James Herriot

IF ONLY THEY COULD TALK

IT SHOULDN'T HAPPEN TO A VET

LET SLEEPING VETS LIE

VET IN HARNESS

VETS MIGHT FLY

VET IN A SPIN

PEERAGE BOOKS

If Only They Could Talk first published in Great Britain in 1970 by Michael Joseph Limited
It Shouldn't Happen to a Vet first published in Great Britain in 1972 by Michael Joseph Limited
Let Sleeping Vets Lie first published in Great Britain in 1973 by Michael Joseph Limited
Vet in Harness first published in Great Britain in 1974 by Michael Joseph Limited
Vets Might Fly first published in Great Britain in 1976 by Michael Joseph Limited
Vet in a Spin first published in Great Britain in 1977 by Michael Joseph Limited

This edition first published in Great Britain in 1990 by Peerage Books

an imprint of
The Octopus Group Limited
Michelin House
Fulham Road
London SW3 6RB

ISBN 1 85052 003 8

Printed and bound in the United Kingdom by The Bath Press, Avon

Contents

If Only They Could Talk

If Only They Could Talk

To
EDDIE STRAITON
with gratitude and affection

Chapter One

They didn't say anything about this in the books, I thought, as the snow blew in through the gaping doorway and settled on my naked back.

I lay face down on the cobbled floor in a pool of nameless muck, my arm deep inside the straining cow, my feet scrabbling for a toe hold between the stones. I was stripped to the waist and the snow mingled with the dirt and the dried blood on my body. I could see nothing outside the circle of flickering light thrown by the smoky oil lamp which the farmer held over me.

No, there wasn't a word in the books about searching for your ropes and instruments in the shadows; about trying to keep clean in a half bucket of tepid water; about the cobbles digging into your chest. Nor about the slow numbing of the arms, the creeping paralysis of the muscles as the fingers tried to work against the cow's powerful expulsive efforts.

There was no mention anywhere of the gradual exhaustion, the feeling of futility and the little far off voice of panic.

My mind went back to that picture in the obstetrics book. A cow standing in the middle of a gleaming floor while a sleek veterinary surgeon in a spotless parturition overall inserted his arm to a polite distance. He was relaxed and smiling, the farmer and his helpers were smiling, even the cow was smiling. There was no dirt or blood or sweat anywhere.

That man in the picture had just finished an excellent lunch and had moved next door to do a bit of calving just for the sheer pleasure of it, as a kind of dessert. He hadn't crawled shivering from his bed at two o'clock in the morning and bumped over twelve miles of frozen snow, staring sleepily ahead till the lonely farm showed in the headlights. He hadn't climbed half a mile of white fell-side to the doorless barn where his patient lay.

I tried to wriggle my way an extra inch inside the cow. The calf's head was back and I was painfully pushing a thin, looped rope towards its lower jaw with my finger tips. All the time my arm was being squeezed between the calf and the bony pelvis. With every straining effort from the cow the pressure became almost unbearable, then she would relax and I would push the rope another inch. I wondered how long I would be able to keep this up. If I didn't snare that jaw soon I would never get the calf away. I groaned, set my teeth and reached forward again.

Another little flurry of snow blew in and I could almost hear the flakes sizzling on my sweating back. There was sweat on my forehead too, and it trickled into my eyes as I pushed.

There is always a time at a bad calving when you begin to wonder if you will ever win the battle. I had reached this stage.

Little speeches began to flit through my brain. 'Perhaps it would be better to slaughter this cow. Her pelvis is so small and narrow that I can't see a calf coming through.' Or 'She's a good fat animal and really of the beef type, so don't you think it would pay you better to get the butcher?' or perhaps 'This is a very bad presentation. In a roomy cow it would be simple enough to bring the head round but in this case it is just about impossible.'

Of course, I could have delivered the calf by embryotomy – by passing a wire over the neck and sawing off the head. So many of these occasions ended with the floor strewn with heads, legs, heaps of intestines. There were thick text books devoted to the countless ways you could cut up a calf.

But none of it was any good here, because this calf was alive. At my furthest stretch I had got my finger as far as the commissure of the mouth and had been startled by a twitch of the little creature's tongue. It was unexpected because calves in this position are usually dead, asphyxiated by the acute flexion of the neck and the pressure of the dam's powerful contractions. But this one had a spark of life in it and if it came out it would have to be in one piece.

I went over to my bucket of water, cold now and bloody, and silently soaped my arms. Then I lay down again, feeling the cobbles harder than ever against my chest. I worked my toes between the stones, shook the sweat from my eyes and for the hundredth time thrust an arm that felt like spaghetti into the cow; alongside the little dry legs of the calf, like sandpaper tearing against my flesh, then to the bend in the neck and so to the ear and then, agonisingly, along the side of the face towards the lower jaw which had become my major goal in life.

It was incredible that I had been doing this for nearly two hours; fighting as my strength ebbed to push a little noose round that jaw. I had tried everything else – repelling a leg, gentle traction with a blunt hook in the eye socket, but I was back to the noose.

It had been a miserable session all through. The farmer, Mr Dinsdale, was a long, sad, silent man of few words who always seemed to be expecting the worst to happen. He had a long, sad, silent son with him and the two of them had watched my efforts with deepening gloom.

But worst of all had been Uncle. When I had first entered the hillside barn I had been surprised to see a little bright-eyed old man in a pork pie hat settling down comfortably on a bale of straw. He was filling his pipe and clearly looking forward to the entertainment.

'Now then, young man,' he cried in the nasal twang of the West Riding. 'I'm Mr Dinsdale's brother. I farm over in Listondale.'

I put down my equipment and nodded. 'How do you do? My name is Herriot.'

The old man looked me over, piercingly. 'My vet is Mr Broomfield. Expect you'll have heard of him – everybody knows him, I reckon. Wonderful man, Mr Broomfield, especially at calving. Do you know, I've never seen 'im beat yet.'

I managed a wan smile. Any other time I would have been delighted to hear how good my colleague was, but somehow not now, not now. In fact, the words set a mournful little bell tolling inside me.

'No, I'm afraid I don't know Mr Broomfield,' I said, taking off my jacket and, more reluctantly, peeling my shirt over my head. 'But I haven't been around these parts very long.'

Uncle was aghast. 'You don't know him! Well you're the only one as doesn't. They think the world of him in Listondale, I can tell you.' He lapsed into a shocked silence and applied a match to his pipe. Then he shot a glance at my goose-pimpled torso. 'Strips like a boxer does Mr Broomfield. Never seen such muscles on a man.'

A wave of weakness coursed sluggishly over me. I felt suddenly leaden-footed and inadequate. As I began to lay out my ropes and instruments on a clean towel the old man spoke again.

'And how long have you been qualified, may I ask?'

'Oh, about seven months.'

'Seven months!' Uncle smiled indulgently, tamped down his tobacco and blew out a cloud of rank, blue smoke. 'Well, there's nowt like a bit of experience, I always says. Mr Broomfield's been doing my work now for over ten years and he really knows what he's about. No, you can 'ave your book learning. Give me experience every time.'

I tipped some antiseptic into the bucket and lathered my arms carefully. I knelt behind the cow.

'Mr Broomfield always puts some special lubricating oils on his arms first,' Uncle said, pulling contentedly on his pipe. 'He says you get infection of the womb if you just use soap and water.'

I made my first exploration. It was the burdened moment all vets go through when they first put their hand into a cow. Within seconds I would know whether I would be putting on my jacket in fifteen minutes or whether I had hours of hard labour ahead of me.

I was going to be unlucky this time; it was a nasty presentation. Head back and no room at all; more like being inside an undeveloped heifer than a second calver. And she was bone dry – the 'waters' must have come away from her hours ago. She had been running out on the high fields and had started to calve a week before her time; that was why they had had to bring her into this half-ruined barn. Anyway, it would be a long time before I saw my bed again.

'Well now, what have you found, young man?' Uncle's penetrating voice cut through the silence. 'Head back, eh? You won't have much trouble, then. I've seen Mr Broomfield do 'em like that – he turns calf right round and brings it out back legs first.'

I had heard this sort of nonsense before. A short time in practice had taught me that all farmers were experts with other farmers' live stock. When their own animals were in trouble they tended to rush to the phone for the vet, but with their neighbours' they were confident, knowledgeable and full of helpful advice. And another phenomenon I had observed was that their advice was usually regarded as more valuable than the vet's. Like now, for instance; Uncle was obviously an accepted sage and the Dinsdales listened with deference to everything he said.

'Another way with a job like this,' continued Uncle 'is to get a few strong chaps with ropes and pull the thing out, head back and all.'

I gasped as I felt my way around. 'I'm afraid it's impossible to turn a calf completely round in this small space. And to pull it out without bringing the head round would certainly break the mother's pelvis.'

The Dinsdales narrowed their eyes. Clearly they thought I was hedging in the face of Uncle's superior knowledge.

And now, two hours later, defeat was just round the corner. I was just about whacked. I had rolled and grovelled on the filthy cobbles while the Dinsdales watched me in morose silence and Uncle kept up a non-stop stream of comment. Uncle, his ruddy face glowing with delight, his little eyes sparkling, hadn't had such a happy night for years. His long trek up the hillside had been repaid a hundredfold. His vitality was undiminished; he had enjoyed every minute.

As I lay there, eyes closed, face stiff with dirt, mouth hanging open, Uncle took his pipe in his hand and leaned forward on his straw bale. 'You're about beat, young man,' he said with deep satisfaction. 'Well, I've never seen Mr Broomfield beat but he's had a lot of experience. And what's more, he's strong, really strong. That's one man you couldn't tire.'

Rage flooded through me like a draught of strong spirit. The right thing to do, of course, would be to get up, tip the bucket of bloody water over Uncle's head, run down the hill and drive away; away from Yorkshire, from Uncle, from the Dinsdales, from this cow.

Instead, I clenched my teeth, braced my legs and pushed with everything I had; and with a sensation of disbelief I felt my noose slide over the sharp little incisor teeth and into the calf's mouth. Gingerly, muttering a prayer, I pulled on the thin rope with my left hand and felt the slipknot tighten. I had hold of that lower jaw.

At last I could start doing something. 'Now hold this rope, Mr Dinsdale, and just keep a gentle tension on it. I'm going to repel the calf and if you pull steadily at the same time, the head ought to come round.'

'What if the rope comes off?' asked Uncle hopefully.

I didn't answer. I put my hand in against the calf's shoulder and began to push against the cow's contractions. I felt the small body moving away from me. 'Now a steady pull, Mr Dinsdale, without jerking.' And to myself, 'Oh God, don't let it slip off.'

The head was coming round. I could feel the neck straightening against my arm, then the ear touched my elbow. I let go the shoulder and grabbed the little muzzle. Keeping the teeth away from the vaginal wall with my hand, I guided the head till it was resting where it should be, on the fore limbs.

Quickly I extended the noose till it reached behind the ears. 'Now pull on the head as she strains.'

'Nay, you should pull on the legs now,' cried Uncle.

'Pull on the bloody head rope, I tell you!' I bellowed at the top of my voice and felt immediately better as Uncle retired, offended, to his bale.

With traction the head was brought out and the rest of the body followed easily. The little animal lay motionless on the cobbles, eyes glassy and unseeing, tongue blue and grossly swollen.

'It'll be dead. Bound to be,' grunted Uncle, returning to the attack.

I cleared the mucus from the mouth, blew hard down the throat and began artificial respiration. After a few pressures on the ribs, the calf gave a gasp and the eyelids flickered. Then it started to inhale and one leg jerked.

Uncle took off his hat and scratched his head in disbelief. 'By gaw, it's alive. I'd have thowt it'd sure to be dead after you'd messed about all that time.' A lot of the fire had gone out of him and his pipe hung down empty from his lips.

'I know what this little fellow wants,' I said. I grasped the calf by its fore legs and pulled it up to its mother's head. The cow was stretched out on her side, her head extended wearily along the rough floor. Her ribs heaved, her eyes were almost closed; she looked past caring about anything. Then she felt the calf's body against her face and there was a transformation; her eyes opened wide and her muzzle began a snuffling exploration of the new object. Her interest grew with every sniff and she struggled on to her chest, nosing and probing all over the calf, rumbling deep in her chest. Then she began to lick him methodically. Nature provides the perfect stimulant massage for a time like this and the little creature arched his back as the coarse papillae on the tongue dragged along his skin. Within a minute he was shaking his head and trying to sit up.

I grinned. This was the bit I liked. The little miracle. I felt it was something that would never grow stale no matter how often I saw it. I cleaned as much of the dried blood and filth from my body as I could, but most of it had caked on my skin and not even my finger nails would move it. It would have to wait for the hot bath at home. Pulling my shirt over my head, I felt as though I had been beaten for a long time with a thick stick. Every muscle ached. My mouth was dried out, my lips almost sticking together.

A long, sad figure hovered near. 'How about a drink?' asked Mr Dinsdale.

I could feel my grimy face cracking into an incredulous smile. A vision of hot tea well laced with whisky swam before me. 'That's very kind of you, Mr Dinsdale, I'd love a drink. It's been a hard two hours.'

'Nay,' said Mr Dinsdale looking at me steadily, 'I meant for the cow.'

I began to babble. 'Oh yes, of course, certainly, by all means give her a drink. She must be very thirsty. It'll do her good. Certainly, certainly, give her a drink.'

I gathered up my tackle and stumbled out of the barn. On the moor it was still dark and a bitter wind whipped over the snow, stinging my eyes. As I plodded down the slope, Uncle's voice, strident and undefeated, reached me for the last time.

'Mr Broomfield doesn't believe in giving a drink after calving. Says it chills the stomach.'

Chapter Two

It was hot in the rickety little bus and I was on the wrong side where the July sun beat on the windows. I shifted uncomfortably inside my best suit and eased a finger inside the constricting white collar. It was a foolish outfit for this weather but a few miles ahead, my prospective employer was waiting for me and I had to make a good impression.

There was a lot hanging on this interview; being a newly qualified veterinary surgeon in this year of 1937 was like taking out a ticket for the dole queue. Agriculture was depressed by a decade of government neglect, the draught horse which had been the mainstay of the profession was fast disappearing. It was easy to be a prophet of doom when the young men emerging from the colleges after a hard five years' slog were faced by a world indifferent to their enthusiasm and bursting knowledge. There were usually two or three situations vacant in the '*Record*' each week and an average of eighty applicants for each one.

It hadn't seemed true when the letter came from Darrowby in the Yorkshire Dales. Mr Siegfried Farnon MRCVS would like to see me on the Friday afternoon; I was to come to tea and if we were mutually suited I could stay on as assistant. I had grabbed at the lifeline unbelievingly; so many friends who had qualified with me were unemployed or working in shops or as labourers in the shipyards that I had given up hope of any other future for myself.

The driver crashed his gears again as he went into another steep bend. We had been climbing steadily now for the last fifteen miles or so, moving closer to the distant blue swell of the Pennines. I had never been in Yorkshire before but the name had always raised a picture of a county as stodgy and unromantic as its pudding; I was prepared for solid worth, dullness and a total lack of charm. But as the bus groaned its way higher I began to wonder. The formless heights were resolving into high, grassy hills and wide valleys. In the valley bottoms, rivers twisted among the trees and solid grey-stone farmhouses lay among islands of cultivated land which pushed bright green promontories up the hillsides into the dark tide of heather which lapped from the summits.

I had seen the fences and hedges give way to dry stone walls which bordered the roads, enclosed the fields and climbed endlessly over the surrounding fells. The walls were everywhere, countless miles of them, tracing their patterns high on the green uplands.

But as I neared my destination the horror stories kept forcing their way into my mind; the tales brought back to college by veterans hardened and embittered by a few months of practice. Assistants were just little bits of dirt to be starved and worked into the ground by the principals who were heartless and vicious to a man. Dave Stevens, lighting a cigarette with trembling hand: 'Never a night off or a half day. He made me wash the car, dig the garden, mow the lawn, do the family shopping. But when he told me to sweep the chimney I left.' Or Willie Johnstone: 'First job I had to do was pass the stomach tube on a horse. Got it into the trachea instead of the oesophagus. Couple of quick pumps and down went the horse with a hell of a crash – dead as a hammer. That's when I started these grey hairs.' Or that dreadful one they passed around about Fred Pringle. Fred had trocharised a bloated cow and the farmer had been so impressed by the pent up gas hissing from the abdomen that Fred had got carried away and applied his cigarette lighter to the canula. A roaring sheet of flame had swept onto some straw bales and burned the byre to the ground. Fred had taken up a colonial appointment immediately afterwards – Leeward Islands wasn't it?

Oh hell, that one couldn't be true. I cursed my fevered imagination and tried to shut out the crackling of the inferno, the terrified bellowing of the cattle as they were led to safety. No, it couldn't be as bad as that; I rubbed my sweating palms on my knees and tried to concentrate on the man I was going to meet.

Siegfried Farnon. Strange name for a vet in the Yorkshire Dales. Probably a German who had done his training in this country and decided to set up in practice. And it wouldn't have been Farnon in the beginning; probably Farrenen. Yes, Siegfried Farrenen. He was beginning to take shape; short, fat, roly poly type with merry eyes and a bubbling laugh. But at the same time I had trouble with the obtruding image of a hulking, cold-eyed, bristle-skulled Teuton more in keeping with the popular idea of the practice boss.

I realised the bus was clattering along a narrow street which opened on to a square where we stopped. Above the window of an unpretentious grocer shop I read 'Darrowby Co-operative Society'. We had arrived.

I got out and stood beside my battered suitcase, looking about me. There was something unusual and I couldn't put my finger on it at first. Then I realised what it was – the silence. The other passengers had dispersed, the driver had switched off his engine and there was not a sound or a movement anywhere. The only visible sign of life was a group of old men sitting round the clock tower in the centre of the square but they might have been carved from stone.

Darrowby didn't get much space in the guide books but when it was mentioned it was described as a grey little town on the river Darrow with a cobbled market place and little of interest except its two ancient bridges. But when you looked at it, its setting was beautiful on the pebbly river where the houses clustered thickly and straggled unevenly along the lower slopes of Herne Fell. Everywhere in Darrowby, in the streets, through the windows of the houses you could see the Fell rearing its calm, green bulk more than two thousand feet above the huddled roofs.

There was a clarity in the air, a sense of space and airiness that made me feel I had shed something on the plain, twenty miles behind. The confinement of the city, the grime, the smoke – already they seemed to be falling away from me.

Trengate was a quiet street leading off the square and I had my first sight of Skeldale House. I knew it was the right place before I was near enough to read 'S. Farnon MRCVS' on the old fashioned brass plate hanging slightly askew on the iron railings. I knew by the ivy which climbed untidily over the mellow brick to the topmost windows. It was what the letter had said – the only house with ivy; and this could be where I would work for the first time as a veterinary surgeon.

Now that I was here, right on the doorstep, I felt breathless, as though I had been running. If I got the job, this was where I would find out about myself. There were many things to prove.

But I liked the look of the old house. It was Georgian with a fine, white-painted doorway. The windows, too, were white – wide and graceful on the ground floor and first storey but small and square where they peeped out from under the overhanging tiles far above. The paint was flaking and the mortar looked crumbly between the bricks, but there was a changeless elegance about the place. There was no front garden and only the railings separated the house from the street a few feet away.

I rang the doorbell and instantly the afternoon peace was shattered by a distant baying like a wolf pack in full cry. The upper half of the door was of glass and, as I peered through, a river of dogs poured round the corner of a long passage and dashed itself with frenzied yells against the door. If I hadn't been used to animals I would have turned and run for my life. As it was I stepped back warily and watched the dogs as they appeared, sometimes two at a time, at the top of their leap, eyes glaring, jaws slavering. After a minute or two of this I was able to sort them out and I realised that my first rough count of about fourteen was exaggerated. There were, in fact, five; a huge fawn greyhound who appeared most often as he hadn't so far to jump as the others, a cocker spaniel, a Scottie, a whippet and a tiny, short-legged hunt terrier. This terrier was seldom seen since the glass was rather high for him, but when he did make it he managed to get an even more frantic note into his bark before he disappeared.

I was thinking of ringing the bell again when I saw a large woman in the passage. She rapped out a single word and the noise stopped as if by magic. When she opened the door the ravening pack was slinking round her feet ingratiatingly, showing the whites of their eyes and wagging their tucked-in tails. I had never seen such a servile crew.

'Good afternoon,' I said with my best smile. 'My name is Herriot.'

The woman looked bigger than ever with the door open. She was about sixty but her hair, tightly pulled back from her forehead, was jet black and hardly streaked with grey. She nodded and looked at me with grim benevolence, but she seemed to be waiting for further information. Evidently, the name struck no answering spark.

'Mr Farnon is expecting me. He wrote asking me to come today.'

'Mr Herriot?' she said thoughtfully. 'Surgery is from six to seven o'clock. If you wanted to bring a dog in, that would be your best time.'

'No, no.' I said, hanging on to my smile. 'I'm applying for the position of assistant. Mr Farnon said to come in time for tea.'

'Assistant? Well, now, that's nice.' The lines in her face softened a little. 'I'm Mrs Hall. I keep house for Mr Farnon. He's a bachelor, you know. He never said anything to me about you, but never mind, come in and have a cup of tea. He shouldn't be long before he's back.'

I followed her between whitewashed walls, my feet clattering on the tiles. We turned right at the end into another passage and I was beginning to wonder just how far back the house extended when I was shown into a sunlit room.

It had been built in the grand manner, high-ceilinged and airy with a massive fireplace flanked by arched alcoves. One end was taken up by a french window which gave on a long, high-walled garden. I could see unkempt lawns, a rockery and many fruit trees. A great bank of paeonies blazed in the hot sunshine and at the far end, rooks cawed in the branches of a group of tall elms. Above and beyond were the green hills with their climbing walls.

Ordinary looking furniture stood around on a very worn carpet. Hunting prints hung on the walls and books were scattered everywhere, some on shelves in the alcoves but others piled on the floor in the corners. A pewter pint pot occupied a prominent place at one end of the mantelpiece. It was an interesting pot. Cheques and bank notes had been stuffed into it till they bulged out of the top and overflowed on to the hearth beneath. I was studying this with astonishment when Mrs Hall came in with a tea tray.

'I suppose Mr Farnon is out on a case.' I said.

'No, he's gone through to Brawton to visit his mother. I can't really say when he'll be back.' She left me with my tea.

The dogs arranged themselves peacefully around the room and, except for a brief dispute between the Scottie and the cocker spaniel about the occupancy of a deep chair, there was no signof their previous violent behaviour. They lay regarding me with friendly boredom and, at the same time, fighting a losing battle against sleep. Soon the last nodding head had fallen back and a chorus of heavy breathing filled the room.

But I was unable to relax with them. A feeling of let-down gripped me; I had screwed myself up for an interview and I was left dangling. This was all very odd. Why should anyone write for an assistant, arrange a time to meet him and then go to visit his mother? Another thing – if I was engaged, I would be living in this house, yet the housekeeper had no instructions to prepare a room for me. In fact, she had never even heard of me.

My musings were interrupted by the door bell ringing and the dogs, as if touched by a live wire, leaped screaming into the air and launched themselves in a solid mass through the door. I wished they didn't take their duties so seriously. There was no sign of Mrs Hall so I went out to the front door where the dogs were putting everything into their fierce act.

'Shut up!' I shouted and the din switched itself off. The five dogs cringed abjectly round my ankles, almost walking on their knees. The big greyhound got the best effect by drawing his lips back from his teeth in an apologetic grin.

I opened the door and looked into a round, eager face. Its owner, a plump man in wellington boots leaned confidently against the railings.

'Hello, 'ello, Mr Farnon in?'

'Not at the moment. Can I help you?'

'Aye, give 'im a message when he comes in. Tell 'im Bert Sharpe of Barrow Hills has a cow wot wants borin' out?'

'Boring out?'

'That's right, she's nobbut going on three cylinders.'

'Three cylinders?'

'Aye and if we don't do summat she'll go wrang in 'er ewer, won't she?'

'Very probably.'

'Don't want felon, do we?'

'Certainly not.'

'O.K., you'll tell 'im, then. Ta-ta.'

I returned thoughtfully to the sitting-room. It was disconcerting but I had listened to my first case history without understanding a word of it.

I had hardly sat down when the bell rang again. This time I unleashed a frightening yell which froze the dogs when they were still in mid air; they took the point and returned, abashed, to their chairs.

This time it was a solemn gentleman with a straightly adjusted cloth cap resting on his ears, a muffler knotted precisely over his adam's apple and a clay pipe growing from the exact centre of his mouth. He removed the pipe and spoke with a rich, unexpected accent.

'Me name's Mulligan and I want Misther Farnon to make up some midicine for me dog.'

'Oh, what's the trouble with your dog, Mr Mulligan?'

He raised a questioning eyebrow and put a hand to his ear. I tried again with a full blooded shout.

'What's the trouble?'

He looked at me doubtfully for a moment. 'He's womitin, sorr. Womitin' bad.'

I immediately felt on secure ground now and my brain began to seethe with diagnostic procedures. 'How long after eating does he vomit?'

The hand went to the ear again. 'Phwhat's that?'

I leaned close to the side of his head, inflated my lungs and bawled: 'When does he womit – I mean vomit?'

Comprehension spread slowly across Mr Mulligan's face. He gave a gentle smile. 'Oh aye, he's womitin'. Womitin' bad, sorr.'

I didn't feel up to another effort so I told him I would see to it and asked him to call later. He must have been able to lipread me because he seemed satisfied and walked away.

Back in the sitting-room, I sank into a chair and poured a cup of tea. I had taken one sip when the bell rang again. This time, a wild glare from me was enough to make the dogs cower back in their chairs; I was relieved they had caught on so quickly.

Outside the front door a lovely, red-haired girl was standing. She smiled, showing a lot of very white teeth.

'Good afternoon,' she said in a loud, well-bred voice. 'I am Diana Brompton. Mr Farnon is expecting me for tea.'

I gulped and clung to the door handle. 'He's asked YOU to tea?'

The smile became fixed. 'Yes, that is correct,' she said, spelling the words out carefully, 'He asked me to tea.'

'I'm afraid Mr Farnon isn't at home. I can't say when he'll be back.'

The smile was plucked away. 'Oh,' she said, and she got a lot into the word. 'At any rate, perhaps I could come in.'

'Oh, certainly, do come in. I'm sorry.' I babbled, suddenly conscious that I had been staring, open mouthed at her.

I held open the door and she brushed past me without a word. She knew her way about because, when I got to the first corner, she had disappeared into the room. I tiptoed past the door and broke into a gallop which took me along another thirty yards or so of twisting passage to a huge, stone-flagged kitchen. Mrs Hall was pottering about there and I rushed at her.

'There's a young lady here, a Miss Brompton. She's come to tea, too.' I had to fight an impulse to pluck at her sleeve.

Mrs Hall's face was expressionless. I thought she might have started to wave her arms about, but she didn't even seem surprised.

'You go through and talk to her and I'll bring a few more cakes,' she said.

'But what the heck am I going to talk to her about? How long is Mr Farnon going to be?'

'Oh, just chat to her for a bit. I shouldn't think he'll be very long,' she said calmly.

Slowly, I made my way back to the sitting-room and when I opened the door the girl turned quickly with the makings of another big smile. She made no attempt to hide her disgust when she saw it was only me.

'Mrs Hall thinks he should be back fairly soon. Perhaps you would join me in a cup of tea while you're waiting.'

She gave me a quick glance which raked me from my rumpled hair to my scuffed old shoes. I realised suddenly how grimy and sweaty I was after the long journey. Then she shrugged her shoulders and turned away. The dogs regarded her apathetically. A heavy silence blanketed the room.

I poured a cup of tea and held it out to her. She ignored me and lit a cigarette. This was going to be tough, but I could only try.

I cleared my throat and spoke lightly. 'I've only just arrived myself. I hope to be the new assistant.'

This time she didn't trouble to look round. She just said 'Oh' and again the monosyllable carried a tremendous punch.

'Lovely part of the world, this.' I said, returning to the attack.

'Yes.'

'I've never been in Yorkshire before, but I like what I've seen.'

'Oh.'

'Have you known Mr Farnon very long?'

'Yes.'

'I believe he's quite young – about thirty?'

'Yes.'

'Wonderful weather.'

'Yes.'

I kept at it with courage and tenacity for about five minutes, hunting for something original or witty, but finally, Miss Brompton, instead of answering, took the cigarette from her mouth, turned towards me and gave me a long, blank stare. I knew that was the end and shrank into silence.

After that, she sat staring out of the french window, pulling deeply at her cigarette, narrowing her eyes as the smoke trickled from her lips. As far as she was concerned, I just wasn't there.

I was able to observe her at will and she was interesting. I had never met a living piece of a society magazine before. Cool, linen dress, expensive-looking cardigan, elegant legs and the glorious red hair falling on her shoulders.

And yet here was a fascinating thought. She was sitting there positively hungering for a little fat German vet. This Farnon must have something.

The tableau was finally broken up when Miss Brompton jumped to her feet. She hurled her cigarette savagely into the fireplace and marched from the room.

Wearily, I got out of my chair. My head began to ache as I shuffled through the french window into the garden. I flopped down among the knee deep grass on the lawn and rested my back against a towering acacia tree. Where the devil was Farnon? Was he really expecting me or had somebody played a horrible practical joke on me? I felt suddenly cold. I had spent my last few pounds getting here and if there was some mistake I was in trouble.

But, looking around me, I began to feel better. The sunshine beat back from the high old walls, bees droned among the bright masses of flowers. A gentle breeze stirred the withered blooms of a magnificent wistaria which almost covered the back of the house. There was peace here.

I leaned my head against the bark and closed my eyes. I could see Herr Farrenen, looking just as I had imagined him, standing over me. He wore a shocked expression.

'Wass is dis you haff done?' he spluttered, his fat jowls quivering with rage. 'You kom to my house under false pretences, you insult Fraulein Brompton, you trink my tea, you eat my food. Vat else you do, hein? Maybe you steal my spoons. You talk about assistant but I vant no assistant. Is best I telephone the police.'

Herr Farrenen seized the phone in a pudgy hand. Even in my dream, I wondered how the man could use such a completely corny accent. I heard the thick voice saying 'Hello, hello.'

And I opened my eyes. Somebody was saying 'Hello', but it wasn't Herr Farrenen. A tall, thin man was leaning against the wall, his hands in his pockets. Something seemed to be amusing him. As I struggled to my feet, he heaved himself away from the wall and held out his hand. 'Sorry you've had to wait. I'm Siegfried Farnon.'

He was just about the most English looking man I had ever seen. Long, humorous, strong-jawed face. Small, clipped moustache, untidy, sandy hair. He was wearing an old tweed jacket and shapeless flannel trousers. The collar of his check shirt was frayed and the tie carelessly knotted. He looked as though he didn't spend much time in front of a mirror.

Studying him, I began to feel better despite the ache in my neck where it had rested against the tree. I shook my head to get my eyes fully open and tufts of grass fell from my hair. 'There was a Miss Brompton here' I blurted out. 'She came to tea. I explained you had been called away.'

Farnon looked thoughtful, but not put out. He rubbed his chin slowly. 'Mm, yes – well, never mind. But I do apologise for being out when you arrived. I have a shocking memory and I just forgot.'

It was the most English voice, too.

Farnon gave me a long, searching look, then he grinned. 'Let's go inside. I want to show you round the place.'

Chapter Three

The long offshoot behind the house had been the servants' quarters in grander days. Here, everything was dark and narrow and poky as if in deliberate contrast with the front.

Farnon led me to the first of several doors which opened off a passage where the smell of ether and carbolic hung on the air. 'This,' he said, with a secret gleam in his eye as though he were about to unveil the mysteries of Aladdin's cave, 'is the dispensary.'

The dispensary was an important place in the days before penicillin and the sulphonamides. Rows of gleaming Winchester bottles lined the white walls from floor to ceiling. I savoured the familiar names: Sweet Spirits of Nitre, Tincture of Camphor, Chlorodyne, Formalin, Salammoniac, Hexamine, Sugar of Lead, Linimentum Album, Perchloride of Mercury, Red Blister. The lines of labels were comforting.

I was an initiate among old friends. I had painfully accumulated their lore, ferreting out their secrets over the years. I knew their origins, actions and uses, and their maddeningly varied dosage. The examiner's voice – 'And what is the dose for the horse? – and the cow? and the sheep? – and the pig? – and the dog? – and the cat?'

These shelves held the vets' entire armoury against disease and, on a bench under the window, I could see the instruments for compounding them; the graduated vessels and beakers, the mortars and pestles. And underneath, in an open cupboard, the medicine bottles, piles of corks of all sizes, pill boxes, powder papers.

As we moved around, Farnon's manner became more and more animated. His eyes glittered and he talked rapidly. Often, he reached up and caressed a Winchester on its shelf; or he would lift out a horse ball or an electuary from its box, give it a friendly pat and replace it with tenderness.

'Look at this stuff, Herriot,' he shouted without warning. 'Adrevan! This is the remedy, par excellence, for red worms in horses. A bit expensive, mind you

– ten bob a packet. And these gentian violet pessaries. If you shove one of these into a cow's uterus after a dirty cleansing, it turns the discharges a very pretty colour. Really looks as though it's doing something. And have you seen this trick?'

He placed a few crystals of resublimated iodine on a glass dish and added a drop of turpentine. Nothing happened for a second then a dense cloud of purple smoke rolled heavily to the ceiling. He gave a great bellow of laughter at my startled face.

'Like witchcraft, isn't it? I use it for wounds in horses' feet. The chemical reaction drives the iodine deep into the tissues.'

'It does?'

'Well, I don't know, but that's the theory, and anyway, you must admit it looks wonderful. Impresses the toughest client.'

Some of the bottles on the shelves fell short of the ethical standards I had learned in college. Like the one labelled 'Colic Drench' and featuring a floridly drawn picture of a horse rolling in agony. The animal's face was turned outwards and wore an expression of very human anguish. Another bore the legend 'Universal Cattle Medicine' in ornate script – 'A sovereign Remedy for coughs, chills, scours, pneumonia, milk fever, gargett and all forms of indigestion. At the bottom of the label, in flaring black capitals was the assurance, 'Never Fails to Give Relief.'

Farnon had something to say about most of the drugs. Each one had its place in his five years' experience of practice; they all had their fascination, their individual mystique. Many of the bottles were beautifully shaped, with heavy glass stoppers and their Latin names cut deeply into their sides; names familiar to physicians for centuries, gathering fables through the years.

The two of us stood gazing at the gleaming rows without any idea that it was nearly all useless and that the days of the old medicines were nearly over. Soon they would be hustled into oblivion by the headlong rush of the new discoveries and they would never return.

'This is where we keep the instruments.' Farnon showed me into another little room. The small animal equipment lay on green baize shelves, very neat and impressively clean. Hypodermic syringes, whelping forceps, tooth scalers, probes, searchers, and, in a place of prominence, an ophthalmoscope.

Farnon lifted it lovingly from its black box. 'My latest purchase,' he murmured, stroking its smooth shaft. 'Wonderful thing. Here, have a peep at my retina.'

I switched on the bulb and gazed with interest at the glistening, coloured tapestry in the depths of his eye. 'Very pretty. I could write you a certificate of soundness.'

He laughed and thumped my shoulder. 'Good, I'm glad to hear it. I always fancied I had a touch of cataract in that one.'

He began to show me the large animal instruments which hung from hooks on the walls. Docking and firing irons, bloodless castrators, emasculators, casting ropes and hobbles, calving ropes and hooks. A new, silvery embryotome hung in the place of honour, but many of the instruments, like the drugs, were museum pieces. Particularly the blood stick and fleam, a relic of medieval times, but still used to bring the rich blood spouting into a bucket.

'You still can't beat it for laminitis,' Farnon declared seriously.

We finished up in the operating room with its bare white walls, high table, oxygen and ether anaesthetic outfit and a small steriliser.

'Not much small animal work in this district.' Farnon smoothed the table with his palm. 'But I'm trying to encourage it. It makes a pleasant change from lying on your belly in a cow house. The thing is, we've got to do the job right. The old castor oil and prussic acid doctrine is no good at all. You probably know that a lot of the old hands won't look at a dog or a cat, but the profession has got to change its ideas.'

He went over to a cupboard in the corner and opened the door. I could see glass shelves with a few scalpels, artery forceps, suture needles and bottles of catgut in spirit. He took out his handkerchief and flicked at an auroscope before closing the doors carefully.

'Well, what do you think of it all?' he asked as he went out into the passage.

'Great,' I replied. 'You've got just about everything you need here. I'm really impressed.'

He seemed to swell visibly. The thin cheeks flushed and he hummed softly to himself. Then he burst loudly into song in a shaky baritone, keeping time with our steps as we marched along.

Back in the sitting-room, I told him about Bert Sharpe. 'Something about boring out a cow which was going on three cylinders. He talked about her ewer and felon – I didn't quite get it.'

Farnon laughed. 'I think I can translate. He wants a Hudson's operation doing on a blocked teat. Ewer is the udder and felon the local term for mastitis.'

'Well, thanks. And there was a deaf Irishman, a Mr Mulligan . . .'

'Wait a minute.' Farnon held up a hand. 'Let me guess – womitin'?'

'Aye, womitin' bad, sorr.'

'Right, I'll put up another pint of bismuth carb for him. I'm in favour of long range treatment for this dog. He looks like an airedale but he's as big as a donkey and has a moody disposition. He's had Joe Mulligan on the floor a few times – just gets him down and worries him when he's got nothing better to do. But Joe loves him.'

'How about the womitin'?'

'Doesn't mean a thing. Natural reaction from eating every bit of rubbish he finds. Well, we'd better get out to Sharpe's. And there are one or two other visits – how about coming with me and I'll show you a bit of the district.'

Outside the house, Farnon motioned me towards a battered Hillman and, as I moved round to the passenger's side, I shot a startled glance at the treadless tyres, the rusty bodywork, the almost opaque windscreen with its network of fine cracks. What I didn't notice was that the passenger seat was not fixed to the floor but stood freely on its sledge-like runners. I dropped into it and went over backwards, finishing with my head on the rear seat and my feet against the roof. Farnon helped me up, apologising with great charm, and we set off.

Once clear of the market place, the road dipped quite suddenly and we could see all of the Dale stretching away from us in the evening sunshine. The outlines of the great hills were softened in the gentle light and a broken streak of silver showed where the Darrow wandered on the valley floor.

Farnon was an unorthodox driver. Apparently captivated by the scene, he drove slowly down the hill, elbows resting on the wheel, his chin cupped in his hands. At the bottom of the hill he came out of his reverie and spurted to seventy miles an hour. The old car rocked crazily along the narrow road and my movable seat slewed from side to side as I jammed my feet against the floor boards.

Then he slammed on the brakes, pointed out some pedigree Shorthorns in a field and jolted away again. He never looked at the road in front; all his attention was on the countryside around and behind him. It was that last bit that worried me, because he spent a lot of time driving fast and looking over his shoulder at the same time.

We left the road at last and made our way up a gated lane. My years of seeing practice had taught me to hop in and out very smartly as students were regarded primarily as gate-opening machines. Farnon, however, thanked me gravely every time and once I got over my surprise I found it refreshing.

We drew up in a farmyard. 'Lame horse here.' Farnon said. A strapping Clydesdale gelding was brought out and we watched attentively as the farmer trotted him up and down.

'Which leg do you make it?' my colleague asked. 'Near fore? Yes, I think so, too. Like to examine it?'

I put my hand on the foot, feeling how much hotter it was than the other. I called for a hammer and tapped the wall of the hoof. The horse flinched, raised the foot and held it trembling for a few seconds before replacing it carefully on the ground. 'Looks like pus in the foot to me.'

'I'll bet you're right,' Farnon said. 'They call it gravel around here, by the way. What do you suggest we do about it?'

'Open up the sole and evacuate the pus.'

'Right.' He held out a hoof knife. 'I'll watch your technique.'

With the uncomfortable feeling that I was on trial, I took the knife, lifted the foot and tucked it between my knees. I knew what I had to do – find the dark mark on the sole where the infection had entered and follow it down till I reached the pus. I scraped away the caked dirt and found not one, but several marks. After more tapping to find the painful area I selected a likely spot and started to cut.

The horn seemed as hard as marble and only the thinnest little shaving came away with each twist of the knife. The horse, too, appeared to appreciate having his sore foot lifted off the ground and gratefully leaned his full weight on my back. He hadn't been so comfortable all day. I groaned and dug him in the ribs with my elbow and, though it made him change his position for a second, he was soon leaning on again.

The mark was growing fainter and, after a final gouge with the knife it disappeared altogether. I swore quietly and started on another mark. With my back at breaking point and the sweat trickling into my eyes, I knew that if this one petered out, too, I would have to let the foot go and take a rest. And with Farnon's eye on me I didn't want to do that.

Agonisingly, I hacked away and, as the hole deepened, my knees began an uncontrollable trembling. The horse rested happily, his fifteen hundredweight cradled by this thoughtful human. I was wondering how it would look when I finally fell flat on my face when, under the knife blade, I saw a thin spurt of pus followed by a steady trickle.

'There it goes,' the farmer grunted. 'He'll get relief now.'

I enlarged the drainage hole and dropped the foot. It took me a long time to straighten up and when I stepped back, my shirt clung to my back.

'Well done, Herriot.' Farnon took the knife from me and slipped it into his pocket. 'It just isn't funny when the horn is as hard as that.'

He gave the horse a shot of tetanus antitoxin then turned to the farmer. 'I wonder if you'd hold up the foot for a second while I disinfect the cavity.' The stocky little man gripped the foot between his knees and looked down with interest as Farnon filled the hole with iodine crystals and added some turpentine. Then he disappeared behind a billowing purple curtain.

I watched, fascinated, as the thick pall mounted and spread. I could locate the little man only by the spluttering noises from somewhere in the middle.

As the smoke began to clear, a pair of round, startled eyes came into view. 'By Gaw, Mr Farnon, I wondered what the 'ell had happened for a minute,' the farmer said between coughs. He looked down again at the blackened hole in the hoof and spoke reverently: 'It's wonderful what science can do nowadays.'

We did two more visits, one to a calf with a cut leg which I stitched, dressed and bandaged, then to the cow with the blocked teat.

Mr Sharpe was waiting, still looking eager. He led us into the byre and Farnon gestured towards the cow. 'See what you can make of it.'

I squatted down and palpated the teat, feeling the mass of thickened tissue half up. It would have to be broken down by a Hudson's instrument and I began to work the thin metal spiral up the teat. One second later, I was sitting gasping in the dung channel with the neat imprint of a cloven hoof on my shirt front, just over the solar plexus.

It was embarrassing, but there was nothing I could do but sit there fighting for breath, my mouth opening and shutting like a stranded fish.

Mr Sharpe held his hand over his mouth, his innate politeness at war with his natural amusement at seeing the vet come to grief. 'I'm sorry, young man, but I owt to 'ave told you that this is a very friendly cow. She allus likes to shake hands.' Then, overcome by his own wit, he rested his forehead on the cow's back and went into a long paroxysm of silent mirth.

I took my time to recover, then rose with dignity from the channel. With Mr Sharpe holding the nose and Farnon lifting up the tail, I managed to get the instrument past the fibrous mass and by a few downward tugs I cleared the obstruction; but, though the precautions cramped the cow's style a little, she still got in several telling blows on my arms and legs.

When it was over, the farmer grasped the teat and sent a long white jet frothing on the floor. 'Capital! She's going on four cylinders now!'

Chapter Four

'We'll go home a different way.' Farnon leaned over the driving wheel and wiped the cracked windscreen with his sleeve. 'Over the Brenkstone Pass and down Sildale. It's not much further and I'd like you to see it.'

We took a steep, winding road, climbing higher and still higher with the hillside falling away sheer to a dark ravine where a rocky stream rushed headlong to the gentler country below. On the top, we got out of the car. In the summer dusk, a wild panorama of tumbling fells and peaks rolled away and lost itself in the crimson and gold ribbons of the Western sky. To the East, a black mountain overhung us, menacing in its naked bulk. Huge, square-cut boulders littered the lower slopes.

I whistled softly as I looked around. This was different from the friendly hill country I had seen on the approach to Darrowby.

Farnon turned towards me. 'Yes, one of the wildest spots in England. A fearsome place in winter. I've known this pass to be blocked for weeks on end.'

I pulled the clean air deeply into my lungs. Nothing stirred in the vastness, but a curlew cried faintly and I could just hear the distant roar of the torrent a thousand feet below.

It was dark when we got into the car and started the long descent into Sildale. The valley was a shapeless blur but points of light showed where the lonely farms clung to the hillsides.

We came to a silent village and Farnon applied his brakes violently. I tobogganed effortlessly across the floor on my mobile seat and collided with the windscreen. My head made a ringing sound against the glass but Farnon didn't seem to notice. 'There's a grand little pub here. Let's go in and have a beer.'

The pub was something new to me. It was, simply, a large kitchen, square and stone-flagged. An enormous fireplace and an old black cooking range took up one end. A· kettle stood on the hearth and a single large log hissed and crackled, filling the room with its resinous scent.

About a dozen men sat on the high-backed settles which lined the walls. In front of them, rows of pint mugs rested on oak tables which were fissured and twisted with age.

There was a silence as we went in. Then somebody said 'Now then, Mr Farnon,' not enthusiastically, but politely, and this brought some friendly grunts and nods from the company. They were mostly farmers or farm workers taking their pleasure without fuss or excitement. Most were burnt red by the sun and some of the younger ones were tieless, muscular necks and chests showing through the open shirt fronts. Soft murmurs and clicks rose from a peaceful domino game in the corner.

Farnon guided me to a seat, ordered two beers and turned to face me. 'Well, you can have this job if you want it. Four quid a week and full board. O.K.?'

The suddenness struck me silent. I was in. And four pounds a week! I remembered the pathetic entries in the *Record*. 'Veterinary surgeon, fully experienced, will work for keep.' The BVMA had had to put pressure on the editor to stop him printing these cries from the heart. It hadn't looked so good to see members of the profession offering their services free. Four pounds a week was affluence.

'Thank you,' I said, trying hard not to look triumphant. 'I accept.'

'Good.' Farnon took a hasty gulp at his beer. 'Let me tell you about the practice. I bought it a year ago from an old man of eighty. Still practising, mind you, a real tough old character. But he'd got past getting up in the middle of the night, which isn't surprising. And, of course, in lots of other ways he had let things slide – hanging on to all the old ideas. Some of those ancient instruments in the surgery were his. One way and another, there was hardly any practice left and I'm trying to work it up again now. There's very little profit in it so far, but if we stick in for a few years, I'm confident we'll have a good business. The farmers are pleased to see a younger man taking over and they welcome new treatments and operations. But I'm having to educate them out of the three and sixpenny consulting fee the old chap used to charge and it's been a hard slog. These Dalesmen are wonderful people and you'll like them, but they don't like parting with their brass unless you can prove they are getting something in return.'

He talked on enthusiastically of his plans for the future, the drinks kept coming and the atmosphere in the pub thawed steadily. The place filled up as the regulars from the village streamed in, the noise and heat increased and by near closing time I had got separated from my colleague and was in the middle of a laughing group I seemed to have known for years.

But there was one odd character who swam repeatedly into my field of vision. An elderly little man with a soiled white panama perched above a smooth, brown, time-worn face like an old boot. He was dodging round the edge of the group, beckoning and winking.

I could see there was something on his mind, so I broke away and allowed myself to be led to a seat in the corner. The old man sat opposite me, rested his hands and chin on the handle of his walking stick and regarded me from under drooping eyelids.

'Now then, young man, ah've summat to tell thee. Ah've been among beasts all me life and I'm going to tell tha summat.'

My toes began to curl. I had been caught this way before. Early in my college career I had discovered that all the older inhabitants of the agricultural world seemed to have the idea that they had something priceless to impart. And it usually took a long time. I looked around me in alarm but I was trapped. The old man shuffled his chair closer and began to talk in a conspiratorial whisper. Gusts of beery breath hit my face from six inches range.

There was nothing new about the old man's tale – just the usual recital of miraculous cures he had wrought, infallible remedies known only to himself and many little sidetracks about how unscrupulous people had tried in vain to worm his secrets from him. He paused only to take expert pulls at his pint pot; his tiny frame seemed to be able to accommodate a surprising amount of beer.

But he was enjoying himself and I let him ramble on. In fact I encouraged him by expressing amazement and admiration at his feats.

The little man had never had such an audience. He was a retired smallholder and it had been years since anybody had shown him the appreciation he deserved. His face wore a lopsided leer and his swimmy eyes were alight with friendship. But suddenly he became serious and sat up straight.

'Now, afore ye go, young man, I'm going to tell thee summat nobody knows but me. Ah could've made a lot o' money out o' this. Folks 'ave been after me for years to tell 'em but I never 'ave.'

He lowered the level in his glass by several inches then narrowed his eyes to slits. 'It's the cure for mallenders and sallenders in 'osses.'

I started up in my chair as though the roof had begun to fall in. 'You can't mean it,' I gasped. 'Not mallenders and sallenders.'

The old man looked smug. 'Ah, but ah do mean it. All you have to do is rub on this salve of mine and the 'oss walks away sound. He's better by that!' His voice rose to a thin shout and he made a violent gesture with his arm which swept his nearly empty glass to the floor.

I gave a low, incredulous whistle and ordered another pint. 'And you're really going to tell me the name of this salve?' I whispered.

'I am, young man, but only on one condition. Tha must tell no one. Tha must keep it to thaself, then nobody'll know but thee and me.' He effortlessly tipped half of his fresh pint down his throat. 'Just thee and me, lad.'

'All right, I promise you. I'll not tell a soul. Now what is this wonderful stuff?'

The old man looked furtively round the crowded room. Then he took a deep breath, laid his hand on my shoulder and put his lips close to my ear. He hiccuped once, solemnly, and spoke in a hoarse whisper. 'Marshmallow ointment.'

I grasped his hand and wrung it silently. The old man, deeply moved, spilled most of his final half pint down his chin.

But Farnon was making signals from the door. It was time to go. We surged out with our new friends, making a little island of noise and light in the quiet village street. A tow-haired young fellow in shirt sleeves opened the car door with natural courtesy and, waving a final good night, I plunged in. This time, the seat went over quicker than usual and I hurtled backwards, coming to rest with my head among some Wellingtons and my knees tucked underneath my chin.

A row of surprised faces peered in at me through the back window, but soon, willing hands were helping me up and the trick seat was placed upright on its rockers again. I wondered how long it had been like that and if my employer had ever thought of having it fixed.

We roared off into the darkness and I looked back at the waving group. I could see the little man, his panama gleaming like new in the light from the doorway. He was holding his finger to his lips.

Chapter Five

The past five years had been leading up to one moment and it hadn't arrived yet. I had been in Darrowby for twenty-four hours now and I still hadn't been to a visit on my own.

Another day had passed in going around with Farnon. It was a funny thing, but, for a man who seemed careless, forgetful and a few other things, Farnon was frustratingly cautious about launching his new assistant.

We had been over into Lidderdale today and I had met more of the clients – friendly, polite farmers who received me pleasantly and wished me success. But working under Farnon's supervision was like being back at college with the professor's eye on me. I felt strongly that my professional career would not start until I, James Herriot, went out and attended a sick animal, unaided and unobserved.

However, the time couldn't be very far away now. Farnon had gone off to Brawton to see his mother again. A devoted son, I thought wonderingly. And he had said he would be back late, so the old lady must keep unusual hours. But never mind about that – what mattered was that I was in charge.

I sat in an armchair with a frayed loose cover and looked out through the french windows at the shadows thrown by the evening sun across the shaggy lawn. I had the feeling that I would be doing a lot of this.

I wondered idly what my first call would be. Probably an anti-climax after the years of waiting. Something like a coughing calf or a pig with constipation. And maybe that would be no bad thing – to start with something I could easily put right. I was in the middle of these comfortable musings when the telephone exploded out in the passage. The insistent clamour sounded abnormally loud in the empty house. I lifted the receiver.

'Is that Mr Farnon?' It was a deep voice with a harsh edge to it. Not a local accent; possibly a trace of the South West.

'No, I'm sorry, he's out. This is his assistant.'

'When will he be back?'

'Not till late, I'm afraid. Can I do anything for you?'

'I don't know whether you can do anything for me or not.' The voice took on a hectoring tone. 'I am Mr Soames, Lord Hulton's farm manager. I have a valuable hunting horse with colic. Do you know anything about colic?'

I felt my hackles rising. 'I am a veterinary surgeon, so I think I should know something about it.'

There was a long pause, and the voice barked again. 'Well, I reckon you'll have to do. In any case, I know the injection the horse wants. Bring some arecoline with you. Mr Farnon uses it. And for God's sake, don't be all night getting here. How long will you be?'

'I'm leaving now.'

'Right.'

I heard the receiver bang down onto its rest. My face felt hot as I walked away from the phone. So my first case wasn't going to be a formality. Colics were tricky things and I had an aggressive know-all called Soames thrown in for good measure.

On the eight mile journey to the case, I re-read from memory that great classic, Caulton Reek's Common Colics of the Horse. I had gone through it so often in my final year that I could recite stretches of it like poetry. The well-thumbed pages hovered in front of me, phantom-like, as I drove.

This would probably be a mild impaction or a bit of spasm. Might have had a change of food or too much rich grass. Yet, that would be it; most colics were like that. A quick shot of arecoline and maybe some chlorodyne to relieve the discomfort and all would be well. My mind went back to the case I had met while seeing practice. The horse standing quietly except that it occasionally eased a hind leg or looked round at its side. There was nothing to it, really.

I was elaborating this happy picture when I arrived. I drove into a spotless, gravelled yard surrounded on three sides by substantial loose boxes. A man was standing there, a broad-shouldered, thick-set figure, very trim in check cap and jacket, well-cut breeches and shiny leggings.

The car drew up about thirty yards away and, as I got out, the man slowly and deliberately turned his back on me. I walked across the yard, taking my time, waiting for the other to turn round, but he stood motionless, hands in pockets, looking in the other direction.

I stopped a few feet away but still the man did not turn. After a long time, and when I had got tired of looking at the back, I spoke.

'Mr Soames?'

At first the man did not move, then he turned very slowly. He had a thick, red neck, a ruddy face and small, fiery eyes. He made no answer but looked me over carefully from head to foot, taking in the worn raincoat, my youth, my air of inexperience. When he had completed his examination he looked away again.

'Yes, I am Mr Soames.' He stressed the 'Mr' as though it meant a lot to him. 'I am a very great friend of Mr Farnon.'

'My name is Herriot.'

Soames didn't appear to have heard. 'Yes, a clever man is Mr Farnon. We are great friends.'

'I understand you have a horse with colic.' I wished my voice didn't sound so high and unsteady.

Soames' gaze was still directed somewhere into the sky. He whistled a little tune softly to himself before replying. 'In there,' he said, jerking his head in the direction of one of the boxes. 'One of his lordship's best hunters. In need of expert assistance, I think.' He put a bit of emphasis on the 'expert'.

I opened the door and went inside. And I stopped as though I had walked into a wall. It was a very large box, deeply bedded with peat moss. A bay horse was staggering round and round the perimeter where he had worn a deep path in the peat. He was lathered in sweat from nose to tail, his nostrils were dilated and his eyes stared blankly in front of him. His head rolled about at every step and, through his clenched teeth, gobbets of foam dripped to the floor. A rank steam rose from his body as though he had been galloping.

My mouth had gone dry. I found it difficult to speak and when I did, it was almost in a whisper. 'How long has he been like this?'

'Oh, he started with a bit of belly ache this morning. I've been giving him black draughts all day, or at least this fellow has. I wouldn't be surprised if he's made a bloody mess of it like he does everything.'

I saw that there was somebody standing in the shadows in the corner; a large, fat man with a head collar in his hand.

'Oh, I got the draughts down him, right enough, Mr Soames, but they haven't done 'im no good.' The big man looked scared.

'You call yourself a horseman,' Soames said, 'but I should have done the damn job myself. I reckon he'd have been better by now.'

'It would take more than a black draught to help him,' I said. 'This is no ordinary colic.'

'What the hell is it, then?'

'Well, I can't say till I've examined him, but severe, continuous pain like that could mean a torsion – a twisted bowel.'

'Twisted bowel, my foot! He's got a bit of belly ache, that's all. He hasn't passed anything all day and he wants something to shift him. Have you got the arecoline with you?'

'If this is a torsion, arecoline would be the worst thing you could give him. He's in agony now, but that would drive him mad. It acts by contracting the muscles of the intestines.'

'God dammit,' snarled Soames, 'Don't start giving me a bloody lecture. Are you going to start doing something for the horse or aren't you?'

I turned to the big man in the corner. 'Slip on that head collar and I'll examine him.'

With the collar on, the horse was brought to a halt. He stood there, trembling and groaning as I passed a hand between ribs and elbows, feeling for the pulse. It was as bad as it could be – a racing, thready beat. I everted an eyelid with my fingers; the mucous membrane was a dark, brick red. The thermometer showed a temperature of a hundred and three.

I looked across the box at Soames. 'Could I have a bucket of hot water, soap and a towel, please?'

'What the devil for? You've done nothing yet and you want to have a wash?'

'I want to make a rectal examination. Will you please bring me the water?'

'God help us, I've never seen anything like this.' Soames passed a hand wearily over his eyes then swung round on the big man. 'Well, come on, don't stand around there. Get him his water and we'll maybe get something done.'

When the water came, I soaped my arm and gently inserted it into the animal's rectum. I could feel plainly the displacement of the small intestine on the left side and a tense, tympanitic mass which should not have been there. As I touched it, the horse shuddered and groaned again.

As I washed and dried my arms, my heart pounded. What was I to do? What could I say?

Soames was stamping in and out of the box, muttering to himself as the pain maddened animal writhed and twisted. 'Hold the bloody thing,' he bellowed at the horseman who was gripping the head collar. 'What the bloody hell are you playing at?'

The big man said nothing. He was in no way to blame but he just stared back stolidly at Soames.

I took a deep breath. 'Everything points to the one thing. I'm convinced this horse has a torsion.'

'All right then, have it your own way. He's got a torsion. Only for God's sake do something, will you? Are we going to stand in here all night?'

'There's nothing anybody can do. There is no cure for this. The important thing is to put him out of his pain as quickly as possible.'

Soames screwed up his face. 'No cure? Put him out of his pain? What rubbish is this you're talking? Just what are you getting at?'

I took a hold on myself. 'I suggest you let me put him down immediately.'

'What do you mean?' Soames' mouth fell open.

'I mean that I should shoot him now, straight away. I have a humane killer in the car.'

Soames looked as if he was going to explode. 'Shoot him! Are you stark raving mad? Do you know how much that horse is worth?'

'It makes no difference what he's worth, Mr Soames. He has been going through hell all day and he's dying now. You should have called me out long ago. He might live a few hours more but the end would be the same. And he's in dreadful pain, continuous pain.'

Soames sunk his head in his hands. 'Oh God, why did this have to happen to me? His lordship is on holiday or I'd call him out to try to make you see some sense. I tell you, if your boss had been here he'd have given that horse an injection and put him right in half an hour. Look here, can't we wait till Mr Farnon gets back tonight and let him have a look at him?'

Something in me leaped gladly at the idea. Give a shot of morphine and get away out of it. Leave the responsibility to somebody else. It would be easy. I looked again at the horse. He had recommenced his blind circling of the box, stumbling round and round in a despairing attempt to leave his agony behind. As I watched, he raised his lolling head and gave a little whinny. It was a desolate, uncomprehending, frantic sound and it was enough for me.

I strode quickly out and got the killer from the car. 'Steady his head,' I said to the big man and placed the muzzle between the glazing eyes. There was a sharp crack and the horse's legs buckled. He thudded down on the peat and lay still.

I turned to Soames who was staring at the body in disbelief. 'Mr Farnon will come round in the morning and carry out a post mortem. I'd like Lord Hulton to have my diagnosis confirmed.'

I put on my jacket and went out to the car. As I started the engine, Soames opened the door and pushed his head in. He spoke quietly but his voice was furious. 'I'm going to inform his lordship about this night's work. And Mr Farnon too. I'll let him know what kind of an assistant he's landed himself with. And let me tell you this. You'll be proved wrong at that post mortem tomorrow and then I'm going to sue you.' He banged the door shut and walked away.

Back at the surgery, I decided to wait up for my boss and I sat there trying to rid myself of the feeling that I had blasted my career before it had got started. Yet, looking back, I knew I couldn't have done anything else. No matter how many times I went over the ground, the conclusion was always the same.

It was 1 a.m. before Farnon got back. His evening with his mother had stimulated him. His thin cheeks were flushed and he smelt pleasantly of gin. I was surprised to see that he was wearing evening dress and though the dinner jacket was of old-fashioned cut and hung in loose folds on his bony frame, he still managed to look like an ambassador.

He listened in silence as I told him about the horse. He was about to comment when the phone rang. 'A late one,' he whispered, then 'Oh, it's you, Mr Soames.' He nodded at me and settled down in his chair. He was a long time saying 'Yes' and 'No' and 'I see', then he sat up decisively and began to speak.

'Thank you for ringing, Mr Soames, and it seems as though Mr Herriot did the only possible thing in the circumstances. No, I cannot agree. It would have been cruel to leave him. One of our duties is to prevent suffering. Well, I'm sorry you feel like that, but I consider Mr Herriot to be a highly capable veterinary surgeon. If I had been there I have no doubt I'd have done the same thing. Good night, Mr Soames, I'll see you in the morning.'

I felt so much better that I almost launched into a speech of gratitude, but in the end, all I said was 'Thanks'.

Farnon reached up into the glass-fronted cupboard above the mantelpiece and pulled out a bottle of whisky. He carelessly slopped out half a tumblerful and pushed it at me. He gave himself a similar measure and fell back into the armchair.

He took a deep swallow, stared for a few seconds at the amber fluid in the glass then looked up with a smile. 'Well, you certainly got chucked in at the deep end tonight, my boy. Your first case! And it had to be Soames, too.'

'Do you know him very well?'

'Oh, I know all about him. A nasty piece of work and enough to put anybody off their stroke. Believe me, he's no friend of mine. In fact, rumour has it that he's a bit of a crook. They say he's been feathering his nest for a long time at his lordship's expense. He'll slip up one day, I expect.'

The neat whisky burned a fiery path down to my stomach but I felt I needed it. 'I wouldn't like too many sessions like tonight's, but I don't suppose veterinary practice is like that all the time.'

'Well, not quite,' Farnon replied, 'but you never know what's in store for you. It's a funny profession, ours, you know. It offers unparalleled opportunities for making a chump of yourself.'

'But I expect a lot depends on your ability.'

'To a certain extent. It helps to be good at the job, of course, but even if you're a positive genius humiliation and ridicule are lurking just round the corner. I once got an eminent horse specialist along here to do a rig operation and the horse stopped breathing half way through. The sight of that man dancing frantically on his patient's ribs taught me a great truth – that I was going to look just as big a fool at fairly regular intervals throughout my career.'

I laughed. 'Then I might as well resign myself to it right at the beginning.'

'That's the idea. Animals are unpredictable things so our whole life is unpredictable. It's a long tale of little triumphs and disasters and you've got to really like it to stick it. Tonight it was Soames, but another night it'll be something else. One thing, you never get bored. Here, have some more whisky.'

I drank the whisky and then some more and we talked. It seemed no time at all before the dark bulk of the acacia tree began to emerge from the grey light beyond the french window, a blackbird tried a few tentative pipes and Farnon was regretfully shaking the last drops from the bottle into his glass.

He yawned, jerked the knot out of his black tie and looked at his watch. 'Well, five o'clock. Who would have thought it? But I'm glad we had a drink together – only right to celebrate your first case. It was a right one, wasn't it?'

Chapter Six

Two and a half hours' sleep was a meagre ration but I made a point of being up by seven thirty and downstairs, shaved and scrubbed, by eight.

But I breakfasted alone. Mrs Hall, impassively placing scrambled eggs before me, told me that my employer had left some time ago to do the PM on Lord Hulton's horse. I wondered if he had bothered to go to bed at all.

I was busy with the last of the toast when Farnon burst into the room. I was getting used to his entrances and hardly jumped at all as he wrenched at the door handle and almost leaped into the middle of the carpet. He looked rosy and in excellent spirits.

'Anything left in that coffee pot? I'll join you for a cup.' He crashed down on a protesting chair. 'Well, you've nothing to worry about. The PM showed a classical torsion. Several loops of bowel involved – black and tympanitic. I'm glad you put the poor beggar down straight away.'

'Did you see my friend Soames?'

'Oh, he was there, of course. He tried to get in a few digs about you but I quietened him. I just pointed out that he had delayed far too long in sending for us and that Lord Hulton wasn't going to be too pleased when he heard how his horse had suffered. I left him chewing over that.'

The news did a lot to lighten my outlook. I went over to the desk and got the day book. 'Here are this morning's calls. What would you like me to do?'

Farnon picked out a round of visits, scribbled the list on a scrap of paper and handed it over. 'Here you are,' he said, 'A few nice, trouble-free cases to get yourself worked in.'

I was turning to leave when he called me back. 'Oh, there's one other thing I'd like you to do. My young brother is hitching from Edinburgh today. He's at the Veterinary College there and the term finished yesterday. When he gets within striking distance he'll probably give us a ring. I wonder if you'd slip out and pick him up?'

'Certainly. Glad to.'

'His name is Tristan, by the way.'

'Tristan?'

'Yes. Oh, I should have told you. You must have wondered about my own queer name. It was my father. Great Wagnerian. It nearly ruled his life. It was music all the time – mainly Wagner.'

'I'm a bit partial myself.'

'Ah well, yes, but you didn't get it morning noon and night like we did. And then to be stuck with a name like Siegfried. Anyway, it could have been worse – Wotan, for instance.'

'Or Pogner.'

Farnon looked startled. 'By golly, you're right. I'd forgotten about old Pogner. I suppose I've a lot to be thankful for.'

It was late afternoon before the expected call came. The voice at the other end was uncannily familiar.

'This is Tristan Farnon.'

'Gosh, you sound just like you brother.'

A pleasant laugh answered me. 'Everybody says that – oh, that's very good of you. I'd be glad of a lift. I'm at the Holly Tree Café on the Great North Road.'

After the voice I had been expecting to find a younger edition of my employer but the small, boyish-faced figure sitting on a rucksack could hardly have been less like him. He got up, pushed back the dark hair from his forehead and held out his hand. The smile was charming.

'Had much walking to do?' I asked.

'Oh, a fair bit, but I needed the exercise. We had a roughish end of term party last night.' He opened the car door and threw the rucksack into the back. As I started the engine he settled himself in the passenger seat as though it were a luxurious armchair, pulled out a paper packet of Woodbines, lit one with tender concentration and gulped the smoke down blissfully. He produced the *Daily Mirror* from a side pocket and shook it open with a sigh of utter content. The smoke, which had been gone a long time, began to wisp from his nose and mouth.

I turned West off the great highway and the rumble of traffic faded rapidly behind us. I glanced round at Tristan. 'You'll have just finished exams?' I said.
'Yes, pathology and parasitology.'

I almost broke one of my steadfast rules by asking him if he had passed, but stopped myself in time. It is a chancy business. But in any case, there was no shortage of conversation. Tristan had something to say about most of the news items and now and then he read out an extract and discussed it with me. I felt a growing conviction that I was in the presence of a quicker and livelier mind than my own. It seemed no time at all before we pulled up outside Skeldale House.

Siegfried was out when we arrived and it was early evening when he returned. He came in through the french window, gave me a friendly greeting and threw himself into an armchair. He had begun to talk about one of his cases when Tristan walked in.

The atmosphere in the room changed as though somebody had clicked a switch. Siegfried's smile became sardonic and he gave his brother a long, appraising look. He grunted a 'hello', then reached up and began to run his finger along the titles of the books in the alcove. He seemed absorbed in this for a few minutes and I could feel the tension building up. Tristan's expression had changed remarkably; his face had gone completely deadpan but his eyes were wary.

Siegfried finally located the book he was looking for, took it down from the shelf and began to leaf through it unhurriedly. Then, without looking up, he said quietly: 'Well, how did the exams go?'

Tristan swallowed carefully and took a deep breath. 'Did all right in parasitology,' he replied in a flat monotone.

Siegfried didn't appear to have heard. He had found something interesting in his book and settled back to read. He took his time over it, then put the book back on the shelf. He began again the business of going along the titles; still with his back to his brother, he spoke again in the same soft voice.

'How about pathology?'

Tristan was on the edge of his chair now, as if ready to make a run for it. His eyes darted from his brother to the book shelves and back again. 'Didn't get it,' he said tonelessly.

There was no reaction from Siegfried. He kept up his patient search for his book, occasionally pulling a volume out, glancing at it and replacing it carefully. Then he gave up the hunt, lay back in the chair with his arms dangling almost to the floor and looked at Tristan. 'So you failed pathology,' he said conversationally.

I was surprised to hear myself babbling with an edge of hysteria in my voice. 'Well now that's pretty good you know. It puts him in the final year and he'll be able to sit path. at Christmas. He won't lose any time that way and, after all, it's a tough subject.'

Siegfried turned a cold eye on me. 'So you think it's pretty good, do you?' There was a pause and a long silence which was broken by a totally unexpected bellow as he rounded on his brother. 'Well, I don't! I think it is bloody awful! It's a damned disgrace, that's what it is. What the hell have you been doing all this term, anyway? Boozing, I should think, chasing women, spending my money, anything but working. And now you've got the bloody nerve to walk in here and tell me you've failed pathology. You're lazy, that's your trouble, isn't it? You're bloody bone idle!'

He was almost unrecognisable. His face was darkly flushed and his eyes glared. He yelled wildly again at his brother. 'But I've had enough this time. I'm sick of you. I'm not going to work my fingers to the bloody bone to keep you up there idling your time away. This is the end. You're sacked, do you hear me. Sacked once and for all. So get out of here – I don't want to see you around any more. Go on, get out!'

Tristan, who had preserved an air of injured dignity throughout, withdrew quietly.

Writhing with embarrassment, I looked at Siegfried. He was showing the strain of the interview. His complexion had gone blotchy; he muttered to himself and drummed his fingers on the arm of the chair.

I was aghast at having to witness this break-up and I was grateful when Siegfried sent me on a call and I was able to get out of the room.

It was nearly dark when I got back and I drove round to the back lane and into the yard at the foot of the garden. The creaking of the garage doors disturbed the rooks in the great elms which overhung the buildings. Far up in the darkness there was a faint fluttering, a muffled cawing then silence. As I stood listening, I became aware of a figure in the gloom, standing by the yard door, looking down the garden. As the face turned towards me I saw it was Tristan.

Again, I felt embarrassed. It was an unfortunate intrusion when the poor fellow had come up here to brood alone. 'Sorry about the way things turned out,' I said awkwardly.

The tip of the cigarette glowed brightly as Tristan took a long pull. 'No, no, that's all right. Could have been a lot worse, you know.'

'Worse? Well, it's bad enough, isn't it? What are you going to do?'

'Do? What do you mean?'

'Well, you've been kicked out, haven't you? Where are you going to sleep tonight?'

'I can see you don't understand,' Tristan said. He took his cigarette from his mouth and I saw the gleam of very white teeth as he smiled. 'You needn't worry, I'm sleeping here and I'll be down to breakfast in the morning.'

'But how about your brother?'

'Siegfried? Oh, he'll have forgotten all about it by then.'

'Are you sure?'

'Dead sure. He's always sacking me and he always forgets. Anyway, things turned out very well. The only tricky bit back there was getting him to swallow that bit about the parasitology.'

I stared at the shadowy form by my side. Again, there was a rustling as the rooks stirred in the tall trees then settled into silence.

'The parasitology?'

'Yes. If you think back, all I said was that I had done all right. I wasn't any more specific than that.'

'Then you mean . . ?'

Tristan laughed softly and thumped my shoulder.

'That's right, I didn't get parasitology. I failed in both. But don't worry, I'll pass them at Christmas.'

Chapter Seven

I huddled deeper in the blankets as the strident brreeng-brreeng, brreeng-brreeng of the telephone echoed through the old house.

It was three weeks since Tristan's arrival and life at Skeldale House had settled into a fairly regular pattern. Every day began much the same with the phone ringing between seven and eight o'clock after the farmers had had the first look at their stock.

There was only one phone in the house. It rested on a ledge in the tiled passage downstairs. Siegfried had impressed on me that I shouldn't get out of bed for these early calls. He had delegated the job to Tristan; the responsibility would be good for him. Siegfried had been emphatic about it.

I listened to the ringing. It went on and on – it seemed to get louder. There was neither sound nor movement from Tristan's room and I waited for the next move in the daily drama. It came, as always, with a door crashing back on its hinges, then Siegfried rushed out on to the landing and bounded down the stairs three at a time.

A long silence followed and I could picture him shivering in the draughty passage, his bare feet freezing on the tiles as he listened to the farmer's leisurely account of the animal's symptoms. Then the ting of the phone in its rest and the mad pounding of feet on the stairs as Siegfried made a dash for his brother's room.

Next a wrenching sound as the door was flung open, then a yell of rage. I detected a note of triumph; it meant Tristan had been caught in bed – a definite victory for Siegfried and he didn't have many victories. Usually, Tristan exploited his quick-dressing technique and confronted his brother fully dressed. It gave him a psychological advantage to be knotting his tie when Siegfried was still in pyjamas.

But this morning Tristan had overplayed his hand; trying to snatch the extra few seconds he was caught between the sheets. I listened to the shouts. 'Why didn't you answer the bloody phone like I told you? Don't tell me you're deaf as well as idle! Come on, out of it, out, out!'

But I knew Tristan would make a quick come-back. When he was caught in bed he usually scored a few points by being half way through his breakfast before his brother came in.

Later, I watched Siegfried's face as he entered the dining-room and saw Tristan munching his toast happily, his *Daily Mirror* balanced against the coffee pot. It was as if he had felt a sudden twinge of toothache.

It all made for a strained atmosphere and I was relieved when I was able to escape to collect my things for the morning round. Down the narrow passage with its familiar, exciting smell of ether and carbolic and out into the high-walled garden which led to the yard where the cars were kept.

It was the same every morning but, to me, there was always the feeling of surprise. When I stepped out into the sunshine and the scent of the flowers it was as though I was doing it for the first time. The clear air held a breath of the nearby moorland; after being buried in a city for five years it was difficult to take it all in.

I never hurried over this part. There could be an urgent case waiting but I still took my time. Along the narrow part between the ivy-covered wall and the long offshoot of the house where the wistaria climbed, pushing its tendrils and its withered blooms into the very rooms. Then past the rockery where the garden widened to the lawn, unkempt and lost looking but lending coolness and softness to the weathered brick. Around its borders flowers blazed in untidy profusion, battling with a jungle of weeds.

And so to the rose garden, then an asparagus bed whose fleshy fingers had grown into tall fronds. Further on were strawberries and raspberries. Fruit trees were everywhere, their branches dangling low over the path. Peaches, pears, cherries and plums were trained against the South wall where they fought for a place with wild-growing rambler roses.

Bees were at work among the flowers and the song of blackbirds and thrushes competed with the cawing of the rooks high up in the elms.

Life was full for me. There were so many things to find out and a lot I had to prove to myself. The days were quick and challenging and they pressed on me with their very newness. But it all stopped here in the garden. Everything seemed to have stopped here a long time ago. I looked back before going through the door into the yard and it was like suddenly coming across a picture in an old book; the empty, wild garden and the tall, silent house beyond. I could never quite believe it was there and that I was a part of it.

And the feeling was heightened when I went into the yard. It was square and cobbled and the grass grew in thick tufts between the stones. Buildings took up two sides; the two garages, once coach houses, a stable and saddle room, a loose box and a pig sty. Against the free wall a rusty iron pump hung over a stone water trough.

Above the stable was a hay loft and over one of the garages a dovecot. And there was old Boardman. He, too, seemed to have been left behind from grander days, hobbling round on his lame leg, doing nothing in particular.

He grunted good morning from his cubby hole where he kept a few tools and garden implements. Above his head his reminders of the war looked down; a row of coloured prints of Bruce Bairnsfather cartoons. He had stuck them up when he came home in 1918 and there they were still, dusty and curled at the edges but still speaking to him of Kaiser Bill and the shell holes and muddy trenches.

Boardman washed a car sometimes or did a little work in the garden, but he was content to earn a pound or two and get back to his yard. He spent a lot of time in the saddle room, just sitting. Sometimes he looked round the empty hooks where the harness used to hang and then he would make a rubbing movement with his fist against his palm.

He often talked to me of the great days. 'I can see t'owd doctor now, standing on top step waiting for his carriage to come round. Big, smart looking feller he was. Allus wore a top hat and frock coat, and I can remember him when I was a lad, standing there, pulling on 'is gloves and giving his hat a tilt while he waited.'

Boardman's features seemed to soften and a light came into his eyes as though he were talking more to himself than to me. 'The old house was different then. A housekeeper and six servants there were and everything just so. And a full time gardener. There weren't a blade of grass out of place in them days and the flowers all in rows and the trees pruned, tidy-like. And this yard – it were t'owd doctor's favourite spot. He'd come and look over t' door at me sitting here polishing the harness and pass time o' day, quiet like. He were a real gentleman but you couldn't cross 'im. A few specks o' dust anywhere down here and he'd go nearly mad.'

'But the war finished it all. Everybody's rushing about now. They don't care about them things now. They've no time, no time at all.'

He would look round in disbelief at the overgrown cobbles, the peeling garage doors hanging crazily on their hinges. At the empty stable and the pump from which no water flowed.

He was always friendly with me in an absent way, but with Siegfried he seemed to step back into his former character, holding himself up smartly and saying 'Very good, sir,' and saluting repeatedly with one finger. It was as though he recognised something there – something of the strength of authority of t'owd doctor – and reached out eagerly towards the lost days.

'Morning, Boardman,' I said, as I opened the garage door. 'How are you today?'

'Oh, middlin' lad, just middlin'.' He limped across and watched me get the starting handle and begin the next part of the daily routine. The car allotted to me was a tiny Austin of an almost forgotten vintage and one of Boardman's voluntary duties was towing it off when it wouldn't start. But this morning, surprisingly, the engine coughed into life after six turns.

As I drove round the corner of the back lane, I had the feeling, as I did every morning, that this was where things really got started. The problems and pressures of my job were waiting for me out there and at the moment I seemed to have plenty.

I had arrived in the Dales, I felt, at a bad time. The farmers, after a generation of neglect, had seen the coming of a prophet, the wonderful new vet, Mr Farnon. He appeared like a comet, trailing his new ideas in his wake. He was able, energetic and charming and they received him as a maiden would a lover. And now, at the height of the honeymoon, I had to push my way into the act, and I just wasn't wanted.

I was beginning to get used to the questions. 'Where's Mr Farnon?' – 'Is he ill or something?' – 'I expected Mr Farnon.' It was a bit daunting to watch their faces fall when they saw me walking on to their farms. Usually they looked past me hopefully and some even went and peered into the car to see if the man they really wanted was hiding in there.

And it was uphill work examining an animal when its owner was chafing in the background, wishing with all his heart that I was somebody else.

But I had to admit they were fair. I got no effusive welcomes and when I started to tell them what I thought about the case they listened with open scepticism, but I found that if I got my jacket off and really worked at the job they began to thaw a little. And they were hospitable. Even though they were disappointed at having me they asked me into their homes. 'Come in and have a bit o' dinner,' was a phrase I heard nearly every day. Sometimes I was glad to accept and I ate some memorable meals with them.

Often, too, they would slip half a dozen eggs or a pound of butter into the car as I was leaving. This hospitality was traditional in the Dales and I knew they would probably do the same for any visitor, but it showed the core of friendliness which lay under the often unsmiling surface of these people and it helped.

I was beginning to learn about the farmers and what I found I liked. They had a toughness and a philosophical attitude which was new to me. Misfortunes which would make the city dweller want to bang his head against a wall were shrugged off with 'Aye, well, these things happen.'

It looked like being another hot day and I wound down the car windows as far as they would go. I was on my way to do a tuberculin test; the national scheme was beginning to make its first impact in the Dales and the more progressive farmers were asking for survey tests.

And this was no ordinary herd. Mr Copfield's Galloway cattle were famous in their way. Siegfried had told me about them. 'The toughest lot in this practice. There's eighty five of them and none has ever been tied up. In fact, they've scarcely been touched by hand. They live out on the fells, they calve and rear their calves outside. It isn't often anybody goes near them so they're practically wild animals.'

'What do you do when there's anything wrong with them?' I had asked.

'Well, you have to depend on Frank and George – they're the two Copfield sons. They've been reared with those cattle since they were babies – started tackling the little calves as soon as they could walk, then worked up to the big ones. They're about as tough as the Galloways.'

Copfield's place was one of the bleak ones. Looking across the sparse pastures to the bald heights with their spreading smudges of heather it was easy to see why the farmer had chosen a breed hardier then the local shorthorns. But this morning the grim outlines were softened by the sunshine and there was a desert peace in the endless greens and browns.

Frank and George were not as I expected. The durable men who helped me in my daily jobs tended to be dark and lean with stringy muscles but the Copfields were golden haired and smooth skinned. They were good looking young men about my own age and their massive necks and wide spread of shoulder made their heads look small. Neither of them was tall but they looked formidable with their shirt sleeves rolled high to reveal wrestlers' arms and their thick legs encased in cloth gaiters. Both wore clogs.

The cattle had been herded into the buildings and they just about filled all the available accommodation. There were about twenty-five in a long passage down the side of the fold yard; I could see the ragged line of heads above the rails, the steam rising from their bodies. Twenty more occupied an old stable and two lots of twenty milled about in large loose boxes.

I looked at the black, untamed animals and they looked back at me, their reddish eyes glinting through the rough fringe of hair which fell over their faces. They kept up a menacing, bad-tempered swishing with their tails.

It wasn't going to be easy to get an intradermal injection into every one of them. I turned to Frank.

'Can you catch these beggars?' I asked.

'We'll 'ave a bloody good try,' he replied calmly, throwing a halter over his shoulder. He and his brother lit cigarettes before climbing into the passage where the biggest beasts were packed. I followed them and soon found that the tales I had heard about the Galloways hadn't been exaggerated. If I approached them from the front they came at me with their great hairy heads and if I went behind them they kicked me as a matter of course.

But the brothers amazed me. One of them would drop a halter on a beast, get his fingers into its nose and then be carried away as the animal took off like a rocket. They were thrown about like dolls but they never let go; their fair heads bobbed about incongruously among the black backs; and the thing that fascinated me was that through all the contortions the cigarettes dangled undisturbed.

The heat increased till it was like an oven in the buildings and the animals, their bowels highly fluid with their grass diet, ejected greenish-brown muck like non-stop geysers.

The affair was conducted in the spirit of a game with encouragement shouted to the man in action: 'Thou 'as 'im, Frank.' 'Sniggle 'im, George.' In moments of stress the brothers cursed softly and without heat: 'Get off ma bloody foot, thou awd bitch.' They both stopped work and laughed with sincere appreciation when a cow slashed me across the face with her sodden tail; and another little turn which was well received was when I was filling my syringe with both arms raised and a bullock, backing in alarm from the halter, crashed its craggy behind into my midriff. The wind shot out of me in a sharp hiccup, then the animal decided to turn round in the narrow passage, squashing me like a fly against the railings. I was pop-eyed as it scrambled round; I wondered whether the creaking was coming from my ribs or the wood behind me.

We finished up with the smallest calves and they were just about the most difficult to handle. The shaggy little creatures kicked, bucked, sprang into the air, ran through our legs and even hurtled straight up the walls. Often the brothers had to throw themselves on top of them and bear them to the ground before I could inject them and when the calves felt the needle they stuck out their tongues and bawled deafeningly; outside, the anxious mothers bellowed back in chorus.

It was midday when I reeled out of the buildings. I seemed to have been a month in there, in the suffocating heat, the continuous din, the fusillade of muck.

Frank and George produced a bucket of water and a scrubbing brush and gave me a rough clean-up before I left. A mile from the farm I drove off the unfenced road, got out of the car and dropped down on the cool fell-side. Throwing wide my arms I wriggled my shoulders and my sweat-soaked shirt into the tough grass and let the sweet breeze play over me. With the sun on my face I looked through half closed eyes at the hazy-blue sky.

My ribs ached and I could feel the bruises of a dozen kicks on my legs. I knew I didn't smell so good either. I closed my eyes and grinned at the ridiculous thought that I had been conducting a diagnostic investigation for tuberculosis back there. A strange way to carry out a scientific procedure; a strange way, in fact, to earn a living.

But then I might have been in an office with the windows tight shut against the petrol fumes and the traffic noise, the desk light shining on the columns of figures, my bowler hat hanging on the wall.

Lazily I opened my eyes again and watched a cloud shadow riding over the face of the green hill across the valley. No, no . . . I wasn't complaining.

Chapter Eight

I hardly noticed the passage of the weeks as I rattled along the moorland roads on my daily rounds; but the district was beginning to take shape, the people to emerge as separate personalities. Most days I had a puncture. The tyres were through to the canvas on all wheels; it surprised me that they took me anywhere at all.

One of the few refinements on the car was a rusty 'sunshine roof'. It grated dismally when I slid it back, but most of the time I kept it open and the windows too, and I drove in my shirt sleeves with the delicious air swirling about me. On wet days it didn't help much to close the roof because the rain dripped through the joints and formed pools on my lap and the passenger seat.

I developed great skill in zig-zagging round puddles. To drive through was a mistake as the muddy water fountained up through the gaps in the floor boards.

But it was a fine Summer and long days in the open gave me a tan which rivalled the farmers'. Even mending a puncture was no penance on the high, unfenced roads with the wheeling curlews for company and the wind bringing the scents of flowers and trees up from the valleys. And I could find other excuses to get out and sit on the crisp grass and look out over the airy roof of Yorkshire. It was like taking time out of life. Time to get things into perspective and assess my progress. Everything was so different that it confused me. This countryside after years of city streets, the sense of release from exams and study, the job with its daily challenge. And then there was my boss.

Siegfried Farnon charged round the practice with fierce energy from dawn till dark and I often wondered what drove him on. It wasn't money because he treated it with scant respect. When the bills were paid, the cash went into the pint pot on the mantelpiece and he grabbed handfuls when he wanted it. I never saw him take out a wallet, but his pockets bulged with loose silver and balled up notes. When he pulled out a thermometer they flew around him in a cloud.

After a week or two of headlong rush he would disappear; maybe for the evening, maybe overnight and often without saying where he was going. Mrs Hall would serve a meal for two, but when she saw I was eating alone she would remove the food without comment.

He dashed off the list of calls each morning with such speed that I was quite often sent hurrying off to the wrong farm or to do the wrong thing. When I told him later of my embarrassment he would laugh heartily.

There was one time when he got involved himself. I had just taken a call from a Mr Heaton of Bronsett about doing a PM on a dead sheep.

'I'd like you to come with me James,' Siegfried said. 'Things are quiet this morning and I believe they teach you blokes a pretty hot post mortem procedure. I want to see you in action.'

We drove into the village of Bronsett and Siegfried swung the car left into a gated lane.

'Where are you going?' I said. 'Heaton's is at the other end of the village.'

'But you said Seaton's.'

'No, I assure you . . .'

'Look, James, I was right by you when you were talking to the man. I distinctly heard you say the name.'

I opened my mouth to argue further but the car was hurtling down the lane and Siegfried's jaw was jutting. I decided to let him find out for himself.

We arrived outside the farmhouse with a screaming of brakes. Siegfried had left his seat and was rummaging in the boot before the car had stopped shuddering. 'Hell!' he shouted, 'No post mortem knife. Never mind, I'll borrow something from the house.' He slammed down the lid and bustled over to the door.

The farmer's wife answered and Siegfried beamed on her. 'Good morning to you, Mrs Seaton, have you a carving knife?'

The good lady raised her eyebrows. 'What was that you said?'

'A carving knife, Mrs Seaton, a carving knife, and a good sharp one, please.'

'You want a carving knife?'

'Yes, that's right, a carving knife!' Siegfried cried, his scanty store of patience beginning to run out. 'And I wonder if you'd mind hurrying. I haven't much time.'

The bewildered woman withdrew to the kitchen and I could hear whispering and muttering. Children's heads peeped out at intervals to get a quick look at

Siegfried stamping irritably on the step. After some delay, one of the daughters advanced timidly, holding out a long, dangerous-looking knife.

Siegfried snatched it from her hand and ran his thumb up and down the edge. 'This is no damn good!' he shouted in exasperation. 'Don't you understand I want something really sharp. Fetch me a steel.'

The girl fled back into the kitchen and there was a low rumble of voices. It was some minutes before another young girl was pushed round the door. She inched her way up to Siegfried, gave him the steel at arm's length and dashed back to safety.

Siegfried prided himself on his skill at sharpening a knife. It was something he enjoyed doing. As he stropped the knife on the steel, he warmed to his work and finally burst into song. There was no sound from the kitchen, only the ring of steel backed by the tuneless singing; there were silent intervals when he carefully tested the edge, then the noise would start again.

When he had completed the job to his satisfaction he peered inside the door. 'Where is your husband?' he called.

There was no reply so he strode into the kitchen, waving the gleaming blade in front of him. I followed him and saw Mrs Seaton and her daughters cowering in the far corner, staring at Siegfried with large, frightened eyes.

He made a sweeping gesture at them with the knife. 'Well, come on, I can get started now!'

'Started what?' the mother whispered, holding her family close to her.

'I want to PM this sheep. You have a dead sheep, haven't you?'

Explanations and apologies followed.

Later, Siegfried remonstrated gravely with me for sending him to the wrong farm.

'You'll have to be a bit more careful in future, James,' he said seriously. 'Creates a very bad impression, that sort of thing.'

Another thing about my new life which interested me was the regular traffic of women through Skeldale House. They were all upper class, mostly beautiful and they had one thing in common – eagerness. They came for drinks, for tea, to dinner, but the real reason was to gaze at Siegfried like parched travellers in the desert sighting an oasis.

I found it damaging to my own ego when their eyes passed over me without recognition or interest and fastened themselves hungrily on my colleague. I wasn't envious, but I was puzzled. I used to study him furtively, trying to fathom the secret of his appeal. Looking at the worn jacket hanging from the thin shoulders, the frayed shirt collar and anonymous tie, I had to conclude that clothes had nothing to do with it.

There was something attractive in the long, bony face and humorous blue eyes, but a lot of the time he was so haggard and sunken-cheeked that I wondered if he was ill.

I often spotted Diana Brompton in the queue and at these times I had to fight down an impulse to dive under the sofa. She was difficult to recognise as the brassy beauty of that afternoon as she looked up meltingly at Siegfried, hanging on his words, giggling like a schoolgirl.

I used to grow cold at the thought that Siegfried might pick her out of the mob and marry her. It worried me a lot because I knew I would have to leave just when I was beginning to enjoy everything about Darrowby.

But Siegfried showed no sign of marrying any of them and the procession continued hopefully. I finally got used to it and stopped worrying.

I got used, too, to my employer's violent changes of front. There was one morning when Siegfried came down to breakfast, rubbing a hand wearily over red-rimmed eyes.

'Out at 4 a.m.,' he groaned, buttering his toast listlessly. 'And I don't like to have to say this, James, but it's all your fault.'

'My fault?' I said, startled.

'Yes, lad, your fault. This was a cow with a mild impaction of the rumen. The farmer had been mucking about with it himself for days; a pint of linseed oil one day, a bit of bicarb and ginger the next, and at four o'clock in the morning he decides it is time to call the vet. When I pointed out it could have waited a few hours more he said Mr Herriot told him never to hesitate to ring – he'd come out any hour of the day or night.'

He tapped the top of his egg as though the effort was almost too much for him. 'Well, it's all very well being conscientious and all that, but if a thing has waited several days it can wait till morning. You're spoiling these chaps, James, and I'm getting the backwash of it. I'm sick and tired of being dragged out of my bed for trifles.'

'I'm truly sorry, Siegfried. I honestly had no wish to do that to you. Maybe it's just my inexperience. If I didn't go out, I'd be worried the animal might die. If I left it till morning and it died, how would I feel?'

'That's all right,' snapped Siegfried. 'There's nothing like a dead animal to bring them to their senses. They'll call us out a bit earlier next time.'

I absorbed this bit of advice and tried to act on it. A week later, Siegfried said he wanted a word with me.

'James, I know you won't mind my saying this, but old Sumner was complaining to me today. He says he rang you the other night and you refused to come out to his cow. He's a good client, you know, and a very nice fellow, but he was quite shirty about it. We don't want to lose a chap like that.'

'But it was just a chronic mastitis,' I said. 'A bit of thickening in the milk, that's all. He'd been dosing it himself for nearly a week with some quack remedy. The cow was eating all right, so I thought it would be quite safe to leave it till next day.'

Siegfried put a hand on my shoulder and an excessively patient look spread over his face. I steeled myself. I didn't mind his impatience; I was used to it and could stand it. But the patience was hard to take.

'James,' he said in a gentle voice, 'There is one fundamental rule in our job which transcends all others, and I'll tell you what it is. YOU MUST ATTEND. That is it and it ought to be written on your soul in letters of fire.' He raised a portentous forefinger. 'YOU MUST ATTEND. Always remember that, James; it is the basis of everything. No matter what the circumstances, whether it be wet or fine, night or day, if a client calls you out, you must go; and go cheerfully. You say this didn't sound like an urgent case. Well, after all, you have only the owner's description to guide you and he is not equipped with the knowledge to decide whether it is urgent or not. No, lad, you have to go. Even if they have been treating the animal themselves, it may have taken a turn for the worse. And don't forget,' wagging the finger solemnly 'the animal may die.'

'But I thought you said there was nothing like a dead animal to bring them to their senses.' I said querulously.

'What's that?' barked Siegfried, utterly astonished. 'Never heard such rubbish. Let's have no more of it. Just remember – YOU MUST ATTEND.'

Sometimes he would give me advice on how to live. As when he found me hunched over the phone which I had just crashed down; I was staring at the wall, swearing softly to myself.

Siegfried smiled whimsically. 'Now what is it, James?'

'I've just have a torrid ten minutes with Rolston. You remember that outbreak of calf pneumonia? Well, I spent hours with those calves, poured expensive drugs into them. There wasn't a single death. And now he's complaining about his bill. Not a word of thanks. Hell, there's no justice.'

Siegfried walked over and put his arm round my shoulders. He was wearing his patient look again. 'My dear chap,' he coo'd. 'Just look at you. Red in the face, all tensed up. You mustn't let yourself get upset like this; you must try to relax. Why do you think professional men are cracking up all over the country with coronaries and ulcers? Just because they allow themselves to get all steamed up over piffling little things like you are doing now. Yes, yes, I know these things are annoying, but you've got to take them in your stride. Keep calm, James, calm. It just isn't worth it – I mean, it will all be the same in a hundred years.'

He delivered the sermon with a serene smile, patting my shoulder reassuringly like a psychiatrist soothing a violent patient.

I was writing a label on a jar of red blister a few days later when Siegfried catapulted into the room He must have kicked the door open because it flew back viciously against the rubber stop and rebounded almost into his face. He rushed over to the desk where I was sitting and began to pound on it with the flat of his hand. His eyes glared wildly from a flushed face.

'I've just come from that bloody swine Holt!' he shouted.

'Ned Holt, you mean?'

'Yes, that's who I mean, damn him!'

I was surprised. Mr Holt was a little man who worked on the roads for the county council. He kept four cows as a sideline and had never been known to pay a veterinary bill; but he was a cheerful character and Siegfried had rendered his unpaid services over the years without objection.

'One of your favourites, isn't he?' I said.

'Was, by God, was,' Siegfried snarled. 'I've been treating Muriel for him. You know, the big red cow second from the far end of his byre. She's had recurrent tympany – coming in from the field every night badly blown – and I'd tried about everything. Nothing did any good. Then it struck me that it might be actinobacillosis of the reticulum. I shot some sodium iodide into the vein and when I saw her today the difference was incredible – she was standing there, chewing her cud, right as rain. I was just patting myself on the back for a smart piece of diagnosis, and do you know what Holt said? He said he knew she'd be better today because last night he gave her half a pound of epsom salts in a bran mash. That was what had cured her.'

Siegfried took some empty cartons and bottles from his pockets and hurled them savagely into the wastepaper basket. He began to shout again.

'Do you know, for the past fortnight I've puzzled and worried and damn nearly dreamt about that cow. Now I've found the cause of the trouble, applied the most modern treatment and the animal has recovered. And what happens? Does the owner express his grateful thanks for my skill? Does he hell – the entire credit goes to the half pound of epsom salts. What I did was a pure waste of time.'

He dealt the desk another sickening blow.

'But I frightened him, James,' he said, his eyes staring, 'By God, I frightened him. When he made that crack about the salts, I yelled out "You bugger!" and made a grab for him. I think I would have strangled him, but he shot into the house and stayed there. I didn't see him again.'

Siegfried threw himself into a chair and began to churn his hair about. 'Epsom salts!' he groaned. 'Oh God, it makes you despair.'

I thought of telling him to relax and pointing out that it would all be the same in a hundred years, but my employer still had an empty serum bottle dangling from one hand. I discarded the idea.

Then there came the day when Siegfried decided to have my car rebored. It had been using a steady two pints of oil a day and he hadn't thought this excessive, but when it got to half a gallon a day he felt something ought to be done. What probably decided him was a farmer on market day saying he always knew when the young vet was coming because he could see the cloud of blue smoke miles away.

When the tiny Austin came back from the garage, Siegfried fussed round it like an old hen. 'Come over here, James,' he called. 'I want to talk to you.'

I saw he was looking patient again and braced myself.

'James,' he said, pacing round the battered vehicle, whisking specks from the paintwork. 'You see this car?'

I nodded.

'Well, it has been rebored, James, rebored at great expense, and that's what I want to talk to you about. You now have in your possession what amounts to a new car.' With an effort he unfastened the catch and the bonnet creaked open in a shower of rust and dirt. He pointed down at the engine, black and oily, with unrelated pieces of flex and rubber tubing hanging around it like garlands. 'You have a piece of fine mechanism here and I want you to treat it with respect. I've seen you belting along like a maniac and it won't do. You've got to nurse this machine for the next two or three thousand miles; thirty miles an hour is quite fast enough. I think it's a crime the way some people abuse a new engine – they should be locked up – so remember, lad, no flogging or I'll be down on you.'

He closed the bonnet with care, gave the cracked windscreen a polish with the cuff of his coat and left.

These strong words made such an impression on me that I crawled round the visits all day almost at walking pace.

The same night, I was getting ready for bed when Siegfried came in. He had two farm lads with him and they both wore silly grins. A powerful smell of beer filled the room.

Siegfried spoke with dignity, slurring his words only slightly. 'James, I met these gentlemen in the Black Bull this evening. We have had several excellent games of dominoes but unfortunately they have missed the last bus. Will you kindly bring the Austin round and I will run them home.'

I drove the car to the front of the house and the farm lads piled in, one in the front, the other in the back. I looked at Siegfried lowering himself unsteadily into the driving seat and decided to go along. I got into the back.

The two young men lived in a farm far up on the North Moors and, three miles out of the town, we left the main road and our headlights picked out a strip of track twisting along the dark hillside.

Siegfried was in a hurry. He kept his foot on the boards, the note of the engine rose to a tortured scream and the little car hurtled on into the blackness. Hanging on grimly, I leaned forward so that I could shout into my employer's ear. 'Remember this is the car which has just been rebored,' I bellowed above the din.

Siegfried look round with an indulgent smile. 'Yes, yes, I remember, James. What are you fussing about?' As he spoke, the car shot off the road and bounded over the grass at sixty miles an hour. We all bounced around like corks till he found his way back. Unperturbed, he carried on at the same speed. The silly grins had left the lads' faces and they sat rigid in their seats. Nobody said anything.

The passengers were unloaded at a silent farmhouse and the return journey began. Since it was downhill all the way, Siegfried found he could go even faster. The car leaped and bumped over the uneven surface with its engine whining. We made several brief but tense visits to the surrounding moors, but we got home.

It was a month later that Siegfried had occasion to take his assistant to task once more. 'James, my boy,' he said sorrowfully, 'you are a grand chap, but by God, you're hard on cars. Look at this Austin. Newly rebored a short time ago, in tip top condition, and look at it now – drinking oil. I don't know how you did it in the time. You're a real terror.'

Chapter Nine

'First, please,' I called as I looked into the waiting room. There was an old lady with a cat in a cardboard box, two small boys trying to keep hold of a rabbit, and somebody I didn't recognise at first. Then I remembered – it was Soames.

When it was his turn, he came into the surgery but he was a vastly different character from the one I knew. He wore an ingratiating smile. His head bobbed up and down as he spoke. He radiated anxiety to please. And the most interesting thing was that his right eye was puffed and closed and surrounded by an extensive area of bluish-black flesh.

'I hope you don't mind my coming to see you, Mr Herriot,' he said. 'The fact is I have resigned my position with his lordship and am looking for another post. I was wondering if you and Mr Farnon would put in a word for me if you heard of anything.'

I was too astonished at the transformation to say much. I replied that we would do what we could and Soames thanked me effusively and bowed himself out.

I turned to Siegfried after he had gone. 'Well, what do you make of that?'

'Oh, I know all about it.' Siegfried looked at me with a wry smile. 'Remember I told you he was working one or two shady sidelines up there – selling a few bags of corn or a hundredweight of fertiliser here and there. It all mounted up. But it didn't last; he got a bit careless and he was out on his ear before he knew what had happened.'

'And how about the lovely black eye?'

'Oh, he got that from Tommy. You must have seen Tommy when you were there. He's the horseman.'

My mind went back to that uncomfortable night and to the quiet man holding the horse's head. 'I remember him – big fat chap.'

'Yes, he's a big lad and I'd hate to have him punch me in the eye. Soames gave him a hell of a life and as soon as Tommy heard about the sacking he paid a visit just to settle the score.'

I was now comfortably settled into the way of life in Skeldale House. At first I wondered where Tristan fitted into the set up. Was he supposed to be seeing practice, having a holiday, working or what? But it soon became clear that he was a factotum who dispensed and delivered medicines, washed the cars, answered the phone and even, in an emergency, went to a case.

At least, that was how Siegfried saw him and he had a repertoire of tricks aimed at keeping him on his toes. Like returning unexpectedly or bursting into a room in the hope of catching him doing nothing. He never seemed to notice the obvious fact that the college vacation was over and Tristan should have been back there. I came to the conclusion over the next few months that Tristan must have had some flexible arrangement with the college authorities because, for a student, he seemed to spend a surprising amount of time at home.

He interpreted his role rather differently from his brother and, while resident in Darrowby, he devoted a considerable amount of his acute intelligence to the cause of doing as little as possible. Tristan did, in fact, spend much of his time sleeping in a chair. When he was left behind to dispense when we went out on our rounds he followed an unvarying procedure. He half filled a sixteen ounce bottle with water, added a few drachms of chlorodyne and a little epicacuanha, pushed the cork in and took it through to the sitting-room to stand by his favourite chair. It was a wonderful chair for his purpose; old fashioned and high backed with wings to support the head.

He would get out his *Daily Mirror*, light a Woodbine and settle down till sleep overcame him. If Siegfried rushed in on him he grabbed the bottle and started to shake it madly, inspecting the contents at intervals. Then he went through to the dispensary, filled up the bottle and labelled it.

It was a sound, workable system but it had one big snag. He never knew whether it was Siegfried or not when the door opened and often I walked in and found him half lying in his chair, staring up with startled, sleep-blurred eyes while he agitated his bottle.

Most evenings found him sitting on a high stool at the bar counter of the Drovers' Arms, conversing effortlessly with the barmaid. At other times he would be out with one of the young nurses from the local hospital which he seemed to regard as an agency to provide him with female company. All in all, he managed to lead a fairly full life.

Saturday night, 10.30 p.m. and I was writing up my visits when the phone rang. I swore, crossed my fingers and lifted the receiver.

'Hello, Herriot speaking.'

'Oh, it's you is it,' growled a dour voice in broadest Yorkshire. 'Well, ah want Mr Farnon.'

'I'm sorry, Mr Farnon is out. Can I help you?'

'Well, I 'ope so, but I'd far raither 'ave your boss. This is Sims of Beal Close.'

(Oh no, please no, not Beal Close on a Saturday night. Miles up in the hills at the end of a rough lane with about eight gates.)

'Yes, Mr Sims, and what is the trouble?'

'Ah'll tell you, there is some trouble an' all. I 'ave a grand big show 'oss here. All of seventeen hands. He's cut 'isself badly on the hind leg, just above the hock. I want him stitched immediately.'

(Glory be! Above the hock! What a charming place to have to stitch a horse. Unless he's very quiet, this is going to be a real picnic.)

'How big is the wound, Mr Sims?'

'Big? It's a gurt big thing about a foot long and bleedin' like 'ell. And this 'oss is as wick as an eel. Could kick a fly's eye out. Ah can't get near 'im nohow. Goes straight up wall when he sees anybody. By gaw, I tell you I had 'im to t'blacksmith t'other day and feller was dead scared of 'im. Twiltin' gurt 'oss 'e is.'

(Damn you, Mr Sims, damn Beal Close and damn your twiltin' gurt 'oss.)

'Well, I'll be along straight away. Try to have some men handy just in case we have to throw him.'

'Throw 'im? Throw 'im? You'd never throw this 'oss. He'd kill yer first. Anyways, I 'ave no men here so you'll have to manage on your own. Ah know Mr Farnon wouldn't want a lot of men to help 'im.'

(Oh lovely, lovely. This is going to be one for the diary.)

'Very well, I'm leaving now, Mr Sims.'

'Oh, ah nearly forgot. My road got washed away in the floods yesterday. You'll 'ave to walk the last mile and a half. So get a move on and don't keep me waiting all night.'

(This is just a bit much.)

'Look here, Mr Sims, I don't like your tone. I said I would leave now and I will get there just as soon as I can.'

'You don't like ma tone, eh? Well, ah don't like useless young apprentices practising on my good stock, so ah don't want no cheek from you. You know nowt about t'damn job, any road.'

(That finally does it.)

'Now just listen to me, Sims. If it wasn't for the sake of the horse I'd refuse to come out at all. Who do you think you are, anyway? If you ever try to speak to me like that again . . .'

'Now, now, Jim, get a grip on yourself. Take it easy old boy. You'll burst a blood vessel if you go on like this.'

'Who the devil . . .?'

'Ah, ah, Jim, calm yourself now. That temper of yours, you know. You'll really have to watch it.'

'Tristan! Where the hell are you speaking from?'

'The kiosk outside the Drovers. Five pints inside me and feeling a bit puckish. Thought I'd give you a ring.'

'By God, I'll murder you one of these days if you don't stop this game. It's putting years on me. Now and again isn't so bad, but this is the third time this week.'

'Ah, but this was by far the best, Jim. It was really wonderful. When you started drawing yourself up to your full height – it nearly killed me. Oh God, I wish you could have heard yourself.' He trailed off into helpless laughter.

And then my feeble attempts at retaliation; creeping, trembling, into some lonely phone box.

'Is that young Mr Farnon?' in a guttural croak. 'Well, this is Tilson of High Woods. Ah want you to come out here immediately. I 'ave a terrible case of . . .'

'Excuse me for interrupting, Jim, but is there something the matter with your tonsils? Oh, good. Well, go on with what you were saying, old lad. Sounds very interesting.'

There was only one time when I was not on the receiving end. It was Tuesday – my half day – and at 11.30 a.m. a call came in. An eversion of the uterus in a cow. This is the tough job in country practice and I felt the usual chill.

It happens when the cow, after calving, continues to strain until it pushes the entire uterus out and it hangs down as far as the animal's hocks. It is a vast organ and desperately difficult to replace, mainly because the cow, having once got rid of it, doesn't want it back. And in a straightforward contest between man and beast the odds were very much on the cow.

The old practitioners, in an effort to even things up a bit, used to sling the cow up by its hind limbs and the more inventive among them came up with all sorts of contraptions like the uterine valise which was supposed to squeeze the organ into smaller bulk. But the result was usually the same – hours of back-breaking work.

The introduction of the epidural anaesthetic made everything easier by removing sensation from the uterus and preventing the cow from straining but, for all that, the words 'calf bed out' coming over the line were guaranteed to wipe the smile off any vet's face.

I decided to take Tristan in case I needed a few pounds of extra push. He came along but showed little enthusiasm for the idea. He showed still less when he saw the patient, a very fat shorthorn lying, quite unconcerned, in her stall. Behind her, a bloody mass of uterus, afterbirth, muck and straw spilled over into the channel.

She wasn't at all keen to get up, but after we had done a bit of shouting and pushing at her shoulder she rose to her feet, looking bored.

The epidural space was difficult to find among the rolls of fat and I wasn't sure if I had injected all the anaesthetic into the right place. I removed the afterbirth, cleaned the uterus and placed it on a clean sheet held by the farmer and his brother. They were frail men and it was all they could do to keep the sheet level. I wouldn't be able to count on them to help me much.

I nodded to Tristan; we stripped off our shirts, tied clean sacks round our waists and gathered the uterus in our arms.

It was badly engorged and swollen and it took us just an hour to get it back. There was a long spell at the beginning when we made no progress at all and the whole idea of pushing the enormous organ through a small hole seemed ludicrous, like trying to thread a needle with a sausage. Then there was a few minutes when we thought we were doing famously only to find we were feeding the thing down through a tear in the sheet, (Siegfried once told me he had spent half a morning trying to stuff a uterus up a cow's rectum. What really worried him, he said, was that he nearly succeeded) and at the end when hope was fading, there was the blissful moment when the whole thing began to slip inside and incredibly disappeared from sight.

Somewhere half way through we both took a breather at the same time and stood panting, our faces almost touching. Tristan's cheeks were prettily patterned where a spouting artery had sprayed him; I was able to look deep into his eyes and I read there a deep distaste for the whole business.

Lathering myself in the bucket and feeling the ache in my shoulders and back, I looked over at Tristan. He was pulling his shirt over his head as though it cost him the last of his strength. The cow, chewing contentedly at a mouthful of hay, had come best out of the affair.

Out in the car, Tristan groaned. 'I'm sure that sort of thing isn't good for me. I feel as though I've been run over by a steam roller. Hell, what a life this is at times.'

After lunch I rose from the table. 'I'm off to Brawton now, Triss, and I think I'd better mention that you may not have seen the last of that cow. These bad cases sometime recur and there's a chance that little lot may come out again. If it does, it's all yours because Siegfried won't be back for hours and nothing is going to stop me having my half day.'

For once Tristan's sense of humour failed him. He became haggard, he seemed to age suddenly. 'Oh God,' he moaned, 'don't even talk about it. I'm all in – another session like that would kill me. And on my own! It would be the end of me, I tell you.'

'Ah well,' I said sadistically, 'try not to worry. It may never happen.'

It was when I saw the phone box about ten miles along the Brawton road that the thought struck me. I slowed down and got out of the car. 'I wonder,' I muttered, 'I wonder if I could do it just once.'

Inside the box, inspiration was strong in me. I wrapped my handkerchief over the mouthpiece, dialled the practice number and when I heard Tristan on the line I shouted at the top of my voice. 'Are you t'young feller that put our cow's calf bed back this morning?'

'Yes, I'm one of them.' Tension sprang into Tristan's voice. 'Why, is there something wrong?'

'Aye, there is summat wrong,' I bawled. 'She's putten it out again.'

'Out again? Out again? All of it?' He was almost screaming.

'Aye, it's a terrible mess. Pourin' blood and about twice size it was this morning. You'll 'ave some job with 'er.'

There was a long silence and I wondered if he had fainted. Then I heard him again, hoarse but resolute. 'Very well, I'll come straight away.'

There was another pause then he spoke again almost in a whisper. 'Is it out completely?'

I broke down then. There was a wistful quality about the words which defeated me; a hint of a wild hope that the farmer may have been exaggerating and that there might be only a tiny piece peeping out. I began to laugh. I would have liked to toy with my victim a little longer but it was impossible. I laughed louder and took my handkerchief from the mouthpiece so that Tristan could hear me.

I listened for a few seconds to the frenzied swearing at the other end then gently replaced the receiver. It would probably never happen again but it was sweet, very sweet.

Chapter Ten

'You want Mr Herriot? Certainly, I'll get him for you.' Siegfried cupped the phone with his hand. 'Come on, James, here's another one prefers you to me.' I glanced at him quickly, but he was smiling. He was pleased.

I thought, as I took the phone, of the tales I had heard of the other kind of boss; the man who couldn't bear to be knocked off his little pedestal. And I thought, too, of the difference a few weeks had made in the farmers' attitude; they didn't look past me now, hoping that Mr Farnon had come with me. They were beginning to accept me, and I liked to think that it wasn't only their hospitable traditions that made them ask me in for a 'bit o' dinner'.

This really meant something, because, with the passage of time, an appreciation of the Dales people had grown in me; a sense of the value of their carefully given friendship. The higher up the country, the more I liked them. At the bottom of the valley, where it widened into the plain, the farmers were like farmers everywhere, but the people grew more interesting as the land heightened, and in the scattered hamlets and isolated farms near the bleak tops I found their characteristics most marked; their simplicity and dignity, their rugged independence and their hospitality.

This Sunday morning it was the Bellerbys and they lived at the top of Halden, a little valley branching off the main Dale. My car bumped and rattled over the last rough mile of an earth road with the tops of boulders sticking up every few yards.

I got out and from where I stood, high at the head, I could see all of the strangely formed cleft in the hills, its steep sides grooved and furrowed by countless streams feeding the boisterous Halden Beck which tumbled over its rocky bed far below. Down there, were trees and some cultivated fields, but immediately behind me the wild country came crowding in on the bowl where the farmhouse lay. Halsten Pike, Alstang, Birnside – the huge fells with their barbarous names were very near.

Up here, the trappings of civilisation seemed far away. The farm buildings had been built massively of stone hundreds of years ago with the simple object of sheltering the animals. Those ancient masons were untroubled by regulations about the light and ventilation and the cow byre was gloomy, thick walled, almost windowless. The floor was broken and pitted, and rotting wooden partitions separated the cows from each other.

I went in, groping my way until my eyes grew accustomed to the dim light. There was nobody there but a roan cow had a label tied to its tail. Since this was a common way of communicating with the vet I lifted the tail and read 'Felon, back quarters.'

I pushed the cow over and began to examine the back teats. I was drawing out the stringy, discoloured milk when a voice addressed me from the doorway: 'Oh, it's you, Mr Herriot. I'm right glad you've come to see us this morning. You could do us such a great favour if you would.'

I looked up and saw Ruth Bellerby, a fine looking woman in her late thirties. She was the go-ahead member of the family and had an intelligent, questing mind. She was a great believer in self-improvement for the Dales people.

'I'll be glad to help you if I can, Miss Bellerby. What is it you'd like me to do?'

'Well, Mr Herriot, you know they are putting on the Messiah at Darrowby church this afternoon and we did badly want to go, but it's such a job getting the pony and trap ready and it's so slow. If you could give us a lift down in your car, I know we'd be able to get a ride back. It would be such a help.'

'Of course I'll run you down,' I replied. 'I'll be delighted to do it. I'm going myself as a matter of fact. You don't get many chances to hear good music in Darrowby.'

It was good to have a chance to help these kindly people. I had always marvelled at the Bellerbys. They seemed to me to be survivors from another age and their world had a timeless quality. They were never in a hurry; they rose when it was light, went to bed when they were tired, ate when they were hungry and seldom looked at a clock.

Ruth led the way over to the house. 'There's just mother and dad and me going. Bob's not interested, I'm afraid.'

I was slightly taken aback when I entered the house. The family were just sitting down to Sunday dinner and were still in their working clothes. I stole a look at my watch; a quarter to twelve and the performance started at 2 p.m. Oh well, I probably had plenty of time.

'Come on, young man,' said little Mr Bellerby. 'Sit down and have a bit o' dinner.'

It was always a bit tricky refusing these invitations without causing offence, but I pointed out that my own meal would be ready when I got back and it would be hard on Mrs Hall if it were wasted.

They were quick to appreciate this argument and settled down round the scrubbed kitchen table. Mrs Bellerby served a large, round Yorkshire pudding to each of them and poured a pool of gravy into it from a quart size enamel jug. I had had a hard morning and the delicious scent that rose from the gravy as it ran over the golden slabs was a sweet torture. But I consoled myself with the thought that the fact of my sitting there would make them hurry.

The pudding was consumed in leisurely silence, then Bob, an amiable, thick-set youth in his twenties, pushed out his empty plate. He did not say anything, but his mother planked down another pudding on the plate and plied the gravy jug again. His parents and sister watched him benevolently as he methodically demolished the thick, doughy mass.

Next, a tremendous roast appeared from the oven and Mr Bellerby hacked and sawed at it till they all had a heap of thick slices on their plates. Then mountains of mashed potatoes were served from something that looked like a washing-up bowl. Chopped turnip followed and the family went into action again.

There was no sign of haste. They ate calmly and quietly without any small talk. Bob had an extra helping of mashed potatoes.

The Bellerbys were relaxed and happy, but I couldn't say the same about myself. Hunger was tearing fiercely at me and the minutes on my watch were ticking away relentlessly.

There was a decent interval before Mrs Bellerby went over to the old fire oven in the corner, opened the door and pulled forth a great flat baking tin of steaming apple pie. She then proceeded to carve off about a square foot for each of them and deluged it with something like a pint of custard from another towering enamel jug.

The family set to as though they were just beginning the meal and once more a busy silence fell on the group. Bob cleared his plate in effortless style and pushed it wordlessly into the middle of the table. His mother was ready with another great rectangle of pie and another copious libation of custard.

It was going to be a close thing, I thought, but this surely must be the end. They would realise time was getting short and start to change. But, to my consternation, Mrs Bellerby moved slowly over to the fire and put the kettle on, while her husband and Bob pushed their chairs back and stretched out their legs. They both wore corduroy breeches with the lacing undone and on their feet were enormous hobnailed boots. Bob, after a search through his pockets, brought out a battered packet of cigarettes and lay back in a happy coma as his mother put a cup of tea in front of him. Mr Bellerby produced a clasp knife and began to cut up some plug tobacco for his pipe.

As they rearranged themselves round the table and began to slowly sip the hot tea, I found I had started to exhibit all the classical symptoms of tension. Pounding pulse, tightly clenched jaws and the beginnings of a headache.

After a second cup of tea, there were signs of activity. Mr Bellerby rose with a groan, scratched his shirt front and stretched luxuriously. 'Well, young man, we'll just have a bit of a wash and get changed. Bob'll stay and talk to you – he's not coming with us.'

There was a lot of splashing and spluttering in the big stone sink at the far end of the kitchen as they made their ablutions, then they disappeared upstairs. I was greatly relieved to find that it didn't take them long to change. Mr Bellerby was down very soon, transformed in appearance by a stiff and shiny suit of navy blue serge with a faint greenish tinge. His wife and daughter followed soon in a blaze of flowered cotton.

'Ah well, now, here we are. All ready, eh?' There was a note of hysteria in my heartiness. 'Right, then, off we go. After you, ladies.'

But Ruth did not move. She was pulling on a pair of white gloves and looking at her brother sprawled in his chair. 'You know, Bob, you're nowt but a disgrace!' she burst out. 'Here we are going off to hear this lovely music and you're lying there in your muck, not caring. You've no interest in culture at all. You care no more about bettering yourself than one of them bullocks out there.'

Bob stirred uneasily under this sudden attack, but there was more to come.

Ruth stamped her foot. 'Really, it makes my blood boil to look at you. And I know we won't be right out of t'door before you're asleep. Aye, snoring there all afternoon like a pig.' She swung round to Mrs Bellerby. 'Mother! I've made up my mind. I'm not going to leave him snoring here. He's got to come with us!'

I felt the sweat start out on my brow. I began to babble. 'But don't you think perhaps . . . might be just a little late . . . starts at two o'clock . . . my lunch . . .'

But my words were utterly lost. Ruth had the bit properly between her teeth. 'Get up out of there, Bob! Get up this minute and get dressed!' She shut her mouth tightly and thrust out her lower jaw.

She was too much for Bob. Although an impressive eater, he didn't seem to have much mind of his own. He mumbled sulkily and shuffled over to the sink. He took off his shirt and they all sat down and watched as he lathered his torso with a large block of White Windsor and sluiced his head and neck by working the pump handle by the side of the sink.

The family regarded him happily, pleased that he was coming with them and content in the knowledge that it would be good for him. Ruth watched his splashings with the light of love in her eyes. She kept looking over at me as if to say 'Isn't this grand.'

For my part, I was only just stopping myself from tearing out my hair in great handfuls. A compulsion to leap up and pace the floor, to scream at the top of my voice showed that I was nearing the end of my tether. I fought this feeling by closing my eyes and I must have kept them closed for a long time because, when I opened them, Bob was standing by my side in a suit exactly like his father's.

I could never remember much about that ride to Darrowby. I had only a vague recollection of the car hurtling down the stony track at forty miles an hour. Of myself staring straight ahead with protruding eyes and the family, tightly packed but cheerful, thoroughly enjoying the ride.

Even the imperturbable Mrs Hall was a little tight lipped as I shot into the house at ten to two and out again at two after bolting her good food.

I was late for the Messiah. The music had started as I crept into the church and I ran a gauntlet of disapproving stares. Out of the corner of my eye I saw the Bellerbys sitting very upright, all in a row. It seemed to me that they looked disapproving, too.

Chapter Eleven

I looked again at the slip of paper where I had written my visits. 'Dean, 3, Thompson's Yard. Old dog ill.'

There were a lot of these 'yards' in Darrowby. They were, in fact, tiny streets, like pictures from a Dickens novel. Some of them opened off the market place and many more were scattered behind the main thoroughfares in the old part of the town. From the outside you could see only an archway and it was always a surprise to me to go down a narrow passage and come suddenly upon the uneven rows of little houses with no two alike, looking into each other's windows across eight feet of cobbles.

In front of some of the houses a strip of garden had been dug out and marigolds and nasturtiums straggled over the rough stones; but at the far end the houses were in a tumbledown condition and some were abandoned with their windows boarded up.

Number three was down at this end and looked as though it wouldn't be able to hold out much longer.

The flakes of paint quivered on the rotten wood of the door as I knocked; above, the outer wall bulged dangerously on either side of a long crack in the masonry.

A small, white haired man answered. His face, pinched and lined, was enlivened by a pair of cheerful eyes; he wore a much-darned woollen cardigan, patched trousers and slippers.

'I've come to see your dog,' I said, and the old man smiled.

'Oh, I'm glad you've come, sir,' he said. 'I'm getting a bit worried about the old chap. Come inside, please.'

He led me into the tiny living-room. 'I'm alone now, sir. Lost my missus over a year ago. She used to think the world of the old dog.'

The grim evidence of poverty was everywhere. In the worn out lino, the fireless hearth, the dank, musty smell of the place. The wallpaper hung away from the damp patches and on the table the old man's solitary dinner was laid; a fragment of bacon, a few fried potatoes and a cup of tea. This was life on the old age pension.

In the corner, on a blanket, lay my patient, a cross-bred labrador. He must have been a big, powerful dog in his time, but the signs of age showed in the white hairs round his muzzle and the pale opacity in the depth of his eyes. He lay quietly and looked at me without hostility.

'Getting on a bit, isn't he, Mr Dean?'

'Aye he is that. Nearly fourteen, but he's been like a pup galloping about until these last few weeks. Wonderful dog for his age, is old Bob and he's never offered to bite anybody in his life. Children can do anything with him. He's my only friend now – I hope you'll soon be able to put him right.'

'Is he off his food, Mr Dean?'

'Yes, clean off, and that's a strange thing because by gum, he could eat. He always sat by me and put his head on my knee at meal times, but he hasn't been doing it lately.'

I looked at the dog with growing uneasiness. The abdomen was grossly distended and I could read the tell-tale symptoms of pain; the catch in the respirations, the retracted commissures of the lips, the anxious, preoccupied expression in the eyes.

When his master spoke, the tail thumped twice on the blankets and a momentary interest showed in the white old eyes; but it quickly disappeared and the blank, inward look returned.

I passed my hand carefully over the dog's abdomen. Ascites was pronounced and the dropsical fluid had gathered till the pressure was intense. 'Come on, old chap,' I said, 'Let's see if we can roll you over.' The dog made no resistance as I eased him slowly on to his other side, but, just as the movement was completed, he whimpered and looked round. The cause of the trouble was now only too easy to find.

I palpated gently. Through the thin muscle of the flank I could feel a hard, corrugated mass; certainly a splenic or hepatic carcinoma, enormous and completely inoperable. I stroked the old dog's head as I tried to collect my thoughts. This wasn't going to be easy.

'Is he going to be ill for long?' the old man asked, and again came the thump, thump of the tail at the sound of the loved voice. 'It's miserable when Bob isn't following me round the house when I'm doing my little jobs.'

'I'm sorry, Mr Dean, but I'm afraid this is something very serious. You see this large swelling. It is caused by an internal growth.'

'You mean . . . cancer?' the little man said faintly.

'I'm afraid so, and it has progressed too far for anything to be done. I wish there was something I could do to help him, but there isn't.'

The old man looked bewildered and his lips trembled. 'Then he's going to die?'

I swallowed hard. 'We really can't just leave him to die, can we? He's in some distress now, but it will soon be an awful lot worse. Don't you think it would be kindest to put him to sleep? After all, he's had a good, long innings.' I always aimed at a brisk, matter-of-fact approach, but the old cliches had an empty ring.

The old man was silent, then he said, 'Just a minute,' and slowly and painfully knelt down by the side of the dog. He did not speak, but ran his hand again and again over the grey old muzzle and the ears, while the tail thump, thump, thumped on the floor.

He knelt there a long time while I stood in the cheerless room, my eyes taking in the faded pictures on the walls, the frayed, grimy curtains, the broken-springed armchair.

At length the old man struggled to his feet and gulped once or twice. Without looking at me, he said huskily, 'All right, will you do it now?'

I filled the syringe and said the things I always said. 'You needn't worry, this is absolutely painless. Just an overdose of an anaesthetic. It is really an easy way out for the old fellow.'

The dog did not move as the needle was inserted, and, as the barbiturate began to flow into the vein, the anxious expression left his face and the muscles began to relax. By the time the injection was finished, the breathing had stopped.

'Is that it?' the old man whispered.

'Yes, that's it,' I said. 'He is out of his pain now.'

The old man stood motionless except for the clasping and unclasping of his hands. When he turned to face me his eyes were bright. 'That's right, we couldn't let him suffer, and I'm grateful for what you've done. And now, what do I owe you for your services, sir?'

'Oh, that's all right, Mr Dean,' I said quickly, 'It's nothing – nothing at all. I was passing right by here – it was no trouble.'

The old man was astonished. 'But you can't do that for nothing.'

'Now please say no more about it, Mr Dean. As I told you, I was passing right by your door.' I said goodbye and went out of the house, through the passage and into the street. In the bustle of people and the bright sunshine, I could still see only the stark, little room, the old man and his dead dog.

As I walked towards my car, I heard a shout behind me. The old man was shuffling excitedly towards me in his slippers. His cheeks were streaked and wet, but he was smiling. In his hand he held a small, brown object.

'You've been very kind, sir. I've got something for you.' He held out the object and I looked at it. It was tattered but just recognisable as a precious relic of a bygone celebration.

'Go on, it's for you,' said the old man. 'Have a cigar.'

Chapter Twelve

It was unfortunate that Siegfried ever had the idea of delegating the book-keeping to his brother, because Skeldale House had been passing through a period of peace and I found it soothing.

For nearly a fortnight there had been hardly a raised voice or an angry word except for one unpleasant interlude when Siegfried had come in and found his brother cycling along the passage. Tristan found all the rage and shouting quite incomprehensible – he had been given the job of setting the table and it was a long way from kitchen to dining-room; it seemed the most natural thing in the world to bring his bike in.

Autumn had come with a sharpness in the air and at nights the log fire burned bright in the big room, sending shadows flickering over the graceful alcoves and up to the high, carved ceiling. It was always a good time when the work of the day was through and the three of us lay back in the shabby arm chairs and stretched our feet out to the blaze.

Tristan was occupied with *The Daily Telegraph* crossword which he did every night. Siegfried was reading and I was dozing. It embarrassed me to be drawn into the crossword; Siegfried could usually make a contribution after a minute's thought but Tristan could have the whole thing worked out while I wrestled with the first clue.

The carpet round our feet was hidden by the dogs, all five of them, draped over each other in heavy-breathing layers and adding to the atmosphere of camaraderie and content.

It seemed to me that a chill breath struck through the comfort of the room as Siegfried spoke. 'Market day tomorrow and the bills have just gone out. They'll be queueing up to give us their money so I want you, Tristan, to devote the entire day to taking it from them. James and I are going to be busy, so you'll be in sole charge. All you have to do is take their cheques, give them a receipt and enter their names in the receipt book. Now do you think you can manage that without making a bloody hash of it?'

I winced. It was the first discordant note for a long time and it struck deep.

'I think I might just about cope with that,' Tristan replied haughtily.

'Good. Let's get to bed then.'

But, next day, it was easy to see that the assignment was right up Tristan's street. Stationed behind the desk, he took in the money in handfuls; and all the time he talked. But he did not talk at random; each character got a personal approach.

With the upright methodist, it was the weather, the price of cows and the activities of the village institute. The raffish type with his cap on one side, exhaling fumes of market ale, got the latest stories which Tristan kept on the backs of envelopes. But with the ladies he rose to his greatest heights. They were on his side from the first because of his innocent, boyish face, and when he turned the full blast of his charm on them their surrender was complete.

I was amazed at the giggles which came from behind the door. I was pleased the lad was doing well. Nothing was going wrong this time.

Tristan was smug at lunch time and cock-a-hoop at tea. Siegfried too, was satisfied with the day's takings which his brother presented in the form of a column of neat figures accurately totalled at the bottom. 'Thank you, Tristan, very efficient.' All was sweetness.

At the end of the day I was in the yard, throwing the used bottles from the boot of my car into a bin. It had been a busy day and I had accumulated a bigger than usual load of empties.

Tristan came panting in from the garden. 'Jim, I've lost the receipt book!'

'Always trying to pull my leg, always joking,' I said, 'Why don't you give your sense of humour a rest some time?' I laughed heartily and sent a liniment bottle crashing among the others.

He plucked at my sleeve, 'I'm not joking, Jim, believe me. I really have lost the bloody thing.' For once, his *sang froid* had deserted him. His eyes were wide, his face pale.

'But it can't just have disappeared,' I said. 'It's bound to turn up.'

'It'll never turn up.' Tristan wrung his hands and did a bit of pacing on the cobbles. 'Do you know I've spent about two hours searching for it. I've ransacked the house. It's gone, I tell you.'

'But it doesn't matter, does it? You'll have transferred all the names into the ledger.'

'That's just it. I haven't. I was going to do it tonight.'

'So that means that all the farmers who have been handing you money today are going to get the same bill next month?'

'Looks like it. I can't remember the names of more than two or three of them.'

I sat down heavily on the stone trough. 'Then God help us all, especially you. These Yorkshire lads don't like parting with their brass once, but when you ask them to do it twice – oh, brother!'

Another thought struck me and I said with a touch of cruelty: 'And how about Siegfried. Have you told him yet?'

A spasm crossed Tristan's face. 'No, he's just come in. I'm going to do it now.' He squared his shoulders and strode from the yard.

I decided not to follow him to the house. I didn't feel strong enough for the scene which was bound to follow. Instead, I went out into the back lane and round behind the house to the market place where the lighted entrance of the Drovers' Arms beckoned in the dusk.

I was sitting behind a pint when Tristan came in looking as though somebody had just drained half a gallon of blood from him.

'How did it go?' I asked.

'Oh, the usual, you know. Bit worse this time, maybe. But I can tell you this, Jim. I'm not looking forward to a month from today.'

The receipt book was never found and, a month later, all the bills were sent out again, timed, as usual, to arrive on market day morning.

The practice was quiet that particular day and I had finished my round by mid morning. I didn't go into the house, because through the waiting room window I could see rows of farmers sitting round the walls; they all wore the same offended, self-righteous expression.

I stole away to the market place. When I had time, I enjoyed moving among the stalls which crowded the ancient square. You could buy fruit, fish, second-hand books, cheeses, clothes, in fact nearly everything; but the china stall was my favourite.

It was run by a Jewish gentleman from Leeds – fat, confident, sweating, and with a hypnotic selling technique. I never got tired of watching him. He fascinated me. He was in his best form today, standing in a little clearing surrounded on all sides by heaps of crockery, while beyond, the farmers' wives listened open-mouthed to his oratory.

'Ah'm not good lookin',' he was saying. 'Ah'm not clever, but by God ah can talk. Ah can talk the hind leg off a donkey. Now look 'ere.' He lifted a cheap cup and held it aloft, but tenderly, gripping it between his thick thumb and forefinger, his little finger daintily outspread. 'Beautiful, isn't it? Now isn't that lovely?' Then he placed it reverently on the palm of his hand and displayed it to the audience. 'Now I tell you ladies, you can buy this self same tea-set in Conners in Bradford for three pounds fifteen. I'm not jokin' nor jestin', it's there and that's the price. But my price, ladies?' and here he fished out an old walking stick with a splintered handle, 'My price for this beautiful tea-set?' He held the stick by its end and brought it crashing down on an empty tea-chest. 'Never mind three pound fifteen.' Crash! 'Never mind three pound.' Crash! 'Never mind two pound.' Crash! 'Never mind thirty bob.' Crash! ' 'ere, 'ere, come on, who'll give me a quid?' Not a soul moved. 'All right, all right, I can see ah've met me match today. Go on, seventeen and a tanner the lot.' A final devastating crash and the ladies began to make signals and fumble in their handbags. A little man emerged from the back of the stall and started to hand out the tea-sets. The ritual had been observed and everybody was happy.

I was waiting, deeply content, for the next item from the virtuoso when I saw a burly figure in a check cap waving wildly at me from the edge of the crowd. He had his hand inside his jacket and I knew what he was feeling for. I didn't hesitate but dodged quickly behind a stall laden with pig troughs and wire netting. I had gone only a few steps before another farmer hailed me purposefully. He was brandishing an envelope.

I felt trapped, then I saw a way of escape. Rapidly skirting a counter displaying cheap jewellery, I plunged into the doorway of the Drovers' Arms and, avoiding the bar which was full of farmers, slipped into the manager's office. I was safe; this was one place where I was always welcome.

The manager looked up from his desk, but he did not smile. 'Look here,' he said sharply, 'I brought my dog in to see you some time ago and in due course I received an account from you.' I cringed inwardly. 'I paid by return and was extremely surprised this morning to find that another account had been rendered. I have here a receipt signed by . . .'

I couldn't stand any more. 'I'm very sorry, Mr Brooke, but there's been a mistake. I'll put it right. Please accept our apologies.'

This became a familiar refrain over the next few days, but it was Siegfried who had the most unfortunate experience. It was in the bar of his favourite pub, the Black Swan. He was approached by Billy Breckenridge, a friendly, jocular little character, one of Darrowby's worthies. 'Hey, remember that three and six I paid at your surgery? I've had another bill for it.'

Siegfried made a polished apology – he'd had a lot of practice – and bought the man a drink. They parted on good terms.

The pity of it was that Siegfried, who seldom remembered anything, didn't remember this. A month later, also in the Swan, he ran into Billy Breckenridge again. This time, Billy wasn't so jocular. 'Hey, remember that bill you sent me twice? Well, I've had it again.'

Siegfried did his best, but his charm bounced off the little man. He was offended. 'Right, I can see you don't believe I paid your bill. I had a receipt from your brother, but I've lost it.' He brushed aside Siegfried's protestations. 'No, no, there's only one way to settle this. I say I've paid the three and six, you say I haven't. All right, I'll toss you for it.'

Miserably, Siegfried demurred, but Billy was adamant. He produced a penny and, with great dignity, balanced it on his thumbnail. 'O.K., you call.'

'Heads,' muttered Siegfried and heads it was. The little man did not change expression. Still dignified, he handed the three and six to Siegfried. 'Perhaps we might be able to consider the matter closed.' He walked out of the bar.

Now there are all kinds of bad memories, but Siegfried's was of the inspired type. He somehow forgot to make a note of this last transaction and, at the end of the moth, Billy Breckenridge received a fourth request for the amount which he had already paid twice. It was about then that Siegfried changed his pub and started going to the Cross Keys.

Chapter Thirteen

As Autumn wore into Winter and the high tops were streaked with the first snows, the discomforts of practice in the Dales began to make themselves felt.

Driving for hours with frozen feet, climbing to the high barns in biting winds which seared and flattened the wiry hill grass. The interminable stripping off in draughty buildings and the washing of hands and chest in buckets of cold water, using scrubbing soap and often a piece of sacking for a towel.

I really found out the meaning of chapped hands. When there was a rush of work, my hands were never quite dry and the little red fissures crept up almost to my elbows.

This was when some small animal work came as a blessed relief. To step out of the rough, hard routine for a while; to walk into a warm drawing-room instead of a cow house and tackle something less formidable than a horse or a bull. And among all those comfortable drawing-rooms there was none so beguiling as Mrs Pumphrey's.

Mrs Pumphrey was an elderly widow. Her late husband, a beer baron whose breweries and pubs were scattered widely over the broad bosom of Yorkshire, had left her a vast fortune and a beautiful house on the outskirts of Darrowby. Here she lived with a large staff of servants, a gardener, a chauffeur and Tricki Woo. Tricki Woo was a Pekingese and the apple of his mistress' eye.

Standing now in the magnificent doorway, I furtively rubbed the toes of my shoes on the backs of my trousers and blew on my cold hands. I could almost see the deep armchair drawn close to the leaping flames, the tray of cocktail biscuits, the bottle of excellent sherry. Because of the sherry, I was always careful to time my visits for half an hour before lunch.

A maid answered my ring, beaming on me as an honoured guest and led me to the room, crammed with expensive furniture and littered with glossy magazines and the latest novels. Mrs Pumphrey, in the high backed chair by the fire, put down her book with a cry of delight. 'Trick! Tricki! Here is your uncle Herriot.' I had been made an uncle very early and, sensing the advantages of the relationship, had made no objection.

Tricki, as always, bounded from his cushion, leaped on to the back of a sofa and put his paws on my shoulders. He then licked my face thoroughly before retiring, exhausted. He was soon exhausted because he was given roughly twice the amount of food needed for a dog of his size. And it was the wrong kind of food.

'Oh, Mr Herriot,' Mrs Pumphrey said, looking at her pet anxiously. 'I'm so glad you've come. Tricki has gone flop-bott again.'

This ailment, not to be found in any text book, was her way of describing the symptoms of Tricki's impacted anal glands. When the glands filled up, he showed discomfort by sitting down suddenly in mid walk and his mistress would rush to the phone in great agitation.

'Mr Herriot! Please come, he's going flop-bott again!'

I hoisted the little dog on to a table and, by pressure on the anus with a pad of cotton wool, I evacuated the glands.

It baffled me that the Peke was always so pleased to see me. Any dog who could still like a man who grabbed him and squeezed his bottom hard every time they met had to have an incredibly forgiving nature. But Tricki never showed any resentment; in fact he was an outstandingly equable little animal, bursting with intelligence, and I was genuinely attached to him. It was a pleasure to be his personal physician.

The squeezing over, I lifted my patient from the table, noticing the increased weight, the padding of extra flesh over the ribs. 'You know, Mrs Pumphrey, you're overfeeding him again. Didn't I tell you to cut out all those pieces of cake and give him more protein?'

'Oh yes, Mr Herriot,' Mrs Pumphrey wailed. 'But what can I do? He's so tired of chicken.'

I shrugged; it was hopeless. I allowed the maid to lead me to the palatial bathroom where I always performed a ritual handwashing after the operation. It was a huge room with a fully stocked dressing table, massive green ware and rows of glass shelves laden with toilet preparations. My private guest towel was laid out next to the slab of expensive soap.

Then I returned to the drawing-room, my sherry glass was filled and I settled down by the fire to listen to Mrs Pumphrey. It couldn't be called a conversation because she did all the talking, but I always found it rewarding.

Mrs Pumphrey was likeable, gave widely to charities and would help anybody in trouble. She was intelligent and amusing and had a lot of waffling charm; but most people have a blind spot and her's was Tricki Woo. The tales she told about her darling ranged far into the realms of fantasy and I waited eagerly for the next instalment.

'Oh Mr Herriot, I have the most exciting news. Tricki has a pen pal! Yes, he wrote a letter to the editor of *Doggy World* enclosing a donation, and told him that even though he was descended from a long line of Chinese emperors, he had decided to come down and mingle freely with the common dogs. He asked the editor to seek out a pen pal for him among the dogs he knew so that they could correspond to their mutual benefit. And for this purpose, Tricki said he would adopt the name of Mr Utterbunkum. And, do you know, he received the most beautiful letter from the editor' (I could imagine the sensible man leaping upon this potential gold mine) 'who said he would like to introduce Bonzo Fotheringham, a lonely Dalmatian who would be delighted to exchange letters with a new friend in Yorkshire.'

I sipped the sherry. Tricki snored on my lap. Mrs Pumphrey went on.

'But I'm so disappointed about the new Summerhouse – you know I got it specially for Tricki so we could sit out together on warm afternoons. It's such a nice little rustic shelter, but he's taken a passionate dislike to it. Simply loathes it – absolutely refuses to go inside. You should see the dreadful expression on his face when he looks at it. And do you know what he called it yesterday? Oh, I hardly dare tell you.' She looked around the room before leaning over and whispering: 'He called it "the bloody hut"!'

The maid struck fresh life into the fire and refilled my glass. The wind hurled a handful of sleet against the window. This, I thought, was the life. I listened for more.

'And did I tell you, Mr Herriot, Tricki had another good win yesterday? You know, I'm sure he must study the racing columns, he's such a tremendous judge of form. Well, he told me to back Canny Lad in the three o'clock at Redcar yesterday and, as usual, it won. He put on a shilling each way and got back nine shillings.'

These bets were always placed in the name of Tricki Woo and I thought with compassion of the reactions of the local bookies. The Darrowby turf accountants were a harassed and fugitive body of men. A board would appear at the end of some alley urging the population to invest with Joe Downs and enjoy perfect security. Joe would live for a few months on a knife edge while he pitted his wits against the knowledgeable citizens, but the end was always the same; a few favourites would win in a row and Joe would be gone in the night, taking his board with him. Once I had asked a local inhabitant about the sudden departure of one of these luckless nomads. He replied unemotionally: 'Oh, we brok 'im.'

Losing a regular flow of shillings to a dog must have been a heavy cross for these unfortunate men to bear.

'I had such a frightening experience last week,' Mrs Pumphrey continued. 'I was sure I would have to call you out. Poor little Tricki – he went completely crackerdog!'

I mentally lined this up with flop-bott among the new canine diseases and asked for more information.

'It was awful. I was terrified. The gardener was throwing rings for Tricki – you know he does this for half an hour every day.' I had witnessed this spectacle several times. Hodgkin, a dour, bent old Yorkshireman who looked as though he hated all dogs and Tricki in particular, had to go out on the lawn every day and throw little rubber rings over and over again. Tricki bounded after them and brought them back, barking madly till the process was repeated. The bitter lines on the old man's face deepened as the game progressed. His lips moved continually, but it was impossible to hear what he was saying.

Mrs Pumphrey went on: 'Well, he was playing his game, and he does adore it so, when suddenly, without warning, he went cracker dog. He forgot all about his rings and began to run around in circles, barking and yelping in such a strange way. Then he fell over on his side and lay like a little dead thing. Do you know, Mr Herriot, I really thought he was dead, he lay so perfectly still. And what hurt me most was that Hodgkin began to laugh. He has been with me for twenty-four years and I have never even seen him smile, and yet, when he looked down at that still form, he broke into a queer, high-pitched cackle. It was horrid. I was just going to rush to the telephone when Tricki got up and walked away – he seemed perfectly normal.'

Hysteria, I thought, brought on by wrong feeding and over-excitement. I put down my glass and fixed Mrs Pumphrey with a severe glare. 'Now look, this is just what I was talking about. If you persist in feeding all that fancy rubbish to Tricki you are going to ruin his health. You really must get him on to a sensible dog diet of one or, at the most, two small meals a day of meat and brown bread or a little biscuit. And nothing in between.'

Mrs Pumphrey shrank into her chair, a picture of abject guilt. 'Oh, please don't speak to me like that. I do try to give him the right things, but it is so difficult. When he begs for his little titbits, I can't refuse him.' She dabbed her eyes with a handkerchief.

But I was unrelenting. 'All right, Mrs Pumphrey, it's up to you, but I warn you that if you go on as you are doing, Tricki will go crackerdog more and more often.'

I left the cosy haven with reluctance, pausing on the gravelled drive to look back at Mrs Pumphrey waving and Tricki, as always, standing against the window, his wide-mouthed face apparently in the middle of a hearty laugh.

Driving home, I mused on the many advantages of being Tricki's uncle. When he went to the seaside he sent me boxes of oak-smoked kippers; and when the tomatoes ripened in his greenhouse, he sent a pound or two every week. Tins of tobacco arrived regularly, sometimes with a photograph carrying a loving inscription.

But it was when the Christmas hamper arrived from Fortnum and Mason's that I decided that I was on a really good thing which should be helped along a bit. Hitherto, I had merely rung up and thanked Mrs Pumphrey for the gifts, and she had been rather cool, pointing out that it was Tricki who had sent the things and he was the one who should be thanked.

With the arrival of the hamper it came to me, blindingly, that I had been guilty of a grave error of tactics. I set myself to compose a letter to Tricki. Avoiding Siegfried's sardonic eye, I thanked my doggy nephew for his Christmas gifts and for all his generosity in the past. I expressed my sincere hopes that the festive fare had not upset his delicate digestion and suggested that if he did experience any discomfort he should have recourse to the black powder his uncle always prescribed. A vague feeling of professional shame was easily swamped by floating visions of kippers, tomatoes and hampers. I addressed the envelope to Master Tricki Pumphrey, Barlby Grange and slipped it into the post box with only a slight feeling of guilt.

On my next visit, Mrs Pumphrey drew me to one side. 'Mr Herriot,' she whispered, 'Tricki adored your charming letter and he will keep it always, but he was very put out about one thing – you addressed it to Master Tricki and he does insist upon Mister. He was dreadfully affronted at first, quite beside himself, but when he saw it was from you he soon recovered his good temper. I can't think why he should have these little prejudices. Perhaps it is because he is an only dog – I do think an only dog develops more prejudices than one from a large family.'

Entering Skeldale House was like returning to a colder world. Siegfried bumped into me in the passage. 'Ah, who have we here? Why I do believe it's dear Uncle Herriot. And what have you been doing, Uncle? Slaving away at Barlby Grange, I expect. Poor fellow, you must be tired out. Do you really think it's worth it, working your fingers to the bone for another hamper?'

Chapter Fourteen

Looking back, I can scarcely believe we used to spend all those hours in making up medicines. But our drugs didn't come to us in proprietary packages and before we could get out on the road we had to fill our cars with a wide variety of carefully compounded and largely useless remedies.

When Siegfried came upon me that morning I was holding a twelve ounce bottle at eye level while I poured syrup of coccilana into it. Tristan was moodily mixing stomach powders with a mortar and pestle and he stepped up his speed of stroke when he saw his brother's eye on him. He was surrounded by packets of the powder and, further along the bench, were orderly piles of pessaries which he had made by filling cellophane cylinders with boric acid.

Tristan looked industrious; his elbow jogged furiously as he ground away at the ammon carb and nux vomica. Siegfried smiled benevolently.

I smiled too. I felt the strain badly when the brothers were at variance, but I could see that this was going to be one of the happy mornings. There had been a distinct improvement in the atmosphere since Christmas when Tristan had slipped casually back to college and, apparently without having done any work, had re-sat and passed his exams. And there was something else about my boss today; he seemed to glow with inner satisfaction as though he knew for certain that something good was on the way. He came in and closed the door.

'I've got a bit of good news.'

I screwed the cork into the bottle. 'Well, don't keep us in suspense. Let's have it.'

Siegfried looked from one of us to the other. He was almost smirking. 'You remember that bloody awful shambles when Tristan took charge of the bills?'

His brother looked away and began to grind still faster, but Siegfried laid a friendly hand on his shoulder. 'No, don't worry, I'm not going to ask you to do it again. In fact, you'll never have to do it again because, from now on, the job will be done by an expert.' He paused and cleared his throat. 'We're going to have a secretary.'

As we stared blankly at him he went on. 'Yes, I picked her myself and I consider she's perfect.'

'Well, what's she like?' I asked.

Siegfried pursed his lips. 'It's difficult to describe her. But just think – what do we want here? We don't want some flighty young thing hanging about the place. We don't want a pretty little blonde sitting behind that desk powdering her nose and making eyes at everybody.'

'We don't?' Tristan interrupted, plainly puzzled.

'No, we don't!' Siegfried rounded on him. 'She'd be day-dreaming about her boy friends half the time and just when we'd got her trained to our ways she'd be running off to get married.'

Tristan still looked unconvinced and it seemed to exasperate his brother. Siegfried's face reddened. 'And there's another thing. How could we have an attractive young girl in here with somebody like you in the house. You'd never leave her alone.'

Tristan was nettled. 'How about you?'

'I'm talking about you, not me!' Siegfried roared. I closed my eyes. The peace hadn't lasted long. I decided to cut in. 'All right, tell us about the new secretary.'

With an effort, he mastered his emotion. 'Well, she's in her fifties and she has retired after thirty years with Green and Moulton in Bradford. She was company secretary there and I've had the most wonderful reference from the firm. They say she is a model of efficiency and that's what we want in this practice – efficiency. We're far too slack. It's just a stroke of luck for us that she decided to come and live in Darrowby. Anyway, you'll be able to meet her in a few minutes – she's coming at ten o'clock this morning.'

The church clock was chiming when the door bell rang. Siegfried hastened out to answer it and led his great discovery into the room in triumph. 'Gentlemen, I want you to meet Miss Harbottle.'

She was a big, high-bosomed woman with a round healthy face and gold-rimmed spectacles. A mass of curls, incongruous and very dark, peeped from under her hat; they looked as if they might be dyed and they didn't go with her severe clothes and brogue shoes.

It occurred to me that we wouldn't have to worry about her rushing off to get married. It wasn't that she was ugly, but she had a jutting chin and an air of effortless command that would send any man running for his life.

I shook hands and was astonished at the power of Miss Harbottle's grip. We looked into each other's eyes and had a friendly trial of strength for a few seconds, then she seemed happy to call it a draw and turned away. Tristan was entirely unprepared and a look of alarm spread over his face as his hand was engulfed; he was released only when his knees started to buckle.

She began a tour of the office while Siegfried hovered behind her, rubbing his hands and looking like a shopwalker with his favourite customer. She paused at the desk, heaped high with in-coming and out-going bills, Ministry of Agriculture forms, circulars from drug firms with here and there stray boxes of pills and tubes of udder ointment.

Stirring distastefully among the mess, she extracted the dog-eared old ledger and held it up between finger and thumb. 'What's this?'

Siegfried trotted forward. 'Oh, that's our ledger. We enter the visits into it from our day book which is here somewhere.' He scrabbled about on the desk. 'Ah, here it is. This is where we write the calls as they come in.'

She studied the two books for a few minutes with an expression of amazement which gave way to a grim humour. 'You gentlemen will have to learn to write if I am going to look after your books. There are three different hands here, but this one is by far the worst. Quite dreadful. Whose it it?'

She pointed to an entry which consisted of a long, broken line with an occasional undulation.

'That's mine, actually,' said Siegfried, shuffling his feet. 'Must have been in a hurry that day.'

'But it's all like that, Mr Farnon. Look here and here and here. It won't do, you know.'

Siegfried put his hands behind his back and hung his head.

'I expect you keep your stationery and envelopes in here.' She pulled open a drawer in the desk. It appeared to be filled entirely with old seed packets, many of which had burst open. A few peas and french beans rolled gently from the top of the heap. The next drawer was crammed tightly with soiled calving ropes which somebody had forgotten to wash. They didn't smell so good and Miss Harbottle drew back hurriedly; but she was not easily deterred and tugged hopefully at the third drawer. It came open with a musical clinking and she looked down on a dusty row of empty pale ale bottles.·

She straightened up slowly and spoke patiently. 'And where, may I ask, is your cash box?'

'Well, we just stuff it in there, you know.' Siegfried pointed to the pint pot on the corner of the mantelpiece. 'Haven't got what you'd call a proper cash box, but this does the job all right.'

Miss Harbottle looked at the pot with horror. 'You just stuff . . .' Crumpled cheques and notes peeped over the brim at her; many of their companions had burst out on to the hearth below. 'And you mean to say that you go out and leave that money there day after day?'

'Never seems to come to any harm,' Siegfried replied.

'And how about your petty cash?'

Siegfried gave an uneasy giggle. 'All in there, you know. All cash – petty and otherwise.'

Miss Harbottle's ruddy face had lost some of its colour. 'Really, Mr Farnon, this is too bad. I don't know how you have gone on so long like this. I simply do not know. However, I'm confident I will be able to straighten things out very soon. There is obviously nothing complicated about your business – a simple card index system would be the thing for your accounts. The other little things,' – she glanced back unbelievingly at the pot – 'I will put right very quickly.'

'Fine, Miss Harbottle, fine.' Siegfried was rubbing his hands harder than ever. 'We'll expect you on Monday morning.'

'Nine o'clock sharp, Mr Farnon.'

After she had gone there was a silence. Tristan had enjoyed her visit and was smiling thoughtfully, but I felt uncertain.

'You know, Siegfried,' I said, 'Maybe she is a demon of efficiency but isn't she just a bit tough?'

'Tough?' Siegfried gave a loud, rather cracked laugh. 'Not a bit of it. You leave her to me. I can handle her.'

Chapter Fifteen

There was little furniture in the dining-room but the noble lines and the very size of the place lent grace to the long sideboard and the modest mahogany table where Tristan and I sat at breakfast.

The single large window was patterned with frost and in the street outside, the footsteps of the passers by crunched in the crisp snow. I looked up from my boiled egg as a car drew up. There was a stamping in the porch, the outer door banged shut and Siegfried burst into the room. Without a word he made for the fire and hung over it, leaning his elbows on the grey marble mantelpiece. He was muffled almost to the eyes in greatcoat and scarf but what you could see of his face was purplish blue.

He turned a pair of streaming eyes to the table. 'A milk fever up at old Heseltine's. One of the high buildings. God, it was cold up there. I could hardly breathe.'

As he pulled off his gloves and shook his numbed fingers in front of the flames, he darted sidelong glances at his brother. Tristan's chair was nearest the fire and he was enjoying his breakfast as he enjoyed everything, slapping the butter happily on to his toast and whistling as he applied the marmalade. His *Daily Mirror* was balanced against the coffee pot. You could almost see the waves of comfort and contentment coming from him.

Siegfried dragged himself unwillingly from the fire and dropped into a chair. 'I'll just have a cup of coffee, James. Heseltine was very kind – asked me to sit down and have breakfast with him. He gave me a lovely slice of home fed bacon – a bit fat, maybe, but what a flavour! I can taste it now.'

He put down his cup with a clatter. 'You know, there's no reason why we should have to go to the grocer for our bacon and eggs. There's a perfectly good hen house at the bottom of the garden and a pig sty in the yard with a boiler for the swill. All our household waste could go towards feeding a pig. We'd probably do it quite cheaply.'

He rounded on Tristan who had just lit a Woodbine and was shaking out his *Mirror* with the air of ineffable pleasure which was peculiar to him. 'And it would be a useful job for you. You're not producing much sitting around here on your arse all day. A bit of stock keeping would do you good.'

Tristan put down his paper as though the charm had gone out of it. 'Stock keeping? Well, I feed your mare as it is.' He didn't enjoy looking after Siegfried's new hunter because every time he turned her out to water in the yard she would take a playful kick at him in passing.

Siegfried jumped up. 'I know you do, and it doesn't take all day, does it? It won't kill you to take on the hens and pigs.'

'Pigs?' Tristan looked startled. 'I thought you said pig?'

'Yes, pigs. I've just been thinking. If I buy a litter of weaners we can sell the others and keep one for ourselves. Won't cost a thing that way.'

'Not with free labour, certainly.'

'Labour? Labour? You don't know what it means! Look at you lying back there puffing your head off. You smoke too many of those bloody cigarettes!'

'So do you.'

'Never mind me, I'm talking about you!' Siegfried shouted.

I got up from the table with a sigh. Another day had begun.

When Siegfried got an idea he didn't muck about. Immediate action was his watchword. Within forty-eight hours a litter of ten little pigs had taken up residence in the sty and twelve Light Sussex pullets were pecking about behind the wire of the hen house. He was particularly pleased with the pullets. 'Look at them, James; just on point of lay and a very good strain, too. There'll be just a trickle of eggs at first, but once they get cracking we'll be snowed under. Nothing like a nice fresh egg warm from the nest.'

It was plain from the first that Tristan didn't share his brother's enthusiasm for the hens. I often found him hanging about outside the hen house, looking bored and occasionally throwing bread crusts over the wire. There was no evidence of the regular feeding, the balanced diet recommended by the experts. As egg producers, the hens held no appeal for him, but he did become mildly interested in them as personalities. An odd way of clucking, a peculiarity in gait – these things amused him.

But there were no eggs and as the weeks passed, Siegfried became increasingly irritable. 'Wait till I see the chap that sold me those hens. Damned scoundrel. Good laying strain my foot!' It was pathetic to see him anxiously exploring empty nesting boxes every morning.

One afternoon, I was going down the garden when Tristan called to me. 'Come over here, Jim. This is something new. I bet you've never seen anything like it before.' He pointed upwards and I saw a group of unusually coloured large birds perched in the branches of the elms. There were more of them in the neighbour's apple trees.

I stared in astonishment. 'You're right, I've never seen anything like them. What are they?'

'Oh, come on,' said Tristan, grinning in delight, 'Surely there's something familiar about them. Take another look.'

I peered upwards again. 'No, I've never seen birds as big as that and with such exotic plumage. What is it – a freak migration?'

Tristan gave a shout of laughter. 'They're our hens!'

'How the devil did they get up there?'

'They've left home. Hopped it.'

'But I can only see seven. Where are the rest of them?'

'God knows. Let's have a look over the wall.'

The crumbling mortar gave plenty of toe holds between the bricks and we looked down into the next garden. The other five hens were there, pecking contentedly among some cabbages.

It took a long time to get them all back into the hen house and the tedious business had to be repeated several times a day thereafter. For the hens had clearly grown tired of life under Tristan and decided that they would do better living off the country. They became nomads, ranging ever further afield in their search for sustenance.

At first the neighbours chuckled. They phoned to say their children were rounding up the hens and would we come and get them; but with the passage of time their jocularity wore thin. Finally Siegfried was involved in some painful interviews. His hens, he was told, were an unmitigated nuisance.

It was after one particularly unpleasant session that Siegfried decided that the hens must go. It was a bitter blow and as usual he vented his fury on Tristan. 'I must have been mad to think that any hens under your care would ever lay eggs. But really, isn't it just a bit hard? I give you this simple little job and one would have thought that even you would be hard put to it to make a mess of it. But look at the situation after only three weeks. Not one solitary egg have we seen. The bloody hens are flying about the countryside like pigeons. We are permanently estranged from our neighbours. You've done a thorough job haven't you?' All the frustrated egg producer in Siegfried welled out in his shrill tones.

Tristan's expression registered only wounded virtue, but he was rash enough to try to defend himself. 'You know, I thought there was something queer about those hens from the start,' he muttered.

Siegfried shed the last vestiges of his self control. 'Queer!' he yelled wildly, 'You're the one that's queer, not the poor bloody hens. You're the queerest bugger there is. For God's sake get out – get out of my sight!'

Tristan withdrew with quiet dignity.

It took some time for the last echoes of the poultry venture to die away but after a fortnight, sitting again at the dining-table with Tristan, I felt sure that all was forgotten. So that it was with a strange sense of the workings of fate that I saw Siegfried stride into the room and lean menacingly over his brother. 'You remember those hens, I suppose,' he said almost in a whisper, 'You'll recall that I gave them away to Mrs Dale, that old aged pensioner down Brown's Yard. Well, I've just been speaking to her. She's delighted with them. Gives them a hot mash night and morning and she's collecting ten eggs a day.' His voice rose almost to a scream. 'Ten eggs, do you hear, ten eggs!'

I hurriedly swallowed the last of my tea and excused myself. I trotted along the passage out the back door and up the garden to my car. On the way I passed the empty hen house. It had a forlorn look. It was a long way to the dining-room but I could still hear Siegfried.

Chapter Sixteen

'Jim! Come over here and look at these little beggars.' Tristan laughed excitedly as he leaned over the door of the pig sty.

I walked across the yard. 'What is it?'

'I've just given them their swill and it's a bit hot. Just look at them!'

The little pigs were seizing the food, dropping it and walking suspiciously round it. Then they would creep up, touch the hot potatoes with their muzzles and leap back in alarm. There was none of the usual meal time slobbering; just a puzzled grunting.

Right from the start Tristan had found the pigs more interesting than the hens which was a good thing because he had to retrieve himself after the poultry disaster. He spent a lot of time in the yard, sometimes feeding or mucking out but more often resting his elbows on the door watching his charges.

As with the hens, he was more interested in their characters than their ability to produce pork or bacon. After he poured the swill into the long trough he always watched, entranced, while the pigs made their first rush. Soon, in the desperate gobbling there would be signs of uneasiness. The tiny animals would begin to glance sideways till their urge to find out what their mates were enjoying so much became unbearable; they would start to change position frantically, climbing over each other's backs and falling into the swill.

Old Boardman was a willing collaborator, but mainly in an advisory capacity. Like all countrymen he considered he knew all about the husbandry and diseases of animals and, it turned out, pigs were his speciality. There were long conferences in the dark room under the Bairnsfather cartoons and the old man grew animated over his descriptions of the vast, beautiful animals he had reared in that very sty.

Tristan listened with respect because he had solid proof of Boardman's expertise in the way he handled the old brick boiler. Tristan could light the thing but it went out if he turned his back on it; but it was docile in Boardman's hands. I often saw Tristan listening wonderingly to the steady blub-blub while the old man rambled on and the delicious scent of cooking pig potatoes drifted over them both.

But no animal converts food more quickly into flesh than a pig and as the weeks passed the little pink creatures changed with alarming speed into ten solid, no-nonsense porkers. Their characters deteriorated, too. They lost all their charm. Meal times stopped being fun and became a battle with the odds growing heavier against Tristan all the time.

I could see that it brought a lot of colour into old Boardman's life and he always dropped whatever he was doing when he saw Tristan scooping the swill from the boiler.

He obviously enjoyed watching the daily contest from his seat on the stone trough. Tristan bracing himself, listening to the pigs squealing at the rattle of the bucket; giving a few fearsome shouts to encourage himself then shooting the bolt and plunging among the grunting, jostling animals; broad, greedy snouts forcing into the bucket, sharp feet grinding his toes, heavy bodies thrusting against his legs.

I couldn't help smiling when I remembered the light-hearted game it used to be. There was no laughter now. Tristan finally took to brandishing a heavy stick at the pigs before he dared to go in. Once inside his only hope of staying on his feet was to clear a little space by beating on the backs.

It was on a market day when the pigs had almost reached bacon weight when I came upon Tristan sprawled in his favourite chair. But there was something unusual about him; he wasn't asleep, no medicine bottle, no Woodbines, no *Daily Mirror*. His arms hung limply over the sides of the chair, his eyes were half closed and sweat glistened on his forehead.

'Jim,' he whispered. 'I've had the most hellish afternoon I've ever had in my life.'

I was alarmed at his appearance. 'What's happened.'

'The pigs,' he croaked. 'They escaped today.'

'Escaped! How the devil could they do that?'

Tristan tugged at his hair. 'It was when I was feeding the mare. I gave her her hay and thought I might as well feed the pigs at the same time. You know what they've been like lately – well, today they went berserk. Soon as I opened the door they charged out in a solid block. Sent me up in the air, bucket and all, then ran over the top of me.' He shuddered and looked up at me wide-eyed. 'I'll tell you this, Jim, when I was lying there on the cobbles, covered with swill and that lot trampling on me, I thought it was all over. But they didn't savage me. They belted out through the yard door at full gallop.'

'The yard door was open then?'

'Too true it was. I would just choose this one day to leave it open.'

Tristan sat up and wrung his hands. 'Well, you know, I thought it was all right at first. You see, they slowed down when they got into the lane and trotted quietly round into the front street with Boardman and I hard on their heels. They formed a group there. Didn't seem to know where to go next. I was sure we were going to be able to head them off, but just then one of them caught sight of itself in Robson's shop window.'

He gave a remarkable impression of a pig staring at its reflection for a few moments then leaping back with a startled grunt.

'Well, that did it, Jim. The bloody animal panicked and shot off into the market place at about fifty miles an hour with the rest after it.'

I gasped. Ten large pigs loose among the packed stalls and market day crowds was difficult even to imagine.

'Oh God, you should have seen it.' Tristan fell back wearily into his chair. 'Women and kids screaming. The stall holders, police and everybody else cursing me. There was a terrific traffic jam too – miles of cars tooting like hell while the policeman on point duty concentrated on browbeating me.' He wiped his brow. 'You know that fast talking merchant on the china stall – well, today I saw him at a loss for words. He was balancing a cup on his palm and in full cry when one of the pigs got its fore feet on his stall and stared him straight in the face. He stopped as if he'd been shot. Any other time it would have been funny but I thought the perishing animal was going to wreck the stall. The counter was beginning to rock when the pig changed its mind and made off.'

'What's the position now?' I asked. 'Have you got them back?'

'I've got nine of them back,' Tristan replied, leaning back and closing his eyes. 'With the help of almost the entire male population of the district I've got nine of them back. The tenth was last seen heading North at a good pace. God knows where it is now. Oh, I didn't tell you – one of them got into the post office. Spent quite some time in there.' He put his hands over his face. 'I'm for it this time, Jim. I'll be in the hands of the law after this lot. There's no doubt about it.'

I leaned over and slapped his leg. 'Oh, I shouldn't worry. I don't suppose there's been any serious damage done.'

Tristan replied with a groan. 'But there's something else. When I finally closed the door after getting the pigs back in their sty I was on the verge of collapse. I was leaning against the wall gasping for breath when I saw the mare had gone. Yes, gone. I'd gone straight out after the pigs and forgot to close her box. I don't know where she is. Boardman said he'd look around – I haven't the strength.'

Tristan lit a trembling Woodbine. 'This is the end, Jim. Siegfried will have no mercy this time.'

As he spoke, the door flew open and his brother rushed in. 'What the hell is going on?' he roared. 'I've just been speaking to the vicar and he says my mare is in his garden eating his wallflowers. He's hopping mad and I don't blame him. Go on, you lazy young scoundrel. Don't lie there, get over to the vicarage this instant and bring her back!'

Tristan did not stir. He lay inert, looking up at his brother. His lips moved feebly.

'No,' he said.

'What's that?' Siegfried shouted incredulously. 'Get out of that chair immediately. Go and get that mare!'

'No,' replied Tristan.

I felt a chill of horror. This sort of mutiny was unprecedented. Siegfried had gone very red in the face and I steeled myself for an eruption; but it was Tristan who spoke.

'If you want your mare you can get her yourself.' His voice was quiet with no note of defiance. He had the air of a man to whom the future is of no account.

Even Siegfried could see that this was one time when Tristan had had enough. After glaring down at his brother for a few seconds he turned and walked. He got the mare himself.

Nothing more was said about the incident but the pigs were moved hurriedly to the bacon factory and were never replaced. The stock keeping project was at an end.

Chapter Seventeen

When I came in, Miss Harbottle was sitting, head bowed, over the empty cash box; she looked bereaved. It was a new, shiny, black box with the words 'Petty Cash' printed on top in white letters. Inside was a red book with the incomings and outgoings recorded in neat columns. But there was no money.

Miss Harbottle's sturdy shoulders sagged. She listlessly took up the red book between finger and thumb and a lonely sixpence rolled from between its pages and tinkled into the box. 'He's been at it again,' she whispered.

A stealthy footstep sounded in the passage. 'Mr Farnon!' she called out. And to me: 'It's really absurd the way the man always tries to slink past the door.'

Siegfried shuffled in. He was carrying a stomach tube and pump, calcium bottles bulged from his jacket pockets and a bloodless castrator dangled from the other hand.

He smiled cheerfully but I could see he was uncomfortable, not only because of the load he carried, but because of his poor tactical position. Miss Harbottle had arranged her desk across the corner diagonally opposite the door and he had to walk across a long stretch of carpet to reach her. From her point of view it was strategically perfect. From her corner she could see every inch of the big room, into the passage when the door was open and out on to the front street from the window on her left. Nothing escaped her – it was a position of power.

Siegfried looked down at the square figure behind the desk. 'Good morning, Miss Harbottle, can I do anything for you?'

The grey eyes glinted behind the gold-rimmed spectacles. 'You can, indeed, Mr Farnon. You can explain why you have once more emptied my petty cash box.'

'Oh, I'm so sorry. I had to rush through to Brawton last night and I found myself a bit short. There was really nowhere else to turn to.'

'But Mr Farnon, in the two months I have been here, we must have been over this a dozen times. What is the good of my trying to keep an accurate record of the money in the practice if you keep stealing it and spending it?'

'Well, I suppose I got into the habit in the old pint pot days. It wasn't a bad system, really.'

'It wasn't a system at all. It was anarchy. You cannot run a business that way. But I've told you this so many times and each time you have promised to alter your ways. I feel almost at my wits' end.'

'Oh, never mind, Miss Harbottle. Get some more out of the bank and put it in your box. That'll put it right.' Siegfried gathered up the loose coils of the stomach tube from the floor and turned to go, but Miss Harbottle cleared her throat warningly.

'There are one or two other matters. Will you please try to keep your other promise to enter your visits in the book every day and to price them as you do so. Nearly a week has gone by since you wrote anything in. How can I possibly get the bills out on the first of the month? This is most important, but how do you expect me to do it when you impede me like this?'

'Yes, yes, I'm sorry, but I have a string of calls waiting. I really must go.' He was halfway across the floor and the tube was uncoiling itself again when he heard the ominous throat clearing behind him.

'And one more thing, Mr Farnon. I still can't decipher your writing. These medical terms are difficult enough, so please take a little care and don't scribble.'

'Very well, Miss Harbottle.' He quickened his pace through the door and into the passage where, it seemed, was safety and peace. He was clattering thankfully over the tiles when the familiar rumbling reached him. She could project that sound a surprising distance by giving it a bit of extra pressure, and it was a summons which had to be obeyed. I could hear him wearily putting the tube and pump on the floor; the calcium bottles must have been digging into his ribs because I heard them go down too.

He presented himself again before the desk. Miss Harbottle wagged a finger at him. 'While I have you here I'd like to mention another point which troubles me. Look at this day book. You see all these slips sticking out of the pages? They are all queries – there must be scores of them – and I am at a standstill until you clear them for me. When I ask you you never have the time. Can you go over them with me now?'

Siegfried backed away hurriedly. 'No, no, not just now. As I said, I have some urgent calls waiting. I'm very sorry but it will have to be some other time. First chance I get I'll come in and see you'. He felt the door behind him and with a last glance at the massive, disapproving figure behind the desk, he turned and fled.

Chapter Eighteen

I could look back now on six months of hard practical experience. I had treated cows, horses, pigs, dogs and cats seven days a week; in the morning, afternoon, evening and through the hours when the world was asleep. I had calved cows and farrowed sows till my arms ached and the skin peeled off. I had been knocked down, trampled on and sprayed liberally with every kind of muck. I had seen a fair cross section of the diseases of animals. And yet a little voice had begun to niggle at the back of my mind; it said I knew nothing, nothing at all.

This was strange, because those six months had been built upon five years of theory; a slow, painful assimilation of thousands of facts and a careful storage of fragments of knowledge like a squirrel with its nuts. Beginning with the study of plants and the lowest forms of life, working up to dissection in the anatomy lab and physiology and the vast, soul-less territory of materia medica. Then pathology which tore down the curtain of ignorance and let me look for the first time into the deep secrets. And parasitology, the teeming other world of the worms and fleas and mange mites. Finally, medicine and surgery, the crystallisation of my learning and its application to the everyday troubles of animals.

And there were many others, like physics, chemistry, hygiene; they didn't seem to have missed a thing. Why then should I feel I knew nothing? Why had I begun to feel like an astronomer looking through a telescope at an unknown galaxy? This sensation that I was only groping about on the fringes of limitless space was depressing. It was a funny thing, because everybody else seemed to know all about sick animals. The chap who held the cow's tail, the neighbour from the next farm, men in pubs, jobbing gardeners; they all knew and were free and confident with their advice.

I tried to think back over my life. Was there any time when I had felt this supreme faith in my own knowledge. And then I remembered.

I was back in Scotland, I was seventeen and I was walking under the arch of the Veterinary College into Montrose Street. I had been a student for three days but not until this afternoon had I felt the thrill of fulfilment. Messing about with botany and zoology was all right but this afternoon had been the real thing; I had had my first lecture in animal husbandry.

The subject had been the points of the horse. Professor Grant had hung up a life size picture of a horse and gone over it from nose to tail, indicating the withers, the stifle, the hock, the poll and all the other rich, equine terms. And the professor had been wise; to make his lecture more interesting he kept throwing in little practical points like 'This is where we find curb,' or 'Here is the site for windgalls.' He talked of thoroughpins and sidebones, splints and quittor; things the students wouldn't learn about for another four years, but it brought it all to life.

The words were still spinning in my head as I walked slowly down the sloping street. This was what I had come for. I felt as though I had undergone an initiation and become a member of an exclusive club. I really knew about horses. And I was wearing a brand new riding mac with all sorts of extra straps and buckles which slapped against my legs as I turned the corner of the hill into busy Newton Road.

I could hardly believe my luck when I saw the horse. It was standing outside the library below Queen's Cross like something left over from another age. It drooped dispiritedly between the shafts of a coal cart which stood like an island in an eddying stream of cars and buses. Pedestrians hurried by, uncaring, but I had the feeling that fortune was smiling on me.

A horse. Not just a picture but a real, genuine horse. Stray words from the lecture floated up into my mind; the pastern, cannon bone, coronet and all those markings – snip, blaze, white sock near hind. I stood on the pavement and examined the animal critically.

I thought it must be obvious to every passer-by that here was a true expert. Not just an inquisitive onlooker but a man who knew and understood all. I felt clothed in a visible aura of horsiness.

I took a few steps up and down, hands deep in the pockets of the new riding mac, eyes probing for possible shoeing faults or curbs or bog spavins. So thorough was my inspection that I worked round to the off side of the horse and stood perilously among the racing traffic.

I glanced around at the people hurrying past. Nobody seemed to care, not even the horse. He was a large one, at least seventeen hands, and he gazed apathetically down the street, easing his hind legs alternatively in a bored manner. I hated to leave him but I had completed my examination and it was time I was on my way. But I felt that I ought to make a gesture before I left; something to communicate to the horse that I understood his problems and that we belonged to the same brotherhood. I stepped briskly forward and patted him on the neck.

Quick as a striking snake, the horse whipped downwards and seized my shoulder in his great strong teeth. He laid back his ears, rolled his eyes wickedly and hoisted me up, almost off my feet. I hung there helplessly, suspended like a lopsided puppet. I wriggled and kicked but the teeth were clamped immovably in the material of my coat.

There was no doubt about the interest of the passers by now. The grotesque sight of a man hanging from a horse's mouth brought them to a sudden halt and a crowd formed with people looking over each other's shoulders and others fighting at the back to see what was going on.

A horrified old lady was crying: 'Oh, poor boy! Help him, somebody!' Some of the braver characters tried pulling at me but the horse whickered ominously and hung on tighter. Conflicting advice was shouted from all sides. With deep shame I saw two attractive girls in the front row giggling helplessly.

Appalled at the absurdity of my position, I began to thrash about wildly; my shirt collar tightened round my throat; a stream of the horse's saliva trickled down the front of my mac. I could feel myself choking and was giving up hope when a man pushed his way through the crowd.

He was very small. Angry eyes glared from a face blackened by coal dust. Two empty sacks were draped over an arm.

'Whit the hell's this?' he shouted. A dozen replies babbled in the air.

'Can ye no leave the bloody hoarse alone?' he yelled into my face. I made no reply, being pop-eyed, half throttled and in no mood for conversation.

The coalman turned his fury on the horse. 'Drop him, ya big bastard! Go on, let go, drop him!'

Getting no response he dug the animal viciously in the belly with his thumb. The horse took the point at once and released me like an obedient dog dropping a bone. I fell on my knees and ruminated in the gutter for a while till I could breathe more easily. As from a great distance I could still hear the little man shouting at me.

After some time I stood up. The coalman was still shouting and the crowd was listening appreciatively. 'Whit d'ye think you're playing at – keep yer hands off ma bloody hoarse – get the poliss tae ye.'

I looked down at my new mac. The shoulder was chewed to a sodden mass. I felt I must escape and began to edge my way through the crowd. Some of the faces were concerned but most were grinning. Once clear I started to walk away rapidly and as I turned the corner the last faint cry from the coalman reached me.

'Dinna meddle wi' things ye ken nuthin' aboot!'

Chapter Nineteen

I flipped idly through the morning mail. The usual stack of bills, circulars, brightly coloured advertisements for new drugs; after a few months the novelty had worn off and I hardly bothered to read them. I had almost reached the bottom of the pile when I came on something different; an expensive looking envelope in heavy, deckle-edged paper addressed to me personally. I ripped it open and pulled out a gilt bordered card which I scanned quickly. I felt my face redden as I slipped the card into an inside pocket.

Siegfried finished ticking off the visits and looked up. 'What are you looking so guilty about, James? Your past catching up with you? What is it, anyway – a letter from an outraged mother?'

'Go on then,' I said sheepishly, pulling out the card and handing it to him, 'have a good laugh. I suppose you'd find out, anyway.'

Siegfried's face was expressionless as he read the card aloud. 'Tricki requests the pleasure of Uncle Herriot's company on Friday February 5th. Drinks and dancing.' He looked up and spoke seriously. 'Now isn't that nice. You know, that must be one of the most generous Pekingeses in England. Sending you kippers and tomatoes and hampers isn't enough – he has to ask you to his home for a party.'

I grabbed the card and slipped it out of sight. 'All right, all right, I know. But what am I supposed to do?'

'Do? What you do is to sit down right away and get a letter off saying thank you very much, you'll be there on February the fifth. Mrs Pumphrey's parties are famous. Mountains of exotic food, rivers of champagne. Don't miss it whatever you do.'

'Will there be a lot of people there?' I asked, shuffling my feet.

Siegfried struck himself on the forehead with his open hand. 'Of course there'll be a lot of people. What d'you think. Did you expect it would be just you and Tricki? You'd have a few beers together and then you'd dance a slow foxtrot with him? The cream of the county will be there in full regalia but my guess is that there will be no more honoured guest than Uncle Herriot. Why? Because Mrs Pumphrey invited the others but Tricki invited you.'

'OK, OK,' I groaned. 'I'll be on my own and I haven't got a proper evening suit. I don't fancy it.'

Siegfried rose and put a hand on my shoulder. 'My dear chap, don't mess about. Sit down and accept the invitation and then go into Brawton and hire a suit for the night. You won't be on your own for long – the debs will be tramping over each other for a dance with you.' He gave the shoulder a final pat before walking to the door. Before leaving he turned round and his expression was grave. 'And remember for Pete's sake don't write to Mrs Pumphrey. Address your letter to Tricki himself or you're sunk.'

I had a lot of mixed feelings churning around in me when I presented myself at the Pumphrey home on the night of February 5th. A maid let me into the hall and I could see Mrs Pumphrey at the entrance to the ballroom receiving her guests and beyond, an elegant throng standing around with drinks. There was a well bred clamour, a general atmosphere of wealth. I straightened the tie on my hired outfit, took a deep breath and waited.

Mrs Pumphrey was smiling sweetly as she shook hands with the couple in front of me but when she saw me her face became radiant. 'Oh Mr Herriot, how nice of you to come. Tricki was so delighted to have your letter – in fact we really must go in and see him now.' She led me across the hall.

'He's in the morning-room,' she whispered. 'Between ourselves he finds these affairs rather a bore, but he'll be simply furious if I don't take you in for a moment.'

Tricki was curled up in an armchair by the side of a bright fire. When he saw me he jumped on the back of the chair barking in delight, his huge, laughing mouth bisecting his face. I was trying to fend off his attempts to lick my face when I caught sight of two large food bowls on the carpet. One contained about a pound of chopped chicken, the other a mass of crumbled cake.

'Mrs Pumphrey!' I thundered, pointing at the bowls. The poor woman put her hand to her mouth and shrank away from me.

'Oh do forgive me,' she wailed, her face a picture of guilt. 'It's just a special treat because he's alone tonight. And the weather is so cold, too.' She clasped her hands and looked at me abjectly.

'I'll forgive you,' I said sternly, 'If you will remove half the chicken and all the cake.'

Fluttering, like a little girl caught in naughtiness, she did as I said.

I parted regretfully from the little Peke. It had been a busy day and I was sleepy from the hours in the biting cold. This room with its fire and soft lighting looked more inviting than the noisy glitter of the ballroom and I would have preferred to curl up here with Tricki on my knee for an hour or two.

Mrs Pumphrey became brisk. 'Now you must come and meet some of my friends.' We went into the ballroom where light blazed down from three cut glass chandeliers and was reflected dazzlingly from the cream and gold, many-mirrored walls. We moved from group to group as Mrs Pumphrey introduced me and I squirmed in embarrassment as I heard myself described as 'Tricki's dear kind uncle'. But either they were people of superb self control or they were familiar with their hostess's blind spot because the information was received with complete gravity.

Along one wall a five piece orchestra was tuning up; white-jacketed waiters hurried among the guests with trays of food and drinks. Mrs Pumphrey stopped one of the waiters. 'François, some champagne for this gentleman.'

'Yes, Madame.' The waiter proffered his tray.

'No, no, no, not those. One of the big glasses.'

François hurried away and returned with something like a soup plate with a stem. It was brimming with champagne.

'François.'

'Yes, Madame?'

'This is Mr Herriot. I want you to take a good look at him.'

The waiter turned a pair of sad, spaniel eyes on me and drank me in for a few moments.

'I want you to look after him. See that his glass is full and that he has plenty to eat.'

'Certainly, Madame.' He bowed and moved away.

I buried my face in the ice cold champagne and when I looked up, there was François holding out a tray of smoked salmon sandwiches.

It was like that all the evening. François seemed always to be at my elbow, filling up the enormous glass or pushing dainties at me. I found it delightful;

the salty snacks brought on a thirst which I quenched with deep draughts of champagne, then I had more snacks which made me thirsty again and François would unfailingly pop up with the magnum.

It was the first time I had had the opportunity of drinking champagne by the pint and it was a rewarding experience. I was quickly aware of a glorious lightness, a heightening of the perceptions. I stopped being overawed by this new world and began to enjoy it. I danced with everybody in sight – sleek young beauties, elderly dowagers and twice with a giggling Mrs Pumphrey.

Or I just talked. And it was witty talk; I repeatedly amazed myself by my lightning shafts. Once I caught sight of myself in a mirror – a distinguished figure, glass in hand, the hired suit hanging on me with quiet grace. It took my breath away.

Eating, drinking, talking, dancing, the evening winged past. When it was time to go and I had my coat on and was shaking hands with Mrs Pumphrey in the hall, François appeared again with a bowl of hot soup. He seemed to be worried lest I grow faint on the journey home.

After the soup, Mrs Pumphrey said: 'And now you must come and say good night to Tricki. He'll never forgive you if you don't.' We went into his room and the little dog yawned from the depths of the chair and wagged his tail. Mrs Pumphrey put her hand on my sleeve. 'While you're here, I wonder if you would be so kind as to examine his claws. I've been so worried in case they might be growing too long.'

I lifted up the paws one by one and scrutinised the claws while Tricki lazily licked my hands. 'No, you needn't worry, they're perfectly all right.'

'Thank you so much, I'm so grateful to you. Now you must wash your hands.'

In the familiar bathroom with the sea green basins and the enamelled fishes on the walls and the dressing-table and the bottles on the glass shelves, I looked around as the steaming water ran from the tap. There was my own towel by the basin and the usual new slab of soap – soap that lathered in an instant and gave off an expensive scent. It was the final touch of balm on a gracious evening. It had been a few hours of luxury and light and I carried the memory back with me to Skeldale House.

I got into bed, switched off the light and lay on my back looking up into the darkness. Snatches of music still tinkled about in my head and I was beginning to swim back to the ballroom when the phone rang.

'This is Atkinson of Beck Cottage,' a far away voice said. 'I 'ave a sow 'ere what can't get pigged. She's been on all night. Will you come?'

I looked at the clock as I put down the receiver. It was two a.m. I felt numbed. A farrowing right on top of the champagne and the smoked salmon and those little biscuits with the black heaps of caviare. And at Beck Cottage, one of the most primitive smallholdings in the district. It wasn't fair.

Sleepily, I took off my pyjamas and pulled on my shirt. As I reached for the stiff, worn corduroys I used for work, I tried not to look at the hired suit hanging on a corner of the wardrobe.

I groped my way down the long garden to the garage. In the darkness of the yard I closed my eyes and the great chandeliers blazed again, the mirrors flashed and the music played.

It was only two miles out to Beck Cottage. It lay in a hollow and in the winter the place was a sea of mud. I left my car and squelched through the blackness to the door of the house. My knock was unanswered and I moved across to the cluster of buildings opposite and opened the half door into the byre. The warm, sweet bovine smell met me as I peered towards a light showing dimly at the far end where a figure was standing.

I went inside past the shadowy row of cows standing side by side with broken wooden partitions between them and past the mounds of manure piled behind them. Mr Atkinson didn't believe in mucking out too often.

Stumbling over the broken floor, splashing through pools of urine, I arrived at the end where a pen had been made by closing off a corner with a gate. I could just make out the form of a pig, pale in the gloom, lying on her side. There was a scanty bed of straw under her and she lay very still except for the trembling of her flanks. As I watched, she caught her breath and strained for a few seconds then the straining began again.

Mr Atkinson received me without enthusiasm. He was middle-aged, sported a week's growth of beard and wore an ancient hat with a brim which flopped round his ears. He stood hunched against a wall, one hand deep in a ragged pocket, the other holding a bicycle lamp with a fast-failing battery.

'Is this all the light we've got?' I asked.

'Aye, it is,' Mr Atkinson replied, obviously surprised. He looked from the lamp to me with a 'what more does he want?' expression.

'Let's have it, then.' I trained the feeble beam on my patient. 'Just a young pig, isn't she?'

'Aye, nobbut a gilt. Fust litter.'

The pig strained again, shuddered and lay still.

'Something stuck there, I reckon,' I said. 'Will you bring me a bucket of hot water some soap and a towel, please.'

'Haven't got no 'ot water. Fire's out.'

'OK, bring me whatever you've got.'

The farmer clattered away down the byre taking the light with him and, with the darkness, the music came back again. It was a Strauss waltz and I was dancing with Lady Frenswick; she was young and very fair and she laughed as I swung her round. I could see her white shoulders and the diamonds winking at her throat and the wheeling mirrors.

Mr Atkinson came shuffling back and dumped a bucket of water on the floor. I dipped a finger in the water; it was ice cold. And the bucket had seen many hard years – I would have to watch my arms on that jagged rim.

Quickly stripping off jacket and shirt, I sucked in my breath as a villainous draught blew through a crack on to my back.

'Soap, please,' I said through clenched teeth.

'In t'bucket.'

I plunged an arm into the water, shivered, and felt my way round till I found a roundish object about the size of a golf ball. I pulled it out and examined it; it was hard and smooth and speckled like a pebble from the sea shore and, optimistically, I began to rub it between my hands and up my arms, waiting for the lather to form. But the soap was impervious; it yielded nothing.

I discarded the idea of asking for another piece in case this would be construed as another complaint. Instead, I borrowed the light and tracked down the byre into the yard, the mud sucking at my Wellingtons, goose pimples rearing on my chest. I searched around in the car boot, listening to my teeth chattering, till I came on a jar of antiseptic lubricating cream.

Back in the pen, I smeared the cream on my arm, knelt behind the pig and gently inserted my hand into the vagina. I moved my hand forward and as wrist and elbow disappeared inside the pig I was forced to roll over on my side. The stones were cold and wet but I forgot my discomfort when my fingers touched something; it was a tiny tail. Almost a transverse presentation, biggish piglet stuck like a cork in a bottle.

Using one finger, I worked the hind legs back until I was able to grasp them and draw the piglet out. 'This is the one that's been causing the trouble. He's dead, I'm afraid – been squashed in there too long. But there could be some live ones still inside. I'll have another feel.'

I greased my arm and got down again. Just inside the os uteri, almost at arm's length, I found another piglet and I was feeling at the face when a set of minute but very sharp teeth sank into my finger.

I yelped and looked up at the farmer from my stony bed. 'This one's alive, anyway. I'll soon have him out.'

But the piglet had other ideas. He showed no desire to leave his warm haven and every time I got hold of his slippery little foot between my fingers he jerked it away. After a minute or two of this game I felt a cramping in my arm. I relaxed and lay back, my head resting on the cobbles, my arm still inside the pig. I closed my eyes and immediately I was back in the ballroom, in the warmth and the brilliant light. I was holding out my immense glass while François poured from the magnum; then I was dancing, close to the orchestra this time and the leader, beating time with one hand, turned round and smiled into my face; smiled and bowed as though he had been looking for me all his life.

I smiled back but the bandleader's face disolved and there was only Mr Atkinson looking down at me expressionlessly, his unshaven jaw and shaggy eyebrows thrown into sinister relief by the light striking up from the bicycle lamp.

I shook myself and raised my cheek from the floor. This wouldn't do. Falling asleep on the job; either I was very tired or there was still some champagne in me. I reached again and grasped the foot firmly between two fingers and this time, despite his struggles, the piglet was hauled out into the world. Once arrived, he seemed to accept the situation and tottered round philosophically to his mother's udder.

'She's not helping at all,' I said. 'Been on so long that she's exhausted. I'm going to give her an injection.'

Another numbing expedition through the mud to the car, a shot of pituitrin into the gilt's thigh and within minutes the action began with powerful contractions of the uterus. There was no obstruction now and soon a wriggling pink piglet was deposited in the straw; then quite quickly another and another.

'Coming off the assembly line now, all right,' I said. Mr Atkinson grunted.

Eight piglets had been born and the light from the lamp had almost given out when a dark mass of afterbirth welled from the gilt's vulva.

I rubbed my cold arms. 'Well, I should say that's the lot now.' I felt suddenly chilled; I couldn't say how long I had been standing there looking at the wonder that never grew stale; the little pigs struggling on to their legs and making their way unguided to the long double row of teats; the mother with her first family easing herself over to expose as much as possible of her udder to the hungry mouths.

Better get dressed quickly. I had another try at the marble-like soap but it defeated me as easily as the first time. I wondered how long it had been in the family. Down my right side my cheek and ribs were caked with dirt and mucus. I did my best to scrape some off with my finger nails then I swilled myself down with the cold water from the bucket.

'Have you a towel there?' I gasped.

Mr Atkinson wordlessly handed me a sack. Its edges were stiff with old manure and it smelled musty from the meal it had long since contained. I took it and began to rub my chest and as the sour grains of the meal powdered my skin, the last bubbles of champagne left me, drifted up through the gaps in the tiles and burst sadly in the darkness beyond.

I dragged my shirt over my gritty back, feeling a sense of coming back to my own world. I buttoned my coat, picked up the syringe and the bottle of pituitrin and climbed out of the pen. I had a last look before I left. The bicycle lamp was shedding its final faint glow and I had to lean over the gate to see the row of little pigs sucking busily, utterly absorbed. The gilt carefully shifted her position and grunted. It was a grunt of deep content.

Yes, I was back and it was all right. I drove through the mud and up the hill where I had to get out to open a gate and the wind, with the cold, clean smell of the frosty grass in it caught at my face. I stood for a while looking across the dark fields, thinking of the night which was ending now. My mind went back to my schooldays and an old gentleman talking to the class about careers. He had said: 'If you decide to become a veterinary surgeon you will never grow rich but you will have a life of endless interest and variety.'

I laughed aloud in the darkness and as I got into the car I was still chuckling. That old chap certainly wasn't kidding. Variety. That was it – variety.

Chapter Twenty

As I checked my list of calls it occurred to me that, this time, Siegfried didn't look so much like a schoolboy as he faced Miss Harbottle. For one thing, he hadn't marched straight in and stood in front of the desk; that was disastrous and he always looked beaten before he started. Instead, he had veered off over the last few yards till he stood with his back to the window. This way she had to turn her head slightly to face him and besides, he had the light at his back.

He thrust his hands into his pockets and leaned back against the window frame. He was wearing his patient look, his eyes were kind and his face was illumined by an almost saintly smile. Miss Harbottle's eyes narrowed.

'I just wanted a word with you, Miss Harbottle. One or two little points I'd like to discuss. First, about your petty cash box. It's a nice box and I think you were quite right to institute it, but I think you would be the first to agree that the main function of a cash box is to have cash in it.' He gave a light laugh. 'Now last night I had a few dogs in the surgery and the owners wanted to pay on the spot. I had no change and went for some to your box – it was quite empty. I had to say I would send them a bill, and that isn't good business, is it Miss Harbottle? It didn't look good, so I really must ask you to keep some cash in your cash box.'

Miss Harbottle's eyes widened incredulously. 'But Mr Farnon, you removed the entire contents to go to the hunt ball at . . .'

Siegfried held up a hand and his smile took on an unearthly quality. 'Please hear me out. There is another very small thing I want to bring to your attention. It is now the tenth day of the month and the accounts have not gone out. Now this is a very undesirable state of affairs and there are several points to consider here.'

'But Mr Farnon . . . !'

'Just one moment, Miss Harbottle, till I explain this to you. It is a known fact that farmers pay their bills more readily if they receive them on the first of the month. And there is another, even more important factor.' The beautiful smile left his face and was replaced by an expression of sorrowing gravity. 'Have you ever stopped to work out just how much interest the practice is losing on all the money lying out there because you are late in sending out the accounts.'

'Mr Farnon . . .!'

'I am almost finished, Miss Harbottle, and, believe me, it grieves me to have to speak like this. But the fact is, I can't afford to lose money in this way.' He spread out his hands in a gesture of charming frankness. 'So if you will just apply yourself to this little matter I'm sure all will be well.'

'But will you tell me how I can possibly send the accounts when you refuse to write up the . . .'

'In conclusion, Miss Harbottle, let me say this. I have been very satisfied with your progress since you joined us, and I am sure that with time you will tighten up on those little points I have just mentioned.' A certain roguishness crept into his smile and he put his head on one side. Miss Harbottle's strong fingers closed tightly round a heavy ebony ruler.

'Efficiency,' he said, crinkling his eyes. 'That's what we must have – efficiency.'

Chapter Twenty-one

I dropped the suture needle into the tray and stepped back to survey the finished job. 'Well though I say it myself, that looks rather nice.'

Tristan leaned over the unconscious dog and examined the neat incision with its row of regular stitches. 'Very pretty indeed, my boy. Couldn't have done better myself.'

The big black labrador lay peacefully on the table, his tongue lolling, his eyes glazed and unseeing. He had been brought in with an ugly growth over his ribs and I had decided that it was a simple lipoma, quite benign and very suitable for surgery. And so it had turned out. The tumour had come away with almost ridiculous ease, round, intact and shining, like a hard boiled egg from its shell. No haemorrhage, no fear of recurrence.

The unsightly swelling had been replaced by this tidy scar which would be invisible in a few weeks. I was pleased.

'We'd better keep him here till he comes round,' I said. 'Give me a hand to get him on to these blankets.' We made the dog comfortable in front of an electric stove and I left to start my morning round.

It was during lunch that we first heard the strange sound. It was something between a moan and a howl, starting quite softly but rising to a piercing pitch before shuddering back down the scale to silence.

Siegfried looked up, startled, from his soup. 'What in God's name is that?'

'Must be that dog I operated on this morning,' I replied. 'The odd one does that coming out of barbiturates. I expect he'll stop soon.'

Siegfried looked at me doubtfully. 'Well, I hope so – I could soon get tired of that. Gives me the creeps.'

We went through and looked at the dog, Pulse strong, respirations deep and regular, mucous membranes a good colour. He was still stretched out, immobile, and the only sign of returning consciousness was the howl which seemed to have settled down into a groove of one every ten seconds.

'Yes, he's perfectly all right,' Siegfried said. 'But what a bloody noise! Let's get out of here.'

Lunch was finished hastily and in silence except for the ceaseless background wailing. Siegfried had scarcely swallowed his last mouthful before he was on his feet. 'Well, I must fly. Got a lot on this afternoon. Tristan, I think it would be a good idea to bring that dog through to the sitting-room and put him by the fire. Then you could stay by him and keep an eye on him.'

Tristan was stunned. 'You mean I have to stay in the same room as that noise all afternoon?'

'Yes, I mean just that. We can't send him home as he is and I don't want anything to happen to him. He needs care and attention.' .

'Maybe you'd like me to hold his paw or perhaps wheel him round the market place?'

'Don't give me any of your bloody cheek. You stay with the dog and that's an order!'

Tristan and I stretchered the heavy animal along the passage on the blankets, then I had to leave for the afternoon round. I paused and looked back at the big black form by the fire and Tristan crouched miserably in his chair. The noise was overpowering. I closed the door hurriedly.

It was dark when I got back and the old house hung over me, black and silent against the frosty sky. Silent, that is, except for the howling which still echoed along the passage and filtered eerily into the deserted street.

I glanced at my watch as I slammed the car door. It was six o'clock, so Tristan had had four hours of it. I ran up the steps and along the passage and when I opened the sitting-room door the noise jarred in my head. Tristan was standing with his back to me, looking through the french window into the darkness of the garden. His hands were deep in his pockets; tufts of cotton wool drooped from his ears. —

'Well, how is it going?' I asked.

There was no reply so I walked over and tapped him on the shoulder. The effect was spectacular. Tristan leaped into the air and cork-screwed round. His face was ashen and he was trembling violently.

'God help us, Jim, you nearly killed me there. I can't hear a damn thing through these ear plugs – except the dog, of course. Nothing keeps that out.'

I knelt by the labrador and examined him. The dog's condition was excellent but, except for a faint eye reflex there was no sign that he was regaining consciousness. And all the time there were the piercing, evenly spaced howls.

'He's taking a hell of a time to come out of it,' I said. 'Has he been like this all afternoon?'

'Yes, just like that. Not one bit different. And don't waste any sympathy on him, the yowling devil. He's as happy as a sandboy down by the fire – doesn't know a thing about it. But how about me? My nerves are about shot to bits listening to him hour after hour. Much more of it and you'll have to give me a shot too.' He ran a shaking hand through his hair and a twitching started in his cheek.

I took his arm. 'Well, come through and eat. You'll feel better after some food.' I led him unresisting into the dining-room.

Siegfried was in excellent form over the meal. He seemed to be in a mood of exhilaration and monopolised the conversation but he did not once refer to the shrill obligato from the other room. There was no doubt, however, that it was still getting through to Tristan.

As they were leaving the room, Siegfried put his hand on my shoulder. 'Remember we've got that meeting in Brawton tonight, James. Old Reeves on diseases of sheep – he's usually very good. Pity you can't come too, Tristan, but I'm afraid you'll have to stay with the dog till he comes round.'

Tristan flinched as if he had been struck. 'Oh not another session with that bloody animal! He's driving me mad!'

'I'm afraid there's nothing else for it. James or I could have taken over tonight but we have to show up at this meeting. It would look bad if we missed it.'

Tristan stumbled back into the room and I put on my coat. As I went out into the street I paused for a moment and listened. The dog was still howling.

The meeting was a success. It was held in one of Brawton's lush hotels and, as usual, the best part was the get together of the vets in the bar afterwards. It was infinitely soothing to hear the other man's problems and mistakes – especially the mistakes.

It amused me to look round the crowded room and try to guess what the little knots of men were talking about. That man over there, bent double and slashing away at the air with one hand – he was castrating a colt in the standing position. And the one with his arm out at full stretch, his fingers working busily at nothing – almost certainly foaling a mare; probably correcting a carpal flexion. And doing it effortlessly too. Veterinary surgery was a childishly simple matter in a warm bar with a few drinks inside you.

It was eleven o'clock before we all got into our cars and headed for our own particular niche in Yorkshire – some to the big industrial towns of the West Riding, others to the seaside places of the East coast and Siegfried and I hurrying thankfully back on the narrow road which twisted between its stone walls into the Northern Pennines.

I thought guiltily that for the last few hours I had completely forgotten about Tristan and his vigil. Still, it must have been better tonight. The dog would surely have quietened down by now. But, jumping from the car in Darrowby, I froze in mid stride as a thin wail came out faintly from Skeldale House. This was incredible; it was after midnight and the dog was still at it. And what of Tristan? I hated to think what kind of shape he'd be in. Almost fearfully I turned the knob on the sitting-room door.

Tristan's chair made a little island in a sea of empty beer bottles. An upturned crate lay against the wall and Tristan was sitting very upright and looking solemn. I picked my way over the debris.

'Well, has it been rough, Triss? How do you feel now?'

'Could be worse, old lad, could be worse. Soon as you'd gone I slipped over to the Drovers for a crate of pint Magnets. Made all the difference. After three or four the dog stopped worrying me – matter of fact, I've been yowling back at him for hours now. We've had quite an interesting evening. Anyway, he's coming out now. Look at him.'

The big dog had his head up and there was recognition in his eyes. The howling had stopped. I went over and patted him and the long black tail jerked in a fair attempt at a wag.

'That's better, old boy,' I said. 'But you'd better behave yourself now. You've given your uncle Tristan one hell of a day.'

The labrador responded immediately by struggling to his feet. He took a few swaying steps and collapsed among the bottles.

Siegfried appeared in the doorway and looked distastefully at Tristan, still very upright and wearing a judicial expression, and at the dog scrabbling among the bottles. 'What an infernal mess! Surely you can do a little job without making an orgy out of it.'

At the sound of his voice the labrador staggered up and, in a flush of over confidence, tried to run towards him, wagging his tail unsteadily. He didn't get very far and went down in a heap, sending a Magnet empty rolling gently up to Siegfried's feet.

Siegfried bent over and stroked the shining black head. 'Nice friendly animal that. I should think he's a grand dog when he's got his senses about him. He'll be normal in the morning, but the problem is what to do with him now. We can't leave him staggering about down here – he could break a leg.' He glanced at Tristan who had not moved a muscle. He was sitting up straighter than ever; stiff and motionless like a Prussian general. 'You know, I think the best thing would be for you to take him up to your room tonight. Now we've got him so far, we don't want him to hurt himself. Yes, that's it, he can spend the night with you.'

'Thank you, thank you very much indeed,' Tristan said in a flat voice, still looking straight to his front.

Siegfried looked at him narrowly for a moment, then turned away. 'Right then, clear away this rubbish and let's get to bed.'

My bedroom and Tristan's were connected by a door. Mine was the main room, huge, square, with a high ceiling, pillared fireplace and graceful alcoves like the ones downstairs. I always felt a little like a duke lying there.

Tristan's had been the old dressing-room and was long and narrow with his small bed crouching at one end as if trying to hide. There were no carpets on the smooth, varnished boards so I laid the dog on a heap of blankets and talked down soothingly at Tristan's wan face on the pillow.

'He's quiet now – sleeping like a baby and looks as though he's going to stay that way. You'll be able to have a well earned rest now.'

I went back to my own room, undressed quickly and got into bed. I went to sleep immediately and I couldn't tell just when the noises started next door, but I came suddenly wide awake with an angry yell ringing in my ears. Then there was a slithering and a bump followed by another distracted cry from Tristan.

I quailed at the idea of going into the dressing-room – there was nothing I could do, anyway – so I huddled closer into the sheets and listened. I kept sliding into a half sleep then starting into wakefulness as more bumping and shouting came through the wall.

After about two hours the noises began to change. The labrador seemed to have gained mastery over his legs and was marching up and down the room, his claws making a regular tck-a-tck, tck-a-tck, tck-a-tck on the wooden floor. It went on and on, interminably. At intervals, Tristan's voice, hoarse now, burst out. 'Stop it, for Christ's sake! Sit down, you bloody dog!'

I must have fallen into a deeper sleep because when I awoke the room was grey with the cold light of morning. I rolled on to my back and listened. I could still hear the tck-a-tck of the claws but it had become irregular as though the labrador was strolling about instead of blundering blindly from one end of the room to the other. There was no sound from Tristan.

I got out of bed, shivering as the icy air of the room gripped me, and pulled on my shirt and trousers. Tiptoeing across the floor, I opened the connecting door and was almost floored as two large feet were planted on my chest. The labrador was delighted to see me and appeared to be thoroughly at home. His fine brown eyes shone with intelligence and well-being and he showed rows of glittering teeth and a flawlessly pink tongue in a wide, panting grin. Far below, the tail lashed ecstatically.

'Well, you're all right, chum,' I said. 'Let's have a look at that wound.' I removed the horny paws from my chest and explored the line of stitches over the ribs. No swelling, no pain, no reaction at all.

'Lovely!' I cried. 'Beautiful. You're as good as new again.' I gave the dog a playful slap on the rump which sent him into a transport of joy. He leaped all over me, clawing and kicking.

I was fighting him off when I heard a dismal groan from the bed. In the dim light Tristan looked ghastly. He was lying on his back, both hands clutching the quilt and there was a wild look in his eyes. 'Not a wink of sleep, Jim,' he whispered. 'Not a bloody wink. He's got a wonderful sense of humour, my brother, making me spend the night with this animal. It'll really make his day when he hears what I've been through. Just watch him – I'll bet you anything you like he'll look pleased.'

Later, over breakfast, Siegfried heard the details of his brother's harrowing night and was very sympathetic. He condoled with him at length and apologised for all the trouble the dog had given him. But Tristan was right. He did look pleased.

Chapter Twenty-two

As I came into the operating room I saw that Siegfried had a patient on the table. He was thoughtfully stroking the head of an elderly and rather woebegone border terrier.

'James,' he said, 'I want you to take this little dog through to Grier.'

'Grier?'

'Vet at Brawton. He was treating the case before the owner moved into our district. I've seen it a couple of times – stones in the bladder. It needs an immediate operation and I think I'd better let Grier do it. He's a touchy devil and I don't want to stand on his toes.'

'Oh, I think I've heard of him,' I said.

'Probably you have. A cantankerous Aberdonian. Since he practises in a fashionable town he gets quite a few students and he gives them hell. That sort of thing gets around.' He lifted the terrier from the table and handed him to me. 'The sooner you get through there the better. You can see the op and bring the dog back here afterwards. But watch yourself – don't rub Grier the wrong way or he'll take it out of you somehow.'

At my first sight of Angus Grier I thought immediately of whisky. He was about fifty and something had to be responsible for the fleshy, mottled cheeks, the swimmy eyes and the pattern of purple veins which chased each other over his prominent nose. He wore a permanently insulted expression.

He didn't waste any charm on me; a nod and a grunt and he grabbed the dog from my arms. Then he stabbed a finger at a slight, fairish youth in a white coat. 'That's Clinton – final year student. Do ye no' think there's some pansy lookin' buggers coming in to this profession?'

During the operation he niggled constantly at the young man and, in an attempt to create a diversion, I asked when he was going back to college.

'Beginning of next week,' he replied.

'Aye, but he's awa hame tomorrow,' Grier rasped. 'Wasting his time when he could be gettin' good experience here.'

The student blushed. 'Well, I've been seeing practice for over a month and I felt I ought to spend a couple of days with my mother before the term starts.'

'Oh, I ken, I ken. You're all the same – canna stay away from the titty.'

The operation was uneventful and as Grier inserted the last stitch he looked up at me. 'You'll no' want to take the dog back till he's out of the anaesthetic. I've got a case to visit – you can come with me to pass the time.'

We didn't have what you could call a conversation in the car. It was a monologue; a long recital of wrongs suffered at the hands of wicked clients and predatory colleagues. The story I liked best was about a retired admiral who had asked Grier to examine his horse for soundness. Grier said the animal had a bad heart and was not fit to ride, whereupon the admiral flew into a fury and got another vet to examine the horse. The second vet said there was nothing the matter with the heart and passed the animal sound.

The admiral wrote Grier a letter and told him what he thought of him in fairly ripe quarter-deck language. Having got this out of his system he felt refreshed and went out for a ride during which, in the middle of a full gallop the horse fell down dead and rolled on the admiral who sustained a compound fracture of the leg and a crushed pelvis.

'Man,' said Grier with deep sincerity, 'Man, I was awfu' glad.'

We drew up in a particularly dirty farmyard and Grier turned to me. 'I've got a cow tae cleanse here.'

'Right,' I said, 'fine'. I settled down in my seat and took out my pipe. Grier paused, half way out of the car. 'Are you no' coming to give me a hand?'

I couldn't understand him. 'Cleansing' of cows is simply the removal of retained afterbirth and is a one man job.

'Well, there isn't much I can do is there?' I said. 'And my Wellingtons and coat are back in my car. I didn't realise it was a farm visit – I'd probably get messed up for nothing.'

I knew immediately that I'd said the wrong thing. The toad-skin jowls flushed darker and he gave me a malevolent glance before turning away; but half way across the yard he stopped and stood for a few moments in thought before coming back to the car. 'I've just remembered. I've got something here you can put on. You might as well come in with me – you'll be able to pass me a pessary when I want one.'

It sounded nutty to me, but I got out of the car and went round to the back. Grier was fishing out a large wooden box from his boot.

'Here, ye can put this on. It's a calving outfit I got a bit ago. I haven't used it much because I found it a mite heavy, but it'll keep ye grand and clean.'

I looked in the box and saw a suit of thick, black, shining rubber. I lifted out the jacket; it bristled with zip fasteners and press studs and felt as heavy as lead. The trousers were even more weighty, with many clips and fasteners. The whole thing was a most imposing creation, obviously designed by somebody who had never seen a cow calved and having the disadvantage that anybody wearing it would be pretty well immobilised.

I studied Grier's face for a moment but the watery eyes told me nothing. I began to take off my jacket – it was crazy but I didn't want to offend the man.

And, in truth, Grier seemed anxious to get me into the suit because he was holding it up in a helpful manner. It was a two man operation. First the gleaming trousers were pulled on and zipped up fore and aft, then it was the turn of the jacket, a wonderful piece of work, fitting tightly round the waist and possessing short sheeves about six inches long with powerful elastic gripping my biceps.

Before I could get it on I had to roll my shirt sleeves to the shoulder, then Grier, heaving and straining, worked me into it. I could hear the zips squeaking into place, the final one being at the back of my neck to close a high, stiff collar which held my head in an attitude of supplication, my chin pointing at the sky.

Grier's heart really seemed to be in his work and, for the final touch, he produced a black rubber skull cap. I shrank away from the thing and began to mouth such objections as the collar would allow, but Grier insisted. 'Stand still a wee minute longer. We might as well do the job right.'

When he had finished he stood back admiringly. I must have been a grotesque sight, sheathed from head to foot in gleaming black, my arms, bare to the shoulders, sticking out almost at right angles. Grier appeared well satisfied. 'Well, come on, it's time we got on wi' the job.' He turned and hurried towards the byre; I plodded ponderously after him like an automaton.

Our arrival in the byre caused a sensation. There were present the farmer, two cowmen and a little girl. The men's cheerful greeting froze on their lips as the menacing figure paced slowly, deliberately in. The little girl burst into tears and ran outside.

'Cleansing' is a dirty, smelly job for the operator and a bore for the onlooker who may have to stand around for twenty minutes without being able to see anything. But this was one time the spectators were not bored. Grier was working away inside the cow and mumbling about the weather, but the men weren't listening; they never took their eyes away from me as I stood rigid, like a suit of armour against the wall. They studied each part of the outfit in turn, wonderingly. I knew what they were thinking. Just what was going to happen when this formidable unknown finally went into action. Anybody dressed like that must have some tremendous task ahead of him.

The intense pressure of the collar against my larynx kept me entirely out of any conversation and this must have added to my air of mystery. I began to sweat inside the suit.

The little girl had plucked up courage and brought her brothers and sisters to look at me. I could see the row of little heads peeping round the door and, screwing my head round painfully, I tried to give them a reassuring smile; but the heads disappeared and I heard their feet clattering across the yard.

I couldn't say how long I stood there, but Grier at last finished his job and called out, 'All right, I'm ready for you now.' The atmosphere became suddenly electric. The men straightened up and stared at me with slightly open mouths. This was the moment they had been waiting for.

I pushed myself away from the wall and did a right turn with some difficulty before heading for the tin of pessaries. It was only a few yards away but it seemed a long way as I approached it like a robot, head in the air, arms extended stiffly on either side. When I arrived at the tin I met a fresh difficulty; I could not bend. After a few contortions I got my hand into the tin, then had to take the paper off the pessary with one hand; a new purgatory. The men watched in fascinated silence.

Having removed the paper, I did a careful about turn and paced back along the byre with measured tread. When I came level with the cow I extended my arm stiffly to Grier who took the pessary and inserted it in the uterus.

I then took up my old position against the wall while my colleague cleaned himself down. I glanced down my nose at the men; their expressions had changed to open disbelief. Surely the mystery man's assignment was tougher than that – he couldn't be wearing that outfit just to hand over a pessary. But when Grier started the complicated business of snapping open the studs and sliding the zips they realised the show was over; and fast on the feeling of let-down came amusement.

As I tried to rub some life back into my swollen arms which had been strangulated by the elastic sleeves, I was surrounded by grinning faces. They could hardly wait, I imagined, to get round to the local that night to tell the tale. Pulling together the shreds of my dignity, I put on my jacket and got into the car. Grier stayed to say a few words to the men, but he wasn't holding their attention; it was all on me, huddling in the seat. They couldn't believe I was true.

Back at the surgery the border terrier was coming out of the anaesthetic. He raised his head and tried bravely to wag his tail when he saw me. I wrapped him in a blanket, gathered him up and was preparing to leave when I saw Grier through the partly open door of a small store room. He had the wooden box on a table and he was lifting out the rubber suit, but there was something peculiar about the way he was doing it; the man seemed to be afflicted by a kind of rigor – his body shook and jerked, the mottled face was strangely contorted and a half stifled wailing issued from his lips.

I stared in amazement. I would have said it was impossible, yet it was happening right in front of me. There was not a shadow of a doubt about it – Angus Grier was laughing.

Chapter Twenty-three

Milk fever is one of the straightforward conditions, but, looking down into the beck in the dreary dawn light, I realised that this was one of its more bizarre manifestations. The illness had struck immediately after calving and the cow had slithered down the muddy bank into the water. She was unconscious when I arrived, her hindquarters completely submerged, the head resting on a shelf of rock. Her calf, sodden and pathetic in the driving rain, trembled by her side.

Dan Cooper's eyes were anxious as we made our way down. 'I doubt we're too late. She's dead, isn't she? I can't see her breathing.'

'Pretty far gone, I'm afraid,' I replied, 'but I think there's still life there. If I can get some calcium into her vein she might still come round.'

'Damn, I 'ope so,' Dan grunted. 'She's one of my best milkers. It allus happens to the good 'uns.'

'It does with milk fever, anyway. Here, hold these bottles for me.' I pulled out the syringe box and selected a wide-bored needle. My fingers, numb with the special kind of cold you felt in the early morning with your circulation sluggish and your stomach empty, could hardly hold it. The water was deeper than I thought and it was over my Wellington tops at the first stride. Gasping, I bent down and dug my thumb into the jugular furrow at the base of the neck. The vein came up and as I pushed the needle in, the blood ran warm and dark over my hand. I fumbled the flutter valve from my pocket, pushed a bottle into the cup end and inserted the other end into the needle. The calcium began to flow into the vein.

Standing there in the icy beck, holding the bottle aloft with bloody fingers and feeling the rain working its way inside my collar, I tried to keep out the black thoughts; about all those people I knew who were still in bed and would only leave it when their alarm clocks rang; and they would read their papers over breakfast and drive out to their cosy banks or insurance offices. Maybe I should have been a doctor – they treated their patients in nice, warm bedrooms.

I pulled the needle from the vein and threw the empty bottle on to the bank. There was no response to the injection. I took the other bottle and began to run more calcium under the skin. Might as well go through the motions, futile though it seemed now. It was when I was rubbing away the subcutaneous injection that I noticed the eyelids quiver.

A quick ripple of relief and excitement went through me. I looked up at the farmer and laughed. 'She's still with us, Dan.' I flicked her ear and her eyes opened wide. 'We'll wait a few minutes and then try to roll her on to her chest.'

Within a quarter of an hour she was beginning to toss her head about and I knew it was time. I caught hold of her horns and pulled while Dan and his tall son pushed at her shoulder. We made slow progress but after several concerted heaves the cow took over herself and settled on her chest. Immediately everything looked rosier; when a cow is lying on her side she always has the look of death on her.

I was pretty sure then that she would recover, but I couldn't go away and leave her lying in the beck. Milk fever cows can stay down for days on end but I had the feeling this one would be up soon. I decided to stick it out a bit longer.

She didn't seem to relish her situation in the peaty water and began to make determined efforts to rise, but it was another half hour and my teeth were chattering uncontrollably before she finally staggered to her feet.

'Well, that's a licker!' Dan said. 'Ah never thought she'd stand again. Must be good stuff you gave her.'

'It's a bit quicker than the old bicycle pump,' I laughed. The spectacular effects of intravenous calcium were still enough of a novelty to intrigue me. For generations, cows with milk fever had just died. Then inflation of the udder had saved many; but the calcium was the thing – when they got up within an hour like this one, I always felt like a successful conjurer.

We guided the cow up the bank and at the top, the full force of the wind and rain struck us. The house was only a hundred yards away and we battled towards it, Dan and his son leading, holding the calf in a sack slung between them. The tiny animal swung to and fro, screwing up its eyes against the hard world it had entered. Close behind followed the anxious mother, still rocky on her legs but doing her best to poke her muzzle into the sack. I squelched along in the rear.

We left the cow knee deep in straw in a warm shed, licking her calf vigorously. In the porch of the house, the others dutifully pulled off their Wellingtons; I did the same, pouring about a pint of beck water from each boot. Mrs Cooper had the reputation of being a firebrand who exercised an iron rule over Dan and her family, but from my previous contacts with her I had the feeling that Dan didn't do so badly.

I thought so again as I saw her, square built but comely, plaiting a little girl's pigtails in readiness for school. A crackling fire was mirrored in the gleaming brass of the hearth and above the clean farmhouse smell there was a hint of home-cured bacon just beginning to fry.

Mrs Cooper sent Dan and the boy scurrying upstairs to change their socks then she turned a calm gaze on me as I dripped on her linoleum. She shook her head as though I were a naughty child.

'All right, off with the socks,' she rapped out. 'And your coat, and roll up your trousers, and sit down here, and dry your hair with this.' A clean towel landed on my lap and Mrs Cooper bent over me. 'Don't you ever think of wearing a hat?'

'Not keen on them, I'm afraid,' I mumbled, and she shook her head again.

She poured hot water from a kettle into a large bowl and added mustard from a pound tin. 'Here, stick your feet in this.'

I had obeyed all her commands with alacrity and I gave an involuntary yelp as I made contact with the bubbling mixture. At this, she shot a fierce glance at me and I took care to keep my feet in the bowl. I was sitting, teeth clenched, enveloped in steam, when she pushed a pint pot of tea into my hand.

It was old fashioned treatment but effective. By the time I was half way down the pint pot I felt as though I were being consumed by fire. The river bed chill was a dream which vanished completely as Mrs Cooper topped up my bowl with another scalding quart from the kettle.

Next, she grabbed chair and bowl and swivelled me round till I was sitting at the table, still with my feet in the water. Dan and the children were already at their breakfast and in front of me was a plate with two eggs, a rough cut piece of bacon and several sausages. I had learned enough of Dales ways to keep quiet at meals; when I first came to the district I had thought it incumbent on me to provide light conversation in return for their hospitality but the questioning glances they exchanged with each other silenced me effectively.

So this morning, I attacked the food without preamble, but the first mouthful almost made me break my new found rule. It was the first time I had tasted a home made Yorkshire sausage and it was an effort to restrain the cries of congratulation which would have been natural in other circles. But Mrs Cooper had been watching me out of the corner of her eye and she must have noticed my rapt expression. Casually, she rose, brought over the frying pan and rolled a few more links on to my plate.

'Killed a pig last week,' she said, pulling open the pantry door. I could see the dishes heaped with chopped meat, spare rib, liver, the rows of pies with the jelly gleaming on their pale gold crusts.

I finished my meal, pulled on a thick pair of socks borrowed from Dan and my dry shoes. I was about to leave when Mrs Cooper tucked a parcel under my arm. I knew it contained further samples from the pantry but her eyes dared me to say much about it. I muttered a few words of thanks and went out to the car.

The church clock was chiming a quarter past nine when I pulled up outside Skeldale House. I felt good – warm, full of superb food and with the satisfying memory of the cow's quick recovery. And there was my parcel on the back seat; it was always a stroke of luck to land on a farm after a pig killing and there was usually a gift from the hospitable farmers, but these sausages were something I would never forget.

I took the surgery steps at a jump and trotted along the passage, but as I rounded the corner my progress was halted. Siegfried was standing there, rigid, his back pressed against the wall. Over his shoulder dangled a long, flexible, leather probang. Between us was the half open door of the office with Miss Harbottle clearly visible at her desk.

I waved cheerfully. 'Hello, hello, off to a choke?'

Siegfried's face twisted in anguish and he held up a warning hand. Then he began to creep past the door, balancing on the balls of his feet like a tightrope walker. He was beyond the door and the tense lines of his body had begun to relax when the brass end of the swinging probang clattered against the wall and, as if in reply came the familiar rumble from Miss Harbottle's corner. Siegfried gave me a single despairing glance then, shoulders drooping, he went slowly into the room.

Watching him go, I thought wonderingly of how things had built up since the secretary's arrival. It was naked war now and it gave life an added interest to observe the tactics of the two sides.

At the beginning it seemed that Siegfried must run out an easy winner. He was the employer; he held the reins and it appeared that Miss Harbottle would be helpless in the face of his obstructive strategy. But Miss Harbottle was a fighter and a resourceful one and it was impossible not to admire the way she made use of the weapons at her command.

In fact, over the past week the tide had been running in her favour. She had been playing Siegfried like an expert fisherman with a salmon; bringing him repeatedly back to her desk to answer footling questions. Her throat clearing had developed into an angry bark which could penetrate the full extent of the house. And she had a new weapon; she had taken to writing Siegfried's clerical idiocies on slips of paper; mis-spellings, errors in addition, wrong entries – they were all faithfully copied down.

Miss Harbottle used these slips as ammunition. She never brought one out when things were slack and her employer was hanging about the surgery. She saved them until he was under pressure, then she would push a slip under his nose and say 'How about this?'

She always kept an expressionless face at these times and it was impossible to say how much pleasure it gave her to see him cower back like a whipped animal. But the end was unvarying – mumbled explanations and apologies from Siegfried and Miss Harbottle, radiating self-righteousness, correcting the entry.

As Siegfried went into the room I watched through the partly open door. I knew my morning round was waiting but I was impelled by morbid curiosity. Miss Harbottle, looking brisk and businesslike, was tapping an entry in the book with her pen while Siegfried shuffled his feet and muttered replies. He made several vain attempts to escape and, as the time passed, I could see he was nearing breaking point. His teeth were clenched and his eyes had started to bulge.

The phone rang and the secretary answered it. Her employer was making again for the door when she called happily, 'Colonel Brent for you.' Like a man in a dream he turned back. The Colonel, a racehorse owner had been a thorn in our flesh for a long time with his complaints and his continual questioning and probing; a call from him was always liable to send up the blood pressure.

I could see it was that way this morning. The minutes ticked away and Siegfried's face got redder. He made his replies in a choked voice which finally rose almost to a shout. At the end he crashed the receiver down and leaned on the desk, breathing heavily.

Then, as I watched, unbelieving, Miss Harbottle began to open the drawer where she kept her slips. She fished one out, coughed and held it in Siegfried's face.

'How about this?' she asked.

I resisted the impulse to close my eyes and stared in horror. For a few seconds nothing happened and there was a tense interval while Siegfried stood quite motionless. Then his face seemed to break up and with a scything sweep of his arm he snatched the slip from the secretary's hand and began to tear at it with fierce intensity. He didn't say a word but as he tore, he leaned forward over the desk and his glaring eyes approached ever nearer to Miss Harbottle who slowly edged her chair back till it was jammed against the wall.

It was a weird picture. Miss Harbottle straining back, her mouth slightly open, her tinted curls bobbing in alarm, and Siegfried, his ravaged features close to hers, still tearing with insane vigour at the piece of paper. The scene ended when Siegfried, putting every ounce of his strength into an action like a javelin thrower, hurled the torn up slip at the waste paper basket. It fell in a gentle shower, like confetti, in and around the basket and Siegfried, still without speaking, wrapped his probang around him and strode from the room.

In the kitchen, Mrs Hall opened the parcel and extracted a pie, a chunk of liver and a cluster of the exquisite sausages. She turned a quizzical eye on me. 'You look kind of pleased with yourself this morning, Mr Herriot.'

I leaned back against the oak dresser. 'Yes, Mrs Hall, I've just been thinking. It must be very nice to be the principal of a practice but, you know, it's not such a bad life being an assistant.'

Chapter Twenty-four

The day had started badly. Tristan had been trapped by his brother at 4 a.m. returning from the Bellringers' Outing.

This function took place annually when a bus load of the bellringers of all the local churches made a trip to Morecambe. They spent very little time on the beach, however, and when they weren't working their way from one pub to another, they were attacking the crates of beer they had brought with them.

When they rolled into Darrowby in the small hours most of the occupants of the bus were unconscious. Tristan, an honoured guest of the party, had been tipped out in the back lane behind Skeldale House. He waved weakly as the bus moved away, but drew no response from the unseeing faces at the windows. Lurching down the garden path, he was horrified to see a light in Siegfried's room. Escape was impossible and, when asked to explain where he had been, he made a series of attempts to articulate 'Bellringers' Outing' without success.

Siegfried, seeing he was wasting his time, had saved his wrath till breakfast time. That was when Tristan told me the story – just before his brother came into the dining-room and started on him.

But, as usual, it seemed to take more out of Siegfried who went off on his rounds glowering and hoarse from shouting. Ten minutes after he had gone I found Tristan closeted cheerfully in Boardman's cubby hole. Boardman listening to some fresh material from the backs of the envelopes and sniggering appreciatively.

The old man had cheered up greatly since Tristan came home and the two of them spent a lot of time in the gloom where the light from the tiny window picked out the rows of rusting tools, the Bairnsfather cartoons looking down from the wall. The place was usually kept locked and visitors were not encouraged; but Tristan was always welcome.

Often, when I was passing by, I would peep in and see Tristan patiently pulling at a Woodbine while Boardman rambled on. 'We was six weeks up the line. The French was on our right and the Jocks on our left ...' or 'Poor old Fred – one minute 'e was standing by me and next 'e was gone. Never found as much as a trouser button ...'

This morning, Tristan hailed me boisterously and I marvelled again at his resilience and his power to bend like a willow before the winds of misfortune and spring back unscathed. He held up two tickets.

'Village dance tonight, Jim, and I can guarantee it. Some of my harem from the hospital are going, so I'll see you're all right. And that's not all – look here.' He went into the saddle room, lifted out a loose board and produced a bottle of sherry. 'We'll be able to have a toothful between dances.'

I didn't ask where the tickets or the sherry had come from. I liked the village dances. The packed hall with the three piece band at one end – piano, scraping fiddle and drums – and at the other end, the older ladies looking after the refreshments. Glasses of milk, mounds of sandwiches, ham, home-made brawn, trifles heaped high with cream.

That evening, Tristan came out with me on my last visit and, in the car, the talk was all about the dance. The case was simple enough – a cow with an infected eye – but the farm was in a village high up the dale, and when we finished, it was dusk. I felt good, and everything seemed to stand out, clear and meaningful. The single, empty, grey stone street, the last red streaks in the sky, the dark purple of the enclosing fells. There was no wind, but a soft breath came from the quiet moors, sweet and fresh and full of promise. Among the houses, the thrilling smell of wood smoke was everywhere.

When we got back to the surgery, Siegfried was out but there was a note for Tristan propped up on the mantelpiece. It said simply: 'Tristan. Go home. Siegfried.'

This had happened before, everything in Skeldale House being in short supply, especially beds and blankets. When unexpected visitors arrived, Tristan was packed off to stay with his mother in Brawton. Normally he would board a train without comment, but tonight was different.

'Good God,' he said. 'Somebody must be coming for the night and, of course, I'm the one who's just expected to disappear. It's a nice bloody carry on, I must say! And isn't that a charming letter! It doesn't matter if I've made any private arrangements. Oh no! There's no question of asking me if it's convenient to leave. It's just "Tristan, go home." Polite and thoughtful, isn't it?'

It was unusual for him to get worked up like this. I spoke soothingly. 'Look, Triss. Maybe we'd better just skip this dance. There'll be others.'

Tristan clenched his fists. 'Why should I let him push me around like this?' he fumed. 'I'm a person, am I not? I have my own life to lead and I tell you I am not going to Brawton tonight. I've arranged to go to a dance and I am damn well going to a dance.'

This was fighting talk but I felt a twinge of alarm. 'Wait a minute. What about Siegfried? What's he going to say when he comes in and finds you still here?'

'To hell with Siegfried!' said Tristan. So I left it at that.

Siegfried came home when we were upstairs, changing. I was first down and found him sitting by the fire, reading. I said nothing but sat down and waited for the explosion.

After a few minutes, Tristan came in. He had chosen with care among his limited wardrobe and was resplendent in a dark grey suit; a scrubbed face shone under carefully combed hair; he was wearing a clean collar.

Siegfried flushed as he looked up from his book. 'What the bloody hell are you doing here? I told you to go to Brawton. Joe Ramage is coming tonight.'

'Couldn't go.'

'Why not?'

'No trains.'

'What the hell do you mean, no trains?'

'Just that – no trains.'

The cross talk was bringing on the usual sense of strain in me. The interview was falling into the habitual pattern; Siegfried red faced, exasperated, his brother expressionless, answering in a flat monotone, fighting a defensive battle with the skill of long practice.

Siegfried sank back in his chair, baffled for the moment, but he kept a slit-eyed gaze on his brother. The smart suit, the slicked hair and polished shoes all seemed to irritate him further.

'All right,' he said suddenly, 'It's maybe just as well you are staying. I want you to do a job for me. You can open that haematoma on Charlie Dent's pig's ear.'

This was a bombshell. Charlie Dent's pig's ear was something we didn't talk about.

A few weeks earlier, Siegfried himself had gone to the smallholding half way along a street on the outskirts of the town to see a pig with a swollen ear. It was an aural haematoma and the only treatment was to lance it, but, for some reason, Siegfried had not done the job but had sent me the following day.

I had wondered about it, but not for long. When I climbed into the sty, the biggest sow I had ever seen rose from the straw, gave an explosive bark and rushed at me with its huge mouth gaping. I didn't stop to argue. I made the wall about six inches ahead of the pig and vaulted over into the passage. I stood there, considering the position, looking thoughtfully at the mean little red eyes, the slavering mouth with its long, yellow teeth.

Usually, I paid no attention when pigs barked and grumbled at me but this one really seemed to mean it. As I wondered what the next step would be, the pig gave an angry roar, reared up on its hind legs and tried to get over the wall at me. I made up my mind quickly.

'I'm afraid I haven't got the right instrument with me, Mr Dent. I'll pop back another day and open the ear for you. It's nothing serious – only a small job. Goodbye.'

There the matter had rested, with nobody caring to mention it till now.

Tristan was aghast. 'You mean you want me to go along there tonight. Saturday night? Surely some other time would do? I'm going to a dance.'

Siegfried smiled bitterly from the depths of his chair. 'It has to be done now. That's an order. You can go to your dance afterwards.'

Tristan started to say something, but he knew he had pushed his luck far enough. 'Right,' he said, 'I'll go and do it.'

He left the room with dignity, Siegfried resumed his book, and I stared into the fire, wondering how Tristan was going to handle this one. He was a lad of infinite resource, but was going to be tested this time.

Within ten minutes he was back. Siegfried looked at him suspiciously, 'Have you opened that ear?'

'No.'

'Why not?'

'Couldn't find the place. You must have given me the wrong address. Number 98, you said.'

'It's number 89 and you know damn well it is. Now get back there and do your job.'

The door closed behind Tristan and again, I waited. Fifteen minutes later it opened again and Tristan reappeared looking faintly triumphant. His brother looked up from his book.

'Done it?'

'No.'

'Why not?'

'The family are all out at the pictures. Saturday night, you know.'

'I don't care a damn where the family are. Just get into that sty and lance that ear. Now get out, and this time I want the job done.'

Again Tristan retreated and a new vigil began. Siegfried did not say a word, but I could feel the tension building up. Twenty minutes passed and Tristan was with us again.

'Have you opened that ear?'

'No.'

'Why not?'

'It's pitch dark in there. How do you expect me to work? I've only got two hands – one for the knife and one for the torch. How can I hold the ear?'

Siegfried had been keeping a tight hold on himself, but now his control snapped. 'Don't give me any more of your bloody excuses,' he shouted, leaping from his chair. 'I don't care how you do it, but, by God, you are going to open that pig's ear tonight or I've finished with you. Now get to hell out of here and don't come back till it's done!'

My heart bled for Tristan. He had been dealt a poor hand and had played his cards with rare skill, but he had nothing left now. He stood silent in the doorway for a few moments, then he turned and walked out.

The next hour was a long one. Siegfried seemed to be enjoying his book and I even tried to read myself; but I got no meaning out of the words and it made my head ache to sit staring at them. It would have helped if I could have paced up and down the carpet but that was pretty well impossible in Siegfried's presence. I had just decided to excuse myself and go out for a walk when I heard the outer door open, then Tristan's footsteps in the passage.

A moment later, the man of destiny entered but the penetrating smell of pig got into the room just ahead of him, and as he walked over to the fire, pungent waves seemed to billow round him. Pig muck was spattered freely over his nice suit, and on his clean collar, his face and hair. There was a great smear of the stuff on the seat of his trousers but despite his ravaged appearance he still maintained his poise.

Siegfried pushed his chair back hurriedly but did not change expression.

'Have you got that ear opened?' he asked quietly.

'Yes.'

Siegfried returned to his book without comment. It seemed that the matter was closed and Tristan, after staring briefly at his brother's bent head, turned and marched from the room. But even after he had gone, the odour of the pigsty hung in the room like a cloud.

Later, in the Drovers', I watched Tristan draining his third pint. He had changed, and if he didn't look as impressive as when he started the evening, at least he was clean and hardly smelt at all. I had said nothing yet, but the old light was returning to his eye. I went over to the bar and ordered my second half and Tristan's fourth pint and, as I set the glasses on the table, I thought that perhaps it was time.

'Well, what happened?'

Tristan took a long, contented pull at his glass and lit a Woodbine. 'Well now, all in all, Jim, it was rather a smooth operation, but I'll start at the beginning. You can imagine me standing all alone outside the sty in the pitch darkness with that bloody great pig grunting and growling on the other side of the wall. I didn't feel so good, I can tell you.

'I shone my torch on the thing's face and it jumped up and ran at me, making a noise like a lion and showing all those dirty yellow teeth. I nearly wrapped it up and came home there and then, but I got to thinking about the dance and all and, on the spur of the moment, I hopped over the wall.

'Two seconds later, I was on my back. It must have charged me but couldn't see enough to get a bite in. I just heard a bark, then a terrific weight against my legs and I was down.

'Well, it's a funny thing, Jim. You know I'm not a violent chap, but as I lay there, all my fears vanished and all I felt was a cold hatred of that bloody animal. I saw it as the cause of all my troubles and before I knew what I was doing I was up on my feet and booting its arse round and round the sty. And, do you know, it showed no fight at all. That pig was a coward at heart.'

I was still puzzled. 'But the ear – how did you manage to open the haematoma?'

'No problem, Jim. That was done for me.'

'You don't mean to say . . .'

'Yes,' Tristan said, holding his pint up to the light and studying a small foreign body floating in the depths. 'Yes, it was really very fortunate. In the scuffle in the dark, the pig ran up against the wall and burst the thing itself. Made a beautiful job.'

Chapter Twenty-five

I realised, quite suddenly, that spring had come. It was late March and I had been examining some sheep in a hillside fold. On my way down, in the lee of a small pine wood I leaned my back against a tree and was aware, all at once, of the sunshine, warm on my closed eyelids, the clamour of the larks, the muted sea-sound of the wind in the high branches. And though the snow still lay in long runnels behind the walls and the grass was lifeless and winter-yellowed, there was the feeling of change; almost of liberation, because, unknowing, I had surrounded myself with a carapace against the iron months, the relentless cold.

It wasn't a warm spring but it was dry with sharp winds which fluttered the white heads of the snowdrops and bent the clumps of daffodils on the village greens. In April the roadside banks were bright with the fresh yellow of the primroses.

And in April, too, came the lambing. It came in a great tidal wave, the most vivid and interesting part of the veterinary surgeon's year, the zenith of the annual cycle, and it came as it always does when we were busiest with our other work.

In the spring the livestock were feeling the effects of the long winter. Cows had stood for months in the same few feet of byre and were in dire need of the green grass and the sun on their backs, while their calves had very little resistance to disease. And just when we were wondering how we could cope with the coughs and colds and pneumonias and acetonaemias the wave struck us.

The odd thing is that for about ten months of the year, sheep hardly entered into the scheme of our lives. They were just woolly things on the hills. But for the other two months they almost blotted out everything else.

First came the early troubles, the pregnancy toxaemias, the prolapses. Then the lambings in a concentrated rush followed by the calcium deficiencies, the horrible gangrenous mastitis when the udder turns black and sloughs away; and the diseases which beset the lambs themselves – swayback, pulpy kidney, dysentery. Then the flood slackened, became a trickle and by the end of May had almost dried up. Sheep became woolly things on the hills again.

But in this first year I found a fascination in the work which has remained with me. Lambing, it seemed to me, had all the thrill and interest of calving without the hard labour. It was usually uncomfortable in that it was performed in the open; either in draughty pens improvised from straw bales and gates or more often out in the fields. It didn't seem to occur to the farmers that the ewe might prefer to produce her family in a warm place or that the vet may not enjoy kneeling for an hour in his shirt sleeves in the rain.

But the actual job was as easy as a song. After my experiences in correcting the malpresentations of calves it was delightful to manipulate these tiny creatures. Lambs are usually born in twos or threes and some wonderful mix-ups occur; tangles of heads and legs all trying to be first out and it is the vet's job to sort them around and decide which leg belonged to which head. I revelled in this. It was a pleasant change to be for once stronger and bigger than my patient, but I didn't over-stress this advantage; I have not changed the opinion I formed then that there are just two things to remember in lambing – cleanliness and gentleness.

And the lambs. All young animals are appealing but the lamb has been given an unfair share of charm. The moments come back; of a bitterly cold evening when I had delivered twins on a wind-scoured hillside; the lambs shaking their heads convulsively and within minutes one of them struggling upright and making its way, unsteady, knock-kneed, towards the udder while the other followed resolutely on its knees.

The shepherd, his purpled, weather-roughened face almost hidden by the heavy coat which muffled him to his ears, gave a slow chuckle. 'How the 'ell do they know?'

He had seen it happen thousands of times and he still wondered. So do I.

And another memory of two hundred lambs in a barn on a warm afternoon. We were inoculating them against pulpy kidney and there was no conversation because of the high pitched protests of the lambs and the unremitting deep baa-ing from nearly a hundred ewes milling anxiously around outside. I couldn't conceive how these ewes could ever get their own families sorted out from that mass of almost identical little creatures. It would take hours.

It took about twenty-five seconds. When we had finished injecting we opened the barn doors and the outpouring lambs were met by a concerted rush of distraught mothers. At first the noise was deafening but it died away rapidly to an occasional bleat as the last stray was rounded up. Then, neatly paired off, the flock headed calmly for the field.

Through May and early June my world became softer and warmer. The cold wind dropped and the air, fresh as the sea, carried a faint breath of the thousands of wild flowers which speckled the pastures. At times it seemed unfair that I should be paid for my work; for driving out in the early morning with the fields glittering under the first pale sunshine and the wisps of mist still hanging on the high tops.

At Skeldale House the wistaria exploded into a riot of mauve blooms which thrust themselves through the open windows and each morning as I shaved I breathed in the heady fragrance from the long clusters drooping by the side of the mirror. Life was idyllic.

There was only one jarring note; it was the time of the horse. In the thirties there were still quite a lot of horses on the farms though the tractors had already sounded their warning knell. In the farms near the foot of the Dale where there was a fair amount of arable land the rows of stables were half empty but there were still enough horses to make May and June uncomfortable. This was when the castrations were done.

Before that came the foaling and it was a common enough thing to see a mare with her foal either trotting beside her or stretched flat on the ground as its mother nibbled at the grass. Nowadays the sight of a cart mare and foal in a field would make me pull up my car to have another look.

There was all the work connected with the foalings; cleansing the mares, docking the foals' tails, treating the illnesses of the new born – joint ill, retained meconium. It was hard and interesting but as the weather grew warmer the farmers began to think of having the year old colts castrated.

I didn't like the job and since there might be up to a hundred to be done, it cast a shadow over this and many subsequent springs. For generations the operation had been done by casting the colt and tying him up very like a trussed chicken. It was a bit laborious but the animal was under complete restraint and it was possible to concentrate entirely on the job; but about the time I qualified, standing castration was coming very much to the fore. It consisted simply of applying a twitch to the colt's upper lip, injecting a shot of local anaesthetic into each testicle and going straight ahead. There was no doubt it was a lot quicker.

The obvious disadvantage was that the danger of injury to the operator and his helpers was increased tenfold, but for all that the method rapidly became more popular. A local farmer called Kenny Bright who considered himself an advanced thinker took the step of introducing it to the district. He engaged Major Farley, the horse specialist, to give a demonstration on one of his colts, and a large gathering of farmers came to spectate. Kenny, smug and full of self importance was holding the twitch and beaming round the company as his protégé prepared to disinfect the operation site, but as soon as the Major touched the scrotum with his antiseptic the colt reared and brought a fore foot crashing down on Kenny's head. He was carried away on a gate with his skull fractured and spent a long time in hospital. The other farmers didn't stop laughing for weeks but the example failed to deter them. Standing castration was in.

I said it was quicker. It was when everything went smoothly, but there were other times when the colt kicked or threw himself on top of us or just went generally mad. Out of ten jobs nine would be easy and the tenth would be a rodeo. I don't know how much apprehension this state of affairs built up in other vets but I was undeniably tense on castration mornings.

Of course, one of the reasons was that I was not, am not and never will be a horseman. It is difficult to define the term but I am convinced that horsemen are either born or acquire the talent in early childhood. I knew it was no good my trying to start in my mid twenties. I had the knowledge of equine diseases, I believed I had the ability to treat sick horses efficiently but that power the real horseman had to soothe and quieten and mentally dominate an animal was beyond my reach. I didn't even try to kid myself.

It was unfortunate because there is no doubt horses know. It is quite different with cows; they don't care either way; if a cow feels like kicking you she will kick you; she doesn't give a damn whether you are an expert or not. But horses know.

So on those mornings my morale was never very high as I drove out with my instruments rattling and rolling about on an enamel tray on the back seat. Would he be wild or quiet? How big would he be? I had heard my colleagues airily stating their preference for big horses – the two year olds were far easier, they said, you could get a better grip on the testicles. But there was never any doubt in my own mind. I liked them small; the smaller the better.

One morning when the season was at its height and I had had about enough of the equine race, Siegfried called to me as he was going out. 'James, there's a horse with a tumour on its belly at Wilkinson's of White Cross. Get along and take it off – today if possible but otherwise fix your own time; I'll leave it with you.'

Feeling a little disgruntled at fate having handed me something on top of the seasonal tasks, I boiled up a scalpel, tumour spoons and syringe and put them on my tray with local anaesthetic, iodine and tetanus antitoxin.

I drove to the farm with the tray rattling ominously behind me. That sound always had a connotation of doom for me. I wondered about the horse – maybe it was just a yearling; they did get those little dangling growths sometimes – nanberries, the farmers called them. Over the six miles I managed to build up a comfortable picture of a soft-eyed little colt with pendulous abdomen and over-long hair; it hadn't done well over the winter and was probably full of worms – shaky on its legs with weakness, in fact.

At Wilkinson's all was quiet. The yard was empty except for a lad of about ten who didn't know where the boss was.

'Well, where is the horse?' I asked.

The lad pointed to the stable. 'He's in there.'

I went inside. At one end stood a high, open-topped loose box with a metal grill topping the wooden walls and from within I heard a deep-throated whinnying and snorting followed by a series of tremendous thuds against the sides of the box. A chill crept through me. That was no little colt in there.

I opened the top half door and there, looking down at me was an enormous animal; I hadn't realised horses ever came quite as big as this; a chestnut stallion with a proud arch to his neck and feet like manhole covers. Surging swathes of muscle shone on his shoulders and quarters and when he saw me he laid back his ears, showed the whites of his eyes and lashed out viciously against the wall. A foot long splinter flew high in the air as the great hoof crashed against the boards.

'God almighty,' I breathed and closed the half door hurriedly. I leaned my back against the door and listened to my heart thumping.

I turned to the lad. 'How old is that horse?'

'Over six years, sir.'

I tried a little calm thinking. How did you go about tackling a man-eater like this. I had never seen such a horse – he must weigh over a ton. I shook myself; I hadn't even had a look at the tumour I was supposed to remove. I lifted the latch, opened the door about two inches and peeped inside. I could see it plainly dangling from the belly; probably a papilloma, about the size of a cricket ball, with a lobulated surface which made it look like a little cauliflower. It swung gently from side to side as the horse moved about.

No trouble to take it off. Nice narrow neck to it; a few c.c.'s of local in there and I could twist it off easily with the spoons.

But the snag was obvious. I would have to go under that shining barrel of an abdomen within easy reach of the great feet and stick a needle into those few inches of skin. Not a happy thought.

But I pulled my mind back to practical things; like a bucket of hot water, soap and a towel. And I'd need a good man on the twitch. I began to walk towards the house.

There was no answer to my knock. I tried again; still nothing – there was nobody at home. It seemed the most natural thing in the world to leave everything till another day; the idea of going round the buildings and fields till I found somebody never entered my head.

I almost broke into a gallop on my way to the car, backed it round with the tyres squealing and roared out of the yard.

Siegfried was surprised. 'Nobody there? Well that's a damn funny thing. I'm nearly sure they were expecting you today. But never mind, it's in your hands, James. Give them a ring and fix it up again as soon as possible.'

I found it wonderfully easy to forget about the stallion over the days and weeks that followed; except when my defences were down. At least once a night it thundered through my dreams with gaping nostrils and flying mane and I developed an uncomfortable habit of coming bolt awake at five o'clock in the morning and starting immediately to operate on the horse. On an average, I took that tumour off twenty times before breakfast each morning.

I told myself it would be a lot easier to fix the job up and get it over. What was I waiting for, anyway? Was there a subconscious hope that if I put it off long enough something would happen to get me off the hook? The tumour might fall off or shrink away and disappear, or the horse might drop down dead.

I could have passed the whole thing on to Siegfried – he was good with horses – but my confidence was low enough without that.

All my doubts were resolved one morning when Mr Wilkinson came on the phone. He wasn't in the least upset at the long delay but he made it quite clear that he could wait no longer. 'You see, I want to sell this 'oss, young man, but I can't let him go with that thing on him, can I?'

My journey to Wilkinson's wasn't enlivened by the familiar clatter of the tray on the back seat; it reminded me of the last time when I was wondering what was ahead of me. This time I knew.

Stepping out of the car, I felt almost disembodied. It was like walking a few inches above the ground. I was greeted by a reverberating din from the loose box; the same angry whinneys and splintering crashes I had heard before. I tried to twist my stiff face into a smile as the farmer came over.

'My chaps are getting a halter on him,' he said, but his words were cut short by an enraged squealing from the box and two tremendous blows against the wooden sides. I felt my mouth going dry.

The noise was coming nearer; then the stable doors flew open and the great horse catapulted out into the yard, dragging two big fellows along on the end of the halter shank. The cobbles struck sparks from the men's boots as they slithered about but they were unable to stop the stallion backing and plunging. I imagined I could feel the ground shudder under my feet as the hooves crashed down.

At length, after much manoeuvring, the men got the horse standing with his off side against the wall of the barn. One of them looped the twitch on to the upper lip and tightened it expertly, the other took a firm grip on the halter and turned towards me. 'Ready for you now, sir.'

I pierced the rubber cap on the bottle of cocaine, withdrew the plunger of the syringe and watched the clear fluid flow into the glass barrel. Seven, eight, ten c.c.'s. If I could get that in, the rest would be easy; but my hands were trembling.

Walking up to the horse was like watching an action from a film. It wasn't really me doing this – the whole thing was unreal. The near side eye flickered dangerously at me as I raised my left hand and passed it over the muscles of the neck, down the smooth, quivering flank and along the abdomen till I was able to grasp the tumour. I had the thing in my hand now, the lobulations firm and lumpy under my fingers. I pulled gently downwards, stretching the brown skin joining the growth to the body. I would put the local in there – a few good weals. It wasn't going to be so bad. The stallion laid back his ears and gave a warning whicker.

I took a long, careful breath, brought up the syringe with my right hand, placed the needle against the skin then thrust it in.

The kick was so explosively quick that at first I felt only surprise that such a huge animal could move so swiftly. It was a lightning outward slash that I never even saw and the hoof struck the inside of my right thigh, spinning me round helplessly. When I hit the ground I lay still, feeling only a curious numbness. Then I tried to move and a stab of pain went through my leg.

When I opened my eyes Mr Wilkinson was bending over me. 'Are you all right, Mr Herriot?' The voice was anxious.

'I don't think so.' I was astonished at the matter of fact sound of my own words; but stranger still was the feeling of being at peace with myself for the first time for weeks. I was calm and completely in charge of the situation.

'I'm afraid not, Mr Wilkinson. You'd better put the horse back in his box for now – we'll have a go at him another day – and I wonder if you'd ring Mr Farnon to come and pick me up. I don't think I'll be able to drive.'

My leg wasn't broken but it developed a massive haematoma at the point of impact and then the whole limb blossomed into an unbelievable range of colours from delicate orange to deepest black. I was still hobbling like a Crimean veteran when, a fortnight later, Siegfried and I with a small army of helpers went back and roped the stallion, chloroformed him and removed that little growth.

I have a cavity in the muscle of my thigh to remind me of that day, but some good came out of the incident. I found that the fear is worse than the reality and horse work has never worried me as much since then.

Chapter Twenty-six

The first time I saw Phin Calvert was in the street outside the surgery when I was talking to Brigadier Julian Coutts-Browne about his shooting dogs. The Brigadier was almost a stage version of an English aristocrat; immensely tall with a pronounced stoop, hawk features and a high drawling voice. As he spoke, smoke from a narrow ciga. trickled from his lips.

I turned my head at the clatter of heavy boots on the pavement. A thick set figure was stumping rapidly towards us, hands tucked behind his braces, ragged jacket pulled wide to display a curving expanse of collarless shirt, wisps of grizzled hair hanging in a fringe beneath a greasy cap. He was smiling widely at nobody in particular and he hummed busily to himself.

The Brigadier glanced at him. 'Morning, Calvert,' he grunted coldly.

Phineas threw up his head in pleased recognition. 'Now then, Charlie, 'ow is ta?' he shouted.

The Brigadier looked as though he had swallowed a swift pint of vinegar. He removed his cigar with a shaking hand and stared after the retreating back. 'Impudent devil,' he muttered.

Looking at Phin, you would never have thought he was a prosperous farmer. I was called to his place a week later and was surprised to find a substantial house and buildings and a fine dairy herd grazing in the fields.

I could hear him even before I got out of the car.

'Hello, 'ello, 'ello! Who's this we've got then? New chap eh? Now we're going to learn summat!' He still had his hands inside his braces and was grinning wider than ever.

'My name is Herriot,' I said.

'Is it now?' Phin cocked his head and surveyed me, then he turned to three young men standing by. 'Hasn't he a nice smile, lads. He's a real Happy Harry!'

He turned and began to lead the way across the yard. 'Come on, then and we'll see what you're made of. I 'ope you know a bit about calves because I've got some here that are right dowly.'

As he went into the calf house I was hoping I would be able to do something impressive – perhaps use some of the new drugs and sera I had in my car; it was going to take something special to make an impact here.

There were six well grown young animals, almost stirk size, and three of them were behaving very strangely; grinding their teeth, frothing at the mouth and blundering about the pen as though they couldn't see. As I watched, one of them walked straight into the wall and stood with his nose pressed against the stone.

Phin, apparently unconcerned, was humming to himself in a corner. When I started to take my thermometer from its case he burst into a noisy commentary. 'Now what's he doing? Ah, we're off now, get up there!'

The half minute which my thermometer spends in an animal's rectum is usually devoted to hectic thought. But this time I didn't need the time to work out my diagnosis; the blindness made it easy. I began to look round the walls of the calf house; it was dark and I had to get my face close to the stone.

Phin gave tongue again. 'Hey, what's going on? You're as bad as t' calves, nosing about there, dozy like. What d'you think you're lookin' for?'

'Paint, Mr Calvert. I'm nearly sure your calves have got lead poisoning.'

Phin said what all farmers say at this juncture. 'They can't have. I've had calves in here for thirty years and they've never taken any harm before. There's no paint in here, anyway.'

'How about this, then?' I peered into the darkest corner and pulled at a piece of loose board.

'Oh, that's nobbut a bit of wood I nailed down there last week to block up a hole. Came off an old hen house.'

I looked at the twenty year old paint hanging off in the loose flakes which calves find so irresistible. 'This is what's done the damage,' I said. 'Look, you can see the tooth marks where they've been at it.'

Phin studied the board at close quarters and grunted doubtfully. 'All right, what do we do now?'

'First thing is to get this painted board out of here and then give all the calves epsom salts. Have you got any?'

Phin gave a bark of laughter. 'Aye, I've got a bloody great sack full, but can't you do owt better than that? Aren't you going to inject them?'

It was a little embarrassing. The specific antidotes to metal poisoning had not been discovered and the only thing which sometimes did a bit of good was magnesium sulphate which caused the precipitation of insoluble lead sulphate. The homely term for magnesium sulphate is of course, epsom salts.

'No,' I said. 'There's nothing I can inject that will help at all and I can't even guarantee the salts will. But I'd like you to give the calves two heaped tablespoonfuls three times a day.'

'Oh 'ell, you'll skitter the poor buggers to death!'

'Maybe so, but there's nothing else for it.' I said.

Phin took a step towards me so that his face, dark-skinned and deeply wrinkled, was close to mine. The suddenly shrewd, mottled brown eyes regarded me steadily for a few seconds then he turned away quickly. 'Right,' he said. 'Come in and have a drink.'

Phin stumped into the farm kitchen ahead of me, threw back his head and let loose a bellow that shook the windows. 'Mother! Feller 'ere wants a glass o' beer. Come and meet Happy Harry!'

Mrs Calvert appeared with magical speed and put down glasses and bottles. I glanced at the labels – 'Smith's Nutty Brown Ale', and filled my glass. It was a historic moment though I didn't know it then; it was the first of an incredible series of Nutty Browns I was to drink at that table.

Mrs Calvert sat down for a moment, crossed her hands on her lap and smiled encouragingly. 'Can you do anything for the calves, then?' she asked.

Phin butted in before I could reply. 'Oh aye, he can an' all. He's put them on to epsom salts.'

'Epsom salts?'

'That's it, Missis. I said when he came that we'd get summat real smart and scientific like. You can't beat new blood and modern ideas.' Phin sipped his beer gravely.

Over the following days the calves gradually improved and at the end of a fortnight they were all eating normally. The worst one still showed a trace of blindness, but I was confident this too would clear up.

It wasn't long before I saw Phin again. It was early afternoon and I was in the office with Siegfried when the outer door banged and the passage echoed to the clumping of hob nails. I heard a voice raised in song – hi-ti-tiddly-rum-te-tum. Phineas was in our midst once more.

'Well, well, well!' he bawled heartily at Miss Harbottle. 'It's Flossie! And what's my little darlin' doing this fine day?'

There was not a flicker from Miss Harbottle's granite features. She directed an icy stare at the intruder but Phin swung round on Siegfried with a yellow-toothed grin. 'Now, gaffer, 'ow's tricks?'

'Everything's fine, Mr Calvert,' Siegfried replied. 'What can we do for you?'

Phin stabbed a finger at me. 'There's my man. I want him out to my place right sharpish.'

'What's the trouble?' I asked. 'Is it the calves again?'

'Damn, no! Wish it was. It's me good bull. He's puffin' like a bellows – bit like pneumonia but worse than I've known. He's in a 'ell of a state. Looks like he's peggin' out.' For an instant Phin lost his jocularity.

I had heard of this bull; pedigree shorthorn, show winner, the foundation of his herd. 'I'll be right after you, Mr Calvert. I'll follow you along.'

'God lad. I'm off, then.' Phin paused at the door, a wild figure, tieless, tattered; baggy trousers ballooning from his ample middle. He turned again to Miss Harbottle and contorted his leathery features into a preposterous leer. 'Ta-ra, Floss!' he cried and was gone.

For a moment the room seemed very empty and quiet except for Miss Harbottle's acid 'Oh, that man! Dreadful! Dreadful!'

I made good time to the farm and found Phin waiting with his three sons. The young men looked gloomy but Phin was still indomitable. 'Here 'e is!' he shouted. 'Happy Harry again. Now we'll be all right.' He even managed a little tune as we crossed to the bull pen but when he looked over the door his head sank on his chest and his hands worked deeper behind his braces.

The bull was standing as though rooted to the middle of the pen. His great rib cage rose and fell with the most laboured respirations I had ever seen. His mouth gaped wide, a bubbling foam hung round his lips and his flaring nostrils; his eyes, almost starting from his head in terror, stared at the wall in front of him. This wasn't pneumonia, it was a frantic battle for breath; and it looked like a losing one.

He didn't move when I inserted my thermometer and though my mind was racing I suspected the half minute wasn't going to be long enough this time. I had expected accelerated breathing, but nothing like this.

'Poor aud beggar,' Phin muttered. 'He's bred me the finest calves I've ever had and he's as quiet as a sheep, too. I've seen me little grandchildren walk under 'is belly and he's took no notice. I hate to see him sufferin' like this. If you can't do no good, just tell me and I'll get the gun out.'

I took the thermometer out and read it. One hundred and ten degrees fahrenheit. This was ridiculous; I shook it vigorously and pushed it back into the rectum.

I gave it nearly a minute this time so that I could get in some extra thinking. The second reading said a hundred and ten again and I had an unpleasant conviction that if the thermometer had been a foot long the mercury would still have been jammed against the top.

What in the name of God was this? Could be Anthrax ... must be ... and yet ... I looked over at the row of heads above the half door; they were waiting for me to say something and their silence accentuated the agonised groaning and panting. I looked above the heads to the square of deep blue and a tufted cloud moving across the sun. As it passed, a single dazzling ray made me close my eyes and a faint bell rang in my mind.

'Has he been out today?' I asked.

'Aye, he's been out on the grass on his tether all morning. It was that grand and warm.'

The bell became a triumphant gong. 'Get a hosepipe in here quick. You can rig it to that tap in the yard.'

'A hosepipe? What the 'ell ...?'

'Yes, quick as you can – he's got sunstroke.'

They had the hose fixed in less than a minute. I turned it full on and began to play the jet of cold water all over the huge form – his face and neck, along the ribs, up and down the legs. I kept this up for about five minutes but it seemed a lot longer as I waited for some sign of improvement. I was beginning to think I was on the wrong track when the bull gulped just once.

It was something – he had been unable to swallow his saliva before in his desperate efforts to get the air into his lungs; and I really began to notice a change in the big animal. Surely he was looking just a little less distressed and wasn't the breathing slowing down a bit?

Then the bull shook himself, turned his head and looked at us. There was an awed whisper from one of the young men: 'By gaw, it's working!'

I enjoyed myself after that. I can't think of anything in my working life that has given me more pleasure than standing in that pen directing the life-saving jet and watching the bull savouring it. He liked it on his face best and as I worked my way up from the tail and along the steaming back he would turn his nose full into the water, rocking his head from side to side and blinking blissfully.

Within half an hour he looked almost normal. His chest was still heaving a little but he was in no discomfort. I tried the temperature again. Down to a hundred and five.

'He'll be all right now,' I said, 'but I think one of the lads should keep the water on him for another twenty minutes or so. I'll have to go now.'

'You've time for a drink,' Phin grunted.

In the farm kitchen his bellow of 'Mother' lacked some of its usual timbre. He dropped into a chair and stared into his glass of Nutty Brown. 'Harry,' he said, 'I'll tell you, you've flummoxed me this time.' He sighed and rubbed his chin in apparent disbelief. 'I don't know what the 'ell to say to you.'

It wasn't often that Phin lost his voice, but he found it again very soon at the next meeting of the farmers' discussion group.

A learned and earnest gentleman had been expounding on the advances in veterinary medicine and how the farmers could now expect their stock to be treated as the doctors treated their human patients with the newest drugs and procedures.

It was too much for Phin. He jumped to his feet and cried: 'Ah think you're talking a lot of rubbish. There's a young feller in Darrowby not long out of college and it doesn't matter what you call 'im out for he uses nowt but epsom salts and cold water.'

Chapter Twenty-seven

It was during one of Siegfried's efficiency drives that Colonel Merrick's cow picked up a wire. The colonel was a personal friend, which made things even more uncomfortable.

Everybody suffered when Siegfried had these spells. They usually came on after he had been reading a technical work or when he had seen a film of some new technical procedure. He would rampage around, calling on the cowering household to stir themselves and be better men. He would be obsessed, for a time, with a craving for perfection.

'We must put on a better show at these operations on the farms. It just isn't good enough to fish out a few old instruments from a bag and start hacking at the animal. We must have cleanliness, asepsis if possible, and an orderly technique.'

So he was jubilant when he diagnosed traumatic reticulitis (foreign body in the second stomach) in the colonel's cow. 'We'll really show old Hubert something. We'll give him a picture of veterinary surgery he'll never forget.'

Tristan and I were pressed into service as assistants, and our arrival at the farm was really impressive. Siegfried led the procession, looking unusually smart in a brand new tweed jacket of which he was very proud. He was a debonair figure as he shook hands with his friend.

The colonel was jovial. 'Hear you're going to operate on my cow. Take out a wire, eh? Like to watch you do it, if it's all right with you.'

'By all means, Hubert, please do. You'll find it very interesting.'

In the byre, Tristan and I had to bustle about. We arranged tables alongside the cow and on these we placed new metal trays with rows of shining, sterilised instruments. Scalpels, directors, probes, artery forceps, hypodermic syringes, suture needles, gut and silk in glass phials, rolls of cotton wool and various bottles of spirit and other antiseptics.

Siegfried fussed around, happy as a schoolboy. He had clever hands and, as a surgeon, he was worth watching. I could read his mind without much trouble. This, he was thinking, was going to be good.

When all was to his liking, he took off his jacket and donned a brilliantly white smock. He handed the jacket to Tristan and almost instantly gave a roar of anger. 'Hey, don't just throw it down on that meal bin! Here, give it to me. I'll find a safe place for it.' He dusted the new garment down tenderly and hung it on a nail on the wall.

Meanwhile, I had shaved and disinfected the operation site on the flank and everything was ready for the local anaesthetic. Siegfried took the syringe and quickly infiltrated the area. 'This is where we go inside, Hubert. I hope you aren't squeamish.'

The colonel beamed. 'Oh, I've seen blood before. You needn't worry, I shan't faint.'

With a bold sweep of the scalpel, Siegfried incised the skin, then the muscles and finally, with delicate, the glistening peritoneum. The smooth wall of the rumen (the large first stomach) lay exposed.

Siegfried reached for a fresh scalpel and looked for the best place to cut in. But as he poised his knife, the wall of the rumen suddenly bulged out through the skin incision. 'Unusual,' he muttered. 'Probably a bit of rumenal gas.' Unflurried, he gently thrust back the protrusion and prepared again to make his cut; but as he withdrew his hand, the rumen welled out after it, a pinkish mass bigger than a football. Siegfried pushed it back and it shot out again immediately, ballooning to a startling size. This time, he took two hands to the job, pushing and pressing till he forced the thing once more out of sight. He stood for a moment with his hands inside the cow, breathing heavily. Two beads of sweat trickled down his forehead.

Carefully, he withdrew his hands. Nothing happened. It must have settled down. He was reaching back for his knife when, like a live thing, the rumen again came leaping and surging out. It seemed almost as though the entire organ had escaped through the incision – a slippery, gleaming mass rising and swelling till it was level with his eyes.

Siegfried had dropped all pretence of calm and was fighting desperately, both arms round the thing, pressing downwards with all his strength. I hastened forward to help and, as I drew near, he whispered hoarsely: 'What the hell is it?' Clearly, he was wondering if this pulsating heap of tissue was some part of the bovine anatomy he had never even heard of.

Silently, we fought the mass down till it was level with the skin. The colonel was watching intently. He hadn't expected the operation to be so interesting. His eyebrows were slightly raised.

'It must be gas that's doing this,' panted Siegfried. 'Pass me the knife and stand back.'

He inserted the knife into the rumen and cut sharply downwards. I was glad I had moved away because through the incision shot a high pressure jet of semi-liquid stomach contents – a greenish-brown, foul-smelling cascade which erupted from the depths of the cow as from an invisible pump.

The first direct hit was on Siegfried's face. He couldn't release his hold of the rumen or it would have slipped back into the abdomen and contaminated the peritoneum. So he hung on to each side of the opening while the evil torrent poured onto his hair, down his neck and all over his lovely white smock.

Now and then, the steady stream would be varied by a sudden explosion which sent the fermenting broth spouting viciously over everything in the immediate vicinity. Within a minute, the trays with their gleaming instruments were thoroughly covered. The tidy rows of swabs, the snowy tufts of cotton wool disappeared without trace, but it was the unkindest cut of all when a particular powerful jet sent a liberal spray over the new jacket hanging on the wall. Siegfried's face was too obscured for me to detect any change of expression but at this disaster, I saw real anguish in his eyes.

The colonel's eyebrows were now raised to the maximum and his mouth hung open as he gazed in disbelief at the chaotic scene. Siegfried, still hanging grimly on, was the centre of it all, paddling about in a reeking swamp which came half way up his Wellington boots. He looked very like a Fiji Islander with his hair stiffened and frizzled and his eyes rolling whitely in the brown face.

Eventually, the flood slowed to a trickle and stopped. I was able to hold the lips of the wound while Siegfried inserted his arm and felt his way to the reticulum. I watched him as he groped inside the honeycombed organ far out of sight against the diaphragm. A satisfied grunt told me he had located the piercing wire and within seconds he had removed it.

Tristan had been frantically salvaging and washing suture materials and soon the incision in the rumen was stitched. Siegfried's heroic stand had not been in vain; there was no contamination of the peritoneum.

Silently and neatly, he secured the skin and muscles with retention sutures and swabbed round the wound. Everything looked fine. The cow seemed unperturbed; under the anaesthetic she had known nothing of the titanic struggle with her insides. In fact, freed from the discomfort of the transfixing wire, she appeared already to be feeling better.

It took quite a time to tidy up the mess and the most difficult job was to make Siegfried presentable. We did our best by swilling him down with buckets of water while, all the time, he scraped sadly at his new jacket with a flat stick. It didn't make much difference.

The colonel was hearty and full of congratulations. 'Come in, my dear chap. Come in and have a drink.' But the invitation had a hollow ring and he took care to stand at least ten feet away from his friend.

Siegfried threw his bedraggled jacket over his shoulder. 'No thank you, Hubert. It's most kind of you, but we must be off.' He went out of the byre. 'I think you'll find the cow will be eating in a day or two. I'll be back in a fortnight to take out the stitches.'

In the confined space of the car, Tristan and I were unable to get as far away from him as we could have liked. Even with our heads stuck out of the windows it was still pretty bad.

Siegfried drove for a mile or two in silence, then he turned to me and his streaked features broke into a grin. There was something indomitable about him. 'You never know what's round the corner in this game, my boys, but just think of this – that operation was a success.'

Chapter Twenty-eight

There were three of us in the cheerless yard, Isaac Cranford, Jeff Mallock and myself. The only one who looked at ease was Mallock and it was fitting that it should be so, since he was, in a manner of speaking, the host. He owned the knacker yard and he looked on benignly as we peered into the carcass of the cow he had just opened.

In Darrowby the name Mallock had a ring of doom. It was the graveyard of livestock, of farmers' ambitions, of veterinary surgeons' hopes. If ever an animal was very ill somebody was bound to say: 'I reckon she'll be off to Mallock's afore long.' or 'Jeff Mallock'll have 'er in t' finish.' And the premises fitted perfectly into the picture; a group of drab, red-brick buildings standing a few fields back from the road with a stumpy chimney from which rolled endlessly a dolorous black smoke.

It didn't pay to approach Mallock's too closely unless you had a strong stomach, so the place was avoided by the townspeople, but if you ventured up the lane and peeped through the sliding metal doors you could look in on a nightmare world. Dead animals lay everywhere. Most of them were dismembered and great chunks of meat hung on hooks, but here and there you could see a bloated sheep or a greenish, swollen pig which not even Jeff could bring himself to open.

Skulls and dry bones were piled to the roof in places and brown mounds of meat meal stood in the corners. The smell was bad at any time but when Jeff was boiling up the carcasses it was indescribable. The Mallock family bungalow stood in the middle of the buildings and strangers could be pardoned if they expected a collection of wizened gnomes to dwell there. But Jeff was a pink-faced, cherubic man in his forties, his wife plump, smiling and comely. Their family ranged from a positively beautiful girl of nineteen down to a robust five year old boy. There were eight young Mallocks and they had spent their lifetimes playing among tuberculous lungs and a vast spectrum of bacteria from Salmonella to Anthrax. They were the healthiest children in the district.

It was said in the pubs that Jeff was one of the richest men in the town but the locals, as they supped their beer, had to admit that he earned his money. At any hour of the day or night he would rattle out into the country in his ramshackle lorry, winch on a carcass, bring it back to the yard and cut it up. A dog food dealer came twice a week from Brawton with a van and bought the fresh meat. The rest of the stuff Jeff shovelled into his boiler to make the meat meal which was in great demand for mixing in pig and poultry rations. The bones went for making fertiliser, the hides to the tanner and the nameless odds and ends were collected by a wild-eyed individual known only as the 'ket feller'. Sometimes, for a bit of variety, Ted would make long slabs of strange-smelling soap which found a brisk sale for scrubbing shop floors. Yes, people said, there was no doubt Jeff did all right. But, by gaw, he earned it.

My contacts with Mallock were fairly frequent. A knacker's yard had a useful function for a vet. It served as a crude post mortem room, a place where he could check on his diagnosis in fatal cases; and on the occasions where he had been completely baffled, the mysteries would be revealed under Jeff's knife.

Often, of course, farmers would send in an animal which I had been treating and ask Jeff to tell them 'what had been wrong wi't' and this was where a certain amount of friction arose. Because Jeff was placed in a position of power and seldom resisted the temptation to wield it. Although he could neither read nor write, he was a man of great professional pride; he didn't like to be called a knacker man but preferred 'fell-monger'. He considered in his heart that, after twenty odd years of cutting up diseased animals he knew more than any vet alive, and it made things rather awkward that the farming community unhesitatingly agreed with him.

It never failed to spoil my day if a farmer called in at the surgery and told me that, once more, Jeff Mallock had confounded my diagnosis. 'Hey, remember that cow you were treating for magnesium deficiency? She never did no good and ah sent 'er into Mallocks. Well, you know what was really the matter wi' 'er? Worm i' the tail. Jeff said if you'd nobbut cut tail off, that cow would have gotten up and walked away.' It was no good arguing or saying there was no such thing as worm in the tail. Jeff knew – that was all about it.

If only Jeff had taken his priceless opportunities to acquire a commonsense knowledge it wouldn't have been so bad. But instead, he had built up a weird pathology of his own and backed it up by black magic remedies gleaned from his contacts with the more primitive members of the farming community. His four stock diseases were Stagnation of t'lungs, Black Rot, Gastric Ulsters and Golf Stones. It was a quartet which made the vets tremble for miles around.

Another cross which the vets had to bear was his unique gift of being able to take one look at a dead animal on a farm and pronounce immediately on the cause of death. The farmers, awe-struck by his powers, were always asking me why I couldn't do it. But I was unable to dislike the man. He would have had to be more than human to resist the chance to be important and there was no malice in his actions. Still, it made things uncomfortable at times and I liked to be on the spot myself whenever possible. Especially when Isaac Cranford was involved.

Cranford was a hard man, a man who had cast his life in a mould of iron austerity. A sharp bargainer, a win-at-all-cost character and, in a region where thrift was general, he was noted for meanness. He farmed some of the best land in the lower Dale, his Shorthorns won prizes regularly at the shows but he was nobody's friend. Mr Bateson, his neighbour to the North, summed it up: 'That feller 'ud skin a flea for its hide.' Mr Dickon, his neighbour to the South, put it differently: 'If he gets haud on a pound note, by gaw it's a prisoner.'

This morning's meeting had had its origin the previous day. A phone call mid afternoon from Mr Cranford. 'I've had a cow struck by lightning. She's laid dead in the field.'

I was surprised. 'Lightning? Are you sure? We haven't had a storm today.'

'Maybe you haven't, but we have 'ere.'

'Mmm, all right, I'll come and have a look at her.'

Driving to the farm, I couldn't work up much enthusiasm for the impending interview. This lightning business could be a bit of a headache. All farmers were insured against lightning stroke – it was usually part of their fire policy – and after a severe thunder storm it was common enough for the vets' phones to start ringing with requests to examine dead beasts.

The insurance companies were reasonable about it. If they received a certificate from the vet that he believed lightning to be the cause of death they would usually pay up without fuss. In cases of doubt they would ask for a post mortem or a second opinion from another practitioner. The difficulty was that there are no diagnostic post mortem features to go on; occasionally a bruising of the tissues under the skin, but very little else. The happiest situation was when the beast was found with the tell-tale scorch marks running from an ear down the leg to earth into the ground. Often the animal would be found under a tree which itself had obviously been blasted and torn by lightning. Diagnosis was easy then.

Ninety-nine per cent of the farmers were looking only for a square deal and if their vet found some other clear cause of death they would accept his verdict philosophically. But the odd one could be very difficult.

I had heard Siegfried tell of one old chap who had called him out to verify a lightning death. The long scorch marks on the carcass were absolutely classical and Siegfried, viewing them, had been almost lyrical. 'Beautiful, Charlie, beautiful, I've never seen more typical marks. But there's just one thing.' He put an arm round the old man's shoulder. 'What a great pity you let the candle grease fall on the skin.'

The old man looked closer and thumped a fist into his palm. 'Dang it, you're right, maister! Ah've mucked t'job up. And ah took pains ower it an' all – been on for dang near an hour.' He walked away muttering. He showed no embarrassment, only disgust at his own technological shortcomings.

But this, I thought, as the stone walls flipped past the car windows, would be very different. Cranford was in the habit of getting his own way, right or wrong, and if he didn't get it today there would be trouble.

I drove through the farm gate and along a neat tarmac road across the single field. Mr Cranford was standing motionless in the middle of the yard and I was struck, not for the first time, by the man's resemblance to a big, hungry bird. The hunched, narrow shoulders, the forward-thrust, sharp-beaked face, the dark overcoat hanging loosely on the bony frame. I wouldn't have been surprised if he had spread his wings and flapped his way on to the byre roof. Instead, he nodded impatiently at me and began to hasten with short, tripping steps to a field at the back of the house.

It was a large field and the dead cow lay almost in the centre. There were no trees, no hedges, not even a small bush. My hopeful picture of the body under a stricken tree melted immediately, leaving an anxious void.

We stopped beside the cow and Mr Cranford was the first to speak. 'Bound to be lightning. Can't be owt else. Nasty storm, then this good beast dropping down dead.'

I looked at the grass around the big Shorthorn. It had been churned and torn out, leaving patches of bare earth. 'But it hasn't exactly dropped down, has it? It died in convulsions – you can see where its feet have kicked out the grass.'

'All right then, it 'ad a convulsion, but it was lightning that caused it.' Mr Cranford had fierce little eyes and they darted flitting glances at my shirt collar, macintosh belt, Wellingtons. He never could quite bring himself to look anybody in the eye.

'I doubt it, Mr Cranford. One of the signs of lightning stroke is that the beast has fallen without a struggle. Some of them even have grass in their mouths.'

'Oh, I know all about that,' Cranford snapped, his thin face flushing. 'I've been among livestock for half a century and this isn't the first beast I've seen that's been struck. They're not all t'same, you know.'

'Oh, I realise that, but, you see, this death could have been caused by so many things.'

'What sort o' things?'

'Well, Anthrax for a start, magnesium deficiency, heart trouble – there's quite a list. I really think we ought to do a post mortem to make sure.'

'Now see here, are you saying I'm trying to do summat I shouldn't?'

'Not at all. I'm only saying we should make sure before I write a certificate. We can go and see her opened at Mallock's and, believe me, if there's no other obvious cause of death you'll get the benefit of the doubt. The insurance people are pretty good about it.'

Mr Cranford's predatory features sank lower into his coat collar. He dug his hands viciously into his pockets. 'I've had vitneries at these jobs afore. Proper, experienced vitneries, too.' The little eyes flashed in the direction of my left ear. 'They've never messed about like this. What's the use of going to all that trouble? Why do you have to be so damn particular?'

Why indeed, I thought. Why make an enemy of this man? He wielded a lot of power in the district. Prominent in the local Farmers' Union, a member of every agricultural committee for miles around. He was a wealthy, successful man and, if people didn't like him they respected his knowledge and listened to him. He could do a young vet a lot of harm. Why not write the certificate and go home? This is to certify that I have examined that above mentioned animal and, in my opinion, lightning stroke was the cause of death. It would be easy and Cranford would be mollified. It would be the end of the whole thing. Why antagonise this dangerous character for nothing? Maybe it really was lightning, anyway.

I turned to face Mr Cranford, trying in vain to look into the eyes that always veered away at the last moment. 'I'm sorry, but I feel we ought to have a look inside this cow. I'll ring Mallock and ask him to pick her up and we can see her in the morning. I'll meet you there at ten o'clock. Will that be all right?'

'Reckon it'll have to be,' Cranford spat out. 'It's a piece o' nonsense, but I suppose I've got to humour you. But just let me remind you – this was a good cow, worth all of eighty pounds. I can't afford to lose that amount of money. I want my rights.'

'I'm sure you'll get them, Mr Cranford. And before I have her moved I'd better take a blood film to eliminate Anthrax.'

The farmer had been under a mounting load of pressure. As a pillar of the methodist chapel his range of language was restricted, so he vented his pent up feelings by kicking out savagely at the carcass. His toe made contact with the unyielding backbone and he hopped around on one leg for a few seconds. Then he limped off towards the house.

I was alone as I nicked the dead ear with my knife and drew a film of blood across a couple of glass slides. It hadn't been a happy session and the one tomorrow didn't hold out much more promise. I enclosed the blood films carefully in a cardboard box and set off for Skeldale House to examine them under the microscope.

So it wasn't a particularly cheerful group which assembled at the knacker yard the following morning. Even Jeff, though he preserved his usual Buddha-like expression, was, in fact, deeply offended. The account he had given me when I first arrived at the yard was fragmentary, but I could piece the scene together. Jeff, leaping from his lorry at Cranford's, sweeping the carcass with a piercing glance and making his brilliant spot diagnosis. 'Stagnation o' t'lungs. I can allus tell by the look in their eyes and the way their hair lies along t'back.' Waiting confidently for the wondering gasps, the congratulatory speeches which always followed his tour de force.

Then Mr Cranford, almost dancing with rage. 'Shut your big, stupid mouth, Mallock, tha knows nowt about it. This cow was struck by lightning and you'd better remember that.'

And now, bending my head over the carcass, I couldn't find a clue anyway. No sign of bruising when the skin was removed. The internal organs clean and normal.

I straightened up and pushed my fingers through my hair. The boiler bubbled softly, puffing out odoriferous wisps into the already highly charged atmosphere. Two dogs licked busily at a pile of meat meal.

Then a chill of horror struck through me. The dogs had competition. A little boy with golden curls was pushing a forefinger into the heap, inserting it in his mouth and sucking with rapt enjoyment.

'Look at that!' I quavered.

The knacker man's face lit up with paternal pride. 'Aye,' he said happily, 'It isn't only the four legged 'uns wot likes my meal. Wonderful stuff – full of nourishment!'

His good humour completely restored, he struck a match and began to puff appreciatively at a short pipe which was thickly encrusted with evidence of his grisly trade.

I dragged my attention back to the job in hand. 'Cut into the heart, will you, Jeff,' I said.

Jeff deftly sliced the big organ from top to bottom and I knew immediately my search was over. The auricles and ventricles were almost completely occluded by a cauliflower-like mass growing from the valves. Verrucose endocarditis, common in pigs but seldom seen in cattle.

'There's what killed your cow, Mr Cranford.' I said.

Cranford aimed his nose at the heart. 'Fiddlesticks! You're not telling me them little things could kill a great beast like that.'

'They're not so little. Big enough to stop the flow of blood. I'm sorry, but there's no doubt about it – your cow died of heart failure.'

'And how about lightning?'

'No sign of it, I'm afraid. You can see for yourself.'

'And what about my eighty pounds?'

'I'm truly sorry about that, but it doesn't alter the facts.'

'Facts! What facts? I've come along this morning and you've shown me nowt to make me change my opinion.'

'Well, there's nothing more I can say. It's a clear cut case.'

Mr Cranford stiffened in his perching stance. He held his hands against the front of his coat and the fingers and thumbs rubbed together unceasingly as though fondling the beloved bank notes which were slipping away from him. His face, sunk deeper in his collar, appeared still sharper in outline.

Then he turned to me and made a ghastly attempt to smile. And his eyes, trained on my lapels, tried valiantly to inch their way upwards. There was a fleeting instance when they met my gaze before flickering away in alarm.

He drew me to one side and addressed himself to my larynx. There was a wheedling note in the hoarse whisper.

'Now look here, Mr Herriot, we're both men of the world. You know as well as I do that the insurance company can afford this loss a lot better nor me. So why can't you just say it is lightning?'

'Even though I think it isn't?'

'Well, what the hangment does it matter? You can say it is, can't you? Nobody's going to know.'

I scratched my head. 'But what would bother me, Mr Cranford, is that I would know.'

'You would know?' The farmer was mystified.

'That's right. And it's no good – I can't give you a certificate for this cow and that's the end of it.'

Dismay, disbelief, frustration chased across Mr Cranford's features. 'Well, I'll tell you this. I'm not leaving the matter here. I'm going to see your boss about you.' He swung round and pointed at the cow. 'There's no sign of disease there. Trying to tell me it's due to little things in the heart. You don't know your job – you don't even know what them things are!'

Jeff Mallock removed his unspeakable pipe from his mouth. 'But ah know. It's what ah said. Stagnation o' t'lungs is caused by milk from milk vein getting back into the body. Finally it gets to t'heart and then it's over wi't. Them's milk clots you're looking at.'

Cranford rounded on him. 'Shut up, you great gumph! You're as bad as this feller here. It was lightning killed my good cow. Lightning!' He was almost screaming. Then he controlled himself and spoke quietly to me. 'You'll hear more of this, Mr Knowledge, and I'll just tell you one thing. You'll never walk on to my farm again.' He turned and hurried away with his quick-stepping gait.

I said good morning to Jeff and climbed wearily into my car. Well, everything had worked out just great. If only vetting just consisted of treating sick animals. But it didn't. There were so many other things. I started the engine and drove away.

Chapter Twenty-nine

It didn't take Mr Cranford long to make good his threat. He called at the surgery shortly after lunch the following day and Siegfried and I, enjoying a post prandial cigarette in the sitting-room, heard the jangle of the door bell. We didn't get up, because most of the farmers walked in after ringing.

The dogs, however, went into their usual routine. They had had a long run on the high moor that morning and had just finished licking out their dinner bowls. Tired and distended, they had collapsed in a snoring heap around Siegfried's feet. There was nothing they wanted more than ten minutes' peace but, dedicated as they were to their self appointed role of fierce guardians of the house, they did not hesitate. They leaped, baying, from the rug and hurled themselves into the passage.

People often wondered why Siegfried kept five dogs. Not only kept them but took them everywhere with him. Driving on his rounds it was difficult to see him at all among the shaggy heads and waving tails; and anybody approaching the car would recoil in terror from the savage barking and the bared fangs and glaring eyes framed in the windows.

'I cannot for the life of me understand,' Siegfried would declare, thumping his fist on his knee, 'why people keep dogs as pets. A dog should have a useful function. Let it be used for farm work, for shooting, for guiding; but why anybody should keep the things just hanging around the place beats me.'

It was a pronouncement he was continually making, often through a screen of flapping ears and lolling tongues as he sat in his car. His listener would look wonderingly from the huge greyhound to the tiny terrier, from the spaniel to the whippet to the Scottie; but nobody ever asked Siegfried why he kept his own dogs.

I judged that the pack fell upon Mr Cranford about the bend of the passage and many a lesser man would have fled; but I could hear him fighting his way doggedly forward. When he came through the sitting-room door he had removed his hat and was beating the dogs off with it. It wasn't a wise move and the barking rose to a higher pitch. The man's eyes stared and his lips moved continuously, but nothing came through.

Siegfried, courteous as ever, rose and indicated a chair. His lips, too, were moving, no doubt in a few gracious words of welcome. Mr Cranford flapped his black coat, swooped across the carpet and perched. The dogs sat in a ring round him and yelled up into his face. Usually they collapsed after their exhausting performance but there was something in the look or smell of Mr Cranford that they didn't like.

Siegfried leaned back in his arm chair, put his fingers together and assumed a judicial expression. Now and again he nodded understandingly or narrowed his eyes as if taking an interesting point. Practically nothing could be heard from Mr Cranford but occasionally a word or phrase penetrated.

'. . . have a serious complaint to make . . .'
'. . . doesn't know his job . . .'
'. . . can't afford . . . not a rich man . . .'
'. . . these danged dogs . . .'
'. . . won't have 'im again . . .'
'. . . down dog, get by . . .'
'. . . nowt but robbery . . .'

Siegfried, completely relaxed and apparently oblivious of the din, listened attentively but as the minutes passed I could see the strain beginning to tell on Mr Cranford. His eyes began to start from their sockets and the veins corded on his scrawny neck as he tried to get his message across. Finally it was too much for him; he jumped up and a leaping brown tide bore him to the door. He gave a last defiant cry, lashed out again with his hat and was gone.

Pushing open the dispensary door a few weeks later, I found my boss mixing an ointment. He was working with great care, turning and returning the glutinous mass on a marble slab.

'What's this you're doing?' I asked.

Siegfried threw down his spatula and straightened his back. 'Ointment for a boar.' He looked past me at Tristan who had just come in. 'And I don't know why the hell I'm doing it when some people are sitting around on their backsides.' He indicated the spatula. 'Right, Tristan, you can have a go. When you've finished your cigarette, that is.'

His expression softened as Tristan hastily nipped out his Woodbine and began to work away on the slab. 'Pretty stiff concoction, that. Takes a bit of mixing,' Siegfried said with satisfaction, looking at his brother's bent head. 'The back of my neck was beginning to ache with it.'

He turned to me. 'By the way, you'll be interested to hear it's for your old friend Cranford. For that prize boar of his. It's got a nasty sore across its back and he's worried to death about it. Wins him a lot of money at the shows and a blemish there would be disastrous.'

'Cranford's still with us, then.'

'Yes, it's a funny thing, but we can't get rid of him. I don't like losing clients but I'd gladly make an exception of this chap. He won't have you near the place after that lightning job and he makes it very clear he doesn't think much of me either. Tells me I never do his beasts any good – says it would have been a lot better if he'd never called me. And moans like hell when he gets his bill. He's more bother than he's worth and on top of everything he gives me the creeps. But he won't leave – he damn well won't leave.'

'He knows which side his bread's buttered,' I said. 'He gets first rate service and the moaning is part of the system to keep the bills down.'

'Maybe you're right, but I wish there was a simple way to get rid of him.' He tapped Tristan on the shoulder. 'All right, don't strain yourself. That'll do. Put it into this ointment box and label it: "Apply liberally to the boar's back three times daily, working it well in with the fingers." And post it to Mr Cranford. And while you're on, will you post this faeces sample to the laboratory at Leeds to test for Johne's disease.' He held out a treacle tin brimming with foul-smelling, liquid diarrhoea.

It was a common thing to collect such samples and send them away for Johne's tests, worm counts, etc., and there was always one thing all the samples had in common – they were very large. All that was needed for the tests was a couple of teaspoonfuls but the farmers were lavish in their quantities. They seemed pleasantly surprised that all the vet wanted was a bit of muck from the dung channel; they threw aside their natural caution and shovelled the stuff up cheerfully into the biggest container they could find. They brushed aside all protests; 'take plenty, we've lots of it' was their attitude.

Tristan took hold of the tin gingerly and began to look along the shelves. 'We don't seem to have any of those little glass sample jars.'

'That's right, we're out of them,' said Siegfried. 'I meant to order some more. But never mind – shove the lid on that tin and press it down tight, then parcel it up well in brown paper. It'll travel to the lab all right.'

It took only three days for Mr Cranford's name to come up again. Siegfried was opening the morning mail, throwing the circulars to one side and making a pile of the bills and receipts when he became suddenly very still. He had frozen over a letter on blue notepaper and he sat like a statue till he read it through. At length he raised his head; his face was expressionless. 'James, this is just about the most vitriolic letter I have ever read. It's from Cranford. He's finished with us for good and all and is considering taking legal action against us.'

'What have we done this time?' I asked.

'He accuses us of grossly insulting him and endangering the health of his boar. He says we sent him a treacle tin full of cow shit with instructions to rub it on the boar's back three times daily.'

Tristan, who had been sitting with his eyes half closed, became fully awake. He rose unhurriedly and began to make his way towards the door. His hand was on the knob when his brother's voice thundered out.

'Tristan! Come back here! Sit down – I think we have something to talk about.'

Tristan looked up resolutely, waiting for the storm to break, but Siegfried was unexpectedly calm. His voice was gentle.

'So you've done it again. When will I ever learn that I can't trust you to carry out the simplest task. It wasn't much to ask, was it? Two little parcels to post – hardly a tough assignment. But you managed to botch it. You got the labels wrong, didn't you?'

Tristan wriggled in his chair. 'I'm sorry, I can't think how . . .'

Siegfried held up his hand. 'Oh, don't worry. Your usual luck has come to your aid. With anybody else this bloomer would be catastrophic but with Cranford – it's like divine providence.' He paused for a moment and a dreamy expression crept into his eyes. 'The label said to work it well in with the fingers, I seem to recall. And Mr Cranford says he opened the package at the breakfast table . . . Yes, Tristan, I think you have found the way. This, I do believe, has done it.'

I said, 'But how about the legal action?'

'Oh, I think we can forget about that. Mr Cranford has a great sense of his own dignity. Just think how it would sound in court.' He crumpled the letter and dropped it into the waste paper basket. 'Well, let's get on with some work.'

He led the way out and stopped abruptly in the passage. He turned to face us. 'There's another thing, of course. I wonder how the lab is making out, testing that ointment for Johne's disease?'

Chapter Thirty

I was really worried about Tricki this time. I had pulled up my car when I saw him in the street with his mistress and I was shocked at his appearance. He had become hugely fat, like a bloated sausage with a leg at each corner. His eyes, bloodshot and rheumy, stared straight ahead and his tongue lolled from his jaws.

Mrs Pumphrey hastened to explain. 'He was so listless, Mr Herriot. He seemed to have no energy. I thought he must be suffering from malnutrition, so I have been giving him some little extras between meals to build him up. Some calf's foot jelly and malt and cod liver oil and a bowl of Horlick's at night to make him sleep – nothing much really.'

'And did you cut down on the sweet things as I told you?'

'Oh, I did for a bit, but he seemed to be so weak. I had to relent. He does love cream cakes and chocolates so. I can't bear to refuse him.'

I looked down again at the little dog. That was the trouble. Tricki's only fault was greed. He had never been known to refuse food; he would tackle a meal at any hour of the day or night. And I wondered about all the things Mrs Pumphrey hadn't mentioned; the pate on thin biscuits, the fudge, the rich trifles – Tricki loved them all.

'Are you giving him plenty of exercise?'

'Well, he has his little walks with me as you can see, but Hodgkin has been down with lumbago, so there has been no ring-throwing lately.'

I tried to sound severe. 'Now I really mean this. If you don't cut his food right down and give him more exercise he is going to be really ill. You must harden your heart and keep him on a very strict diet.'

Mrs Pumphrey wrung her hands. 'Oh I will, Mr Herriot. I'm sure you are right, but it is so difficult, so very difficult.' She set off, head down, along the road, as if determined to put the new regime into practice immediately.

I watched their progress with growing concern. Tricki was tottering along in his little tweed coat; he had a whole wardrobe of these coats – warm tweed or tartan ones for the cold weather and macintoshes for the wet days. He struggled on, drooping in his harness. I thought it wouldn't be long before I heard from Mrs Pumphrey.

The expected call came within a few days. Mrs Pumphrey was distraught. Tricki would eat nothing. Refused even his favourite dishes; and besides, he had bouts of vomiting. He spent all his time lying on a rug, panting. Didn't want to go walks, didn't want to do anything.

I had made my plans in advance. The only way was to get Tricki out of the house for a period. I suggested that he be hospitalised for about a fortnight to be kept under observation.

The poor lady almost swooned. She had never been separated from her darling before; she was sure he would pine and die if he did not see her every day.

But I took a firm line. Tricki was very ill and this was the only way to save him; in fact, I thought it best to take him without delay and, followed by Mrs Pumphrey's wailings, I marched out to the car carrying the little dog wrapped in a blanket.

The entire staff was roused and maids rushed in and out bringing his day bed, his night bed, favourite cushions, toys and rubber rings, breakfast bowl, lunch bowl, supper bowl. Realising that my car would never hold all the stuff, I started to drive away. As I moved off, Mrs Pumphrey, with a despairing cry, threw an armful of the little coats through the window. I looked in the mirror before I turned the corner of the drive; everybody was in tears.

Out on the road, I glanced down at the pathetic little animal gasping on the seat by my side. I patted the head and Tricki made a brave effort to wag his tail. 'Poor old lad,' I said, 'You haven't a kick in you but I think I know a cure for you.'

At the sugery, the household dogs surged round me. Tricki looked down at the noisy pack with dull eyes and, when put down, lay motionless on the carpet. The other dogs, after sniffing round him for a few seconds, decided he was an uninteresting object and ignored him.

I made up a bed for him in a warm loose box next to the one where the other dogs slept. For two days I kept an eye on him, giving him no food but plenty of water. At the end of the second day he started to show some interest in his surroundings and on the third he began to whimper when he heard the dogs in the yard.

When I opened the door, Tricki trotted out and was immediately engulfed by Joe the greyhound and his friends. After rolling him over and thoroughly inspecting him, the dogs moved off down the garden. Tricki followed them, rolling slightly with his surplus fat but obviously intrigued.

Later that day, I was present at feeding time. I watched while Tristan slopped the food into the bowls. There was the usual headlong rush followed by the sounds of high-speed eating; every dog knew that if he fell behind the others he was liable to have some competition for the last part of his meal.

When they had finished. Tricki took a walk round the shining bowls, licking

casually inside one or two of them. Next day, an extra bowl was put out for him
and I was pleased to see him jostling his way towards it.

From then on, his progress was rapid. He had no medicinal treatment of any
kind but all day he ran about with the dogs, joining in their friendly scrimmages.
He discovered the joys of being bowled over, trampled on and squashed every
few minutes. He became an accepted member of the gang, an unlikely, silky
little object among the shaggy crew, fighting like a tiger for his share at meal
times and hunting rats in the old hen house at night. He had never had such
a time in his life.

All the while, Mrs Pumphrey hovered anxiously in the background, ringing
a dozen times a day for the latest bulletins. I dodged the questions about whether
his cushions were being turned regularly or his correct coat worn according to
the weather; but I was able to tell her that the little fellow was out of danger
and convalescing rapidly.

The word 'convalescing' seemed to do something to Mrs Pumphrey. She
started to bring round fresh eggs, two dozen at a time, to build up Tricki's
strength. For a happy period there were two eggs each for breakfast, but when
the bottles of sherry began to arrive, the real possibilities of the situation began
to dawn on the household.

It was the same delicious vintage that I knew so well and it was to enrich
Tricki's blood. Lunch became a ceremonial occasion with two glasses before and
several during the meal. Siegfried and Tristan took turns at proposing Tricki's
health and the standard of speech-making improved daily. As the sponsor, I was
always called upon to reply.

We could hardly believe it when the brandy came. Two bottles of Cordon
Bleu, intended to put a final edge on Tricki's constitution. Siegfried dug out
some balloon glasses belonging to his mother. I had never seen them before, but
for a few nights they saw constant service as the fine spirit was rolled around,
inhaled and reverently drunk.

They were days of deep content, starting well with the extra egg in the
morning, bolstered up and sustained by the midday sherry and finishing
luxuriously round the fire with the brandy.

It was a temptation to keep Tricki on as a permanent guest, but I knew Mrs
Pumphrey was suffering and after a fortnight, felt compelled to phone and tell
her that the little dog had recovered and was awaiting collection.

Within minutes, about thirty feet of gleaming black metal drew up outside
the surgery. The chauffeur opened the door and I could just make out the figure
of Mrs Pumphrey almost lost in the interior. Her hands were tightly clasped
in front of her; her lips trembled. 'Oh, Mr Herriot, do tell me the truth. Is he
really better?'

'Yes, he's fine. There's no need for you to get out of the car – I'll go and fetch
him.'

I walked through the house into the garden. A mass of dogs was hurtling
round and round the lawn and in their midst, ears flapping, tail waving, was
the little golden figure of Tricki. In two weeks he had been transformed into a
lithe, hard-muscled animal; he was keeping up well with the pack, stretching
out in great bounds, his chest almost brushing the ground.

I carried him back along the passage to the front of the house. The chauffeur
was still holding the car door open and when Tricki saw his mistress he took
off from my arms in a tremendous leap and sailed into Mrs Pumphrey's lap.
She gave a startled 'Ooh!' and then had to defend herself as he swarmed over
her, licking her face and barking.

During the excitement, I helped the chauffeur to bring out the beds, toys,
cushions, coats and bowls, none of which had been used. As the car moved

away, Mrs Pumphrey leaned out of the window. Tears shone in her eyes. Her lips trembled.

'Oh, Mr Herriot,' she cried, 'How can I ever thank you? This is a triumph of surgery!'

Chapter Thirty-one

I came suddenly and violently awake, my heart thudding and pounding in time with the insistent summons of the telephone. These bedside phones were undoubtedly an improvement on the old system when you had to gallop downstairs and stand shivering with your bare feet on the tiles of the passage; but this explosion a few inches from your ear in the small hours when the body was weak and the resistance low was shattering. I felt sure it couldn't be good for me.

The voice at the other end was offensively cheerful. 'I have a mare on foaling. She doesn't seem to be getting on wi' t'job. Reckon foal must be laid wrong – can you come and give me a hand?'

My stomach contracted to a tight ball. This was just a little bit too much; once out of bed in the middle of the night was bad enough, but twice was unfair, in fact it was sheer cruelty. I had had a hard day and had been glad to crawl between the sheets at midnight. I had been hauled out at one o'clock to a damned awkward calving and hadn't got back till nearly three. What was the time now? Three fifteen. Good God, I had only had a few minutes sleep. And a foaling! Twice as difficult as a calving as a rule. What a life! What a bloody awful life!

I muttered into the receiver, 'Right, Mr Dixon, I'll come straight away' and shuffled across the room, yawning and stretching, feeling the ache in my shoulders and arms. I looked down at the pile of clothing in the chair; I had taken them off, put them on again, taken them off already tonight and something in me rebelled at the thought of putting them on yet again. With a weary grunt I took my macintosh from the back of the door and donned it over my pyjamas, went downstairs to where my Wellingtons stood outside the dispensary door and stuck my feet into them. It was a warm night, what was the point of getting dressed up; I'd only have to strip off again at the farm.

I opened the back door and trailed slowly down the long garden, my tired mind only faintly aware of the fragrance that came from the darkness. I reached the yard at the bottom, opened the double doors into the lane and got the car out of the garage. In the silent town the buildings glowed whitely as the headlights swept across the shuttered shop fronts, the tight-drawn curtains. Everybody was asleep. Everybody except me, James Herriot, creeping sore and exhausted towards another spell of hard labour. Why the hell had I ever decided to become a country vet? I must have been crazy to pick a job where you worked seven days a week and through the night as well. Sometimes I felt as though the practice was a malignant, living entity; testing me, trying me out; putting the pressure on more and more to see just when at what point I would drop down dead.

It was a completely unconscious reaction which hoisted me from my bath of self pity and left me dripping on the brink, regarding the immediate future with a return of some of my natural optimism. For one thing, Dixon's place was down at the foot of the Dale just off the main road and they had that unusual luxury, electric light in the buildings. And I couldn't be all that tired; not at the age of twenty-four with all my faculties unimpaired. I'd take a bit of killing yet.

I smiled to myself and relapsed into the state of half suspended animation which was normal to me at these times; a sleepy blanketing of all the senses except those required for the job in hand. Many times over the past months I had got out of bed, driven far into the country, done my job efficiently and returned to bed without ever having been fully awake.

I was right about Dixon's. The graceful Clydesdale mare was in a well-lit loose box and I laid out my ropes and instruments with a feeling of deep thankfulness. As I tipped antiseptic into the steaming bucket I watched the mare straining and paddling her limbs. The effort produced nothing; there were no feet protruding from the vulva. There was almost certainly a malpresentation.

Still thinking hard, I removed my macintosh and was jerked out of my reverie by a shout of laughter from the farmer. 'God 'elp us, what's this, the Fol-de-rols?'

I looked down at my pyjamas which were pale blue with an arresting broad red stripe. 'This, Mr Dixon,' I replied with dignity, 'is my night attire. I didn't bother to dress.'

'Oh, I see now.' The farmer's eyes glinted impishly. 'I'm sorry, but I thought I'd got the wrong chap for a second. I saw a feller just like you at Blackpool last year – same suit exactly, but he 'ad a stripy top hat too and a stick. Did a champion little dance.'

'Can't oblige you, I'm afraid,' I said with a wan smile. 'I'm just not in the mood right now.'

I stripped off, noting with interest the deep red grooves caused by the calf's teeth a couple of hours ago. Those teeth had been like razors, peeling off neat little rolls of skin every time I pushed my arm past them.

The mare trembled as I felt my way inside her. Nothing, nothing, then just a tail and the pelvic bones and the body and hind legs disappearing away beyond my reach. Breech presentation; easy in the cow for a man who knew his job but tricky in the mare because of the tremendous length of the foal's legs.

It took me a sweating, panting half hour with ropes and a blunt hook on the end of a flexible cane to bring the first leg round. The second leg came more easily and the mare seemed to know there was no obstruction now. She gave a great heave and the foal shot out onto the straw with myself, arms around its body, sprawling on top of it. To my delight I felt the small form jerking convulsively; I had felt no movement while I was working and had decided that it was dead, but the foal was very much alive, shaking its head and snorting out the placental fluid it had inhaled during its delayed entry.

When I had finished towelling myself I turned to see the farmer with an abnormally straight face, holding out my colourful jacket like a valet. 'Allow me, sir,' he said gravely.

'O.K., O.K.,' I laughed, 'I'll get properly dressed next time.' As I was putting my things in the car boot the farmer carelessly threw a parcel on to the back seat.

'Bit o' butter for you,' he muttered. When I started the engine he bent level with the window. 'I think a bit about that mare and I've been badly wanting a foal out of her. Thank ye lad, thank ye very much.'

He waved as I moved away and I heard his parting cry. 'You did all right for a Kentucky Minstrel!'

I leaned back in my seat and peered through heavy lids at the empty road unwinding in the pale morning light. The sun had come up – a dark crimson ball hanging low over the misted fields. I felt utterly content, warm with the memory of the foal trying to struggle on to its knees, its absurdly long legs still out of control. Grand that the little beggar had been alive after all – there was something desolate about delivering a lifeless creature.

The Dixon farm was in the low country where the Dale widened out and gave on to the great plain of York. I had to cross a loop of the busy road which connected the West Riding with the industrial North East. A thin tendril of smoke rose from the chimney of the all night transport café which stood there and as I slowed down to take the corner a faint but piercing smell of cooking found its way into the car; the merest breath but rich in the imagery of fried sausages and beans and tomatoes and chips.

God, I was starving. I looked at my watch; five fifteen, I wouldn't be eating for a long time yet. I turned in among the lorries on the broad strip of tarmac.

Hastening towards the still lighted building I decided that I wouldn't be greedy. Nothing spectacular, just a nice sandwich. I had been here a few times before and the sandwiches were very good; and I deserved some nourishment after my hard night.

I stepped into the warm interior where groups of lorry drivers sat behind mounded plates, but as I crossed the floor the busy clatter died and was replaced by a tense silence. A fat man in a leather jacket sat transfixed, a loaded fork half way to his mouth, while his neighbour, gripping a huge mug of tea in an oily hand stared with bulging eyes at my ensemble.

It occurred to me then that bright red striped pyjamas and Wellingtons might seem a little unusual in those surroundings and I hastily buttoned my macintosh which had been billowing behind me. Even closed, it was on the short side and at least a foot of pyjama leg showed above my boots.

Resolutely I strode over to the counter. An expressionless blonde bulging out of a dirty white overall on the breast pocket of which was inscribed 'Dora' regarded me blankly.

'A ham sandwich and a cup of Bovril, please,' I said huskily. As the blonde put a teaspoonful of Bovril into a cup and filled it with a hissing jet of hot water I was uncomfortably aware of the silence behind me and of the battery of eyes focused on my legs. On my right I could just see the leather jacketed man. He filled his mouth and chewed reflectively for a few moments.

'Takes all kinds, don't it Ernest,' he said in a judicial tone.

'Does indeed, Kenneth, does indeed,' replied his companion.

'Would you say, Ernest, that this is what the Yorkshire country gentleman is wearing this spring?'

'Could be, Kenneth, could be.'

Listening to the titters from the rear, I concluded that these two were the accepted café wags. Best to eat up quickly and get out. Dora pushed the thickly meated sandwich across the counter and spoke with all the animation of a sleep walker. 'That'll be a shillin'.'

I slipped my hand inside my coat and encountered the pocketless flannelette beneath. God almighty, my money was in my trousers back in Darrowby! A wave of sickly horror flooded me as I began a frantic, meaningless search through my macintosh.

I looked wildly at the blonde and saw her slip the sandwich under the counter.
'Look, I've come out without any money. I've been in here before – do you know who I am?'

Dora gave a single bored shake of her head.

'Well, never mind,' I babbled, 'I'll pop in with the money next time I'm passing.'

Dora's expression did not alter but she raised one eyebrow fractionally; she made no effort to retrieve the sandwich from its hiding place.

Escape was the only thing in my mind now. Desperately I sipped at the scalding fluid.

Kenneth pushed back his plate and began to pick his teeth with a match. 'Ernest,' he said as though coming to a weighty conclusion. 'It's my opinion that this 'ere gentleman is eccentric.'

'Eccentric?' Ernest sniggered into his tea. 'Bloody daft, more like.'

'Ah, but not so daft, Ernest. Not daft enough to pay for 'is grub.'

'You 'ave a point there, Kenneth, a definite point.'

'You bet I have. He's enjoying a nice cup of Bovril on the house and if 'e hadn't mistimed his fumble he'd be at the sandwich too. Dora moved a bit sharpish for 'im there – another five seconds and he'd have had 'is choppers in the ham.'

'True, true,' muttered Ernest, seemingly content with his role of straight man.

Kenneth put away his match, sucked his teeth noisily and leaned back. 'There's another possibility we 'aven't considered. He could be on the run.'

'Escaped convict, you mean, Kenneth?'

'I do, Ernest, I do indeed.'

'But them fellers allus have arrows on their uniforms.'

'Ah, some of 'em do. But I 'eard somewhere that some of the prisons is going in for stripes now.'

I had had enough. Tipping the last searing drops of Bovril down my throat I made headlong for the door. As I stepped out into the early sunshine Kenneth's final pronouncement reached me.

'Prob'ly got away from a working party. Look at them Wellingtons . . .'

Postscript

I remember it was an afternoon when the sun blazed. I filled my car with Siegfried's dogs and drove to where an old mine track climbed green and inviting on the side of a steep hill. We walked a mile or two on the smooth turf then turned off and headed straight up the hillside through the hot bracken scent and the hum of flies to the very top where the wind was sweet and welcome and you could see nearly all of the Dale laid out there beneath; nearly all of it from the head where the great bare hills stood on the edge of the wild right down to the rich plain, chequered and hazy, at the foot.

I was sitting in the heather with the dogs in an expectant ring when the Dales smell came up on the breeze, the fragrance which the wind stole from the miles of warm grass and the shy flowers of the moorland. It had met me when I first stepped off the bus at Darrowby a year ago. And I realised that I had worked my way through the full cycle: I had travelled that magical first time round.

And it had all happened down there. Many of the farms in the practice were visible from where I sat; splashes of grey stone with their livestock, motionless dots from this distance, scattered in the fields around them. They were unrecognisable as the battle grounds of the past year, the scenes of my first struggles where everything had happened from heady success to abject failure.

There were people down there who thought I was a pretty fair vet, some who regarded me as an amiable idiot, a few who were convinced I was a genius and one or two who would set their dogs on me if I put a foot inside their gates.

All this in a year. What would be the position in thirty years? Well, as it has turned out, very much the same.

And what of the animals around whom the whole little drama revolves? It is a pity they cannot talk because it would be charming to have their views. There are a few things I would like to know. What do they think of their widely varying lives? What do they think of us? And do they manage to get a laugh out of it all?

It Shouldn't Happen to a Vet

It Shouldn't Happen to a Vet
To
DONALD and BRIAN SINCLAIR
Still my friends

Chapter One

I could see that Mr Handshaw didn't believe a word I was saying. He looked down at his cow and his mouth tightened into a stubborn line.

'Broken pelvis? You're trying to tell me she'll never get up n'more? Why, look at her chewing her cud! I'll tell you this, young man – me dad would've soon got her up if he'd been alive today.'

I had been a veterinary surgeon for a year now and I had learned a few things. One of them was that farmers weren't easy men to convince – especially Yorkshire Dalesmen.

And that bit about his dad. Mr Handshaw was in his fifties and I suppose there was something touching about his faith in his late father's skill and judgement. But I could have done very nicely without it.

It had acted as an additional irritant in a case in which I felt I had troubles enough. Because there are few things which get more deeply under a vet's skin than a cow which won't get up. To the layman it may seem strange that an animal can be apparently cured of its original ailment and yet be unable to rise from the floor, but it happens. And it can be appreciated that a completely recumbent milk cow has no future.

The case had started when my boss, Siegfried Farnon, who owned the practice in the little Dales market town of Darrowby, sent me to a milk fever. This suddenly occurring calcium deficiency attacks high yielding animals just after calving and causes collapse and progressive coma. When I first saw Mr Handshaw's cow she was stretched out motionless on her side, and I had to look carefully to make sure she wasn't dead.

But I got out my bottles of calcium with an airy confidence because I had been lucky enough to qualify just about the time when the profession had finally got on top of this hitherto fatal condition. The breakthrough had come many years earlier with inflation of the udder and I still carried a little blowing-up outfit around with me (the farmers used bicycle pumps), but with the advent of calcium therapy one could bask in a cheap glory by jerking an animal back from imminent death within minutes. The skill required was minimal but it looked very very good.

By the time I had injected the two bottles – one into the vein, the other under the skin – and Mr Handshaw had helped me roll the cow on to her chest the improvement was already obvious; she was looking about her and shaking her head as if wondering where she had been for the last few hours. I felt sure that if I had the time to hang about for a bit I could see her on her feet. But other jobs were waiting.

'Give me a ring if she isn't up by dinner time,' I said, but it was a formality. I was pretty sure I wouldn't be seeing her again.

When the farmer rang at midday to say she was still down it was just a pinprick. Some cases needed an extra bottle – it would be all right. I went out and injected her again.

I wasn't really worried when I learned she hadn't got up the following day, but Mr Handshaw, hands deep in pockets, shoulders hunched as he stood over his cow, was grievously disappointed at my lack of success.

'It's time t'awd bitch was up. She's doin' no good laid there. Surely there's summat you can do. I poured a bottle of water into her lug this morning but even that hasn't shifted her.'

'You what?'

'Poured some cold water down her lug 'ole. Me dad used to get 'em up that way and he was a very clever man with stock was me dad.'

'I've no doubt he was,' I said primly. 'But I really think another injection is more likely to help her.'

The farmer watched glumly as I ran yet another bottle of calcium under the skin. The procedure had lost its magic for him.

As I put the apparatus away I did my best to be hearty. 'I shouldn't worry. A lot of them stay down for a day or two – you'll probably find her walking about in the morning.'

The phone rang just before breakfast and my stomach contracted sharply as I heard Mr Handshaw's voice. It was heavy with gloom. 'Well, she's no different. Lyin' there eating her 'ead off, but never offers to rise. What are you going to do now?'

What indeed, I thought as I drove out to the farm. The cow had been down for forty-eight hours now – I didn't like it a bit.

The farmer went into the attack immediately. 'Me dad allus used to say they had a worm in the tail when they stayed down like this. He said if you cut tail end off it did the trick.'

My spirits sagged lower. I had had trouble with this myth before. The insidious thing was that the people who still practised this relic of barbarism could often claim that it worked because, after the end of the tail had been chopped off, the pain of the stump touching the ground forced many a sulky cow to scramble to her feet.

'There's no such thing as worm in the tail, Mr Handshaw,' I said. 'And don't you think it's a cruel business, cutting off a cow's tail? I hear the RSPCA had a man in court last week over a job like that.'

The farmer narrowed his eyes. Clearly he thought I was hedging. 'Well, if you won't do that, what the hangment are you going to do? We've got to get this cow up somehow.'

I took a deep breath. 'Well, I'm sure she's got over the milk fever because she's eating well and looks quite happy. It must be a touch of posterior paralysis that's keeping her down. There's no point in giving her any more calcium so I'm going to try this stimulant injection.' I filled the syringe with a feeling of doom. I hadn't a scrap of faith in the stimulant injection but I just couldn't do nothing. I was scraping the barrel out now.

I was turning to go when Mr Handshaw called after me. 'Hey, Mister, I remember summat else me dad used to do. Shout in their lugs. He got many a cow up that way. I'm not very strong in the voice – how about you having a go?'

It was a bit late to stand on my dignity. I went over to the animal and seized her by the ear. Inflating my lungs to the utmost I bent down and bawled wildly into the hairy depths. The cow stopped chewing for a moment and looked at me enquiringly, then her eyes drooped and she returned contentedly to her cudding. 'We'll give her another day,' I said wearily. 'And if she's still down tomorrow we'll have a go at lifting her. Could you get a few of your neighbours to give us a hand?'

Driving round my other cases that day I felt tied up inside with sheer frustration. Damn and blast the thing! What the hell was keeping her down? And what else could I do? This was 1938 and my resources were limited. Thirty years later there are still milk fever cows which won't get up but the vet has a much wider armoury if the calcium has failed to do the job. The excellent Bagshaw hoist which clamps on to the pelvis and raises the animal in a natural manner, the phosphorus injections, even the electric goad which administers a swift shock when applied to the rump and sends many a comfortably ensconced cow leaping to her feet with an offended bellow.

As I expected, the following day brought no change and as I got out of the car in Mr Handshaw's yard I was surrounded by a group of his neighbours. They were in festive mood, grinning, confident, full of helpful advice as farmers always are with somebody else's animals.

There was much laughter and legpulling as we drew sacks under the cow's body and a flood of weird suggestions to which I tried to close my ears. When we all finally gave a concerted heave and lifted her up, the result was predictable; she just hung there placidly with her legs dangling whilst her owner leaned against the wall watching us with deepening gloom.

After a lot of puffing and grunting we lowered the inert body and everybody looked at me for the next move. I was hunting round desperately in my mind when Mr Handshaw piped up again.

'Me dad used to say a strange dog would allus get a cow up.'

There were murmurs of assent from the assembled farmers and immediate offers of dogs. I tried to point out that one would be enough but my authority had dwindled and anyway everybody seemed anxious to demonstrate their dogs' cow-raising potential. There was a sudden excited exodus and even Mr Smedley the village shopkeeper pedalled off at frantic speed for his border terrier. It seemed only minutes before the byre was alive with snapping, snarling curs but the cow ignored them all except to wave her horns warningly at the ones which came too close.

The flash-point came when Mr Handshaw's own dog came in from the fields where he had been helping to round up the sheep. He was a skinny, hard-bitten little creature with lightning reflexes and a short temper. He stalked, stiff-legged and bristling, into the byre, took a single astounded look at the pack of foreigners on his territory and flew into action with silent venom.

Within seconds the finest dog fight I had ever seen was in full swing and I stood back and surveyed the scene with a feeling of being completely superfluous. The yells of the farmers rose above the enraged yapping and growling. One intrepid man leaped into the mêlée and reappeared with a tiny Jack Russell hanging on determinedly to the heel of his wellington boot. Mr Reynolds of Clover Hill was rubbing the cow's tail between two short sticks and shouting 'Cush! Cush!' and as I watched helplessly a total stranger tugged at my sleeve and whispered: 'Hasta tried a teaspoonful of Jeyes' Fluid in a pint of old beer every two hours?'

It seemed to me that all the forces of black magic had broken through and were engulfing me and that my slender resources of science had no chance of shoring up the dyke. I don't know how I heard the creaking sound above the din – probably because I was bending low over Mr Reynolds in an attempt to persuade him to desist from his tail rubbing. But at that moment the cow shifted her position slightly and I distinctly heard it. It came from the pelvis.

It took me some time to attract attention – I think everybody had forgotten I was there – but finally the dogs were separated and secured with innumerable lengths of binder twine, everybody stopped shouting, Mr Reynolds was pulled away from the tail and I had the stage.

I addressed myself to Mr Handshaw. 'Would you get me a bucket of hot water, some soap and a towel, please.'

He trailed off, grumbling, as though he didn't expect much from the new gambit. My stock was definitely low.

I stripped off my jacket, soaped my arms and pushed a hand into the cow's rectum until I felt the hard bone of the pubis. Gripping it through the wall of the rectum I looked up at my audience. 'Will two of you get hold of the hook bones and rock the cow gently from side to side.'

Yes, there it was again, no mistake about it. I could both hear and feel it – a looseness, a faint creaking, almost a grating.

I got up and washed my arm. 'Well, I know why your cow won't get up – she has a broken pelvis. Probably did it during the first night when she was staggering about with the milk fever. I should think the nerves are damaged, too. It's hopeless, I'm afraid.' Even though I was dispensing bad news it was a relief to come up with something rational.

Mr Handshaw stared at me. 'Hopeless? How's that?'

'I'm sorry,' I said, 'but that's how it is. The only thing you can do is get her off to the butcher. She has no power in her hind legs. She'll never get up again.'

That was when Mr Handshaw really blew his top and started a lengthy speech. He wasn't really unpleasant or abusive but firmly pointed out my shortcomings and bemoaned again the tragic fact that his dad was not there to put everything right. The other farmers stood in a wide-eyed ring, enjoying every word.

At the end of it I took myself off. There was nothing more I could do and anyway Mr Handshaw would have to come round to my way of thinking. Time would prove me right.

I thought of that cow as soon as I awoke next morning. It hadn't been a happy episode but at least I did feel a certain peace in the knowledge that there were no more doubts. I knew what was wrong, I knew that there was no hope. There was nothing more to worry about.

I was surprised when I heard Mr Handshaw's voice on the phone so soon. I had thought it would take him two or three days to realise he was wrong.

'Is that Mr Herriot? Aye, well, good mornin' to you. I'm just ringing to tell you that me cow's up on her legs and doing fine.'

I gripped the receiver tightly with both hands.

'What? What's that you say?'

'I said me cow's up. Found her walking about byre this morning, fit as a fiddle. You'd think there'd never been owt the matter with her.' He paused for a few moments then spoke with grave deliberation like a disapproving school-master. 'And you stood there and looked at me and said she'd never get up n'more.'

'But . . . but . . .'

'Ah, you're wondering how I did it? Well, I just happened to remember another old trick of me dad's. I went round to t'butcher and got a fresh-killed sheep skin and put it on her back. Had her up in no time – you'll 'ave to come round and see her. Wonderful man was me dad.'

Blindly I made my way into the dining-room. I had to consult my boss about this. Siegfried's sleep had been broken by a 3 a.m. calving and he looked a lot older than his thirty-odd years. He listened in silence as he finished his breakfast then pushed away his plate and poured a last cup of coffee. 'Hard luck, James. The old sheep skin, eh? Funny thing – you've been in the Dales over a year now and never come across that one. Suppose it must be going out of fashion a bit now but you know it has a grain of sense behind it like a lot of these old remedies. You can imagine there's a lot of heat generated under a fresh sheep skin and it acts like a great hot poultice on the back – really tickles them up after a while, and if a cow is lying there out of sheer cussedness she'll often get up just to get rid of it.'

'But damn it, how about the broken pelvis? I tell you it was creaking and wobbling all over the place!'

'Well, James, you're not the first to have been caught that way. Sometimes the pelvic ligaments don't tighten up for a few days after calving and you get this effect.'

'Oh God,' I moaned, staring down at the table cloth. 'What a bloody mess I've made of the whole thing.'

'Oh, you haven't really.' Siegfried lit a cigarette and leaned back in his chair. 'That old cow was probably toying with the idea of getting up for a walk just when old Handshaw dumped the skin on her back. She could just as easily have done it after one of your injections and then you'd have got the credit. Don't you remember what I told you when you first came here? There's a very fine dividing line between looking a real smart vet on the one hand and an immortal fool on the other. This sort of thing happens to us all, so forget it, James.'

But forgetting wasn't so easy. That cow became a celebrity in the district. Mr Handshaw showed her with pride to the postman, the policeman, corn merchants, lorry drivers, fertiliser salesmen, Ministry of Agriculture officials and they all told me about it frequently with pleased smiles. Mr Handshaw's speech was always the same, delivered, they said, in ringing, triumphant tones:

'There's the cow that Mr Herriot said would never get up n'more!'

I'm sure there was no malice behind the farmer's actions. He had put one over on the young clever-pants vet and nobody could blame him for preening himself a little. And in a way I did that cow a good turn; I considerably extended her life span, because Mr Handshaw kept her long beyond her normal working period just as an exhibit. Years after she had stopped giving more than a couple of gallons of milk a day she was still grazing happily in the field by the roadside.

She had one curiously upturned horn and was easy to recognise. I often pulled up my car and looked wistfully over the wall at the cow that would never get up n'more.

Chapter Two

Siegfried came away from the telephone; his face was expressionless. 'That was Mrs Pumphrey. She wants you to see her pig.'

'Peke, you mean,' I said.

'No, pig. She has a six-week-old pig she wants you to examine for soundness.'

I laughed sheepishly. My relations with the elderly widow's Peke was a touchy subject. 'All right, all right, don't start again. What did she really want? Is Tricki Woo's bottom playing him up again?'

'James,' said Siegfried gravely. 'It is unlike you to doubt my word in this way. I will repeat the message from Mrs Pumphrey and then I shall expect you to act upon it immediately and without further question. The lady informed me that she has become the owner of a six-week-old piglet and she wants the animal thoroughly vetted. You know how I feel about these examinations and I don't want the job scamped in any way. I should pay particular attention to its wind

– have it well galloped round a paddock before you get your stethoscope on it and for heaven's sake don't miss anything obvious like curbs or ringbones. I think I'd take its height while you're about it; you'll find the measuring stick in . . .'

His words trailed on as I hurried down the passage. This was a bit baffling; I usually had a bit of leg-pulling to stand ever since I became Tricki the Peke's adopted uncle and received regular presents and letters and signed photographs from him, but Siegfried wasn't in the habit of flogging the joke to this extent. The idea of Mrs Pumphrey with a pig was unthinkable; there was no room in her elegant establishment for livestock. Oh, he must have got it wrong somehow.

But he hadn't. Mrs Pumphrey received me with a joyful cry. 'Oh, Mr Herriot, isn't it wonderful! I have the most darling little pig. I was visiting some cousins who are farmers and I picked him out. He will be such company for Tricki – you know how I worry about his being an only dog.'

I shook my head vigorously in bewilderment as I crossed the oak-panelled hall. My visits here were usually associated with a degree of fantasy but I was beginning to feel out of my depth.

'You mean you actually have this pig in the house?'

'But of course.' Mrs Pumphrey looked surprised. 'He's in the kitchen. Come and see him.'

I had been in this kitchen a few times and had been almost awestruck by its shining spotlessness; the laboratory look of the tiled walls and floors, the gleaming surfaces of sink unit, cooker, refrigerator. Today, a cardboard box occupied one corner and inside I could see a tiny pig; standing on his hind legs, his forefeet resting on the rim, he was looking round him appreciatively at his new surroundings.

The elderly cook had her back to us and did not look round when we entered; she was chopping carrots and hurling them into a saucepan with, I thought, unnecessary vigour.

'Isn't he adorable!' Mrs Pumphrey bent over and tickled the little head. 'It's so exciting having a pig of my very own! Mr Herriot, I have decided to call him Nugent.'

I swallowed. 'Nugent?' The cook's broad back froze into immobility.

'Yes, after my great uncle Nugent. He was a little pink man with tiny eyes and a snub nose. The resemblance is striking.'

'I see,' I said, and the cook started her splashing again.

For a few moments I was at a loss; the ethical professional man in me rebelled at the absurdity of examining this obviously healthy little creature. In fact I was on the point of saying that he looked perfectly all right to me when Mrs Pumphrey spoke.

'Come now, Nugent,' she said, 'You must be a good boy and let your Uncle Herriot look at you.'

That did it. Stifling my finer feelings I seized the string-like tail and held Nugent almost upside down as I took his temperature. I then solemnly auscultated his heart and lungs, peered into his eyes, ran my fingers over his limbs and flexed his joints.

The cook's back radiated stiff disapproval but I carried on doggedly. Having a canine nephew, I had found, carried incalculable advantages; it wasn't only the frequent gifts – and I could still taste the glorious kippers Tricki had posted to me from Whitby – it was the vein of softness in my rough life, the sherry before lunch, the warmth and luxury of Mrs Pumphrey's fireside. The way I saw it, if a piggy nephew of the same type had been thrown in my path then Uncle Herriot was going to be the last man to interfere with the inscrutable workings of fate.

The examination over, I turned to Mrs Pumphrey who was anxiously awaiting the verdict. 'Sound in all respects,' I said briskly. 'In fact you've got a very fine pig there. But there's just one thing – he can't live in the house.'

For the first time the cook turned towards me and I read a mute appeal in her face. I could sympathise with her because the excretions of the pig are peculiarly volatile and even such a minute specimen as Nugent had already added his own faint pungency to the atmosphere in the kitchen.

Mrs Pumphrey was appalled at the idea at first but when I assured her that he wouldn't catch pneumonia and in fact would be happier and healthier outside, she gave way.

An agricultural joiner was employed to build a palatial sty in a corner of the garden; it had a warm sleeping apartment on raised boards and an outside run. I saw Nugent installed in it, curled up blissfully in a bed of clean straw. His trough was filled twice daily with the best meal and he was never short of an extra titbit such as a juicy carrot or some cabbage leaves. Every day he was allowed out to play and spent a boisterous hour frisking round the garden with Tricki.

In short, Nugent had it made, but it couldn't have happened to a nicer pig; because, though most of his species have an unsuspected strain of friendliness, this was developed in Nugent to an extraordinary degree. He just liked people and over the next few months his character flowered under the constant personal contact with humans.

I often saw him strolling companionably in the garden with Mrs Pumphrey and in his pen he spent much of the time standing upright with his cloven feet against the wire netting, waiting eagerly for his next visitor. Pigs grow quickly and he soon left the pink baby stage behind, but his charm was undiminished. His chief delight was to have his back scratched; he would grunt deeply, screwing up his eyes in ecstasy, then gradually his legs would start to buckle until finally he toppled over on his side.

Nugent's existence was sunny and there was only one cloud in the sky; old Hodgkin, the gardener, whose attitude to domestic pets had been permanently soured by having to throw rubber rings for Tricki every day, now found himself appointed personal valet to a pig. It was his duty to feed and bed down Nugent and to supervise his play periods. The idea of doing all this for a pig who was never ever going to be converted into pork pies must have been nearly insupportable for the old countryman; the harsh lines on his face deepened whenever he took hold of the meal bucket.

On the first of my professional visits to his charge he greeted me gloomily with 'Hasta come to see Nudist?' I knew Hodgkin well enough to realise the impossibility of any whimsical word-play; it was a genuine attempt to grasp the name and throughout my nephew's long career he remained 'Nudist' to the old man.

There is one memory of Nugent which I treasure. The telephone rang one day just after lunch; it was Mrs Pumphrey and I knew by the stricken voice that something momentous had happened; it was the same voice which had described Tricki Woo's unique symptoms of flop-bott and crackerdog.

'Oh, Mr Herriot, thank heavens you are in. It's Nugent! I'm afraid he's terribly ill.'

'Really? I'm sorry to hear that. What's he doing?'

There was a silence at the other end except for gasping breathing then Mrs Pumphrey spoke again. 'Well, he can't manage . . . he can't do . . . do his little jobs.'

I was familiar with her vocabulary of big jobs and little jobs. 'You mean he can't pass his urine?'

'Well . . . well . . .' she was obviously confused. 'Not properly.'

'That's strange,' I said. 'Is he eating all right?'

'I think so, but . . .' then she suddenly blurted out: 'Oh, Mr Herriot, I'm so terribly worried! I've heard of men being dreadfully ill . . . just like this. It's a gland, isn't it?'

'Oh, you needn't worry about that. Pigs don't have that trouble and anyway, I think four months is a bit young for hypertrophy of the prostate.'

'Oh, I'm so glad, but something is . . . stopping it. You will come, won't you!'

'I'm leaving now.'

I had quite a long wait outside Nugent's pen. He had grown into a chunky little porker and grunted amiably as he surveyed me through the netting. Clearly he expected some sort of game and, growing impatient, he performed a few stiff-legged little gallops up and down the run.

I had almost decided that my visit was fruitless when Mrs Pumphrey, who had been pacing up and down, wringing her hands, stopped dead and pointed a shaking finger at the pig.

'Oh God,' she breathed. 'There! There! There it is now!' All the colour had drained from her face leaving her deathly pale. 'Oh, it's awful! I can't look any longer.' With a moan she turned away and buried her face in her hands.

I scrutinised Nugent closely. He had halted in mid gallop and was contentedly relieving himself by means of the intermittent spurting jets of the normal male pig.

I turned to Mrs Pumphrey. 'I really can't see anything wrong there.'

'But he's . . . he's . . .' she still didn't dare to look. 'He's doing it in . . . in fits and starts!'

I had had considerable practice at keeping a straight face in Mrs Pumphrey's presence and it stood me in good stead now.

'But they all do it that way, Mrs Pumphrey.'

She half turned and looked tremblingly out of the corner of her eye at Nugent. 'You mean . . . all boy pigs . . .?'

'Every single boy pig I have ever known has done it like that.'

'Oh . . . Oh . . . how odd, how very odd.' The poor lady fanned herself with her handkerchief. Her colour had come back in a positive flood.

To cover her confusion I became very business-like. 'Yes, yes indeed. Lots of people make the same mistake, I assure you. Ah well, I suppose I'd better be on my way now – it's been nice to see the little fellow looking so well and happy.'

Nugent enjoyed a long and happy life and more than fulfilled my expectations of him; he was every bit as generous as Tricki with his presents and, as with the little Peke, I was able to salve my conscience with the knowledge that I was really fond of him. As always, Siegfried's sardonic attitude made things a little uncomfortable; I had suffered in the past when I got the signed photographs from the little dog – but I never dared let him see the one from the pig.

Chapter Three

Angus Grier MRCVS was never pretty to look at, but the sight of him propped up in bed, his mottled, pop-eyed face scowling above a pink quilted bed jacket was enough to daunt the bravest. Especially at eight in the morning when I usually had the first of my daily audiences with him.

'You're late again,' he said, his voice grating. 'Can ye no' get out of your bed in the morning? I've told you till I'm tired that I want ye out on the road by eight o'clock.'

As I mumbled apologies he tugged fretfully at the counterpane and looked me up and down with deepening distaste. 'And another thing, that's a terrible pair o' breeches you're wearing. If you must wear breeches to your work, for heaven's sake go and get a pair made at a proper tailor. There's nae cut about those things at all – they're not fit to be worn by a veterinary surgeon.'

The knife really went in then. I was attached to those breeches. I had paid thirty shillings for them at the Army and Navy Stores and cherished a private conviction that they gave me a certain air. And Grier's attack on them was all the more wounding when I considered that the man was almost certainly getting my services free; Siegfried, I felt sure, would wave aside any offers of payment.

I had been here a week and it seemed like a lifetime. Somewhere, far back, I knew, there had been a brighter, happier existence but the memory was growing dim. Siegfried had been sincerely apologetic that morning back in Darrowby.

'James, I have a letter here from Grier of Brawton. It seems he was castrating a colt and the thing threw itself on top of him; he has a couple of cracked ribs. Apparently his assistant walked out on him recently, so there's nobody to run his practice. He wants me to send you along there for a week or two.'

'Oh no! There's a mistake somewhere. He doesn't like me.'

'He doesn't like anybody. But there's no mistake, it's down here – and honestly, what can I do?'

'But the only time I met him he worked me into a horrible rubber suit and made me look a right chump.'

Siegfried smiled sadly. 'I remember, James, I remember. He's a mean old devil and I hate to do this to you, but I can't turn him down, can I?'

At the time I couldn't believe it. The whole idea was unreal. But it was real enough now as I stood at the foot of Grier's bed listening to him ranting away. He was at me again.

'Another thing – my wife tells me you didna eat your porridge. Did you not like it?'

I shuffled my feet. 'Oh yes, it was very nice. I just didn't feel hungry this morning.' I had pushed the tasteless mass about with my spoon and done my best with it but it had defeated me in the end.

'There's something wrong with a man that canna eat his good food.' Grier peered at me suspiciously then held out a slip of paper. 'Here's a list of your visits for this morning. There's a good few so you'll no' have to waste your time getting round. This one here of Adamson's of Grenton – a prolapse of the cervix in a cow. What would you do about that, think ye?'

I put my hand in my pocket, got hold of my pipe then dropped it back again. Grier didn't like smoking.

'Well, I'd give her an epidural anaesthetic, replace the prolapse and fasten it with retention sutures through the vulva.'

'Havers, man, havers!' snorted Grier. 'What a lot of twaddle. There's no need for a' that. It'll just be constipation that's doing it. Push the thing back, build the cow up with some boards under her hind feet and put her on to linseed oil for a few days.'

'Surely it'll come out again if I don't stitch it in?' I said.

'Na, na, na, not at all,' Grier cried angrily. 'Just you do as I tell you now. I ken more about this than you.'

He probably did. He should, anyway – he had been qualified for thirty years and I was starting my second. I looked at him glowering from his pillow and pondered for a moment on the strange fact of our uncomfortable relationship. A Yorkshireman listening to the two outlandish accents – Grier's rasping Aberdeen, my glottal Clydeside – might have expected that some sort of rapport would exist between us, if only on national grounds. But there was none.

'Right, just as you say.' I left the room and went downstairs to gather up my equipment.

As I set off on the round I had the same feeling as every morning – relief at getting out of the house. I had had to go flat out all week to get through the work but I had enjoyed it. Farmers are nearly always prepared to make allowances for a young man's inexperience and Grier's clients had treated me kindly, but I still had to come back to that joyless establishment for meals and it was becoming more and more wearing.

Mrs Grier bothered me just as much as her husband. She was a tight-lipped woman of amazing thinness and she kept a spartan board in which soggy porridge figured prominently. It was porridge for breakfast, porridge for supper and, in between, a miserable procession of watery stews, anaemic mince and nameless soups. Nothing she cooked ever tasted of anything. Angus Grier had come to Yorkshire thirty years ago, a penniless Scot just like myself, and acquired a lucrative practice by the classical expedient of marrying the boss's daughter; so he got a good living handed to him on a plate, but he also got Mrs Grier.

It seemed to me that she felt she was still in charge – probably because she had always lived in this house with its memories of her father who had built up the practice. Other people would seem like interlopers and I could understand how she felt; after all, she was childless, she didn't have much of a life and she had Angus Grier for a husband. I could feel sorry for her.

But that didn't help because I just couldn't get her out of my hair; she hung over my every move like a disapproving spectre. When I came back from a round she was always there with a barrage of questions. 'Where have you been all this time?' or 'I wondered wherever you'd got to, were you lost?' or 'There's an urgent case waiting. Why are you always so slow?' Maybe she thought I'd nipped into a cinema for an hour or two.

There was a pretty full small animal surgery every night and she had a nasty habit of lurking just outside the door so that she could listen to what I was saying to the clients. She really came into her own in the dispensary where she watched me narrowly, criticising my prescriptions and constantly pulling me up for being extravagant with the drugs. 'You're putting in far too much chlorodyne – don't you know it's very expensive?'

I developed a deep sympathy for the assistant who had fled without warning; jobs were hard to come by and young graduates would stand nearly anything just to be at work, but I realised that there had been no other choice for that shadowy figure.

Adamson's place was a small-holding on the edge of the town and maybe it was because I had just been looking at Grier but by contrast the farmer's lined, patient face and friendly eyes seemed extraordinarily warming and attractive. A ragged khaki smock hung loosely on his gaunt frame as he shook hands with me.

'Now then, we've got a new man today, have we?' He looked me over for a second or two. 'And by the look of you you're pretty fresh to t'job.'

'That's right,' I replied. 'But I'm learning fast.'

Mr Adamson smiled. 'Don't worry about that, lad. I believe in new blood and new ideas – it's what we want in farming. We've stood still too long at this game. Come into t'byre and I'll show you the cow.'

There were about a dozen cows, not the usual Shorthorns but Ayrshires, and they were obviously well kept and healthy. My patient was easy to pick out by the football-sized rose-pink protrusion of the vaginal wall and the corrugated uterine cervix. But the farmer had wasted no time in calling for assistance; the mass was clean and undamaged.

He watched me attentively as I swabbed the prolapse with antiseptic and pushed it back out of sight, then he helped me build a platform with soil and planks for the cow's hind feet. When we had finished she was standing on a slope with her tail higher than her head.

'And you say that if I give her linseed oil for a few days that thing won't come out again?'

'That's the idea,' I said. 'Be sure to keep her built up like this.'

'I will, young man, and thank you very much. I'm sure you've done a good job for me and I'll look forward to seeing you again.'

Back in the car, I groaned to myself. Good job! How the hell could that thing stay in without stitches? But I had to do as I was told and Grier, even if he was unpleasant, wasn't a complete fool. Maybe he was right. I put it out of my mind and got on with the other visits.

It was less than a week later at the breakfast table and I was prodding at the inevitable porridge when Grier, who had ventured downstairs, barked suddenly at me.

'I've got a card here frae Adamson. He says he's not satisfied with your work. We'd better get out there this morning and see what's wrong. I dinna like these complaints.' His normal expression of being perpetually offended deepened and the big pale eyes swam and brimmed till I was sure he was going to weep into his porridge.

At the farm, Mr Adamson led us into the byre. 'Well, what do you think of that, young man?'

I looked at the prolapse and my stomach lurched. The innocuous-looking pink projection had been transformed into a great bloated purple mass. It was caked with filth and an ugly wound ran down one side of it.

'It didn't stay in very long, did it?' the farmer said quietly.

I was too ashamed to speak. This was a dreadful thing to do to a good cow. I felt my face reddening, but luckily I had my employer with me; he would be able to explain everything. I turned towards Grier who snuffled, mumbled, blinked his eyes rapidly but didn't say anything.

The farmer went on. 'And you see she's damaged it. Must have caught it on something. I'll tell you I don't like the look of it.'

It was against this decent man's nature to be unpleasant, but he was upset all right. 'Maybe it would be better if you would take the job on this time, Mr Grier,' he said.

Grier, who still had not uttered an intelligible word, now sprang into action. He clipped the hair over the base of the spine, inserted an epidural anaesthetic, washed and disinfected the mass and, with an effort, pushed it back to its place. Then he fastened it in with several strong retention sutures with little one-inch lengths of rubber tubing to stop them cutting into the flesh. The finished job looked neat and workmanlike.

The farmer took me gently by the shoulder. 'Now that's something like. You can see it's not going to come out again now, can't you? Why didn't you do something like that when you came before?'

I turned again to Grier, but this time he was seized by a violent fit of coughing. I continued to stare at him but when he still said nothing I turned and walked out of the byre.

'No hard feelings, though, young man,' Mr Adamson called after me. 'I reckon we've all got to learn and there's no substitute for experience. That's so, Mr Grier, isn't it?'

'Aye, och aye, that's right enough. Aye, aye, rightly so, rightly so, there's no doubt aboot that,' Grier mumbled. We got into the car.

I settled down and waited for some explanation from him. I was interested to know just what he would say. But the blue-veined nose pointed straight ahead and the bulging eyes fixed themselves blankly on the road ahead of us.

We drove back to the surgery in silence.

Chapter Four

It wasn't long before Grier had to return to bed; he began to groan a lot and hold his injured ribs and soon he was reinstalled upstairs with the pillows at his back and the little pink jacket buttoned to the neck. Whisky was the only thing that gave him relief from his pain and the level of his bedside bottle went down with remarkable speed.

Life resumed its dreary pattern. Mrs Grier was usually around when I had to report to her husband; beyond the bedroom door there would be a lot of whispering which stopped as soon as I entered. I would receive my instructions while Mrs Grier fussed round the bed tucking things in, patting her husband's brow with a folded handkerchief and all the time darting little glances of dislike at me. Immediately I got outside the door the whispering started again.

It was quite late one evening – about ten o'clock –when the call from Mrs Mallard came in. Her dog had a bone in its throat and would Mr Grier come at once. I was starting to say that he was ill and I was doing his work but it was too late; there was a click as the receiver went down at the other end.

Grier reacted to the news by going into a sort of trance; his chin sank on his chest and he sat immobile for nearly a minute while he gave the matter careful thought. Then he straightened up suddenly and stabbed a finger at me.

'It'll not be a bone in its throat. It'll only be a touch of pharyngitis making it cough.'

I was surprised at his confidence. 'Don't you think I'd better take some long forceps just in case?'

'Na, na, I've told ye now. There'll be no bone, so go down and put up some of the syrup of squills and ipecacuanha mixture. That's all it'll want. And another thing – if ye can't find anything wrong don't say so. Tell the lady it's pharyngitis and how to treat it – you have to justify your visit, ye ken.'

I felt a little bewildered as I filled a four ounce bottle in the dispensary, but I took a few pairs of forceps with me too; I had lost a bit of faith in Grier's long-range diagnosis.

I was surprised when Mrs Mallard opened the door of the smart semi-detached house. For some reason I had been expecting an old lady, and here was a striking-looking blonde woman of about forty with her hair piled high in glamorous layers as was the fashion at that time. And I hadn't expected the long ballroom dress in shimmering green, the enormous swaying earrings, the heavily made up face.

Mrs Mallard seemed surprised too. She stared blankly at me till I explained the position. 'I've come to see your dog – I'm Mr Grier's locum. He's ill at the moment, I'm afraid.'

It took a fair time for the information to get through because she still stood on the doorstep as if she didn't know what I was talking about; then she came to life and opened the door wide. 'Oh yes, of course, I'm sorry, do come in.' I walked past her through an almost palpable wall of perfume and into a room on the left of the hall. The perfume was even stronger in here but it was in keeping with the single, pink-tinted lamp which shed a dim but rosy light on the wide divan drawn close to the flickering fire. Somewhere in the shadows a radiogram was softly pouring out 'Body and Soul'.

There was no sign of my patient and Mrs Mallard looked at me irresolutely, fingering one of her earrings.

'Do you want me to see him in here?' I asked.

'Oh yes, certainly.' She became brisk and opened a door at the end of the room. Immediately a little West Highland Terrier bounded across the carpet and hurled himself at me with a woof of delight. He tried his best to lick my face by a series of mighty springs and this might have gone on for quite a long time had I not caught him in mid air.

Mrs Mallard smiled nervously. 'He seems a lot better now,' she said.

I flopped down on the divan still with the little dog in my arms and prised open his jaws. Even in that dim light it was obvious that there was nothing in his throat. I gently slid my forefinger over the back of his tongue and the terrier made no protest as I explored his gullet. Then I dropped him down on the carpet and took his temperature – normal.

'Well, Mrs Mallard,' I said, 'there is certainly no bone in his throat and he has no fever.' I was about to add that the dog seemed perfectly fit to me when I remembered Grier's parting admonition – I had to justify my visit.

I cleared my throat. 'It's just possible, though, that he has a little pharyngitis which has been making him cough or retch.' I opened the terrier's mouth again. 'As you see, the back of his throat is rather inflamed. He may have got a mild infection in there or perhaps swallowed some irritant. I have some medicine in the car which will soon put him right.' Realising I was beginning to gabble, I brought my speech to a close.

Mrs Mallard hung on every word, peering anxiously into the little dog's mouth and nodding her head rapidly. 'Oh yes, I do see,' she said. 'Thank you so much. What a good thing I sent for you!'

On the following evening I was half way through a busy surgery when a fat man in a particularly vivid tweed jacket bustled in and deposited a sad-eyed Basset Hound on the table.

'Shaking his head about a bit,' he boomed. 'Think he must have a touch of canker.'

I got an auroscope from the instrument cupboard and had begun to examine the ear when the fat man started again.

'I see you were out our way last night. I live next door to Mrs Mallard.'

'Oh yes,' I said peering down the lighted metal tube. 'That's right, I was.'

The man drummed his fingers on the table for a moment. 'Aye, that dog must have a lot of ailments. The vet's car seems always to be outside the house.'

'Really, I shouldn't have thought so. Seemed a healthy little thing to me.' I finished examining one ear and started on the other.

'Well, it's just as I say,' said the man. 'The poor creature's always in trouble, and it's funny how often it happens at night.'

I looked up quickly. There was something odd in the way he said that. He looked at me for a moment with a kind wide-eyed innocence, then his whole face creased into a knowing leer.

I stared at him. 'You can't mean . . .'

'Not with that ugly old devil, you mean, eh? Takes a bit of reckoning up, doesn't it?' The eyes in the big red face twinkled with amusement.

I dropped the auroscope on the table with a clatter and my arms fell by my sides.

'Don't look like that, lad!' shouted the fat man, giving me a playful punch in the chest. 'It's a rum old world, you know!'

But it wasn't just the thought of Grier that was filling me with horror; it was the picture of myself in that harem atmosphere pontificating about pharyngitis against a background of 'Body and Soul' to a woman who knew I was talking rubbish.

In another two days Angus Grier was out of bed and apparently recovered; also, a replacement assistant had been engaged and was due to take up his post immediately. I was free to go.

Having said I would leave first thing in the morning I was out of the house by 6.30 a.m. in order to make Darrowby by breakfast. I wasn't going to face any more of that porridge.

As I drove west across the Plain of York I began to catch glimpses over the hedge tops and between the trees of the long spine of the Pennines lifting into the morning sky; they were pale violet at this distance and still hazy in the early sunshine but they beckoned to me. And later, when the little car pulled harder against the rising ground and the trees became fewer and the hedges gave way to the clean limestone walls I had the feeling I always had of the world opening out, of shackles falling away. And there, at last, was Darrowby sleeping under the familiar bulk of Herne Fell and beyond, the great green folds of the Dales.

Nothing stirred as I rattled across the cobbled market place then down the quiet street to Skeldale House with the ivy hanging in untidy profusion from its old bricks and 'Siegfried Farnon MRCVS' on the lopsided brass plate.

I think I would have galloped along the passage beyond the glass door but I had to fight my way through the family dogs, all five of them, who surged around me, leaping and barking in delight.

I almost collided with the formidable bulk of Mrs Hall who was carrying the coffee-pot out of the dining-room. 'You're back then,' she said and I could see she was really pleased because she almost smiled. 'Well, go in and get sat down. I've got a bit of home-cured in the pan for you.'

My hand was on the door when I heard the brothers' voices inside. Tristan was mumbling something and Siegfried was in full cry. 'Where the hell were you last night, anyway? I heard you banging about at three o'clock in the morning and your room stinks like a brewery. God, I wish you could see yourself – eyes like piss-holes in the snow!'

Smiling to myself, I pushed open the door, I went over to Tristan who stared up in surprise as I seized his hand and began to pump it; he looked as boyishly innocent as ever except for the eyes which, though a little sunken, still held their old gleam. Then I approached Siegfried at the head of the table. Obviously startled at my formal entry, he had choked in mid-chew; he reddened, tears coursed down his thin cheeks and the small sandy moustache quivered. Nevertheless, he rose from his chair, inclined his head and extended his hand with the grace of a marquis.

'Welcome, James,' he spluttered, spraying me lightly with toast crumbs. 'Welcome home.'

Chapter Five

I had been away for only two weeks but it was enough to bring it home to me afresh that working in the high country had something for me that was missing elsewhere. My first visit took me up on one of the narrow, unfenced roads which join Sildale and Cosdale and when I had ground my way to the top in bottom gear I did what I so often did – pulled the car on to the roadside turf and got out.

That quotation about not having time to stand and stare has never applied to me. I seem to have spent a good part of my life – probably too much – in just standing and staring and I was at it again this morning. From up here you could see away over the Plain of York to the sprawl of the Hambleton Hills forty miles to the east, while behind me, the ragged miles of moorland rolled away, dipping and rising over the flat fell-top. In my year at Darrowby I must have stood here scores of times and the view across the plain always looked different; sometimes in the winter the low country was a dark trough between the snow-covered Pennines and the distant white gleam of the Hambletons, and in April the rain squalls drifted in slow, heavy veils across the great green and brown dappled expanse. There was a day, too, when I stood in brilliant sunshine looking down over miles of thick fog like a rippling layer of cotton wool with dark tufts of trees and hilltops pushing through here and there.

But today the endless patchwork of fields slumbered in the sun, and the air, even on the hill, was heavy with the scents of summer. There must be people working among the farms down there, I knew, but I couldn't see a living soul; and the peace which I always found in the silence and the emptiness of the moors filled me utterly.

At these times I often seemed to stand outside myself, calmly assessing my progress. It was easy to flick back over the years – right back to the time I had decided to become a veterinary surgeon. I could remember the very moment. I was thirteen and I was reading an article about careers for boys in the Meccano Magazine and as I read, I felt a surging conviction that this was for me. And yet what was it based upon? Only that I liked dogs and cats and didn't care much for the idea of an office life; it seemed a frail basis on which to build a career. I knew nothing about agriculture or about farm animals and though, during the years in college, I learned about these things I could see only one future for myself; I was going to be a small animal surgeon. This lasted right up to the time I qualified – a kind of vision of treating people's pets in my own animal hospital where everything would be not just modern but revolutionary. The fully equipped operating theatre, laboratory and X-ray room; they had all stayed crystal clear in my mind until I had graduated MRCVS.

How on earth, then, did I come to be sitting on a high Yorkshire moor in shirt sleeves and wellingtons, smelling vaguely of cows?

The change in my outlook had come quite quickly – in fact almost immediately after my arrival in Darrowby. The job had been a godsend in those days of high unemployment, but only, I had thought, a stepping-stone to my real ambition. But everything had switched round, almost in a flash.

Maybe it was something to do with the incredible sweetness of the air which still took me by surprise when I stepped out into the old wild garden at Skeldale House every morning. Or perhaps the daily piquancy of life in the graceful old house with my gifted but mercurial boss, Siegfried, and his reluctant student brother, Tristan. Or it could be that it was just the realisation that treating cows and pigs and sheep and horses had a fascination I had never even suspected; and this brought with it a new concept of myself as a tiny wheel in the great machine of British agriculture. There was a kind of solid satisfaction in that.

Probably it was because I hadn't dreamed there was a place like the Dales. I hadn't thought it possible that I could spend all my days in a high, clean-blown land where the scent of grass or trees was never far away; and where even in the driving rain of winter I could snuff the air and find the freshness of growing things hidden somewhere in the cold clasp of the wind.

Anyway, it had all changed for me and my work consisted now of driving from farm to farm across the roof of England with a growing conviction that I was a privileged person.

I got back into the car and looked at my list of visits; it was good to be back and the day passed quickly. It was about seven o'clock in the evening, when I thought I had finished, that I had a call from Terry Watson, a young farm worker who kept two cows of his own. One of them, he said, had summer mastitis. Mid-July was a bit early for this but in the later summer months we saw literally hundreds of these cases; in fact a lot of the farmers called it 'August Bag'. It was an unpleasant condition because it was just about incurable and usually resulted in the cow losing a quarter (the area of the udder which supplies each teat with milk) and sometimes even her life.

Terry Watson's cow looked very sick. She had limped in from the field at milking time, swinging her right hind leg wide to keep it away from the painful udder, and now she stood trembling in her stall, her eyes staring anxiously in front of her. I drew gently at the affected teat and, instead of milk, a stream of dark, foul-smelling serum spurted into the tin can I was holding.

'No mistaking that stink, Terry,' I said. 'It's the real summer type all right.' I felt my way over the hot, swollen quarter and the cow lifted her leg quickly as I touched the tender tissue. 'Pretty hard, too. It looks bad, I'm afraid.'

Terry's face was grim as he ran his hand along the cow's back. He was in his early twenties, had a wife and a small baby and was one of the breed who was prepared to labour all day for somebody else and then come home and start work on his own few stock. His two cows, his few pigs and hens made a big difference to somebody who had to live on thirty shillings a week.

'Ah can't understand it,' he muttered. 'It's usually dry cows that get it and this 'uns still giving two gallons a day. I'd have been on with tar if only she'd been dry.' (The farmers used to dab the teats of the dry cows with Stockholm tar to keep off the flies which were blamed for carrying the infection.)

'No, I'm afraid all cows can get it, especially the ones that are beginning to dry off.' I pulled the thermometer from the rectum – it said a hundred and six.

'What's going to happen, then? Can you do owt for her?'

'I'll do what I can, Terry. I'll give her an injection and you must strip the teat out as often as you can, but you know as well as I do that it's a poor outlook with these jobs.'

'Aye, ah know all about it.' He watched me gloomily as I injected the Coryne pyogenes toxoid into the cow's neck. (Even now we are still doing this for summer mastitis because it is a sad fact none of the modern range of antibiotics has much effect on it.) 'She'll lose her quarter, won't she, and maybe she'll even peg out?'

I tried to be cheerful. 'Well, I don't think she'll die, and even if the quarter goes she'll make it up on the other three.' But there was the feeling of helplessness I always had when I could do little about something which mattered a great deal. Because I knew what a blow this was to the young man; a three-teated cow has lost a lot of her market value and this was about the best outcome I could see. I didn't like to think about the possibility of the animal dying.

'Look, is there nowt at all I can do myself? Is the job a bad 'un do you think?' Terry Watson's thin cheeks were pale and as I looked at the slender figure with the slightly stooping shoulders I thought, not for the first time, that he didn't look robust enough for his hard trade.

'I can't guarantee anything,' I said. 'But the cases that do best are the ones that get the most stripping. So work away at it this evening – every half hour if you can manage it. That rubbish in her quarter can't do any harm if you draw it out as soon as it is formed. And I think you ought to bathe the udder with warm water and massage it well.'

'What'll I rub it with?'

'Oh, it doesn't matter what you use. The main thing is to move the tissue about so that you can get more of that stinking stuff out. Vaseline would do nicely.'

'Ah've got a bowl of goose grease.'

'O.K. use that.' I reflected that there must be a bowl of goose grease on most farms; it was the all-purpose lubricant and liniment for man and beast.

Terry seemed relieved at the opportunity to do something. He fished out an old bucket, tucked the milking stool between his legs and crouched down against the cow. He looked up at me with a strangely defiant expression. 'Right,' he said. 'I'm startin' now.'

As it happened, I was called out early the next morning to a milk fever and on the way home I decided to look in at the Watsons' cottage. It was about eight o'clock and when I entered the little two-stalled shed, Terry was in the same position as I had left him on the previous night. He was pulling at the infected teat, eyes closed, cheek resting against the cow's flank. He started as though roused from sleep when I spoke.

'Hello, you're having another go, I see.'

The cow looked round, too, at my words and I saw immediately, with a thrill of pleasure that she was immeasurably improved. She had lost her blank stare and was looking at me with the casual interest of the healthy bovine and best of all, her jaws were moving with that slow, regular, lateral grind that every vet loves to see.

'My God, Terry, she looks a lot better. She isn't like the same cow!'

The young man seemed to have difficulty in keeping his eyes open but he smiled. 'Aye, and come and have a look at this end.' He rose slowly from the stool, straightened his back a little bit at a time and leaned his elbow on the cow's rump.

I bent down by the udder, feeling carefully for the painful swelling of last night, but my hand came up against a smooth, yielding surface and, in disbelief,

I kneaded the tissue between my fingers. The animal showed no sign of discomfort. With a feeling of bewilderment I drew on the teat with thumb and forefinger; the quarter was nearly empty but I did manage to squeeze a single jet of pure white milk on to my palm.

'What's going on here, Terry? You must have switched cows on me. You're having me on, aren't you?'

'Nay, guvnor,' the young man said with his slow smile. 'It's same cow all right – she's better, that's all.'

'But it's impossible! What the devil have you done to her?'

'Just what you told me to do. Rub and strip.'

I scratched my head. 'But she's back to normal. I've never seen anything like it.'

'Aye, I know you haven't.' It was a woman's voice and I turned and saw young Mrs Watson standing at the door holding her baby. 'You've never seen a man that would rub and strip a cow right round the clock, have you?'

'Round the clock?' I said.

She looked at her husband with a mixture of concern and exasperation. 'Yes, he's been there on that stool since you left last night. Never been to bed, never been in for a meal. I've been bringing him bits and pieces and cups of tea. Great fool – it's enough to kill anybody.'

I looked at Terry and my eyes moved from the pallid face over the thin, slightly swaying body to the nearly empty bowl of goose grease at his feet. 'Good Lord, man,' I said. 'You've done the impossible but you must be about all in. Anyway, your cow is as good as new – you don't need to do another thing to her, so you can go in and have a bit of rest.'

'Nay, I can't do that.' He shook his head and straightened his shoulders. 'I've got me work to go to and I'm late as it is.'

Chapter Six

I couldn't help feeling just a little bit smug as I squeezed the bright red rubber ball out through the incision in the dog's stomach. We got enough small animal work in Darrowby to make a pleasant break from our normal life around the farms but not enough to make us blasé. No doubt the man with an intensive town practice looks on a gastrotomy as a fairly routine and unexciting event but as I watched the little red ball roll along the table and bounce on the surgery floor a glow of achievement filled me.

The big, lolloping Red Setter pup had been brought in that morning; his mistress said that he had been trembling, miserable and occasionally vomiting for two days – ever since their little girl's ball had mysteriously disappeared. Diagnosis had not been difficult.

I inverted the lips of the stomach wound and began to close it with a continuous suture. I was feeling pleasantly relaxed unlike Tristan who had been unable to light a Woodbine because of the ether which bubbled in the glass bottle behind him and out through the anaesthetic mask which he held over the dog's face; he stared moodily down at the patient and the fingers of his free hand drummed on the table.

But it was soon my turn to be tense because the door of the operating room burst open and Siegfried strode in. I don't know why it was but whenever Siegfried watched me do anything I started to go to pieces; great waves seemed to billow from him – impatience, frustration, criticism, irritation. I could feel the waves buffeting me now although my employer's face was expressionless; he was standing quietly at the end of the table but as the minutes passed I had the growing impression of a volcano on the bubble. The eruption came when I began to stitch the deep layer of the abdominal muscle. I was pulling a length of catgut from a glass jar when I heard a sharp intake of breath.

'God help us, James!' cried Siegfried. 'Stop pulling at that bloody gut! Do you know how much that stuff costs per foot? Well it's a good job you don't or you'd faint dead away. And that expensive dusting powder you've been chucking about – there must be about half a pound of it inside that dog right now.' He paused and breathed heavily for a few moments. 'Another thing, if you want to swab, a little bit of cotton wool is enough – you don't need a square foot at a time like you've been using. Here, give me that needle. Let me show you.'

He hastily scrubbed his hands and took over. First he took a minute pinch of the iodoform powder and sprinkled it daintily into the wound rather like an old lady feeding her goldfish, then he cut off a tiny piece of gut and inserted a continuous suture in the muscle; he had hardly left himself enough to tie the knot at the end and it was touch and go, but he just made it after a few moments of intense concentration.

This process was repeated about ten times as he closed the skin wound with interrupted silk sutures, his nose almost touching the patient as he laboriously tied off each little short end with forceps. When he had finished he was slightly pop-eyed.

'Right, turn off the ether, Tristan,' he said as he pulled off half an inch of wool and primly wiped the wound down.

He turned to me and smiled gently. With dismay I saw that his patient look was spreading over his face. 'James, please don't misunderstand me. You've made a grand job of this dog but you've got to keep one eye on the economic side of things. I know it doesn't matter a hoot to you just now but some day, no doubt, you'll have your own practice and then you'll realise some of the worries I have on my shoulders.' He patted my arm and I steeled myself as he put his head on one side and a hint of roguishness crept into his smile.

'After all, James, you'll agree it is desirable to make some sort of profit in the end.'

It was a week later and I was kneeling on the neck of a sleeping colt in the middle of a field, the sun was hot on the back of my neck as I looked down at the peacefully closed eyes, the narrow face disappearing into the canvas chloroform muzzle. I tipped a few more drops of the anaesthetic on to the sponge and screwed the cap on to the bottle. He had had about enough now.

I couldn't count the number of times Siegfried and I have enacted this scene; the horse on his grassy bed, my employer cutting away at one end while I watched the head. Siegfried was a unique combination of born horseman and dexterous surgeon with which I couldn't compete, so I had inevitably developed into an anaesthetist. We liked to do the operations in the open; it was cleaner and if the horse was wild he stood less chance of injuring himself. We just hoped for a fine morning and today we were lucky. In the early haze I looked over the countless buttercups; the field was filled with them and it was like sitting in a shimmering yellow ocean. Their pollen had powdered my shoes and the neck of the horse beneath me.

Everything had gone off more or less as it usually did. I had gone into the box with the colt, buckled on the muzzle underneath his head collar then walked him quietly out to a soft, level spot in the field. I left a man at the head holding a long shank on the head collar and poured the first half ounce of chloroform on to the sponge, watching the colt snuffling and shaking his head at the strange scent. As the man walked him slowly round I kept adding a little more chloroform till the colt began to stagger and sway; this stage always took a few minutes and I waited confidently for Siegfried's little speech which always came about now. I was not disappointed.

'He isn't going to go down, you know, James. Don't you think we should tie a foreleg up?'

I adopted my usual policy of feigning deafness and a few seconds later the colt gave a final lurch and collapsed on his side. Siegfried, released from his enforced inactivity, sprang into action. 'Sit on his head!' he yelled. 'Get a rope on that upper hind leg and pull it forward! Bring me that bucket of water over here! Come on – move!'

It was a violent transition. Just moments ago, peace and silence and now men scurrying in all directions, bumping into each other, urged on by Siegfried's cries.

Thirty years later I am still dropping horses for Siegfried and he is still saying 'He isn't going to go down, James'.

These days I mostly use an intravenous injection of Thiopentone and it puts a horse out in about ten seconds. It doesn't give Siegfried much time to say his piece but he usually gets it in somewhere between the seventh and tenth seconds.

This morning's case was an injury. But it was a pretty dramatic one, justifying general anaesthetic to repair it. The colt, bred from a fine hunter mare, had been galloping round his paddock and had felt the urge to visit the outside world. He had chosen the only sharp fence post to try to jump over and had been impaled between the forelegs; in his efforts to escape he had caused so much damage in the breast region that it looked like something from a butcher's shop with the skin extensively lacerated and the big sternal muscles hanging out, chopped through as though by a cleaver.

'Roll him on his back,' said Siegfried. 'That's better.' He took a probe from the tray which lay on the grass near by and carefully explored the wound. 'No damage to the bone,' he grunted, still peering into the depths. Then he took a pair of forceps and fished out all the loose debris he could find before turning to me.

'It's just a big stitching job. You can carry on if you like.'

As we changed places it occurred to me that he was disappointed it was not something more interesting. I couldn't see him asking me to take over in a rig operation or something like that. Then, as I picked up the needle, my mind clicked back to that gastrotomy on the dog. Maybe I was on trial for my wasteful ways. This time I would be on my guard.

I threaded the needle with a minute length of gut, took a bite at the severed muscle and, with an effort, stitched it back into place. But it was a laborious business tying the little short ends – it was taking me at least three times as long as it should. However, I stuck to it doggedly. I had been warned and I didn't want another lecture.

I had put in half a dozen sutures in this way when I began to feel the waves. My employer was kneeling close to me on the horse's neck and the foaming breakers of disapproval were crashing into me from close range. I held out for another two sutures then Siegfried exploded in a fierce whisper.

'What the hell are you playing at, James?'

'Well, just stitching. What do you mean?'

'But why are you buggering about with those little bits of gut? We'll be here all bloody day!'

I fumbled another knot into the muscle. 'For reasons of economy.' I whispered back virtuously.

Siegfried leaped from the neck as though the horse had bitten him. 'I can't stand any more of this! Here, let me have a go.'

He strode over to the tray, selected a needle and caught hold of the free end of the catgut protruding from the jar. With a scything sweep of his arm he pulled forth an enormous coil of gut, setting the bobbin inside the jar whirring wildly like a salmon reel with a big fish on the line. He returned to the horse, stumbling slightly as the gut caught round his ankles and began to stitch. It wasn't easy because even at the full stretch of his arm he was unable to pull the suture tight and had to keep getting up and down; by the time he had tacked the muscles back into their original positions he was puffing and I could see a faint dew of perspiration on his forehead.

'Drop of blood seeping from somewhere down there,' he muttered and visited the tray again where he tore savagely at a huge roll of cotton wool. Trailing untidy white streamers over the buttercups he returned and swabbed out the wound with one corner of the mass.

Back to the tray again. 'Just a touch of powder before I stitch the skin,' he said lightly and seized a two pound carton. He poised for a moment over the wound then began to dispense the powder with extravagant jerks of the wrist. A considerable amount did go into the wound but much more floated over other parts of the horse, over me, over the buttercups, and a particularly wayward flick obscured the sweating face of the man on the foot rope. When he had finished coughing he looked very like Coco the clown.

Siegfried completed the closure of the skin, using several yards of silk, and when he stood back and surveyed the tidy result I could see he was in excellent humour.

'Well now, that's fine. A young horse like that will heal in no time. Shouldn't be surprised if it doesn't even leave a mark.'

He came over and addressed me as I washed the instruments in the bucket. 'Sorry I pushed you out like that, James, but honestly I couldn't think what had come over you – you were like an old hen. You know it looks bad trying to work with piddling little amounts of materials. One has to operate with a certain ... well ... panache, if I can put it that way, and you just can't do that if you stint yourself.'

I finished washing the instruments, dried them off and laid them on the enamel tray. Then I lifted the tray and set off for the gate at the end of the field. Siegfried, walking alongside me, laid his hand on my shoulder. 'Mind you, don't think I'm blaming you, James. It's probably your Scottish upbringing. And don't misunderstand me, this same upbringing has inculcated in you so many of the qualities I admire – integrity, industry, loyalty. But I'm sure you will be the first to admit,' and here he stopped and wagged a finger at me 'that you Scots sometimes overdo the thrift.' He gave a light laugh. 'So remember, James, don't be too – er – canny when you are operating.'

I measured him up. If I dropped the tray quickly I felt sure I could fell him with a right hook.

Siegfried went on. 'But I know I don't have to ramble on at you, James. You always pay attention to what I say, don't you?'

I tucked the tray under my arm and set off again. 'Yes,' I replied. 'I do. Every single time.'

Chapter Seven

'I can see you like pigs,' said Mr Worley as I edged my way into the pen.

'You can?'

'Oh yes, I can always tell. As soon as you went in there nice and quiet and scratched Queenie's back and spoke to her I said "There's a young man as likes pigs".'

'Oh good. Well, as a matter of fact you're absolutely right. I do like pigs.' I had, in truth, been creeping very cautiously past Queenie, wondering just how she was going to react. She was a huge animal and sows with litters can be very hostile to strangers. When I had come into the building she had got up from where she was suckling her piglets and eyed me with a non-committal grunt, reminding me of the number of times I had left a pig pen a lot quicker than I had gone in. A big, barking, gaping-mouthed sow has always been able to make me move very smartly.

Now that I was right inside the narrow pen, Queenie seemed to have accepted me. She grunted again, but peaceably, then carefully collapsed on the straw and exposed her udder to the eager little mouths. When she was in this position I was able to examine her foot.

'Aye, that's the one,' Mr Worley said anxiously. 'She could hardly hobble when she got up this morning.'

There didn't seem to be much wrong. A flap of the horn of one claw was a bit overgrown and was rubbing on the sensitive sole, but we didn't usually get called out for little things like that. I cut away the overgrown part and dressed the sore place with our multi-purpose ointment, ung pini sedativum, while all the time Mr Worley knelt by Queenie's head and patted her and sort of crooned into her ear. I couldn't make out the words he used – maybe it was pig language because the sow really seemed to be answering him with little soft grunts. Anyway, it worked better than an anaesthetic and everybody was happy including the long row of piglets working busily at the double line of teats.

'Right, Mr Worley.' I straightened up and handed him the jar of ung pini. 'Keep rubbing in a little of that twice a day and I think she'll be sound in no time.'

'Thank ye, thank ye, I'm very grateful.' He shook my hand vigorously as though I had saved the animal's life. 'I'm very glad to meet you for the first time, Mr Herriot. I've know Mr Farnon for a year or two, of course, and I think a bit about him. Loves pigs does that man, loves them. And his young brother's been here once or twice – I reckon he's fond of pigs, too.'

'Devoted to them, Mr Worley.'

'Ah yes, I thought so. I can always tell.' He regarded me for a while with a moist eye, then smiled, well satisfied.

We went out into what was really the back yard of an inn. Because Mr Worley wasn't a regular farmer, he was the landlord of the Langthorpe Falls Hotel and his precious livestock were crammed into what had once been the stables and coach houses of the inn. They were all Tamworths and whichever door you opened you found yourself staring into the eyes of ginger-haired pigs;

there were a few porkers and the odd one being fattened for bacon but Mr Worley's pride was his sows. He had six of them – Queenie, Princess, Ruby, Marigold, Delilah and Primrose.

For years expert farmers had been assuring Mr Worley that he'd never do any good with his sows. If you were going in for breeding, they said, you had to have proper premises; it wasn't a bit of use shoving sows into converted buildings like his. And for years Mr Worley's sows had responded by producing litters of unprecedented size and raising them with tender care. They were all good mothers and didn't savage their families or crush them clumsily under their bodies so it turned out with uncanny regularity that at the end of eight weeks Mr Worley had around twelve chunky weaners to take to market.

It must have spoiled the farmers' beer – none of them could equal that, and the pill was all the more bitter because the landlord had come from the industrial West Riding – Halifax, I think it was – a frail, short-sighted little retired newsagent with no agricultural background. By all the laws he just didn't have a chance.

Leaving the yard we came on to the quiet loop of road where my car was parked. Just beyond, the road dipped steeply into a tree-lined ravine where the Darrow hurled itself over a great broken shelf of rock in its passage to the lower Dale. I couldn't see down there from where I was standing, but I could hear the faint roar of the water and could picture the black cliff lifting sheer from the boiling river and on the other bank the gentle slope of turf where people from the towns came to sit and look in wonder.

Some of them were here now. A big, shiny car had drawn up and its occupants were disembarking. The driver, sleek, fat and impressive, strolled towards us and called out: 'We would like some tea.'

Mr Worley swung round on him. 'And you can 'ave some, maister, but when I'm ready. I have some very important business with this gentleman.' He turned his back on the man and began to ask me for final instructions about Queenie's foot.

The man was obviously taken aback and I couldn't blame him. It seemed to me that Mr Worley might have shown a little more tact – after all serving food and drink was his living – but as I came to know him better I realised that his pigs came first and everything else was an irritating intrusion.

Knowing Mr Worley better had its rewards. The time when I feel most like a glass of beer is not in the evening when the pubs are open but at around four-thirty on a hot afternoon after wrestling with young cattle in some stifling cow-shed. It was delightful to retire, sweating and weary, to the shaded sanctuary of Mr Worley's back kitchen and sip at the bitter ale, cool, frothing, straight from the cellar below.

The smooth working of the system was facilitated by the attitude of the local constable, P.C. Dalloway, a man whose benign disposition and elastic interpretation of the licensing laws had made him deeply respected in the district. Occasionally he joined us, took off his uniform jacket and, in shirt and braces, consumed a pint with a massive dignity which was peculiar to him.

But mostly Mr Worley and I were on our own and when he had brought the tall jug up from the cellar he would sit down and say 'Well now, let's have a piggy talk!' His use of this particular phrase made me wonder if perhaps he had some humorous insight into his obsessive preoccupation with the porcine species. Maybe he had but for all that our conversations seemed to give him the deepest pleasure.

We talked about erysipelas and swine fever, brine poisoning and paratyphoid, the relative merits of dry and wet mash, while pictures of his peerless sows with their show rosettes looked down at us from the walls.

On one occasion, in the middle of a particularly profound discussion on the ventilation of farrowing houses Mr Worley stopped suddenly and, blinking rapidly behind his thick spectacles, burst out:

'You know, Mr Herriot, sitting here talking like this with you, I'm 'appy as king of England!'

His devotion resulted in my being called out frequently for very trivial things and I swore freely under my breath when I heard his voice on the other end of the line at one o'clock one morning.

'Marigold pigged this afternoon, Mr Herriot, and I don't think she's got much milk. Little pigs look very hungry to me. Will you come?'

I groaned my way out of bed and downstairs and through the long garden to the yard. By the time I had got the car out into the lane I had begun to wake up and when I rolled up to the inn was able to greet Mr Worley fairly cheerfully.

But the poor man did not respond. In the light from the oil lamp his face was haggard with worry.

'I hope you can do something quick. I'm real upset about her – she's just laid there doing nothin' and it's such a lovely litter. Fourteen she's had.'

I could understand his concern as I looked into the pen. Marigold was stretched motionless on her side while the tiny piglets swarmed around her udder; they were rushing from teat to teat, squealing and falling over each other in their desperate quest for nourishment. And the little bodies had the narrow, empty look which meant they had nothing in their stomachs. I hated to see a litter die off from sheer starvation but it could happen so easily. There came a time when they stopped trying to suck and began to lie about the pen. After that it was hopeless.

Crouching behind the sow with my thermometer in her rectum I looked along the swelling flank, the hair a rich copper red in the light from the lamp. 'Did she eat anything tonight?'

'Aye, cleaned up just as usual.'

The thermometer reading was normal. I began to run my hands along the udder, pulling in turn at the teats. The ravenous piglets caught at my fingers with their sharp teeth as I pushed them to one side but my efforts failed to produce a drop of milk. The udder seemed full, even engorged, but I was unable to get even a bead down to the end of the teat.

'There's nowt there, is there?' Mr Worley whispered anxiously.

I straightened up and turned to him 'This is simply agalactia. There's no mastitis and Marigold isn't really ill, but there's something interfering with the let-down mechanism of the milk. She's got plenty of milk and there's an injection which ought to bring it down.'

I tried to keep the triumphant look off my face as I spoke, because this was one of my favourite party tricks. There is a flavour of magic in the injection of pituitrin in these cases; it works within a minute and though no skill is required the effect is spectacular.

Marigold didn't complain as I plunged in the needle and administered 3 c.c. deep into the muscle of her thigh. She was too busy conversing with her owner – they were almost nose to nose, exchanging soft pig noises.

After I had put away my syringe and listened for a few moments to the cooing sounds from the front end I thought it might be time. Mr Worley looked up in surprise as I reached down again to the udder.

'What are you doing now?'

'Having a feel to see if the milk's come down yet.'

'Why damn, it can't be! You've only just given t'stuff and she's bone dry!'

Oh, this was going to be good. A roll of drums would be appropriate at this moment. With finger and thumb I took hold of one of the teats at the turgid back end of the udder. I suppose it is a streak of exhibitionism in me which always makes me send the jet of milk spraying against the opposite wall in these circumstances; this time I thought it would be more impressive if I directed my shot past the innkeeper's left ear, but I got my trajectory wrong and sprinkled his spectacles instead.

He took them off and wiped them slowly as if he couldn't believe what he had seen. Then he bent over and tried for himself.

'It's a miracle!' he cried as the milk spouted eagerly over his hand. 'I've never seen owt like it!'

It didn't take the little pigs long to catch on. Within a few seconds they had stopped their fighting and squealing and settled down in a long, silent row. Their utterly rapt expressions all told the same story – they were going to make up for lost time.

I went into the kitchen to wash my hands and was using the towel hanging behind the door when I noticed something odd; there was a subdued hum of conversation, the low rumble of many voices. It seemed unusual in a pub at 2 a.m. and I looked through the partly open door into the bar. The place was crowded. In the light of a single weak electric bulb I could see a row of men drinking at the counter while others sat behind foaming pint pots on the wooden settles against the walls.

Mr Worley grinned as I turned to him in surprise.

'Didn't expect to see this lot, did you? Well, I'll tell you, the real drinkers don't come in till after closing time. Aye, it's a rum 'un – every night I lock front door and these lads come in the back.'

I pushed my head round the door for another look. It was a kind of rogue's gallery of Darrowby. All the dubious characters in the town seemed to be gathered in that room; the names which regularly enlivened the columns of the weekly newspaper with their activities. Drunk and disorderly, non-payment of rates, wife-beating, assault and battery – I could almost see the headings as I went from face to face.

I had been spotted. Beery cries of welcome rang out and I was suddenly conscious that all eyes were fixed on me in the smoky atmosphere. Above the rest a voice said 'Are you going to have a drink?' What I wanted most was to get back to my bed, but it wouldn't look so good just to close the door and go. I went inside and over to the bar. I seemed to have plenty of friends there and within seconds was in the centre of a merry group with a pint glass in my hand.

My nearest neighbour was a well-known Darrowby worthy called Gobber Newhouse, an enormously fat man who had always seemed able to get through life without working at all. He occupied his time with drinking, brawling and gambling. At the moment he was in a mellow mood and his huge, sweating face, pushed close to mine, was twisted into a comradely leer.

'Nah then, Herriot, ow's dog trade?' he enquired courteously.

I had never heard my profession described in this way and was wondering how to answer when I noticed that the company were looking at me expectantly. Mr Worley's niece who served behind the bar was looking at me expectantly too.

'Six pints of best bitter – six shillings please,' she said, clarifying the situation.

I fumbled the money from my pocket. Obviously my first impression that somebody had invited me to have a drink with them had been mistaken. Looking round the faces, there was no way of telling who had called out, and as the beer disappeared, the group round the bar thinned out like magic; the members just drifted away as though by accident till I found myself alone. I was no longer an object of interest and nobody paid any attention as I drained my glass and left.

The glow from the pig pen showed through the darkness of the yard and as I crossed over, the soft rumble of pig and human voices told me that Mr Worley was still talking things over with his sow. He looked up as I came in and his face in the dim light was ecstatic.

'Mr Herriot,' he whispered. 'Isn't that a beautiful sight?'

He pointed to the little pigs who were lying motionless in a layered heap, sprawled over each other without plan or pattern, eyes tightly closed, stomachs bloated with Marigold's bountiful fluid.

'It is indeed,' I said, prodding the sleeping mass with my finger but getting no response beyond the lazy opening of an eye. 'You'd have to go a long way to beat it.'

And I did share his pleasure; it was one of the satisfying little jobs. Climbing into the car I felt that the nocturnal visit had been worth while even though I had been effortlessly duped into buying a round with no hope of reciprocation. Not that I wanted to drink any more – my stomach wasn't used to receiving pints of ale at 2 a.m. and a few whimpers of surprise and indignation were already coming up – but I was just a bit ruffled by the offhand, professional way those gentlemen in the tap room had handled me.

But, winding my way home through the empty, moonlit roads, I was unaware that the hand of retribution was hovering over that happy band. This was, in fact, a fateful night, because ten minutes after I had left, Mr Worley's pub was raided. Perhaps that is a rather dramatic word, but it happened that it was the constable's annual holiday and the relief man, a young policeman who did not share Mr Dalloway's liberal views, had come up on his bicycle and pinched everybody in the place.

The account of the court proceedings in the *Darrowby and Houlton Times* made good reading. Gobber Newhouse and company were all fined £2 each and warned as to their future conduct. The magistrates, obviously a heartless lot, had remained unmoved by Gobber's passionate protestations that the beer in the glasses had all been purchased before closing time and that he and his friends had been lingering over it in light conversation for the subsequent four hours.

Mr Worley was fined £15 but I don't think he really minded; Marigold and her litter were doing well.

Chapter Eight

This was the last gate. I got out to open it since Tristan was driving, and looked back at the farm, a long way below us now, and at the marks our tyres had made on the steep, grassy slopes. Strange places, some of these Dales farms; this one had no road to it – not even a track. From down there you just drove across the fields from gate to gate till you got to the main road above the valley. And this was the last one; ten minutes' driving and we'd be home.

Tristan was acting as my chauffeur, as my left hand had been infected after a bad calving and I had my arm in a sling. He didn't drive up through the gate but got out of the car, leaned his back against the gate post and lit a Woodbine.

Obviously he wasn't in any rush to leave. And with the sun warm on the back of his neck and the two bottles of Whitbread's nestling comfortably in his stomach I could divine that he felt pretty good. Come to think of it, it had been all right back there. He had taken some warts off a heifer's teats and the farmer had said he shaped well for a young 'un, ('Aye, you really framed at t'job, lad') and asked us in for a bottle of beer since it was so hot. Impressed by the ecstatic speed with which Tristan had consumed his, he had given him another.

Yes, it had been all right, and I could see Tristan thought so too. With a smile of utter content he took a long, deep gulp of moorland air and Woodbine smoke and closed his eyes.

He opened them quickly as a grinding noise came from the car. 'Christ! She's off, Jim!' he shouted.

The little Austin was moving gently backwards down the slope – it must have slipped out of gear and it had no brakes to speak of. We both leaped after it. Tristan was nearest and he just managed to touch the bonnet with one finger; the speed was too much for him. We gave it up and watched.

The hillside was steep and the little car rapidly gathered momentum, bouncing crazily over the uneven ground. I glanced at Tristan; his mind invariably worked quickly and clearly in a crisis and I had a good idea what he was thinking. It was only a fortnight since he had turned the Hillman over, taking a girl home from a dance. It had been a complete write-off and the insurance people had been rather nasty about it; and of course Siegfried had gone nearly berserk and had finished by sacking him finally, once and for all – never wanted to see his face in the place again.

But he had been sacked so often; he knew he had only to keep out of his way for a bit and his brother would forget. And he had been lucky this time because Siegfried had talked his bank manager into letting him buy a beautiful new Rover and this had blotted everything else from his mind.

It was distinctly unfortunate that this should happen when he, as driver, was technically in charge of the Austin. The car appeared now to be doing about 70 m.p.h. hurtling terrifyingly down the long, green hill. One by one the doors burst open till all four flapped wildly and the car swooped downwards looking like a huge, ungainly bird.

From the open doors, bottles, instruments, bandages, cotton wool cascaded out onto the turf, leaving a long, broken trail. Now and again a packet of nux vomica and bicarb stomach powder would fly out and burst like a bomb, splashing vivid white against the green.

Tristan threw up his arms. 'Look! The bloody thing's going straight for that hut.' He drew harder on his Woodbine.

There was indeed only one obstruction on the bare hillside – a small building near the foot where the land levelled out and the Austin, as if drawn by a magnet, was thundering straight towards it.

I couldn't bear to watch. Just before the impact I turned away and focused my attention on the end of Tristan's cigarette which was glowing bright red when the crash came. When I looked back down the hill the building was no longer there. It had been completely flattened and everything I had ever heard about houses of cards surged into my mind. On top of the shattered timbers the little car lay peacefully on its side, its wheels still turning lazily.

As we galloped down the hill it was easy to guess Tristan's thoughts. He wouldn't be looking forward to telling Siegfried he had wrecked the Austin; in fact it was something the mind almost refused to contemplate. But as we neared the scene of devastation, passing on our way syringes, scalpels, bottles of vaccine, it was difficult to see any other outcome.

Arriving at the car, we made an anxious inspection. The body had been so bashed and dented before that it wasn't easy to identify any new marks. Certainly the rear end was pretty well caved in but it didn't show up very much. The only obvious damage was a smashed rear light. Our hopes rising, we set off for the farm for help.

The farmer greeted us amiably. 'Now then, you lads, hasta come back for more beer?'

'It wouldn't come amiss,' Tristan replied. 'We've had a bit of an accident.'

We went into the house and the hospitable man opened some more bottles. He didn't seem disturbed when he heard of the demolition of the hut. 'Nay, that's not mine. Belongs to t'golf club – it's t'club house.'

Tristan's eyebrows shot up. 'Oh no! Don't say we've flattened the headquarters of the Darrowby Golf Club!'

'Aye, lad, you must have. It's t'only wooden building in them fields. I rent that part of my land to the club and they've made a little nine hole course. Don't worry, hardly anybody plays on it – mainly t'bank manager and ah don't like that feller.'

Mr Prescott got a horse out of the stable and we went back to the car and pulled it upright again. Trembling a little, Tristan climbed in and pressed the starter. The sturdy little engine burst into a confident roar immediately and he drove carefully over the prostrate wooden walls on to the grass.

'Well thanks a lot, Mr Prescott,' he shouted. 'We seem to have got away with it.'

'Champion, lad, champion. You're as good as new.' Then the farmer winked and held up a finger. 'Now you say nowt about this job and I'll say nowt. Right?'

'Right! Come on, Jim, get in.' Tristan put his foot down and we chugged thankfully up the hill once more.

He seemed thoughtful on the way and didn't speak till we got on to the road. Then he turned to me.

'You know, Jim, it's all very well, but I've still got to confess to Siegfried about that rear light. And of course I'll get the lash again. Don't you think it's just a bit hard the way I get blamed for everything that happens to his cars? You've seen it over and over again – he gives me a lot of bloody old wrecks to drive and when they start to fall to bits it's always my fault. The bloody tyres are all down to the canvas but if I get a puncture there's hell to pay. It isn't fair.'

'Well Siegfried isn't the man to suffer in silence, you know.' I said. 'He's got to lash out and you're nearest.'

Tristan was silent for a moment then he took a deeper drag at his Woodbine, blew out his cheeks and assumed a judicial expression. 'Mind you, I'm not saying I was entirely blameless with regard to the Hillman – I was taking that sharp turn in Dringley at sixty with my arm round a little nurse – but all in all I've just had sheer bad luck. In fact, Jim, I'm a helpless victim of prejudice.'

Siegfried was out of sorts when we met in the surgery. He was starting a summer cold and was sniffly and listless, but he still managed to raise a burst of energy at the news.

'You bloody young maniac! It's the rear light now, is it? God help me, I think all I work for is to pay for the repair bills you run up. You'll ruin me before you're finished. Go on, get to hell out of it. I'm finished with you.'

Tristan retired with dignity and followed his usual policy of lying low. He didn't see his brother until the following morning. Siegfried's condition had deteriorated; the cold had settled in his throat, always his weak spot, and he was down with laryngitis. His neck was swathed in vinegar-soaked Thermogene and when Tristan and I came into the bedroom he was feebly turning over the pages of the *Darrowby and Houlton Times*.

He spoke in a tortured whisper. 'Have you seen this? It says here that the golf clubhouse was knocked down yesterday and there's no clue as to how it happened. Damn funny thing. On Prescott's land, isn't it?' His head jerked suddenly from the pillow and he glared at his brother. 'You were there yesterday!' he croaked, then he fell back, muttering. 'Oh no, no, I'm sorry, it's too ridiculous – and it's wrong of me to blame you for everything.'

Tristan stared. He had never heard this kind of talk from Siegfried before. I too felt a pang of anxiety; could my boss be delirious?

Siegfried swallowed painfully. 'I've just had an urgent call from Armitage of Sorton. He's got a cow down with milk fever and I want you to drive James out there straight away. Go on, now – get moving.'

'Afraid I can't, Tristan shrugged. 'Jim's car is in Hammond's garage. They're fixing that light – it'll take them about an hour.'

'Oh God, yes, and they said they couldn't let us have a spare. Well, Armitage is in a bit of a panic – that cow could be dead in an hour. What the hell can we do?'

'There's the Rover,' Tristan said quietly.

Siegfried's form stiffened suddenly under the blankets and wild terror flickered in his eyes. For a few moments his head rolled about on the pillow and his long, bony fingers picked nervously at the quilt, then with an effort he heaved himself on to his side and stared into his brother's eyes. He spoke slowly and the agonised hissing of his voice lent menace to his words.

'Right, so you'll have to take the Rover. I never thought I'd see the day when I'd let a wrecker like you drive it, but just let me tell you this. If you put a scratch on that car I'll kill you. I'll kill you with my own two hands.'

The old pattern was asserting itself. Siegfried's eyes had begun to bulge, a dark flush was creeping over his cheeks while Tristan's face had lost all expression.

Using the last remnants of his strength, Siegfried hoisted himself even higher. 'Now do you really think you are capable of driving that car five miles to Sorton and back without smashing it up? All right then, get on with it and just remember what I've said.'

Tristan withdrew in offended silence and as I followed him I took a last look at the figure in the bed. Siegfried had fallen back and was staring at the ceiling with feverish eyes. His lips moved feebly as though he were praying.

Outside the room, Tristan rubbed his hands delightedly. 'What a break, Jim! A chance in a lifetime! You know I never thought I'd get behind the wheel of that Rover in a hundred years.' He dropped his voice to a whisper. 'Just shows you – everything happens for the best.'

Five minutes later he was backing carefully out of the yard and into the lane and once on the Sorton road I saw he was beginning to enjoy himself. For two miles the way ahead stretched straight and clear except for a milk lorry approaching in the far distance; a perfect place to see what the Rover could do. He nestled down in the rich leather upholstery and pressed his foot hard on the accelerator.

We were doing an effortless eighty when I saw a car beginning to overtake the milk lorry; it was an ancient, square-topped, high-built vehicle like a biscuit tin on wheels and it had no business trying to overtake anything. I waited for it to pull back but it still came on. And the lorry, perhaps with a sporting driver, seemed to be spurting to make a race of it.

With increasing alarm I saw the two vehicles abreast and bearing down on us only a few hundred yards away and not a foot of space on either side of them. Of course the old car would pull in behind the lorry – it had to, there was no other way – but it was taking a long time about it. Tristan jammed on his brakes. If the lorry did the same, the other car would just be able to dodge between. But within seconds I realised nothing like that was going to happen and as they thundered towards us I resigned myself with dumb horror to a head-on collision.

Just before I closed my eyes I had a fleeting glimpse of a large, alarmed face behind the wheel of the old car, then something hit the left side of the Rover with a rending crash.

When I opened my eyes we were stationary. There was just Tristan and myself staring straight ahead at the road, empty and quiet, curving ahead of us into the peaceful green of the hills.

I sat motionless, listening to my thumping heart then I looked over my shoulder and saw the lorry disappearing at high speed round a distant bend; in passing I studied Tristan's face with interest – I had never seen a completely green face before.

After quite a long time, feeling a draught from the left, I looked carefully round in that direction. There were no doors on that side – one was lying by the roadside a few yards back and the other hung from a single broken hinge; as I watched, this one too, clattered on to the tarmac with a note of flat finality. Slowly, as in a dream, I got out and surveyed the damage; the left side of the Rover was a desert of twisted metal where the old car, diving for the verge at the last split second, had ploughed its way.

Tristan had flopped down on the grass, his face blank. A nasty scratch on the paintwork might have sent him into a panic but this wholesale destruction seemed to have numbed his senses. But this state didn't last long; he began to blink, then his eyes narrowed and he felt for his Woodbines. His agile mind was back at work and it wasn't difficult to read his thoughts. What was he going to do now?

It seemed to me after a short appraisal of the situation that he had three possible courses of action. First, and most attractive, he could get out of Darrowby permanently – emigrate if necessary. Second, he could go straight to the railway station and board a train for Brawton where he could live quietly with his mother till this had blown over. Third, and it didn't bear thinking about, he could go back to Skeldale House and tell Siegfried he had smashed up his new Rover.

As I weighed up the possibilities I spotted the old car which had hit us; it was lying upside down in a ditch about fifty yards down the road. Hurrying towards it, I could hear a loud cackling coming from the interior and I remembered it was market day and many of the farmers would be bringing in crates of hens and maybe twenty or thirty dozen eggs to sell. We peered in through a window and Tristan gasped. A fat man, obviously unhurt, was lying in a great pool of smashed eggs. His face wore a wide, reassuring smile – in fact, his whole expression was ingratiating as far as it could be seen through the mask of egg which covered his features. The rest of the interior was filled with frantic hens which had escaped from their crates in the crash and were hunting for a way out.

The fat man, smiling up happily from his bed of eggs, was shouting something, but it was difficult to hear him above the wild cackling. I managed to pick up odd phrases: 'Very sorry indeed – entirely my fault – I'll make good the damage.' The words floated up cheerfully while the hens scampered across the man's beaming face and yolks coursed sluggishly down his clothes.

With an effort, Tristan managed to wrench open a door and was driven back immediately by a rush of hens. Some of them galloped off in various directions till they were lost to sight, while their less adventurous companions began to peck about philosophically by the roadside.

'Are you all right?' Tristan shouted.

'Yes, yes, young man. I'm not hurt. Please don't worry about me.' The fat man struggled vainly to rise from the squelching mass. 'Ee, I am sorry about this, but I'll see you right, you can be sure.'

He held up a dripping hand and we helped him out on to the road. Despite his saturated clothes and the pieces of shell sticking to his hair and moustache he hadn't lost his poise. In fact he radiated confidence, the same confidence, I thought, which made him think his old car could overtake that speeding lorry.

He laid a hand on Tristan's shoulder. 'There's a simple explanation, you know. The sun got in my eyes.'

It was twelve noon and the fat man had been driving due north, but there didn't seem much point in arguing.

We lifted the shattered doors from the road, put them inside the Rover, drove to Sorton, treated the milk fever cow and returned to Darrowby. Tristan gave me a single despairing look then squared his shoulders and marched straight to his brother's room. I followed close on his heels.

Siegfried was worse. His face was red with fever and his eyes burned deeply in their sockets. He didn't move when Tristan walked over to the foot of the bed.

'Well, how did you get on?' The whisper was barely audible.

'Oh fine, the cow was on her feet when we left. But there's just one thing – I had a bit of a bump with the car.'

Siegfried had been wheezing stertorously and staring at the ceiling but the breathing stopped as if it had been switched off. There was an eerie silence then from the completely motionless figure two strangled words escaped. 'What happened?'

'Wasn't my fault. Chap tried to overtake a lorry and didn't make it. Caught one side of the Rover.'

Again the silence and again the whisper.

'Much damage?'

'Front and rear wings pretty well mangled, I'm afraid – and both doors torn off the left side.'

As if operated by a powerful spring, Siegfried came bolt upright in the bed. It was startlingly like a corpse coming to life and the effect was heightened by the coils of Thermogene which had burst loose and trailed in shroud-like garlands from the haggard head. The mouth opened wide in a completely soundless scream.

'You bloody fool! You're sacked!'

He crashed back on to the pillow as though the mechanism had gone into reverse and lay very still. We watched him for a few moments in some anxiety, but when we heard the breathing restart we tiptoed from the room.

On the landing Tristan blew out his cheeks and drew a Woodbine from its packet. 'A tricky little situation, Jim, but you know what I always say.' He struck a match and pulled the smoke down blissfully. 'Things usually turn out better than you expect.'

Chapter Nine

A lot of the Dales farms were anonymous and it was a help to find this one so plainly identified. 'Heston Grange' it said on the gate in bold black capitals.

I got out of the car and undid the latch. It was a good gate, too, and swung easily on its hinges instead of having to be dragged round with a shoulder under the top spar. The farmhouse lay below me, massive, grey-stoned, with a pair of bow windows which some prosperous Victorian had added to the original structure.

It stood on a flat, green neck of land in a loop of the river and the lushness of the grass and the quiet fertility of the surrounding fields contrasted sharply with the stark hills behind. Towering oaks and beeches sheltered the house and a thick pine wood covered the lower slopes of the fell.

I walked round the buildings shouting as I always did, because some people considered it a subtle insult to go to the house and ask if the farmer was in. Good farmers are indoors only at meal times. But my shouts drew no reply, so I went over and knocked at the door set deep among the weathered stones.

A voice answered 'Come in,' and I opened the door into a huge, stone-flagged kitchen with hams and sides of bacon hanging from hooks in the ceiling. A dark girl in a check blouse and green linen slacks was kneading dough in a bowl. She looked up and smiled.

'Sorry I couldn't let you in. I've got my hands full.' She held up her arms, floury-white to the elbow.

'That's all right. My name is Herriot. I've come to see a calf. It's lame, I understand.'

'Yes, we think he's broken his leg. Probably got his foot in a hole when he was running about. If you don't mind waiting a minute, I'll come with you. My father and the men are in the fields. I'm Helen Alderson, by the way.'

She washed and dried her arms and pulled on a pair of short wellingtons. 'Take over this bread will you, Meg,' she said to an old woman who came through from an inner room. 'I have to show Mr Herriot the calf.'

Outside, she turned to me and laughed. 'We've got a bit of a walk, I'm afraid. He's in one of the top buildings. Look, you can just see it up there.' She pointed to a squat, stone barn, high on the fell-side. I knew all about these top buildings; they were scattered all over the high country and I got a lot of healthy exercise going round them. They were used for storing hay and other things and as shelters for the animals on the hill pastures.

I looked at the girl for a few seconds. 'Oh, that's all right, I don't mind. I don't mind in the least.'

We went over the field to a narrow bridge spanning the river, and, following her across, I was struck by a thought; this new fashion of women wearing slacks might be a bit revolutionary but there was a lot to be said for it. The path led upward through the pine wood and here the sunshine was broken up into islands of brightness among the dark trunks, the sound of the river grew faint and we walked softly on a thick carpet of pine needles. It was cool in the wood and silent except when a bird call echoed through the trees.

Ten minutes of hard walking brought us out again into the hot sun on the open moor and the path curved steeper still round a series of rocky outcrops. I was beginning to puff, but the girl kept up a brisk pace, swinging along with easy strides. I was glad when we reached the level ground on the top and the barn came in sight again.

When I opened the half door I could hardly see my patient in the dark interior which was heavy with the fragrance of hay piled nearly to the roof. He looked very small and sorry for himself with his dangling foreleg which trailed uselessly along the strawed floor as he tried to walk.

'Will you hold his head while I examine him, please?' I said.

The girl caught the calf expertly, one hand under its chin, the other holding an ear. As I felt my way over the leg the little creature stood trembling, his face a picture of woe.

'Well, your diagnosis was correct. Clean fracture of the radius and ulna, but there's very little displacement so it should do well with a plaster on it.' I opened my bag, took out some plaster bandages then filled a bucket with water from a near-by spring. I soaked one of the bandages and applied it to the leg, following it with a second and a third till the limb was encased in a rapidly hardening white sheath from elbow to foot.

'We'll just wait a couple of minutes till it hardens, then we can let him go.' I kept tapping the plaster till I was satisfied it was set like stone. 'All right,' I said finally. 'He can go now.'

The girl released the head and the little animal trotted away. 'Look,' she cried. 'He's putting his weight on it already! And doesn't he look a lot happier!' I smiled. I felt I had really done something. The calf felt no pain now that the broken ends of the bone were immobilised; and the fear which always demoralises a hurt animal had magically vanished.

'Yes,' I said. 'He certainly has perked up quickly.' My words were almost drowned by a tremendous bellow and the patch of blue above the half door was suddenly obscured by a large shaggy head. Two great liquid eyes stared down anxiously at the little calf and it answered with a high-pitched bawl. Soon a deafening duet was in progress.

'That's his mother,' the girl shouted above the din. 'Poor old thing, she's been hanging about here all morning wondering what we've done with her calf. She hates being separated from him.'

I straightened up and drew the bolt on the door. 'Well she can come in now.'

The big cow almost knocked me down as she rushed past me. Then she started a careful, sniffing inspection of her calf, pushing him around with her muzzle and making muffled lowing noises deep in her throat.

The little creature submitted happily to all the fuss and when it was over and his mother was finally satisfied, he limped round to her udder and began to suck heartily.

'Soon got his appetite back,' I said and we both laughed.

I threw the empty tins into my bag and closed it. 'He'll have to keep the plaster on for a month, so if you'll give me a ring then I'll come back and take it off. Just keep an eye on him and make sure his leg doesn't get sore round the top of the bandage.'

As we left the barn the sunshine and the sweet warm air met us like a high wave. I turned and looked across the valley to the soaring green heights, smooth, enormous, hazy in the noon heat. Beneath my feet the grassy slopes fell away steeply to where the river glimmered among the trees.

'It's wonderful up here,' I said. 'Just look at that gorge over there. And that great hill – I suppose you could call it a mountain.' I pointed at a giant which heaved its heather-mottled shoulders high above the others.

'That's Heskit Fell – nearly two and a half thousand feet. And that's Eddleton just beyond, and Wedder Fell on the other side and Colver and Sennor.' The names with their wild, Nordic ring fell easily from her tongue; she spoke of them like old friends and I could sense the affection in her voice.

We sat down on the warm grass of the hillside, a soft breeze pulled at the heads of the moorland flowers, somewhere a curlew cried. Darrowby and Skeldale House and veterinary practice seemed a thousand miles away.

'You're lucky to live here,' I said. 'But I don't think you need me to tell you that.'

'No, I love this country. There's nowhere else quite like it.' She paused and looked slowly around her. 'I'm glad it appeals to you too – a lot of people find it too bare and wild. It almost seems to frighten them.'

I laughed. 'Yes, I know, but as far as I'm concerned I can't help feeling sorry for all the thousands of vets who don't work in the Yorkshire Dales.'

I began to talk about my work, then almost without knowing, I was going back over my student days, telling her of the good times, the friends I had made and our hopes and aspirations.

I surprised myself with my flow of talk – I wasn't much of a chatterbox usually – and I felt I must be boring my companion. But she sat quietly looking over the valley, her arms around her green-clad legs, nodding at times as though she understood. And she laughed in all the right places.

I wondered too, at the silly feeling that I would like to forget all about the rest of the day's duty and stay up here on this sunny hillside. It came to me that it had been a long time since I had sat down and talked to a girl of my own age. I had almost forgotten what it was like.

I didn't hurry back down the path and through the scented pine wood but it seemed no time at all before we were walking across the wooden bridge and over the field to the farm.

I turned with my hand on the car door. 'Well, I'll see you in a month.' It sounded like an awful long time.

The girl smiled. 'Thank you for what you've done.' As I started the engine she waved and went into the house.

'Helen Alderson?' Siegfried said later over lunch. 'Of course I know her. Lovely girl.'

Tristan, across the table, made no comment, but he laid down his knife and fork, raised his eyes reverently to the ceiling and gave a long, low whistle. Then he started to eat again.

Siegfried went on. 'Oh yes, I know her very well. And I admire her. Her mother died a few years ago and she runs the whole place. Cooks and looks after her father and a younger brother and sister.' He spooned some mashed potatoes on to his plate. 'Any men friends? Oh, half the young bloods in the district are chasing her but she doesn't seem to be going steady with any of them. Choosy sort, I think.'

Chapter Ten

It was when I was plodding up Mr Kay's field for the ninth time that it began to occur to me that this wasn't going to be my day. For some time now I had been an LVI, the important owner of a little certificate informing whosoever it may concern that James Herriot MRCVS was a Local Veterinary Inspector of the Ministry of Agriculture and Fisheries. It meant that I was involved in a lot of routine work like clinical examinations and tuberculin testing. It also highlighted something which I had been suspecting for some time – the Dales farmers' attitude to time was different from my own.

It had been all right when I was calling on them to see a sick animal; they were usually around waiting for me and the beast would be confined in some building when I arrived. It was very different, however, when I sent them a card saying I was coming to inspect their dairy cows or test their herd. It stated quite clearly on the card that the animals must be assembled indoors and that I would be there at a certain time and I planned my day accordingly; fifteen minutes or so for a clinical and anything up to several hours for a test depending on the size of the herd. If I was kept waiting for ten minutes at every clinical while they got the cows in from the field it meant simply that after six visits I was running an hour late.

So when I drove up to Mr Kay's farm for a tuberculin test and found his cows tied up in their stalls I breathed a sigh of relief. We were through them in no time at all and I thought I was having a wonderful start to the day when the farmer said he had only half a dozen young heifers to do to complete the job. It was when I left the buildings and saw the group of shaggy roans and reds grazing contentedly at the far end of a large field that I felt the old foreboding.

'I thought you'd have them inside, Mr Kay,' I said apprehensively.

Mr Kay tapped out his pipe on to his palm, mixed the sodden dottle with a few strands of villainous looking twist and crammed it back into the bowl. 'Nay, nay,' he said, puffing appreciatively, 'Ah didn't like to put them in on a grand 'ot day like this. We'll drive them up to that little house.' He pointed to a tumbledown grey-stone barn at the summit of the long, steeply sloping pasture and blew out a cloud of choking smoke. 'Won't take many minutes.'

At his last sentence a cold hand clutched at me. I'd heard these dreadful words so many times before. But maybe it would be all right this time. We made our way to the bottom of the field and got behind the heifers.

'Cush, cush!' cried Mr Kay.

'Cush, cush!' I added encouragingly, slapping my hands against my thighs.

The heifers stopped pulling the grass and regarded us with mild interest, their jaws moving lazily, then in response to further cries they began to meander casually up the hill. We managed to coax them up to the door of the barn but there they stopped. The leader put her head inside for a moment then turned suddenly and made a dash down the hill. The others followed suit immediately and though we danced about and waved our arms they ran past us as if we weren't there. I looked thoughtfully at the young beasts thundering down the slope, their tails high, kicking up their heels like mustangs; they were enjoying this new game.

Down the hill once more and again the slow wheedling up to the door and again the sudden breakaway. This time one of them tried it on her own and as I galloped vainly to and fro trying to turn her the others charged with glee through the gap and down the slope again.

It was a long, steep hill and as I trudged up for the third time with the sun blazing on my back I began to regret being so conscientious about my clothes; in the instructions to the new LVI's the Ministry had been explicit that they expected us to be properly attired to carry out our duties. I had taken it to heart and rigged myself out in the required uniform but I realised now that a long oilskin coat and wellingtons was not an ideal outfit for the job in hand. The sweat was trickling into my eyes and my shirt was beginning to cling to me.

When, for the third time, I saw the retreating backs careering joyously down the hill, I thought it was time to do something about it.

'Just a minute,' I called to the farmer, 'I'm getting a bit warm.'

I took off the coat, rolled it up and placed it on the grass well away from the barn. And as I made a neat pile of my syringe, the box of tuberculin, my calipers, scissors, notebook and pencil, the thought kept intruding that I was being cheated in some way. After all, Ministry work was easy – any practitioner would tell you that. You didn't have to get up in the middle of the night, you had nice set hours and you never really had to exert yourself. In fact it was money for old rope – a pleasant relaxation from the real thing. I wiped my streaming brow and stood for a few seconds panting gently – this just wasn't fair.

We started again and at the fourth visit to the barn I thought we had won because all but one of the heifers strolled casually inside. But that last one just wouldn't have it. We cushed imploringly, waved and even got near enough to poke at its rump but it stood in the entrance regarding the interior with deep suspicion. Then the heads of its mates began to reappear in the doorway and I knew we had lost again; despite my frantic dancing and shouting they wandered out one by one before joining again in their happy downhill dash. This time I found myself galloping down after them in an agony of frustration.

We had another few tries during which the heifers introduced touches of variation by sometimes breaking away half way up the hill or occasionally trotting round the back of the barn and peeping at us coyly from behind the old stones before frisking to the bottom again.

After the eighth descent I looked appealingly at Mr Kay who was relighting his pipe calmly and didn't appear to be troubled in any way. My time schedule was in tatters but I don't think he had noticed that we had been going on like this for about forty minutes.

'Look, we're getting nowhere,' I said. 'I've got a lot of other work waiting for me. Isn't there anything more we can do?'

The farmer stamped down the twist with his thumb, drew deeply and pleasurably a few times then looked at me with mild surprise. 'Well, let's see. We could bring a dog out but I don't know as he'll be much good. He's nobbut a young 'un.'

He sauntered back to the farmhouse and opened a door. A shaggy cur catapulted out, barking in delight, and Mr Kay brought him over to the field. 'Get away by!' he cried gesturing towards the cattle who had resumed their grazing and the dog streaked behind them. I really began to hope as we went up the hill with the hairy little figure darting in, nipping at the heels, but at the barn the rot set in again. I could see the heifers beginning to sense the inexperience of the dog and one of them managed to kick him briskly under the chin as he came in. The little animal yelped and his tail went down. He stood uncertainly, looking at the beasts, advancing on him now, shaking their horns threateningly, then he seemed to come to a decision and slunk away. The young cattle went after him at increasing speed and in a moment I was looking at the extraordinary spectacle of the dog going flat out down the hill with the heifers drumming close behind him. At the foot he disappeared under a gate and we saw him no more.

Something seemed to give way in my head. 'Oh God,' I yelled, 'we're never going to get these damn things tested! I'll just have to leave them. I don't know what the Ministry is going to say, but I've had enough!'

The farmer looked at me ruminatively. He seemed to recognise that I was at breaking point. 'Aye, it's no good,' he said, tapping his pipe out on his heel. 'We'll have to get Sam.'

'Sam?'

'Aye, Sam Broadbent. Works for me neighbour. He'll get 'em in all right.'

How's he going to do that?'

'Oh, he can imitate a fly.'

For a moment my mind reeled. 'Did you say imitate a fly?'

'That's right. A warble fly, tha knows. He's a bit slow is t'lad but by gaw he can imitate a fly. I'll go and get him – he's only two fields down the road.'

I watched the farmer's retreating back in disbelief then threw myself down on the ground. At any other time I would have enjoyed lying there on the slope with the sun on my face and the grass cool against my sweating back; the air was still and heavy with the fragrance of clover and when I opened my eyes the gentle curve of the valley floor was a vision of peace. But my mind was a turmoil. I had a full day's Ministry work waiting for me and I was an hour behind time already. I could picture the long succession of farmers waiting for me and cursing me heartily. The tension built in me till I could stand it no longer; I jumped to my feet and ran down to the gate at the foot. I could see along the road from there and was relieved to find that Mr Kay was on his way back.

Just behind him a large, fat man was riding slowly on a very small bicycle, his heels on the pedals, his feet and knees sticking out at right angles. Tufts of greasy black hair stuck out at random from under a kind of skull cap which looked like an old bowler without the brim.

'Sam's come to give us a hand,' said Mr Kay with an air of quiet triumph.

'Good morning,' I said and the big man turned slowly and nodded. The eyes in the round, unshaven face were vacant and incurious and I decided that Sam did indeed look a bit slow. I found it difficult to imagine how he could possibly be of any help.

The heifers, standing near by, watched with languid interest as we came through the gate. They had obviously enjoyed every minute of the morning's entertainment and it seemed they were game for a little more fun if we so desired; but it was up to us, of course – they weren't worried either way.

Sam propped his bicycle against the wall and paced solemnly forward. He made a circle of his thumb and forefinger and placed it to his lips. His cheeks worked as though he was getting everything into place then he took a deep breath. And, from nowhere it seemed came a sudden swelling of angry sound, a vicious humming and buzzing which made me look round in alarm for the enraged insect zooming in for the kill.

The effect on the heifers was electric. Their superior air vanished and was replaced by rigid anxiety; then, as the noise increased in volume, they turned and charged up the hill. But it wasn't the carefree frolic of before – no tossing heads, waving tails and kicking heels; this time they kept shoulder to shoulder in a frightened block.

Mr Kay and I, trotting on either side, directed them yet again up to the building where they formed a group, looking nervously around them.

We had to wait for a short while for Sam to arrive. He was clearly a one-pace man and ascended the slope unhurriedly. At the top he paused to regain his breath, fixed the animals with a blank gaze and carefully adjusted his fingers against his mouth. A moment's tense silence then the humming broke out again, even more furious and insistent than before.

The heifers knew when they were beaten. With a chorus of startled bellows they turned and rushed into the building and I crashed the half door behind them; I stood leaning against it unable to believe my troubles were over. Sam joined me and looked into the dark interior. As if to finally establish his mastery he gave a sudden sharp blast, this time without his fingers, and his victims huddled still closer against the far wall.

A few minutes later, after Sam had left us, I was happily clipping and injecting the necks. I looked up at the farmer. 'You know, I can still hardly believe what I saw there. It was like magic. That chap has a wonderful gift.'

Mr Kay looked over the half door and I followed his gaze down the grassy slope to the road. Sam was riding away and the strange black headwear was just visible, bobbing along the top of the wall.

'Aye, he can imitate a fly all right. Poor awd lad, it's t'only thing he's good at.'

Chapter Eleven

Hurrying away from Mr Kay's to my second test I reflected that if I had to be more than an hour late for an appointment it was a lucky thing that my next call was at the Hugills. The four brothers and their families ran a herd which, with cows, followers and calves must have amounted to nearly two hundred and I had to test the lot of them; but I knew that my lateness wouldn't bring any querulous remarks on my heads because the Hugills had developed the Dales tradition of courtesy to an extraordinary degree. The stranger within their gates was treated like royalty.

As I drove into the yard I could see everybody leaving their immediate tasks and advancing on me with beaming faces. The brothers were in the lead and they stopped opposite me as I got out of the car, and I thought as I always did that I had never seen such healthy-looking men. Their ages ranged from Walter, who was about sixty, down through Thomas and Fenwick to William, the youngest, who would be in his late forties, and I should say their average weight would be about fifteen stones. They weren't fat, either, just huge, solid men with bright red, shining faces and clear eyes.

William stepped forward from the group and I knew what was coming; this was always his job. He leaned forward, suddenly solemn, and looked into my face.

'How are you today, sorr?' he asked.

'Very well, thank you, Mr Hugill,' I replied.

'Good!' said William fervently, and the other brothers all repeated 'Good, good, good,' with deep satisfaction.

William took a deep breath. 'And how is Mr Farnon?'

'Oh, he's very fit, thanks.'

'Good!' Then the rapid fire of the responses from behind him: 'Good, good, good.'

William hadn't finished yet. He cleared his throat. 'And how is young Mr Farnon?'

'In really top form.'

'Good!' But this time William allowed himself a gentle smile and from behind him came a few dignified ho-ho's. Walter closed his eyes and his great shoulders shook silently. They all knew Tristan.

William stepped back into line, his appointed task done and we all went into the byre. I braced myself as I looked at the long row of backs, the tails swishing at the flies. There was some work ahead here.

'Sorry I'm so late,' I said, as I drew the tuberculin into the syringe. 'I was held up at the last place. It's difficult to forecast how long these tests will take.'

All four brothers replied eagerly. 'Aye, you're right, sorr. It's difficult. It IS difficult. You're right, you're right, it's difficult.' They went on till they had thrashed the last ounce out of the statement.

I finished filling the syringe, got out my scissors and began to push my way between the first two cows. It was a tight squeeze and I puffed slightly in the stifling atmosphere.

'It's a bit warm in here,' I said.

Again the volley of agreement. 'You're right, sorr. Aye, it's warm. It IS warm. You're right. It's warm. It's warm. Aye, you're right.' This was all delivered with immense conviction and vigorous nodding of heads as though I had made some incredible discovery; and as I looked at the grave, intent faces still pondering over my brilliant remark, I could feel my tensions beginning to dissolve. I was lucky to work here. Where else but in the high country of Yorkshire would I meet people like these?

I pushed along the cow and got hold of its ear, but Walter stopped me with a gentle cough.

'Nay, Mr Herriot, you won't have to look in the ears. I have all t'numbers wrote down.'

'Oh, that's fine. It'll save us a lot of time.' I had always found scratching the wax away to find ear tattoos an overrated pastime. And it was good to hear that the Hugills were attending to the clerical side; there was a section in the Ministry form which said: 'Are the herd records in good order?' I always wrote 'Yes,' keeping my fingers crossed as I thought of the scrawled figures on the backs of old bills, milk recording sheets, anything.

'Aye,' said Walter. 'I have 'em all set down proper in a book.'

'Great! Can you go and get it, then?'

'No need, sorr, I have it 'ere.' Walter was the boss, there was no doubt about it. They all seemed to live in perfect harmony but when the chips were down Walter took over automatically. He was the organiser, the acknowledged brains of the outfit. The battered trilby which he always wore in contrast with the others' caps gave him an extra air of authority.

Everybody watched respectfully as he slowly and deliberately extracted a spectacle case from an inside pocket. He opened it and took out an old pair of steel-rimmed spectacles, blowing away fragments of the hay and corn chaff with which the interior of the case was thickly powdered. There was a quiet dignity and importance in the way he unhurriedly threaded the side pieces over his ears and stood grimacing slightly to work everything into place. Then he put his hand into his waistcoat pocket.

When he took it out he was holding some object but it was difficult to identify, being almost obscured by his enormous thumb. Then I saw that it was a tiny, black-covered miniature diary about two inches square – the sort of novelty people give each other at Christmas.

'Is that the herd record?' I asked.

'Yes, this is it. It's all set down in here.' Walter daintily flicked over the pages with a horny forefinger and squinted through his spectacles. 'Now that fust cow – she's number eighty-fower.'

'Splendid!' I said. 'I'll just check this one and then we can go by the book.' I peered into the ear. 'That's funny, I make it twenty-six.'

The brothers had a look. 'You're right, sorr, you're right. It IS twenty-six.'

Walter pursed his lips. 'Why, that's Bluebell's calf isn't it?'

'Nay,' said Fenwick, 'she's out of awd Buttercup.'

'Can't be,' mumbled Thomas. 'Awd Buttercup was sold to Tim Jefferson afore this 'un was born. This is Brenda's calf.'

William shook his head. 'Ah'm sure we got her as a heifer at Bob Ashby's sale.'

'All right,' I said, holding up a hand. 'We'll put in twenty-six.' I had to cut in. It was in no way an argument, just a leisurely discussion but it looked as if it could go on for some time. I wrote the number in my notebook and injected the cow. 'Now how about this next one?'

'Well ah DO know that 'un,' said Walter confidently, stabbing at an entry in the diary. 'Can't make no mistake, she's number five.'

I looked in the ear. 'Says a hundred and thirty-seven here.'

It started again. 'She was brought in, wasn't she?' 'Nay, nay, she's out of awd Dribbler.' 'Don't think so – Dribbler had nowt but bulls . . .'

I raised my hand again. 'You know, I really think it might be quicker to look in all the ears. Time's getting on.'

'Aye, you're right, sorr, it IS getting on.' Walter returned the herd record to his waistcoat pocket philosophically and we started the laborious business of clipping, measuring and injecting every animal, plus rubbing the inside of the ears with a cloth soaked in spirit to identify the numbers which had often faded to a few unrelated dots. Occasionally Walter referred to his tiny book. 'Ah, that's right, ninety-two. I thowt so. It's all set down here.'

Fighting with the loose animals in the boxes round the fold yard was like having a dirty Turkish bath while wearing oil-skins. The brothers caught the big beasts effortlessly and even the strongest bullock grew quickly discouraged when it tried to struggle against those mighty arms. But I noticed one strange phenomenon: the men's fingers were so thick and huge that they often slipped out of the animals' noses through sheer immobility.

It took an awful long time but we finally got through. The last little calf had a space clipped in his shaggy neck and bawled heartily as he felt the needle, then I was out in the sweet air throwing my coat in the car boot. I looked at my watch – three o'clock. I was nearly two hours behind my schedule now and already I was hot and weary, with skinned toes on my right foot where a cow had trodden and a bruised left instep caused by the sudden descent of Fenwick's size thirteen hobnails during a particularly violent mêlée. As I closed the boot and limped round to the car door I began to wonder a little about this easy Ministry work.

Walter loomed over me and inclined his head graciously. 'Come in and sit down and have a drink o' tea.'

'It's very kind of you and I wish I could, Mr Hugill. But I've got a long string of inspections waiting and I don't know when I'll get round them. I've fixed up far too many and I completely underestimated the time needed for your test. I really am an absolute fool.'

And the brothers intoned sincerely. 'Aye, you're right, sorr, you're right, you're right.'

Well, there was no more testing today, but ten inspections still to do and I should have been at the first one two hours ago. I roared off, feeling that little ball tightening in my stomach as it always did when I was fighting the clock. Gripping the wheel with one hand and exploring my lunch packet with the other, I pulled out a piece of Mrs Hall's ham and egg pie and began to gnaw at it as I went along.

But I had gone only a short way when reason asserted itself. This was no good. It was an excellent pie and I might as well enjoy it. I pulled off the unfenced road on to the grass, switched off the engine and opened the windows wide. The farm back there was like an island of activity in the quiet landscape and now that I was away from the noise and the stuffiness of the buildings the silence and the emptiness enveloped me like a soothing blanket. I leaned my head against the back of the seat and looked out at the checkered greens of the little fields along the flanks of the hills; thrusting upwards between their walls till they gave way to the jutting rocks and the harsh brown of the heather which flooded the wild country above.

I felt better when I drove away and didn't particularly mind when the farmer at the first inspection greeted me with a scowl.

'This isn't one o'clock, Maister!' he snapped. 'My cows have been in all afternoon and look at the bloody mess they've made. Ah'll never get the place clean again!'

I had to agree with him when I saw the muck piled up behind the cows; it was one of the snags about housing animals in grass time. And the farmer's expression grew blacker as most of them cocked their tails as though in welcome and added further layers to the heaps.

'I won't keep you much longer,' I said briskly, and began to work my way down the row. Before the tuberculin testing scheme came into being, these clinical examinations were the only means of detecting tuberculous cows and I moved from animal to animal palpating the udders for any unusual induration. The routine examinations were known jocularly in the profession as 'bag-snatching' or 'cow-punching' and it was a job that soon got tedious.

I found the only way to stop myself going nearly mad with boredom was to keep reminding myself what I was there for. So when I came to a gaunt red cow with a pendulous udder I straightened up and turned to the farmer.

'I'm going to take a milk sample from this one. She's a bit hard in the left hind quarter.'

The farmer sniffed. 'Please yourself. There's nowt wrong with her but I suppose it'll make a job for somebody.'

Squirting milk from the quarter into a two ounce bottle, I thought about Siegfried's veterinary friend who always took a pint sample from the healthiest udder he could find to go with his lunchtime sandwiches.

I labelled the bottle and put it into the car. We had a little electric centrifuge at Skeldale House and tonight I would spin this milk and examine the sediment on a slide after staining by Ziehl-Neelsen. Probably I would find nothing but at times there was the strange excitement of peering down the microscope at a clump of bright red, iridescent TB bacilli. When that happened the cow was immediately slaughtered and there was always the thought that I might have lifted the death sentence from some child – the meningitis, the spinal and lung infections which were so common in those days.

Returning to the byre I finished the inspection by examining the wall in front of each cow.

The farmer watched me dourly. 'What you on with now?'

'Well, if a cow has a cough you can often find some spit on the wall.' I had, in truth, found more tuberculous cows this way than any other – by scraping a little sputum on to a glass slide and then staining it as for the milk.

The modern young vet just about never sees a TB cow, thank heavens, but 'screws' were all too common thirty years ago. There were very few in the high Pennines but in the low country on the plain you found them; the cows that 'weren't doing right', the ones with the soft, careful cough and slightly accelerated breathing. Often they were good milkers and ate well, but they were killers and I was learning to spot them. And there were the others, the big, fat, sleek animals which could still be riddled with the disease. They were killers of a more insidious kind and nobody could pick them out. It took the tuberculin test to do that.

At the next four places I visited, the farmers had got tired of waiting for me and had turned their cows out. They had all to be brought in from the field and they came slowly and reluctantly; there was nothing like the rodeo I had had with Mr Kay's heifers but a lot more time was lost. The animals kept trying to turn back to the field while I sped around their flanks like a demented sheep dog; and as I panted to and fro each farmer told me the same thing – that cows only liked to come in at milking time.

Milking time did eventually come and I caught three of my herds while they were being milked, but it was after six when I came tired and hungry to my second last inspection. A hush hung over the place and after shouting my way round the buildings without finding anybody I walked over to the house.

'Is your husband in, Mrs Bell?' I asked.

'No, he's had to go into t'village to get the horse shod but he won't be long before he's back. He's left cows in for you,' the farmer's wife replied.

That was fine. I'd soon get through this lot. I almost ran into the byre and started the old routine, feeling sick to death of the sight and smell of cows and fed up with pawing at their udders. I was working along almost automatically when I came to a thin, rangy cow with a narrow red and white face; she could be a crossed Shorthorn-Ayrshire. I had barely touched her udder when she lashed out with the speed of light and caught me just above the kneecap.

I hopped round the byre on one leg, groaning and swearing in my agony. It was some time before I was able to limp back to have another try and this time I scratched her back and cush-cushed her in a wheedling tone before sliding my hand gingerly between her legs. The same thing happened again only this time the sharp-edged cloven foot smacked slightly higher up my leg.

Crashing back against the wall, I huddled there, almost weeping with pain and rage. After a few minutes I reached a decision. To hell with her. If she didn't want to be examined she could take her luck. I had had enough for one day – I was in no mood for heroics.

Ignoring her, I proceeded down the byre till I had inspected the others. But I had to pass her on my way back and paused to have another look; and whether it was sheer stubbornness or whether I imagined she was laughing at me, I don't know, but I decided to have just one more go. Maybe she didn't like me coming from behind. Perhaps if I worked from the side she wouldn't mind so much.

Carefully I squeezed my way between her and her neighbour, gasping as the craggy pelvic bones dug into my ribs. Once in the space beyond, I thought, I would be free to do my job; and that was my big mistake. Because as soon as I had got there the cow went to work on me in earnest. Switching her back end round quickly to cut off my way of escape, she began to kick me systematically from head to foot. She kicked forward, reaching at times high on my chest as I strained back against the wall.

Since then I have been kicked by an endless variety of cows in all sorts of situations but never by such an expert as this one. There must be very few really venomous bovines and when one of them uses her feet it is usually an instinctive reaction to being hurt or frightened; and they kick blindly. But this cow measured me up before each blow and her judgement of distance was beautiful. And as she drove me further towards her head she was able to hook me in the back with her horns by way of variety. I am convinced she hated the human race.

My plight was desperate. I was completely trapped and it didn't help when the apparently docile cow next door began to get into the act by prodding me off with her horns as I pressed against her.

I don't know what made me look up, but there, in the thick wall of the byre was a hole about two feet square where some of the crumbling stone had fallen out. I pulled myself up with an agility that amazed me and as I crawled through head first a sweet fragrance came up to me. I was looking into a hay barn and, seeing a deep bed of finest clover just below I launched myself into space and did a very creditable roll in the air before landing safely on my back.

Lying there, bruised and breathless, with the front of my coat thickly patterned with claw marks I finally abandoned any lingering illusions I had had that Ministry work was a soft touch.

I was rising painfully to my feet when Mr Bell strolled in. 'Sorry ah had to go out,' he said, looking me over with interest, 'But I'd just about given you up. You're 'ellish late.'

I dusted myself down and picked a few strands of hay from my hair. 'Yes, sorry about that. But never mind, I managed to get the job done.'

'But . . . were you havin' a bit of a kip, then?'

'No, not exactly. I had some trouble with one of your cows.' There wasn't much point in standing on my dignity. I told him the story.

Even the friendliest farmer seems to derive pleasure from a vet's discomfiture and Mr Bell listened with an ever-widening grin of delight. By the time I had finished he was doubled up, beating his breeches knees with his hands.

'I can just imagine it. That Ayrshire cross! She's a right bitch. Picked her up cheap at market last spring and thought ah'd got a bargain, but ah soon found out. Took us a fortnight to get bugger tied up!'

'Well, I just wish I'd known,' I said, rather tight lipped.

The farmer looked up at the hole in the wall. 'And you crawled through . . .' he went into another convulsion which lasted some time, then he took off his cap and wiped his eyes with the lining.

'Oh dear, oh dear,' he murmured weakly. 'By gaw, I wish I'd been here.'

My last call was just outside Darrowby and I could hear the church clock striking a quarter past seven as I got stiffly out of the car. After my easy day in the service of the government I felt broken in mind and body; I had to suppress a scream when I saw yet another long line of cows' backsides awaiting me. The sun was low, and dark thunder clouds piling up in the west had thrown the countryside into an eerie darkness; and in the old-fashioned, slit-windowed byre the animals looked shapeless and ill-defined in the gloom.

Right, no messing about. I was going to make a quick job of this and get off home; home to some food and an armchair. I had no further ambitions. So left hand on the root of the tail, right hand between the hind legs, a quick feel around and on to the next one. Eyes half closed, my mind numb, I moved from cow to cow going through the motions like a robot with the far end of the byre seeming like the promised land.

And finally here it was, the very last one up against the wall. Left hand on tail, right hand between legs . . . At first my tired brain didn't take in the fact that there was something different here, but there was . . . something vastly different. A lot of space and instead of the udder a deeply cleft, pendulous something with no teats anywhere.

I came awake suddenly and looked along the animal's side. A huge woolly head was turned towards me and two wide-set eyes regarded me enquiringly. In the dull light I could just see the gleam of the copper ring in the nose.

The farmer who had watched me in silence, spoke up.

'You're wasting your time there, young man. There's nowt wrong wi' HIS bag.'

Chapter Twelve

The card dangled above the old lady's bed. It read 'God is Near' but it wasn't like the usual religious text. It didn't have a frame or ornate printing. It was just a strip of cardboard about eight inches long with plain lettering which might have said 'No smoking' or 'Exit' and it was looped carelessly over an old gas bracket so that Miss Stubbs from where she lay could look up at it and read 'God is Near' in square black capitals.

There wasn't much more Miss Stubbs could see; perhaps a few feet of privet hedge through the frayed curtains but mainly it was just the cluttered little room which had been her world for so many years.

The room was on the ground floor and in the front of the cottage, and as I came up through the wilderness which had once been a garden I could see the dogs watching me from where they had jumped on to the old lady's bed. And when I knocked on the door the place almost erupted with their barking. It was always like this. I had been visiting regularly for over a year and the pattern never changed; the furious barking, then Mrs Broadwith who looked after Miss Stubbs would push all the animals but my patient into the back kitchen and open the door and I would go in and see Miss Stubbs in the corner in her bed with the card hanging over it.

She had been there for a long time and would never get up again. But she never mentioned her illness and pain to me; all her concern was for her three dogs and two cats.

Today it was old Prince and I was worried about him. It was his heart – just about the most spectacular valvular incompetence I had ever heard. He was waiting for me as I came in, pleased as ever to see me, his long, fringed tail waving gently.

The sight of that tail used to make me think there must be a lot of Irish Setter in Prince but I was inclined to change my mind as I worked my way forward over the bulging black and white body to the shaggy head and upstanding Alsatian ears. Miss Stubbs often used to call him 'Mr Heinz' and though he may not have had 57 varieties in him his hybrid vigour had stood him in good stead. With his heart he should have been dead long ago.

'I thought I'd best give you a ring, Mr Herriot,' Mrs Broadwith said. She was a comfortable, elderly widow with a square, ruddy face contrasting sharply with the pinched features on the pillow. 'He's been coughing right bad this week and this morning he was a bit staggery. Still eats well, though.'

'I bet he does.' I ran my hands over the rolls of fat on the ribs. 'It would take something really drastic to put old Prince off his grub.'

Miss Stubbs laughed from the bed and the old dog, his mouth wide, eyes dancing, seemed to be joining in the joke. I put my stethoscope over his heart and listened, knowing well what I was going to hear. They say the heart is supposed to go 'Lub-dup, lub-dup', but Prince's went 'swish-swoosh, swish-swoosh'. There seemed to be nearly as much blood leaking back as was being pumped into the circulatory system. And another thing, the 'swish-swoosh' was a good bit faster than last time; he was on oral digitalis but it wasn't quite doing its job.

Gloomily I moved the stethoscope over the rest of the chest. Like all old dogs with a chronic heart weakness he had an ever-present bronchitis and I listened without enthusiasm to the symphony of whistles, rales, squeaks and bubbles which signalled the workings of Prince's lungs. The old dog stood very erect and proud, his tail still waving slowly. He always took it as a tremendous compliment when I examined him and there was no doubt he was enjoying himself now. Fortunately his was not a very painful ailment.

Straightening up, I patted his head and he responded immediately by trying to put his paws on my chest. He didn't quite make it and even that slight exertion started his ribs heaving and his tongue lolling. I gave him an intramuscular injection of digitalin and another of morphine hydrochloride which he accepted with apparent pleasure as part of the game.

'I hope that will steady his heart and breathing, Miss Stubbs. You'll find he'll be a bit dopey for the rest of the day and that will help, too. Carry on with the tablets, and I'm going to leave you some more medicine for his bronchitis.' I handed over a bottle of my old standby mixture of ipecacuanha and ammonium acetate.

The next stage of the visit began now as Mrs Broadwith brought in a cup of tea and the rest of the animals were let out of the kitchen. There were Ben, a Sealyham, and Sally, a Cocker Spaniel, and they started a deafening barking contest with Prince. They were closely followed by the cats, Arthur and Susie, who stalked in gracefully and began to rub themselves against my trouser legs.

It was the usual scenario for the many cups of tea I had drunk with Miss Stubbs under the little card which dangled above her bed.

'How are you today?' I asked.

'Oh, much better,' she replied and immediately, as always, changed the subject.

Mostly she liked to talk about her pets and the ones she had known right back to her girlhood. She spoke a lot, too, about the days when her family were alive. She loved to describe the escapades of her three brothers and today she showed me a photograph which Mrs Broadwith had found at the bottom of a drawer.

I took it from her and three young men in the knee breeches and little round caps of the nineties smiled up at me from the yellowed old print; they all held long church warden pipes and the impish humour in their expressions came down undimmed over the years.

'My word, they look really bright lads, Miss Stubbs,' I said.

'Oh, they were young rips!' she exclaimed. She threw back her head and laughed and for a moment her face was radiant, transfigured by her memories.

The things I had heard in the village came back to me; about the prosperous father and his family who lived in the big house many years ago. Then the foreign investments which crashed and the sudden change in circumstances.

'When t'owd feller died he was about skint,' one old man had said. 'There's not much brass there now.'

Probably just enough brass to keep Miss Stubbs and her animals alive and to pay Mrs Broadwith. Not enough to keep the garden dug or the house painted or for any of the normal little luxuries.

And, sitting there, drinking my tea, with the dogs in a row by the bedside and the cats making themselves comfortable on the bed itself, I felt as I had often felt before – a bit afraid of the responsibility I had. The one thing which brought some light into the life of the brave old woman was the transparent devotion of this shaggy bunch whose eyes were never far from her face. And the snag was that they were all elderly.

There had, in fact, been four dogs originally, but one of them, a truly ancient golden Labrador, had died a few months previously. And now I had the rest of them to look after and none of them less than ten years old.

They were perky enough but all showing some of the signs of old age; Prince with his heart, Sally beginning to drink a lot of water which made me wonder if she was starting with a pyometra. Ben growing steadily thinner with his nephritis. I couldn't give him new kidneys and I hadn't much faith in the hexamine tablets I had prescribed. Another peculiar thing about Ben was that I was always having to clip his claws; they grew at an extraordinary rate.

The cats were better, though Susie was a bit scraggy and I kept up a morbid kneading of her furry abdomen for signs of lymphosarcoma. Arthur was the best of the bunch; he never seemed to ail anything beyond a tendency for his teeth to tartar up.

This must have been in Miss Stubbs' mind because, when I had finished my tea, she asked me to look at him. I hauled him across the bedspread and opened his mouth.

'Yes, there's a bit of the old trouble there. Might as well fix it while I'm here.'

Arthur was a huge, grey, neutered Tom, a living denial of all those theories that cats are cold-natured, selfish and the rest. His fine eyes, framed in the widest cat face I have ever seen, looked out on the world with an all-embracing benevolence and tolerance. His every movement was marked by immense dignity.

As I started to scrape his teeth his chest echoed with a booming purr like a distant outboard motor. There was no need for anybody to hold him; he sat there placidly and moved only once – when I was using forceps to crack off a tough piece of tartar from a back tooth and accidentally nicked his gum. He casually raised a massive paw as if to say 'Have a care, chum', but his claws were sheathed.

My next visit was less than a month later and was in response to an urgent summons from Mrs Broadwith at six o'clock in the evening. Ben had collapsed. I jumped straight into my car and in less than ten minutes was threading my way through the overgrown grass in the front garden with the animals watching from their window. The barking broke out as I knocked, but Ben's was absent. As I went into the little room I saw the old dog lying on his side, very still, by the bed.

DOA is what we write in the day book. Dead on arrival. Just three words but they covered all kinds of situations – the end of milk fever cows, bloated bullocks, calves in fits. And tonight they meant that I wouldn't be clipping old Ben's claws any more.

It wasn't often these nephritis cases went off so suddenly but his urine albumen had been building up dangerously lately.

'Well, it was quick, Miss Stubbs. I'm sure the old chap didn't suffer at all.' My words sounded lame and ineffectual.

The old lady was in full command of herself. No tears, only a fixity of expression as she looked down from the bed at her companion for so many years. My idea was to get him out of the place as quickly as possible and I pulled a blanket under him and lifted him up. As I was moving away, Miss Stubbs said, 'Wait a moment.' With an effort she turned on to her side and gazed at Ben. Still without changing expression, she reached out and touched his head lightly. Then she lay back calmly as I hurried from the room.

In the back kitchen I had a whispered conference with Mrs Broadwith. 'I'll run down t'village and get Fred Manners to come and bury him,' she said. 'And if you've got the time could you stay with the old lady while I'm gone. Talk to her, like, it'll do her good.'

I went back and sat down by the bed. Miss Stubbs looked out of the window for a few moments then turned to me. 'You know, Mr Herriot,' she said casually. 'It will be my turn next.'

'What do you mean?'

'Well, tonight Ben has gone and I'm going to be the next one. I just know it.'

'Oh, nonsense! You're feeling a bit low, that's all. We all do when something like this happens.' But I was disturbed. I had never heard her even hint at such a thing before.

'I'm not afraid,' she said. 'I know there's something better waiting for me. I've never had any doubts.' There was silence between us as she lay calmly looking up at the card on the gas bracket.

Then the head on the pillow turned to me again. 'I have only one fear.' Her expression changed with startling suddenness as if a mask had dropped. The brave face was almost unrecognisable. A kind of terror flickered in her eyes and she quickly grasped my hand.

'It's my dogs and cats, Mr Herriot. I'm afraid I might never see them when I'm gone and it worries me so. You see, I know I'll be reunited with my parents and my brothers but ... but ...'

'Well, why not with your animals?'

'That's just it.' She rocked her head on the pillow and for the first time I saw tears on her cheeks. 'They say animals have no souls.'

'Who says?'

'Oh, I've read it and I know a lot of religious people believe it.'

'Well I don't believe it.' I patted the hand which still grasped mine. 'If having a soul means being able to feel love and loyalty and gratitude, then animals are better off than a lot of humans. You've nothing to worry about there.'

'Oh, I hope you're right. Sometimes I lie at night thinking about it.'

'I know I'm right, Miss Stubbs, and don't you argue with me. They teach us vets all about animals' souls.'

The tension left her face and she laughed with a return of her old spirit. 'I'm sorry to bore you with this and I'm not going to talk about it again. But before you go, I want you to be absolutely honest with me. I don't want reassurance from you – just the truth. I know you are very young but please tell me – what are your beliefs? Will my animals go with me?'

She stared intently into my eyes. I shifted in my chair and swallowed once or twice.

'Miss Stubbs, I'm afraid I'm a bit foggy about all this,' I said. 'But I'm absolutely certain of one thing. Wherever you are going, they are going too.'

She still stared at me but her face was calm again. 'Thank you, Mr Herriot, I know you are being honest with me. That is what you really believe, isn't it?'

'I do believe it,' I said. 'With all my heart I believe it.'

It must have been about a month later and it was entirely by accident that I learned I had seen Miss Stubbs for the last time. When a lonely, penniless old woman dies people don't rush up to you in the street to tell you. I was on my rounds and a farmer happened to mention that the cottage in Corby village was up for sale.

'But what about Miss Stubbs?' I asked.

'Oh, went off sudden about three weeks ago. House is in a bad state, they say – nowt been done at it for years.'

'Mrs Broadwith isn't staying on, then?'

'Nay, I hear she's staying at t'other end of village.'

'Do you know what's happened to the dogs and cats?'

'What dogs and cats?'

I cut my visit short. And I didn't go straight home though it was nearly lunch time. Instead I urged my complaining little car at top speed to Corby and asked the first person I saw where Mrs Broadwith was living. It was a tiny house but attractive and Mrs Broadwith answered my knock herself.

'Oh, come in, Mr Herriot. It's right good of you to call.' I went inside and we sat facing each other across a scrubbed table top.

'Well, it was sad about the old lady,' she said.

'Yes, I've only just heard.'

'Any road, she had a peaceful end. Just slept away at finish.'

'I'm glad to hear that.'

Mrs Broadwith looked round the room. 'I was real lucky to get this place – it's just what I've always wanted.'

I could contain myself no longer. 'What's happened to the animals?' I blurted out.

'Oh, they're in t'garden,' she said calmly. 'I've got a grand big stretch at back.' She got up and opened the door and with a surge of relief I watched my old friends pour in.

Arthur was on my knee in a flash, arching himself ecstatically against my arm while his outboard motor roared softly above the barking of the dogs. Prince, wheezy as ever, tail fanning the air, laughing up at me delightedly between barks.

'They look great, Mrs Broadwith. How long are they going to be here?'

'They're here for good. I think just as much about them as t'old lady ever did and I couldn't be parted from them. They'll have a good home with me as long as they live.'

I looked at the typical Yorkshire country face, at the heavy cheeks with their grim lines belied by the kindly eyes. 'This is wonderful,' I said. 'But won't you find it just a bit . . . er . . . expensive to feed them?'

'Nay, you don't have to worry about that. I 'ave a bit put away.'

'Well fine, fine, and I'll be looking in now and then to see how they are. I'm through the village every few days.' I got up and started for the door.

Mrs Broadwith held up her hand. 'There's just one thing I'd like you to do before they start selling off the things at the cottage. Would you please pop in and collect what's left of your medicines. They're in t'front room.'

I took the key and drove along to the other end of the village. As I pushed open the rickety gate and began to walk through the tangled grass the front of the cottage looked strangely lifeless without the faces of the dogs at the window; and when the door creaked open and I went inside the silence was like a heavy pall.

Nothing had been moved. The bed with its rumpled blankets was still in the corner. I moved around, picking up half empty bottles, a jar of ointment, the cardboard box with old Ben's tablets – a lot of good they had done him.

When I had got everything I looked slowly round the little room. I wouldn't be coming here any more and at the door I paused and read for the last time the card which hung over the empty bed.

Chapter Thirteen

I was spending Tuesday evening as I spent all the Tuesday evenings – staring at the back of Helen Alderson's head at the Darrowby Music Society. It was a slow way of getting to know her better but I had been unable to think of a better idea.

Since the morning on the high moor when I had set the calf's leg, I had scanned the day book regularly in the hope of getting another visit to the farm. But the Aldersons seemed to have lamentably healthy stock. I had to be content with the thought that there was the visit at the month end to take off the plaster. The really crushing blow came when Helen's father rang up to say that, since the calf was going sound he had removed the plaster himself. He was pleased to say that the fracture had knitted perfectly and there was no sign of lameness.

I had come to admire the self-reliance and initiative of the Dalesmen but I cursed it now at great length; and I joined the Music Society. I had seen Helen going into the schoolroom where the meetings were held and, with the courage of desperation, had followed her inside.

That was weeks ago and, I reflected miserably, I had made no progress at all. I couldn't remember how many tenors, sopranos and male voice choirs had come and gone and on one occasion the local brass band had packed themselves into the little room and almost burst my ear drums; but I was no further forward.

Tonight a string quartet was scraping away industriously, but I hardly heard them. My eyes, as usual, were focused on Helen, several rows in front of me, sitting between the two old ladies she always seemed to bring with her. That was part of the trouble; those two old girls were always there, cutting out any chance of private conversation, even at the half-time break for tea. And there was the general atmosphere of the place; the members were nearly all elderly, and over everything hung the powerful schoolroom scent of ink and exercise books and chalk and lead pencils. It was the sort of place where you just couldn't say without warning 'Are you doing anything on Saturday night?'

The scraping stopped and everybody clapped. The vicar got up from the front row and beamed on the company. 'And now, ladies and gentlemen, I think we might stop for fifteen minutes as I see our willing helpers have prepared tea. The price, as usual is threepence.' There was laughter and a general pushing back of chairs.

I went to the back of the hall with the others, put my threepence on the plate and collected a cup of tea and a biscuit. This was when I tried to get near Helen in the blind hope that something might happen. It wasn't always easy, because I was often buttonholed by the school headmaster and others who regarded a vet who liked music as an interesting curiosity, but tonight I managed to edge myself as if by accident into her group.

She looked at me over the top of her cup. 'Good evening, Mr Herriot, are you enjoying it?' Oh God, she always said that. And Mr Herriot! But what could I do? 'Call me Jim', would sound great. I replied, as always, 'Good evening,

Miss Alderson. Yes, it's very nice, isn't it.' Things were going with a bang again.

I munched my biscuit while the old ladies talked about Mozart. It was going to be the same as all the other Tuesdays. It was about time I gave up the whole thing. I felt beaten.

The vicar approached our group, still beaming. 'I'm afraid I have to call on somebody for the washing-up rota. Perhaps our two young friends would take it on tonight.' His friendly gaze twinkled from Helen to me and back again.

The idea of washing up teacups had never held much attraction for me but suddenly it was like sighting the promised land. 'Yes, certainly, delighted – that is if it's all right with Miss Alderson.'

Helen smiled. 'Of course it's all right. We all have to take a turn, don't we?'

I wheeled the trolley of cups and saucers into the scullery. It was a cramped, narrow place with a sink and a few shelves and there was just about room for the two of us to get inside.

'Would you like to wash or dry?' Helen asked.

'I'll wash,' I replied and began to run the hot water into the sink. It shouldn't be too difficult now, I thought, to work the conversation round to where I wanted it. I'd never have a better chance than now, jammed into this little room with Helen.

But it was surprising how the time went by. Five whole minutes and we hadn't talked about anything but music. With mounting frustration I saw that we had nearly got through the pile of crockery and I had achieved nothing. The feeling changed to near panic when I lifted the last cup from the soapy water.

It had to be now. I held out the cup to Helen and she tried to take it from me; but I kept a grip on the handle while I waited for inspiration. She pulled gently but I clung to it tenaciously. It was developing into a tug of war. Then I heard a hoarse croak which I only just recognised as my own voice. 'Can I see you some time?'

For a moment she didn't answer and I tried to read her face. Was she surprised, annoyed, even shocked? She flushed and replied, 'If you like.' I heard the croak again. 'Saturday evening?' She nodded, dried the cup and was gone.

I went back to my seat with my heart thudding. The strains of mangled Haydn from the quartet went unheeded. I had done it at last. But did she really want to come out? Had she been hustled into it against her will? My toes curled with embarrassment at the thought, but I consoled myself with the knowledge that for better or for worse it was a step forward. Yes, I had done it at last.

Chapter Fourteen

As I sat at breakfast I looked out at the autumn mist dissolving in the early sunshine. It was going to be another fine day but there was a chill in the old house this morning, a shiveriness as though a cold hand had reached out to remind us that summer had gone and the hard months lay just ahead.

'It says here,' Siegfried said, adjusting his copy of the *Darrowby and Houlton Times* with care against the coffee-pot, 'that farmers have no feeling for their animals.'

I buttered a piece of toast and looked across at him.

'Cruel, you mean?'

'Well, not exactly, but this chap maintains that to a farmer, livestock are purely commercial – there's no sentiment in his attitude towards them, no affection.'

'Well, it wouldn't do if they were all like poor Kit Bilton, would it? They'd all go mad.'

Kit was a lorry driver who, like so many of the working men of Darrowby, kept a pig at the bottom of his garden for family consumption. The snag was that when killing time came, Kit wept for three days. I happened to go into the house on one of these occasions and found his wife and daughter hard at it cutting up the meat for pies and brawn while Kit huddled miserably by the kitchen fire, his eyes swimming with tears. He was a huge man who could throw a twelve stone sack of meal on to his wagon with a jerk of his arms, but he seized my hand in his and sobbed at me 'I can't bear it, Mr Herriot. He was like a Christian was that pig, just like a Christian.'

'No, I agree,' Siegfried leaned over and sawed off a slice of Mrs Hall's home-baked bread. 'But Kit isn't a real farmer. This article is about people who own large numbers of animals. The question is, is it possible for such men to become emotionally involved? Can the dairy farmer milking maybe fifty cows become really fond of any of them or are they just milk producing units?'

'It's an interesting point,' I said, 'And I think you've put your finger on it with the numbers. You know there are a lot of our farmers up in the high country who have only a few stock. They always have names for their cows – Daisy, Mabel, I even came across one called Kipperlugs the other day. I do think these small farmers have an affection for their animals but I don't see how the big men can possibly have.'

Siegfried rose from the table and stretched luxuriously. 'You're probably right. Anyway, I'm sending you to see a really big man this morning. John Skipton of Dennaby Close – he's got some tooth rasping to do. Couple of old horses losing condition. You'd better take all the instruments, it might be anything.'

I went through to the little room down the passage and surveyed the tooth instruments. I always felt at my most mediaeval when I was caught up in large animal dentistry and in the days of the draught horse it was a regular task. One of the commonest jobs was knocking the wolf teeth out of young horses. I have no idea how it got its name but you found the little wolf tooth just in front of the molars and if a young horse was doing badly it always got the blame.

It was no good the vets protesting that such a minute, vestigial object couldn't possibly have any effect on the horse's health and that the trouble was probably due to worms. The farmers were adamant; the tooth had to be removed.

We did this by having the horse backed into a corner, placing the forked end of a metal rod against the tooth and giving a sharp tap with an absurdly large wooden mallet. Since the tooth had no proper root the operation was not particularly painful, but the horse still didn't like it. We usually had a couple of fore-feet waving around our ears at each tap.

And the annoying part was that after we had done the job and pointed out to the farmer that we had only performed this bit of black magic to humour him, the horse would take an immediate turn for the better and thrive consistently from then on. Farmers are normally reticent about our successful efforts for fear we might put a bit more on the bill but in these cases they cast aside all caution. They would shout at us across the market place: 'Hey, remember that 'oss you knocked wolf teeth out of? Well he never looked back. It capped him.'

I looked again with distaste at the tooth instruments; the vicious forceps with two-feet-long arms, sharp-jawed shears, mouth gags, hammers and chisels, files and rasps; it was rather like a quiet corner in the Spanish Inquisition. We kept a long wooden box with a handle for carrying the things and I staggered out to the car with a fair selection.

Dennaby Close was not just a substantial farm, it was a monument to a man's endurance and skill. The fine old house, the extensive buildings, the great sweep of lush grassland along the lower slopes of the fell were all proof that old John Skipton had achieved the impossible; he had started as an uneducated farm labourer and he was now a wealthy landowner.

The miracle hadn't happened easily; old John had a lifetime of grinding toil behind him that would have killed most men, a lifetime with no room for a wife or family or creature comforts, but there was more to it than that; there was a brilliant acumen in agricultural matters that had made the old man a legend in the district. 'When all t'world goes one road, I go t'other' was one of his quoted sayings and it is true that the Skipton farms had made money in the hard times when others were going bankrupt. Dennaby was only one of John's farms; he had two large arable places of about four hundred acres each lower down the Dale.

He had conquered, but to some people it seemed that he had himself been conquered in the process. He had battled against the odds for so many years and driven himself so fiercely that he couldn't stop. He could be enjoying all kinds of luxuries now but he just hadn't the time; they said that the poorest of his workers lived in better style than he did.

I paused as I got out of the car and stood gazing at the house as though I had never seen it before; and I marvelled again at the elegance which had withstood over three hundred years of the harsh climate. People came a long way to see Dennaby Close and take photographs of the graceful manor with its tall, leaded windows, the massive chimneys towering over the old moss-grown tiles; or to wander through the neglected garden and climb up the sweep of steps to the entrance with its wide stone arch over the great studded door.

There should have been a beautiful woman in one of those pointed hats peeping out from that mullioned casement or a cavalier in ruffles and hose pacing beneath the high wall with its pointed copings. But there was just old John stumping impatiently towards me, his tattered, buttonless coat secured only by a length of binder twine round his middle.

'Come in a minute, young man,' he cried. 'I've got a little bill to pay you.' He led the way round to the back of the house and I followed, pondering on the odd fact that it was always a 'little bill' in Yorkshire. We went in through a flagged kitchen to a room which was graceful and spacious but furnished only with a table, a few wooden chairs and a collapsed sofa.

The old man bustled over to the mantelpiece and fished out a bundle of papers from behind the clock. He leafed through them, threw an envelope on to the table then produced a cheque book and slapped it down in front of me. I did the usual – took out the bill, made out the amount on the cheque and pushed it over for him to sign. He wrote with a careful concentration, the small-featured, weathered face bent low, the peak of the old cloth cap almost touching the pen. His trousers had ridden up his legs as he sat down showing the skinny calves and bare ankles. There were no socks underneath the heavy boots.

When I had pocketed the cheque, John jumped to his feet. 'We'll have to walk down to t'river; 'osses are down there.' He left the house almost at a trot.

I eased my box of instruments from the car boot. It was a funny thing but whenever I had heavy equipment to lug about, my patients were always a long way away. This box seemed to be filled with lead and it wasn't going to get any lighter on the journey down through the walled pastures.

The old man seized a pitch fork, stabbed it into a bale of hay and hoisted it effortlessly over his shoulder. He set off again at the same brisk pace. We made our way down from one gateway to another, often walking diagonally across the fields. John didn't reduce speed and I stumbled after him, puffing a little and trying to put away the thought that he was at least fifty years older than me.

About half way down we came across a group of men at the age-old task of 'walling' – repairing a gap in one of the dry stone walls which trace their patterns everywhere on the green slopes of the Dales. One of the men looked up. 'Nice mornin', Mr Skipton,' he sang out cheerfully.

'Bugger t'mornin'. Get on wi' some work,' grunted old John in reply and the man smiled contentedly as though he had received a compliment.

I was glad when we reached the flat land at the bottom. My arms seemed to have been stretched by several inches and I could feel a trickle of sweat on my brow. Old John appeared unaffected; he flicked the fork from his shoulder and the bale thudded on to the grass.

The two horses turned towards us at the sound. They were standing fetlock deep in the pebbly shallows just beyond a little beach which merged into the green carpet of turf; nose to tail, they had been rubbing their chins gently along each other's backs, unconscious of our approach. A high 'cliff overhanging the far bank made a perfect wind break while on either side of us clumps of oak and beech blazed in the autumn sunshine.

'They're in a nice spot, Mr Skipton,' I said.

'Aye, they can keep cool in the hot weather and they've got the barn when winter comes.' John pointed to a low, thick-walled building with a single door. 'They can come and go as they please.'

The sound of his voice brought the horses out of the river at a stiff trot and as they came near you could see they really were old. The mare was a chestnut and the gelding was a light bay but their coats were so flecked with grey that they almost looked like roans. This was most pronounced on their faces where the sprinkling of white hairs, the sunken eyes and the deep cavity above the eyes gave them a truly venerable appearance.

For all that, they capered around John with a fair attempt at skittishness, stamping their feet, throwing their heads about, pushing his cap over his eyes with their muzzles.

'Get by, leave off!' he shouted. 'Daft awd beggars.' But he tugged absently at the mare's forelock and ran his hand briefly along the neck of the gelding.

'When did they last do any work?' I asked.

'Oh, about twelve years ago, I reckon.'

I stared at John. 'Twelve years! And have they been down here all that time?'

'Aye, just lakin' about down here, retired like. They've earned it an' all.' For a few moments he stood silent, shoulders hunched, hands deep in the pockets of his coat, then he spoke quietly as if to himself. 'They were two slaves when I was a slave.' He turned and looked at me and for a revealing moment I read in the pale blue eyes something of the agony and struggle he had shared with the animals.

'But twelve years! How old are they, anyway?'

John's mouth twisted up at one corner. 'Well you're t'vet. You tell me.'

I stepped forward confidently, my mind buzzing with Galvayne's groove, shape of marks, degree of slope and the rest; I grasped the unprotesting upper lip of the mare and looked at her teeth.

'Good God!' I gasped, 'I've never seen anything like this.' The incisors were immensely long and projecting forward till they met at an angle of about forty-five degrees. There were no marks at all – they had long since gone.

I laughed and turned back to the old man. 'It's no good, I'd only be guessing. You'll have to tell me.'

'Well she's about thirty and gelding's a year or two younger. She's had fifteen grand foals and never ailed owt except a bit of teeth trouble. We've had them rasped a time or two and it's time they were done again, I reckon. They're both losing ground and dropping bits of half chewed hay from their mouths. Gelding's the worst – has a right job champin' his grub.'

I put my hand into the mare's mouth, grasped her tongue and pulled it out to one side. A quick exploration of the molars with my other hand revealed what I suspected; the outside edges of the upper teeth were overgrown and jagged and were irritating the cheeks while the inside edges of the lower molars were in a similar state and were slightly excoriating the tongue.

'I'll soon make her more comfortable, Mr Skipton. With those sharp edges rubbed off she'll be as good as new.' I got the rasp out of my vast box, held the tongue in one hand and worked the rough surface along the teeth, checking occasionally with my fingers till the points had been sufficiently reduced.

'That's about right,' I said after a few minutes. 'I don't want to make them too smooth or she won't be able to grind her food.'

John grunted. 'Good enough. Now have a look a t'other. There's summat far wrong with him.'

I had a feel at the gelding's teeth. 'Just the same as the mare. Soon put him right, too.'

But pushing at the rasp, I had an uncomfortable feeling that something was not quite right. The thing wouldn't go fully to the back of the mouth; something was stopping it. I stopped rasping and explored again, reaching with my fingers as far as I could. And I came upon something very strange, something which shouldn't have been there at all. It was like a great chunk of bone projecting down from the roof of the mouth.

It was time I had a proper look. I got out my pocket torch and shone it over the back of the tongue. It was easy to see the trouble now; the last upper molar was overlapping the lower one resulting in a gross overgrowth of the posterior border. The result was a sabre-like barb about three inches long stabbing down into the tender tissue of the gum.

That would have to come off – right now. My jauntiness vanished and I suppressed a shudder; it meant using the horrible shears – those great long-handled things with the screw operated by a cross bar. They gave me the willies because I am one of those people who can't bear to watch anybody blowing up a balloon and this was the same sort of thing only worse. You fastened the sharp blades of the shears on to the tooth and began to turn the bar slowly, slowly. Soon the tooth began to groan and creak under the tremendous leverage and you knew that any second it would break off and when it did it was like somebody letting off a rifle in your ear. That was when all hell usually broke loose but mercifully this was a quiet old horse and I wouldn't expect him to start dancing around on his hind legs. There was no pain for the horse because the overgrown part had no nerve supply – it was the noise that caused the trouble.

Returning to my crate I produced the dreadful instrument and with it a Haussman's gag which I inserted on the incisors and opened on its ratchet till the mouth gaped wide. Everything was easy to see then and, of course, there it was – a great prong at the other side of the mouth exactly like the first. Great, great, now I had two to chop off.

The old horse stood patiently, eyes almost closed, as though he had seen it all and nothing in the world was going to bother him. I went through the motions with my toes curling and when the sharp crack came, the white-bordered eyes opened wide, but only in mild surprise. He never even moved. When I did the other side he paid no attention at all; in fact, with the gag prising his jaws apart he looked exactly as though he was yawning with boredom.

As I bundled the tools away, John picked up the bony spicules from the grass and studied them with interest. 'Well, poor awd beggar. Good job I got you along, young man. Reckon he'll feel a lot better now.'

On the way back, old John, relieved of his bale, was able to go twice as fast and he stumped his way up the hill at a furious pace, using the fork as a staff. I panted along in the rear, changing the box from hand to hand every few minutes.

About half way up, the thing slipped out of my grasp and it gave me a chance to stop for a breather. As the old man muttered impatiently I looked back and could just see the two horses; they had returned to the shallows and were playing together, chasing each other jerkily, their feet splashing in the water. The cliff made a dark backcloth to the picture – the shining river, the trees glowing bronze and gold and the sweet green of the grass.

Back in the farm yard, John paused awkwardly. He nodded once or twice, said 'Thank ye, young man,' then turned abruptly and walked away.

I was dumping the box thankfully into the boot when I saw the man who had spoken to us on the way down. He was sitting, cheerful as ever, in a sunny corner, back against a pile of sacks, pulling his dinner packet from an old army satchel.

'You've been down to see t'pensioners, then? By gaw, awd John should know the way.'

'Regular visitor, is he?'

'Regular? Every day God sends you'll see t'awd feller ploddin' down there. Rain, snow or blow, never misses. And allus has summat with him – bag o' corn, straw for their bedding.'

'And he's done that for twelve years?'

The man unscrewed his thermos flask and poured himself a cup of black tea. 'Aye, them 'osses haven't done a stroke o' work all that time and he could've got good money for them from the horse flesh merchants. Rum 'un, isn't it?'

'You're right,' I said, 'it is a rum 'un.'

Just how rum it was occupied my thoughts on the way back to the surgery. I went back to my conversation with Siegfried that morning; we had just about decided that the man with a lot of animals couldn't be expected to feel affection for individuals among them. But those buildings back there were full of John Skipton's animals – he must have hundreds.

Yet what made him trail down that hillside every day in all weathers? Why had he filled the last years of those two old horses with peace and beauty? Why had he given them a final ease and comfort which he had withheld from himself?

It could only be love.

Chapter Fifteen

The longer I worked in Darrowby the more the charms of the Dales beguiled me. And there was one solid advantage of which I became more aware every day – the Dales farmers were all stocksmen. They really knew how to handle animals, and to a vet whose patients are constantly trying to thwart him or injure him it was a particular blessing.

So this morning I looked with satisfaction at the two men holding the cow. It wasn't a difficult job – just an intravenous injection of magnesium lactate – but still it was reassuring to have two such sturdy fellows to help me. Maurice Bennison, medium sized but as tough as one of his own hill beasts, had a horn in his right hand while the fingers of his left gripped the nose; I had the comfortable impression that the cow wouldn't jump very far when I pushed the needle in. His brother George whose job it was to raise the vein, held the choke rope limply in his enormous hands like bunches of carrots. He grinned down at me amiably from his six feet four inches.

'Right, George,' I said. 'Tighten up that rope and lean against the cow to stop her coming round on me.' I pushed my way between the cow and her neighbour, past George's unyielding bulk and bent over the jugular vein. It was standing out very nicely. I poised the needle, feeling the big man's elbow on me as he peered over my shoulder, and thrust quickly into the vein.

'Lovely!' I cried as the dark blood fountained out and spattered thickly on the straw bedding beneath. 'Slacken your rope, George.' I fumbled in my pocket for the flutter valve. 'And for God's sake, get your weight off me!'

Because George had apparently decided to rest his full fourteen stones on me instead of the cow, and as I tried desperately to connect the tube to the needle I felt my knees giving way. I shouted again, despairingly, but he was inert, his chin resting on my shoulder, his breathing stertorous in my ear.

There could only be one end to it. I fell flat on my face and lay there writhing under the motionless body. My cries went unheeded; George was unconscious.

Mr Bennison, attracted by the commotion, came in to the byre just in time to see me crawling out from beneath his eldest son. 'Get him out, quick!' I gasped, 'before the cows trample on him.' Wordlessly, Maurice and his father took an ankle apiece and hauled away in unison. George shot out from under the cows, his head beating a brisk tattoo on the cobbles, traversed the dung channel, then resumed his sleep on the byre floor.

Mr Bennison moved back to the cow and waited for me to continue with my injection but I found the presence of the sprawled body distracting. 'Look, couldn't we sit him up against the wall and put his head between his legs?' I suggested apologetically. The others glanced at each other then, as though deciding to humour me, grabbed George's shoulders and trundled him over the floor with the expertise of men used to throwing around bags of fertiliser and potatoes. But even propped against the rough stones, his head slumped forward and his great long arms hanging loosely, the poor fellow still didn't look so good.

I couldn't help feeling a bit responsible. 'Don't you think we might give him a drink?'

But Mr Bennison had had enough. 'Nay, nay, he'll be right,' he muttered testily. 'Let's get on with t'job.' Evidently he felt he had pampered George too much already.

The incident started me thinking about this question of people's reactions to the sight of blood and other disturbing realities. Even though it was only my second year of practice I had already formulated certain rules about this and one was that it was always the biggest men who went down. (I had, by this time, worked out a few other, perhaps unscientific theories, e.g. big dogs were kept by people who lived in little houses and vice versa. Clients who said 'spare no expense' never paid their bills, ever. When I asked my way in the Dales and was told 'you can't miss it', I knew I'd soon be hopelessly lost.)

I had begun to wonder if perhaps country folk, despite their closer contact with fundamental things, were perhaps more susceptible than city people. Ever since Sid Blenkhorn had staggered into Skeldale House one evening. His face was ghastly white and he had obviously passed through a shattering experience. 'Have you got a drop o' whisky handy, Jim?' he quavered, and when I had guided him to a chair and Siegfried had put a glass in his hand he told us he had been at a first aid lecture given by Dr Allinson, a few doors down the street. 'He was talking about veins and arteries and things,' groaned Sid, passing a hand across his forehead. 'God, it was awful!' Apparently Fred Ellison the fishmonger had been carried out unconscious after only ten minutes and Sid himself had only just made it to the door. It had been a shambles.

I was interested because this sort of thing, I had found, was always just round the corner. I suppose we must have more trouble in this way than the doctors because in most cases when our medical colleagues have any cutting or carving to do they send their patients to hospital while the vets just have to get their jackets off and operate on the spot. It means that the owners and attendants of the animals are pulled in as helpers and are subjected to some unusual sights.

So, even in my short experience, I had become a fair authority on the various manifestations of 'coming over queer'. I suppose it was a bit early to start compiling statistics but I had never seen a woman or a little man pass out even though they might exhibit various shadings of the squeamish spectrum. The big chap was the best bet every time, especially the boisterous, super-confident type.

I have a vivid recollection of a summer evening when I had to carry out a rumenotomy on a cow. As a rule I was inclined to play for time when I suspected a foreign body – there were so many other conditions with similar symptoms that I was never in a hurry to make a hole in the animal's side. But this time diagnosis was easy; the sudden fall in milk yield, loss of cudding; grunting, and the rigid, sunken-eyed appearance of the cow. And to clinch it the farmer told me he had been repairing a hen house in the cow pasture – nailing up loose boards. I knew where one of the nails had gone.

The farm, right on the main street of the village, was a favourite meeting place for the local lads. As I laid out my instruments on a clean towel draped over a straw bale a row of grinning faces watched from above the half door of the box; not only watched but encouraged me with ribald shouts. When I was about ready to start it occurred to me that an extra pair of hands would be helpful and I turned to the door. 'How would one of you lads like to be my assistant?' There was even more shouting for a minute or two, then the door was opened and a huge young man with a shock of red hair ambled into the box; he was a magnificent sight with his vast shoulders and the column of sunburned neck rising from the open shirt. It needed only the bright blue eyes and the ruddy, high-cheekboned face to remind me that the Norsemen had been around the Dales a thousand years ago. This was a Viking.

I had him roll up his sleeves and scrub his hands in a bucket of warm water and antiseptic while I infiltrated the cow's flank with local anaesthetic. When I gave him artery forceps and scissors to hold he pranced around, making stabbing motions at the cow and roaring with laughter.

'Maybe you'd like to do the job yourself?' I asked. The Viking squared his great shoulders. 'Aye, I'll 'ave a go,' and the heads above the door cheered lustily.

As I finally poised my Bard Parker scalpel with its new razor-sharp blade over the cow, the air was thick with earthy witticisms. I had decided that this time I really would make the bold incision recommended in the surgery books; it was about time I advanced beyond the stage of pecking nervously at the skin. 'A veritable blow,' was how one learned author had described it. Well, that was how it was going to be.

I touched the blade down on the clipped area of the flank and with a quick motion of the wrist laid open a ten-inch wound. I stood back for a few seconds admiring the clean-cut edges of the skin with only a few capillaries spurting on to the glistening, twitching abdominal muscles. At the same time I noticed that the laughter and shouting from the heads had been switched off and was replaced by an eerie silence broken only by a heavy, thudding sound from behind me.

'Forceps please,' I said, extending my hand back. But nothing happened. I looked round; the top of the half door was bare – not a head in sight. There was only the Viking spreadeagled in the middle of the floor, arms and legs flung wide, chin pointing to the roof. The attitude was so theatrical that I thought he was still acting the fool, but a closer examination erased all doubts: the Viking was out cold. He must have gone straight over backwards like a stricken oak.

The farmer, a bent little man who couldn't have scaled much more than eight stones, had been steadying the cow's head. He looked at me with the faintest flicker of amusement in his eyes. 'Looks like you and me for it, then, guvnor.' He tied the halter to a ring on the wall, washed his hands methodically and took up his place at my side. Throughout the operation, he passed me my instruments, swabbed away the seeping blood and clipped the sutures, whistling tunelessly through his teeth in a bored manner; the only time he showed any real emotion was when I produced the offending nail from the depths of the reticulum. He raised his eyebrows slightly, said ' 'ello, 'ello,' then started whistling again.

We were too busy to do anything for the Viking. Halfway through, he sat up, shook himself a few times then got to his feet and strolled with elaborate nonchalance out of the box. The poor fellow seemed to be hoping that perhaps we had noticed nothing unusual.

I don't suppose we could have done much to bring him round anyway. There was only one time I discovered a means of immediate resuscitation and that was by accident.

It was when Henry Dickson asked me to show him how to castrate a ruptured pig without leaving a swelling. Henry was going in for pigs in a big way and had a burning ambition to equip himself with veterinary skills.

When he showed me the young pig with the gross scrotal swelling I demurred. 'I really think this is a vet's job, Henry. Castrate your normal pigs by all means but I don't think you could make a proper job of this sort of thing.'

'How's that, then?'

'Well, there's the local anaesthetic, danger of infection – and you really need a knowledge of anatomy to know what you're doing.'

All the frustrated surgeon in Henry showed in his eyes. 'Gaw, I'd like to know how to do it.'

'I'll tell you what,' I said. 'How about if I do this one as a demonstration and you can make up your own mind. I'll give him a general anaesthetic so you don't have to hold him.'

'Right, that's a good idea.' Henry thought for a moment. 'What'll you charge me to do 'im?'

'Seven and six.'

'Well I suppose you have to have your pound of flesh. Get on.'

I injected a few cc's of Nembutal into the little pig's peritoneum and after some staggering he rolled over in the straw and lay still. Henry had rigged up a table in the yard and we laid the sleeping animal on it. I was preparing to start when Henry pulled out a ten-shilling note.

'Better pay you now before I forget.'

'All right, but my hands are clean now – push it into my pocket and I'll give you the change when we finish.'

I rather fancy myself as a teacher and soon warmed to my task. I carefully incised the skin over the inguinal canal and pulled out the testicle, intact in its tunics. 'See there, Henry, the bowels have come down the canal and are lying in with the testicle.' I pointed to the loops of intestine, pale pink through the translucent membranes. 'Now if I do this, I can push them right back into the abdomen, and if I press here, out they pop again. You see how it works? There, they've gone; now they're out again. Once more I make them disappear and whoops, there they are back with us! Now in order to retain them permanently in the abdomen I take the spermatic cord and wind it in its coverings tightly down to the . . .'

But my audience was no longer with me. Henry had sunk down on an upturned oil drum and lay slumped across the table, his head cradled on his arms. My disappointment was acute, and finishing off the job and inserting the sutures was a sad anticlimax with my student slumbering at the end of the table.

I put the pig back in his pen and gathered up my gear: then I remembered I hadn't given Henry his change. I don't know why I did it but instead of half-a-crown, I slapped down a shilling and sixpence on the wood a few inches from his face. The noise made him open his eyes and he gazed dully at the coins for a few seconds, then with almost frightening suddenness he snapped upright, ashenfaced but alert and glaring.

'Hey!' he shouted. 'I want another shillin'!'

Chapter Sixteen

Vets are useless creatures, parasites on the agricultural community, expensive layabouts who really know nothing about animals or their diseases. You might as well get Jeff Mallock the knacker man as send for a vet.

At least that was the opinion, frequently expressed, of the Sidlow family. In fact, when you came right down to it, just about the only person for miles around who knew how to treat sick beasts was Mr Sidlow himself. If any of their cows or horses fell ill it was Mr Sidlow who stepped forward with his armoury of sovereign remedies. He enjoyed a God-like prestige with his wife and large family and it was an article of their faith that father was infallible in these matters; the only other being who had ever approached his skill was long-dead Grandpa Sidlow from whom father had learned so many of his cures.

Mind you, Mr Sidlow was a just and humane man. After maybe five or six days of dedicated nursing during which he would perhaps push half-a-pound of lard and raisins down the cow's throat three times a day, rub its udder vigorously with turpentine or maybe cut a bit off the end of the tail to let the bad out, he always in the end called the vet. Not that it would do any good, but he liked to give the animal every chance. When the vet arrived he invariably found a sunken-eyed, dying creature and the despairing treatment he gave was like a figurative administration of the last rites. The animal always died so the Sidlows were repeatedly confirmed in their opinion – vets were useless.

The farm was situated outside the normal area of the practice and we were the third firm Mr Sidlow had dealt with. He had been a client of Grier of Brawton but had found him wanting and moved to Wallace away over in Mansley. Wallace had disappointed him grievously so he had decided to try Darrowby. He had been with us for over a year but it was an uncomfortable relationship because Siegfried had offended him deeply on his very first visit. It was to a moribund horse, and Mr Sidlow, describing the treatment to date, announced that he had been pushing raw onions up the horse's rectum; he couldn't understand why it was so uneasy on its legs. Siegfried had pointed out that if he were to insert a raw onion in Mr Sidlow's rectum, he, Mr Sidlow, would undoubtedly be uneasy on his legs.

It was a bad start but there were really no other available vets left. He was stuck with us.

I had been uncannily lucky in that I had been at Darrowby for more than a year and had never had to visit this farm. Mr Sidlow rarely called us up during normal working hours as, after wrestling with his conscience for a few days, he always seemed to lose the battle around eleven o'clock at night (he made exceptions in the case of the occasional Sunday afternoon) and it had always landed on Siegfried's duty nights. It was Siegfried who had trailed out, swearing quietly and returned, slightly pop-eyed in the small hours.

So when it did finally come round to my turn I didn't rush out with any great enthusiasm, even though the case was just a choking bullock and should present no difficulties. (This was when a beast got a piece of turnip or a potato stuck in its gullet, preventing regurgitation of gases and causing bloating which can be fatal. We usually either relieved the bloat by puncturing the stomach or we carefully pushed the obstruction down into the stomach by means of a long flexible leather instrument called a probang.) Anyway, they had realised they couldn't wait for days this time and by way of a change it was only four o'clock in the afternoon.

The farm was nearer Brawton than Darrowby and lay in the low country down on the Plain of York. I didn't like the look of the place; there was something depressing about the dilapidated brick buildings in the dreary setting of ploughing land with only the occasional mound of a potato clamp to relieve the flatness.

My first sight of Mr Sidlow reminded me that he and his family were members of a fanatically narrow religious sect. I had seen that gaunt, blue-jowled face with the tortured eyes staring at me from the pages of history books long ago. I had the feeling that Mr Sidlow would have burnt me at the stake without a qualm.

The bullock was in a gloomy box off the fold yard. Several of the family had filed in with us; two young men in their twenties and three teenage girls, all good-looking in a dark gipsy way, but all with the same taut, unsmiling look as their father. As I moved around, examining the animal, I noticed another peculiarity – they all looked at me, the bullock, each other, with quick sideways glances without any head movement. Nobody said anything.

I would have liked to break the silence but couldn't think of anything cheerful to say. This beast didn't have the look of an ordinary choke. I could feel the potato quite distinctly from the outside, half-way down the oesophagus but all around was an oedematous mass extending up and down the left side of the neck. Not only that, but there was a bloody foam dripping from the mouth. There was something funny here.

A thought struck me. 'Have you been trying to push the potato down with something?'

I could almost feel the battery of flitting glances, and the muscles of Mr Sidlow's clenched jaw stood out in a twitching ridge. He swallowed carefully. 'Aye, we've tried a bit.'

'What did you use?'

Again the rippling jaw muscles under the dark skin. 'Broom handle and a bit of hose pipe. Same as usual.'

That was enough; a sense of doom enveloped me. It would have been nice to be the first vet to make a good impression here but it wasn't to be. I turned to the farmer. 'I'm afraid you've ruptured the gullet. It's a very delicate tube, you know, and you only have to push a bit too hard and you're through. You can see the fluid collection round the rupture.'

A quivering silence answered me. I ploughed on. 'I've seen this happen before. It's a pretty black outlook.'

'All right,' Mr Sidlow ground out. 'What are you going to do about it?'

Well, we were at it now. What was I going to do about it? Maybe now, thirty years later, I might have tried to repair the gullet, packed the wound with antibiotic powder and given a course of penicillin injections. But there, in that cheerless place, looking at the patient animal gulping painfully, coughing up the gouts of blood, I knew I was whacked. A ruptured oesophagus was as near hopeless as anything could be. I searched my mind for a suitable speech.

'I'm sorry, Mr Sidlow, but I can't do anything about it.' The glances crackled around me and the farmer breathed in sharply through his nose. I didn't need to be told what they were all thinking – another no-good, useless vet. I took a deep breath and continued. 'Even if I shifted the potato the wound would get contaminated when the beast tried to eat. He'd have gangrene in no time and that means a painful death. He's in pretty good condition – if I were you I'd have him slaughtered immediately.'

The only reply was a virtuoso display from the jaw muscles. I tried another tack. 'I'll give you a certificate. I'm sure the meat will pass for the butcher.'

No cries of joy greeted this remark. If anything, Mr Sidlow's expression became still more bleak.

'That beast isn't ready for killin' yet,' he whispered.

'No, but you'd be sending him in before long – another month, maybe. I'm sure you won't lose much. I tell you what,' with a ghastly attempt at heartiness, 'if I can come into the house I'll write you this chit now and we'll get the job over. There's really nothing else for it.'

I turned and headed across the fold yard for the farm kitchen. Mr Sidlow followed wordlessly with the family. I wrote the certificate quickly, waves of disapproval washing around me in the silent room. As I folded the paper I had the sudden conviction that Mr Sidlow wasn't going to pay the slightest attention to my advice. He was going to wait a day or two to see how things turned out. The picture of the big, uncomprehending animal trying vainly to swallow as his hunger and thirst increased was too strong for me. I walked over to the phone on the window sill.

'I'll just give Harry Norman a ring at the abattoir. I know he'll come straight up if I ask him.' I made the arrangements, hung up the receiver and started for the door, addressing Mr Sidlow's profile as I left. 'It's fixed. Harry will be along within half-an-hour. Much better to get it done immediately.'

Going across the yard, I had to fight the impulse to break into a gallop. As I got into the car I recalled Siegfried's advice: 'In sticky situations always get your car backed round before you examine the animal. Leave the engine running if necessary. The quick getaway is essential.' He was right, it took a long time reversing and manoeuvring under the battery of unseen eyes. I don't blush easily but my face was burning as I finally left the farm.

That was my first visit to the Sidlows and I prayed that it might be my last. But my luck had run out. From then on, every time they sent for us it happened to be me on duty. I would rather not say anything about the cases I treated there except to record that something went wrong every time. The very name Sidlow became like a jinx. Try as I might I couldn't do a thing right on that farm so that within a short time I was firmly established with the family as the greatest menace to the animal population they had ever encountered. They didn't think much of vets as a whole and they'd met some real beauties in their time, but I was by far the worst. My position as the biggest nincompoop of them all was unassailable.

It got so bad that if I saw any Sidlows in the town I would dive down an alley to avoid them and one day in the market place I had the unnerving experience of seeing the entire family, somehow jammed into a large old car, passing within a few feet of me. Every face looked rigidly to the front but every eye, I knew, was trained balefully on me. Fortunately I was just outside the Drovers' Arms, so I was able to reel inside and steady myself with a half-pint of Younger's Special Heavy.

However, the Sidlows were far from my mind on the Saturday morning when Siegfried asked me if I would go through and officiate at Brawton races.

'They've asked me to do it as Grier is on holiday,' he said. 'But I'd already promised to go through to Casborough to help Dick Henley with a rig operation. I can't let him down. There's nothing much to the race job: the regular course vet will be there and he'll keep you right.'

He hadn't been gone more than a few minutes when there was a call from the racecourse. One of the horses had fallen while being unloaded from its box and had injured its knee. Would I come right away.

Even now I am no expert on racehorses; they form a little branch of practice all by itself, with its own stresses, its own mystique. In my short spell in Darrowby I had had very little to do with them as Siegfried was fascinated by anything equine and usually gobbled up anything in that line which came along. So my practical experience was negligible.

I wasn't at all reassured when I saw my patient. The knee was a terrible mess. He had tripped at the bottom of the ramp and come down with his full weight on the stony ground. The lacerated skin hung down in bloody ribbons exposing the joint capsule over an area of about six inches and the extensor tendons gleamed through a tattered layer of fascia. The beautiful three-year-old held the limb up, trembling, with the toe just touching the ground; the ravaged knee made a violent contrast with the sleek, carefully groomed coat.

Examining the wound, gently feeling round the joint, I was immediately thankful for one thing – it was a quiet animal. Some light horses are so highly strung that the slightest touch sends them up in the air, but this one hardly moved as I tried to piece together the jigsaw of skin pieces. Another lucky break – there was nothing missing.

I turned to the stable head lad, small, square, hands deep in his coat pockets who was standing watching. 'I'll clean up the wound and stitch it but he'll need some expert care when you get him home. Can you tell me who will be treating him?'

'Yes sir, Mr Brayley-Reynolds. He'll have charge of 'im.'

I came bolt upright from my crouching position. The name was like a trumpet call echoing down from my student days. When you talked about horses you usually talked about Brayley-Reynolds sooner or later. I could imagine the great man inspecting my handiwork. 'And who did you say treated this? Herriot . . .? Herriot . . .?'

I got down to the job again with my heart beating faster. Mercifully the joint capsule and tendon sheaths were undamaged – no escape of synovia. Using a solution of Chinosol, I swabbed out every last cranny of the wound till the ground around me was white with cotton wool pledgets, then I puffed in some iodoform powder and tacked down the loose shreds of fascia. Now the thing was to make a really good job of the skin to avoid disfigurement if possible. I chose some fine silk and a very small suture needle and squatted down again.

I must have stayed there for nearly an hour, pulling the flaps of skin carefully into position and fastening them down with innumerable tiny sutures. There is a fascination in repairing a ragged wound and I always took pains over it even without an imaginary Brayley-Reynolds peering over my shoulder. When I finally straightened up I did so slowly, like an old man, easing the kinks from neck and back. With shaking knees I looked down at the head lad almost without recognition. He was smiling.

'You've made a proper job of that,' he said. 'It looks nearly as good as new. I want to thank you, sir – he's one of my favourites, not just because he's a good 'orse, but he's kind.' He patted the three-year-old's flank.

'Well, I hope he does all right.' I got out a packet of gauze and a bandage. 'I'm just going to cover up the knee with this and then you can put on a stable bandage. I'll give him a shot against tetanus and that's it.'

I was packing my gear away in the car when the head lad hovered again at my side. 'Do you back 'orses?'

I laughed. 'No, hardly ever. Don't know much about it.'

'Well never mind.' The little man looked around him and lowered his voice. 'But I'll tell you something to back this afternoon. Kemal in the first race. He's one of ours and he's going to win. You'll get a nice price about him.'

'Well, thanks, it'll give me something to do. I'll have half-a-crown on him.'

The tough little face screwed up in disgust. 'No, no, put a fiver on him. This is the goods, I mean it. Keep it to yourself but get a fiver on him.' He walked rapidly away.

I don't know what madness took hold of me, but by the time I had got back to Darrowby I had decided to take his advice. There had been something compelling about that last hoarse whisper and the utter confidence in the black pebble eyes. The little chap was trying to do me a good turn. I had noticed him glancing at my old jacket and rumpled flannels, so different from the natty outfit of the typical horse vet; maybe he thought I needed the money.

I dropped in at the Midland Bank and drew out five pounds which at the time represented approximately half my available capital. I hurried round the remaining visits, had a quick lunch and got into my best suit. There was plenty of time to get to the course, meet the officials and get my fiver on Kemal before the first race at 2.30.

The phone rang just as I was about to leave the house. It was Mr Sidlow. He had a scouring cow which needed attention immediately. It was fitting, I thought dully, that in my moment of eager anticipation it should be my old jinx who should stretch out his cold hand and grasp me. And it was Saturday afternoon; that was fitting too. But I shook myself – the farm was near Brawton and it shouldn't take long to deal with a scouring cow; I could still make it.

When I arrived, my immaculate appearance set up an immediate flurry of oblique glances among the assembled family while Mr Sidlow's rigid lips and squared shoulders bore witness that he was prepared to endure another visit from me with courage.

A numbness filled me as we went into the byre. It continued as Mr Sidlow described how he had battled against this cow's recurring bouts of diarrhoea for several months; how he had started quietly with ground eggshells in gruel and worked up to his most powerful remedy, blue vitriol and dandelion tea, but all to no avail. I hardly heard him because it was fairly obvious at a glance that the cow had Jöhne's disease.

Nobody could be quite sure, of course, but the animal's advanced emaciation, especially in the hind end, and the stream of bubbly, foetid scour which she had ejected as I walked in were almost diagnostic. Instinctively I grasped her tail and thrust my thermometer into the rectum: I wasn't much interested in her temperature but it gave me a couple of minutes to think.

However, in this instance I got only about five seconds because, without warning, the thermometer disappeared from my fingers. Some sudden suction had drawn it inside the cow. I ran my fingers round just inside the rectum – nothing; I pushed my hand inside without success; with a feeling of rising panic I rolled up my sleeve and groped about in vain.

There was nothing else for it – I had to ask for a bucket of hot water, soap and a towel and strip off as though preparing for some large undertaking. Over my thirty-odd years in practice I can recall many occasions when I looked a complete fool, but there is a peculiarly piercing quality about the memory of myself, bare to the waist, the centre of a ring of hostile stares, guddling frantically inside that cow. At the time, all I could think of was that this was the Sidlow place; anything could happen here. In my mental turmoil I had discarded all my knowledge of pathology and anatomy and could visualise the little glass tube working its way rapidly along the intestinal tract until it finally pierced some vital organ. There was another hideous image of myself carrying out a major operation, a full-scale laparotomy on the cow to recover my thermometer.

It is difficult to describe the glorious relief which flooded through me when at last I felt the thing between my fingers; I pulled it out, filthy and dripping and stared down stupidly at the graduations on the tube.

Mr Sidlow cleared his throat. 'Well, wot does it say? Has she got a temperature?'

I whipped round and gave him a piercing look. Was it possible that this man could be making a joke? But the dark, tight-shut face was expressionless.

'No,' I mumbled in reply. 'No temperature.'

The rest of that visit has always been mercifully blurred in my mind. I know I got myself cleaned up and dressed and told Mr Sidlow that I thought his cow had Jöhne's disease which was incurable but I would take away a faeces sample to try to make sure. The details are cloudy but I do know that at no point was there the slightest gleam of light or hope.

I left the farm, bowed down by an ever greater sense of disgrace than usual and drove with my foot on the boards all the way to Brawton. I roared into the special car park at the race-course, galloped through the owners' and trainers' entrance and seized the arm of the gatekeeper.

'Has the first race been run?' I gasped.

'Aye, just finished,' he replied cheerfully. 'Kemal won it – ten to one.'

I turned and walked slowly towards the paddock. Fifty pounds! A fortune snatched from my grasp by cruel fate. And hanging over the whole tragedy was the grim spectre of Mr Sidlow. I could forgive Mr Sidlow, I thought, for dragging me out at all sorts of ungodly hours; I could forgive him for presenting me with a long succession of hopeless cases which had lowered my self-esteem to rock bottom; I could forgive him for thinking I was the biggest idiot in

Yorkshire and for proclaiming his opinion far and wide. But I'd never forgive him for losing me that fifty pounds.

Chapter Seventeen

'The Reniston, eh?' I fidgeted uneasily. 'Bit grand, isn't it?'

Tristan lay rather than sat in his favourite chair and peered up through a cloud of cigarette smoke. 'Of course it's grand. It's the most luxurious hotel in the country outside of London, but for your purpose it's the only possible place. Look, tonight is your big chance isn't it? You want to impress this girl, don't you? Well, ring her up and tell her you're taking her to the Reniston. The food is wonderful and there's a dinner dance every Saturday night. And today is Saturday.' He sat up suddenly and his eyes widened. 'Can't you see it, Jim? The music oozing out of Benny Thornton's trombone and you, full of lobster thermidor, floating round the floor with Helen snuggling up to you. The only snag is that it will cost you a packet, but if you are prepared to spend about a fortnight's wages you can have a really good night.'

I hardly heard the last part, I was concentrating on the blinding vision of Helen snuggling up to me. It was an image which blotted out things like money and I stood with my mouth half open listening to the trombone. I could hear it quite clearly.

Tristan broke in. 'There's one thing – have you got a dinner-jacket? You'll need one.'

'Well, I'm not very well off for evening-dress. In fact, when I went to Mrs Pumphrey's party I hired a suit from Brawton, but I wouldn't have time for that now.' I paused and thought for a moment. 'I do have my first and only dinner-suit but I got it when I was about seventeen and I don't know whether I'd be able to get into it.'

Tristan waved this aside. He dragged the Woodbine smoke into the far depths of his lungs and released it reluctantly in little wisps and trickles as he spoke. 'Doesn't matter in the least, Jim. As long as you're wearing the proper gear they'll let you in, and with a big, good-looking chap like you the fit of the suit is unimportant.'

We went upstairs and extracted the garment from the bottom of my trunk. I had cut quite a dash in this suit at the college dances and though it had got very tight towards the end of the course it had still been a genuine evening-dress outfit and as such had commanded a certain amount of respect.

But now it had a pathetic, lost look. The fashion had changed and the trend was towards comfortable jackets and soft, unstarched shirts. This one was rigidly of the old school and included an absurd little waistcoat with lapels and a stiff, shiny-fronted shirt with a tall, winged collar.

My problems really started when I got the suit on. Hard work, Pennine air and Mrs Hall's good food had filled me out and the jacket failed to meet across my stomach by six inches. I seemed to have got taller, too, because there was a generous space between the bottom of the waistcoat and the top of the trousers. The trousers themselves were skin tight over the buttocks, yet seemed foolishly baggy lower down.

Tristan's confidence evaporated as I paraded before him and he decided to call on Mrs Hall for advice. She was an unemotional woman and endured the irregular life at Skeldale House without noticeable reaction, but when she came into the bedroom and looked at me her facial muscles went into a long, twitching spasm. She finally overcame the weakness, however, and .became very businesslike.

'A little gusset at the back of your trousers will work wonders, Mr Herriot, and I think if I put a bit of silk cord across the front of your jacket it'll hold it nicely. Mind you, there'll be a bit of a space, like, but I shouldn't think that'll worry you. And I'll give the whole suit a good press – makes all the difference in the world.'

I had never gone in much for intensive grooming, but that night I really went to work on myself, scrubbing and anointing and trying a whole series of different partings in my hair before I was satisfied. Tristan seemed to have appointed himself master of the wardrobe and carried the suit tenderly upstairs, still warm from Mrs Hall's ironing board. Then, like a professional valet, he assisted in every step of the robing. The high collar gave most trouble and he drew strangled oaths from me as he trapped the flesh of my neck under the stud.

When I was finally arrayed he walked around me several times, pulling and patting the material and making delicate adjustments here and there.

Eventually he stopped his circling and surveyed me from the front. I had never seen him look so serious. 'Fine, Jim, fine – you look great. Distinguished, you know. It's not everybody who can wear a dinner-jacket – so many people look like conjurers, but not you. Hang on a minute and I'll get your overcoat.'

I had arranged to pick up Helen at seven o'clock and as I climbed from the car in the darkness outside her house a strange unease crept over me. This was different. When I had come here before it had been as a veterinary surgeon – the man who knew, who was wanted, who came to render assistance in time of need. It had never occurred to me how much this affected my outlook every time I walked on to a farm. This wasn't the same thing at all. I had come to take this man's daughter out. He might not like it, might positively resent it.

Standing outside the farmhouse door I took a deep breath. The night was very dark and still. No sound came from the great trees near by and only the distant roar of the Darrow disturbed the silence. The recent heavy rains had transformed the leisurely, wandering river into a rushing torrent which in places overflowed its banks and flooded the surrounding pastures.

I was shown into the large kitchen by Helen's young brother. The boy had a hand over his mouth in an attempt to hide a wide grin. He seemed to find the situation funny. His little sister sitting at a table doing her homework was pretending to concentrate on her writing but she, too, wore a fixed smirk as she looked down at her book.

Mr Alderson was reading the *Farmer and Stockbreeder*, his breeches unlaced, his stockinged feet stretched out towards a blazing pile of logs. He looked up over his spectacles.

'Come in, young man, and sit by the fire,' he said absently. I had the uncomfortable impression that it was a frequent and boring experience for him to have young men calling for his eldest daughter.

I sat down at the other side of the fire and Mr Alderson resumed his study of the *Farmer and Stockbreeder*. The ponderous tick-tock of a large wall clock boomed out into the silence. I stared into the red depths of the fire till my eyes began to ache, then I looked up at a big oil painting in a gilt frame hanging above the mantelpiece. It depicted shaggy cattle standing knee-deep in a lake of an extraordinary bright blue; behind them loomed a backcloth of fearsome, improbable mountains, their jagged summits wreathed in a sulphurous mist.

Averting my eyes from this, I examined, one by one, the sides of bacon and the hams hanging from the rows of hooks in the ceiling. Mr Alderson turned over a page. The clock ticked on. Over by the table, spluttering noises came from the children.

After about a year I heard footsteps on the stairs, then Helen came into the room. She was wearing a blue dress – the kind, without shoulder straps, that seems to stay up by magic. Her dark hair shone under the single pressure lamp which lit the kitchen, shadowing the soft curves of her neck and shoulders. Over one white arm she held a camel-hair coat.

I felt stunned. She was like a rare jewel in the rough setting of stone flags and whitewashed walls. She gave me her quiet, friendly smile and walked towards me. 'Hello, I hope I haven't kept you waiting too long.'

I muttered something in reply and helped her on with her coat. She went over and kissed her father who didn't look up but waved his hand vaguely. There was another outburst of giggling from the table. We went out.

In the car I felt unusually tense and for the first mile or two had to depend on some inane remarks about the weather to keep a conversation going. I was beginning to relax when I drove over a little hump-backed bridge into a dip in the road. Then the car suddenly stopped. The engine coughed gently and then we were sitting silent and motionless in the darkness. And there was something else; my feet and ankles were freezing cold.

'My God!' I shouted. 'We've run into a bit of flooded road. The water's right into the car.' I looked round at Helen. 'I'm terribly sorry about this – your feet must be soaked.'

But Helen was laughing. She had her feet tucked up on the seat, her knees under her chin. 'Yes, I am a bit wet, but it's no good sitting about like this. Hadn't we better start pushing?'

Wading out into the black icy waters was a nightmare but there was no escape. Mercifully it was a little car and between us we managed to push it beyond the flooded patch. Then by torchlight I dried the plugs and got the engine going again.

Helen shivered as we squelched back into the car. 'I'm afraid I'll have to go back and change my shoes and stockings. And so will you. There's another road back through Fensley. You take the first turn on the left.'

Back at the farm, Mr Alderson was still reading the *Farmer and Stockbreeder* and kept his finger on the list of pig prices while he gave me a baleful glance over his spectacles. When he learned that I had come to borrow a pair of his shoes and socks he threw the paper down in exasperation and rose, groaning, from his chair. He shuffled out of the room and I could hear him muttering to himself as he mounted the stairs.

Helen followed him and I was left alone with the two young children. They studied my sodden trousers with undisguised delight. I had wrung most of the surplus water out of them but the final result was remarkable. Mrs Hall's knife-edge crease reached to just below the knee, but then there was chaos. The trousers flared out at that point in a crumpled, shapeless mass and as I stood by the fire to dry them a gentle steam rose about me. The children stared at me, wide-eyed and happy. This was a big night for them.

Mr Alderson reappeared at length and dropped some shoes and rough socks at my feet. I pulled on the socks quickly but shrank back when I saw the shoes. They were a pair of dancing slippers from the early days of the century and their cracked patent leather was topped by wide, black silk bows.

I opened my mouth to protest but Mr Alderson had dug himself deep into his chair and had found his place again among the pig prices. I had the feeling that if I asked for another pair of shoes Mr Alderson would attack me with the poker. I put the slippers on.

We had to take a roundabout road to avoid the floods but I kept my foot down and within half-an-hour we had left the steep sides of the Dale behind us and were heading out on to the rolling plain. I began to feel better. We were making good time and the little car, shuddering and creaking, was going well. I was just thinking that we wouldn't be all that late when the steering-wheel began to drag to one side.

I had a puncture most days and recognised the symptoms immediately. I had become an expert at changing wheels and with a word of apology to Helen was out of the car like a flash. With my rapid manipulation of the rusty jack and brace the wheel was off within three minutes. The surface of the crumpled tyre was quite smooth except for the lighter, frayed parts where the canvas showed through. Working like a demon, I screwed on the spare, cringing inwardly as I saw that this tyre was in exactly the same condition as the other. I steadfastly refused to think of what I would do if its frail fibres should give up the struggle.

By day, the Reniston dominated Brawton like a vast mediaeval fortress, bright flags fluttering arrogantly from its four turrets, but tonight it was like a dark cliff with a glowing cavern at street level where the Bentleys discharged their expensive cargoes. I didn't take my vehicle to the front entrance but tucked it away quietly at the back of the car park. A magnificent commissionaire opened the door for us and we trod noiselessly over the rich carpeting of the entrance hall.

We parted there to get rid of our coats, and in the men's cloakroom I scrubbed frantically at my oily hands. It didn't do much good; changing that wheel had given my finger nails a border of deep black which defied ordinary soap and water. And Helen was waiting for me.

I looked up in the mirror at the white-jacketed attendant hovering behind me with a towel. The man, clearly fascinated by my ensemble, was staring down at the wide-bowed pierrot shoes and the rumpled trouser bottoms. As he handed over the towel he smiled broadly as if in gratitude for this little bit of extra colour in his life.

I met Helen in the reception hall and we went over to the desk. 'What time does the dinner dance start?' I asked.

The girl at the desk looked surprised. 'I'm sorry, sir, there's no dance tonight. We only have them once a fortnight.'

I turned to Helen in dismay but she smiled encouragingly. 'It doesn't matter,' she said. 'I don't really care what we do.'

'We can have dinner, anyway,' I said. I tried to speak cheerfully but a little black cloud seemed to be forming just above my head. Was anything going to go right tonight? I could feel my morale slumping as I padded over the lush carpet and my first sight of the dining-room didn't help.

It looked as big as a football field with great marble pillars supporting a carved, painted ceiling. The Reniston had been built in the late Victorian period and all the opulence and ornate splendour of those days had been retained in this tremendous room. Most of the tables were occupied by the usual clientele, a mixture of the county aristocracy and industrialists from the West Riding. I had never seen so many beautiful women and masterful-looking men under one roof and I noticed with a twinge of alarm that, though the men were wearing everything from dark lounge suits to hairy tweeds, there wasn't another dinner jacket in sight.

A majestic figure in white tie and tails bore down on us. With his mane of white hair falling back from the lofty brow, the bulging waistline, the hooked nose and imperious expression he looked exactly like a Roman emperor. His eyes flickered expertly over me and he spoke tonelessly.

'You want a table, sir?'

'Yes please,' I mumbled, only just stopping myself saying 'sir' to the man in return. 'A table for two.'

'Are you staying, sir?'

This question baffled me. How could I possibly have dinner here if I wasn't staying.

'Yes, I am staying.'

The emperor made a note on a pad. 'This way, sir.'

He began to make his way with great dignity among the tables while I followed abjectly in his wake with Helen. It was a long way to the table and I tried to ignore the heads which turned to have a second look at me as I passed. It was Mrs Hall's gusset that worried me most and I imagined it standing out like a beacon below the short jacket. It was literally burning my buttocks by the time we arrived.

The table was nicely situated and a swarm of waiters descended on us, pulling out our chairs and settling us into them, shaking out our napkins and spreading them on our laps. When they had dispersed the emperor took charge again. He poised a pencil over his pad.

'May I have your room number, sir?'

I swallowed hard and stared up at him over my dangerously billowing shirt front. 'Room number? Oh, I'm not living in the hotel.'

'Ah, NOT staying.' He fixed me for a moment with an icy look before crossing out something on the pad with unnecessary violence. He muttered something to one of the waiters and strode away.

It was about then that the feeling of doom entered into me. The black cloud over my head spread and descended, enveloping me in a dense cloud of misery. The whole evening had been a disaster and would probably get worse. I must have been mad to come to this sumptuous place dressed up like a knockabout comedian. I was as hot as hell inside this ghastly suit and the stud was biting viciously into my neck.

I took a menu card from a waiter and tried to hold it with my fingers curled inwards to hide my dirty nails. Everything was in French and in my numbed state the words were largely meaningless, but somehow I ordered the meal and, as we ate, I tried desperately to keep a conversation going. But long deserts of silence began to stretch between us; it seemed that only Helen and I were quiet among all the surrounding laughter and chatter.

Worst of all was the little voice which kept telling me that Helen had never really wanted to come out with me anyway. She had done it out of politeness and was getting through a boring evening as best she could.

The journey home was a fitting climax. We stared straight ahead as the headlights picked out the winding road back into the Dales. We made stumbling remarks then the strained silence took over again. By the time we drew up outside the farm my head had begun to ache.

We shook hands and Helen thanked me for a lovely evening. There was a tremor in her voice and in the moonlight her face was anxious and withdrawn. I said goodnight, got into the car and drove away.

Chapter Eighteen

If only my car had had any brakes I would certainly have enjoyed looking down on Worton village from the high moor. The old stone houses straggling unevenly along the near bank of the river made a pleasant splash of grey on the green floor of the valley and the little gardens with their clipped lawns gave a touch of softness to the bare, rising sweep of the fellside on the other side of the Dale.

But the whole scene was clouded by the thought that I had to get down that road with its 1 in 4 gradient and those two villainous S bends. It was like a malevolent snake coiling almost headlong from where I sat. And, as I said, I had no brakes.

Of course the vehicle had originally been fitted with the means of bringing it to a halt, and during most of the year I had ridden in it a violent pressure on the pedal would have the desired effect even though it caused a certain amount of veering about on the road. But lately the response had been growing weaker and now it was nil.

During the gradual deterioration I had brought the matter up with Siegfried now and then and he had expressed sympathy and concern.

'That won't do at all, James. I'll have a word with Hammond about it. Leave it with me.'

And then a few days later when I made a further appeal.

'Oh Lord, yes. I've been meaning to fix it up with Hammond. Don't worry, James, I'll see to it.'

Finally I had to tell him that when I put my foot on the pedal there was nothing at all and the only way I had of stopping the car was to crash it into bottom gear.

'Oh bad luck, James. Must be a nuisance for you. But never mind, I'll arrange everything.'

Some time later I asked Mr Hammond down at the garage if he had heard anything from Siegfried, but he hadn't. The motor man did, however, hop into the car and drive it slowly down the street. He came to a jerking, shuddering halt about fifty yards away and then got out. He made no attempt to back up but walked thoughtfully towards me. Normally an imperturbable man, he had gone rather pale and he looked at me wonderingly.

'And you mean to tell me, lad, that you do all your rounds in that car?'

'Well, yes, I do.'

'You ought to have a medal, then. I dursn't drive across market place in that bloody thing.'

There wasn't much I could do. The car was Siegfried's property and I'd have to await his pleasure. Of course I had had experience of this sort of thing before in the shape of the movable passenger seat he had in his own vehicle when I first came to Darrowby. He never seemed to notice when I went over backwards every time I sat in it and I don't suppose he would ever have done anything about it but for an incident one market day when he noticed an old lady with a large basket of vegetables walking into Darrowby and courteously offered her a lift.

'Poor old girl's feet went straight up in the air and she just disappeared into the back. Had a hell of a job getting her out – thought we'd have to get a block and tackle. Cabbages and cauliflowers rolling all over the place.'

I looked again down the steep track. The sensible thing, of course, would be to go back into Darrowby and take the low road into Worton. No danger that way. But it meant a round trip of nearly ten miles and I could actually see the smallholding I wanted to visit just a thousand feet below. The calf with joint ill was in that shed with the green door – in fact there was old Mr Robinson coming out of the house now and pottering across the yard with a bucket. I could almost reach out and touch him.

I thought, not for the first time, that if you had to drive a car with no brakes one of the last places in England you'd want to be was the Yorkshire Dales. Even on the flat it was bad enough but I got used to it after a week or two and often forgot all about it. As when one day I was busy with a cow and the farmer jumped into my car to move it so that one of his men could get past with a tractor. I never said a word as the unsuspecting man backed round quickly and confidently and hit the wall of the barn with a sickening crash. With typical Yorkshire understatement, all he said was; 'Your brakes aren't ower savage, mister.'

Anyway, I had to make up my mind. Was it to be back to Darrowby or straight over the top? It had become a common situation and every day I had the experience of sitting wrestling with myself on the edge of a hill with my heart thumping as it was now. There must have been scores of these unwitnessed dramas played out in the green silence of the fells. At last, I started the engine and did what I always did – took the quick way down.

But this hill really was a beauty, a notorious road even in this country, and as I nosed gingerly on to it, the whole world seemed to drop away from me. With the gear lever in bottom and my hand jammed against it I headed, dry-mouthed, down the strip of tarmac which now looked to be almost vertical.

It is surprising what speed you can attain in bottom gear if you have nothing else to hold you back and as the first bend rushed up at me the little engine started a rising scream of protest. When I hit the curve, I hauled the wheel round desperately to the right, the tyres spun for a second in the stones and loose soil of the verge, then we were off again.

This was a longer stretch and even steeper and it was like being on the big dipper with the same feeling of lack of control over one's fate. Hurtling into the bend, the idea of turning at this speed was preposterous but it was that or straight over the edge. Terror-stricken, I closed my eyes and dragged the wheel to the left. This time, one side of the car lifted and I was sure we were over, then it rocked back on to the other side and for a horrible second or two kept this up till it finally decided to stay upright and I was once more on my way.

Again a yawning gradient. But as the car sped downwards, engine howling, I was aware of a curious numbness. I seemed to have reached the ultimate limits of fear and hardly noticed as we shot round the third bend. One more to go and at last the road was levelling out; my speed dropped rapidly and at the last bend I couldn't have been doing more than twenty. I had made it.

It wasn't till I was right on to the final straight that I saw the sheep. Hundreds of them, filling the road. A river of woolly backs lapping from wall to wall. They were only yards from me and I was still going downhill. Without hesitation I turned and drove straight into the wall.

There didn't seem to be much damage. A few stones slithered down as the engine stalled and fell silent.

Slowly I sank back in my seat, relaxing my clenched jaws, releasing, finger by finger, the fierce grip on the wheel. The sheep continued to flow past and I took a sideways glance at the man who was shepherding them. He was a stranger to me and I prayed he didn't recognise me either because at that moment the role of unknown madman seemed to be the ideal one. Best not to say anything; appearing round a corner and driving deliberately into a wall is no basis for a rewarding conversation.

The sheep were still passing by and I could hear the man calling to his dogs. 'Get by, Jess. Come by, Nell.' But I kept up a steady stare at the layered stones in front of me, even though he passed within a few feet.

I suppose some people would have asked me what the hell I was playing at, but not a Dales shepherd. He went quietly by without invading my privacy, but when I looked in the mirror after a few moments I could see him in the middle of the road staring back at me, his sheep temporarily forgotten.

My brakeless period has always been easy to recall. There is a piercing clarity about the memory which has kept it fresh over the years. I suppose it lasted only a few weeks but it could have gone on indefinitely if Siegfried himself hadn't become involved.

It was when we were going to a case together. For some reason he decided to take my car and settled in the driver's seat. I huddled apprehensively next to him as he set off at his usual brisk pace.

Hinchcliffe's farm lies about a mile on the main road outside Darrowby. It is a massive place with a wide straight drive leading down to the house. We weren't going there, but as Siegfried spurted to full speed I could see Mr Hinchcliffe in his big Buick ahead of us proceeding in a leisurely way along the middle of the road. As Siegfried pulled out to overtake, the farmer suddenly stuck out his hand and began to turn right towards his farm – directly across our path. Siegfried's foot went hard down on the brake pedal and his eyebrows shot right up as nothing happened. We were going straight for the side of the Buick and there was no room to go round on the left.

Siegfried didn't panic. At the last moment he turned right with the Buick and the two cars roared side by side down the drive, Mr Hinchcliffe staring at me with bulging eyes from close range. The farmer stopped in the yard, but we continued round the back of the house because we had to.

Fortunately, it was one of those places where you could drive right round and we rattled through the stackyard and back to the front of the house behind Mr Hinchcliffe who had got out and was looking round the corner to see where we had gone. The farmer whipped round in astonishment and, open-mouthed watched us as we passed, but Siegfried, retaining his aplomb to the end, inclined his head and gave a little wave before we shot back up the drive.

Before we returned to the main road I had a look back at Mr Hinchcliffe. He was still watching us and there was a certain rigidity in his pose which reminded me of the shepherd.

Once on the road, Siegfried steered carefully into a layby and stopped. For a few moments he stared straight ahead without speaking and I realised he was having a little difficulty in getting his patient look properly adjusted; but when he finally turned to me his face was transfigured, almost saintly.

I dug my nails into my palms as he smiled at me with kindly eyes.

'Really, James,' he said, 'I can't understand why you keep things to yourself. Heaven knows how long your car has been in this condition, yet never a word from you.' He raised a forefinger and his patient look was replaced by one of sorrowing gravity. 'Don't you realise we might have been killed back there? You really ought to have told me.'

Chapter Nineteen

There didn't seem much point in a millionaire filling up football pools coupons but it was one of the motive forces in old Harold Denham's life. It made a tremendous bond between us because, despite his devotion to the pools, Harold knew nothing about football, had never seen a match and was unable to name a single player in league football; and when he found that I could discourse knowledgeably not only about Everton and Preston North End but even about Arbroath and Cowdenbeath the respect with which he had always treated me deepened into a wide-eyed deference.

Of course we had first met over his animals. He had an assortment of dogs, cats, rabbits, budgies and goldfish which made me a frequent visitor to the dusty mansion whose Victorian turrets peeping above their sheltering woods could be seen for miles around Darrowby. When I first knew him, the circumstances of my visits were entirely normal – his fox terrier had cut its pad or the old grey tabby was having trouble with its sinusitis, but later on I began to wonder. He called me out so often on a Wednesday and the excuse was at times so trivial that I began seriously to suspect that there was nothing wrong with the animal but that Harold was in difficulties with his Nine Results or the Easy Six.

I could never be quite sure, but it was funny how he always received me with the same words. 'Ah, Mr Herriot, how are your pools?' He used to say the word in a long-drawn, loving way – poools. This enquiry had been unvarying ever since I had won sixteen shillings one week on the Three Draws. I can never forget the awe with which he fingered the little slip from Littlewoods, looking unbelievingly from it to the postal order. That was the only time I was a winner but it made no difference – I was still the oracle, unchallenged, supreme. Harold never won anything, ever.

The Denhams were a family of note in North Yorkshire. The immensely wealthy industrialists of the last century had become leaders in the world of agriculture. They were 'gentlemen farmers' who used their money to build up pedigree herds of dairy cows or pigs; they ploughed out the high, stony moorland and fertilised it and made it grow crops, they drained sour bogs and made them yield potatoes and turnips; they were the chairmen of committees, masters of fox hounds, leaders of the county society.

But Harold had opted out of all that at an early age. He had refuted the age old dictum that you can't be happy doing absolutely nothing; all day and every day he pottered around his house and his few untidy acres, uninterested in the world outside, not entirely aware of what was going on in his immediate vinicity, but utterly content. I don't think he ever gave a thought to other people's opinions which was just as well because they were often unkind; his brother, the eminent Basil Denham, referred to him invariably as 'that bloody fool' and with the country people it was often 'nobbut ninepence in t'shillin'.'

Personally I always found something appealing in him. He was kind, friendly, with a sense of fun and I enjoyed going to his house. He and his wife ate all their meals in the kitchen and in fact seemed to spend most of their time there, so I usually went round the back of the house.

On this particular day it was to see his Great Dane bitch which had just had pups and seemed unwell; since it wasn't Wednesday I felt that there really might be something amiss with her and hurried round. Harold gave me his usual greeting; he had the most attractive voice – round, fruity, mellow, like a bishop's, and for the hundredth time I thought how odd it was to hear those organ-like vocal cords intoning such incongruities as Mansfield Town or Bradford City.

'I wonder if you could advise me, Mr Herriot,' he said as we left the kitchen and entered a long, ill-lit passage. 'I'm searching for an away winner and I wondered about Sunderland at Aston Villa?'

I stopped and fell into an attitude of deep thought while Harold regarded me anxiously. 'Well, I'm not sure, Mr Denham,' I replied. 'Sunderland are a good side but I happen to know that Raich Carter's auntie isn't too well at present and it could easily affect his game this Saturday.'

Harold looked crestfallen and he nodded his head gravely a few times; then he looked closely at me for a few seconds and broke into a shout of laughter. 'Ah, Mr Herriot, you're pulling my leg again.' He seized my arm, gave it a squeeze and shuffled off along the passage, chuckling deeply.

We traversed a labyrinth of gloomy, cobwebbed passages before he led the way into a little gun room. My patient was lying on a raised wooden dog bed and I recognised her as the enormous Dane I had seen leaping around at previous visits. I had never treated her, but my first sight of her had dealt a blow at one of my new-found theories – that you didn't find big dogs in big houses. Times without number I had critically observed Bull Mastiffs, Alsatians and Old English Sheep Dogs catapulting out of the tiny, back street dwellings of Darrowby, pulling their helpless owners on the end of a lead, while in the spacious rooms and wide acres of the stately homes I saw nothing but Border Terriers and Jack Russells. But Harold would have to be different.

He patted the bitch's head. 'She had the puppies yesterday and she's got a nasty dark discharge. She's eating well, but I'd like you to look her over.'

Great Danes, like most of the big breeds, are usually placid animals and the bitch didn't move as I took her temperature. She lay on her side, listening contentedly to the squeals of her family as the little blind creatures climbed over each other to get at the engorged teats.

'Yes, she's got a slight fever and you're right about the discharge.' I gently palpated the long hollow of the flank. 'I don't think there's another pup there but I'd better have a feel inside her to make sure. Could you bring me some warm water, soap and towel please?'

As the door closed behind Harold I looked idly around the gun room. It wasn't much bigger than a cupboard and, since another of Harold's idiosyncrasies was that he never killed anything, was devoid of guns. The glass cases contained only musty bound volumes of *Blackwood's Magazine* and *Country Life*. I stood there for maybe ten minutes, wondering why the old chap was taking so long, then I turned to look at an old print on the wall; it was the usual hunting scene and I was peering through the grimy glass and wondering why they always drew those horses flying over the stream with such impossible long legs when I heard a sound behind me.

It was a faint growl, a deep rumble, soft but menacing. I turned and saw the bitch rising very slowly from her bed. She wasn't getting to her feet in the normal way of dogs, it was as though she were being lifted up by strings somewhere in the ceiling, the legs straightening almost imperceptibly, the body rigid, every hair bristling. All the time she glared at me unblinkingly and for the first time in my life I realised the meaning of blazing eyes. I had only once seen anything like this before and it was on the cover of an old copy of *The Hound of the Baskervilles*. At the time I had thought the artist ridiculously fanciful but here were two eyes filled with the same yellow fire and fixed unwaveringly on mine.

She thought I was after her pups, of course. After all, her master had gone and there was only this stranger standing motionless and silent in the corner of the room, obviously up to no good. One thing was sure – she was going to come at me any second, and I blessed the luck that had made me stand right by the door. Carefully I inched my left hand towards the handle as the bitch still rose with terrifying slowness, still rumbling deep in her chest. I had almost reached the handle when I made the mistake of making a quick grab for it. Just as I touched the metal the bitch came out of the bed like a rocket and sank her teeth into my wrist.

I thumped her over the head with my right fist and she let go and seized me high up on the inside of the left thigh. This really made me yell out and I don't know just what my immediate future would have been if I hadn't bumped up against the only chair in the room; it was old and flimsy but it saved me. As the bitch, apparently tiring of gnawing my leg, made a sudden leap at my face I snatched the chair up and fended her off.

The rest of my spell in the gun room was a sort of parody of a lion-taming act and would have been richly funny to an impartial observer. In fact, in later years I have often wished I could have a cine film of the episode; but at the time, with that great animal stalking me round those few cramped yards of space, the blood trickling down my leg and only a rickety chair to protect me I didn't feel a bit like laughing. There was a dreadful dedication in the way she followed me and those maddened eyes never left my face for an instant.

The pups, furious at the unceremonious removal of their delightful source of warmth and nourishment, were crawling blindly across the bed and bawling, all nine of them, at the top of their voices. The din acted as a spur to the bitch and the louder it became the more she pressed home her attack. Every few seconds she would launch herself at me and I would prance about, stabbing at her with my chair in best circus fashion. Once she bore me back against the wall, chair and all; on her hind legs she was about as tall as me and I had a disturbing close-up of the snarling gaping jaws.

My biggest worry was that my chair was beginning to show signs of wear; the bitch had already crunched two of the spars effortlessly away and I tried not to think of what would happen if the whole thing finally disintegrated. But I was working my way back to the door and when I felt the handle at my back I knew I had to do something about it. I gave a final, intimidating shout, threw the remains of the chair at the bitch and dived out into the corridor. As I slammed the door behind me and leaned against it I could feel the panels quivering as the big animal threw herself against the wood.

I was sitting on the floor with my back against the passage wall, pants round my ankles, examining my wounds when I saw Harold pass across the far end, pottering vaguely along with a basin of steaming water held in front of him and a towel over his shoulder. I could understand now why he had been so long – he had been wandering around like that all the time; being Harold it was just possible he had been lost in his own house. Or maybe he was just worrying about his Four Aways.

Back at Skeldale House I had to endure some unkind remarks about my straddling gait, but later, in my bedroom, the smile left Siegfried's face as he examined my leg.

'Right up there, by God.' He gave a low, awed whistle. 'You know, James, we've often made jokes about what a savage dog might do to us one day. Well, I tell you boy, it damn nearly happened to you.'

Chapter Twenty

This was my second winter in Darrowby so I didn't feel the same sense of shock when it started to be really rough in November. When they were getting a drizzle of rain down there on the plain the high country was covered in a few hours by a white blanket which filled in the roads, smoothed out familiar landmarks, transformed our world into something strange and new. This was what they meant on the radio when they talked about 'snow on high ground'.

When the snow started in earnest it had a strangling effect on the whole district. Traffic crawled laboriously between the mounds thrown up by the snow ploughs. Herne Fell hung over Darrowby like a great gleaming whale and in the town the people dug deep paths to their garden gates and cleared the drifts from their front doors. They did it without fuss, with the calm of long use and in the knowledge that they would probably have to do it again tomorrow.

Every new fall struck a fresh blow at the vets. We managed to get to most of our cases but we lost a lot of sweat in the process. Sometimes we were lucky and were able to bump along in the wake of a council plough but more often we drove as far as we could and walked the rest of the way.

On the morning when Mr Clayton of Pike House rang up we had had a night of continuous snow.

'Young beast with a touch o' cold,' he said. 'Will you come?'

To get to his place you had to cross over Pike Edge and then drop down into a little valley. It was a lovely drive in the summer, but I wondered.

'What's the road like?' I asked.

'Road? road?' Mr Clayton's reaction was typically airy. Farmers in the less accessible places always brushed aside such queries. 'Road's right enough. Just tek a bit o' care and you'll get here without any trouble.'

Siegfried wasn't so sure. 'You'll certainly have to walk over the top and it's doubtful whether the ploughs will have cleared the lower road. It's up to you.'

'Oh, I'll have a go. There's not much doing this morning and I feel like a bit of exercise.'

In the yard I found that old Boardman had done a tremendous job in his quiet way; he had dug open the big double doors and cleared a way for the cars to get out. I put what I thought I would need into a small rucksack – some expectorant mixture, a tub of electuary, a syringe and a few ampoules of pneumonia serum. Then I threw the most important item of my winter equipment, a broad-bladed shovel, into the back and left.

The bigger roads had already been cleared by the council ploughs which had been clanking past Skeldale House since before dawn, but the surface was rough and I had a slow, bumpy ride. It was more than ten miles to the Clayton farm and it was one of those iron days when the frost piled thickly on the windscreen blotting out everything within minutes. But this morning I was triumphant. I had just bought a wonderful new invention – a couple of strands of wire mounted on a strip of bakelite and fastened to the windscreen with rubber suckers. It worked from the car batteries and cleared a small space of vision.

No more did I have to climb out wearily and scrub and scratch at the frozen glass every half mile or so. I sat peering delightedly through a flawlessly clear semicircle about eight inches wide at the countryside unwinding before me like a film show; the grey stone villages, silent and withdrawn under their smothering white cloak; the low, burdened branches of the roadside trees.

I was enjoying it so much that I hardly noticed the ache in my toes. Freezing feet were the rule in those days before car heaters, especially when you could see the road flashing past through the holes in the floor boards. On long journeys I really began to suffer towards the end. It was like that today when I got out of the car at the foot of the Pike Edge road; my fingers too, throbbed painfully as I stamped around and swung my arms.

The ploughs hadn't even attempted to clear the little side road which wound its way upwards and into the valley beyond. Its solid, creamy, wall-to-wall filling said 'No, you can't come up here', with that detached finality I had come to know so well. But as always, even in my disappointment, I looked with wonder at the shapes the wind had sculpted in the night; flowing folds of the most perfect smoothness tapering to the finest of points, deep hollows with knife-edge rims, soaring cliffs with overhanging margins almost transparent in their delicacy.

Hitching the rucksack on my shoulder I felt a kind of subdued elation. With a leather golf jacket buttoned up to my neck and an extra pair of thick socks under my wellingtons I felt ready for anything. No doubt I considered there was something just a bit dashing and gallant in the picture of the dedicated young vet with his magic potions on his back battling against the odds to succour a helpless animal.

I stood for a moment gazing at the fell, curving clean and cold into the sullen sky. An expectant hush lay on the fields, the frozen river and the still trees as I started off.

I kept up a good pace. First over a bridge with the river white and silent beneath then up and up, picking my way over the drifts till the road twisted, almost invisible, under some low cliffs. Despite the cold, the sweat was beginning to prick on my back when I got to the top.

I looked around me. I had been up here several times in June and July and I could remember the sunshine, the smell of the warm grass, and the scent of flowers and pines that came up the hill from the valley below. But it was hard to relate the smiling landscape of last summer with this desolation.

The flat moorland on the fell top was a white immensity rolling away to the horizon with the sky pressing down like a dark blanket. I could see the farm down there in its hollow and it, too, looked different; small, remote, like a charcoal drawing against the hills bulking smooth and white beyond. A pine wood made a dark smudge on the slopes but the scene had been wiped clean of most of its familiar features.

I could see the road only in places – the walls were covered over most of their length, but the farm was visible all the way. I had gone about half a mile towards it when a sudden gust of wind blew up the surface snow into a cloud of fine particles. Just for a few seconds I found myself completely alone. The farm, the surrounding moor, everything disappeared and I had an eerie sense of isolation till the veil cleared.

It was hard going in the deep snow and in the drifts I sank over the tops of my wellingtons. I kept at it, head down, to within a few hundred yards of the stone buildings. I was just thinking that it had all been pretty easy, really, when I looked up and saw a waving curtain of a million black dots bearing down on me. I quickened my steps and just before the blizzard hit me I marked the position of the farm. But after ten minutes' stumbling and slithering I realised

I had missed the place. I was heading for a shape that didn't exist; it was etched only in my mind.

I stood for a few moments feeling again the chilling sense of isolation. I was convinced I had gone too far to the left and after a few gasping breaths, struck off to the right. It wasn't long before I knew I had gone in the wrong direction again. I began to fall into deep holes, up to the arm-pits in the snow reminding me that the ground was not really flat on these high moors but pitted by countless peat haggs.

As I struggled on I told myself that the whole thing was ridiculous. I couldn't be far from the warm fireside at Pike House – this wasn't the North Pole. But my mind went back to the great empty stretch of moor beyond the farm and I had to stifle a feeling of panic.

The numbing cold seemed to erase all sense of time. Soon I had no idea of how long I had been falling into the holes and crawling out. I did know that each time it was getting harder work dragging myself out. And it was becoming more and more tempting to sit down and rest, even sleep; there was something hypnotic in the way the big, soft flakes brushed noiselessly across my skin and mounted thickly on my closed eyes.

I was trying to shut out the conviction that if I fell down many more times I wouldn't get up when a dark shape hovered suddenly ahead. Then my outflung arms touched something hard and rough. Unbelievingly I felt my way over the square stone blocks till I came to a corner. Beyond that was a square of light – it was the kitchen window of the farm.

Thumping on the door, I leaned against the smooth timbers, mouth gaping, chest heaving agonisingly. My immense relief must have bordered on hysteria because it seemed to me that when the door was opened the right thing would be to fall headlong into the room. My mind played with the picture of the family crowding round the prostrate figure, plying him with brandy.

When the door did open, however, something kept me on my feet. Mr Clayton stood there for a few seconds, apparently unmoved by the sight of the distraught snowman in front of him.

'Oh, it's you, Mr Herriot. You couldn't have come better – I've just finished me dinner. Hang on a minute till I get me 'at. Beast's just across yard.'

He reached behind the door, stuck a battered trilby on his head, put his hands in his pockets and sauntered over the cobbles, whistling. He knocked up the latch of the calf house and with a profound sense of release I stepped inside; away from the relentless cold, the sucking swirling snow into an animal warmth and the scent of hay.

As I rid myself of my rucksack, four long-haired little bullocks regarded me calmly from over a hurdle, their jaws moving rhythmically. They appeared as unconcerned at my appearance as their owner. They showed a mild interest, nothing more. Behind the shaggy heads I could see a fifth small beast with a sack tied round it and a purulent discharge coming from its nose.

It reminded me of the reason for my visit. As my numb fingers fumbled in a pocket for my thermometer a great gust of wind buffeted the door, setting the latch clicking softly and sending a faint powdering of snow into the dark interior.

Mr Clayton turned and rubbed the pane of the single small window with his sleeve. Picking his teeth with his thumb-nail he peered out at the howling blizzard.

'Aye,' he said, and belched pleasurably. 'It's a plain sort o' day.'

Chapter Twenty-one

As I waited for Siegfried to give me my morning list I pulled my scarf higher till it almost covered my ears, turned up the collar of my overcoat and buttoned it tightly under my chin. Then I drew on a pair of holed woollen gloves.

A biting north wind was driving the snow savagely past the window almost parallel with the ground, obliterating the street and everything else with big, swirling flakes.

Siegfried bent over the day book. 'Now let's see what we've got. Barnett, Gill, Sunter, Dent, Cartwright . . .' He began to scribble on a pad. 'Oh, and I'd better see Scruton's calf – you've been attending it, I know, but I'm going right past the door. Can you tell me about it?'

'Yes, it's been breathing a bit fast and running a temperature around 103 – I don't think there's any pneumonia there. In fact I rather suspect it may be developing diphtheria – it has a bit of a swelling on the jaw and the throat glands are up.'

All the time I was speaking, Siegfried continued to write on the pad and only stopped once to whisper to Miss Harbottle. Then he looked up brightly. 'Pneumonia, eh? How have you been treating it?'

'No, I said I didn't think it was pneumonia. I've been injecting Prontosil and I left some liniment to rub into the throat region.'

But Siegfried was writing hard again. He said nothing till he had made out two lists. He tore one from the pad and gave it to me. 'Right, you've been applying liniment to the chest. Suppose it might do a bit of good. Which liniment exactly?'

'Lin. methyl. sal., but they're rubbing it on the calf's throat, not the chest.' But Siegfried had turned away to tell Miss Harbottle the order of his visits and I found myself talking to the back of his head.

Finally he straightened up and came away from the desk. 'Well, that's fine. You have your list – let's get on.' But half way across the floor he hesitated in his stride and turned back. 'Why the devil are you rubbing that liniment on the calf's throat?'

'Well, I thought it might relieve the inflammation a bit.'

'But James, why should there be any inflammation there? Don't you think the liniment would do more good on the chest wall?' Siegfried was wearing his patient look again.

'No, I don't. Not in a case of calf diphtheria.'

Siegfried put his head on one side and a smile of saintly sweetness crept over his face. He laid his hand on my shoulder. 'My dear old James, perhaps it would be a good idea if you started right at the beginning. Take all the time you want – there's no hurry. Speak slowly and calmly and then you won't become confused. You told me you were treating a calf with pneumonia – now take it from there.'

I thrust my hands deep into my coat pockets and began to churn among the thermometers and scissors and little bottles which always dwelt there. 'Look, I told you right at the start that I didn't think there was any pneumonia but that I suspected early diphtheria. There was also a bit of fever – 103.'

Siegfried was looking past me at the window. 'God, just look at that snow. We're going to have some fun getting round today.' He dragged his eyes back to my face. 'Don't you think that with a temperature of 103 you should be injecting some Prontosil?' He raised his arms sideways and let them fall. 'Just a suggestion, James – I wouldn't interfere for the world but I honestly think that the situation calls for a little Prontosil.'

'But hell, I am using it!' I shouted. 'I told you that way back but you weren't listening. I've been doing my damnedest to get this across to you but what chance have I got . . .'

'Come come, dear boy, come come. No need to upset yourself.' Siegfried's face was transfigured by an internal radiance. Sweetness and charity, forgiveness, tolerance and affection flowed from him in an enveloping wave. I battled with an impulse to kick him swiftly on the shin.

'James, James.' The voice was caressing. 'I've not the slightest doubt you tried in your own way to tell me about this case, but we haven't all got the gift of communication. You're the most excellent fellow but must apply yourself to this. It is simply a matter of marshalling your facts and presenting them in an orderly manner. Then you wouldn't get confused and mixed up as you've done this morning; it's only a question of practice, I'm sure.' He gave an encouraging wave of the hand and was gone.

I strode quickly through to the stock room and, seeing a big, empty cardboard box on the floor, dealt it a vicious kick. I put so much venom into it that my foot went clear through the cardboard and I was trying to free myself when Tristan came in. He had been stoking the fire and had witnessed the conversation.

He watched silently as I plunged about the room swearing and trying to shake the box loose. 'What's up, Jim? Has my big brother been getting under your skin?'

I got rid of the box at last and sank down on one of the lower shelves. 'I don't know. Why should he be getting under my skin now? I've known him quite a long time and he's always been the same. He's never been any different but it hasn't bothered me before – not like this, anyway. Any other time I'd laugh that sort of thing off. What the hell's wrong with me?'

Tristan put down his coal bucket and looked at me thoughtfully. 'There's nothing much wrong with you, Jim, but I can tell you one thing – you've been just a bit edgy since you went out with the Alderson woman.'

'Oh God,' I groaned and closed my eyes. 'Don't remind me. Anyway, I've not seen her or heard from her since, so that's the end of that and I can't blame her.'

Tristan pulled out his Woodbines and squatted down by the coal bucket. 'Yes, that's all very well, but look at you. You're suffering and there's no need for it. All right, you had a disastrous night and she's given you the old heave ho. Well, so what? Do you know how many times I've been spurned?'

'Spurned? I never even got started.'

'Very well then, but you're still going around like a bullock with bellyache. Forget it, lad, and get out into the big world. The rich tapestry of life is waiting for you out there. I've been watching you – working all hours and when you're not working you're reading up your cases in the text books – and I tell you this dedicated vet thing is all right up to a point. But you've got to live a little. Think of all the lovely little lasses in Darrowby – you can hardly move for them. And every one just waiting for a big handsome chap like you to gallop up on his white horse. Don't disappoint them.' He leaned over and slapped my knee. 'Tell you what. Why don't you let me fix something up? A nice little foursome – just what you need.'

'Ach I don't know. I'm not keen, really.'

'Nonsense!' Tristan said. 'I don't know why I haven't thought of it before. This monkish existence is bad for you. Leave all the details to me.'

I decided to have an early night and was awakened around eleven o'clock by a heavy weight crashing down on the bed. The room was dark but I seemed to be enveloped in beer-scented smoke. I coughed and sat up. 'Is that you, Triss?'

'It is indeed,' said the shadowy figure on the end of the bed. 'And I bring you glad tidings. You remember Brenda?'

'That little nurse I've seen you around with?'

'The very same. Well, she's got a pal, Connie, who's even more beautiful. The four of us are going dancing at the Poulton Institute on Tuesday night.' The voice was thick with beery triumph.

'You mean me, too?'

'By God I do, and you're going to have the best time you've ever had. I'll see to that.' He blew a last choking blast of smoke into my face and left, chuckling.

Chapter Twenty-two

'We're having a 'ot dinner and entertainers.'

My reaction to the words surprised me. They stirred up a mixture of emotions, all of them pleasant; fulfilment, happy acceptance, almost triumph.

I know by now that there is not the slightest chance of anybody asking me to be President of the Royal College of Veterinary Surgeons, but if they had, I wonder if I'd have been more pleased than when I heard about the 'ot dinner.

The reason, I suppose, was that the words reflected the attitude of a typical Dales farmer towards myself. And this was important because, though after just over a year I was becoming accepted as a vet, I was always conscious of the gulf which was bound to exist between these hill folk and a city product like me. Much as I admired them I was aware always that we were different; it was inevitable, I knew, but it still rankled so that a sincere expression of friendship from one of them struck a deep answering chord in me.

Especially when it came from somebody like Dick Rudd. I had first met Dick last winter on the doorstep of Skeldale House at six o'clock on the kind of black morning when country vets wonder about their choice of profession. Shivering as the ever-present passage draught struck at my pyjamaed legs, I switched on the light and opened the door. I saw a small figure muffled in an old army greatcoat and balaclava leaning on a bicycle. Beyond him the light spilled onto a few feet of streaming pavement where the rain beat down in savage swathes.

'Sorry to ring your bell at this hour, guvnor,' he said. 'My name's Rudd, Birch Tree Farm, Coulston. I've got a heifer calvin' and she's not getting on with t'job. Will you come?'

I looked closer at the thin face, at the water trickling down the cheeks and dripping from the end of the nose. 'Right, I'll get dressed and come straight along. But why don't you leave your bike here and come with me in the car? Coulston's about four miles isn't it and you must be soaked through.'

'Nay, nay, it'll be right.' The face broke into the most cheerful of grins and under the sopping balaclava a pair of lively blue eyes glinted at me. 'I'd only have to come back and get it another time. I'll get off now and you won't be there long afore me.'

He mounted his bike quickly and pedalled away. People who think farming is a pleasant, easy life should have been there to see the hunched figure disappear into the blackness and the driving rain. No car, no telephone, a night up with the heifer, eight miles biking in the rain and a back-breaking day ahead of him. Whenever I thought of the existence of the small farmer it made my own occasional bursts of activity seem small stuff indeed.

I produced a nice live heifer calf for Dick that first morning and later, gratefully drinking a cup of hot tea in the farmhouse kitchen, I was surprised at the throng of young Rudds milling around me; there were seven of them and they were unexpectedly grown up. Their ages ranged from twenty odd down to about ten and I hadn't thought of Dick as middle-aged; in the dim light of the doorway at Skeldale House and later in the byre lit only by a smoke-blackened oil lamp his lively movements and perky manner had seemed those of a man in his thirties. But as I looked at him now I could see that the short, wiry hair was streaked with grey and a maze of fine wrinkles spread from around his eyes onto his cheeks.

In their early married life the Rudds, anxious like all farmers for male children, had observed with increasing chagrin the arrival of five successive daughters. 'We nearly packed up then,' Dick confided to me once; but they didn't and their perseverance was rewarded at last by the appearance of two fine boys. A farmer farms for his sons and Dick had something to work for now.

As I came to know them better I used to observe the family with wonder. The five girls were all tall, big-limbed, handsome, and already the two chunky young boys gave promise of massive growth. I kept looking from them to their frail little parents – 'not a pickin' on either of us', as Mrs Rudd used to say – and wonder how the miracle had happened.

It puzzled me, too, how Mrs Rudd, armed only with the milk cheque from Dick's few shaggy cows, had managed to feed them all, never mind bring them to this state of physical perfection. I gained my first clue one day when I had been seeing some calves and I was asked to have a 'bit o' dinner' with them. Butcher's meat was a scarce commodity on the hill farms and I was familiar with the usual expedients for filling up the eager stomachs before the main course – the doughy slab of Yorkshire pudding or the heap of suet dumpling. But Mrs Rudd had her own method – a big bowl of rice pudding with lots of milk was her *hors d'oeuvres*. It was a new one on me and I could see the family slowing down as they ploughed their way through. I was ravenous when I sat down but after the rice I viewed the rest of the meal with total detachment.

Dick believed in veterinary advice for everything so I was a frequent visitor at Birch Tree Farm. After every visit there was an unvarying ritual; I was asked into the house for a cup of tea and the whole family downed tools and sat down to watch me drink it. On weekdays the eldest girl was out at work and the boys were at school but on Sundays the ceremony reached its full splendour with myself sipping the tea and all nine Rudds sitting around in what I can only call an admiring circle. My every remark was greeted with nods and smiles all round. There is no doubt it was good for my ego to have an entire family literally hanging on my words, but at the same time it made me feel curiously humble.

I suppose it was because of Dick's character. Not that he was unique in any way – there were thousands of small farmers just like him – but he seemed to embody the best qualities of the Dalesman; the indestructibility, the tough philosophy, the unthinking generosity and hospitality. And there were the things that were Dick's own; the integrity which could be read always in his steady eyes and the humour which was never very far away. Dick was no wit but he was always trying to say ordinary things in a funny way. If I asked him to get hold of a cow's nose for me he would say solemnly 'Ah'll endeavour to do so', or I remember when I was trying to lift a square of plywood which was penning a calf in a corner he said 'Just a minute till ah raise portcullis'. When he broke into a smile a kind of radiance flooded his pinched features.

When I held my audiences in the kitchen with all the family reflecting Dick's outlook in their eager laughter I marvelled at their utter contentment with their lot. None of them had known ease or softness but it didn't matter; and they looked on me as a friend and I was proud.

Whenever I left the farm I found something on the seat of my car – a couple of home-made scones, three eggs. I don't know how Mrs Rudd spared them but she never failed.

Dick had a burning ambition – to upgrade his stock until he had a dairy herd which would live up to his ideals. Without money behind him he knew it would be a painfully slow business but he was determined. It probably wouldn't be in his own lifetime but some time, perhaps when his sons were grown up, people would come and look with admiration at the cows of Birch Tree.

I was there to see the very beginning of it. When Dick stopped me on the road one morning and asked me to come up to his place with him I knew by his air of suppressed excitement that something big had happened. He led me into the byre and stood silent. He didn't need to say anything because I was staring unbelievingly at a bovine aristocrat.

Dick's cows had been scratched together over the years and they were a motley lot. Many of them were old animals discarded by more prosperous farmers because of their pendulous udders or because they were 'three titted 'uns'. Others had been reared by Dick from calves and tended to be rough-haired and scruffy. But half way down the byre, contrasting almost violently with her neighbours was what seemed to me a perfect Dairy Shorthorn cow.

In these days when the Friesian has surged over England in a black and white flood and inundated even the Dales which were the very home of the Shorthorn, such cows as I looked at that day at Dick Rudd's are no longer to be seen, but she represented all the glory and pride of her breed. The wide pelvis tapering to fine shoulders and a delicate head, the level udder thrusting back between the hind legs, and the glorious colour – dark roan. That was what they used to call a 'good colour' and whenever I delivered a dark roan calf the farmer would say 'It's good-coloured 'un', and it would be more valuable accordingly. The geneticists are perfectly right, of course: the dark roaned cows gave no more milk than the reds or the whites, but we loved them and they were beautiful.

'Where did she come from, Dick?' I said, still staring.

Dick's voice was elaborately casual. 'Oh, ah went over to Weldon's of Cranby and picked her out. D'you like her?'

'She's a picture – a show cow. I've never seen one better.' Weldons were the biggest pedigree breeders in the northern Dales and I didn't ask whether Dick had cajoled his bank manager or had been saving up for years just for this.

'Aye, she's a seven galloner when she gets goin' and top butter fat, too. Reckon she'll be as good as two of my other cows and a calf out of her'll be worth a bit.' He stepped forward and ran his hand along the perfectly level, smoothly-fleshed back. 'She's got a great fancy pedigree name but missus 'as called her Strawberry.'

I knew as I stood there in the primitive, cobbled byre with its wooden partitions and rough stone walls that I was looking not just at a cow but at the foundation of the new herd, at Dick Rudd's hopes for the future.

It was about a month later that he phoned me. 'I want you to come and look

at Strawberry for me,' he said. 'She's been doing grand, tipplin' the milk out,
but there's summat amiss with her this morning.'

The cow didn't really look ill and, in fact, she was eating when I examined
her, but I noticed that she gulped slightly when she swallowed. Her temperature
was normal and her lungs clear but when I stood up by her head I could just
hear a faint snoring sound.

'It's her throat, Dick,' I said. 'It may be just a bit of inflammation but there's
a chance that she's starting a little abscess in there.' I spoke lightly but I wasn't
happy. Post-pharyngeal abscesses were, in my limited experience, nasty things.
They were situated in an inaccessible place, right away behind the back of the
throat and if they got very large could interfere seriously with the breathing. I
had been lucky with the few I had seen; they had either been small and regressed
or had ruptured spontaneously.

I gave an injection of Prontosil and turned to Dick. 'I want you to foment this
area behind the angle of the jaw with hot water and rub this salve well in
afterwards. You may manage to burst it that way. Do this at least three times
a day.'

I kept looking in at her over the next ten days and the picture was one of
steady development of the abscess. The cow was still not acutely ill but she was
eating a lot less, she was thinner and was going off her milk. Most of the time
I felt rather helpless as I knew that only the rupture of the abscess would bring
relief and the various injections I was giving her were largely irrelevant. But the
infernal thing was taking a long time to burst.

It happened that just then Siegfried went off to an equine conference which
was to last a week; for a few days I was at full stretch and hardly had time to
think about Dick's cow until he biked in to see me one morning. He was cheerful
as usual but he had a strained look.

'Will you come and see Strawberry? She's gone right down t'nick over the
last three days. I don't like look of her.'

I dashed straight out and was in the byre at Birch Tree before Dick was half
way home. The sight of Strawberry stopped me in mid-stride and I stared,
dry-mouthed at what had once been a show cow. The flesh had melted from her
incredibly and she was little more than a hide-covered skeleton. Her rasping
breathing could be heard all over the byre and she exhaled with a curious
out-puffing of the cheeks which I had never seen before. Her terrified eyes were
fixed rigidly on the wall in front of her. Occasionally she gave a painful little
cough which brought saliva drooling from her mouth.

I must have stood there a long time because I became aware of Dick at my
shoulder.

'She's the worst screw in the place now,' he said grimly.

I winced inwardly. 'Hell, Dick, I'm sorry. I'd no idea she'd got to this state.
I can't believe it.'

'Aye well it all happened sudden like. I've never seen a cow alter so fast.'

'The abscess must be right at its peak,' I said. 'She hasn't much space to
breathe through now.' As I spoke the cow's limbs began to tremble and for a
moment I thought she would fall. I ran out to the car and got a tin of Kaolin
poultice. 'Come on, let's get this on to her throat. It just might do the trick.'

When we had finished I looked at Dick. 'I think tonight will do it. It's just
got to burst.'

'And if it doesn't she'll snuff it tomorrow,' he grunted. I must have looked
very woebegone because suddenly his undefeated grin flashed out. 'Never mind,
lad, you've done everything anybody could do.'

But as I walked away I wasn't so sure. Mrs Rudd met me at the car. It was
her baking day and she pushed a little loaf into my hand. It made me feel worse.

Chapter Twenty-three

That night I sat alone in the big room at Skeldale House and brooded. Siegfried was still away, I had nobody to turn to and I wished to God I knew what I was going to do with that cow of Dick's in the morning. By the time I went up to bed I had decided that if nothing further had happened I would have to go in behind the angle of the jaw with a knife.

I knew just where the abscess was but it was a long way in and en route there were such horrific things as the carotid artery and the jugular vein. I tried hard to keep them out of my mind but they haunted my dreams; huge, throbbing, pulsating things with their precious contents threatening to burst at any moment through their fragile walls. I was awake by six o'clock and after an hour of staring miserably at the ceiling I could stand it no longer. I got up and, without washing or shaving, drove out to the farm.

As I crept fearfully into the byre I saw with a sick dismay that Strawberry's stall was empty. So that was that. She was dead. After all, she had looked like it yesterday. I was turning away when Dick called to me from the doorway.

'I've got her in a box on t'other side of the yard. Thought she'd be a bit more comfortable in there.'

I almost ran across the cobbles and as we approached the door the sound of the dreadful breathing came out to us. Strawberry was off her legs now – it had cost her the last of her strength to walk to the box and she lay on her chest, her head extended straight in front of her, nostrils dilated, eyes staring, cheeks puffing in her desperate fight for breath.

But she was alive and the surge of relief I felt seemed to prick me into action, blow away my hesitations.

'Dick,' I said, 'I've just got to operate on your cow. This thing is never going to burst in time, so it's now or never. But there's one thing I want you to know – the only way I can think of doing it is to go in from behind the jaw. I've never done this before, I've never seen it before and I've never heard of anybody doing it. If I nick any of those big blood vessels in there it'll kill her within a minute.'

'She can't last much longer like this,' Dick grunted. 'There's nowt to lose – get on with it.'

In most operations in large bovines we have to pull the animal down with ropes and then use general anaesthesia, but there was no need for this with Strawberry. She was too far gone. I just pushed gently at her shoulder and she rolled on to her side and lay still.

I quickly infiltrated the area from beneath the ear to the angle of the jaw with local anaesthetic then laid out my instruments.

'Stretch her head straight out and slightly back, Dick,' I said. Kneeling in the straw I incised the skin, cut carefully through the long thin layer of the brachiocephalic muscle and held the fibres apart with retractors. Somewhere down there was my objective and I tried to picture the anatomy of the region clearly in my mind. Just there the maxillary veins ran together to form the great jugular and, deeper and more dangerous, was the branching, ramifying carotid. If I pushed my knife straight in there, behind the mandibular salivary gland,

I'd just about hit the spot. But as I held the razor-sharp blade over the small space I had cleared, my hand began to tremble. I tried to steady it but I was like a man with malaria. The fact had to be faced that I was too scared to cut any further. I put the scalpel down, lifted a pair of long artery forceps and pushed them steadily down through the hole in the muscle. It seemed that I had gone an incredibly long way when, almost unbelievably, I saw a thin trickle of pus along the gleaming metal. I was into the abscess.

Gingerly, I opened the forceps as wide as possible to enlarge the drainage hole and as I did the trickle became a creamy torrent which gushed over my hand, down the cow's neck and onto the straw. I stayed quite still till it had stopped, then withdrew the forceps.

Dick looked at me from the other side of the head. 'Now what, boss?' he said softly.

'Well, I've emptied the thing, Dick,' I said, 'and by all the laws she should soon be a lot better. Come on, let's roll her on to her chest again.'

When we had got the cow settled comfortably with a bale of straw supporting her shoulder, I looked almost entreatingly at her. Surely she would show some sign of improvement. She must feel some relief from that massive evacuation. But Strawberry looked just the same. The breathing, if anything, was worse.

I dropped the soiled instruments into a bucket of hot water and antiseptic and began to wash them. 'I know what it is. The walls of the abscess have become indurated – thickened and hardened, you know – because it's been there a long time. We'll have to wait for them to collapse.'

Next day as I hurried across the yard I felt buoyantly confident. Dick was just coming out of the loose box and I shouted across to him, 'Well, how is she this morning?'

He hesitated and my spirits plummeted to zero. I knew what this meant; he was trying to find something good to say.

'Well, I reckon she's about t'same.'

'But dammit,' I shouted, 'she should be much better! Let's have a look at her.'

The cow wasn't just the same, she was worse. And on top of all the other symptoms she had a horribly sunken eye – the sign, usually, of approaching death in the bovine.

We both stood looking at the grim wreck of the once beautiful cow, then Dick broke the silence, speaking gently. 'Well, what do you think? Is it Mallock for her?'

The sound of the knacker man's name added the final note of despair. And indeed, Strawberry looked just like any of the other broken down animals that man came to collect.

I shuffled my feet miserably. 'I don't know what to say, Dick. There's nothing more I can do.' I took another look at the gasping staring head, the mass of bubbling foam around the lips and nostrils. 'You don't want her to suffer any more and neither do I. But don't get Mallock yet – she's distressed but not actually in pain, and I want to give her another day. If she's just the same tomorrow, send her in.' The very words sounded futile – every instinct told me the thing was hopeless. I turned to go, bowed down by a sense of failure heavier than I had ever known. As I went out into the yard, Dick called after me.

'Don't worry, lad, these things happen. Thank ye for all you've done.'

The words were like a whip across my back. If he had cursed me thoroughly I'd have felt a lot better. What had he to thank me for with his cow dying back there, the only good cow he'd ever owned? This disaster would just about floor Dick Rudd and he was telling me not to worry.

When I opened the car door I saw a cabbage on the seat. Mrs Rudd, too, was still at it. I leaned my elbow on the roof of the car and the words flowed from me. It was as if the sight of the cabbage had tapped the deep well of my frustration and I directed a soliloquy at the unheeding vegetable in which I ranged far over my many inadequacies. I pointed out the injustice of a situation where kindly people like the Rudds, in dire need of skilled veterinary assistance, had called on Mr Herriot who had responded by falling flat on his face. I drew attention to the fact that the Rudds, instead of hounding me off the place as I deserved, had thanked me sincerely and started to give me cabbages.

I went on for quite a long time and when I had finally finished I felt a little better. But not much, because, as I drove home I could not detect a glimmer of hope. If the walls of that abscess had been going to collapse they would have done so by now. I should have sent her in – she would be dead in the morning anyway.

I was so convinced of this that I didn't hurry to Birch Tree next day. I took it in with the round and it was almost midday when I drove through the gates. I knew what I would find – the usual grim signs of a vet's failure; the box door open and the drag marks where Mallock had winched the carcass across the yard on to his lorry. But everything was as usual and as I walked over to the silent box I steeled myself. The knacker man hadn't arrived yet but there was nothing surer than that my patient was lying dead in there. She couldn't possibly have hung on till now. My fingers fumbled at the catch as though something in me didn't want to look inside, but with a final wrench I threw the door wide.

Strawberry was standing there, eating hay from the rack; and not just eating it but jerking it through the bars almost playfully as cows do when they are really enjoying their food. It looked as though she couldn't get it down fast enough, pulling down great fragrant tufts and dragging them into her mouth with her rasp-like tongue. As I stared at her an organ began to play somewhere in the back of my mind; not just a little organ but a mighty instrument with gleaming pipes climbing high into the shadows of the cathedral roof. I went into the box, closed the door behind me and sat down in the straw in a corner. I had waited a long time for this. I was going to enjoy it.

The cow was almost a walking skeleton with her beautiful dark roan skin stretched tightly over the jutting bones. The once proud udder was a shrivelled purse dangling uselessly above her hocks. As she stood, she trembled from sheer weakness, but there was a light in her eye, a calm intensity in the way she ate which made me certain she would soon fight her way back to her old glory.

There was just the two of us in the box and occasionally Strawberry would turn her head towards me and regard me steadily, her jaws moving rhythmically. It seemed like a friendly look to me – in fact I wouldn't have been surprised if she had winked at me.

I don't know just how long I sat in there but I savoured every minute. It took some time for it to sink in that what I was watching was really happening; the swallowing was effortless, there was no salivation, no noise from her breathing. When I finally went out and closed the door behind me the cathedral organ was really blasting with all stops out, the exultant peals echoing back from the vaulted roof.

The cow made an amazing recovery. I saw her three weeks later and her bones were magically clothed with flesh, her skin shone and, most important, the magnificent udder bulged turgid beneath her, a neat little teat proudly erect at each corner.

I was pretty pleased with myself but of course a cold assessment of the case would show only one thing – that I had done hardly anything right from start to finish. At the very beginning I should have been down that cow's throat with a knife, but at that time I just didn't know how. In later years I have opened many a score of these abscesses by going in through a mouth gag with a scalpel tied to my fingers. It was a fairly heroic undertaking as the cow or bullock didn't enjoy it and was inclined to throw itself down with me inside it almost to the shoulder. It was simply asking for a broken arm.

When I talk about this to the present-day young vets they are inclined to look at me blankly because most of these abscesses undoubtedly had a tuberculous origin and since attestation they are rarely seen. But I can imagine it might bring a wry smile to the faces of my contemporaries as their memories are stirred.

The post-pharyngeal operation had the attraction that recovery was spectacular and rapid and I have had my own share of these little triumphs. But none of them gave me as much satisfaction as the one I did the wrong way.

It was a few weeks after the Strawberry episode and I was back in my old position in the Rudds' kitchen with the family around me. This time I was in no position to drop my usual pearls of wisdom because I was trying to cope with a piece of Mrs Rudd's apple tart. Mrs Rudd, I knew, could make delicious apple tarts but this was a special kind she produced for ' 'lowance' time – for taking out to Dick and the family when they were working in the fields. I had chewed at the two-inch pastry till my mouth had dried out. Somewhere inside there was no doubt a sliver of apple but as yet I had been unable to find it. I didn't dare try to speak in case I blew out a shower of crumbs and in the silence which followed I wondered if anybody would help me out. It was Mrs Rudd who spoke up.

'Mr Herriot,' she said in her quiet matter-of-fact way, 'Dick has something to say to you.'

Dick cleared his throat and sat up straighter in his chair. I turned towards him expectantly, my cheeks still distended by the obdurate mass. He looked unusually serious and I felt a twinge of apprehension.

'What I want to say is this,' he said. 'It'll soon be our silver wedding anniversary and we're going to 'ave a bit of a do. We want you to be our guest.'

I almost choked. 'Dick, Mrs Rudd, that's very kind of you. I'd love that – I'd be honoured to come.'

Dick inclined his head gravely. He still looked portentous as though there was something big to follow. 'Good, I think you'll enjoy it, because it's goin' to be a right do. We've got a room booked at t'King's Head at Carsley.'

'Gosh, sounds great!'

'Aye, t'missus and me have worked it all out.' He squared his thin shoulders and lifted his chin proudly.

'We're having a 'ot dinner and entertainers.'

Chapter Twenty-four

As time passed and I painfully clothed the bare bones of my theoretical knowledge with practical experience I began to realise there was another side to veterinary practice they didn't mention in the books. It had to do with money. Money has always formed a barrier between the farmer and the vet. I think this is because there is a deeply embedded, maybe subconscious conviction in many farmers' minds that they know more about their stock than any outsider and it is an admission of defeat to pay somebody else to doctor them.

The wall was bad enough in those early days when they had to pay the medical practitioners for treating their own ailments and when there was no free agricultural advisory service. But it is worse now when there is the Health Service and NAAS and the veterinary surgeon stands pitilessly exposed as the only man who has to be paid.

Most farmers, of course, swallow the pill and get out their cheque books, but there is a proportion – maybe about ten per cent – who do their best to opt out of the whole business.

We had our own ten per cent in Darrowby and it was a small but constant irritation. As an assistant I was not financially involved and it didn't seem to bother Siegfried unduly except when the quarterly bills were sent out. Then it really got through to him.

Miss Harbottle used to type out the accounts and present them to him in a neat pile and that was when it started. He would go through them one by one and it was a harrowing experience to watch his blood pressure gradually rising.

I found him crouched over his desk one night. It was about eleven o'clock and he had had a hard day. His resistance was right down. He was scrutinising each bill before placing it face down on a pile to his left. On his right there was a smaller pile and whenever he placed one there it was to the accompaniment of a peevish muttering or occasionally a violent outburst.

'Would you believe it?' he grunted as I came in. 'Henry Bransom – more than two years since we saw a penny of his money, yet he lives like a sultan. Never misses a market for miles around, gets as tight as an owl several nights a week and I saw him putting ten pounds on a horse at the races last month.'

He banged the piece of paper down and went on with his job, breathing deeply. Then he froze over another account. 'And look at this one! Old Summers of Low Ness. I bet he's got thousands of pounds hidden under his bed but by God he won't part with any of it to me.'

He was silent for a few moments as he transferred several sheets to the main pile then he swung round on me with a loud cry, waving a paper in my face.

'Oh no! Oh Christ, James, this is too much! Bert Mason here owes me twenty-seven and sixpence. I must have spent more than that sending him bills year in year out and do you know I saw him driving past the surgery yesterday in a brand new car. The bloody scoundrel!'

He hurled the bill down and started his crutiny again. I noticed he was using only one hand while the other churned among his hair. I hoped fervently that he might hit upon a seam of good payers because I didn't think his nervous system could take much more. And it seemed that my hopes were answered because several minutes went by with only the quiet lifting and laying of the paper sheets. Then Siegfried stiffened suddenly in his chair and sat quite motionless as he stared down at his desk. He lifted an account and held it for several seconds at eye level. I steeled myself. This must be a beauty.

But to my surprise Siegfried began to giggle softly then he threw back his head and gave a great bellow of laughter. He laughed until he seemed to have no strength to laugh any more, then he turned to me.

'It's the Major, James,' he said weakly. 'The dear old gallant Major. You know, you can't help admiring the man. He owed my predecessor a fair bit when I bought the practice and he still owes it. And I've never had a sou for all the work I've done for him. The thing is he's the same with everybody and yet he gets away with it. He's a genuine artist – these other fellows are just fumbling amateurs by comparison.'

He got up, reached up into the glass-fronted cupboard above the mantelpiece and pulled out the whisky bottle and two glasses. He carelessly tipped a prodigal measure into each glass and handed one to me, then he sank back into his chair, still grinning. The Major had magically restored his good humour.

Sipping my drink, I reflected that there was no doubt Major Bullivant's character had a rich, compelling quality. He presented an elegant, patrician front to the world; beautiful Shakespearean actor voice, impeccable manners and an abundance of sheer presence. Whenever he unbent sufficiently to throw me a friendly word I felt honoured even though I knew I was doing his work for nothing.

He had a small, cosy farm, a tweed-clad wife and several daughters who had ponies and were active helpers for the local hunt. Everything in his entire ménage was right and fitting. But he never paid anybody.

He had been in the district about three years and on his arrival the local tradesmen, dazzled by his façade, had fallen over each other to win his custom. After all, he appeared to be just their type because they preferred inherited wealth in Darrowby. In contrast to what I had always found in Scotland, the self-made man was regarded with deep suspicion and there was nothing so damning among the townsfolk as the darkly muttered comment: 'He had nowt when he first came 'ere.'

Of course, when the scales had fallen from their eyes they fought back, but ineffectually. The local garage impounded the Major's ancient Rolls Royce and hung on to it fiercely for a while but he managed to charm it back. His one failure was that his telephone was always being cut off; it seemed that the Postmaster General was one of the few who were immune to his blandishments.

But time runs out for even the most dedicated expert. I was driving one day through Hollerton, a neighbouring market town about ten miles away, and I noticed the Bullivant girls moving purposefully among the shops armed with large baskets. The Major, it seemed, was having to cast his net a little wider and I wondered at the time if perhaps he was ready to move on. He did, in fact, disappear from the district a few weeks later leaving a lot of people licking their wounds. I don't know if he ever paid anybody before he left but Siegfried didn't get anything.

Even after his departure Siegfried wasn't at all bitter, preferring to regard the Major as a unique phenomenon, a master of his chosen craft. 'After all, James,' he said to me once, 'putting ethical considerations to one side, you must admit that anybody who can run up a bill of fifty pounds for shaves and haircuts at the Darrowby barber's shop must command a certain amount of respect.'

Siegfried's attitude to his debtors was remarkably ambivalent. At times he would fly into a fury at the mention of their names, at others he would regard them with a kind of wry benevolence. He often said that if ever he threw a cocktail party for the clients he'd have to invite the non-payers first because they were all such charming fellows.

Nevertheless he waged an inexorable war against them by means of a series of letters graduated according to severity which he called his PNS. system (Polite, Nasty, Solicitor's) and in which he had great faith. It was a sad fact, however, that the system seldom worked with the real hard cases who were accustomed to receiving threatening letters with their morning mail. These people yawned over the polite and nasty ones and were unimpressed by the solicitor's because they knew from experience that Siegfried always shrank from following through to the limit of the law.

When the PNS system failed Siegfried was inclined to come up with some unorthodox ideas to collect his hard-earned fees. Like the scheme he devised for Dennis Pratt. Dennis was a tubby, bouncy little man and his high opinion of himself showed in the way he always carried his entire five feet three inches proudly erect. He always seemed to be straining upwards, his chest thrust forward, his fat little bottom stuck out behind him at an extraordinary angle.

Dennis owed the practice a substantial amount and about eighteen months ago had been subjected to the full rigour of the PNS system. This had induced him to part with five pounds 'on account' but since then nothing more had been forthcoming. Siegfried was in a quandary because he didn't like getting tough with such a cheerful, hospitable man.

Dennis was always either laughing or about to laugh. I remember when we had to anaesthetise a cow on his farm to remove a growth from between its cleats. Siegfried and I went to the case together and on the way we were talking about something which had amused us. As we got out of the car we were both laughing helplessly and just then the farmhouse door opened and Dennis emerged.

We were at the far end of the yard and we must have been all of thirty yards away. He couldn't possibly have heard anything of our conversation but when he saw us laughing he threw back his head immediately and joined in at the top of his voice. He shook so much on his way across the yard that I thought he would fall over. When he arrived he was wiping the tears from his eyes.

After a job he always asked us in to sample Mrs Pratt's baking. In fact on cold days he used to keep a thermos of hot coffee ready for our arrival and he had an endearing habit of sloshing rum freely into each cup before pouring in the coffee.

'You can't put a man like that in court,' Siegfried said. 'But we've got to find some way of parting him from his brass.' He looked ruminatively at the ceiling for a few moments then thumped a fist into his palm.

'I think I've got it, James! You know it's quite possible it just never occurs to Dennis to pay a bill. So I'm going to pitch him into an environment where it will really be brought home to him. The accounts have just gone out and I'll arrange to meet him in here at two o'clock next market day. I'll say I want to discuss his mastitis problem. He'll be right in the middle of all the other farmers paying their bills and I'll deliberately leave him with them for half an hour or so. I'm sure it will give him the notion.'

I couldn't help feeling dubious. I had known Siegfried long enough to realise that some of his ideas were brilliant and others barmy; and he had so many ideas and they came in such a constant torrent that I often had difficulty in deciding which was which. Clearly in this case he was working on the same lines as a doctor who turns on a water tap full force to induce a pent up patient to urinate into a bottle.

The scheme may have merit – it was possible that the flutter of cheque books, the chink of coins, the rustle of notes might tap the long-buried well of debt in Dennis and bring it gushing from him in a mighty flood; but I doubted it.

My doubts must have shown on my face because Siegfried laughed and thumped me on the shoulder. 'Don't look so worried – we can only try. And it'll work. Just you wait.'

After lunch on market day I was looking out of the window when I saw Dennis heading our way. The street was busy with the market bustle but he was easy to pick out. Chin in air, beaming around him happily, every springing step taking him high on tiptoe he was a distinctive figure. I let him in at the front door and he strutted past me along the passage, the back of his natty sports jacket lying in a neat fold over his protruding buttocks.

Siegfried seated him strategically by Miss Harbottle's elbow, giving him an unimpeded view of the desk. Then he excused himself, saying he had a dog to attend to in the operating room. I stayed behind to answer the clients' queries and to watch developments. I hadn't long to wait; the farmers began to come in, a steady stream of them, clutching their cheque books. Some of them stood patiently by the desk, others sat in the chairs along the walls waiting their turn.

It was a typical bill-paying day with the usual quota of moans. The most common expression was that Mr Farnon had been 'ower heavy wi' t'pen' and many of them wanted a 'bit knockin' off'. Miss Harbottle used her discretion in these matters and if the animal had died or the bill did seem unduly large she would make some reduction.

There was one man who didn't get away with it. He had truculently demanded a 'bit of luck' on an account and Miss Harbottle fixed him with a cold eye.

'Mr Brewiss,' she said. 'This account has been owing for over a year. You should really be paying us interest. I can only allow discount when a bill is paid promptly. It's too bad of you to let it run on for this length of time.'

Dennis, sitting bolt upright, his hands resting on his knees, obviously agreed with every word. He pursed his lips in disapproval as he looked at the farmer and turned towards me with a positively scandalised expression.

Among the complaints was an occasional bouquet. A stooping old man who had received one of the polite letters was full of apologies. 'I'm sorry I've missed paying for a few months. The vets allus come out straight away when I send for them so I reckon it's not fair for me to keep them waiting for their money.'

I could see that Dennis concurred entirely with this sentiment. He nodded vigorously and smiled benevolently at the old man.

Another farmer, a hard-looking character, was walking out without his receipt when Miss Harbottle called him back. 'You'd better take this with you or we might ask you to pay again,' she said with a heavy attempt at roguishness.

The man paused with his hand on the door knob. 'I'll tell you summat, missis, you're bloody lucky to get it once – you'd never get it twice.'

Dennis was right in the thick of it all. Watching closely as the farmers slapped their cheque books on the desk for Miss Harbottle to write (they never wrote their own cheques) then signed them slowly and painstakingly. He looked with open fascination at the neat bundles of notes being tucked away in the desk drawer and I kept making little provocative remarks like 'It's nice to see the money coming in. We can't carry on without that, can we?'

The queue began to thin out and sometimes we were left alone in the room. On these occasions we conversed about many things – the weather, Dennis's stock, the political situation. Finally, Siegfried came in and I left to do a round.

When I got back, Siegfried was at his evening meal. I was eager to hear how his scheme had worked out but he was strangely reticent. At length I could wait no longer.

'Well, how did it go?' I asked.

Siegfried speared a piece of steak with his fork and applied some mustard. 'How did what go?'

'Well – Dennis. How did you make out with him?'

'Oh, fine. We went into his mastitis problem very thoroughly. I'm going out there on Tuesday morning to infuse every infected quarter in the herd with acriflavine solution. It's a new treatment – they say it's very good.'

'But you know what I mean. Did he show any sign of paying his bill?'

Siegfried chewed impassively for a few moments and swallowed. 'No, never a sign.' He put down his knife and fork and a haggard look spread over his face. 'It didn't work, did it?'

'Oh well, never mind. As you said, we could only try.' I hesitated. 'There's something else, Siegfried. I'm afraid you're going to be annoyed with me. I know you've told me never to dish out stuff to people who don't pay, but he talked me into letting him have a couple of bottles of fever drink. I don't know what came over me.'

'He did, did he?' Siegfried stared into space for a second then gave a wintry smile. 'Well, you can forget about that. He got six tins of stomach powder out of me.'

Chapter Twenty-five

There was one client who would not have been invited to the debtors' cocktail party. He was Mr Horace Dumbleby, the butcher of Aldgrove. As an inveterate non-payer he fulfilled the main qualification for the function but he was singularly lacking in charm.

His butcher shop in the main street of picturesque Aldgrove village was busy and prosperous but most of his trade was done in the neighbouring smaller villages and among the scattered farmhouses of the district. Usually the butcher's wife and married daughter looked after the shop while Mr Dumbleby himself did the rounds. I often saw his blue van standing with the back doors open and a farmer's wife waiting while he cut the meat, his big, shapeless body hunched over the slab. Sometimes he would look up and I would catch a momentary glimpse of a huge, bloodhound face and melancholy eyes.

Mr Dumbleby was a farmer himself in a small way. He sold milk from six cows which he kept in a tidy little byre behind his shop and he fattened a few bullocks and pork pigs which later appeared as sausages, pies, roasting cuts and chops in his front window. In fact Mr Dumbleby seemed to be very nicely fixed and it was said he owned property all over the place. But Siegfried had only infrequent glimpses of his money.

All the slow payers had one thing in common – they would not tolerate slowness from the vets. When they were in trouble they demanded immediate action. 'Will you come at once?', 'How long will you be?', 'You won't keep me waiting, will you?', 'I want you to come out here straight away'. It used to alarm me to see the veins swelling on Siegfried's forehead, the knuckles whitening as he gripped the phone.

After one such session with Mr Dumbleby at ten o'clock on a Sunday night he had flown into a rage and unleashed the full fury of the PNS system on him. It had no loosening effect on the butcher's purse strings but it did wound his feelings deeply. He obviously considered himself a wronged man. From that time on, whenever I saw him with his van out in the country he would turn slowly and direct a blank stare at me till I was out of sight. And strangely, I seemed to see him more and more often – the thing became unnerving.

And there was something worse. Tristan and I used to frequent the little Aldgrove pub where the bar was cosy and the beer measured up to Tristan's stringent standards. I had never taken much notice of Mr Dumbleby before although he always occupied the same corner, but now, every time I looked up, the great sad eyes were trained on me in disapproval. I tried to forget about him and listen to Tristan relating his stories from the backs of envelopes but all the time I could feel that gaze upon me. My laughter would trail away and I would have to look round. Then the excellent bitter would be as vinegar in my mouth.

In an attempt to escape, I took to visiting the snug instead of the bar and Tristan, showing true nobility of soul, came with me into an environment which was alien to him; where there was a carpet on the floor, people sitting around at little shiny tables drinking gin and hardly a pint in sight. But even this sacrifice was in vain because Mr Dumbleby changed his position in the bar so that he could look into the snug through the communicating hatch. The odd hours I was able to spend there took on a macabre quality. I was like a man trying desperately to forget. But quaff the beer as I might, laugh, talk, even sing, half of me was waiting in a state of acute apprehension for the moment when I knew I would have to look round. And when I did, the great sombre face looked even more forbidding framed by the wooden surround of the hatch. The hanging jowls, the terraced chins, the huge, brooding eyes – all were dreadfully magnified by their isolation in that little hole in the wall.

It was no good, I had to stop going to the place. This was very sad because Tristan used to wax lyrical about a certain unique, delicate nuttiness which he could discern in the draught bitter. But it had lost its joy for me; I just couldn't take any more of Mr Dumbleby.

In fact I did my best to forget all about the gentleman, but he was brought back forcibly into my mind when I heard his voice on the phone at 3 a.m. one morning. It was nearly always the same thing when the bedside phone exploded in your ear in the small hours – a calving.

Mr Dumbleby's call was no exception but he was more peremptory than might have been expected. There was no question about apologising about ringing at such an hour as most farmers would do. I said I would come immediately but that wasn't good enough – he wanted to know exactly in minutes how long I would be. In a sleepy attempt at sarcasm I started to recite a programme of so many minutes to get up and dressed, so many to go downstairs and get the car out etc. but I fear it was lost on him.

When I drove into the sleeping village a light was showing in the window of the butcher's shop. Mr Dumbleby almost trotted out into the street and paced up and down, muttering, as I fished out my ropes and instruments from the boot. Very impatient, I thought, for a man who hadn't paid his vet bill for over a year.

We had to go through the shop to get to the byre in the rear. My patient was a big, fat white cow which didn't seem particularly perturbed by her situation. Now and then she strained, pushing a pair of feet a few inches from her vulva. I took a keen look at those feet – it is the vet's first indication of how tough the job is going to be. Two huge hooves sticking out of a tiny heifer have always been able to wipe the smile off my face. These feet were big enough but not out of the way, and in truth the mother looked sufficiently roomy. I wondered what was stopping the natural sequence.

'I've had me hand in,' said Mr Dumbleby. 'There's a head there but I can't shift owt. I've been pulling them legs for half an hour.'

As I stripped to the waist (it was still considered vaguely cissy to wear a calving overall) I reflected that things could be a lot worse. So many of the buildings where I had to take my shirt off were primitive and draughty but this was a modern cow house and the six cows provided a very adequate central heating. And there was electricity in place of the usual smoke-blackened oil lamp.

When I had soaped and disinfected my arms I made my first exploration and it wasn't difficult to find the cause of the trouble.

There was a head and two legs all right, but they belonged to different calves. 'We've got twins here,' I said. 'These are hind legs you've been pulling – a posterior presentation.'

'Arse fust, you mean?'

'If you like. And the calf that's coming the right way has both his legs back along his sides. I'll have to push him back out of the way and get the other one first.'

This was going to be a pretty tight squeeze. Normally I like a twin calving because the calves are usually so small, but these seemed to be quite big. I put my hand against the little muzzle in the passage, poked a finger into the mouth and was rewarded by a jerk and flip of the tongue; he was alive, anyway.

I began to push him steadily back into the uterus, wondering at the same time what the little creature was making of it all. He had almost entered the world – his nostrils had been a couple of inches from the outside air – and now he was being returned to the starting post.

The cow didn't think much of the idea either because she started a series of straining heaves with the object of frustrating me. She did a pretty fair job, too, since a cow is a lot stronger than a man, but I kept my arm rigid against the calf and though each heave forced me back I maintained a steady pressure till I had pushed him to the brim of the pelvis.

I turned to Mr Dumbleby and gasped: 'I've got this head out of the way. Get hold of those feet and pull the other calf out.'

The butcher stepped forward ponderously and each of his big, meaty hands engulfed a foot. Then he closed his eyes and with many facial contortions and noises of painful effort he began to go through the motions of tugging. The calf didn't move an inch and my spirits drooped. Mr Dumbleby was a grunter. (This expression had its origin in an occasion when Siegfried and a farmer had a foot apiece at a calving and the farmer was making pitiful sounds without exerting himself in the slightest. Siegfried had turned to him and said: 'Look, let's come to an arrangement – you do the pulling and I'll do the grunting.')

It was clear I was going to get no help from the big butcher and decided to have one go by myself. I might be lucky. I let go the muzzle and made a quick grab for those hind feet, but the cow was too quick for me. I had just got a slippery grasp when she made a single expulsive effort and pushed calf number two into the passage again. I was back where I started.

Once more I put my hand against the wet little muzzle and began the painful process of repulsion. And as I fought against the big cow's straining I was reminded that it was 4 a.m. when none of us feels very strong. By the time I had worked the head back to the pelvic inlet I was feeling the beginning of that deadly creeping weakness and it seemed as though somebody had removed most of the bones from my arm.

This time I took a few seconds to get my breath back before I made my dive for the feet, but it was no good. The cow beat me easily with a beautifully timed contraction. Again that intruding head was jammed tight in the passage.

I had had enough. And it occurred to me that the little creature inside must also be getting a little tired of this back and forth business. I shivered my way through the cold, empty shop out into the silent street and collected the local anaesthetic from the car. Eight cc's into the epidural space and the cow, its uterus completely numbed, lost all interest in the proceedings. In fact she pulled a little hay from her rack and began to chew absently.

From then on it was like working inside a mail bag; whatever I pushed stayed put instead of surging back at me. The only snag was that once I had got everything straight there were no uterine contractions to help me. It was a case of pulling. Leaning back on a hind leg and with Mr Dumbleby panting in agony on the other, the posterior presentation was soon delivered. He had inhaled a fair amount of placental fluid but I held him upside down till he had coughed it up. When I laid him on the byre floor he shook his head vigorously and tried to sit up.

Then I had to go in after my old friend the second calf. He was lying well inside now, apparently sulking. When I finally brought him snuffling and kicking into the light I couldn't have blamed him if he had said 'Make up your mind, will you!'

Towelling my chest I looked with the sharp stab of pleasure I always felt at the two wet little animals wriggling on the floor as Mr Dumbleby rubbed them down with a handful of straw.

'Big 'uns for twins,' the butcher muttered.

Even this modest expression of approval surprised me and it seemed I might as well push things along a bit.

'Yes, they're two grand calves. Twins are often dead when they're mixed up like that – good job we got them out alive.' I paused a moment. 'You know, those two must be worth a fair bit.'

Mr Dumbleby didn't answer and I couldn't tell whether the shaft had gone home.

I got dressed, gathered up my gear and followed him out of the byre and into the silent shop past the rows of beef cuts hanging from hooks, the trays of offal, the mounds of freshly-made sausages. Near the outside door the butcher halted and stood, irresolute, for a moment. He seemed to be thinking hard. Then he turned to me.

'Would you like a few sausages?'

I almost reeled in my astonishment. 'Yes, thank you very much, I would.' It was scarcely credible but I must have touched the man's heart.

He went over, cut about a pound of links, wrapped them quickly in grease-proof paper and handed the parcel to me.

I looked down at the sausages, feeling the cold weight on my hand. I still couldn't believe it. Then an unworthy thought welled in my mind. It wasn't fair, I know – the poor fellow couldn't have known the luxury of many generous impulses – but some inner demon drove me to put him to the test. I put a hand in my trouser pocket, jingled my loose change and looked him in the eye.

'Well, how much will that be?' I asked.

Mr Dumbleby's big frame froze suddenly into immobility and he stood for a few seconds perfectly motionless. His face, as he stared at me, was almost without expression, but a single twitch of the cheek and a slowly rising anguish in the eyes betrayed the internal battle which was raging. When he did speak it was in a husky whisper as though the words had been forced from him by a power beyond his control.

'That,' he said, 'will be two and sixpence.'

Chapter Twenty-six

It was a new experience for me to be standing outside the hospital waiting for the nurses to come off duty, but it was old stuff to Tristan who was to be found there several nights a week. His experience showed in various ways, but mainly in the shrewd position he took up in a dark corner of the doorway of the gas company office just beyond the splash of light thrown by the street lamp. From there he could look straight across the road into the square entrance of the hospital and the long white corridor leading to the nurses' quarters. And there was the other advantage that if Siegfried should happen to pass that way, Tristan would be invisible and safe.

At half past seven he nudged me. Two girls had come out of the hospital and down the steps and were standing expectantly in the street. Tristan looked warily in both directions before taking my arm. 'Come on, Jim, here they are. That's Connie on the left – the coppery blonde – lovely little thing.'

We went over and Tristan introduced me with characteristic charm. I had to admit that if the evening had indeed been arranged for therapeutic purposes I was beginning to feel better already. There was something healing in the way the two pretty girls looked up at me with parted lips and shining eyes as though I was the answer to every prayer they had ever offered.

They were remarkably alike except for the hair. Brenda was very dark but Connie was fair with a deep, fiery glow where the light from the doorway touched her head. Both of them projected a powerful image of bursting health – fresh cheeks, white teeth, lively eyes and something else which I found particularly easy to take; a simple desire to please.

Tristan opened the back door of the car with a flourish. 'Be careful with him in there Connie, he looks quiet but he's a devil with women. Known far and wide as a great lover.'

The girls giggled and studied me with even greater interest. Tristan leaped into the driver's seat and we set off at breakneck speed.

As the dark countryside hastened past the windows I leaned back in the corner and listened to Tristan who was in full cry; maybe in a kindly attempt to cheer me or maybe because he just felt that way, but his flow of chatter was unceasing. The girls made an ideal audience because they laughed in delight at everything he said. I could feel Connie shaking against me. She was sitting very close with a long stretch of empty seat on the other side of her. The little car swayed round a sharp corner and threw her against me and she stayed there quite naturally with her head on my shoulder. I felt her hair against my cheek. She didn't use much perfume but smelt cleanly of soap and antiseptic. My mind went back to Helen – I didn't think much about her these days. It was just a question of practice; to scotch every thought of her as soon as it came up. I was getting pretty good at it now. Anyway, it was over – all over before it had begun.

I put my arm round Connie and she lifted her face to me. Ah well, I thought as I kissed her. Tristan's voice rose in song from the front seat, Brenda giggled, the old car sped over the rough road with a thousand rattles.

We came at last to Poulton, a village on the road to nowhere. Its single street straggled untidily up the hillside to a dead end where there was a circular green with an ancient stone cross and a steep mound on which was perched the institute hall.

This was where the dance was to be held, but Tristan had other plans first. 'There's a lovely little pub here. We'll just have a toothful to get us in the mood.' We got out of the car and Tristan ushered us into a low stone building.

There was nothing of the olde worlde about the place; just a large, square, whitewashed room with a black cooking range enclosing a bright fire and a long high-backed wooden settle facing it. Over the fireplace stretched a single immense beam, gnarled and pitted with the years and blackened with smoke.

We hurried over to the settle, feeling the comfort of it as a screen against the cold outside. We had the place to ourselves.

The landlord came in. He was dressed informally – no jacket, striped, collarless shirt, trousers and braces which were reinforced by a broad, leather belt around his middle. His cheerful round face lit up at the sight of Tristan. 'Now then, Mr Farnon, are you very well?'

'Never better, Mr Peacock, and how are you?'

'Nicely, sir, very nicely. Can't complain. And I recognise the other gentleman. Been in my place before, haven't you?'

I remembered then. A day's testing in the Poulton district and I had come in here for a meal, freezing and half starved after hours of wrestling with young beasts on the high moor. The landlord had received me unemotionally and had set to immediately with his frying-pan on the old black range while I sat looking at his shirt back and the braces and the shining leather belt. The meal had taken up the whole of the round oak table by the fire – a thick steak of home cured ham overlapping the plate with two fresh eggs nestling on its bosom, a newly baked loaf with the knife sticking in it, a dish of farm butter, some jam, a vast pot of tea and a whole Wensleydale cheese, circular, snow white, about eighteen inches high.

I could remember eating unbelievingly for a long time and finishing with slice after slice of the moist, delicately flavoured cheese. The entire meal had cost me half a crown.

'Yes, Mr Peacock, I have been here before and if I'm ever starving on a desert island I'll think of that wonderful meal you gave me.'

The landlord shrugged. 'Well it was nowt much, sir. Just t'usual stuff.' But he looked pleased.

'That's fine, then,' Tristan said impatiently. 'But we haven't come to eat, we've come for a drink and Mr Peacock keeps some of the finest draught Magnet in Yorkshire. I'd welcome your opinion on it, Jim. Perhaps you would be kind enough to bring us up two pints and two halves, Mr Peacock.'

I noticed there was no question of asking the girls what they would like to have, but they seemed quite happy with the arrangement. The landlord reappeared from the cellar, puffing slightly. He was carrying a tall, white enamelled jug from which he poured a thin brown stream, varying the height expertly till he had produced a white, frothy head on each glass.

Tristan raised his pint and looked at it with quiet reverence. He sniffed it carefully and then took a sip which he retained in his mouth for a few seconds while his jaw moved rapidly up and down. After swallowing he smacked his lips a few times with the utmost solemnity then closed his eyes and took a deep gulp. He kept his eyes closed for a long time and when he opened them they were rapturous, as though he had seen a beautiful vision.

'It's an experience coming here,' he whispered. 'Keeping beer in the wood is a skilful business, but you, Mr Peacock, are an artist.'

The landlord inclined his head modestly and Tristan, raising his glass in salute, drained it with an easy upward motion of the elbow.

Little oohs of admiration came from the girls but I saw that they, in their turn, had little difficulty in emptying their glasses. With an effort I got my own pint down and the enamel jug was immediately in action again.

I was always at a disadvantage in the company of a virtuoso like Tristan, but as the time passed and the landlord kept revisiting the cellar with his jug it seemed to become easier. In fact, a long time later, as I drew confidently on my eighth pint, I wondered why I had ever had difficulty with large amounts of fluid. It was easy and it soothed and comforted. Tristan was right – I had been needing this.

It puzzled me that I hadn't realised until now that Connie was one of the most beautiful creatures I had ever seen. Back there in the street outside the hospital she had seemed attractive, but obviously the light had been bad and I had failed to notice the perfection of her skin, the mysterious greenish depths of her eyes and the wonderful hair catching lights of gold and deep red-bronze from the flickering fire. And the laughing mouth, shining, even teeth and little pink tongue – she hardly ever stopped laughing except to drink her beer.

Everything I said was witty, brilliantly funny in fact, and she looked at me all the time, peeping over the top of her glass in open admiration. It was profoundly reassuring.

As the beer flowed, time slowed down and finally lurched to a halt and there was neither past nor future, only Connie's face and the warm, untroubled present.

I was surprised when Tristan pulled at my arm, I had forgotten he was there and when I focused on him it was the same as with Connie – there was just the face swimming disembodied in an empty room. Only this face was very red and puffy and glassy-eyed.

'Would you care for the mad conductor?' the face said.

I was deeply touched. Here was another sign of my friend's concern for me. Of all Tristan's repértoire his imitation of a mad conductor was the most exacting. It involved tremendous expenditure of energy and since Tristan was unused to any form of physical activity, it really took it out of him. Yet here he was, ready and willing to sacrifice himself. A wave of treacly sentiment flooded through me and I wondered for a second if it might not be the proper thing to burst into tears; but instead I contented myself with wringing Tristan's hand.

'There's nothing I would like more, my dear old chap,' I said thickly. 'I greatly appreciate the kind thought. And may I take this opportunity of telling you that I consider that in all Yorkshire there is no finer gentleman breathing than T. Farnon.'

The big red face grew very solemn. 'You honour me with those words, old friend.'

'Not a bit of it,' I slurred. 'My stumbling sentences cannot hope to express my extremely high opinion of you.'

'You are too kind,' hiccuped Tristan.

'Nothing of the sort. It's a privlish, a rare privlish to know you.'

'Thank you, thank you,' Tristan nodded gravely at me from a distance of about six inches. We were staring into each other's eyes with intense absorption and the conversation might have gone on for a long time if Brenda hadn't broken in.

'Hey, when you two have finished rubbing noses I'd rather like another drink.'

Tristan gave her a cold look. 'You'll have to wait just a few minutes. There's something I have to do.' He rose, shook himself and walked with dignity to the centre of the floor. When he turned to face his audience he looked exalted. I felt that this would be an outstanding performance.

Tristan raised his arms and gazed imperiously over his imaginary orchestra, taking in the packed rows of strings, the woodwind, brass and tympani in one sweeping glance. Then with a violent downswing he led them into the overture. Rossini, this time, I thought or maybe Wagner as I watched him throwing his head about, bringing in the violins with a waving clenched fist or exhorting the trumpets with a glare and a trembling, outstretched hand.

It was somewhere near the middle of the piece that the rot always set in and I watched enthralled as the face began to twitch and the lips to snarl. The arm waving became more and more convulsive then the whole body jerked with uncontrollable spasms. It was clear that the end was near – Tristan's eyes were rolling, his hair hung over his face and he had lost control of the music which crashed and billowed about him. Suddenly he grew rigid, his arms fell to his sides and he crashed to the floor.

I was joining the applause and laughter when I noticed that Tristan was very still. I bent over him and found that he had struck his head against the heavy oak leg of the settle and was almost unconscious. The nurses were quickly into action. Brenda expertly propped up his head while Connie ran for a basin of hot water and a cloth. When he opened his eyes they were bathing a tender lump above his ear. Mr Peacock hovered anxiously in the background. 'Ista all right? Can ah do anything?'

Tristan sat up and sipped weakly at his beer. He was very pale. 'I'll be all right in a minute and there is something you can do. You can bring us one for the road and then we must be getting on to this dance.'

The landlord hurried away and returned with the enamel jug brimming. The final pint revived Tristan miraculously and he was soon on his feet. Then we shook hands affectionately with Mr Peacock and took our leave. After the brightness of the inn the darkness pressed on us like a blanket and we groped our way up the steep street till we could see the institute standing on its grassy mound. Faint rays of light escaped through the chinks in the curtained windows and we could hear music and a rhythmic thudding.

A cheerful young farmer took our money at the door and when we went into the hall we were swallowed up in a tight mass of dancers. The place was packed solidly with young men in stiff-looking dark suits and girls in bright dresses all sweating happily as they swayed and wheeled to the music.

On the low platform at one end, four musicians were playing their hearts out – piano, accordion, violin and drums. At the other end, several comfortable, middle-aged women stood behind a long table on trestles, presiding over the thick sandwiches of ham and brawn, home made pies, jugs of milk and trifles generously laid with cream.

All round the walls more lads were standing, eyeing the unattached girls. I recognised a young client. 'What do you call this dance?' I yelled above the din.

'The Eva Three Step,' came back the reply.

This was new to me but I launched out confidently with Connie. There was a lot of twirling and stamping and when the men brought their heavy boots down on the boards the hall shook and the noise was deafening. I loved it – I was right on the peak and I whirled Connie effortlessly among the throng. I was dimly aware of bumping people with my shoulders but, try as I might, I couldn't feel my feet touching the floor. The floating sensation was delicious. I decided that I had never been so happy in my life.

After half a dozen dances I felt ravenous and floated with Connie towards the food table. We each ate an enormous wedge of ham and egg pie which was so exquisite that we had the same again. Then we had some trifle and plunged again into the crush. It was about half way through a St. Bernard's Waltz that I began to feel my feet on the boards again – quite heavy and dragging somewhat. Connie felt heavy too. She seemed to be slumped in my arms.

She looked up. Her face was very white. 'Jus' feeling a bit queer – 'scuse me.' She broke away and began to tack erratically towards the ladies' room. A few minutes later she came out and her face was no longer white. It was green. She staggered over to me. 'Could do with some fresh air. Take me outside.'

I took her out into the darkness and it was as if I had stepped aboard a ship; the ground pitched and heaved under my feet and I had to straddle my legs to stay upright. Holding Connie's arm, I retreated hastily to the wall of the institute and leaned my back against it. This didn't help a great deal because the wall, too, was heaving about. Waves of nausea swept over me. I thought of the ham and egg pie and groaned loudly.

Open mouthed, gulping in the sharp air, I looked up at the clean, austere sweep of the night sky and at the ragged clouds driving across the cold face of the moon. 'Oh God,' I moaned at the unheeding stars, 'Why did I drink all that bloody beer?'

But I had to look after Connie. I put my arm round her. 'Come on, we'd better start walking.' We began to reel blindly round the building, pausing after every two or three circuits while I got my breath back and shook my head violently to try to clear my brain.

But our course was erratic and I forgot that the institute was perched on a little steep-sided hill. There was an instant when we were treading on nothing, then we were sprawling down a muddy bank. We finished in a tangled heap on the hard road at the bottom.

I lay there peacefully till I heard a pitiful whimpering near by. Connie! Probably a compound fracture at least; but when I helped her up I found she was unhurt and so, surprisingly, was I. After our large intake of alcohol we must have been as relaxed as rag dolls when we fell.

We went back into the institute and stood just inside the door. Connie was unrecognisable; her beautiful hair hung across her face in straggling wisps, her eyes were vacant and tears coursed slowly through the muddy smears on her cheeks. My suit was plastered with clay and I could feel more of it drying on one side of my face. We stood close, leaning miserably on each other in the doorway. The dancers were a shapeless blur. My stomach heaved and tossed.

Then I heard somebody say 'Good evening'. It was a woman's voice and very close. There were two figures looking at us with interest. They seemed to have just come through the door.

I concentrated fiercely on them and they swam into focus for a few seconds. It was Helen and a man. His pink, scrubbed-looking face, the shining fair hair plastered sideways across the top of his head was in keeping with the spotless British warm overcoat. He was staring at me distastefully. They went out of focus again and there was only Helen's voice. 'We thought we would just look in for a few moments to see how the dance was going. Are you enjoying it?'

Then, unexpectedly, I could see her clearly. She was smiling her kind smile but her eyes were strained as she looked from me to Connie and back again. I couldn't speak but stood gazing at her dully, seeing only her calm beauty in the crush and noise. It seemed, for a moment, that it would be the most natural thing in the world to throw my arms around her but I discarded the idea and, instead, just nodded stupidly.

'Well then, we must be off,' she said and smiled again. 'Good night.'

The fair haired man gave me a cold nod and they went out.

Chapter Twenty-seven

It looked as though I was going to make it back to the road all right. And I was thankful for it because seven o'clock in the morning with the wintry dawn only just beginning to lighten the eastern rim of the moor was no time to be digging my car out of the snow.

This narrow, unfenced road skirted a high tableland and gave on to a few lonely farms at the end of even narrower tracks. It hadn't actually been snowing on my way out to this early call – a uterine haemorrhage in a cow – but the wind had been rising steadily and whipping the top surface from the white blanket which had covered the fell-tops for weeks. My headlights had picked out the creeping drifts; pretty, pointed fingers feeling their way inch by inch across the strip of tarmac.

This was how all blocked roads began, and at the farm as I injected pituitrin and packed the bleeding cervix with a clean sheet I could hear the wind buffeting the byre door and wondered if I would win the race home.

On the way back the drifts had stopped being pretty and lay across the road like white bolsters; but my little car had managed to cleave through them, veering crazily at times, wheels spinning, and now I could see the main road a few hundred yards ahead, reassuringly black in the pale light.

But just over there on the left, a field away, was Cote House. I was treating a bullock there – he had eaten some frozen turnips – and a visit was fixed for today. I didn't fancy trailing back up here if I could avoid it and there was a light in the kitchen window. The family were up, anyway. I turned and drove down into the yard.

The farmhouse door lay within a small porch and the wind had driven the snow inside forming a smooth, two-foot heap against the timbers. As I leaned across to knock, the surface of the heap trembled a little, then began to heave. There was something in there, something quite big. It was eerie standing in the half light watching the snow parting to reveal a furry body. Some creature of the wild must have strayed in, searching for warmth – but it was bigger than a fox or anything else I could think of.

Just then the door opened and the light from the kitchen streamed out. Peter Trenholm beckoned me inside and his wife smiled at me from the bright interior. They were a cheerful young couple.

'What's that?' I gasped, pointing at the animal which was shaking the snow vigorously from its coat.

'That?' Peter grinned, 'That's awd Tip.'

'Tip? Your dog? But what's he doing under a pile of snow?'

'Just blew in on him, I reckon. That's where he sleeps, you know, just outside back door.'

I stared at the farmer. 'You mean he sleeps there, out in the open, every night?'

'Aye, allus. Summer and winter. But don't look at me like that Mr Herriot – it's his own choice. The other dogs have a warm bed in the cow house but Tip won't entertain it. He's fifteen now and he's been sleeping out there since he were a pup. I remember when me father was alive he tried all ways to get t'awd feller to sleep inside but it was no good.'

I looked at the old dog in amazement. I could see him more clearly now; he wasn't the typical sheep dog type, he was bigger boned, longer in the hair, and he projected a bursting vitality that didn't go with his fifteen years. It was difficult to believe that any animal living in these bleak uplands should choose to sleep outside – and thrive on it. I had to look closely to see any sign of his great age. There was the slightest stiffness in his gait as he moved around, perhaps a fleshless look about his head and face and of course the tell-tale lens opacity in the depths of his eyes. But the general impression was of an unquenchable jauntiness.

He shook the last of the snow from his coat, pranced jerkily up to the farmer and gave a couple of reedy barks. Peter Trenholm laughed. 'You see he's ready to be off – he's a beggar for work is Tip.' He led the way towards the buildings and I followed, stumbling over the frozen ruts, like iron under the snow, and bending my head against the knife-like wind. It was a relief to open the byre door and escape into the sweet bovine warmth.

There was a fair mixture of animals in the long building. The dairy cows took up most of the length, then there were a few young heifers, some bullocks and finally, in an empty stall deeply bedded with straw, the other farm dogs. The cats were there too, so it had to be warm. No animal is a better judge of comfort than a cat and they were just visible as furry balls in the straw. They had the best place, up against the wooden partition where the warmth came through from the big animals.

Tip strode confidently among his colleagues – a young dog and a bitch with three half-grown pups. You could see he was boss.

One of the bullocks was my patient and he was looking a bit better. When I had seen him yesterday his rumen (the big first stomach) had been completely static and atonic following an over eager consumption of frozen turnips. He had been slightly bloated and groaning with discomfort. But today as I leaned with my ear against his left side I could hear the beginnings of the surge and rumble of the normal rumen instead of the deathly silence of yesterday. My gastric lavage had undoubtedly tickled things up and I felt that another of the same would just about put him right. Almost lovingly I got together the ingredients of one of my favourite treatments, long since washed away in the flood of progress; the ounce of formalin, the half pound of common salt, the can of black treacle from the barrel which you used to find in most cow houses, all mixed up in a bucket with two gallons of hot water.

I jammed the wooden gag into the bullock's mouth and buckled it behind the horns, then as Peter held the handles I passed the stomach tube down into the rumen and pumped in the mixture. When I had finished the bullock opened his eyes wide in surprise and began to paddle his hind legs. Listening again at his side, I could hear the reassuring bubbling of the stomach contents. I smiled to myself in satisfaction. It worked, it always worked.

Wiping down the tube I could hear the hiss-hiss as Peter's brother got on with the morning's milking, and as I prepared to leave he came down the byre with a full bucket on the way to the cooler. As he passed the dogs' stall he tipped a few pints of the warm milk into their dishes and Tip strolled forward casually for his breakfast. While he was drinking, the young dog tried to push his way in but a soundless snap from Tip's jaws missed his nose by a fraction and he retired to another dish. I noticed, however, that the old dog made no protest as the bitch and pups joined him. The cats, black and white, tortoise-shell, tabby grey, appeared, stretching, from the straw and advanced in a watchful ring. Their turn would come.

Mrs Trenholm called me in for a cup of tea and when I came out it was full daylight. But the sky was a burdened grey and the sparse trees near the house strained their bare branches against the wind which drove in long, icy gusts over the white empty miles of moor. It was what the Yorkshiremen called a 'thin wind' or sometimes a 'lazy wind' – the kind that couldn't be bothered to blow round you but went straight through instead. It made me feel that the best place on earth was by the side of that bright fire in the farmhouse kitchen.

Most people would have felt like that, but not old Tip. He was capering around as Peter loaded a flat cart with some hay bales for the young cattle in the outside barns; and as Peter shook the reins and the cob set off over the fields, he leapt on to the back of the cart.

As I threw my tackle into the boot I looked back at the old dog, legs braced against the uneven motion, tail waving, barking defiance at the cold world. I carried away the memory of Tip who scorned the softer things and slept in what he considered the place of honour – at his master's door.

A little incident like this has always been able to brighten my day and fortunately I have the kind of job where things of this kind happened. And sometimes it isn't even a happening – just a single luminous phrase.

As when I was examining a cow one morning while its neighbour was being milked. The milker was an old man and he was having trouble. He was sitting well into the cow, his cloth-capped head buried in her flank, the bucket gripped tightly between his knees, but the stool kept rocking about as the cow fidgeted and weaved. Twice she kicked the bucket over and she had an additional little trick of anointing her tail with particularly liquid faeces than lashing the old man across the face with it.

Finally he could stand it no longer. Leaping to his feet he dealt a puny blow at the cow's craggy back and emitted an exasperated shout.

'Stand still, thou shittin' awd bovril!'

Or the day when I had to visit Luke Benson at his smallholding in Hillom village. Luke was a powerful man of about sixty and had the unusual characteristic of speaking always through his clenched teeth. He literally articulated every word by moving only his lips, showing the rows of square, horse-like incisors clamped tightly together. It leant a peculiar intensity to his simplest utterance; and as he spoke, his eyes glared.

Most of his conversation consisted of scathing remarks about the other inhabitants of Hillom. In fact he seemed to harbour a cordial dislike of the human race in general. Yet strangely enough I found him a very reasonable man to deal with; he accepted my diagnoses of his animals' ailments without question and appeared to be trying to be friendly by addressing me repeatedly as 'Jems', which was the nearest he could get to my name with his teeth together.

His fiercest hatred was reserved for his neighbour and fellow smallholder, a little lame man called Gill to whom Luke referred invariably and unkindly as 'Yon 'oppin youth'. A bitter feud had raged between them for many years and I had seen Luke smile on only two occasions – once when Mr Gill's sow lost its litter and again when he had a stack burnt down.

When Mr Gill's wife ran away with a man who came round the farm selling brushes it caused a sensation. Nothing like that had ever happened in Hillom before and a wave of delighted horror swept through the village. This, I thought, would be the high point of Luke Benson's life and when I had to visit a heifer of his I expected to find him jubilant. But Luke was gloomy.

As I examined and treated his animal he remained silent and it wasn't until I went into the kitchen to wash my hands that he spoke. He glanced round warily at his wife, a gaunt, grim-faced woman who was applying blacklead to the grate.

'You'll have heard about yon 'oppin youth's missus runnin' off?' he said.

'Yes,' I replied. 'I did hear about it.' I waited for Luke to gloat but he seemed strangely ill at ease. He fidgeted until I had finished drying my hands then he glared at me and bared his strong teeth.

'Ah'll tell you something, Jems,' he ground out. 'Ah wish somebody would tek MA bugger!'

And there was that letter from the Bramleys – that really made me feel good. You don't find people like the Bramleys now; radio, television and the motorcar have carried the outside world into the most isolated places so that the simple people you used to meet on the lonely farms are rapidly becoming like people anywhere else. There are still a few left, of course – old folk who cling to the ways of their fathers and when I come across any of them I like to make some excuse to sit down and talk with them and listen to the old Yorkshire words and expressions which have almost disappeared.

But even in the thirties when there were many places still untouched by the flood of progress the Bramleys were in some ways unique. There were four of them; three brothers, all middle-aged bachelors, and an older sister, also unmarried, and their farm lay in a wide, shallow depression in the hills. You could just see the ancient tiles of Scar House through the top branches of the sheltering trees if you stood outside the pub in Drewburn village and in the summer it was possible to drive down over the fields to the farm. I had done it a few times, the bottles in the boot jingling and crashing as the car bounced over the rig and furrow. The other approach to the place was right on the other side through Mr Broom's stackyard and then along a track with ruts so deep that only a tractor could negotiate it.

There was, in fact, no road to the farm, but that didn't bother the Bramleys because the outside world held no great attraction for them. Miss Bramley made occasional trips to Darrowby on market days for provisions and Herbert, the middle brother, had come into town in the spring of 1929 to have a tooth out, but apart from that they stayed contentedly at home.

A call to Scar House always came as rather a jolt because it meant that at least two hours had been removed from the working day. In all but the driest weather it was safer to leave the car at Mr Broom's and make the journey on foot. One February night at about eight o'clock I was splashing my way along the track, feeling the mud sucking at my wellingtons; it was to see a horse with colic and my pockets were stuffed with the things I might need – arecoline, phials of morphia, a bottle of Paraphyroxia. My eyes were half closed against the steady drizzle but about half a mile ahead I could see the lights of the house winking among the trees.

After twenty minutes of slithering in and out of the unseen puddles and opening a series of broken, string-tied gates, I reached the farm yard and crossed over to the back door. I was about to knock when I stopped with my hand poised. I found I was looking through the kitchen window and in the interior, dimly lit by an oil lamp, the Bramleys were sitting in a row.

They weren't grouped round the fire but were jammed tightly on a long, high-backed wooden settle which stood against the far wall. The strange thing was the almost exact similarity of their attitudes; all four had their arms folded, chins resting on their chests, feet stretched out in front of them. The men had removed their heavy boots and were stocking-footed, but Miss Bramley wore an old pair of carpet slippers.

I stared, fascinated by the curious immobility of the group. They were not asleep, not talking or reading or listening to the radio – in fact they didn't have one – they were just sitting.

I had never seen people just sitting before and I stood there for some minutes to see if they would make a move or do anything at all, but nothing happened. It occurred to me that this was probably a typical evening; they worked hard all day, had their meal, then they just sat till bedtime.

A month or two later I discovered another unsuspected side of the Bramleys when they started having trouble with their cats. I knew they were fond of cats by the number and variety which swarmed over the place and perched confidently on my car bonnet on cold days with their unerring instinct for a warm place. But I was unprepared for the family's utter desolation when the cats started to die. Miss Bramley was on the doorstep of Skeldale House nearly every day carrying an egg basket with another pitiful patient – a cat or sometimes a few tiny kittens – huddling miserably inside.

Even today with the full range of modern antibiotics, the treatment of feline enteritis is unrewarding and I had little success with my salicylates and non-specific injections. I did my best. I even took some of the cats in and kept them at the surgery so that I could attend them several times a day, but the mortality rate was high.

The Bramleys were stricken as they saw their cats diminishing. I was surprised at their grief because most farmers look on cats as pest killers and nothing more. But when Miss Bramley came in one morning with a fresh consignment of invalids she was in a sorry state. She stared at me across the surgery table and her rough fingers clasped and unclasped on the handle of the egg basket.

'Is it going to go through 'em all?' she quavered.

'Well, it's very infectious and it looks as though most of your young cats will get it anyway.'

For a moment Miss Bramley seemed to be struggling with herself, then her chin began to jerk and her whole face twitched uncontrollably. She didn't actually break down but her eyes brimmed and a couple of tears wandered among the network of wrinkles on her cheeks. I looked at her helplessly as she stood there, wisps of grey hair straggling untidily from under the incongruous black beret which she wore pulled tightly over her ears.

'It's Topsy's kittens I'm worried about,' she gasped out at length. 'There's five of 'em and they're the best we've got.'

I rubbed my chin. I had heard a lot about Topsy, one of a strain of incomparable ratters and mousers. Her last family were only about ten weeks old and it would be a crushing blow to the Bramleys if anything happened to them. But what the devil could I do? There was, as yet, no protective vaccine against the disease – or wait a minute, was there? I remembered that I'd heard a rumour that Burroughs Wellcome were working on one.

I pulled out a chair. 'Just sit down a few minutes, Miss Bramley. I'm going to make a phone call.' I was soon through to the Wellcome Laboratory and half expected a sarcastic reply. But they were kind and co-operative. They had had encouraging results with the new vaccine and would be glad to let me have five doses if I would inform them of the result.

I hurried back to Miss Bramley. 'I've ordered something for your kittens. I can't guarantee anything but there's nothing else to do. Have them down here on Tuesday morning.'

The vaccine arrived promptly and as I injected the tiny creatures Miss Bramley extolled the virtues of the Topsy line. 'Look at the size of them ears! Did you ever see bigger 'uns on kittens?'

I had to admit that I hadn't. The ears were enormous, sail-like and they made the ravishingly pretty little faces look even smaller.

Miss Bramley nodded and smiled with satisfaction. 'Aye, you can allus tell. It's the sure sign of a good mouser.'

The injection was repeated a week later. The kittens were still looking well.

'Well that's it,' I said. 'We'll just have to wait now. But remember I want to know the outcome of this, so please don't forget to let me know.'

I didn't hear from the Bramleys for several months and had almost forgotten about the little experiment when I came upon a grubby envelope which had apparently been pushed under the surgery door. It was the promised report and was, in its way, a model of conciseness. It communicated all the information I required without frills or verbiage.

It was in a careful, spidery scrawl and said simply: 'Dere Sir, Them kittens is now big cats. Yrs trly, R. Bramley.'

Chapter Twenty-eight

As I stopped my car by the group of gipsies I felt I was looking at something which should have been captured by a camera. The grass verge was wide on this loop of the road and there were five of them squatting round the fire; it seemed like the mother and father and three little girls. They sat very still, regarding me blankly through the drifting smoke while a few big snowflakes floated across the scene and settled lazily on the tangled hair of the children. Some unreal quality in the wild tableau kept me motionless in my seat, staring through the glass, forgetful of the reason for my being here. Then I wound down the window and spoke to the man.

'Are you Mr Myatt? I believe you have a sick pony.' The man nodded. 'Aye, that's right. He's over here.' It was a strange accent with no trace of Yorkshire in it. He got up from the fire, a thin, dark-skinned unshaven little figure, and came over to the car holding out something in his hand. It was a ten shilling note and I recognised it as a gesture of good faith.

The gipsies who occasionally wandered into Darrowby were always regarded with a certain amount of suspicion. They came, unlike the Myatts, mainly in the summer to camp down by the river and sell their horses and we had been caught out once or twice before. A lot of them seemed to be called Smith and it wasn't uncommon to go back on the second day and find that patient and owner had gone. In fact Siegfried had shouted to me as I left the house this morning: 'Get the brass if you can.' But he needn't have worried – Mr Myatt was on the up and up.

I got out of the car and followed him over the grass, past the shabby, ornate caravan and the lurcher dog tied to the wheel to where a few horses and ponies were tethered. My patient was easy to find; a handsome piebald of about thirteen hands with good, clean legs and a look of class about him. But he was in a sorry state. While the other animals moved around on their tethers, watching us with interest, the piebald stood as though carved from stone.

Even from a distance I could tell what was wrong with him. Only acute laminitis could produce that crouching posture and as I moved nearer I could see that all four feet were probably affected because the pony had his hind feet right under his body in a desperate attempt to take his full weight on his heels.

I pushed my thermometer into the rectum. 'Has he been getting any extra food, Mr Myatt?'

'Aye, he getten into a bag of oats last night.' The little man showed me the big, half empty sack in the back of the caravan. It was difficult to understand him but he managed to convey that the pony had broken loose and gorged himself on the oats. And he had given him a dose of castor oil – he called it 'casta ile'.

The thermometer read 104 and the pulse was rapid and bounding. I passed my hand over the smooth, trembling hooves, feeling the abnormal heat, then I looked at the taut face, the dilated nostrils and terrified eyes. Anybody who has had an infection under a finger-nail can have an inkling of the agony a horse goes through when the sensitive laminae of the foot are inflamed and throbbing against the unyielding wall of the hoof.

'Can you get him to move?' I asked.

The man caught hold of the head collar and pulled, but the pony refused to budge.

I took the other side of the collar. 'Come on, it's always better if they can get moving.'

We pulled together and Mrs Myatt slapped the pony's rump. He took a couple of stumbling steps but it was as though the ground was red hot and he groaned as his feet came down. Within seconds he was crouching again with his weight on his heels.

'It seems he just won't have it.' I turned and went back to the car. I'd have to do what I could to give him relief and the first thing was to get rid of as much as possible of that bellyful of oats. I fished out the bottle of arecoline and gave an injection into the muscle of the neck, then I showed the little man how to tie cloths round the hooves so that he could keep soaking them with cold water.

Afterwards I stood back and looked again at the pony. He was salivating freely from the arecoline and he had cocked his tail and evacuated his bowel; but his pain was undiminished and it would stay like that until the tremendous inflammation subsided – if it ever did. I had seen cases like this where serum had started to ooze from the coronet; that usually meant shedding of the hooves – even death.

As I turned over the gloomy thoughts the three little girls went up to the pony. The biggest put her arms round his neck and laid her cheek against his shoulder while the others stroked the shivering flanks. There were no tears, no change in the blank expressions, but it was easy to see that that pony really meant something to them.

Before leaving I handed over a bottle of tincture of aconite mixture. 'Get a dose of this down him every four hours, Mr Myatt, and be sure to keep putting cold water on the feet. I'll come and see him in the morning.'

I closed the car door and looked through the window again at the slow-rising smoke, the drifting snowflakes and the three children with their ragged dresses and uncombed hair still stroking the pony.

'Well you got the brass, James,' Siegfried said at lunch, carelessly stuffing the ten shilling note into a bulging pocket. 'What was the trouble?'

'Worst case of laminitis I've ever seen. Couldn't move the pony at all and he's going through hell. I've done the usual things but I'm pretty sure they aren't going to be enough.'

'Not a very bright prognosis, then?'

'Really black. Even if he gets over the acute stage he'll have deformed feet, I'd like to bet. Grooved hooves, dropped soles, the lot. And he's a grand little animal, lovely piebald. I wish to God there was something else I could do.'

Siegfried sawed two thick slices off the cold mutton and dropped them on my plate. He looked thoughtfully at me for a moment. 'You've been a little distrait since you came back. These are rotten jobs, I know, but it's no good worrying.'

'Ach, I'm not worrying, exactly, but I can't get it off my mind. Maybe it's those people – the Myatts. They were something new to me. Right out of the world. And three raggedy little girls absolutely crazy about that pony. They aren't going to like it at all.'

As Siegfried chewed his mutton I could see the old glint coming into his eyes; it showed when the talk had anything to do with horses. I knew he wouldn't push in but he was waiting for me to make the first move. I made it.

'I wish you'd come along and have a look with me. Maybe there's something you could suggest. Do you think there could be?'

Siegfried put down his knife and fork and stared in front of him for a few seconds, then he turned to me. 'You know, James, there just might be. Quite obviously this is a right pig of a case and the ordinary remedies aren't going to do any good. We have to pull something out of the bag and I've got an idea. There's just one thing.' He gave me a crooked smile. 'You may not like it.'

'Don't bother about me,' I said. 'You're the horseman. If you can help this pony I don't care what you do.'

'Right, eat up then and we'll go into action together.' We finished our meal and he led me through to the instrument room. I was surprised when he opened the cupboard where old Mr Grant's instruments were kept. It was a kind of museum.

When Siegfried had bought the practice from the old vet who had worked on into his eighties these instruments had come with it and they lay there in rows, unused but undisturbed. It would have been logical to throw them out, but maybe Siegfried felt the same way about them as I did. The polished wooden boxes of shining, odd-shaped scalpels, the enema pumps and douches with their perished rubber and brass fittings, the seaton needles, the ancient firing irons – they were a silent testament to sixty years of struggle. I often used to open that cupboard door and try to picture the old man wrestling with the same problems as I had, travelling the same narrow roads as I did. He had done it absolutely on his own and for sixty years. I was only starting but I knew a little about the triumphs and disasters, the wondering and worrying, the hopes and disappointments – and the hard labour. Anyway, Mr Grant was dead and gone, taking with him all the skills and knowledge I was doggedly trying to accumulate.

Siegfried reached to the back of the cupboard and pulled out a long flat box. He blew the dust from the leather covering and gingerly unfastened the clasp. Inside, a fleam, glittering on its bed of frayed velvet, lay by the side of a round, polished blood stick.

I looked at my employer in astonishment. 'You're going to bleed him, then?'

'Yes, my boy, I'm going to take you back to the Middle Ages.' He looked at my startled face and put a hand on my arm. 'But don't start beating me over the head with all the scientific arguments against blood-letting. I've no strong views either way.'

'But have you ever done it? I've never seen you use this outfit.'

'I've done it. And I've seen some funny things after it, too.' Siegfried turned away as if he wanted no more discussion. He cleaned the fleam thoroughly and dropped it into the steriliser. His face was expressionless as he stood listening to the hiss of the boiling water.

The gipsies were again hunched over the fire when we got there and Mr Myatt, sensing that reinforcements had arrived, scrambled to his feet and shuffled forward holding out another ten shilling note.

Siegfried waved it away. 'Let's see how we get on, Mr Myatt,' he grunted. He strode across the grass to where the pony still trembled in his agonised crouch. There was no improvement; in fact the eyes stared more wildly and I could hear little groans as the piebald carefully eased himself from foot to foot.

Siegfried spoke softly without looking at me, 'Poor beggar. You weren't exaggerating, James. Bring that box from the car, will you?'

When I came back he was tying a choke rope round the base of the pony's neck. 'Pull it up tight,' he said. As the jugular rose up tense and turgid in its furrow he quickly clipped and disinfected a small area and inserted a plaque of local anaesthetic. Finally he opened the old leather-covered box and extracted the fleam, wrapped in sterile lint.

Everything seemed to start happening then. Siegfried placed the little blade of the fleam against the bulging vein and without hesitation gave it a confident smack with the stick. Immediately an alarming cascade of blood spouted from the hole and began to form a dark lake on the grass. Mr Myatt gasped and the little girls set up a sudden chatter. I could understand how they felt. In fact I was wondering how long the pony could stand this tremendous outflow without dropping down.

It didn't seem to be coming out fast enough for Siegfried, however, because he produced another stick from his pocket, thrust it into the pony's mouth and began to work the jaws. And as the animal champed, the blood gushed more fiercely.

When at least a gallon had come away Siegfried seemed satisfied. 'Slacken the rope, James,' he cried, then rapidly closed the wound on the neck with a pin suture. Next he trotted over the grass and looked over a gate in the roadside wall. 'Thought so,' he shouted. 'There's a little beck in that field. We've got to get him over to it. Come on, lend a hand everybody!'

He was clearly enjoying himself and his presence was having its usual effect. The Myatts were spurred suddenly into action and began to run around aimlessly, bumping into each other. I was gripped by a sudden tension and preparedness and even the pony seemed to be taking an interest in his surroundings for the first time.

All five of the gipsies pulled at the halter, Siegfried and I looped our arms behind the pony's thighs, everybody gave encouraging shouts and at last he began to move forward. It was a painful process but he kept going – through the gate and across the field to where the shallow stream wandered among its rushes. There were no banks to speak of and it was easy to push him out into the middle. As he stood there with the icy water rippling round his inflamed hooves I fancied I could read in his eyes a faint dawning of an idea that things were looking up at last.

'Now he must stand in there for an hour,' Siegfried said. 'And then you'll have to make him walk round the field. Then another hour in the beck. As he gets better you can give him more and more exercise but he must come back to the beck. There's a lot of work for somebody here, so who's going to do it?'

The three little girls came shyly round him and looked up, wide-eyed, into his face. Siegfried laughed. 'You three want the job, do you? Right, I'll tell you just what to do.'

He pulled out the bag of peppermint drops which was an ever-present among his widely-varied pocket luggage and I settled myself for a long wait. I had seen him in action with the children on the farms and when that bag of sweets came out, everything stopped. It was the one time Siegfried was never in a hurry.

The little girls each solemnly took a sweet, then Siegfried squatted on his heels and began to address them like a professor with his class. They soon began to thaw and put a word in for themselves. The smallest launched into a barely intelligible account of the remarkable things the pony had done when he was a foal and Siegfried listened intently, nodding his head gravely now and then. There was all the time in the world.

His words obviously went home because, over the next few days, whenever I passed the gipsy camp I could see the three wild little figures either grouped around the pony in the beck or dragging him round the field on a long halter shank. I didn't need to butt in – I could see he was improving all the time.

It was about a week later that I saw the Myatts on their way out of Darrowby, the red caravan rocking across the market place with Mr Myatt up front wearing a black velvet cap, his wife by his side. Tethered to various parts of the caravan the family of horses clopped along and right at the rear was the piebald, a bit stiff perhaps, but going very well. He'd be all right.

The little girls were looking out of the back door and as they spotted me I waved. They looked back at me unsmilingly until they had almost turned the corner into Hallgate then one of them shyly lifted her hand. The others followed suit and my last sight was of them waving eagerly back.

I strolled into the Drovers and took a thoughtful half pint into a corner. Siegfried had done the trick there all right but I was wondering what to make of it because in veterinary practice it is difficult to draw definite conclusions even after spectacular results. Was it my imagination or did that pony seem to feel relief almost immediately after the blood-letting? Would we ever have got him moving without it? Was it really the right thing in these cases to bash a hole in the jugular and release about a bucketful of the precious fluid? I still don't have the answers because I never dared try it for myself.

Chapter Twenty-nine

'Could Mr Herriot see my dog, please?'

Familiar enough words coming from the waiting-room but it was the voice that brought me to a slithering halt just beyond the door.

It couldn't be, no of course it couldn't, but it sounded just like Helen. I tiptoed back and applied my eye without hesitation to the crack in the door. Tristan was standing there looking down at somebody just beyond my range of vision. All I could see was a hand resting on the head of a patient sheep dog, the hem of a tweed skirt and two silk stockinged legs.

They were nice legs - not skinny - and could easily belong to a big girl like Helen. My cogitations were cut short as a head bent over to speak to the dog and I had a close up in profile of the small straight nose and the dark hair falling across the milky smoothness of the cheek.

I was still peering, bemused, when Tristan shot out of the room and collided with me. Stifling an oath, he grabbed my arm and hauled me along the passage into the dispensary. He shut the door and spoke in a hoarse whisper.

'It's her! The Alderson woman! And she wants to see you! Not Siegfried, not me, but you, Mr Herriot himself!'

He looked at me wide-eyed for a few moments then, as I stood hesitating he opened the door and tried to propel me into the passage.

'What the hell are you waiting for?' he hissed.

'Well, it's a bit embarrassing, isn't it? After that dance, I mean. Last time she saw me I was a lovely sight - so pie-eyed I couldn't even speak.'

Tristan struck his forehead with his hand. 'God help us! You worry about details, don't you? She's asked to see you - what more do you want? Go on, get in there!'

I was shuffling off irresolutely when he raised a hand. 'Just a minute. Stay right there.' He trotted off and returned in a few seconds holding out a white lab coat.

'Just back from the laundry,' he said as he began to work my arms into the starched sleeves. 'You'll look marvellous in this, Jim - the immaculate young surgeon.'

I stood unresisting as he buttoned me into the garment but struck away his hand when he started to straighten my tie. As I left him he gave me a final encouraging wave before heading for the back stairs.

I didn't give myself any more time to think but marched straight into the waiting-room. Helen looked up and smiled. And it was just the same smile. Nothing behind it. Just the same friendly, steady-eyed smile as when I first met her.

We faced each other in silence for some moments then when I didn't say anything she looked down at the dog.

'It's Dan in trouble this time,' she said. 'He's our sheep dog but we're so fond of him that he's more like one of the family.'

The dog wagged his tail furiously at the sound of his name but yelped as he came towards me. I bent down and patted his head. 'I see he's holding up a hind leg.'

'Yes, he jumped over a wall this morning and he's been like that ever since. I think it's something quite bad – he can't put any weight on the leg.'

'Right bring him through to the other room and I'll have a look at him. But take him on in front of me, will you, and I'll be able to watch how he walks.'

I held the door open and she went through ahead of me with the dog.

Watching how Helen walked distracted me over the first few yards, but it was a long passage and by the time we had reached the second bend I had managed to drag my attention back to my patient.

And glory be, it was a dislocated hip. It had to be with that shortening of the limb and the way he carried it underneath his body with the paw just brushing the ground.

My feelings were mixed. This was a major injury but on the other hand the chances were I could put it right quickly and look good in the process. Because I had found, in my brief experience, that one of the most spectacular procedures in practice was the reduction of a dislocated hip. Maybe I had been lucky, but with the few I had seen I had been able to convert an alarmingly lame animal into a completely sound one as though by magic.

In the operating room I hoisted Dan on to the table. He stood without moving as I examined the hip. There was no doubt about it at all – the head of the femur was displaced upwards and backwards, plainly palpable under my thumb.

The dog looked round only once – when I made a gentle attempt to flex the limb – but turned away immediately and stared resolutely ahead. His mouth hung open a little as he panted nervously but like a lot of the placid animals which arrived on our surgery table he seemed to have resigned himself to his fate. I had the strong impression that I could have started to cut his head off and he wouldn't have made much fuss.

'Nice, good-natured dog,' I said. 'And a bonny one, too.'

Helen patted the handsome head with the broad blaze of white down the face; the tail waved slowly from side to side.

'Yes,' she said. 'He's just as much a family pet as a working dog. I do hope he hasn't hurt himself too badly.'

'Well, he has a dislocated hip. It's a nasty thing but with a bit of luck I ought to be able to put it back.'

'What happens if it won't go back?'

'He'd have to form a false joint up there. He'd be very lame for several weeks and probably always have a slightly short leg.'

'Oh dear, I wouldn't like that,' Helen said. 'Do you think he'll be all right?'

I looked at the docile animal still gazing steadfastly to his front. 'I think he's got a good chance, mainly because you haven't hung about for days before bringing him in. The sooner these things are tackled the better.'

'Oh good. When will you be able to start on him?'

'Right now.' I went over to the door. 'I'll just give Tristan a shout. This is a two man job.'

'Couldn't I help?' Helen said. 'I'd very much like to if you wouldn't mind.'

I looked at her doubtfully. 'Well I don't know. You mightn't like playing tug of war with Dan in the middle. He'll be anaesthetised of course but there's usually a lot of pulling.'

Helen laughed. 'Oh, I'm quite strong. And not a bit squeamish. I'm used to animals, you know, and I like working with them.'

'Right,' I said. 'Slip on this spare coat and we'll begin.'

The dog didn't flinch as I pushed the needle into his vein and as the Nembutal flowed in, his head began to slump against Helen's arm and his supporting paw to slide along the smooth top of the table. Soon he was stretched unconscious on his side.

I held the needle in the vein as I looked down at the sleeping animal. 'I might have to give him a bit more. They have to be pretty deep to overcome the muscular resistance.'

Another cc. and Dan was as limp as any rag doll. I took hold of the affected leg and spoke across the table. 'I want you to link your hands underneath his thigh and try to hold him there when I pull. O.K.? Here we go, then.'

It takes a surprising amount of force to pull the head of a displaced femur over the rim of the acetabulum. I kept up a steady traction with my right hand, pressing on the head of the femur at the same time with my left. Helen did her part efficiently, leaning back against the pull, her lips pushed forward in a little pout of concentration.

I suppose there must be a foolproof way of doing this job – a method which works the very first time – but I have never been able to find it. Success has always come to me only after a fairly long period of trial and error and it was the same today. I tried all sorts of angles, rotations and twists on the flaccid limb, trying not to think of how it would look if this just happened to be the one I couldn't put back. I was wondering what Helen, still hanging on determinedly to her end, must be thinking of this wrestling match when I heard the muffled click. It was a sweet and welcome sound.

I flexed the hip joint once or twice. No resistance at all now. The femoral head was once more riding smoothly in its socket.

'Well that's it,' I said. 'Hope it stays put – we'll have to keep our fingers crossed. The odd one does pop out again but I've got a feeling this is going to be all right.'

Helen ran her hand over the silky ears and neck of the sleeping dog. 'Poor old Dan. He wouldn't have jumped over that wall this morning if he'd known what was in store for him. How long will it be before he comes round?'

'Oh, he'll be out for the rest of the day. When he starts to wake up tonight I want you to be around to steady him in case he falls and puts the thing out again. Perhaps you'd give me a ring. I'd like to know how things are.'

I gathered Dan up in my arms and was carrying him along the passage, staggering under his weight, when I met Mrs Hall. She was carrying a tray with two cups.

'I was just having a drink of tea, Mr Herriot,' she said. 'I thought you and the young lady might fancy a cup.'

I looked at her narrowly. This was unusual. Was it possible she had joined Tristan in playing Cupid? But the broad, dark-skinned face was as unemotional as ever. It told me nothing.

'Well, thanks very much, Mrs Hall. I'll just put this dog outside first.' I went out and settled Dan on the back seat of Helen's car; with only his eyes and nose sticking out from under a blanket he looked at peace with the world.

Helen was already sitting with a cup in her lap and I thought of the other time I had drunk tea in this room with a girl. On the day I had arrived in Darrowby. She had been one of Siegfried's followers and surely the toughest of them all.

This was a lot different. During the struggle in the operating room I had been able to observe Helen at close range and I had discovered that her mouth turned up markedly at the corners as though she was just going to smile or had just been smiling; also that the deep warm blue of the eyes under the smoothly arching brows made a dizzying partnership with the rich black-brown of her hair.

And this time the conversation didn't lag. Maybe it was because I was on my own ground – perhaps I never felt fully at ease unless there was a sick animal involved somewhere, but at any rate I found myself prattling effortlessly just as I had done up on that hill when we had first met.

Mrs Hall's teapot was empty and the last of the biscuits gone before I finally saw Helen off and started on my round.

The same feeling of easy confidence was on me that night when I heard her voice on the phone.

'Dan is up and walking about,' she said. 'He's still a bit wobbly but he's perfectly sound on that leg.'

'Oh great, he's got the first stage over. I think everything's going to be fine.'

There was a pause at the other end of the line, then: 'Thank you so much for what you've done. We were terribly worried about him, especially my young brother and sister. We're very grateful.'

'Not at all, I'm delighted too. He's a grand dog.' I hesitated for a moment – it had to be now. 'Oh, you remember we were talking about Scotland today. Well, I was passing the Plaza this afternoon and I see they're showing a film about the Hebrides. I thought maybe . . . I wondered if perhaps, er . . . you might like to come and see it with me.'

Another pause and my heart did a quick thud-thud.

'All right.' Helen said. 'Yes, I'd like that. When? Friday night? Well, thank you – goodbye till then.'

I replaced the receiver with a trembling hand. Why did I make such heavy weather of these things? But it didn't matter – I was back in business.

Chapter Thirty

Rheumatism is a terrible thing in a dog. It is painful enough in humans but an acute attack can reduce an otherwise healthy dog to terrified, screaming immobility.

Very muscular animals suffered most and I went carefully as my fingers explored the bulging triceps and gluteals of the little Staffordshire bull terrier. Normally a tough little fellow, afraid of nothing, friendly, leaping high in an attempt to lick people's faces; but today, rigid, trembling, staring anxiously in front of him. Even to turn his head a little brought a shrill howl of agony.

Mercifully it was something you could put right and quickly too. I pulled the Novalgin into the syringe and injected it rapidly. The little dog, oblivious to everything but the knife-like stabbing of the rheumatism did not stir at the prick of the needle. I counted out some salicylate tablets into a box, wrote the directions on the lid and handed the box to the owner.

'Give him one of those as soon as the injection has eased him, Mr Tavener. Then repeat in about four hours. I'm pretty sure he'll be greatly improved by then.'

Mrs Tavener snatched the box away as her husband began to read the directions. 'Let me see it,' she snapped. 'No doubt I'll be the one who has the job to do.'

It had been like that all the time, ever since I had entered the beautiful house with the terraced gardens leading down to the river. She had been at him ceaselessly while he was holding the dog for me. When the animal had yelped she had cried: 'Really, Henry, don't grip the poor thing like that, you're hurting him!' She had kept him scuttling about for this and that and when he was out of the room she said: 'You know, this is all my husband's fault. He will let the dog swim in the river. I knew this would happen.'

Half-way through, daughter Julia had come in and it was clear from the start that she was firmly on Mama's side. She helped out with plenty of 'How could you, Daddy!' and 'For God's sake, Daddy!' and generally managed to fill in the gaps when her mother wasn't in full cry.

The Taveners were in their fifties. He was a big, floridly handsome man who had made millions in the Tyneside shipyards before pulling out of the smoke to this lovely place. I had taken an instant liking to him; I had expected a tough tycoon and had found a warm, friendly, curiously vulnerable man, obviously worried sick about his dog.

I had reservations about Mrs Tavener despite her still considerable beauty. Her smile had a switched-on quality and there was a little too much steel in the blue of her eyes. She had seemed less concerned about the dog than with the necessity of taking it out on her husband.

Julia, a scaled-down model of her mother, drifted about the room with the aimless, bored look of the spoiled child; glancing blankly at the dog or me, staring without interest through the window at the smooth lawns, the tennis court, the dark band of river under the trees.

I gave the terrier a final reassuring pat on the head and got up from my knees. As I put away the syringe, Tavener took my arm. 'Well, that's fine, Mr Herriot. We're very grateful to you for relieving our minds. I must say I thought the old boy's time had come when he started yelling. And now you'll have a drink before you go.'

The man's hand trembled on my arm as he spoke. It had been noticeable, too, when he had been holding the dog's head and I had wondered; maybe Parkinson's disease, or nerves, or just drink. Certainly he was pouring a generous measure of whisky into his glass, but as he tipped up the bottle his hand was seized by an even more violent tremor and he slopped the spirit on to the polished sideboard.

'Oh God! Oh God!' Mrs Tavener burst out. There was a bitter note of oh no, not again, in her cry and Julia struck her forehead with her hand and raised her eyes to heaven. Tavener shot a single hunted look at the women then grinned as he handed me my glass.

'Come and sit down, Mr Herriot,' he said. 'I'm sure you have time to relax for a few minutes.'

We moved over to the fireside and Tavener talked pleasantly about dogs and the countryside and the pictures which hung on the walls of the big room. Those pictures were noted in the district; many of them were originals by famous painters and they had become the main interest in Tavener's life. His other passion was clocks and as I looked round the room at the rare and beautiful timepieces standing among elegant period furniture it was easy to believe the rumours I had heard about the wealth within these walls.

The women did not drink with us; they had disappeared when the whisky was brought out, but as I drained my glass the door was pushed open and they stood there, looking remarkably alike in expensive tweed coats and fur-trimmed hats. Mrs Tavener pulling on a pair of motoring gloves, looked with distaste at her husband. 'We're going into Brawton,' she said. 'Don't know when we'll be back.'

Behind her, Julia stared coldly at her father; her lip curled slightly.

Tavener did not reply. He sat motionless as I listened to the roar of the car engine and the spatter of whipped-up gravel beyond the window; then he looked out, blank-faced, empty-eyed at the drifting cloud of exhaust smoke in the drive.

There was something in his expression which chilled me. I put down my glass and got to my feet. 'Afraid I must be moving on, Mr Tavener. Thanks for the drink.'

He seemed suddenly to be aware of my presence; the friendly smile returned. 'Not at all. Thank you for looking after the old boy. He seems better already.'

In the driving mirror, the figure at the top of the steps looked small and alone till the high shrubbery hid him from my view.

The next call was to a sick pig, high on Marstang Fell. The road took me at first along the fertile valley floor, winding under the riverside trees past substantial farmhouses and rich pastures; but as the car left the road and headed up a steep track the country began to change. The transition was almost violent as the trees and bushes thinned out and gave way to the bare, rocky hillside and the miles of limestone walls.

And though the valley had been rich with the fresh green of the new leaves, up here the buds were unopened and the naked branches stretched against the sky still had the look of winter.

Tim Alton's farm lay at the top of the track and as I pulled up at the gate I wondered as I always did how the man could scrape a living from those few harsh acres with the grass flattened and yellowed by the wind which always blew. At any rate, many generations had accomplished the miracle and had lived and struggled and died in that house with its outbuildings crouching in the lee of a group of stunted, wind-bent trees, its massive stones crumbling under three centuries of fierce weathering.

Why should anybody want to build a farm in such a place? I turned as I opened the gate and looked back at the track threading between the walls down and down to where the white stones of the river glittered in the spring sunshine. Maybe the builder had stood here and looked across the green vastness and breathed in the cold, sweet air and thought it was enough.

I saw Tim Alton coming across the yard. There had been no need to lay down concrete or cobbles here; they had just swept away the thin soil and there, between house and buildings was a sloping stretch of fissured rock. It was more than a durable surface – it was everlasting.

'It's your pig this time, then, Tim,' I said and the farmer nodded seriously.

'Aye, right as owt yesterday and laid flat like a dead 'un this morning. Never looked up when I filled his trough and by gaw when a pig won't tackle his grub there's summat far wong.' Tim dug his hands inside the broad leather belt which encircled his oversized trousers and which always seemed to be about to nip his narrow frame in two and led the way gloomily into the sty. Despite the bitter poverty of his existence he was a man who took misfortune cheerfully. I had never seen him look like this and I thought I knew the reason; there is something personal about the family pig.

Smallholders like Tim Alton made their meagre living from a few cows; they sold their milk to the big dairies or made butter. And they killed a pig or two each year and cured it themselves for home consumption. On the poorer places it seemed to me that they ate little else; whatever meal I happened to stumble in on, the cooking smell was always the same – roasting fat bacon.

It appeared to be a matter of pride to make the pig as fat as possible; in fact, on these little wind-blown farms where the people and the cows and the dogs were lean and spare, the pig was about the only fat thing to be seen.

I had seen the Alton pig before. I had been stitching a cow's torn teat about a fortnight ago and Tim had patted me on the shoulder and whispered: 'Now come along wi' me, Mr Herriot and I'll show tha summat.' We had looked into the sty at a twenty-five-stone monster effortlessly emptying a huge trough of wet meal. I could remember the pride in the farmer's eyes and the way he listened to the smacking and slobbering as if to great music.

It was different today. The pig looked, if possible, even more enormous as it lay on its side, eyes closed, filling the entire floor of the sty like a beached whale. Tim splashed a stick among the untouched meal in the trough and made encouraging noises but the animal never stirred. The farmer looked at me with haggard eyes.

'He's bad, Mr Herriot. It's serious whatever it is.'

I had been taking the temperature and when I read the thermometer I whistled. 'A hundred and seven. That's some fever.'

The colour drained from Tim's face. 'Oh 'ell! A hundred and seven! It's hopeless, then. It's ower with him.'

I had been feeling along the animal's side and I smiled reassuringly. 'No, don't worry, Tim. I think he's going to be all right. He's got erysipelas. Here, put your fingers along his back. You can feel a lot of flat swellings on his skin – those are the diamonds. He'll have a beautiful rash within a few hours but at the moment you can't see it, you can only feel it.'

'And you can make him better?'

'I'm nearly sure I can. I'll give him a whacking dose of serum and I'd like to bet you he'll have his nose in that trough in a couple of days. Most of them get over it all right.'

'Well that's a bit o' good news, any road,' said Tim, a smile flooding over his face. 'You had me worried there with your hundred and seven, dang you!'

I laughed. 'Sorry, Tim, didn't mean to frighten you. I'm often happier to see a high temperature than a low one. But it's a funny time for erysipelas. We usually see it in late summer.'

'All right, I'll let ye off this time. Come in and wash your hands.'

In the kitchen I ducked my head but couldn't avoid bumping the massive side of bacon hanging from the beamed ceiling. The heavy mass rocked gently on its hooks; it was about eight inches thick in parts – all pure white fat. Only by close inspection was it possible to discern a thin strip of lean meat.

Mrs Alton produced a cup of tea and as I sipped I looked across at Tim who had fallen back into a chair and lay with his hands hanging down; for a moment he closed his eyes and his face became a mask of weariness. I thought for the hundredth time about the endless labour which made up the lives of these little farmers. Alton was only forty but his body was already bent and ravaged by the constant demands he made on it; you could read his story in the corded forearm, the rough, work-swollen fingers. He told me once that the last time he missed a milking was twelve years ago and that was for his father's funeral.

I was taking my leave when I saw Jennie. She was the Altons' eldest child and was pumping vigorously at the tyre of her bicycle which was leaning against the wall just outside the kitchen door.

'Going somewhere?' I asked and the girl straightened up quickly, pushing back a few strands of dark hair from her forehead. She was about eighteen with delicate features and large, expressive eyes; in her wild, pinched prettiness there was something of the wheeling curlews, the wind and sun, the wide emptiness of the moors.

'I'm going down to t'village.' She stole a glance into the kitchen. 'I'm going to get a bottle of Guinness for dad.'

'The village! It's a long way to go for a bottle of Guinness. It must be two miles and then you've got to push back up this hill. Are you going all that way just for one bottle?'

'Ay, just one,' she whispered, counting out a sixpence and some coppers into her palm with calm absorption. 'Dad's been up all night waiting for a heifer to calve – he's tired out. I won't be long and he can have his Guinness with his dinner. That's what he likes.' She looked up at me conspiratorially. 'It'll be a surprise for him.'

As she spoke, her father, still sprawled in the chair, turned his head and looked at her; he smiled and for a moment I saw a serenity in the steady eyes, a nobility in the seamed face.

Jennie looked at him for a few seconds, a happy secret look from under her lowered brows; then she turned quickly, mounted her bicycle and began to pedal down the track at surprising speed.

I followed her more slowly, the car, in second gear, bumping and swaying over the stones. I stared straight ahead, lost in thought. I couldn't stop my mind roaming between the two houses I had visited; between the gracious mansion by the river and the crumbling farmhouse I had just left; from Henry Tavener with his beautiful clothes, his well-kept hands, his rows of books and pictures and clocks to Tim Alton with his worn, chest-high trousers nipped in by that great belt, his daily, monthly, yearly grind to stay alive on that unrelenting hilltop.

But I kept coming back to the daughters; to the contempt in Julia Tavener's eyes when she looked at her father and the shining tenderness in Jennie Alton's.

It wasn't so easy to work out as it seemed; in fact it became increasingly difficult to decide who was getting the most out of their different lives. But as I guided the car over the last few yards of the track and pulled on to the smooth tarmac of the road it came to me with unexpected clarity. Taking it all in all, if I had the choice to make, I'd settle for the Guinness.

Chapter Thirty-one

Tristan was unpacking the UCM's. These bottles contained a rich red fluid which constituted our last line of defence in the battle with animal disease. Its full name, Universal Cattle Medicine, was proclaimed on the label in big black type and underneath it pointed out that it was highly efficacious for coughs, chills, scours, garget, milk fever, pneumonia, felon and bloat. It finished off on a confident note with the assurance: 'Never Fails to Give Relief' and we had read the label so often that we half believed it.

It was a pity it didn't do any good because there was something compelling about its ruby depths when you held it up to the light and about the solid camphor-ammonia jolt when you sniffed at it and which made the farmers blink and shake their heads and say 'By gaw, that's powerful stuff,' with deep respect. But our specific remedies were so few and the possibilities of error so plentiful that it was comforting in cases of doubt to be able to hand over a bottle of the old standby. Whenever an entry of Siegfried's or mine appeared in the day book stating 'Visit attend cow, advice, 1 UCM' it was a pretty fair bet we didn't know what was wrong with the animal.

The bottles were tall and shapely and they came in elegant white cartons, so much more impressive than the unobtrusive containers of the antibiotics and steroids which we use today. Tristan was lifting them out of the tea chest and stacking them on the shelves in deep rows. When he saw me he ceased his labours, sat on the chest and pulled out a packet of Woodbines. He lit one, pulled the smoke a long way down then fixed me with a noncommittal stare.

'You're taking her to the pictures then?'

Feeling vaguely uneasy under his eye, I tipped a pocketful of assorted empties into the waste basket. 'Yes, that's right. In about an hour.'

'Mm.' He narrowed his eyes against the slowly escaping smoke. 'Mm, I see.'

'Well what are you looking like that for?' I said defensively. 'Anything wrong with going to the pictures?'

'No-no. No-no-no. Nothing at all, Jim. Nothing, nothing. A very wholesome pursuit.'

'But you don't think I should be taking Helen there.'

'I never said that. No, I'm sure you'll have a nice time. It's just that . . .' He scratched his head. 'I thought you might have gone in for something a bit more . . . well . . . enterprising.'

I gave a bitter laugh. 'Look, I tried enterprise at the Reniston. Oh, I'm not blaming you, Triss, you meant well, but as you know it was a complete shambles. I just don't want anything to go wrong tonight. I'm playing safe.'

'Well, I won't argue with you there,' Tristan said. 'You couldn't get much safer than the Darrowby Plaza.'

And later, shivering in the tub in the vast, draughty bathroom, I couldn't keep out the thought that Tristan was right. Taking Helen to the local cinema was a form of cowardice, a shrinking away from reality into what I hoped would be a safe, dark intimacy. But as I towelled myself, hopping about to keep warm, and looked out through the fringe of wistaria at the darkening garden there was comfort in the thought that it was another beginning, even though a small one.

And as I closed the door of Skeldale House and looked along the street to where the first lights of the shops beckoned in the dusk I felt a lifting of the heart. It was as though a breath from the near-by hills had touched me. A fleeting fragrance which said winter had gone. It was still cold – it was always cold in Darrowby until well into May – but the promise was there, of sunshine and warm grass and softer days.

You had to look closely or you could easily miss the Plaza, tucked in as it was between Pickersgills the ironmongers and Howarths the chemists. There had never been much attempt at grandeur in its architecture and the entrance was hardly wider than the average shop front. But what puzzled me as I approached was that the place was in darkness. I was in good time but the show was due to start in ten minutes or so and there was no sign of life.

I hadn't dared tell Tristan that my precautions had extended as far as arranging to meet Helen here. With a car like mine there was always an element of doubt about arriving anywhere in time or indeed at all and I had thought it prudent to eliminate all transport hazards.

'Meet you outside the cinema.' My God, it wasn't very bright was it? It took me back to my childhood, to the very first time I had taken a girl out. I was just fourteen and on my way to meet her I tendered my only half-crown to a bloody-minded Glasgow tram conductor and asked for a penny fare. He vented his spleen on me by ransacking his bag and giving me my change entirely in halfpennies. So when the cinema queue reached the pay box I had to stand there with my little partner and everybody else watching while I paid for our shilling tickets with great handfuls of copper. The shame of it left a scar – it was another four years before I took out a girl again.

But the black thoughts were dispelled when I saw Helen picking her way across the market-place cobbles. She smiled and waved cheerfully as if being taken to the Darrowby Plaza was the biggest treat a girl could wish for, and when she came right up to me there was a soft flush on her cheeks and her eyes were bright.

Everything was suddenly absolutely right. I felt a surging conviction that this was going to be a good night – nothing was going to spoil it. After we had said hello she told me that Dan was running about like a puppy with no trace of a limp and the news was another wave on the high tide of my euphoria.

The only thing that troubled me was the blank, uninhabited appearance of the cinema entrance.

'Strange there's nobody here,' I said. 'It's nearly starting time. I suppose the place is open?'

'Must be,' Helen said. 'It's open every night but Sunday. Anyway, I'm sure these people are waiting too.'

I looked around. There was no queue as such but little groups were standing here and there; a few couples, mostly middle-aged, a bunch of small boys rolling and fighting on the pavement. Nobody seemed worried.

And indeed there was no cause. Exactly two minutes before the picture was due to start a figure in a mackintosh coat pedalled furiously round the corner of the street, head down, legs pistoning, the bicycle lying over at a perilous angle with the ground. He came to a screeching halt outside the entrance, inserted a key in the lock and threw wide the doors. Reaching inside, he flicked a switch and a single neon strip flickered fitfully above our heads and went out. It did this a few times and seemed bent on mischief till he stood on tiptoe and beat it into submission with a masterful blow of his fist. Then he whipped off the mackintosh revealing faultless evening-dress. The manager had arrived.

While this was going on a very fat lady appeared from nowhere and wedged herself into the pay box. The show was ready to roll.

We all began to shuffle inside. The little boys put down their ninepences and punched each other as they passed through a curtain into the stalls, while the rest of us proceeded decorously upstairs to the one-and-sixpenny seats in the balcony. The manager, his white shirt front and silk lapels gleaming, smiled and bowed with great courtesy as we passed.

We paused at a row of pegs at the top of the stairs while some people hung up their coats. I was surprised to see Maggie Robinson the blacksmith's daughter there, taking the tickets, and she appeared to be intrigued by the sight of us. She simpered and giggled, darted glances at Helen and did everything but dig me in the ribs. Finally she parted the curtains and we went inside.

It struck me immediately that the management were determined that their patrons wouldn't feel cold because if it hadn't been for the all-pervading smell of old sofas we might have been plunging into a tropical jungle. Maggie steered us through the stifling heat to our places and as I sat down I noticed that there was no arm between the two seats.

'Them's the courting seats,' she blurted out and fled with her hand to her mouth.

The lights were still on and I looked round the tiny balcony. There were only about a dozen people dotted here and there sitting in patient silence under the plain distempered walls. By the side of the screen the hands of a clock stood resolutely at twenty-past four.

But it was all right sitting there with Helen. I felt fine except for a tendency to gasp like a goldfish in the airless atmosphere. I was settling down cosily when a little man seated in front of us with his wife turned slowly round. The mouth in the haggard face was pursed grimly and he fixed his eyes on mine in a long, challenging stare. We faced each other for several silent moments before he finally spoke.

'She's dead,' he said.

A thrill of horror shot through me. 'Dead?'

'Aye, she is. She's dead.' He dragged the word out slowly with a kind of mournful satisfaction while his eyes still stared into mine.

I swallowed a couple of times. 'Well, I'm sorry to hear that. Truly sorry.'

He nodded grimly and continued to regard me with a peculiar intensity as though he expected me to say more. Then with apparent reluctance he turned away and settled in his seat.

I looked helplessly at the rigid back, at the square, narrow shoulders muffled in a heavy overcoat. Who in God's name was this? And what was he talking about? I knew the face from somewhere – must be a client. And what was dead? Cow? Ewe? Sow? My mind began to race over the cases I had seen during the past week but that face didn't seem to fit in anywhere.

Helen was looking at me questioningly and I managed a wan smile. But the spell was shattered. I started to say something to her when the little man began to turn again with menacing deliberation.

He fixed me once more with a hostile glare. 'Ah don't think there was ever owt wrong with her stomach,' he declared.

'You don't, eh?'

'No, young man, ah don't.' He dragged his eyes unwillingly from my face and turned towards the screen again.

The effect of this second attack was heightened because the lights went off suddenly and an incredible explosion of noise blasted my ear drums. It was the Gaumont News. The sound machine, like the heating system, had apparently been designed for something like the Albert Hall and for a moment I cowered back under the assault. As a voice bellowed details of fortnight-old events I closed my eyes and tried again to place the man in front of me.

I often had trouble identifying people outside their usual environment and had once discussed the problem with Siegfried.

He had been airy. 'There's an easy way, James. Just ask them how they spell their names. You'll have no trouble at all.

I had tried this on one occasion and the farmer had looked at me strangely, replied 'S-M-I-T-H' and hurried away. So there seemed nothing to do now but sit sweating with my eyes on the disapproving back and search through my memory. When the news finished with a raucous burst of music I had got back about three weeks without result.

There was a blessed respite of a few seconds before the uproar broke out again. This was the main feature – the film about Scotland was on later – and was described outside as a tender love story. I can't remember the title but there was a lot of embracing which would have been all right except that every kiss was accompanied by a chorus of long-drawn sucking noises from the little boys downstairs. The less romantic blew raspberries.

And all the time it got hotter. I opened my jacket wide and unbuttoned my shirt collar but I was beginning to feel decidedly light-headed. The little man in front, still huddled in his heavy coat, seemed unperturbed. Twice the projector broke down and we stared for several minutes at a blank screen while a storm of whistling and stamping came up from the stalls.

Maggie Robinson, standing in the dim light by the curtain, still appeared to be fascinated by the sight of Helen and me. Whenever I looked up I found her eyes fixed upon us with a knowing leer. About half-way through the film, however, her concentration was disturbed by a commotion on the other side of the curtain and she was suddenly brushed aside as a large form burst through.

With a feeling of disbelief I recognised Gobber Newhouse. I had had previous experience of his disregard of the licensing laws and it was clear he had been at it again. He spent most afternoons in the back rooms of the local pubs and here he was, come to relax after a rough session.

He reeled up the aisle, turned, to my dismay, into our row, rested briefly on Helen's lap, trod on my toe and finally spread his enormous carcass over the seat on my left. Fortunately it was another courting seat with no central arm to get in his way but for all that he had great difficulty in finding a comfortable position. He heaved and squirmed about and the wheezing and snuffing and grunting in the darkness might have come from a pen of bacon pigs. But at last he found a spot and with a final cavernous belch composed himself for slumber.

The tender love story never did have much of a chance but Gobber sounded its death knell. With his snores reverberating in my ear and a dense pall of stale beer drifting over me I was unable to appreciate any of the delicate nuances.

It was a relief when the last close-up came to an end and the lights went up. I was a bit worried about Helen. I had noticed as the evening wore on that her lips had a tendency to twitch occasionally and now and then she drew her brows down in a deep frown. I wondered if she was upset. But Maggie appeared providentially with a tray round her neck and stood over us, still leering while I purchased two chocolate ices.

I had taken only one bite when I noticed a stirring under the overcoat in front of me. The little man was returning to the attack. The eyes staring from the grim mask were as chilling as ever.

'Ah knew,' he said. 'Right from start, that you were on the wrong track.'

'Is that so?'

'Aye, I've been among beasts for fifty years and they never go on like that when it's the stomach.'

'Don't they? You're probably right.'

The little man twisted higher in his seat and for a moment I thought he was going to climb over at me. He raised a forefinger. 'For one thing a beast wi' a bad stomach is allus hard in its muck.'

'I see.'

'And if you think back, this un's muck was soft, real soft.'

'Yes, yes, quite,' I said hastily, glancing across at Helen. This was great – just what I needed to complete the romantic atmosphere.

He sniffed and turned away and once again, as if the whole thing had been stage-managed, we were plunged into blackness and the noise blasted out again. I was lying back quivering when it came through to me that something was wrong. What was this strident Western music? Then the title flashed on the screen. *Arizona Guns*.

I turned to Helen in alarm. 'What's going on? This is supposed to be the Scottish film, isn't it? The one we came to see?'

'It's supposed to be.' Helen paused and looked at me with a half-smile. 'But I'm afraid it isn't going to be. The thing is they often change the supporting film without warning. Nobody seems to mind.'

I slumped wearily in my seat. Well I'd done it again. No dance at the Reniston, wrong picture tonight. I was a genius in my own way.

'I'm sorry,' I said. 'I hope you don't mind too much.'

She shook her head. 'Not a bit. Anyway, let's give this one a chance. It may be all right.'

But as the ancient horse opera crackled out its cliché-ridden message I gave up hope. This was going to be another of those evenings. I watched apathetically as the posse galloped for the fourth time past the same piece of rock and I was totally unprepared for the deafening fusillade of shots which rang out. It made me jump and it even roused Gobber from his sleep.

"Ellow! 'ellow! 'ellow!" he bawled jerking upright and thrashing around him with his arms. A backhander on the side of the head drove me violently against Helen's shoulder and I was beginning to apologise when I saw that her twitching and frowning had come on again. But this time it spread and her whole face seemed to break up. She began to laugh, silently and helplessly.

I had never seen a girl laugh like this. It was as though it was something she had wanted to do for a long time. She abandoned herself utterly to it, lying back with her head on the back of the seat, legs stretched out in front of her, arms dangling by her side. She took her time and waited until she had got it all out of her system before she turned to me.

She put her hand on my arm. 'Look,' she said faintly. 'Next time, why don't we just go for a walk?'

I settled down. Gobber was asleep again and his snores, louder than ever, competed with the bangs and howls from the screen. I still hadn't the slightest idea who that little man in front could be and I had the feeling he wasn't finished with me yet. The clock still stood at twenty-past four. Maggie was still staring at us and a steady strickle of sweat ran down my back.

The environment wasn't all I could have desired, but never mind. There was going to be a next time.

Chapter Thirty-two

Siegfried had a habit of pulling at the lobe of his ear and staring blankly ahead when preoccupied. He was doing it now, his other hand, outstretched, crumbling a crust of bread on his plate.

I didn't usually pry into my boss's meditations and anyway, I wanted to be off on the morning round, but there was something portentous in his face which made me speak.

'What's the matter? Something on your mind?'

Siegfried turned his head slowly and his eyes glared sightlessly for a few moments until recognition dawned. He stopped his lobe-pulling, got to his feet, walked over to the window and looked out at the empty street.

'There is, James, there is indeed. In fact, I was just about to ask your advice. It's about this letter I got this morning.' He ransacked his pockets impatiently, pulling out handkerchiefs, thermometers, crumpled bank-notes, lists of calls, till he found a long blue envelope. 'Here, read it.'

I opened the envelope and quickly scanned the single sheet. I looked up, puzzled. 'Sorry, I don't get it. All it says here is that H. W. St. J. Ransom, Maj. Gen., would like the pleasure of your company at Brawton races on Saturday. No problem there, is there? You like racing.'

'Ah, but it's not so simple as that,' Siegfried said, starting again on the lobe. 'This is in the nature of a trial. General Ransom is one of the big boys in the North West Racing Circuit and he's bringing one of his pals along on Saturday to vet me. They're going to examine me for soundness.'

I must have looked alarmed because he grinned. 'Look, I'd better start at the beginning. And I'll cut it short. The officials of the North West Circuit are looking for a veterinary surgeon to supervise all meetings. You know the local man attends if there's a racecourse in his town and he is on call in case of injury to the horses, but this would be different. This supervisory vet would deal with cases of suspected doping and the like – in fact he'd have to be a bit of a specialist. Well I've had a whisper that they think I might be the man for the job and that's what Saturday's about. I know old Ransom but I haven't met his colleague. The idea is to have a day at the races with me and size me up.'

'If you got the job would it mean giving up general practice?' I asked. And a chill wind seemed to creep around me at the idea.

'No, no, but it would mean spending something like three days a week on racecourses and I'm wondering if that wouldn't be just a bit much.'

'Well, I don't know,' I finished my coffee and pushed back my chair. 'I'm not really the one to advise you on this. I haven't had a lot of experience with racehorses and I'm not interested in racing. You'll have to make up your own mind. But you've often talked of specialising in horse work and you love the atmosphere of a racecourse.'

'You're right there, James, I do. And there's no doubt the extra money would come in very useful. It's what every practice needs – a contract of some sort, a regular income from somewhere to make you less dependent on the farmers paying their bills.' He turned away from the window. 'Anyway, I'll go to Brawton races with them on Saturday and we'll see how it turns out. And you must come too.'

'Me! Why?'

'Well it says in the letter "and partner".'

'That means some woman. They'll have their wives with them, no doubt.'

'Doesn't matter what it means, James, you're coming with me. A day out and a bit of free food and booze will do you good. Tristan can hold the fort for a few hours.'

It was nearly noon on Saturday when I answered the door bell. As I walked along the passage it was easy to identify the people beyond the glass door.

General Ransom was short and square with a moustache of surprising blackness thrusting aggressively from his upper lip. Colonel Tremayne was tall, hawk-nosed and stooping but he shared with his companion the almost tangible aura of authority which comes from a lifetime of command. Two tweedy women stood behind them on the lower step.

I opened the door, feeling my shoulders squaring and my heels coming together under the battery of fierce, unsmiling glares.

'Mr Farnon!' barked the general. 'Expectin' us, I think.'

I retreated a pace and opened the door. 'Oh yes, certainly, please come in.'

The two women swept in first, Mrs Ransom as squat and chunky and even tougher-looking than her husband, then Mrs Tremayne, much younger and attractive in a hard-boiled fashion. All of them completely ignored me except the colonel who brought up the rear and fixed me for a moment with a fishy eye.

I had been instructed to dispense sherry, and once inside the sitting-room I began to pour from a decanter. I was half-way up the second glass when Siegfried walked in. I spilt some of the sherry. My boss had really spruced up for the occasion. His lean frame was draped in cavalry twill of flawless cut; the long, strong-boned face was freshly shaven, the small sandy moustache neatly clipped. He swept off a brand-new bowler as he came in and I put down my decanter and gazed at him with proprietary pride. Maybe there had been a few dukes or the odd earl in Siegfried's family tree but be that as it may, the two army men seemed in an instant to have become low bred and a trifle scruffy.

There was something almost ingratiating in the way the general went up to Siegfried. 'Farnon, me dear feller, how are you? Good to see you again. Let me introduce you to me wife, Mrs Tremayne, Colonel Tremayne.'

The colonel astonishingly dug up a twisted smile, but my main interest was in the reaction of the ladies. Mrs Ransom, looking up at Siegfried as he bent over her, just went to pieces. It was unbelievable that this formidable fortress should crumble at the first shot, but there it was; the tough lines melted from her face and she was left with a big sloppy smile looking like anybody's dear old mum.

Mrs Tremayne's response was different but no less dramatic. As the steady grey eyes swept her she seemed to wither and it was as if a spasm of exquisite pain twisted her cheeks. She controlled herself with an effort but looked after Siegfried with wistful hunger as he turned back to the men.

I began to slosh the sherry violently into the glasses. Damn it, there it was again. The same old thing. And yet he didn't do anything. Just looked at them. Hell, it wasn't fair.

Sherry over, we moved outside and installed ourselves in Siegfried's Rover on which an immaculate coach-building job had been done since the disaster of last summer. It was an impressive turnout. The car, after a morning's forced labour by Tristan with hose and leather, shone like a mirror. Siegfried, in the driver's seat, extended an elegant arm to his brother as we drove away. I couldn't help feeling that the only superfluous object was myself, squatting uncomfortably on a little let-down seat, facing the two army men who sat to attention in the back seat, their bowlers pointing rigidly to the front. Between them Mrs Tremayne stared wonderingly at the back of Siegfried's head.

We lunched on the course, Siegfried comfortably at home with the smoked salmon, the cold chicken and the champagne. There was no doubt he had scored a tremendous success during the meal, discussing racing knowledgeably with the men and dispensing charm equally to their wives. The tough Mrs Ransom positively simpered as he marked her card for her. It was quite certain that if the new appointment hung upon his behaviour today, a vote at this time would have seen him home and dry.

After lunch we went down to the paddock and had a look at the horses parading for the first race. I could see Siegfried expanding as he took in the scene; the jostling crowds, the shouting bookies, the beautiful animals pacing round, the jockeys, tiny, colourful, durable, chatting to the trainers out in the middle. He had got through enough champagne at lunch to sharpen his appreciation and he was the very picture of a man who just knew he was going to have a successful day.

Merryweather, the course vet, joined us to watch the first race. Siegfried knew him slightly and they were chatting after the race when the 'vet wanted' sign went up. A man hurried up to Merryweather. 'That horse that slipped at the last bend is still down and doesn't look like getting up.'

The vet started for his car which was parked in readiness near the rails. He turned towards us 'You two want to come?' Siegfried looked enquiringly at his party and received gracious nods of assent. We hurried after our colleague.

Within seconds we were racing down the course towards the last bend. Merryweather, hanging on to the wheel as we sped over the grass, grunted half to himself: 'Hell, I hope this thing hasn't got a fracture – if there's one thing I mortally hate it's shooting horses.'

It didn't look good when we got to the spot. The sleek animal lay flat on its side showing no movement apart from the laboured rise and fall of its ribs. The jockey, blood streaming from a cut brow, knelt by its head. 'What do you think, sir? Has he broken a leg?'

'Let's have a look.' Merryweather began to palpate the extended limbs, running strong fingers over one bone then another, carefully flexing the joints of fetlock, knee, shoulder, hock. 'Nothing wrong there. Certainly no fracture.' Then he pointed suddenly at the head. 'Look at his eyes.'

We looked; they were glazed and there was a slight but unmistakable nystagmus.

'Concussion?' Siegfried said.

'That's it, he's just had a bang on the head.' Merryweather got off his knees, looking happier. 'Come on, we'll push him on to his chest. I think he ought to be able to get up with a bit of help.'

There were plenty of helpers from the crowd and the horse was rolled easily till he rested on his sternum, forelegs extended forward. After a couple of minutes in this position he struggled to his feet and stood swaying slightly. A stable lad walked him away.

Merryweather laughed. 'Well, that wasn't so bad. Good horse that. I think he'll be all right after a rest.'

Siegfried had started to reply when we heard a 'Psst, psst!' from beyond the rails. We looked up and saw a stout, red-faced figure gesturing at us eagerly. 'Hey! Hey!' it was saying. 'Come over here a minute.'

We went over. There was something about the face which Siegfried seemed to find intriguing. He looked closer at the grinning, pudgy features, the locks of oily black hair falling over the brow and cried out in delight.

'God help us! Stewie Brannon! Here, James, come and meet another colleague – we came through college together.'

Siegfried had told me a lot about Stewie Brannon. So much, in fact, that I seemed to be shaking hands with an old, well-remembered friend. Sometimes, when the mood was on us, Siegfried and I would sit up nearly till dawn over a bottle in the big room at Skeldale House chewing over old times and recalling the colourful characters we had known. I remembered he had told me he had overtaken Stewie about half way through the course and had qualified while Stewie was still battling in his third year. Siegfried had described him as totally unambitious, averse to study, disinclined to wash or shave; in fact, his idea of the young man least likely to succeed. But there had been something touching about him; the ingenuousness of a child, a huge, all-embracing affection for his fellow humans, an impregnable cheerfulness.

Siegfried called over to Merryweather. 'Will you give my apologies to my friends when you go back? There's a chap here I have to see – I'll only be a few minutes.'

Merryweather waved, got into his car and drove back up the course as we ducked under the rails.

Siegfried seized the bulky figure by the arm. 'Come on, Stewie, where can we get a drink?'

Chapter Thirty-three

We went into a long, low bar under the stand and I experienced a slight shock of surprise. This was the four and sixpenny end and the amenities were rather different from the paddock. The eating and drinking was done mainly in the vertical position and the cuisine seemed to consist largely of pies and sausage rolls.

Siegfried fought his way to the bar and collected three whiskies. We sat down at one of the few available tables – an unstable, metal-topped structure. At the next table a sharp faced character studied the *Pink 'Un* while he took great swigs at a pint and tore savagely at a pork pie.

'Now, my lad,' Siegfried said. 'What have you been doing for the past six years?'

'Well, let's see,' said Stewie, absently downing his whisky at a gulp. 'I got into finals shortly after you left and I didn't do so bad at all, really. Pipped them both first go, then I had a bit of bother with surgery a couple of times, but I was launched on the unsuspecting animal population four years ago. I've been around quite a lot since then. North, South, even six months in Ireland. I've been trying to find a place with a living wage. This three or four quid a week lark isn't much cop when you have a family to keep.'

'Family? You're married then?'

'Not half. You remember little Meg Hamilton – I used to bring her to the college dances. We got married when I got into final year. We've got five kids now and another on the way.'

Siegfried choked on his whisky. 'Five kids! For God's sake, Stewie!'

'Ah, it's wonderfully really, Siegfried. You probably wonder how we manage to exist. Well I couldn't tell you. I don't know myself. But we've kept one jump ahead of ruin and we've been happy, too. I think we're going to be OK now. I stuck up my plate in Hensfield a few months ago and I'm doing all right. Been able to clear the housekeeping and that's all that matters.'

'Hensfield, eh?' Siegfried said. I pictured the grim West Riding town. A wilderness of decaying brick bristling with factory chimneys. It was the other Yorkshire. 'Mainly small animal, I suppose?'

'Oh yes. I earn my daily bread almost entirely by separating the local tom cats from their knackers. Thanks to me, the feline females of Hensfield can walk the streets unmolested.'

Siegfried laughed and caught the only waitress in the place lightly by the arm as she hurried by. She whipped round with a frown and an angry word but took another look and smiled. 'Yes, sir?'

Siegfried looked into her face seriously for a few moments, still holding her arm. Then he spoke quietly. 'I wonder if you'd be kind enough to bring us three large whiskies and keep repeating the order whenever you see our glasses are empty. Would you be able to do that?'

'Certainly, sir, of course.' The waitress was over forty but she was blushing like a young girl.

Stewie's chins quivered with silent laugher. 'You old bugger, Farnon. It does me good to see you haven't changed.'

'Really? Well that's rather nice, isn't it?'

'And the funny thing is I don't think you really try.'

'Try? Try what?'

'Ah, nothing, Forget it – here's our whisky.'

As the drinks kept coming they talked and talked. I didn't butt in – I sat listening, wrapped in a pleasant euphoria and pushing every other glassful unobtrusively round to Stewie who put it out of sight with a careless jerk of the wrist.

As Siegfried sketched out his own progress, I was struck by the big man's total absence of envy. He was delighted to hear about the rising practice, the pleasant house, the assistant. Siegfried had described him as plump in the old days but he was fat now, despite his hard times. And I had heard about that overcoat; it was the 'navy nap' which had been his only protection through the years at college. It couldn't have looked so good then, but it was a sad thing now, the seams strained to bursting by the bulging flesh.

'Look, Stewie.' Siegfried fumbled uncomfortably with his glass. 'I'm sure you're going to do well at Hensfield but if by some mischance things got a bit rough, I hope you wouldn't hesitate to turn to me. I'm not so far off in Darrowby, you know. In fact.' He paused and swallowed. 'Are you all right now? If a few quid would help, I've got 'em here.'

Stewie tossed back what must have been the tenth double whisky and gazed at his old friend with gentle benevolence. 'You're a kind old bugger, Siegfried, but no thanks. As I said we're clearing the housekeeping and we'll be OK. But I appreciate it – you always were kind. A strange old bugger, but kind.'

'Strange?' Siegfried was interested.

'No, not strange. Wrong word. Different. That's it, you were as different as hell.'

'Different?' queried Siegfried, swallowing his whisky as if it had stopped tasting of anything a long time ago. 'I'm sure you're wrong there, Stewie.'

'Don't worry your head about it,' Stewie said, and reached across the table to thump his friend on the shoulder. But his judgement was way out and instead he swept Siegfried's bowler from his head. It rolled to the feet of the man at the next table.

During the conversation I had been aware of this gentleman rushing out and trailing slowly back to resume his study of the *Pink 'Un* and renew his attack on the food and drink. The man looked down at the hat. His face was a picture of misery and frustration born of too much beer, semi-masticated pork pies and unwise investment. Convulsively he lashed out with a foot at the bowler and looked better immediately.

The hat, deeply dented, soared back to Siegfried who caught it and replaced it on his head with unruffled aplomb. He didn't seem in the least annoyed; apparently considered the man's reaction perfectly normal.

We all stood up and I was mildly surprised by a slight swaying and blurring of my surroundings. When things came to rest I had another surprise; the big bar was nearly empty. The beer machines were hidden by white cloths. The barmaids were collecting the empty glasses.

'Stewie,' Siegfried said. 'The meeting's over. Do you realise we've been nattering here for over two hours?'

'And very nice, too. For better than giving the hard-earned coppers to the bookies.' As Stewie rose to his feet he clutched at the table and stood blinking for a few seconds.

'There's one thing, though,' Siegfried said. 'My friends. I came here with a party and they must be wondering where I've got to. Tell you what, come and meet them. They'll understand when they realise we haven't seen each other for years.'

We worked our way round to the paddock. No sign of the general and company. We finally found them in the car park grouped unsmilingly around the Rover. Most of the other cars had gone. Siegfried strode up confidently, his dented bowler cocked at a jaunty angle.

'I'm sorry to have left you but a rather wonderful thing happened back there. I would like to present Mr Stewart Brannon, a professional colleague and a very dear friend.'

Four blank stares turned on Stewie. His big, meaty face was redder than ever and he smiled sweetly through a faint dew of perspiration. I noticed that he had made a lopsided job of buttoning the navy nap overcoat; there was a spare button hole at the top and a lack of alignment at the bottom. It made the straining, tortured garment look even more grotesque.

The general nodded curtly, the colonel appeared to be grinding his teeth, the ladies froze visibly and looked away.

'Yes, yes, quite,' grunted the general. 'But we've been waitin' here some time and we want to be gettin' home.' He stuck out his jaw and his moustache bristled.

Siegfried waved a hand. 'Certainly, certainly, by all means. We'll leave right away.' He turned to Stewie. 'Well, goodbye for now, my lad. We'll get together again soon. I'll ring you.'

He began to feel through his pockets for his ignition key. He started quite slowly but gradually stepped up his pace. After he had explored the pockets about five times he stopped, closed his eyes and appeared to give himself over to intense thought. Then, as though he had decided to do the thing systematically, he commenced to lay out the contents of his pockets one by one, using the car bonnet as a table, and as the pile grew so did my conviction that doom was very near.

It wasn't just the key that worried me. Siegfried had consumed a lot more whisky than I had and with its usual delayed action it had begun to creep up on him. He was swaying slightly, his dented bowler had slid forward over one eyebrow and he kept dropping things as he pulled them from his pocket and examined them owlishly.

A man with a long brush and a handcart was walking slowly across the car park when Siegfried grabbed his arm. 'Look, I want you to do something for me. Here's five bob.'

'Right mister.' The man pocketed the money. 'What d'you want me to do?'

'Find my car key.'

The man began to peer round Siegfried's feet. 'I'll do me best. Dropped it round 'ere, did you?'

'No, no. I've no idea where I dropped it.' Siegfried waved vaguely. 'It's somewhere on the course.'

The man looked blank for a moment then he gazed out over the acres of littered ground, the carpet of discarded race cards, torn up tickets. He turned back to Siegfried and giggled suddenly then he walked away, still giggling.

I stole a glance at our companions. They had watched the search in stony silence and none of them seemed to be amused. The general was the first to explode.

'Great heavens, Farnon, have you got the blasted key or haven't you? If the damn thing's lost, then we'd better make other arrangements. Can't keep the ladies standing around here.'

A gentle cough sounded in the background. Stewie was still there. He shambled forward and whispered in his friend's ear and after a moment Siegfried wrung his hand fervently.

'By God, Stewie, that's kind of you! You've saved the situation.' He turned back to the party. 'There's nothing to worry about – Mr Brannon has kindly offered to provide us with transport. He's gone to get his car from the other park.' He pointed triumphantly at the shiny back of the bulging navy overcoat navigating unsteadily through the gate.

Siegfried did his best to keep a conversation going but it was hard slogging. Nobody replied to any of his light sallies and he stopped abruptly when he saw a look of rage and disbelief spread over the general's face. Stewie had come back.

The car was a tiny Austin Seven dwarfed even further by the massive form in the driver's seat. I judged from the rusted maroon paintwork and cracked windows that it must be one of the very earliest models, a 'tourer' whose hood had long since disintegrated and been replaced by a home-made canvas cover fastened to the twisted struts by innumerable loops of string.

Stewie struggled out, dragged open the passenger door and inclined his head with modest pride. He motioned towards a pile of sacks which lay on the bare boards where the passenger seat should have been; there were no seats in the back either, only a couple of rough wooden boxes bearing coloured labels with the legend 'Finest American Apples'. From the boxes peeped a jumble of medicine bottles, stethoscopes, powders, syringe cases.

'I thought,' said Stewie. 'If we put the sacks on top of the boxes . . .'

The general didn't let him finish. 'Dammit, is this supposed to be a joke?' His face was brick red and the veins on his neck were swelling dangerously. 'Are you tryin' to insult me friend and these ladies? You want horsewhippin' for this afternoon's work, Farnon. That's what you want – horsewhippin'!'

He was halted by a sudden roar from the Rover's engine. The colonel, a man of resource as befitted his rank, had shorted the ignition. Fortunately the doors were not locked.

The ladies took their places in the back with the colonel and I slunk miserably on to my little seat. The general had regained control of himself. 'Get in! I'll drive!' he barked at Siegfried as though addressing an erring lance corporal.

But Siegfried held up a restraining hand. 'Just one moment,' he slurred. 'The windscreen is very dirty. I'll give it a rub for you.'

The ladies watched him silently as he weaved round to the back of the car and began to rummage in the boot. The love light had died from their eyes. I don't know why he took the trouble; possibly it was because, through the whisky mists, he felt he must re-establish himself as a competent and helpful member of the party.

But the effort fell flat; the effect was entirely spoiled. He was polishing the glass with a dead hen.

It was a couple of weeks later, again at the breakfast table that Siegfried, reading the morning paper with his third cup of coffee, called out to me.

'Ah, I see Herbert Jarvis MRCVS, one time Captain RAVC, has been appointed to the North West Circuit as supervisory veterinary surgeon. I know Jarvis. Nice chap. Just the man for the job.'

I looked across at my boss for some sign of disappointment or regret. I saw none.

Siegfried put down his cup, wiped his lips on his napkin and sighed contentedly.

'You know, James, everything happens for the best. Old Stewie was sent by providence or heaven or anything you like. I was never meant to get that job and I'd have been as miserable as hell if I had got it. Come on, lad, let's get off into those hills.'

Let Sleeping Vets Lie

Let Sleeping Vets Lie

To
my Wife with love

Chapter One

As the faint rumbling growl rolled up from the rib cage into the ear pieces of my stethoscope the realisation burst upon me with uncomfortable clarity that this was probably the biggest dog I had ever seen. In my limited past experience some Irish Wolfhounds had undoubtedly been taller and a certain number of Bull Mastiffs had possibly been broader, but for sheer gross poundage this one had it. His name was Clancy.

It was a good name for an Irishman's dog and Joe Mulligan was very Irish despite his many years in Yorkshire. Joe had brought him in to the afternoon surgery and as the huge hairy form ambled along, almost filling the passage, I was reminded of the times I had seen him out in the fields around Darrowby enduring the frisking attentions of smaller animals with massive benignity. He looked like a nice friendly dog.

But now there was this ominous sound echoing round the great thorax like a distant drum roll in a subterranean cavern, and as the chest piece of the stethoscope bumped along the ribs the sound swelled in volume and the lips fluttered over the enormous teeth as though a gentle breeze had stirred them. It was then that I became aware not only that Clancy was very big indeed but that my position, kneeling on the floor with my right ear a few inches from his mouth, was infinitely vulnerable.

I got to my feet and as I dropped the stethoscope into my pocket the dog gave me a cold look – a sideways glance without moving his head; and there was a chilling menace in his very immobility. I didn't mind my patients snapping at me but this one, I felt sure, wouldn't snap. If he started something it would be on a spectacular scale.

I stepped back a pace. 'Now what did you say his symptoms were, Mr Mulligan?'

'Phwaat's that?' Joe cupped his ear with his hand. I took a deep breath. 'What's the trouble with him?' I shouted.

The old man looked at me with total incomprehension from beneath the straightly adjusted cloth cap. He fingered the muffler knotted immediately over his larynx and the pipe which grew from the dead centre of his mouth puffed blue wisps of puzzlement.

Then, remembering something of Clancy's past history, I moved close to Mr Mulligan and bawled with all my power into his face. 'Is he vomiting?'

The response was immediate. Joe smiled in great relief and removed his pipe. 'Oh aye, he's womitin' sorr. He's womitin' bad.' Clearly he was on familiar ground.

Over the years Clancy's treatment had all been at long range. My young boss, Siegfried Farnon, had told me on the first day I had arrived in Darrowby two years ago that there was nothing wrong with the dog which he had described as a cross between an Airedale and a donkey, but his penchant for eating every bit of rubbish in his path had the inevitable result. A large bottle of bismuth, mag carb mixture had been dispensed at regular intervals. He had also told me that Clancy, when bored, used occasionally to throw Joe to the ground and worry him like a rat just for a bit of light relief. But his master still adored him.

Prickings of conscience told me I should carry out a full examination. Take his temperature, for instance. All I had to do was to grab hold of that tail, lift it and push a thermometer into his rectum. The dog turned his head and met my eye with a blank stare; again I heard the low booming drum roll and the upper lip lifted a fraction to show a quick gleam of white.

'Yes, yes, right, Mr Mulligan,' I said briskly. 'I'll get you a bottle of the usual.'

In the dispensary, under the rows of bottles with their Latin names and glass stoppers I shook up the mixture in a ten ounce bottle, corked it, stuck on a label and wrote the directions. Joe seemed well satisfied as he pocketed the familiar white medicine but as he turned to go my conscience smote me again. The dog did look perfectly fit but maybe he ought to be seen again.

'Bring him back again on Thursday afternoon at two o'clock,' I yelled into the old man's ear. 'And please come on time if you can. You were a bit late today.'

I watched Mr Mulligan going down the street, preceded by his pipe from which regular puffs rose upwards as though from a departing railway engine. Behind him ambled Clancy, a picture of massive calm. With his all-over covering of tight brown curls he did indeed look like a gigantic Airedale.

Thursday afternoon, I ruminated. That was my half day and at two o'clock I'd probably be watching the afternoon cinema show in Brawton.

The following Friday morning Siegfried was sitting behind his desk, working out the morning rounds. He scribbled a list of visits on a pad, tore out the sheet and handed it to me.

'Here you are, James, I think that'll just about keep you out of mischief till lunch time.' Then something in the previous day's entries caught his eye and he turned to his younger brother who was at his morning task of stoking the fire.

'Tristan, I see Joe Mulligan was in yesterday afternoon with his dog and you saw it. What did you make of it?'

Tristan put down his bucket. 'Oh, I gave him some of the bismuth mixture.'

'Yes, but what did your examination of the patient disclose?'

'Well now, let's see.' Tristan rubbed his chin. 'He looked pretty lively, really.'

'Is that all?'

'Yes . . . yes . . . I think so.'

Siegfried turned back to me. 'And how about you, James? You saw the dog the day before. What were your findings?'

'Well it was a bit difficult,' I said. 'That dog's as big as an elephant and there's something creepy about him. He seemed to me to be just waiting his chance and there was only old Joe to hold him. I'm afraid I wasn't able to make a close examination but I must say I thought the same as Tristan – he did look pretty lively.'

Siegfried put down his pen wearily. On the previous night, fate had dealt him one of the shattering blows which it occasionally reserves for vets – a call at each end of his sleeping time. He had been dragged from his bed at 1 a.m. and again at 6 a.m. and the fires of his personality were temporarily damped.

He passed a hand across his eyes. 'Well God help us. You, James, a veterinary surgeon of two years experience and you, Tristan, a final year student can't come up with anything better between you than the phrase "pretty lively". It's a bloody poor thing! Hardly a worthy description of clinical findings is it? When an animal comes in here I expect you to record pulse, temperature and respiratory rate. To auscultate the chest and thoroughly palpate the abdomen. To open his mouth and examine teeth, gums and pharynx. To check the condition of the skin. To catheterise him and examine the urine if necessary.'

'Right,' I said.

'OK,' said Tristan.

My employer rose from his seat. 'Have you fixed another appointment?'

'I have, yes.' Tristan drew his packet of Woodbines from his pocket. 'For Monday. And since Mr Mulligan's always late for the surgery I said we'd visit the dog at his home in the evening.'

'I see.' Siegfried made a note on the pad, then he looked up suddenly. 'That's when you and James are going to the young farmers' meeting, isn't it?'

The young man drew on his cigarette. 'That's right. Good for the practice for us to mix with the young clients.'

'Very well,' Siegfried said as he walked to the door. 'I'll see the dog myself.'

On the following Tuesday I was fairly confident that Siegfried would have something to say about Mulligan's dog, if only to point out the benefits of a thorough clinical examination. But he was silent on the subject.

It happened that I came upon old Joe in the market place sauntering over the cobbles with Clancy inevitably trotting at his heels.

I went up to him and shouted in his ear. 'How's your dog?'

Mr Mulligan removed his pipe and smiled with slow benevolence. 'Oh foine, sorr, foine. Still womitin' a bit, but not bad.'

'Mr Farnon fixed him up, then?'

'Aye, gave him some more of the white medicine. It's wonderful stuff, sorr, wonderful stuff.'

'Good, good,' I said. 'He didn't find anything else when he examined him?'

Joe took another suck at his pipe. 'No he didn't now, he didn't. He's a clever man, Mr Farnon – I've niver seen a man work as fast, no I haven't.'

'What do you mean?'

'Well now he saw all he wanted in tree seconds, so he did.'

I was mystified. 'Three seconds?'

'Yis,' said Mr Mulligan firmly. 'Not a moment more.'

'Amazing. What happened?'

Joe tapped out his pipe on his heel and without haste took out a knife and began to carve a refill from an evil looking coil of black twist. 'Well now I'll tell ye. Mr Farnon is a man who moves awful sudden, and that night he banged on our front door and jumped into the room.' (I knew those cottages. There was no hall or lobby – you walked straight from the street into the living room.) 'And as he came in he was pullin' his thermometer out of its case. Well now Clancy was lyin' by the fire and he rose up in a flash and he gave a bit of a wuff, so he did.'

'A bit of a wuff, eh?' I could imagine the hairy monster leaping up and baying into Siegfried's face. I could see the gaping jaws, the gleaming teeth.

'Aye, just a bit of a wuff. Well, Mr Farnon just put the thermometer straight back in its case turned round and went out the door.'

'Didn't he say anything?' I asked.

'No, divil a word. Just turned about like a soldier and marched out the door, so he did.'

It sounded authentic. Siegfried was a man of instant decision. I put my hand out to pat Clancy but something in his eyes made me change my mind.

'Well, I'm glad he's better,' I shouted.

The old man ignited his pipe with an ancient brass lighter, puffed a cloud of choking blue smoke into my face and tapped a little metal lid on to the bowl.

'Aye, Mr Farnon sent round a big bottle of the white stuff and it's done 'im good. Mind yous', he gave a beatific smile, 'Clancy's allus been one for the womitin', so he has.'

Nothing more was said about the big dog for over a week, but Siegfried's professional conscience must have been niggling at him because he came into the dispensary one afternoon when Tristan and I were busy at the tasks which have passed into history – making up fever drinks, stomach powders, boric acid pessaries. He was elaborately casual.

'Oh by the way, I dropped a note to Joe Mulligan. I'm not entirely convinced that we have adequately explored the causes of his dog's symptoms. This womiting . . . er, vomiting is almost certainly due to depraved appetite but I just want to make sure. So I have asked him to bring him round tomorrow afternoon between two and two thirty when we'll all be here.'

No cries of joy greeted his statement, so he continued. 'I suppose you could say that this dog is to some degree a difficult animal and I think we should plan accordingly.' He turned to me. 'James, when he arrives you get hold of his back end, will you?'

'Right,' I replied without enthusiasm.

He faced his brother. 'And you, Tristan, can deal with the head. OK?'

'Fine, fine,' the young man muttered, his face expressionless.

His brother continued. 'I suggest you get a good grip with your arms round his neck and I'll be ready to give him a shot of sedative.'

'Splendid, splendid,' said Tristan.

'Ah well, that's capital.' My employer rubbed his hands together. 'Once I get the dope into him the rest will be easy. I do like to satisfy my mind about these things.'

It was a typical Dales practice at Darrowby; mainly large animal and we didn't have packed waiting rooms at surgery times. But on the following afternoon we had nobody in at all, and it added to the tension of waiting. The three of us mooched about the office, making aimless conversation, glancing with studied carelessness into the front street, whistling little tunes to ourselves. By two twenty-five we had all fallen silent. Over the next five minutes we consulted our watches about every thirty seconds, then at exactly two thirty Siegfried spoke up.

'This is no damn good. I told Joe he had to be here before half past but he's taken not a bit of notice. He's always late and there doesn't seem to be any way to get him here on time.' He took a last look out of the window at the empty street. 'Right we're not waiting any longer. You and I, James, have got that colt to cut and you, Tristan, have to see that beast of Wilson's. So let's be off.'

Up till then, Laurel and Hardy were the only people I had ever seen getting jammed together in doorways but there was a moment when the three of us gave a passable imitation of the famous comics as we all fought our way into the passage at the same time. Within seconds we were in the street and Tristan was roaring off in a cloud of exhaust smoke. My employer and I proceeded almost as rapidly in the opposite direction.

At the end of Trengate we turned into the market place and I looked around in vain for signs of Mr Mulligan. It wasn't until we had reached the outskirts of the town that we saw him. He had just left his house and was pacing along under a moving pall of blue smoke with Clancy as always bringing up the rear.

'There he is!' Siegfried exclaimed. 'Would you believe it? At the rate he's going he'll get to the surgery around three o'clock. Well we won't be there and it's his own fault.' He looked at the great curly-coated animal tripping along, a picture of health and energy. 'Well, I suppose we'd have been wasting our time examining that dog in any case. There's nothing really wrong with him.'

For a moment he paused, lost in thought, then he turned to me.

'He does look pretty lively, doesn't he?'

Chapter Two

This was my second spring in the Dales but it was like the one before – and all the springs after. The kind of spring, that is, that a country vet knows; the din of the lambing pens, the bass rumble of the ewes and the high, insistent bawling of the lambs. This, for me, has always heralded the end of winter and the beginning of something new. This and the piercing Yorkshire wind and the hard, bright sunshine flooding the bare hillsides.

At the top of the grassy slope the pens, built of straw bales, formed a long row of square cubicles each holding a ewe with her lambs and I could see Rob Benson coming round the far end carrying two feeding buckets. Rob was hard at it; at this time of the year he didn't go to bed for about six weeks; he would maybe take off his boots and doze by the kitchen fire at night but he was his own shepherd and never very far from the scene of action.

'Ah've got a couple of cases for you today, Jim.' His face, cracked and purpled by the weather, broke into a grin, 'It's not really you ah need, it's that little lady's hand of yours and right sharpish, too.'

He led the way to a bigger enclosure, holding several sheep. There was a scurry as we went in but he caught expertly at the fleece of a darting ewe. 'This is the first one. You can see we haven't a deal o' time.'

I lifted the woolly tail and gasped. The lamb's head was protruding from the vagina, the lips of the vulva clamped tightly behind the ears, and it had swollen enormously to more than twice its size. The eyes were mere puffed slits in the great oedematous ball and the tongue, blue and engorged, lolled from the mouth.

'Well I've seen a few big heads, Rob, but I think this takes the prize.'

'Aye, the little beggar came with his legs back. Just beat me to it. Ah was only away for an hour but he was up like a football. By hell it doesn't take long. I know he wants his legs bringin' round but what can I do with bloody great mitts like mine.' He held out his huge hands, rough and swollen with the years of work.

While he spoke I was stripping off my jacket and as I rolled my shirt sleeves high the wind struck like a knife at my shrinking flesh. I soaped my fingers quickly and began to feel for a space round the lamb's neck. For a moment the little eyes opened and regarded me disconsolately.

'He's alive, anyway,' I said. 'But he must feel terrible and he can't do a thing about it.'

Easing my way round, I found a space down by the throat where I thought I might get through. This was where my 'lady's hand' came in useful and I blessed it every spring; I could work inside the ewes with the minimum of discomfort to them and this was all-important because sheep, despite their outdoor hardiness, just won't stand rough treatment.

With the utmost care I inched my way along the curly wool of the neck to the shoulder. Another push forward and I was able to hook a finger round the leg and draw it forward until I could feel the flexure of the knee; a little more twiddling and I had hold of the tiny cloven foot and drew it gently out into the light of day.

Well that was half the job done. I got up from the sack where I was kneeling and went over to the bucket of warm water; I'd use my left hand for the other leg and began to soap it thoroughly while one of the ewes, marshalling her lambs around her, glared at me indignantly and gave a warning stamp of her foot.

Turning, I knelt again and began the same procedure and as I once more groped forward a tiny lamb dodged under my arm and began to suck at my patient's udder. He was clearly enjoying it, too, if the little tail, twirling inches from my face, meant anything.

'Where did this bloke come from?' I asked, still feeling round.

The farmer smiled. 'Oh that's Herbert. Poor little youth's mother won't have 'im at any price. Took a spite at him at birth though she thinks world of her other lamb.'

'Do you feed him, then?'

'Nay, I was going to put him with the pet lambs but I saw he was fendin' for himself. He pops from one ewe to t'other and gets a quick drink whenever he gets chance. I've never seen owt like it.'

'Only a week old and an independent spirit, eh?'

'That's about the size of it, Jim. I notice 'is belly's full every mornin' so I reckon his ma must let him have a do during the night. She can't see him in the dark – it must be the look of him she can't stand.'

I watched the little creature for a moment. To me he seemed as full of knock-kneed charm as any of the others. Sheep were funny things.

I soon had the other leg out and once that obstruction was removed the lamb followed easily. He was a grotesque sight lying on the strawed grass, his enormous head dwarfing his body, but his ribs were heaving reassuringly and I knew the head would shrink back to normal as quickly as it had expanded. I had another search round inside the ewe but the uterus was empty.

'There's no more, Rob,' I said.

The farmer grunted. 'Aye, I thowt so, just a big single 'un. They're the ones that cause the trouble.'

Drying my arms, I watched Herbert. He had left my patient when she moved round to lick her lamb and he was moving speculatively among the other ewes. Some of them warned him off with a shake of the head but eventually he managed to sneak up on a big, wide-bodied sheep and pushed his head underneath her. Immediately she swung round and with a fierce upward butt of her hard skull she sent the little animal flying high in the air in a whirl of flailing legs. He landed with a thud on his back and as I hurried towards him he leaped to his feet and trotted away.

'Awd bitch!' shouted the farmer and as I turned to him in some concern he shrugged. 'I know, poor little sod, it's rough, but I've got a feelin' he wants it this way rather than being in the pen with the pet lambs. Look at 'im now.'

Herbert, quite unabashed, was approaching another ewe and as she bent over her feeding trough he nipped underneath her and his tail went into action again. There was no doubt about it – that lamb had guts.

'Rob,' I said as he caught my second patient, 'why do you call him Herbert?'

'Well that's my younger lad's name and that lamb's just like 'im the way he puts his head down and gets stuck in, fearless like.'

I put my hand into the second ewe. Here was a glorious mix up of three lambs; little heads, legs, a tail, all fighting their way towards the outside world and effectively stopping each other from moving an inch.

'She's been hanging about all morning and painin',' Rob said. 'I knew summat was wrong.'

Moving a hand carefully around the uterus I began the fascinating business of sorting out the tangle which is just about my favourite job in practice. I had to bring a head and two legs up together in order to deliver a lamb; but they had to belong to the same lamb or I was in trouble. It was a matter of tracing each leg back to see if it was hind or fore, to find if it joined the shoulder or disappeared into the depths.

After a few minutes I had a lamb assembled inside with his proper appendages but as I drew the legs into view the neck telescoped and the head slipped back; there was barely room for it to come through the pelvic bones along with the shoulders and I had to coax it through with a finger in the eye socket. This was groaningly painful as the bones squeezed my hand but only for a few seconds because the ewe gave a final strain and the little nose was visible. After that it was easy and I had him on the grass within seconds. The little creature gave a convulsive shake of his head and the farmer wiped him down quickly with straw before pushing him to his mother's head.

The ewe bent over him and began to lick his face and neck with little quick darts of her tongue; and she gave the deep chuckle of satisfaction that you hear from a sheep only at this time. The chuckling continued as I produced another pair of lambs from inside her, one of them hind end first, and, towelling my arms again, I watched her nosing round her triplets delightedly.

Soon they began to answer her with wavering, high-pitched cries and as I drew my coat thankfully over my cold-reddened arms, lamb number one began to struggle to his knees; he couldn't quite make it to his feet and kept toppling on to his face but he knew where he was going, all right; he was headed for that udder with a singleness of purpose which would soon be satisfied.

Despite the wind cutting over the straw bales into my face I found myself grinning down at the scene; this was always the best part, the wonder that was always fresh, the miracle you couldn't explain.

I heard from Rob Benson again a few days later. It was a Sunday afternoon and his voice was strained, almost panic-stricken.

'Jim, I've had a dog in among me in-lamb ewes. There was some folk up here with a car about dinner time and my neighbour said they had an Alsatian and it was chasing the sheep all over the field. There's a hell of a mess – I tell you I'm frightened to look.'

'I'm on my way.' I dropped the receiver and hurried out to the car. I had a sinking dread of what would be waiting for me; the helpless animals lying with their throats torn, the terrifying lacerations of limbs and abdomen. I had seen it all before. The ones which didn't have to be slaughtered would need stitching and on the way I made a mental check of the stock of suture silk in the boot.

The in-lamb ewes were in a field by the roadside and my heart gave a quick thump as I looked over the wall; arms resting on the rough loose stones I gazed with sick dismay across the pasture. This was worse than I had feared. The long slope of turf was dotted with prostrate sheep – there must have been about fifty of them, motionless woolly mounds scattered at intervals on the green.

Rob was standing just inside the gate. He hardly looked at me. Just gestured with his head.

'Tell me what you think. I daren't go in there.'

I left him and began to walk among the stricken creatures, rolling them over, lifting their legs, parting the fleece of their necks to examine them. Some were completely unconscious, others comatose; none of them could stand up. But as I worked my way up the field I felt a growing bewilderment. Finally I called back to the farmer.

'Rob, come over here. There's something very strange.'

'Look,' I said as the farmer approached hesitantly. 'There's not a drop of blood nor a wound anywhere and yet all the sheep are flat out. I can't understand it.'

Rob went over and gently raised a lolling head. 'Aye, you're right. What the hell's done it, then?'

At that moment I couldn't answer him, but a little bell was tinkling far away in the back of my mind. There was something familiar about that ewe the farmer had just handled. She was one of the few able to support herself on her chest and she was lying there, blank-eyed, oblivious of everything; but . . . that drunken nodding of the head, that watery nasal discharge . . . I had seen it before. I knelt down and as I put my face close to hers I heard a faint bubbling – almost a rattling – in her breathing. I knew then.

'It's calcium deficiency,' I cried and began to gallop down the slope towards the car.

Rob trotted alongside me. 'But what the 'ell? They get that after lambin', don't they?'

'Yes, usually,' I puffed. 'But sudden exertion and stress can bring it on.'

'Well ah never knew that,' panted Rob. 'How does it happen?'

I saved my breath. I wasn't going to start an exposition on the effects of sudden derangement of the parathyroid. I was more concerned with wondering if I had enough calcium in the boot for fifty ewes. It was reassuring to see the long row of round tin caps peeping from their cardboard box; I must have filled up recently.

I injected the first ewe in the vein just to check my diagnosis – calcium works as quickly as that in sheep – and felt a quiet elation as the unconscious animal began to blink and tremble, then tried to struggle on to its chest.

'We'll inject the others under the skin,' I said. 'It'll save time.'

I began to work my way up the field. Rob pulled forward the fore leg of each sheep so that I could insert the needle under the convenient patch of unwoolled skin just behind the elbow; and by the time I was half way up the slope the ones at the bottom were walking about and getting their heads into the food troughs and hay racks.

It was one of the most satisfying experiences of my working life. Not clever, but a magical transfiguration; from despair to hope, from death to life within minutes.

I was throwing the empty bottles into the boot when Rob spoke. He was looking wonderingly up at the last of the ewes getting to its feet at the far end of the field.

'Well Jim, I'll tell you. I've never seen owt like that afore. But there's one thing bothers me.' He turned to me and his weathered features screwed up in puzzlement. 'Ah can understand how gettin' chased by a dog could affect some of them ewes, but why should the whole bloody lot go down?'

'Rob,' I said. 'I don't know.'

And, thirty years later, I still wonder. I still don't know why the whole bloody lot went down.

I thought Rob had enough to worry about at the time, so I didn't point out to him that other complications could be expected after the Alsatian episode. I wasn't surprised when I had a call to the Benson farm within days.

I met him again on the hillside with the same wind whipping over the straw bale pens. The lambs had been arriving in a torrent and the noise was louder than ever. He led me to my patient.

'There's one with a bellyful of dead lambs, I reckon,' he said, pointing to a ewe with her head drooping, ribs heaving. She stood quite motionless and made no attempt to move away when I went up to her; this one was really sick and as the stink of decomposition came up to me I knew the farmer's diagnosis was right.

'Well I suppose it had to happen to one at least after that chasing round,' I said. 'Let's see what we can do, anyway.'

This kind of lambing is without charm but it has to be done to save the ewe. The lambs were putrid and distended with gas and I used a sharp scalpel to skin the legs to the shoulders so that I could remove them and deliver the little bodies with the least discomfort to the mother. When I had finished, the ewe's head was almost touching the ground, she was panting rapidly and grating her teeth. I had nothing to offer her – no wriggling new creature for her to lick and revive her interest in life. What she needed was an injection of penicillin, but this was 1939 and the antibiotics were still a little way round the corner.

'Well I wouldn't give much for her,' Rob grunted. 'Is there owt more you can do?'

'Oh, I'll put some pessaries in her and give her an injection, but what she needs most is a lamb to look after. You know as well as I do that ewes in this condition usually give up if they've nothing to occupy them. You haven't a spare lamb to put to her, have you?'

'Not right now, I haven't. And it's now she needs it. Tomorrow'll be too late.'

Just at that moment a familiar figure wandered into view. It was Herbert, the unwanted lamb, easily recognisable as he prowled from sheep to sheep in search of nourishment.

'Hey, do you think she'd take that little chap?' I asked the farmer.

He looked doubtful. 'Well I don't know – he's a bit old. Nearly a fortnight and they like 'em newly born.'

'But it's worth a try isn't it? Why not try the old trick on her?'

Rob grinned. 'OK, we'll do that. There's nowt to lose. Anyway the little youth isn't much bigger than a new-born 'un. He hasn't grown as fast as his mates.' He took out his penknife and quickly skinned one of the dead lambs, then he tied the skin over Herbert's back and round his jutting ribs.

'Poor little bugger, there's nowt on 'im,' he muttered. 'If this doesn't work he's going in with the pet lambs.'

When he had finished he set Herbert on the grass and the lamb, resolute little character that he was, bored straight in under the sick ewe and began to suck. It seemed he wasn't having much success because he gave the udder a few peremptory thumps with his hard little head; then his tail began to wiggle.

'She's lettin' him have a drop, any road,' Rob laughed.

Herbert was a type you couldn't ignore and the big sheep, sick as she was, just had to turn her head for a look at him. She sniffed along the tied-on skin in a non-committal way, then after a few seconds she gave a few quick licks and the merest beginning of the familiar deep chuckle.

I began to gather up my gear. 'I hope he makes it,' I said. 'Those two need each other.' As I left the pen Herbert, in his new jacket, was still working away.

For the next week I hardly seemed to have my coat on. The flood of sheep work was at its peak and I spent hours of every day with my arms in and out of buckets of water in all corners of the district – in the pens, in dark nooks in farm buildings or very often in the open fields, because the farmers of those days didn't find anything disturbing in the sight of a vet kneeling in his shirt sleeves for an hour in the rain.

I had one more visit to Rob Benson's place. To a ewe with a prolapsed uterus after lambing – a job whose chief delight was comparing it with the sweat of replacing a uterus in a cow.

It was so beautifully easy. Rob rolled the animal on to her side then held her more or less upside down by tying a length of rope to her hind legs and passing it round his neck. In that position she couldn't strain and I disinfected the organ and pushed it back with the minimum of effort, gently inserting an arm at the finish to work it properly into place.

Afterwards the ewe trotted away unperturbed with her family to join the rapidly growing flock whose din was all around us.

'Look!' Rob cried. 'There's that awd ewe with Herbert. Over there on t'right!—in the middle of that bunch.' They all looked the same to me but to Rob, like all shepherds, they were as different as people and he picked out these two effortlessly.

The were near the top of the field and as I wanted to have a close look at them we manoeuvred them into a corner. The ewe, fiercely possessive, stamped her foot at us as we approached, and Herbert, who had discarded his woolly jacket, held close to the flank of his new mother. He was, I noticed, faintly obese in appearance.

'You couldn't call him a runt now, Rob,' I said.

The farmer laughed. 'Nay, t'awd lass has a bag like a cow and Herbert's gettin' the lot. By gaw, he's in clover is that little youth and I reckon he saved the ewe's life—she'd have pegged out all right, but she never looked back once he came along.'

I looked away, over the noisy pens, over the hundreds of sheep moving across the fields. I turned to the farmer. 'I'm afraid you've seen a lot of me lately, Rob. I hope this is the last visit.'

'Aye well it could be. We're getting well through now . . . but it's a hell of a time, lambin' isn't it?'

'It is that. Well I must be off—I'll leave you to it.' I turned and made my way down the hillside, my arms raw and chafing in my sleeves, my cheeks whipped by the eternal wind gusting over the grass. At the gate I stopped and gazed back at the wide landscape, ribbed and streaked by the last of the winter's snow, and at the dark grey banks of cloud riding across on the wind followed by lakes of brightest blue; and in seconds the fields and walls and woods burst into vivid life and I had to close my eyes against the sun's glare. As I stood there the distant uproar came faintly down to me, the tumultuous harmony from deepest bass to highest treble; demanding, anxious, angry, loving.

The sound of the sheep, the sound of spring.

Chapter Three

'Them masticks,' said Mr Pickersgill judicially, 'is a proper bugger.'

I nodded my head in agreement that his mastitis problem was indeed giving cause for concern; and reflected at the same time that while most farmers would have been content with the local word 'felon' it was typical that Mr Pickersgill should make a determined if somewhat inaccurate attempt at the scientific term.

Sometimes he got very wide of the mark as one time long after this when Artificial Insemination or AI was gaining a foothold in the Dales he made my day by telling me he had a cow in calf to the ICI.

However he usually did better than this – most of his efforts were near misses or bore obvious evidence of their derivation – but I could never really fathom where he got the masticks. I did know that once he fastened on to an expression it never changed; mastitis had always been 'them masticks' with him and it always would be. And I knew, too, that nothing would ever stop him doggedly trying to be right.

Because Mr Pickersgill had what he considered to be a scholastic background. He was a man of about sixty and when in his teens he had attended a two week course of instruction for agricultural workers at Leeds University. This brief glimpse of the academic life had left an indelible impression on his mind, and it was as if the intimation of something deep and true behind the facts of his everyday work had kindled a flame in him which had illumined his subsequent life.

No capped and gowned don ever looked back to his years among the spires of Oxford with more nostalgia than did Mr Pickersgill to his fortnight at Leeds and his conversation was usually laced with references to a godlike Professor Malleson who had apparently been in charge of the course.

'Ah don't know what to make of it,' he continued. 'In ma college days I was allus told that you got a big swollen bag and dirty milk with them masticks but this must be another kind. Just little bits of flakes in the milk off and on – neither nowt nor something, but I'm right fed up with it, I'll tell you.'

I took a sip from the cup of tea which Mrs Pickersgill had placed in front of me on the kitchen table. 'Yes, it's very worrying the way it keeps going on and on. I'm sure there's a definite factor behind it all – I wish I could put my finger on it.'

But in fact I had a good idea what was behind it. I had happened in at the little byre late one afternoon when Mr Pickersgill and his daughter Olive were milking their ten cows. I had watched the two at work as they crouched under the row of roan and red backs and one thing was immediately obvious; while Olive drew the milk by almost imperceptible movements of her fingers and with a motionless wrist, her father hauled away at the teats as though he was trying to ring in the new year.

This insight coupled with the fact that it was always the cows Mr Pickersgill milked that gave trouble was enough to convince me that the chronic mastitis was of traumatic origin.

But how to tell the farmer that he wasn't doing his job right and that the only solution was to learn a more gentle technique or let Olive take over all the milking?

It wouldn't be easy because Mr Pickersgill was an impressive man. I don't suppose he had a spare penny in the world but even as he sat there in the kitchen in his tattered, collarless flannel shirt and braces he looked, as always, like an industrial tycoon. You could imagine that massive head with its fleshy cheeks, noble brow and serene eyes looking out from the financial pages of *The Times*. Put him in a bowler and striped trousers and you'd have the perfect chairman of the board.

I was very chary of affronting such natural dignity and anyway, Mr Pickersgill was fundamentally a fine stocksman. His few cows, like all the animals of that fast-dying breed of small farmer, were fat and sleek and clean. You had to look after your beasts when they were your only source of income and somehow Mr Pickersgill had brought up a family by milk production eked out by selling a few pigs and the eggs from his wife's fifty hens.

I could never quite work out how they did it but they lived, and they lived graciously. All the family but Olive had married and left home but there was still a rich decorum and harmony in that house. The present scene was typical. The farmer expounding gravely, Mrs Pickersgill bustling about in the background, listening to him with quiet pride. Olive too, was happy. Though in her late thirties, she had no fears of spinsterhood because she had been assiduously courted for fifteen years by Charlie Hudson from the Darrowby fish shop and though Charlie was not a tempestuous suitor there was nothing flighty about him and he was confidently expected to pop the question over the next ten years or so.

Mr Pickersgill offered me another buttered scone and when I declined he cleared his throat a few times as though trying to find words. 'Mr Herriot,' he said at last, 'I don't like to tell nobody his job, but we've tried all your remedies for them masticks and we've still got trouble. Now when I studied under Professor Malleson I noted down a lot of good cures and I'd like to try this 'un. Have a look at it.'

He put his hand in his hip pocket and produced a yellowed slip of paper almost falling apart at the folds. 'It's an udder salve. Maybe if we gave the bags a good rub with it it'd do t'trick.'

I read the prescription in the fine copperplate writing. Camphor, eucalyptus, zinc oxide – a long list of the old familiar names. I couldn't help feeling a kind of affection for them but it was tempered by a growing disillusion. I was about to say that I didn't think rubbing anything on the udder would make the slightest difference when the farmer groaned loudly.

The action of reaching into his hip pocket had brought on a twinge of his lumbago and he sat very upright, grimacing with pain.

'This bloody old back of mine! By gaw, it does give me some stick, and doctor can't do nowt about it. I've had enough pills to make me rattle but ah get no relief.'

I'm not brilliant but I do get the odd blinding flash and I had one now.

'Mr Pickersgill,' I said solemnly, 'you've suffered from that lumbago ever since I've known you and I've just thought of something. I believe I know how to cure it.'

The farmer's eyes widened and he stared at me with a childlike trust in which there was no trace of scepticism. This could be expected, because just as people place more reliance on the words of knacker men and meal travellers than their vets' when their animals are concerned it was natural that they would believe the vet rather than their doctor with their own ailments.

'You know how to put me right?' he said faintly.

'I think so, and it has nothing to do with medicine. You'll have to stop milking.'

'Stop milking! What the 'ell . . . ?'

'Of course. Don't you see, it's sitting crouched on that little stool night and morning every day of the week that's doing it. You're a big chap and you've got to bend to get down there – I'm sure it's bad for you.'

Mr Pickersgill gazed into space as though he had seen a vision. 'You really think . . .'

'Yes, I do. You ought to give it a try, anyway. Olive can do the milking. She's always saying she ought to do it all.'

'That's right, Dad,' Olive chimed in. 'I like milking, you know I do, and it's time you gave it up – you've done it ever since you were a lad.'

'Dang it, young man, I believe you're right! I'll pack it in, now – I've made my decision!' Mr Pickersgill threw up his fine head, looked imperiously around him and crashed his fist on the table as though he had just concluded a merger between two oil companies.

I stood up. 'Fine, fine. I'll take this prescription with me and make up the udder salve. It'll be ready for you tonight and I should start using it immediately.'

It was about a month later that I saw Mr Pickersgill. He was on a bicycle, pedalling majestically across the market place and he dismounted when he saw me.

'Now then, Mr Herriot,' he said, puffing slightly. 'I'm glad I've met you. I've been meaning to come and tell you that we don't have no flakes in the milk now. Ever since we started with t'salve they began to disappear and milk's as clear as it can be now.'

'Oh, great. And how's your lumbago?'

'Well I'll tell you, you've really capped it and I'm grateful. Ah've never milked since that day and I hardly get a twinge now.' He paused and smiled indulgently. 'You gave me some good advice for me back, but we had to go back to awd Professor Malleson to cure them masticks, didn't we?'

My next encounter with Mr Pickersgill was on the telephone.

'I'm speaking from the cossack,' he said in a subdued shout.

'From the what?'

'The cossack, the telephone cossack in t'village.'

'Yes, indeed,' I said, 'and what can I do for you?'

'I want you to come out as soon as possible, to treat a calf for semolina.'

'I beg your pardon?'

'I 'ave a calf with semolina.'

'Semolina?'

'Aye, that's right. A feller was on about it on t'wireless the other morning.'

'Oh! Ah yes, I see.' I too had heard a bit of the farming talk on Salmonella infection in calves. 'What makes you think you've got this trouble?'

'Well it's just like that feller said. Me calf's bleeding from the rectrum.'

'From the . . . ? Yes, yes, of course. Well I'd better have a look at him – I won't be long.'

The calf was pretty ill when I saw him and he did have rectal bleeding, but it wasn't like Salmonella.

'There's no diarrhoea, you see, Mr Pickersgill,' I said. 'In fact, he seems to be constipated. This is almost pure blood coming away from him. And he hasn't got a very high temperature.'

The farmer seemed a little disappointed. 'Dang, I thowt it was just same as that feller was talking about. He said you could send samples off to the labrador.'

'Eh? To the what?'

'The investigation labrador – you know.'

'Oh yes, quite, but I don't think the lab would be of any help in this case.'

'Aye well, what's wrong with him, then? Is something the matter with his rectrum?'

'No, no,' I said. 'But there seems to be some obstruction high up his bowel which is causing this haemorrhage.' I looked at the little animal standing motionless with his back up. He was totally preoccupied with some internal discomfort and now and then he strained and grunted softly.

And of course I should have known straight away – it was so obvious. But I suppose we all have blind spells when we can't see what is pushed in front of our eyes, and for a few days I played around with that calf in a haze of ignorance, giving it this and that medicine which I'd rather not talk about.

But I was lucky. He recovered in spite of my treatment. It wasn't until Mr

Pickersgill showed me the little roll of necrotic tissue which the calf had passed that the thing dawned on me.

I turned, shame-faced, to the farmer. 'This is a bit of dead bowel all telescoped together – an intussusception. It's usually a fatal condition but fortunately in this case the obstruction has sloughed away and your calf should be all right now.'

'What was it you called it?'

'An intussusception.'

Mr Pickersgill's lips moved tentatively and for a moment I thought he was going to have a shot at it. But he apparently decided against it. 'Oh,' he said. 'That's what it was, was it?'

'Yes, and it's difficult to say just what caused it.'

The farmer sniffed. 'I'll bet I know what was behind it. I always said this one 'ud be a weakly calf. When he was born he bled a lot from his biblical cord.'

Mr Pickersgill hadn't finished with me yet. It was only a week later that I heard him on the phone again.

'Get out here, quick. There's one of me pigs going bezique.'

'Bezique?' With an effort I put away from me a mental picture of two porkers facing each other over a green baize table. 'I'm afraid I don't quite . . .'

'Aye, ah gave him a dose of worm medicine and he started jumpin' about and rollin' on his back. I tell you he's going proper bezique.'

'Ah! Yes, yes I see, right. I'll be with you in a few minutes.'

The pig had quietened down a bit when I arrived but was still in considerable pain, getting up, lying down, trotting in spurts round the pen. I gave him half a grain of morphine hydrochloride as a sedative and within a few minutes he began to relax and finally curled up in the straw.

'Looks as though he's going to be all right,' I said. 'But what's this worm medicine you gave him?'

Mr Pickersgill produced the bottle sheepishly.

'Bloke was coming round sellin' them. Said it would shift any worms you cared to name.'

'It nearly shifted your pig, didn't it?' I sniffed at the mixture. 'And no wonder. It smells almost like pure turpentine.'

'Turpentine! Well by gaw is that all it is? And bloke said it was summat new. Charged me an absorbent price for it too.'

I gave him back the bottle. 'Well never mind, I don't think there's any harm done, but I think the dustbin's the best place for that.'

As I was getting into my car I looked up at the farmer. 'You must be about sick of the sight of me. First the mastitis, then the calf and now your pig. You've had a bad run.'

Mr Pickersgill squared his shoulders and gazed at me with massive composure. Again I was conscious of the sheer presence of the man.

'Young feller,' he said. 'That don't bother me. Where there's stock there's trouble and ah know from experience that trouble allus comes in cyclones.'

Chapter Four

I knew I shouldn't do it, but the old Drovers' Road beckoned to me irresistibly. I ought to be hurrying back to the surgery after my morning call but the broad green path wound beguilingly over the moor top between its crumbling walls and almost before I knew, I was out of the car and treading the wiry grass.

The wall skirted the hill's edge and as I looked across and away to where Darrowby huddled far below between its folding green fells the wind thundered in my ears; but when I squatted in the shelter of the grey stones the wind was only a whisper and the spring sunshine hot on my face. The best kind of sunshine – not heavy or cloying but clear and bright and clean as you find it down behind a wall in Yorkshire with the wind singing over the top.

I slid lower till I was stretched on the turf, gazing with half closed eyes into the bright sky, luxuriating in the sensation of being detached from the world and its problems.

This form of self-indulgence had become part of my life and still is; a reluctance to come down from the high country; a penchant for stepping out of the stream of life and loitering on the brink for a few minutes as an uninvolved spectator.

And it was easy to escape, lying up here quite alone with no sound but the wind sighing and gusting over the empty miles and, far up in the wide blue, the endless brave trilling of the larks.

Not that there was anything unpleasant about going back down the hill to Darrowby. I had worked there for two years now and Skeldale House had become home and the two bright minds in it my friends. It didn't bother me that both the brothers were cleverer than I was. Siegfried – unpredictable, explosive, generous; I had been lucky to have him as a boss. As a city bred youth trying to tell expert stock farmers how to treat their animals I had needed all his skill and guidance behind me. And Tristan; a rum lad as they said, but very sound. His humour and zest for life had lightened my days.

And all the time I was adding practical experience to my theory. The mass of facts I had learned at college were all coming to life, and there was the growing realisation, deep and warm, that this was for me. There was nothing else I'd rather do.

It must have been fifteen minutes later when I finally rose, stretched pleasurably, took a last deep gulp of the crisp air and pottered slowly back to the car for the six mile journey back down the hill to Darrowby.

When I drew up by the railings with Siegfried's brass plate hanging lopsidedly by the fine Georgian doorway I looked up at the tall old house with the ivy swarming untidily over the weathered brick. The white paint on windows and doors was flaking and that ivy needed trimming but the whole place had style, a serene unchangeable grace.

But I had other things on my mind at the moment. I went inside, stepping quietly over the coloured tiles which covered the floor of the long passage till I reached the long offshoot at the back of the house. And I felt as I always did the subdued excitement as I breathed the smell of our trade which always hung there; ether, carbolic and pulv aromat. The latter was the spicy powder which we mixed with the cattle medicines to make them more palatable and it had a distinctive bouquet which even now can take me back thirty years with a single sniff.

And today the thrill was stronger than usual because my visit was of a surreptitious nature. I almost tiptoed along the last stretch of passage, dodged quickly round the corner and into the dispensary. Gingerly I opened the cupboard door at one end and pulled out a little drawer. I was pretty sure Siegfried had a spare hoof knife hidden away within and I had to suppress a cackle of triumph when I saw it lying there; almost brand new with a nicely turned gleaming blade and a polished wooden handle.

My hand was outstretched to remove it when a cry of anger exploded in my right ear.

'Caught in the act! Bloody red-handed, by God!' Siegfried, who had apparently shot up through the floorboards was breathing fire into my face.

The shock was so tremendous that the instrument dropped from my trembling fingers and I cowered back against a row of bottles of formalin bloat mixture.

'Oh hello, Siegfried,' I said with a ghastly attempt at nonchalance. 'Just on my way to that horse of Thompson's. You know – the one with the pus in the foot. I seem to have mislaid my knife so I thought I'd borrow this one.'

'Thought you'd nick it, you mean! My spare hoof knife! By heaven, is nothing sacred, James?'

I smiled sheepishly. 'Oh you're wrong. I'd have given it back to you straight away.'

'A likely story!' Siegfried said with a bitter smile. 'I'd never have seen it again and you know damn well I wouldn't. Anyway, where's your own knife? You've left it on some farm, haven't you?'

'Well as a matter of fact I laid it down at Willie Denholm's place after I'd finished trimming his cow's overgrown foot and I must have forgotten to pick it up.' I gave a light laugh.

'But God help us, James, you're always forgetting to pick things up. And you're always making up the deficiency by purloining my equipment.' He stuck his chin out. 'Have you any idea how much all this is costing me?'

'Oh but I'm sure Mr Denholm will drop the knife in at the surgery the first time he's in town.'

Siegfried nodded gravely. 'He may, I'll admit that, he may. But on the other hand he might think it is the ideal tool for cutting up his plug tobacco. Remember when you left your calving overall at old Fred Dobson's place? The next time I saw it was six months later and Fred was wearing it. He said it was the best thing he'd ever found for stooking corn in wet weather.'

'Yes, I remember. I'm really sorry about it all.' I fell silent, breathing in the pungency of the pulv aromat. Somebody had let a bagful burst on the floor and the smell was stronger than ever.

My employer kept his fiery gaze fixed on me for a few moments more then he shrugged his shoulders. 'Ah well, there's none of us perfect, James. And I'm sorry I shouted at you. But you know I'm deeply attached to that knife and this business of leaving things around is getting under my skin.' He took down a Winchester of his favourite colic draught and polished it with his handkerchief before replacing it carefully on its shelf. 'I tell you what, let's go and sit down for a few minutes and talk about this problem.'

We went back along the passage and as I followed him into the big sitting room Tristan got up from his favourite chair and yawned deeply. His face looked as boyish and innocent as ever but the lines of exhaustion round his eyes and mouth told an eloquent story. Last night he had travelled with the darts team from the Lord Nelson and had taken part in a gruelling match against the Dog and Gun at Drayton. The contest had been followed by a pie and peas supper and the consumption of something like twelve pints of bitter a man. Tristan had crawled into bed at 3 a.m. and was clearly in a delicate condition.

'Ah, Tristan,' Siegfried said. 'I'm glad you're here because what I have to say concerns you just as much as James. It's about leaving instruments on farms and you're as guilty as he is.' (It must be remembered that before the Veterinary Surgeons' act of 1948 it was quite legal for students to treat cases and they regularly did so. Tristan in fact had done much sterling work when called on and was very popular with the farmers.)

'Now I mean this very seriously,' my employer said, leaning his elbow on the mantelpiece and looking from one of us to the other. 'You two are bringing me to the brink of ruin by losing expensive equipment. Some of it is returned but a lot of it is never seen again. What's the use of sending you to visits when you come back without your artery forceps or scissors or something else? The profit's gone, you see?'

We nodded silently.

'After all, there's nothing difficult about bringing your instruments away, is there? You may wonder why I never leave anything behind – well I can tell you it's just a matter of concentration. When I lay a thing down I always impress on my mind that I've got to lift it up again. That's all there is to it.'

The lecture over, he became very brisk. 'Right, let's get on. There's nothing much doing, James, so I'd like you to come with me to Kendall's of Brookside. He's got a few jobs including a cow with a tumour to remove. I don't know the details but we may have to cast her. You can go on to Thompson's later.' He turned to his brother. 'And you'd better come too, Tristan. I don't know if we'll need you but an extra man might come in handy.'

We made quite a procession as we trooped into the farm yard and Mr Kendall met us with his customary ebullience.

'Hello, 'ello, we've got plenty of man power today, I see. We'll be able to tackle owt with this regiment.'

Mr Kendall had the reputation in the district of being a 'bit clever' and the phrase has a different meaning in Yorkshire from elsewhere. It meant he was something of a know-all; and the fact that he considered himself a wag and legpuller of the first degree didn't endear him to his fellow farmers either.

I always felt he was a good-hearted man, but his conviction that he knew everything and had seen it all before made him a difficult man to impress.

'Well what d'you want to see first, Mr Farnon?' he asked. He was a thickset little man with a round, smooth-skinned face and mischievous eyes.

'I believe you have a cow with a bad eye,' Siegfried said. 'Better begin with that.'

'Right squire,' the farmer cried, then he put his hand in his pocket. 'But before we start, here's something for you.' He pulled forth a stethoscope. 'You left it last time you were 'ere.'

There was a silence, then Siegfried grunted a word of thanks and grabbed it hastily from his hand.

Mr Kendall continued. 'And the time afore that you left your bloodless castrators. We did a swop over, didn't we? I gave you back the nippers and you left me the earphones.' He burst into a peal of laughter.

'Yes, yes, quite,' Siegfried snapped, glancing uneasily round at us, 'but we must be getting on. Where is . . . ?'

'You know lads,' chuckled the farmer, turning to us. 'Ah don't think I've ever known 'im come here without leaving summat.'

'Really?' said Tristan interestedly.

'Aye, if I'd wanted to keep 'em all I'd have had a drawerful by now.'

'Is that so?' I said.

'Aye it is, young man. And it's the same with all me neighbours. One feller said to me t'other day. "He's a kind man is Mr Farnon – never calls without leavin' a souvenir." ' He threw back his head and laughed again.

We were enjoying the conversation but my employer was stalking up the byre. 'Where's this damn cow, Mr Kendall? We haven't got all day.'

The patient wasn't hard to find; a nice light roan cow which looked round at us carefully, one eye almost closed. From between the lashes a trickle of tears made a dark stain down the hair of the face, and there was an eloquent story of pain in the cautious movement of the quivering lids.

'There's something in there,' murmured Siegfried.

'Aye, ah know!' Mr Kendall always knew. 'She's got a flippin' great lump of chaff stuck on her eyeball but I can't get to it. Look here.' He grabbed the cow's nose with one hand and tried to prise the eyelids apart with the fingers of the other, but the third eyelid came across and the whole orbit rolled effortlessly out of sight leaving only a blank expanse of white sclera.

'There!' he cried. 'Nowt to see. You can't make her keep her eye still.'

'I can, though.' Siegfried turned to his brother. 'Tristan, get the chloroform muzzle from the car. Look sharp!'

The young man was back in seconds and Siegfried quickly drew the canvas bag over the cow's face and buckled it behind the ears. From a bottle of spirit he produced a small pair of forceps of an unusual type with tiny jaws operated by a spring. He poised them just over the closed eye.

'James,' he said, 'Give her about an ounce.'

I dribbled the chloroform on to the sponge in the front of the muzzle. Nothing happened for a few moments while the animal took a few breaths then her eyes opened wide in surprise as the strange numbing vapour rolled into her lungs.

The whole area of the affected eye was displayed, with a broad golden piece of chaff splayed out across the dark cornea. I only had a glimpse of it before Siegfried's little forceps had seized it and whisked it away.

'Squeeze in some of that ointment, Tristan,' said my employer. 'And get the muzzle off, James, before she starts to rock.'

With the bag away from her face and the tormenting little object gone from her eye the cow looked around her, vastly relieved. The whole thing had taken only a minute or two and was as slick a little exhibition as you'd wish to see, but Mr Kendall didn't seem to think a great deal of it.

'Aye right,' he grunted. 'Let's get on with t'next job.'

As we went down the byre I looked out and saw a horse being led across the yard. Siegfried pointed to it.

'Is that the gelding I operated on for fistulous withers?' he asked.

'That's the one.' The farmer's voice was airy.

We went out and Siegfried ran his hand over the horse's shoulders. The broad fibrous scar over the withers was all that was left of the discharging, stinking sinus of a few weeks back. Healing was perfect. These cases were desperately difficult to treat and I remembered my boss cutting and chiselling at the mass of necrotic tissue, curetting deeply till only healthy flesh and bone remained. His efforts had been rewarded; it was a brilliant success.

Siegfried gave the gelding a final pat on the neck. 'That's done rather well.'

Mr Kendall shrugged and turned back towards the byre. 'Aye, not so bad, I suppose.' But he really wasn't impressed.

The cow with the tumour was standing just inside the door. The growth was in the perineal region, a smooth round object like an apple projecting from the animal's rear end, clearly visible an inch to the right of the tail.

Mr Kendall was in full cry again. 'Now we'll see what you're made of. How are you chaps going to get that thing off, eh? It's a big 'un – you'll need a carving knife or a hack saw for t'job. And are you goin' to put her to sleep or tie her up or what?' He grinned and his bright little eyes darted at each of us in turn.

Siegfried reached out and grasped the tumour, feeling round the base with his fingers. 'Hmm . . . yes . . . hmm . . . bring me some soap and water and a towel, will you please?'

'I have it just outside t'door.' The farmer scuttled into the yard and back again with the bucket.

'Thank you very much,' Siegfried said. He washed his hands and gave them a leisurely towelling. 'Now I believe you have another case to see. A scouring calf, wasn't it?'

The farmer's eyes widened. 'Yes, I 'ave. But how about getting this big lump off the cow first?'

Siegfried folded the towel and hung it over the half door. 'Oh, I've removed the tumour,' he said quietly.

'What's that?' Mr Kendall stared at the cow's backside. We all stared at it. And there was no doubt about it – the growth was gone. And there was another funny thing – there wasn't even a scar or mark remaining. I was standing quite close to the animal and I could see exactly to a fraction of an inch where that big ugly projection had been; and there was nothing, not a drop of blood, nothing.

'Aye,' Mr Kendall said irresolutely. 'You've er . . . you've removed . . . you've removed it, aye, that's right.' The smile had vanished from his face and his entire personality seemed suddenly deflated. Being a man who knew everything and was surprised by nothing he was unable to say, 'When the devil did you do it? And how? And what on earth have you done with it?' He had to maintain face at all costs, but he was rattled. He darted little glances around the byre, along the channel. The cow was standing in a clean-swept stall with no straw and there was nothing lying on the floor there or anywhere. Casually, as though by accident, he pushed a milking stool to one side with his foot – still nothing.

'Well now, perhaps we can see the calf.' Siegfried began to move away.

Mr Kendall nodded. 'Yes . . . yes . . . the calf. He's in t'corner there. I'll just lift bucket first.'

It was a blatant excuse. He went over to the bucket and as he passed behind the cow he whipped out his spectacles, jammed them on his nose and directed a piercing glare at the cow's bottom. He only took an instant because he didn't want to show undue concern, but when he turned back towards us his face registered utter despair and he put his spectacles away with a weary gesture of defeat.

As he approached I turned and brushed against my employer.

'Where the hell is it?' I hissed.

'Up my sleeve,' murmured Siegfried without moving his lips or changing expression.

'What . . . ?' I began, but Siegfried was climbing over a gate into the makeshift pen where the calf was cornered.

He was in expansive mood as he examined the little creature and injected it. He kept up a steady flow of light conversation and Mr Kendall, showing great character, managed to get his smile back on and answer back. But his preoccupied manner, the tortured eyes and the repeated incredulous glances back along the byre floor in the direction of the cow betrayed the fact that he was under immense strain.

Siegfried didn't hurry over the calf and when he had finished he lingered a while in the yard, chatting about the weather, the way the grass was springing, the price of fat bullocks.

Mr Kendall hung on grimly but by the time Siegfried finally waved farewell the farmer's eyes were popping and his face was an anguished mask. He bolted back into the byre and as the car backed round I could see him bent double with his glasses on again, peering into the corners.

'Poor fellow,' I said. 'He's still looking for that thing. And for God's sake where is it, anyway?'

'I told you, didn't I?' Siegfried removed one arm from the wheel and shook it. A round fleshy ball rolled down into his hand.

I stared at it in amazement. 'But . . . I never saw you take it off . . . what happened?'

'I'll tell you.' My employer smiled indulgently. 'I was fingering it over to see how deeply it was attached when I felt it begin to move. The back of it was merely encapsulated by the skin and when I gave another squeeze it just popped out and shot up my sleeve. And after it had gone the lips of the skin sprang back together again so that you couldn't see where it had been. Extraordinary thing.'

Tristan reached over from the back seat. 'Give it to me,' he said. 'I'll take it back to college with me and get it sectioned. We'll find out what kind of tumour it is.'

His brother smiled. 'Yes, I expect they'll give it some fancy name, but I'll always remember it as the only thing that shook Mr Kendall.'

'That was an interesting session in there,' I said. 'And I must say I admired the way you dealt with that eye, Siegfried. Very smooth indeed.'

'You're very kind, James,' my boss murmured. 'That was just one of my little tricks – and of course the forceps helped a lot.'

I nodded. 'Yes, wonderful little things. I've never seen anything like them. Where did you get them?'

'Picked them up on an instrument stall at the last Veterinary Congress. They cost me a packet but they've been worth it. Here, let me show them to you.' He put his hand in his breast pocket, then his side pockets, and as he continued to rummage all over his person a look of sick dismay spread slowly across his face.

Finally he abandoned the search, cleared his throat and fixed his eyes on the road ahead.

'I'll er . . . I'll show you them some other time, James,' he said huskily.

I didn't say anything but I knew and Siegfried knew and Tristan knew.

He'd left them on the farm.

Chapter Five

'Well, it's a good sign.' Tristan reluctantly expelled a lungful of Woodbine smoke and looked at me with wide, encouraging eyes.

'You think so?' I said doubtfully.

Tristan nodded. 'Sure of it. Helen just rang you up, did she?'

'Yes, out of the blue. I haven't seen her since I took her to the pictures that night and it's been hectic ever since with the lambing – and suddenly there she was asking me to tea on Sunday.'

'I like the sound of it,' Tristan said. 'But of course you don't want to get the idea you're home and dry or anything like that. You know there are others in the field?'

'Hell, yes, I suppose I'm one of a crowd.'

'Not exactly, but Helen Alderson is really something. Not just a looker but . . . mm-mm, very nice. There's a touch of class about that girl.'

'Oh I know, I know. There's bound to be a mob of blokes after her. Like young Richard Edmundson – I hear he's very well placed.'

'That's right,' Tristan said. 'Old friends of the family, big farmers, rolling in brass. I understand old man Alderson fancies Richard strongly as a son-in-law.'

I dug my hands into my pockets. 'Can't blame him. A ragged-arsed young vet isn't much competition.'

'Well, don't be gloomy, old lad, you've made a bit of progress, haven't you?'

'In a way,' I said with a wry smile. 'I've taken her out twice – to a dinner dance which wasn't on and to a cinema showing the wrong film. A dead loss the first time and not much better the second. I just don't seem to have any luck there – something goes wrong every time. Maybe this invitation is just a polite gesture – returning hospitality or something like that.'

'Nonsense!' Tristan laughed and patted me on the shoulder. 'This is the beginning of better things. You'll see – nothing will go wrong this time.'

And on Sunday afternoon as I got out of the car to open the gate to Heston Grange it did seem as if all was right with the world. The rough track snaked down from the gate through the fields to Helen's home slumbering in the sunshine by the curving river, and the grey-stoned old building was like a restful haven against the stark backcloth of the fells beyond.

I leaned on the gate for a moment, breathing in the sweet air. There had been a change during the last week; the harsh winds had dropped, everything had softened and greened and the warming land gave off its scents. On the lower slopes of the fell, in the shade of the pine woods, a pale mist of bluebells drifted among the dead bronze of the bracken and their fragrance came up to me on the breeze.

I drove down the track among the cows relishing the tender young grass after their long winter in the byres and as I knocked on the farmhouse door I felt a surge of optimism and well-being. Helen's younger sister answered and it wasn't until I walked into the big flagged kitchen that I experienced a qualm. Maybe it was because it was so like that first disastrous time I had called for Helen; Mr Alderson was there by the fireside, deep in the *Farmer and Stockbreeder* as before, while above his head the cows in the vast oil painting still paddled in the lake of startling blue under the shattered peaks. On the whitewashed wall the clock still tick-tocked inexorably.

Helen's father looked up over his spectacles just as he had done before. 'Good afternoon, young man, come and sit down.' And as I dropped into the chair opposite to him he looked at me uncertainly for a few seconds. 'It's a better day,' he murmured, then his eyes were drawn back irresistibly to the pages on his knee. As he bent his head and started to read again I gained the strong impression that he hadn't the slightest idea who I was.

It came back to me forcibly that there was a big difference in coming to a farm as a vet and visiting socially. I was often in farm kitchens on my rounds, washing my hands in the sink after kicking my boots off in the porch, chatting effortlessly to the farmer's wife about the sick beast. But here I was in my good suit sitting stiffly across from a silent little man whose daughter I had come to court. It wasn't the same at all.

I was relieved when Helen came in carrying a cake which she placed on the big table. This wasn't easy as the table was already loaded; ham and egg pies rubbing shoulders with snowy scones, a pickled tongue cheek by jowl with a bowl of mixed salad, luscious-looking custard tarts jockeying for position with sausage rolls, tomato sandwiches, fairy cakes. In a clearing near the centre a vast trifle reared its cream-topped head. It was a real Yorkshire tea.

Helen came over to me. 'Hello, Jim, it's nice to see you – you're quite a stranger.' She smiled her slow, friendly smile.

'Hello, Helen. Yes, you know what lambing time's like. I hope things will ease up a bit now.'

'Well I hope so too. Hard work's all right up to a point but you need a break some time. Anyway, come and have some tea. Are you hungry?'

'I am now,' I said, gazing at the packed foodstuffs. Helen laughed. 'Well come on, sit in. Dad, leave your precious *Farmer and Stockbreeder* and come over here. We were going to sit you in the dining room, Jim, but Dad won't have his tea anywhere but in here, so that's all about it.'

I took my place along with Helen, young Tommy and Mary her brother and sister, and Auntie Lucy, Mr Alderson's widowed sister who had recently come to live with the family. Mr Alderson groaned his way over the flags, collapsed on to a high-backed wooden chair and began to saw phlegmatically at the tongue.

As I accepted my laden plate I can't say I felt entirely at ease. In the course of my work I had eaten many meals in the homes of the hospitable Dalesmen and I had discovered that light chatter was not welcomed at table. The accepted thing, particularly among the more old-fashioned types, was to put the food away in silence and get back on the job, but maybe this was different. Sunday tea might be a more social occasion; I looked round the table, waiting for somebody to lead the way.

Helen spoke up. 'Jim's had a busy time among the sheep since we saw him last.'

'Oh yes?' Auntie Lucy put her head on one side and smiled. She was a little bird-like woman, very like her brother and the way she looked at me made me feel she was on my side.

The young people regarded me fixedly with twitching mouths. The only other time I had met them they had found me an object of some amusement and things didn't seem to have changed. Mr Alderson sprinkled some salt on a radish, conveyed it to his mouth and crunched it impassively.

'Did you have much twin lamb disease this time, Jim?' Helen asked, trying again.

'Quite a bit,' I replied brightly. 'Haven't had much luck with treatment, though. I tried dosing the ewes with glucose this year and I think it did a bit of good.'

Mr Alderson swallowed the last of his radish. 'I think nowt to glucose,' he grunted. 'I've had a go with it and I think nowt to it.'

'Really?' I said. 'Well now that's interesting. Yes . . . yes . . . quite.'

I buried myself in my salad for a spell before offering a further contribution.

'There's been a lot of sudden deaths in the lambs,' I said. 'Seems to be more Pulpy Kidney about.'

'Fancy that,' said Auntie Lucy, smiling encouragingly.

'Yes,' I went on, getting into my stride. 'It's a good job we've got a vaccine against it now.'

'Wonderful things, those vaccines,' Helen chipped in. 'You'll soon be able to prevent a lot of the sheep diseases that way.' The conversation was warming up.

Mr Alderson finished his tongue and pushed his plate away. 'I think nowt to the vaccines. And those sudden deaths you're on about – they're caused by wool ball on t'stomach. Nowt to do wi' the kidneys.'

'Ah yes, wool ball eh? I see, wool ball.' I subsided and decided to concentrate on the food.

And it was worth concentrating on. As I worked my way through I was aware of a growing sense of wonder that Helen had probably baked the entire spread. It was when my teeth were sinking into a poem of a curd tart that I really began to appreciate the miracle that somebody of Helen's radiant attractiveness should be capable of this.

I looked across at her. She was a big girl, nothing like her little wisp of a father. She must have taken after her mother. Mrs Alderson had been dead for many years and I wondered if she had had that same wide, generous mouth that smiled so easily, those same warm blue eyes under the soft mass of black-brown hair.

A spluttering from Tommy and Mary showed that they had been appreciatively observing me gawping at their sister.

'That's enough, you two,' Auntie Lucy reproved. 'Anyway you can go now, we're going to clear the table.'

Helen and she began to move the dishes to the scullery beyond the door while Mr Alderson and I returned to our chairs by the fireside.

The little man ushered me to mine with a vague wave of the hand. 'Here . . . take a seat, er . . . young man.'

A clattering issued from the kitchen as the washing-up began. We were alone.

Mr Alderson's hand strayed automatically towards his *Farmer and Stock-breeder*, but he withdrew it after a single hunted glance in my direction and began to drum his fingers on the arm of the chair, whistling softly under his breath.

I groped desperately for an opening gambit but came up with nothing. The ticking of the clock boomed out into the silence. I was beginning to break out into a sweat when the little man cleared his throat.

'Pigs were a good trade on Monday,' he vouchsafed.

'They were, eh? Well, that's fine – jolly good.'

Mr Alderson nodded, fixed his gaze somewhere above my left shoulder and started drumming his fingers again. Once more the heavy silence blanketed us and the clock continued to hammer out its message.

After several years Mr Alderson stirred in his seat and gave a little cough. I looked at him eagerly.

'Store cattle were down, though,' he said.

'Ah, too bad, what a pity,' I babbled. 'But that's how it goes, I suppose, eh?'

Helen's father shrugged and we settled down again. This time I knew it was hopeless. My mind was a void and my companion had the defeated look of a man who has shot his conversational bolt. I lay back and studied the hams and sides of bacon hanging from their hooks in the ceiling, then I worked my way along the row of plates on the big oak dresser to a gaudy calendar from a cattle cake firm which dangled from a nail on the wall. I took a chance then and stole a glance at Mr Alderson out of the corner of my eye and my toes curled as I saw he had chosen that precise moment to have a sideways peep at me. We both looked away hurriedly.

By shifting round in my seat and craning my neck I was able to get a view of the other side of the kitchen where there was an old-fashioned roll top desk surmounted by a wartime picture of Mr Alderson looking very stern in the uniform of the Yorkshire Yeomanry, and I was proceeding along the wall from there when Helen opened the door and came quickly into the room.

'Dad,' she said, a little breathlessly. 'Stan's here. He says one of the cows is down with staggers.'

Her father jumped up in obvious relief. I think he was delighted he had a sick cow and I, too, felt like a released prisoner as I hurried out with him.

Stan, one of the cowmen, was waiting in the yard.

'She's at t'top of t'field, boss,' he said. 'I just spotted 'er when I went to get them in for milkin'.'

Mr Alderson looked at me questioningly and I nodded at him as I opened the car door.

'I've got the stuff with me,' I said. 'We'd better drive straight up.'

The three of us piled in and I set course to where I could see the stretched-out form of a cow near the wall in the top corner. My bottles and instruments rattled and clattered as we bumped over the rig and furrow.

This was something every vet gets used to in early summer; the urgent call to milk cows which have collapsed suddenly a week or two after being turned out to grass. The farmers called it grass staggers and as its scientific name of hypomagesaemia implied it was associated with lowered magnesium level in the blood. An alarming and highly fatal condition but fortunately curable by injection of magnesium in most cases.

Despite the seriousness of the occasion I couldn't repress a twinge of satisfaction. It had got me out of the house and it gave me a chance to prove myself by doing something useful. Helen's father and I hadn't established anything like a rapport as yet, but maybe when I gave his unconscious cow my magic injection and it leaped to its feet and walked away he might look at me in a different light. And it often happened that way; some of the cures were really dramatic.

'She's still alive, any road,' Stan said as we roared over the grass. 'I saw her legs move then.'

He was right, but as I pulled up and jumped from the car I felt a tingle of apprehension. Those legs were moving too much.

This was the kind that often died; the convulsive type. The animal, prone on her side, was pedalling frantically at the air with all four feet, her head stretched backwards, eyes staring, foam bubbling from her mouth. As I hurriedly unscrewed the cap from the bottle of magnesium lactate she stopped and went into a long, shuddering spasm, legs stiffly extended, eyes screwed tightly shut; then she relaxed and lay inert for a frightening few seconds before recommencing the wild thrashing with her legs.

My mouth had gone dry. This was a bad one. The strain on the heart during these spasms was enormous and each one could be her last.

I crouched by her side, my needle poised over the milk vein. My usual practice was to inject straight into the bloodstream to achieve the quickest possible effect, but in this case I hesitated. Any interference with the heart's action could kill this cow; best to play safe – I reached over and pushed the needle under the skin of the neck.

As the fluid ran in, bulging the subcutaneous tissues and starting a widening swelling under the roan-coloured hide, the cow went into another spasm. For an agonising few seconds she lay there, the quivering limbs reaching desperately out at nothing, the eyes disappearing deep down under tight-twisted lids. Helplessly I watched her, my heart thudding, and this time as she came out of the rigor and started to move again it wasn't with the purposeful pedalling of before; it was an aimless laboured pawing and as even this grew weaker her eyes slowly opened and gazed outwards with a vacant stare.

I bent and touched the cornea with my finger, there was no response.

The farmer and cowman looked at me in silence as the animal gave a final jerk then lay still.

'I'm afraid she'd dead, Mr Alderson,' I said.

The farmer nodded and his eyes moved slowly over the still form, over the graceful limbs, the fine dark roan flanks, the big, turgid udder that would give no more milk.

'I'm sorry,' I said. 'I'm afraid her heart must have given out before the magnesium had a chance to work.'

'It's a bloody shame,' grunted Stan. 'She was a right good cow, that 'un.'

Mr Alderson turned quietly back to the car. 'Aye well, these things happen,' he muttered.

We drove down the field to the house.

Inside, the work was over and the family was collected in the parlour. I sat with them for a while but my overriding emotion was an urgent desire to be elsewhere. Helen's father had been silent before but now he sat hunched miserably in an armchair taking no part in the conversation. I wondered whether he thought I had actually killed his cow. It certainly hadn't looked very good, the vet walking up to the sick animal, the quick injection and hey presto, dead. No, I had been blameless but it hadn't looked good.

On an impulse I jumped to my feet.

'Thank you very much for the lovely tea,' I said, 'but I really must be off. I'm on duty this evening.'

Helen came with me to the door. 'Well it's been nice seeing you again, Jim.' She paused and looked at me doubtfully. 'I wish you'd stop worrying about that cow. It's a pity but you couldn't help it. There was nothing you could do.'

'Thanks, Helen, I know. But it's a nasty smack for your father isn't it?'

She shrugged and smiled her kind smile. Helen was always kind.

Driving back through the pastures up to the farm gate I could see the motionless body of my patient with her companions sniffing around her curiously in the gentle evening sunshine. Any time now the knacker man would be along to winch the carcase on to his wagon. It was the grim epilogue to every vet's failure.

I closed the gate behind me and looked back at Heston Grange. I had thought everything would be all right this time but it hadn't worked out that way.

The jinx was still on.

Chapter Six

'Monday morning disease' they used to call it. The almost unbelievably gross thickening of the hind limb in cart horses which had stood in the stable over the weekend. It seemed that the sudden suspension of their normal work and exercise produced the massive lymphangitis and swelling which gave many a farmer a nasty jolt right at the beginning of the week.

But it was Wednesday evening now and Mr Crump's big Shire gelding was greatly improved.

'That leg's less than half the size it was,' I said, running my hand over the inside of the hock feeling the remains of the oedema pitting under my fingers. 'I can see you've put in some hard work here.'

'Aye, ah did as you said.' Mr Crump's reply was typically laconic, but I knew he must have spent hours fomenting and massaging the limb and forcibly exercising the horse as I had told him when I gave the arecoline injection on Monday.

I began to fill the syringe for a repeat injection. 'He's having no corn, is he?' 'Nay, nowt but bran.'

'That's fine. I think he'll be back to normal in a day or two if you keep up the treatment.'

The farmer grunted and no sign of approval showed in the big, purple-red face with its perpetually surprised expression. But I knew he was pleased all right; he was fond of the horse and had been unable to hide his concern at the animal's pain and distress on my first visit.

I went into the house to wash my hands and Mr Crump led the way into the kitchen, his big frame lumbering clumsily ahead of me. He proffered soap and towel in his slow-moving way and stood back in silence as I leaned over the long shallow sink of brown earthenware.

As I dried my hands he cleared his throat and spoke hesitantly. 'Would you like a drink of ma wine?'

Before I could answer, Mrs Crump came bustling through from an inner room. She was pulling on her hat and behind her her teenage son and daughter followed, dressed ready to go out.

'Oh Albert, stop it!' she snapped, looking up at her husband. 'Mr Herriot doesn't want your wine. I wish you wouldn't pester people so with it!'

The boy grinned. 'Dad and his wine, he's always looking for a victim.' His sister joined in the general laughter and I had an uncomfortable feeling that Mr Crump was the odd man out in his own home.

'We're going down t'village institute to see a school play, Mr Herriot,' the wife said briskly. 'We're late now so we must be off.' She hurried away with her children, leaving the big man looking after her sheepishly.

There was a silence while I finished drying my hands, then I turned to the farmer. 'Well, how about that drink, Mr Crump?'

He hesitated for a moment and the surprised look deepened. 'Would you . . . you'd really like to try some?'

'I'd love to. I haven't had my evening meal yet – I could just do with an aperitif.'

'Right, I'll be back in a minute.' He disappeared into the large pantry at the end of the kitchen and came back with a bottle of amber liquid and glasses.

'This is ma rhubarb,' he said, tipping out two good measures.

I took a sip and then a good swallow, and gasped as the liquid blazed a fiery trail down to my stomach.

'It's strong stuff,' I said a little breathlessly, 'but the taste is very pleasant. Very pleasant indeed.'

Mr Crump watched approvingly as I took another drink. 'Aye, it's just right. Nearly two years old.'

I drained the glass and this time the wine didn't burn so much on its way down but seemed to wash around the walls of my empty stomach and send glowing tendrils creeping along my limbs.

'Delicious,' I said. 'Absolutely delicious.'

The farmer expanded visibly. He refilled the glasses and watched with rapt attention as I drank. When we had finished the second glass he jumped to his feet.

'Now for a change I want you to try summat different.' He almost trotted to the pantry and produced another bottle, this time of colourless fluid. 'Elder-flower,' he said, panting slightly.

When I tasted it I was amazed at the delicate flavour, the bubbles sparkling and dancing on my tongue.

'Gosh, this is terrific! It's just like champagne. You know, you really have a gift – I never thought home made wines could taste like this.'

Mr Crump stared at me for a moment then one corner of his mouth began to twitch and incredibly a shy smile spread slowly over his face. 'You're about fust I've heard say that. You'd think I was trying to poison folks when I offer them ma wine – they always shy off but they can sup plenty of beer and whisky.'

'Well they don't know what they're missing, Mr Crump.' I watched while the farmer replenished my glass. 'I wouldn't have believed you could make stuff as good as this at home.' I sipped appreciatively at the elderflower. It still tasted like champagne.

I hadn't got more than half way down the glass before Mr Crump was clattering and clinking inside the pantry again. He emerged with a bottle with contents of a deep blood red. 'Try that,' he gasped.

I was beginning to feel like a professional taster and rolled the first mouthful around my mouth with eyes half closed. 'Mm, mm, yes. Just like an excellent port, but there's something else here – a fruitiness in the background – something familiar about it – it's . . . it's . . .'

'Blackberry!' shouted Mr Crump triumphantly. 'One of t'best I've done. Made it two back-ends since – it were a right good year for it.'

Leaning back in the chair I took another drink of the rich, dark wine; it was round-flavoured, warming, and behind it there was always the elusive hint of the brambles. I could almost see the heavy-hanging clusters of berries glistening black and succulent in the autumn sunshine. The mellowness of the image matched my mood which was becoming more expansive by the minute and I looked round with leisurely appreciation at the rough comfort of the farmhouse kitchen; at the hams and sides of bacon hanging from their hooks in the ceiling, and at my host sitting across the table, watching me eagerly. He was, I noticed for the first time, still wearing his cap.

'You know,' I said, holding the glass high and studying its ruby depths against the light. 'I can't make up my mind which of your wines I like best. They're all excellent and yet so different.'

Mr Crump, too, had relaxed. He threw back his head and laughed delightedly before hurriedly refilling both of our tumblers. 'But you haven't started yet. Ah've got dozens of bottles in there – all different. You must try a few more.' He shambled again over to the pantry and this time when he reappeared he was weighed down by an armful of bottles of differing shapes and colours.

What a charming man he was, I thought. How wrong I had been in my previous assessment of him; it had been so easy to put him down as lumpish and unemotional but as I looked at him now his face was alight with friendship, hospitality, understanding. He had cast off his inhibitions and as he sat down surrounded by the latest batch he began to talk rapidly and fluently about wines and wine making.

Wide-eyed and impassioned he ranged at length over the niceties of fermentation and sedimentation, of flavour and bouquet. He dealt learnedly with the relative merits of Chambertin and Nuits St George, Montrachet and Chablis. Enthusiasts are appealing but a fanatic is irresistible and I sat spellbound while Mr Crump pushed endless samples of his craft in front of me, mixing and adjusting expertly.

'How did you find that 'un?'

'Very nice . . .'

'But sweet, maybe?'

'Well, perhaps . . .'

'Right, try some of this with it.' The meticulous addition of a few drops of nameless liquid from the packed rows of bottles. 'How's that?'

'Marvellous!'

'Now this 'un. Perhaps a bit sharpish, eh?'

'Possibly . . . yes . . .'

Again the tender trickling of a few mysterious droplets into my drink and again the anxious enquiry.

'Is that better?'

'Just right.'

The big man drank with me, glass by glass. We tried parsnip and dandelion, cowslip and parsley, clover, gooseberry, beetroot and crab apple. Incredibly we had some stuff made from turnips which was so exquisite that I insisted on a refill.

Everything gradually slowed down as we sat there. Time slowed down till it was finally meaningless. Mr Crump and I slowed down and our speech and actions became more and more deliberate. The farmer's visits to the pantry developed into laboured, unsteady affairs; sometimes he took a roundabout route to reach the door and on one occasion there was a tremendous crash from within and I feared he had fallen among his bottles. But I couldn't be bothered to get up to see and in due course he reappeared, apparently unharmed.

It was around nine o'clock that I heard the soft knocking on the outer door. I ignored it as I didn't want to interrupt Mr Crump who was in the middle of a deep exposition.

'Thish,' he was saying, leaning close to me and tapping a bulbous flagon with his forefinger. 'Thish is, in my 'pinion, comp'rable to a fine Moselle. Made it lash year and would. 'preciate it if you'd tell me what you think.' He went low over the glass, blinking, heavy-eyed as he poured.

'Now then, wha' d'you say? Ish it or ishn't it?'

I took a gulp and paused for a moment. It all tasted the same now and I had never drunk Moselle anyway, but I nodded and hiccuped solemnly in reply.

The farmer rested a friendly hand on my shoulder and was about to make a further speech when he, too, heard the knocking. He made his way across the floor with some difficulty and opened the door. A young lad was standing there and I heard a few muttered words.

'We 'ave a cow on calving and we 'phoned surgery and they said vitnery might still be here.'

Mr Crump turned to face me. 'It's the Bamfords of Holly Bush. They wan' you to go there – jush a mile along t'road.'

'Right,' I heaved myself to my feet then gripped the table tightly as the familiar objects of the room began to whirl rapidly around me. When they came to rest Mr Crump appeared to be standing at the head of a fairly steep slope. The kitchen floor had seemed perfectly level when I had come in but now it was all I could do to fight my way up the gradient.

When I reached the door Mr Crump was staring owlishly into the darkness. ' 'Sraining,' he said. ' 'Sraining like 'ell.'

I peered out at the steady beat of the dark water on the cobbles of the yard, but my car was just a few yards away and I was about to set out when the farmer caught my arm.

'Jus' minute, can't go out like that.' He held up a finger then went over and groped about in a drawer. At length he produced a tweed cap which he offered me with great dignity.

I never wore anything on my head whatever the weather but I was deeply touched and wrung my companion's hand in silence. It was understandable that a man like Mr Crump who wore his cap at all times, indoors and out, would recoil in horror from the idea of anybody venturing uncovered into the rain.

The tweed cap which I now put on was the biggest I had ever seen; a great round flat pancake of a thing which even at that moment I felt would keep not only my head but my shoulders and entire body dry in the heaviest downpour.

I took my leave of Mr Crump with reluctance and as I settled in the seat of the car trying to remember where first gear was situated I could see his bulky form silhouetted against the light from the kitchen; he was waving his hand with gentle benevolence and it struck me as I at length drove away what a deep and wonderful friendship had been forged that night.

Driving at walking pace along the dark narrow road, my nose almost touching the windscreen, I was conscious of some unusual sensations. My mouth and lips felt abnormally sticky as though I had been drinking liquid glue instead of wine, my breath seemed to be whistling in my nostrils like a strong wind blowing under a door, and I was having difficulty focusing my eyes. Fortunately I met only one car and as it approached and flashed past in the other direction I was muzzily surprised by the fact that it had two complete sets of headlights which kept merging into each other and drawing apart again.

In the yard at Holly Bush I got out of the car, nodded to the shadowy group of figures standing there, fumbled my bottle of antiseptic and calving ropes from the boot and marched determinedly into the byre. One of the men held an oil lamp over a cow lying on a deep bed of straw in one of the standings; from the vulva a calf's foot protruding a few inches and as the cow strained a little muzzle showed momentarily then disappeared as she relaxed.

Far away inside me a stone cold sober veterinary surgeon murmured: 'Only a leg back and a big roomy cow. Shouldn't be much trouble.' I turned and looked at the Bamfords for the first time. I hadn't met them before but it was easy to classify them; simple, kindly anxious-to-please people – two middle-aged men, probably brothers, and two young men who would be the sons of one or the other. They were all staring at me in the dim light, their eyes expectant, their mouths slightly open as though ready to smile or laugh if given half a chance.

I squared my shoulders, took a deep breath and said in a loud voice: 'Would you please bring me a bucket of hot water, some soap and a towel.' Or at least that's what I meant to say, because what actually issued from my lips was a torrent of something that sounded like Swahili. The Bamfords, poised, ready to spring into action to do my bidding, looked at me blankly. I cleared my throat, swallowed, took a few seconds' rest and tried again. I cleared my throat, swallowed, another volley of gibberish echoing uselessly round the cow house.

Clearly I had a problem. It was essential to communicate in some way, particularly since these people didn't know me and were waiting for some action. I suppose I must have appeared a strange and enigmatic figure standing there, straight and solemn, surmounted and dominated by the vast cap. But through the mists a flash of insight showed me where I was going wrong. It was over-confidence. It wasn't a bit of good trying to speak loudly like that. I tried again in the faintest of whispers.

'Could I have a bucket of hot water, some soap and a towel, please.' It came out beautifully though the oldest Mr Bamford didn't quite get it first time. He came close, cupped an ear with his hand and watched my lips intently. Then he nodded eagerly in comprehension, held up a forefinger at me, tiptoed across the floor like a tight rope walker to one of the sons and whispered in his ear. The young man turned and crept out noiselessly, closing the door behind him with the utmost care; he was back in less than a minute, padding over the cobbles daintily in his heavy boots and placing the bucket gingerly in front of me.

I managed to remove my jacket, tie and shirt quite efficiently and they were taken from me in silence and hung upon nails by the Bamfords who were moving around as though in church. I thought I was doing fine till I started to wash my arms. The soap kept shooting from my arms, slithering into the dung channel, disappearing into the dark corners of the byre with the Bamfords in hot pursuit. It was worse still when I tried to work up to the top of my arms. The soap flew over my shoulders like a live thing, at times cannoning off the walls, at others gliding down my back. The farmers never knew where the next shot was going and they took on the appearance of a really sharp fielding side crouching around me with arms outstretched waiting for a catch.

However I did finally work up a lather and was ready to start, but the cow refused firmly to get to her feet, so I had to stretch out behind her face down on the unyielding cobbles. It wasn't till I got down there that I felt the great cap dropping over my ears; I must have put it on again after removing my shirt though it was difficult to see what purpose it might serve.

Inserting a hand gently into the vagina I pushed along the calf's neck, hoping to come upon a flexed knee or even a foot, but I was disappointed; the leg really was right back, stretching from the shoulder away flat against the calf's side. Still, I would be all right – it just meant a longer reach.

And there was one reassuring feature; the calf was alive. As I lay, my face was almost touching the rear end of the cow and I had a close up of the nose which kept appearing every few seconds; it was good to see the little nostrils twitching as they sought the outside air. All I had to do was get that leg round.

But the snag was that as I reached forward the cow kept straining, squeezing my arm cruelly against her bony pelvis, making me groan and roll about in agony for a few seconds till the pressure went off. Quite often in these crises my cap fell on to the floor and each time gentle hands replaced it immediately on my head.

At last the foot was in my hand – there would be no need for ropes this time – and I began to pull it round. It took me longer than I thought and it seemed to me that the calf was beginning to lose patience with me because when its head was forced out by the cow's contractions we were eye to eye and I fancied the little creature was giving me a disgusted 'For heaven's sake get on with it' look.

When the leg did come round it was with a rush and in an instant everything was laid as it should have been.

'Get hold of the feet,' I whispered to the Bamfords and after a hushed consultation they took up their places. In no time at all a fine heifer calf was wriggling on the cobbles shaking its head and snorting the placental fluid from its nostrils.

In response to my softly hissed instructions the farmers rubbed the little creature down with straw wisps and pulled it round for its mother to lick.

It was a happy ending to the most peaceful calving I have ever attended. Never a voice raised, everybody moving around on tiptoe. I got dressed in a cathedral silence, went out to the car, breathed a final goodnight and left with the Bamfords waving mutely.

To say I had a hangover next morning would be failing even to hint at the utter disintegration of my bodily economy and personality. Only somebody who had consumed two or three quarts of assorted home-made wines at a sitting could have an inkling of the quaking nausea, the raging inferno within, the jangling nerves, the black despairing outlook.

Tristan had seen me in the bathroom running the cold tap on my tongue and had intuitively administered a raw egg, aspirins and brandy which, as I came downstairs, lay in a cold, unmoving blob in my outraged stomach.

'What are you walking like that for, James?' asked Siegfried in what sounded like a bull's bellow as I came in on him at breakfast. 'You look as though you'd pee'd yourself.'

'Oh it's nothing much.' It was no good telling him I was treading warily across the carpet because I was convinced that if I let my heels down too suddenly it would jar my eyeballs from their sockets. 'I had a few glasses of Mr Crump's wine last night and it seems to have upset me.'

'A few glasses! You ought to be more careful – that stuff's dynamite. Could knock anybody over.' He crashed his cup into its saucer then began to clatter about with knife and fork as if trying to give a one man rendering of the Anvil Chorus. 'I hope you weren't any the worse to go to Bamford's.'

I listlessly crumbled some dry toast on my plate. 'Well I did the job all right, but I'd had a bit too much – no use denying it.'

Siegfried was in one of his encouraging moods. 'By God, James, those Bamfords are very strict Methodists. They're grand chaps but absolutely dead nuts against drink – if they thought you were under the influence of alcohol they'd never have you on the place again.' He ruthlessly bisected an egg yolk. 'I hope they didn't notice anything. Do you think they knew?'

'Oh maybe not. No, I shouldn't think so.' I closed my eyes and shivered as Siegfried pushed a forkful of sausage and fried bread into his mouth and began to chew briskly. My mind went back to the gentle hands replacing the monstrous cap on my head and I groaned inwardly.

Those Bamfords knew all right. Oh yes, they knew.

Chapter Seven

The silvery haired old gentleman with the pleasant face didn't look the type to be easily upset but his eyes glared at me angrily and his lips quivered with indignation.

'Mr Herriot,' he said. 'I have come to make a complaint. I strongly object to your callousness in subjecting my dog to unnecessary suffering.'

'Suffering? What suffering?' I was mystified.

'I think you know, Mr Herriot. I brought my dog in a few days ago. He was very lame and I am referring to your treatment on that occasion.'

I nodded. 'Yes, I remember it well . . . but where does the suffering come in?'

'Well, the poor animal is going around with his leg dangling and I have it on good authority that the bone is fractured and should have been put in plaster immediately.' The old gentleman stuck his chin out fiercely.

'All right, you can stop worrying,' I said. 'Your dog has a radial paralysis caused by a blow on the ribs and if you are patient and follow my treatment he'll gradually improve. In fact I think he'll recover completely.'

'But he trails his leg when he walks.'

'I know – that's typical, and to the layman it does give the appearance of a broken leg. But he shows no sign of pain, does he?'

'No, he seems quite happy, but this lady seemed to be absolutely sure of her facts. She was adamant.'

'Lady?'

'Yes, said the old gentleman. 'She is very clever with animals and she came round to see if she could help in my dog's convalescence. She brought some excellent condition powders with her.'

'Ah!' A blinding shaft pierced the fog in my mind. All was suddenly clear. 'It was Mrs Donovan, wasn't it?'

'Well . . . er, yes. That was her name.'

Old Mrs Donovan was a woman who really got around. No matter what was going on in Darrowby – weddings, funerals, house-sales – you'd find the dumpy little figure and walnut face among the spectators, the darting, black-button eyes taking everything in. And always, on the end of its lead, her terrier dog.

When I say 'old', I'm only guessing, because she appeared ageless; she seemed to have been around a long time but she could have been anything between fifty-five and seventy-five. She certainly had the vitality of a young woman because she must have walked vast distances in her dedicated quest to keep abreast of events. Many people took an uncharitable view of her acute curiosity but whatever the motivation, her activities took her into almost every channel of life in the town. One of these channels was our veterinary practice.

Because Mrs Donovan, among her other widely ranging interests, was an animal doctor. In fact I think it would be safe to say that this facet of her life transcended all the others.

She could talk at length on the ailments of small animals and she had a whole armoury of medicines and remedies at her command, her two specialities being her miracle working condition powders and a dog shampoo of unprecedented value for improving the coat. She had an uncanny ability to sniff out a sick animal and it was not uncommon when I was on my rounds to find Mrs Donovan's dark gipsy face poised intently over what I had thought was my patient while she administered calf's foot jelly or one of her own patent nostrums.

I suffered more than Siegfried because I took a more active part in the small animal side of our practice. I was anxious to develop this aspect and to improve my image in this field and Mrs Donovan didn't help at all. 'Young Mr Herriot,' she would confide to my clients, 'is all right with cattle and such like, but he don't know nothing about dogs and cats.'

And of course they believed her and had implicit faith in her. She had the irresistible mystic appeal of the amateur and on top of that there was her habit, particularly endearing in Darrowby, of never charging for her advice, her medicines, her long periods of diligent nursing.

Older folk in the town told how her husband, an Irish farm worker, had died many years ago and how he must have had a 'bit put away' because Mrs Donovan had apparently been able to indulge all her interests over the years without financial strain. Since she inhabited the streets of Darrowby all day and every day I often encountered her and she always smiled up at me sweetly and told me how she had been sitting up all night with Mrs So-and-so's dog that I'd been treating. She felt sure she'd be able to pull it through.

There was no smile on her face, however, on the day when she rushed into the surgery while Siegfried and I were having tea.

'Mr Herriot!' she gasped. 'Can you come? My little dog's been run over!'

I jumped up and ran out to the car with her. She sat in the passenger seat with her head bowed, her hands clasped tightly on her knees.

'He slipped his collar and ran in front of a car,' she murmured. 'He's lying in front of the school half way up Cliffend Road. Please hurry.'

I was there within three minutes but as I bent over the dusty little body stretched on the pavement I knew there was nothing I could do. The fast-glazing eyes, the faint, gasping respirations, the ghastly pallor of the mucous membranes all told the same story.

'I'll take him back to the surgery and get some saline into him, Mrs Donovan,' I said. 'But I'm afraid he's had a massive internal haemorrhage. Did you see what happened exactly?'

She gulped. 'Yes, the wheel went right over him.'

Ruptured liver, for sure. I passed my hands under the little animal and began to lift him gently, but as I did so the breathing stopped and the eyes stared fixedly ahead.

Mrs Donovan sank to her knees and for a few moments she gently stroked the rough hair of the head and chest. 'He's dead, isn't he?' she whispered at last.

'I'm afraid he is,' I said.

She got slowly to her feet and stood bewilderedly among the little group of bystanders on the pavement. Her lips moved but she seemed unable to say any more.

I took her arm, led her over to the car and opened the door. 'Get in and sit down,' I said. 'I'll run you home. Leave everything to me.'

I wrapped the dog in my calving overall and laid him in the boot before driving away. It wasn't until we drew up outside Mrs Donovan's house that she began to weep silently. I sat there without speaking till she had finished. Then she wiped her eyes and turned to me.

'Do you think he suffered at all?'

'I'm certain he didn't. It was all so quick – he wouldn't know a thing about it.'

She tried to smile. 'Poor little Rex, I don't know what I'm doing to do without him. We've travelled a few miles together, you know.'

'Yes, you have. He had a wonderful life, Mrs Donovan. And let me give you a bit of advice – you must get another dog. You'd be lost without one.'

She shook her head. 'No, I couldn't. That little dog meant too much to me. I couldn't let another take his place.'

'Well I know that's how you feel just now but I wish you'd think about it. I don't want to seem callous – I tell everybody this when they lose an animal and I know it's good advice.'

'Mr Herriot, I'll never have another one.' She shook her head again, very decisively. 'Rex was my faithful friend for many years and I just want to remember him. He's the last dog I'll ever have.'

I often saw Mrs Donovan around the town after this and I was glad to see she was still as active as ever, though she looked strangely incomplete without the little dog on its lead. But it must have been over a month before I had the chance to speak to her.

It was on the afternoon that Inspector Halliday of the RSPCA rang me.

'Mr Herriot,' he said, 'I'd like you to come and see an animal with me. A cruelty case.'

'Right, what is it?'

'A dog, and it's pretty grim. A dreadful case of neglect.' He gave me the name of a row of old brick cottages down by the river and said he'd meet me there.

Halliday was waiting for me, smart and business-like in his dark uniform, as I pulled up in the back lane behind the houses. He was a big, blond man with cheerful blue eyes but he didn't smile as he came over to the car.

'He's in here,' he said, and led the way towards one of the doors in the long, crumbling wall. A few curious people were hanging around and with a feeling

of inevitability I recognised a gnome-like brown face. Trust Mrs Donovan, I
thought, to be among those present at a time like this.

We went through the door into the long garden. I had found that even the
lowliest dwellings in Darrowby had long strips of land at the back as though
the builders had taken it for granted that the country people who were going
to live in them would want to occupy themselves with the pursuits of the soil;
with vegetable and fruit growing, even stock keeping in a small way. You usually
found a pig there, a few hens, often pretty beds of flowers.

But this garden was a wilderness. A chilling air of desolation hung over the
few gnarled apple and plum trees standing among a tangle of rank grass as
though the place had been forsaken by all living creatures.

Halliday went over to a ramshackle wooden shed with peeling paint and a
rusted corrugated iron roof. He produced a key, unlocked the padlock and
dragged the door partly open. There was no window and it wasn't easy to
identify the jumble inside; broken gardening tools, an ancient mangle, rows of
flower pots and partly used paint tins. And right at the back, a dog sitting
quietly.

I didn't notice him immediately because of the gloom and because the smell
in the shed started me coughing, but as I drew closer I saw that he was a big
animal, sitting very upright, his collar secured by a chain to a ring in the wall.
I had seen some thin dogs but this advanced emaciation reminded me of my text
books on anatomy; nowhere else did the bones of pelvis, face and rib cage stand
out with such horrifying clarity. A deep, smoothed out hollow in the earth floor
showed where he had lain, moved about, in fact lived for a very long time.

The sight of the animal had a stupefying effect on me; I only half took in the
rest of the scene – the filthy shreds of sacking scattered nearby, the bowl of
scummy water.

'Look at his back end,' Halliday muttered.

I carefully raised the dog from his sitting position and realised that the stench
in the place was not entirely due to the piles of excrement. The hindquarters
were a welter of pressure sores which had turned gangrenous and strips of
sloughing tissue hung down from them. There were similar sores along the
sternum and ribs. The coat, which seemed to be a dull yellow, was matted and
caked with dirt.

The Inspector spoke again. 'I don't think he's ever been out of here. He's only
a young dog – about a year old – but I understand he's been in this shed since
he was an eight-week-old pup. Somebody out in the lane heard a whimper or
he'd never have been found.'

I felt a tightening of the throat and a sudden nausea which wasn't due to the
smell. It was the thought of this patient animal sitting starved and forgotten in
the darkness and filth for a year. I looked again at the dog and saw in his eyes
only a calm trust. Some dogs would have barked their heads off and soon been
discovered, some would have become terrified and vicious, but this was one of
the totally undemanding kind, the kind which had complete faith in people and
accepted all their actions without complaint. Just an occasional whimper perhaps
as he sat interminably in the empty blackness which had been his world and at
times wondered what it was all about.

'Well, Inspector, I hope you're going to throw the book at whoever's responsible,' I said.

Halliday grunted. 'Oh, there won't be much done. It's a case of diminished
responsibility. The owner's definitely simple. Lives with an aged mother who
hardly knows what's going on either. I've seen the fellow and it seems he threw
in a bit of food when he felt like it and that's about all he did. They'll fine him
and stop him keeping an animal in the future but nothing more than that.'

'I see.' I reached out and stroked the dog's head and he immediately responded by resting a paw on my wrist. There was a pathetic dignity about the way he held himself erect, the calm eyes regarding me, friendly and unafraid. 'Well, you'll let me know if you want me in court.'

'Of course, and thank you for coming along.' Halliday hesitated for a moment. 'And now I expect you'll want to put this poor thing out of his misery right away.'

I continued to run my hand over the head and ears while I thought for a moment. 'Yes ... yes, I suppose so. We'd never find a home for him in this state. It's the kindest thing to do. Anyway, push the door wide open will you so that I can get a proper look at him.'

In the improved light I examined him more thoroughly. Perfect teeth, well-proportioned limbs with a fringe of yellow hair. I put my stethoscope on his chest and as I listened to the slow, strong thudding of the heart the dog again put his paw on my hand.

I turned to Halliday, 'You know, Inspector, inside this bag of bones there's a lovely healthy Golden Retriever. I wish there was some way of letting him out.'

As I spoke I noticed there was more than one figure in the door opening. A pair of black pebble eyes were peering intently at the big dog from behind the Inspector's broad back. The other spectators had remained in the lane but Mrs Donovan's curiosity had been too much for her. I continued conversationally as though I hadn't seen her.

'You know, what this dog needs first of all is a good shampoo to clean up his matted coat.'

'Huh?' said Halliday.

'Yes. And then he wants a long course of some really strong condition powders.'

'What's that?' The Inspector looked startled.

'There's no doubt about it,' I said. 'It's the only hope for him, but where are you going to find such things? Really powerful enough, I mean.' I sighed and straightened up. 'Ah well, I suppose there's nothing else for it. I'd better put him to sleep right away. I'll get the things from my car.'

When I got back to the shed Mrs Donovan was already inside examining the dog despite the feeble remonstrances of the big man.

'Look!' she said excitedly, pointing to a name roughly scratched on the collar. 'His name's Roy.' She smiled up at me. 'It's a bit like Rex, isn't it, that name?'

'You know, Mrs Donovan, now you mention it, it is. It's very like Rex, the way it comes off your tongue.' I nodded seriously.

She stood silent for a few moments, obviously in the grip of a deep emotion, then she burst out.

'Can I have 'im? I can make him better, I know I can. Please, please let me have 'im!'

'Well I don't know,' I said. 'It's really up to the Inspector. You'll have to get his permission.'

Halliday looked at her in bewilderment, then he said: 'Excuse me, Madam,' and drew me to one side. We walked a few yards through the long grass and stopped under a tree.

'Mr Herriot,' he whispered, 'I don't know what's going on here, but I can't just pass over an animal in this condition to anybody who has a casual whim. The poor beggar's had one bad break already – I think it's enough. This woman doesn't look a suitable person ...'

I held up a hand. 'Believe me, Inspector, you've nothing to worry about. She's

a funny old stick but she's been sent from heaven today. If anybody in Darrowby
can give this dog a new life it's her.'

Halliday still looked very doubtful. 'But I still don't get it. What was all that
stuff about him needing shampoos and condition powders?'

'Oh never mind about that. I'll tell you some other time. What he needs is
lots of good grub, care and affection and that's just what he'll get. You can take
my word for it.'

'All right, you seem very sure.' Halliday looked at me for a second or two
then turned and walked over to the eager little figure by the shed.

I had never before been deliberately on the look out for Mrs Donovan: she had
just cropped up wherever I happened to be, but now I scanned the streets of
Darrowby anxiously day by day without sighting her. I didn't like it when
Gobber Newhouse got drunk and drove his bicycle determinedly through a
barrier into a ten foot hole where they were laying the new sewer and Mrs
Donovan was not in evidence among the happy crowd who watched the council
workmen and two policemen trying to get him out; and when she was nowhere
to be seen when they had to fetch the fire engine to the fish and chip shop the
night the fat burst into flames I became seriously worried.

Maybe I should have called round to see how she was getting on with that
dog. Certainly I had trimmed off the necrotic tissue and dressed the sores before
she took him away, but perhaps he needed something more than that. And yet
at the time I had felt a strong conviction that the main thing was to get him out
of there and clean and feed him and nature would do the rest. And I had a lot
of faith in Mrs Donovan – far more than she had in me – when it came to
animal doctoring; it was hard to believe I'd been completely wrong.

It must have been nearly three weeks and I was on the point of calling at her
home when I noticed her stumping briskly along the far side of the market
place, peering closely into every shop window exactly as before. The only
difference was that she had a big yellow dog on the end of the lead.

I turned the wheel and sent my car bumping over the cobbles till I was abreast
of her. When she saw me getting out she stopped and smiled impishly but she
didn't speak as I bent over Roy and examined him. He was still a skinny dog
but he looked bright and happy, his wounds were healthy and granulating and
there was not a speck of dirt in his coat or on his skin. I knew then what Mrs
Donovan had been doing all this time; she had been washing and combing and
teasing at that filthy tangle till she had finally conquered it.

As I straightened up she seized my wrist in a grip of surprising strength and
looked up into my eyes.

'Now Mr Herriot,' she said. 'Haven't I made a difference to this dog!'

'You've done wonders, Mrs Donovan,' I said. 'And you've been at him with
that marvellous shampoo of yours, haven't you?'

She giggled and walked away and from that day I saw the two of them
frequently but at a distance and something like two months went by before I
had a chance to talk to her again. She was passing by the surgery as I was
coming down the steps and again she grabbed my wrist.

'Mr Herriot,' she said, just as she had done before. 'Haven't I made a
difference to this dog!'

I looked down at Roy with something akin to awe. He had grown and filled
out and his coat, no longer yellow but a rich gold, lay in luxuriant shining
swathes over the well-fleshed ribs and back. A new, brightly studded collar
glittered on his neck and his tail, beautifully fringed, fanned the air gently. He
was now a Golden Retriever in full magnificence. As I stared at him he reared
up, plunked his fore paws on my chest and looked into my face, and in his eyes

I read plainly the same calm affection and trust I had seen back in that black, noisome shed.

'Mrs Donovan,' I said softly, 'he's the most beautiful dog in Yorkshire.' Then, because I knew she was waiting for it. 'It's those wonderful condition powders. Whatever do you put in them?'

'Ah, wouldn't you like to know!' She bridled and smiled up at me coquettishly and indeed she was nearer being kissed at that moment than for many years.

I suppose you could say that that was the start of Roy's second life. And as the years passed I often pondered on the beneficent providence which had decreed that an animal which had spent his first twelve months abandoned and unwanted, staring uncomprehendingly into that unchanging, stinking darkness, should be whisked in a moment into an existence of light and movement and love. Because I don't think any dog had it quite so good as Roy from then on.

His diet changed dramatically from odd bread crusts to best stewing steak and biscuit, meaty bones and a bowl of warm milk every evening. And he never missed a thing. Garden fetes, school sports, evictions, gymkhanas – he'd be there. I was pleased to note that as time went on Mrs Donovan seemed to be clocking up an even greater daily mileage. Her expenditure on shoe leather must have been phenomenal, but of course it was absolute pie for Roy – a busy round in the morning, home for a meal then straight out again; it was all go.

Mrs Donovan didn't confine her activities to the town centre; there was a big stretch of common land down by the river where there were seats, and people used to take their dogs for a gallop and she liked to get down there fairly regularly to check on the latest developments on the domestic scene. I often saw Roy loping majestically over the grass among a pack of assorted canines, and when he wasn't doing that he was submitting to being stroked or patted or generally fussed over. He was handsome and he just liked people; it made him irresistible.

It was common knowledge that his mistress had bought a whole selection of brushes and combs of various sizes with which she laboured over his coat. Some people said she had a little brush for his teeth, too, and it might have been true, but he certainly wouldn't need his nails clipped – his life on the roads would keep them down.

Mrs Donovan, too, had her reward; she had a faithful companion by her side every hour of the day and night. But there was more to it than that; she had always had the compulsion to help and heal animals and the salvation of Roy was the high point of her life – a blazing triumph which never dimmed.

I know the memory of it was always fresh because many years later I was sitting on the sidelines at a cricket match and I saw the two of them; the old lady glancing keenly around her, Roy gazing placidly out at the field of play, apparently enjoying every ball. At the end of the match I watched them move away with the dispersing crowd; Roy would be about twelve then and heaven only knows how old Mrs Donovan must have been, but the big golden animal was trotting along effortlessly and his mistress, a little more bent perhaps and her head rather nearer the ground, was going very well.

When she saw me she came over and I felt the familiar tight grip on my wrist.

'Mr Herriot,' she said, and in the dark probing eyes the pride was still as warm, the triumph still as bursting new as if it had all happened yesterday.

'Mr Herriot, haven't I made a difference to this dog!'

Chapter Eight

'How would you like to officiate at Darrowby Show, James?' Siegfried threw the letter he had been reading on to the desk and turned to me.

'I don't mind, but I thought you always did it.'

'I do, but it says in that letter that they've changed the date this year and it happens I'm going to be away that weekend.'

'Oh well, fine. What do I have to do?'

Siegfried ran his eye down his list of calls. 'It's a sinecure, really. More a pleasant day out than anything else. You have to measure the ponies and be on call in case any animals are injured. That's about all. Oh and they want you to judge the Family Pets.'

'Family Pets?'

'Yes, they run a proper dog show but they have an expert judge for that. This is just a bit of fun – all kinds of pets. You've got to find a first, second and third.'

'Right,' I said. 'I think I should just about be able to manage that.'

'Splendid.' Siegfried tipped up the envelope in which the letter had come. 'Here are your car park and luncheon tickets for self and friend if you want to take somebody with you. Also your vet's badge. O.K.?'

The Saturday of the show brought the kind of weather that must have had the organisers purring with pleasure; a sky of wide, unsullied blue, hardly a whiff of wind and the kind of torrid, brazen sunshine you don't often find in North Yorkshire.

As I drove down towards the show ground I felt I was looking at a living breathing piece of old England; the group of tents and marquees vivid against the green of the riverside field, the women and children in their bright summer dresses, the cattle with their smocked attendants, a line of massive Shire horses parading in the ring.

I parked the car and made for the stewards' tent with its flag hanging limply from the mast. Tristan parted from me there. With the impecunious student's unerring eye for a little free food and entertainment he had taken up my spare tickets. He headed purposefully for the beer tent as I went in to report to the show secretary.

Leaving my measuring stick there I looked around for a while.

A country show is a lot of different things to a lot of different people. Riding horses of all kinds from small ponies to hunters were being galloped up and down and in one ring the judges hovered around a group of mares and their beautiful little foals.

In a corner four men armed with buckets and brushes were washing and grooming a row of young bulls with great concentration, twiddling and crimping the fuzz over the rumps like society hairdressers.

Wandering through the marquees I examined the bewildering variety of produce from stalks of rhubarb to bunches of onions, the flower displays, embroidery, jams, cakes, pies. And the children's section; a painting of 'The Beach at Scarborough' by Annie Heseltine, aged nine; rows of wobbling copperplate handwriting – 'A thing of beauty is a joy for ever', Bernard Peacock, aged twelve.

Drawn by the occasional gusts of melody I strolled across the grass to where the Darrowby and Houlton Silver Band was rendering *Poet and Peasant*. The bandsmen were of all ages from seventies down to one or two boys of about fourteen and most of them had doffed their uniform tunics as they sweated in the hot sun. Pint pots reposed under many of the chairs and the musicians refreshed themselves frequently with leisurely swigs.

I was particularly fascinated by the conductor, a tiny frail man who looked about eighty. He alone had retained his full uniform, cap and all, and he stood apparently motionless in front of the crescent of bandsmen, chin sunk on chest, arms hanging limply by his sides. It wasn't until I came right up to him that I realised his fingers were twitching in time with the music and that he was, in fact, conducting. And the more I watched him the more fitting it seemed that he should do it like that. The Yorkshireman's loathing of exhibitionism or indeed any outward show of emotion made it unthinkable that he should throw his arms about in the orthodox manner; no doubt he had spent weary hours rehearsing and coaching his players but here, when the results of his labours were displayed to the public he wasn't going to swank about it. Even the almost imperceptible twitching of the finger-ends had something guilty about it as if the old man felt he was being caught out in something shameful.

But my attention was jerked away as a group of people walked across on the far side of the band. It was Helen with Richard Edmundson and behind them Mr Alderson and Richard's father deep in conversation. The young man walked very close to Helen, his shining, plastered-down fair hair hovering possessively over her dark head, his face animated as he talked and laughed.

There were no clouds in the sky but it was as if a dark hand had reached across and smudged away the brightness of the sunshine. I turned quickly and went in search of Tristan.

I soon picked out my colleague as I hurried into the marquee with 'Refreshments' over the entrance. He was leaning with an elbow on the makeshift counter of boards and trestles chatting contentedly with a knot of cloth-capped locals, a Woodbine in one hand, a pint glass in the other. There was a general air of earthy bonhomie. Drinking of a more decorous kind would be taking place at the president's bar behind the stewards' headquarters with pink gins or sherry as the main tipple but here it was beer, bottled and draught, and the stout ladies behind the counter were working with the fierce concentration of people who knew they were in for a hard day.

'Yes, I saw her,' Tristan said when I gave him my news. 'In fact there she is now.' He nodded in the direction of the family group as they strolled past the entrance. 'I've had my eye on them for some time – I don't miss much from in here you know, Jim.'

'Ah well.' I accepted a half of bitter from him. 'It all looks pretty cosy. The two dads like blood brothers and Helen hanging on to that bloke's arm.'

Tristan squinted over the top of his pint at the scene outside and shook his head. 'Not exactly. He's hanging on to HER arm.' He looked at me judicially. 'There's a difference, you know.'

'I don't suppose it makes much difference to me either way,' I grunted.

'Well don't look so bloody mournful.' He took an effortless swallow which lowered the level in his glass by about six inches. 'What do you expect an attractive girl to do? Sit at home waiting for you to call? If you've been pounding on her door every night you haven't told me about it.'

'It's all right you talking. I think old man Alderson would set his dogs on me if I showed up there. I know he doesn't like me hanging around Helen and on top of that I've got the feeling he thinks I killed his cow on my last visit.'

'And did you?'

'No, I didn't. But I walked up to a living animal, gave it an injection and it promptly died, so I can't blame him.'

I took a sip at my beer and watched the Alderson party who had changed direction and were heading away from our retreat. Helen was wearing a pale blue dress and I was thinking how well the colour went with the deep brown of her hair and how I like the way she walked with her legs swinging easily and her shoulders high and straight when the loudspeaker boomed across the show ground.

'Will Mr Herriot, Veterinary Surgeon, please report to the stewards immediately.'

It made me jump but at the same time I felt a quick stab of pride. It was the first time I had heard myself and my profession publicly proclaimed. I turned to Tristan. He was supposed to be seeing practice and this could be something interesting. But he was immersed in a story which he was trying to tell to a little stocky man with a fat, shiny face, and he was having difficulty because the little man, determined to get his full measure of enjoyment, kept throwing himself into helpless convulsions at the end of every sentence, and the finish was a long way away. Tristan took his stories very seriously; I decided not to interrupt him.

A glow of importance filled me as I hurried over the grass, my official badge with 'Veterinary Surgeon' in gold letters dangling from my lapel. A steward met me on the way.

'It's one of the cattle. Had an accident, I think.' He pointed to a row of pens along the edge of the field.

A curious crowd had collected around my patient which had been entered in the in-calf heifers class. The owner, a stranger from outside the Darrowby practice, came up to me, his face glum.

'She tripped coming off the cattle wagon and went 'ead first into the wall. Knocked one of 'er horns clean off.'

The heifer, a bonny little light roan, was a pathetic sight. She had been washed, combed, powdered and primped for the big day and there she was with one horn dangling drunkenly down the side of her face and an ornamental fountain of bright arterial blood climbing gracefully in three jets from the broken surface high into the air.

I opened my bag. I had brought a selection of the things I might need and I fished out some artery forceps and suture material. The rational way to stop haemorrhage of this type is to grasp the bleeding vessel and ligate it, but it wasn't always as easy as that. Especially when the patient won't co-operate.

The broken horn was connected to the head only by a band of skin and I quickly snipped it away with scissors; then, with the farmer holding the heifer's nose I began to probe with my forceps for the severed vessels. In the bright sunshine it was surprisingly difficult to see the spurting blood and as the little animal threw her head about I repeatedly felt the warm spray across my face and heard it spatter on my collar.

It was when I was beginning to lose heart with my ineffectual groping that I looked up and saw Helen and her boy friend watching me from the crowd. Young Edmundson looked mildly amused as he watched my unavailing efforts but Helen smiled encouragingly as she caught my eye. I did my best to smile back at her through my bloody mask but I don't suppose it showed.

I gave it up when the heifer gave a particularly brisk toss which sent my forceps flying on to the grass. I did what I should probably have done at the beginning – clapped a pad of cotton wool and antiseptic powder on to the stump and secured it with a figure of eight bandage round the other horn.

'That's it, then,' I said to the farmer as I tried to blink the blood out of my eyes. 'The bleeding's stopped, anyway. I'd advise you to have her properly de-horned soon or she's going to look a bit odd.'

Just then Tristan appeared from among the spectators.

'What's got you out of the beer tent?' I enquired with a touch of bitterness.

'It's lunch time, old lad,' Tristan replied equably. 'But we'll have to get you cleaned up a bit first. I can't be seen with you in that condition. Hang on, I'll get a bucket of water.'

The show luncheon was so excellent that it greatly restored me. Although it was taken in a marquee the committee men's wives had somehow managed to conjure up a memorable cold spread. There was fresh salmon and home fed ham and slices of prime beef with mixed salads and apple pie and the big brimming jugs of cream you only see at farming functions. One of the ladies was a noted cheese maker and we finished with some delicious goat cheese and coffee. The liquid side was catered for too with a bottle of Magnet Pale Ale and a glass at every place.

I didn't have the pleasure of Tristan's company at lunch because he had strategically placed himself well down the table between two strict Methodists so that his intake of Magnet was trebled.

I had hardly emerged into the sunshine when a man touched me on the shoulder.

'One of the dog show judges wants you to examine a dog. He doesn't like the look of it.'

He led me to where a thin man of about forty with a small dark moustache was standing by his car. He held a wire-haired fox terrier on a leash and he met me with an ingratiating smile.

'There's nothing whatever the matter with my dog,' he declared, 'but the chap in there seems very fussy.'

I looked down at the terrier. 'I see he has some matter in the corner of his eyes.'

The man shook his head vigorously. 'Oh no, that's not matter. I've been using some white powder on him and a bit's got into his eyes, that's all.'

'Hmm, well let's see what his temperature says, shall we?'

The little animal stood uncomplaining as I inserted the thermometer. When I took the reading my eyebrows went up.

'It's a hundred and four. I'm afraid he's not fit to go into the show.'

'Wait a minute.' The man thrust out his jaw. 'You're talking like that chap in there. I've come a long way to show this dog and I'm going to show him.'

'I'm sorry but you can't show him with a temperature of a hundred and four.'

'But he's had a car journey. That could put up his temperature.'

I shook my head. 'Not as high as that it couldn't. Anyway he looks sick to me. Do you see how he's half closing his eyes as though he's frightened of the light? It's possible he could have distemper.'

'What? That's rubbish and you know it. He's never been fitter!' The man's mouth trembled with anger.

I looked down at the little dog. He was crouching on the grass miserably. Occasionally he shivered, he had a definite photophobia and there was that creamy blob of pus in the corner of each eye. 'Has he been inoculated against distemper?'

'Well no, he hasn't, but why do you keep on about it?'

'Because I think he's got it now and for his sake and for the sake of the other dogs here you ought to take him straight home and see your own vet.'

He glared at me. 'So you won't let me take him into the show tent?'

'That's right. I'm very sorry, but it's out of the question.' I turned and walked away.

I had gone only a few yards when the loudspeaker boomed again. 'Will Mr Herriot please go to the measuring stand where the ponies are ready for him.'

I collected my stick and trotted over to a corner of the field where a group of ponies had assembled; Welsh, Dales, Exmoor, Dartmoor – all kinds of breeds were represented.

For the uninitiated, horses are measured in hands which consist of four inches and a graduated stick is used with a cross piece and a spirit level which rests on the withers, the highest point of the shoulders. I had done a fair bit of it in individual animals but this was the first time I had done the job at a show. With my stick at the ready I stood by the two wide boards which had been placed on the turf to give the animals a reasonably level standing surface.

A smiling young woman led the first pony, a smart chestnut, on to the boards.

'Which class?' I asked.

'Thirteen hands.'

I tried the stick on him. He was well under.

'Fine, next please.'

A few more came through without incident then there was a lull before the next group came up. The ponies were arriving on the field all the time in their boxes and being led over to me, some by their young riders, others by the parents. It looked as though I could be here quite a long time.

During one of the lulls a little man who had been standing near me spoke up.

'No trouble yet?' he asked.

'No, everything's in order,' I replied.

He nodded expressionlessly and as I took a closer look at him his slight body, dark, leathery features and high shoulders seemed to give him the appearance of a little brown gnome. At the same time there was something undeniably horsy about him.

'You'll 'ave some awkward 'uns,' he grunted. 'And they allus say the same thing. They allus tell you the vet at some other show passed their pony.' His swarthy cheeks crinkled in a wry smile.

'Is that so?'

'Aye, you'll see.'

Another candidate, led by a beautiful blonde, was led on to the platform. She gave me the full blast of two big greenish eyes and flashed a mouthful of sparkling teeth at me.

'Twelve two,' she murmured seductively.

I tried the stick on the pony and worked it around, but try as I might I couldn't get it down to that.

'I'm afraid he's a bit big,' I said.

The blonde's smile vanished. 'Have you allowed half an inch for his shoes?'

'I have indeed, but you can see for yourself, he's well over.'

'But he passed the vet without any trouble at Hickley.' She snapped and out of the corner of my eye I saw the gnome nodding sagely.

'I can't help that,' I said. 'I'm afraid you'll have to put him into the next class.'

For a moment two green pebbles from the cold sea bed fixed me with a frigid glare then the blonde was gone taking her pony with her.

Next, a little bay animal was led on to the stand by a hard faced gentleman in a check suit and I must say I was baffled by its behaviour. Whenever the stick touched the withers it sank at the knees so that I couldn't be sure whether I was getting the right reading or not. Finally I gave up and passed him through.

The gnome coughed. 'I know that feller.'

'You do?'

'Aye, he's pricked that pony's withers with a pin so many times that it drops down whenever you try to measure 'im.'

'Never!'

'Sure as I'm standing here.'

I was staggered, but the arrival of another batch took up my attention for a few minutes. Some I passed, others I had to banish to another class and the owners took it in different ways – some philosophically, a few with obvious annoyance. One or two of the ponies just didn't like the look of the stick at all and I had to dance around them as they backed away and reared.

The last pony in this group was a nice grey led by a bouncy man wearing a great big matey smile.

'How are you, all right?' he enquired courteously. 'This 'un's thirteen two.'

The animal went under the stick without trouble but after he had trotted away the gnome spoke up again.

'I know that feller, too.'

'Really?'

'Not 'alf. Weighs down 'is ponies before they're measured. That grey's been standing in 'is box for the last hour with a twelve stone sack of corn on 'is back. Knocks an inch off.'

'Good God! Are you sure?'

'Don't worry, I've seen 'im at it.'

My mind was beginning to reel just a little. Was the man making it all up or were there really these malign forces at work behind all this innocent fun?

'That same feller,' continued the gnome. 'I've seen 'im bring a pony to a show and get half an inch knocked off for shoes when it never 'ad no shoes on.'

I wished he'd stop. And just then there was an interruption. It was the man with the moustache. He sidled up to me and whispered confidentially in my ear.

'Now I've just been thinking. My dog must have got over his journey by now and I expect his temperature will be normal. I wonder if you'd just try him again. I've still got time to show him.'

I turned wearily. 'Honestly, it'll be a waste of time. I've told you, he's ill.'

'Please! Just as a favour.' He had a desperate look and a fanatical light flickered in his eye.

'All right.' I went over to the car with him and produced my thermometer. The temperature was still a hundred and four.

'Now I wish you'd take this poor little dog home,' I said. 'He shouldn't be here.'

For a moment I thought the man was going to strike me. 'There's nothing wrong with him!' he hissed, his whole face working with emotion.

'I'm sorry,' I said, and went back to the measuring stand.

A boy of about fifteen was waiting for me with his pony. It was supposed to be in the thirteen two class but was nearly one and a half inches over.

'Much too big, I'm afraid,' I said. 'He can't go in that class.'

The boy didn't answer. He put his hand inside his jacket and produced a sheet of paper. 'This is a veterinary certificate to say he's under thirteen two.'

'No good, I'm sorry,' I replied. 'The stewards have told me not to accept any certificates. I've turned down two others today. Everything has to go under the stick. It's a pity, but there it is.'

His manner changed abruptly. 'But you've GOT to accept it!' he shouted in my face. 'There doesn't have to be any measurements when you have a certificate.'

'You'd better see the stewards. Those are my instructions.'

'I'll see my father about this, that's what!' he shouted and led the animal away.

Father was quickly on the scene. Big, fat, prosperous-looking, confident. He obviously wasn't going to stand any nonsense from me.

'Now look here, I don't know what this is all about but you have no option in this matter. You have to accept the certificate.'

'I don't, I assure you,' I answered. 'And anyway, it's not as though your pony was slightly over the mark. He's miles over – nowhere near the height.'

Father flushed dark red. 'Well let me tell you he was passed through by the vet at . . .'

'I know, I know,' I said, and I heard the gnome give a short laugh. 'But he's not going through here.'

There was a brief silence then both father and son began to scream at me. And as they continued to hurl abuse I felt a hand on my arm. It was the man with the moustache again.

'I'm going to ask you just once more to take my dog's temperature,' he whispered with a ghastly attempt at a smile. 'I'm sure he'll be all right this time. Will you try him again?'

I'd had enough. 'No, I bloody well won't!' I barked. 'Will you kindly stop bothering me and take that poor animal home.'

It's funny how the most unlikely things motivate certain people. It didn't seem a life and death matter whether a dog got into a show or not but it was to the man with the moustache. He started to rave at me.

'You don't know your job, that's the trouble with you! I've come all this way and you've played a dirty trick on me. I've got a friend who's a vet, a proper vet, and I'm going to tell him about you, yes I am. I'm going to tell him about you!'

At the same time the father and son were still in full cry, snarling and mouthing at me and I became suddenly aware that I was in the centre of a hostile circle. The blonde was there too, and some of the others whose ponies I had outed and they were all staring at me belligerently, making angry gestures.

I felt very much alone because the gnome, who had seemed an ally, was nowhere to be seen. I was disappointed in the gnome; he was a big talker but had vanished at the first whiff of danger. As I surveyed the threatening crowd I moved my measuring stick round in front of me; it wasn't much of a weapon but it might serve to fend them off if they rushed me.

And just at that moment, as the unkind words were thick upon the air, I saw Helen and Richard Edmundson on the fringe of the circle, taking it all in. I wasn't worried about him but again it struck me as strange that it should be my destiny always to be looking a bit of a clown when Helen was around.

Anyway, the measuring was over and I felt in need of sustenance. I retreated and went to find Tristan.

Chapter Nine

The atmosphere in the beer tent was just what I needed. The hot weather had made the place even more popular than usual and it was crowded; many of the inhabitants had been there since early morning and the air was thick with earthy witticisms, immoderate laughter, cries of joy; and the nice thing was that nobody in there cared a damn about the heights of ponies or the temperatures of dogs.

I had to fight my way through the crush to reach Tristan who was leaning across the counter in earnest conversation with a comely young barmaid. The other serving ladies were middle-aged but his practised eye had picked this one out; glossy red hair, a puckish face and an inviting smile. I had been hoping for a soothing chat with him but he was unable to give me his undivided attention, so after juggling with a glass among the throng for a few minutes I left.

Out on the field the sun still blazed, the scent of the trampled grass rose into the warm air, the band was playing a selection from *Rose Marie* and peace began to steal into my soul. Maybe I could begin to enjoy the show now the pinpricks were over; there was only the Family Pets to judge and I was looking forward to that.

For about an hour I wandered among the pens of mountainous pigs and haughty sheep; the rows of Shorthorn cows with their classical wedge-shaped grace, their level udders and dainty feet.

I watched in fascination a contest which was new to me; shirt-sleeved young men sticking a fork into a straw bale and hurling it high over a bar with a jerk of their thick brown arms.

Old Steve Bramley, a local farmer, was judging the heavy horses and I envied him his massive authority as he stumped, bowler-hatted and glowering around each animal, leaning occasionally on his stick as he took stock of the points. I couldn't imagine anyone daring to argue with him.

It was late in the afternoon when the loudspeaker called me to my final duty. The Family Pets contestants were arranged on wooden chairs drawn up in a wide circle on the turf. They were mainly children but behind them an interested ring of parents and friends watched me warily as I arrived.

The fashion for exotic pets was still in its infancy but I experienced a mild shock of surprise when I saw the variety of creatures on show. I suppose I must have had a vague mental picture of a few dogs and cats but I walked round the circle in growing bewilderment looking down at rabbits – innumerable rabbits of all sizes and colours – guinea pigs, white mice, several budgerigars, two tortoises, a canary, a kitten, a parrot, a mynah bird, a box of puppies, a few dogs and cats and a goldfish in a bowl. The smaller pets rested on their owners' knees, the others squatted on the ground.

How, I asked myself was I going to come to a decision here? How did you choose between a parrot and a puppy, a budgie and a bulldog, a mouse and a mynah? Then as I circled it came to me; it couldn't be done. The only way was to question the children in charge and find which ones looked after their pets best, which of them knew most about their feeding and general husbandry. I rubbed my hands together and repressed a chuckle of satisfaction; I had something to work on now.

I don't like to boast but I think I can say in all honesty that I carried out an exhaustive scientific survey of that varied group. From the outset I adopted an attitude of cold detachment, mercilessly banishing any ideas of personal preference. If I had been pleasing only myself I would have given first prize to a gleaming black Labrador sitting by a chair with massive composure and offering me a gracious paw every time I came near. And my second would have been a benevolent tabby – I have always had a thing about tabby cats – which rubbed its cheek against my hand as I talked to its owner. The pups, crawling over each other and grunting obesely, would probably have come third. But I put away these unworthy thoughts and pursued my chosen course.

I was distracted to some extent by the parrot which kept saying 'Hellow' in a voice of devastating refinement like a butler answering a telephone and the mynah which repeatedly adjured me to 'Shut door as you go out,' in a booming Yorkshire baritone.

The only adult in the ring was a bosomy lady with glacial pop eyes and a white poodle on her knee. As I approached she gave me a challenging stare as though defying me to place her pet anywhere but first.

'Hello, little chap,' I said, extending my hand. The poodle responded by drawing its lips soundlessly back from its teeth and giving me much the same kind of look as its owner. I withdrew my hand hastily.

'Oh you needn't be afraid of him,' the lady said frigidly. 'He won't hurt you.'

I gave a light laugh. 'I'm sure he won't.' I held out my hand again. 'You're a nice little dog, aren't you?' Once more the poodle bared his teeth and when I persevered by trying to stroke his ears he snapped noiselessly, his teeth clicking together an inch from my fingers.

'He doesn't like you, I can see that. Do you, darling?' The lady put her cheek against the dog's head and stared at me distastefully as though she knew just how he felt.

'Shut door as you go out,' commanded the mynah gruffy from somewhere behind me.

I gave the lady my questionnaire and moved on.

And among the throng there was one who stood out; the little boy with the goldfish. In reply to my promptings he discoursed knowledgeably about his fish, its feeding, life history and habits. He even had a fair idea of the common diseases. The bowl, too, was beautifully clean and the water fresh; I was impressed.

When I had completed the circuit I swept the ring for the last time with a probing eye. Yes, there was no doubt about it; I had the three prize winners fixed in my mind beyond any question and in an order based on strictly scientific selection. I stepped out into the middle.

'Ladies and gentlemen,' I said, scanning the company with an affable smile.

'Hellow,' responded the parrot fruitily.

I ignored him and continued. 'These are the successful entrants. First, number six, the goldfish. Second, number fifteen, the guinea pig. And third, number ten, the white kitten.'

I half expected a little ripple of applause but there was none. In fact my announcement was greeted by a tight-lipped silence. I had noticed an immediate change in the atmosphere when I mentioned the goldfish. It was striking – a sudden cold wave which swept away the expectant smiles and replaced them with discontented muttering.

I had done something wrong, but what? I looked around helplessly as the hum of voices increased. 'What do you think of that, then?' 'Not fair, is it?'

'Wouldn't have thought it of him?' 'All them lovely rabbits and he hardly looked at them.'

I couldn't make it out, but my job was done, anyway. I pushed between the chairs and escaped to the open field.

'Shut door as you go out,' the mynah requested in deepest bass as I departed.

I sought out Tristan again. The atmosphere in the beer tent had changed, too. The drinkers were long since past their peak and the hilarious babel which had met me on my last visit had died to an exhausted murmur. There was a general air of satiation. Tristan, pint in hand, was being addressed with great solemnity by a man in a flat cap and braces. The man swayed slightly as he grasped Tristan's free hand and gazed into his eyes. Occasionally he patted him on the shoulder with the utmost affection. Obviously my colleague had been forging deep and lasting friendships in here while I was making enemies outside.

I sidled up to him and spoke into his ear. 'Ready to go soon, Triss?'

He turned slowly and looked at me. 'No, old lad,' he said, articulating carefully. 'I'm afraid I shan't be coming with you. They're having a dance here on the showfield later and Doreen has consented to accompany me.' He cast a loving glance across the counter at the red-head who crinkled her nose at him.

I was about to leave when a snatch of conversation from behind made me pause.

'A bloody goldfish!' a voice was saying disgustedly.

'Aye, it's a rum 'un, George,' a second voice replied.

There was a slurping sound of beer being downed.

'But tha knows, Fred,' the first voice said. 'That vet feller had to do it. Didn't 'ave no choice. He couldn't pass over t'squire's son.'

'Reckon you're right, but it's a bugger when you get graft and corruption in t'Family Pets.'

A heavy sigh, then 'It's the way things are nowadays, Fred. Everything's hulterior.'

'You're right there, George. It's hulterior, that's what it is.'

I fought down a rising panic. The Pelhams had been Lords of the Manor of Darrowby for generations and the present squire was Major Pelham. I knew him as a friendly farmer client, but that was all. I'd never heard of his son.

I clutched at Tristan's arm. 'Who is that little boy over there?'

Tristan peered out glassily across the sward. 'The one with the goldfish bowl, you mean?'

'That's right.'

'It's young Nigel Pelham, the squire's son.'

'Oh Gawd,' I moaned. 'But I've never seen him before. Where's he been?'

'Boarding school down south, I believe. On holiday just now.'

I stared at the boy again. Tousled fair hair, grey open-necked shirt, sunburned legs. Just like all the others.

George was at it again. 'Lovely dogs and cats there was, but squire's lad won it with a bloody goldfish.

'Well, let's be right,' his companion put in. 'If that lad 'ad brought along a bloody stuffed monkey he'd still 'ave got fust prize with it.'

'No doubt about it, Fred. T'other kids might as well 'ave stopped at 'ome.'

'Aye, it's not like it used to be, George. Nobody does owt for nowt these days.'

'True, Fred, very true.' There was a gloomy silence punctuated by noisy gulpings. Then, in weary tones: 'Well you and me can't alter it. It's the kind of world we're living in today.'

I reeled out into the fresh air and the sunshine. Looking round at the tranquil scene, the long stretch of grass, the loop of pebbly river with the green hills rising behind, I had a sense of unreality. Was there any part of this peaceful cameo of rural England without its sinister undertones? As if by instinct I made my way into the long marquee which housed the produce section. Surely among those quiet rows of vegetables I would find repose.

The place was almost empty but as I made my way down the long lines of tables I came upon the solitary figure of old John William Enderby who had a little grocer's shop in the town.

'Well how are things?' I enquired.

'Nobbut middlin' lad,' the old man replied morosely.

'Why, what's wrong?'

'Well, ah got a second with me broad beans but only a highly commended for me shallots. Look at 'em.'

I looked. 'Yes, they're beautiful shallots, Mr Enderby.'

'Aye, they are, and nobbut a highly commended. It's a insult, that's what it is a insult.'

'But Mr Enderby . . . highly commended . . . I mean, that's pretty good isn't it?'

'No it isn't, it's a insult!'

'Oh bad luck.'

John William stared at me wide-eyed for a moment. 'It's not bad luck, lad, it's nowt but a twist.'

'Oh surely not!'

'Ah'm tellin' you. Jim Houlston got first with 'is shallots and judge is his wife's cousin.'

'Never!'

'It's true,' grunted John William, nodding solemnly. 'It's nowt but a twist.'

'Well I've never heard of such a thing!'

'You don't know what goes on, young man. Ah wasn't even placed with me taties. Frank Thompson got first wi' that lot.' He pointed to a tray of noble tubers.

I studied them. 'I must admit they look splendid potatoes.'

'Aye, they are, but Frank pinched 'em.'

'What?'

'Aye, they took first prize at Brisby show last Thursday and Frank pinched 'em off t'stand.'

I clutched at the nearby table. The foundations of my world were crumbling. 'That can't be true, Mr Enderby.'

'Ah'm not jokin' nor jestin',' declared John William. 'Them's self and same taties, ah'd know them anywhere. It's nowt but a . . .'

I could take no more. I fled.

Outside the evening sunshine was still warm and the whole field was awash with the soft light which, in the Dales, seems to stream down in a golden flood from the high tops. But it was as if the forces of darkness were pressing on me; all I wanted was to get home.

I hurried to the stewards' tent and collected my measuring stick, running a gauntlet of hostile stares from the pony people I had outed earlier in the day. They were still waving their certificates and arguing.

On the way to the car I had to pass several of the ladies who had watched me judge the pets and though they didn't exactly draw their skirts aside they managed to convey their message. Among the rows of vehicles I spotted the man with the moustache. He still hadn't taken his terrier away and his eyes, full of wounded resentment, followed my every step.

I was opening my door when Helen and her party, also apparently on the way home, passed about fifty yards away. Helen waved, I waved back, and

Richard Edmundson gave me a nod before helping her into the front seat of a gleaming, silver Daimler. The two fathers got into the back.

As I settled into the seat of my little Austin, braced my feet against the broken floor boards and squinted through the cracked windscreen I prayed that just this once the thing would go on the starter. Holding my breath I pulled at the knob but the engine gave a couple of lazy turns then fell silent.

Fishing the starting handle from under the seat I crept out and inserted it in its hole under the radiator; and as I began the old familiar winding the silver monster purred contemptuously past me and away.

Dropping into the driver's seat again I caught sight of my face in the mirror and could see the streaks and flecks of blood still caked on my cheek and around the roots of my hair. Tristan hadn't done a very good job with his bucket of cold water.

I looked back at the emptying field and at the Daimler disappearing round a distant bend. It seemed to me that in more ways than one the show was over.

Chapter Ten

Ben Ashby the cattle dealer looked over the gate with his habitual deadpan expression. It always seemed to me that after a lifetime of buying cows from farmers he had developed a terror of showing any emotion which might be construed as enthusiasm. When he looked at a beast his face registered nothing beyond, occasionally, a gentle sorrow.

This was how it was this morning as he leaned on the top spar and directed a gloomy stare at Harry Sumner's heifer. After a few moments he turned to the farmer.

'I wish you'd had her in for me, Harry. She's too far away. I'm going to have to get over the top.' He began to climb stiffly upwards and it was then that he spotted Monty. The bull hadn't been so easy to see before as he cropped the grass among the group of heifers but suddenly the great head rose high above the others, the nose ring gleamed, and an ominous, strangled bellow sounded across the grass. And as he gazed at us he pulled absently at the turf with a fore foot.

Ben Ashby stopped climbing, hesitated for a second then returned to ground level.

'Aye well,' he muttered, still without changing expression. 'It's not that far away. I reckon I can see all right from here.'

Monty had changed a lot since the first day I saw him about two years ago. He had been a fortnight old then, a skinny, knock-kneed little creature, his head deep in a calf bucket.

'Well, what do you think of me new bull?' Harry Sumner had asked, laughing. 'Not much for a hundred quid is he?'

I whistled. 'As much as that?'

'Aye, it's a lot for a new-dropped calf, isn't it? But I can't think of any other way of getting into the Newton strain. I haven't the brass to buy a big 'un.'

Not all the farmers of those days were as farseeing as Harry and some of them would use any type of male bovine to get their cows in calf.

One such man produced a gaunt animal for Siegfried's inspection and asked him what he thought of his bull. Siegfried's reply of 'All horns and balls' didn't please the owner but I still treasure it as the most graphic description of the typical scrub bull of that period.

Harry was a bright boy. He had inherited a little place of about a hundred acres on his father's death and with his young wife had set about making it go. He was in his early twenties and when I first saw him I had been deceived by his almost delicate appearance into thinking that he wouldn't be up to the job; the pallid face, the large, sensitive eyes and slender frame didn't seem fitted for the seven days a week milking, feeding, mucking-out slog that was dairy farming. But I had been wrong.

The fearless way he plunged in and grabbed at the hind feet of kicking cows for me to examine and his clenched-teeth determination as he hung on to the noses of the big loose beasts at testing time made me change my mind in a hurry. He worked endlessly and tirelessly and it was natural that his drive should have taken him to the south of Scotland to find a bull.

Harry's was an Ayrshire herd – unusual among the almost universal shorthorns in the Dales – and there was no doubt an injection of the famous Newton blood would be a sure way of improving his stock.

'He's got prize winners on both his sire and dam's side,' the young farmer said. 'And a grand pedigree name, too. Newton Montmorency the Sixth – Monty for short.'

As though recognising his name, the calf raised his head from the bucket and looked at us. It was a comic little face – wet-muzzled, milk slobbered half way up his cheeks and dribbling freely from his mouth. I bent over into the pen and scratched the top of the hard little head, feeling the tiny horn buds no bigger than peas under my fingers. Limpid-eyed and unafraid, Monty submitted calmly to the caress for a few moments then sank his head again in the bucket.

I saw quite a bit of Harry Sumner over the next few weeks and usually had a look at his expensive purchase. And as the calf grew you could see why he had cost £100. He was in a pen with three of Harry's own calves and his superiority was evident at a glance; the broad forehead and wide-set eyes; the deep chest and short straight legs; the beautifully even line of the back from shoulder to tail head. Monty had class; and small as he was he was all bull.

He was about three months old when Harry rang to say he thought the calf had pneumonia. I was surprised because the weather was fine and warm and I knew Monty was in a draught-free building. But when I saw him I thought immediately that his owner's diagnosis was right. The heaving of the rib cage, the temperature of 105 degrees – it looked fairly straightforward. But when I got my stethoscope on his chest and listened for the pneumonic sounds I heard nothing. His lungs were perfectly clear. I went over him several times but there was not a squeak, not a râle, not the slightest sign of consolidation.

This was a facer. I turned to the farmer. 'It's a funny one, Harry. He's sick, all right, but his symptoms don't add up to anything recognisable.'

I was going against my early training because the first vet I ever saw practice with in my student days told me once: 'If you don't know what's wrong with an animal for God's sake don't admit it. Give it a name – call it McLuskie's Disease or Galloping Dandruff – anything you like, but give it a name.' But no inspiration came to me as I looked at the panting, anxious-eyed little creature.

Treat the symptoms. That was the thing to do. He had a temperature so I'd try to get that down for a start. I brought out my pathetic armoury of febrifuges; the injection of non-specific antiserum, the 'fever drink' of sweet spirit of nitre; but over the next two days it was obvious that the time-honoured remedies were having no effect.

On the fourth morning, Harry Sumner met me as I got out of my car. 'He's walking funny, this morning, Mr Herriot – and he seems to be blind.'

Blind! An unusual form of lead-poisoning – could that be it? I hurried into the calf pen and began to look round the walls, but there wasn't a scrap of paint anywhere and Monty had spent his entire life in there.

And anyway, as I looked at him I realised that he wasn't really blind; his eyes were staring and slightly upturned and he blundered unseeingly around the pen, but he blinked as I passed my hand in front of his face. To complete my bewilderment he walked with a wooden, stiff-legged gait almost like a mechanical toy and my mind began to snatch at diagnostic straws – tetanus, no – meningitis – no, no; I always tried to maintain the calm, professional exterior but I had to fight an impulse to scratch my head and stand gaping.

I got off the place as quickly as possible and settled down to serious thought as I drove away. My lack of experience didn't help, but I did have a knowledge of pathology and physiology and when stumped for a diagnosis I could usually work something out on rational grounds. But this thing didn't make sense.

That night I got out my books, notes from college, back numbers of the Veterinary Record and anything else I could find on the subject of calf diseases. Somewhere here there would surely be a clue. But the volumes on medicine and surgery were barren of inspiration and I had about given up hope when I came upon the passage in a little pamphlet on calf diseases. 'Peculiar, stilted gait, staring eyes with a tendency to gaze upwards, occasionally respiratory symptoms with high temperature.' The words seemed to leap out at me from the printed page and it was as though the unknown author was patting me on the shoulder and murmuring reassuringly: 'This is it, you see. It's all perfectly clear.'

I grabbed the phone and rang Harry Sumner. 'Harry, have you ever noticed Monty and those other calves in the pen licking each other?'

'Aye, they're allus at it, the little beggars. It's like a hobby with them. Why?'

'Well I know what's wrong with your bull. He's got a hair ball.'

'A hair ball? Where?'

'In the abomasum – the fourth stomach. That's what's setting up all those strange symptoms.'

'Well I'll go to hell. What do we do about it, then?'

'It'll probably mean an operation, but I'd like to try dosing him with liquid paraffin first. I'll put a pint bottle on the step for you if you'll come and collect it. Give him half a pint now and the same first thing in the morning. It might just grease the thing through. I'll see you tomorrow.'

I hadn't a lot of faith in the liquid paraffin. I suppose I suggested it for the sake of doing something while I played nervously with the idea of operating. And next morning the picture was as I expected; Monty was still rigid-limbed, still staring sightlessly ahead of him, and an oiliness round his rectum and down his tail showed that the paraffin had by-passed the obstruction.

'He hasn't had a bite now for three days,' Harry said. 'I doubt he won't stick it much longer.'

I looked from his worried face to the little animal trembling in the pen. 'You're right. We'll have to open him up straight away to have any hope of saving him. Are you willing to let me have a go?'

'Oh, aye, let's be at t'job – sooner the better.' He smiled at me. It was a confident smile and my stomach gave a lurch. His confidence could be badly misplaced because in those days abdominal surgery in the bovine was in a primitive state. There were a few jobs we had begun to tackle fairly regularly but removal of a hair-ball wasn't one of them and my knowledge of the procedure was confined to some rather small-print reading in the text books.

But this young farmer had faith in me. He thought I could do the job so it was no good letting him see my doubts. It was at times like this that I envied our colleagues in human medicine. When a surgical case came up they packed their patient off to a hospital but the vet just had to get his jacket off on the spot and make an operating theatre out of the farm buildings.

Harry and I busied ourselves in boiling up the instruments, setting out buckets of hot water and laying a clean bed of straw in an empty pen. Despite his weakness the calf took nearly sixty c.c.'s of Nembutal into his vein before he was fully anaesthetised but finally he was asleep, propped on his back between two straw bales, his little hooves dangling above him. I was ready to start.

It's never the same as it is in the books. The pictures and diagrams look so simple and straightforward but it is a different thing when you are cutting into a living, breathing creature with the abdomen rising and falling gently and the blood oozing beneath your knife. The abomasum, I knew, was just down there, slightly to the right of the sternum but as I cut through the peritoneum there was this slippery mass of fat-streaked omentum obscuring everthing; and as I pushed it aside one of the bales moved and Monty tilted to his left causing a sudden gush of intestines into the wound. I put the flat of my hand against the shining pink loops – it would be just great if my patient's insides started spilling out on to the straw before I had started.

'Pull him upright, Harry, and shove that bale back into place,' I gasped. The farmer quickly complied but the intestines weren't at all anxious to return to their place and kept intruding coyly as I groped for the abomasum. Frankly I was beginning to feel just a bit lost and my heart was thudding when I came upon something hard. It was sliding about beyond the wall of one of the stomachs – at the moment I wasn't sure which. I gripped it and lifted it into the wound. I had hold of the abomasum and that hard thing inside must be the hair-ball.

Repelling the intestines which had made another determined attempt to push their way into the act, I incised the stomach and had my first look at the cause of the trouble. It wasn't a ball at all, rather a flat plaque of densely matted hair mixed freely with strands of hay, sour curd and a shining covering of my liquid paraffin. The whole thing was jammed against the pyloric opening.

Gingerly I drew it out through the incision and dropped it in the straw. It wasn't till I had closed the stomach wound with the gut, stitched up the muscle layer and had started on the skin that I realised that the sweat was running down my face. As I blew away a droplet from my nose end Harry broke the silence.

'It's a hell of a tricky job, isn't it?' he said. Then he laughed and thumped my shoulder. 'I bet you felt a bit queer the first time you did one of these!'

I pulled another strand of suture silk through and knotted it. 'You're right, Harry,' I said. 'How right you are.'

·When I had finished we covered Monty with a horse rug and piled straw on top of that, leaving only his head sticking out. I bent over and touched a corner of the eye. Not a vestige of a corneal reflex. God, he was deep – had I given him too much anaesthetic? And of course there'd be surgical shock, too. As I left I glanced back at the motionless little animal. He looked smaller than ever and very vulnerable under the bare walls of the pen.

I was busy for the rest of the day but that evening my thoughts kept coming back to Monty. Had he come out of it yet? Maybe he was dead. I hadn't the experience of previous cases to guide me and I simply had no idea of how a calf reacted to an operation like that. And I couldn't rid myself of the nagging consciousness of how much it all meant to Harry Sumner. The bull is half the herd, they say, and half of Harry's future herd was lying there under the straw – he wouldn't be able to find that much money again.

I jumped suddenly from my chair. It was no good, I had to find out what was happening. Part of me rebelled at the idea of looking amateurish and unsure of myself by going fussing back, but, I thought, I could always say I had returned to look for an instrument.

The farm was in darkness as I crept into the pen. I shone my torch on the mound of straw and saw with a quick thump of the heart that the calf had not moved. I dropped to my knees and pushed a hand under the rug; he was breathing anyway. But there was still no eye reflex – either he was dying or he was taking a hell of a time to come out.

In the shadows of the yard I looked across at the soft glow from the farmhouse kitchen. Nobody had heard me. I slunk over to the car and drove off with the sick knowledge that I was no further forward. I still didn't know how the job was going to turn out.

Next morning I had to go through the same thing again and as I walked stiffly across to the calf pen I knew for sure I'd see something this time. Either he'd be dead or better. I opened the outer door and almost ran down the passage. It was the third pen along and I stared hungrily into it.

Monty was sitting up on his chest. He was still under the rug and straw and he looked sorry for himself but when a bovine animal is on its chest I always feel hopeful. The tensions flowed from me in a great wave. He had survived the operation – the first stage was over; and as I knelt rubbing the top of his head I had the feeling that we were going to win.

And, in fact, he did get better, though I have always found it difficult to explain to myself scientifically why the removal of that pad of tangled fibres could cause such a dramatic improvement in so many directions. But there it was. His temperature did drop and his breathing returned to normal, his eyes did stop staring and the weird stiffness disappeared from his limbs.

But though I couldn't understand it, I was none the less delighted. Like a teacher with his favourite pupil, I developed a warm proprietary affection for the calf and when I happened to be on the farm I found my feet straying unbidden to his pen. He always walked up to me and regarded me with friendly interest; it was as if he had a fellow feeling for me, too.

He was rather more than a year old when I noticed the change. The friendly interest gradually disappeared from his eyes and was replaced by a thoughtful, speculative look; and he developed a habit of shaking his head at me at the same time.

'I'd stop going in there, Mr Herriot, if I were you,' Harry said one day. 'He's getting big and I reckon he's going to be a cheeky bugger before he's finished.'

But cheeky was the wrong word. Harry had a long, trouble-free spell and Monty was nearly two years old when I saw him again. It wasn't a case of illness this time. One or two of Harry's cows had been calving before their time and it was typical of him that he should ask me to blood test his entire herd for Brucellosis.

We worked our way easily through the cows and I had a long row of glass tubes filled with blood in just over an hour.

'Well, that's the lot in here,' the farmer said. 'We only have bull to do and we're finished.' He led the way across the yard through the door into the calf pens and along a passage to the bull box at the end. He opened the half door and as I looked inside I felt a sudden sense of shock.

Monty was enormous. The neck with its jutting humps of muscle supported a head so huge that the eyes looked tiny. And there was nothing friendly in those eyes now; no expression at all, in fact, only a cold black glitter. He was standing sideways to me, facing the wall, but I knew he was watching me as he pushed his head against the stones, his great horns scoring the whitewash with slow, menacing deliberation. Occasionally he snorted from deep in his chest but apart from that he remained ominously still. Monty wasn't just a bull – he was a vast, brooding presence.

Harry grinned as he saw me staring over the door. 'Well, do you fancy popping inside to scratch his head? That's what you allus used to do.'

'No thanks.' I dragged my eyes away from the animal. 'But I wonder what my expectation of life would be if I did go in.'

'I reckon you'd last about a minute,' Harry said thoughtfully. 'He's a grand bull – all I ever expected – but by God he's a mean 'un. I never trust him an inch.'

'And how,' I asked without enthusiasm, ''am I supposed to get a sample of blood from him?'

'Oh I'll trap his head in yon corner.' Harry pointed to a metal yoke above a trough in an opening into the yard at the far side of the box. 'I'll give him some meal to 'tice him in.' He went back down the passage and soon I could see him out in the yard scooping meal into the trough.

The bull at first took no notice and continued to prod at the wall with his horns, then he turned with awesome slowness, took a few unhurried steps across the box and put his nose down to the trough. Harry, out of sight in the yard, pulled the lever and the yoke crashed shut on the great neck.

'All right,' the farmer cried, hanging on to the lever, 'I have 'im. You can go in now.'

I opened the door and entered the box and though the bull was held fast by the head there was still the uneasy awareness that he and I were alone in that small space together. And as I passed along the massive body and put my hand on the neck I sensed a quivering emanation of pent up power and rage. Digging my fingers into the jugular furrow I watched the vein rise up and poised my needle. It would take a good hard thrust to pierce that leathery skin.

The bull stiffened but did not move as I plunged the needle in and with relief I saw the blood flowing darkly into the syringe. Thank God I had hit the vein first time and didn't have to start poking around. I was withdrawing the needle and thinking that the job had been so simple after all when everything started to happen. The bull gave a tremendous bellow and whipped round at me with no trace of his former lethargy. I saw that he had got one horn out of the yoke and though he couldn't reach me with his head his shoulder knocked me on my back with a terrifying revelation of unbelievable strength. I heard Harry shouting from outside and as I scrambled up and headed for the box door I saw that the madly plunging creature had almost got his second horn clear and when I reached the passage I heard the clang of the yoke as he finally freed himself.

Anybody who has travelled a narrow passage a few feet ahead of about a ton of snorting, pounding death will appreciate that I didn't dawdle. I was spurred on by the certain knowledge that if Monty caught me he would plaster me against the wall as effortlessly as I would squash a ripe plum, and though I was clad in a long oilskin coat and Wellingtons I doubt whether an olympic sprinter in full running kit would have bettered my time.

I made the door at the end with a foot to spare, dived through and crashed it shut. The first thing I saw was Harry Sumner running round from the outside of the box. He was very pale. I couldn't see my face but it felt pale; even my lips were cold and numb.

'God, I'm sorry!' Harry said hoarsely. 'The yoke couldn't have closed properly – that bloody great neck of his. The lever just jerked out of my hand. Damn, I'm glad to see you – I thought you were a goner!'

I looked down at my hand. The blood-filled syringe was still tightly clutched there. 'Well I've got my sample anyway, Harry. And it's just as well, because it would take some fast talking to get me in there to try for another. I'm afraid you've just seen the end of a beautiful friendship.'

'Aye, the big sod!' Harry listened for a few moments to the thudding of Monty's horns against the door. 'And after all you did for him. That's gratitude for you.'

Chapter Eleven

I suppose if it hadn't been for the Tuberculin Testing scheme I'd never have come to know Ewan and Ginny Ross.

Siegfried broached the matter to me one morning as I was making up some colic mixture in the dispensary.

'All this extra testing work is a bit much for a one-man practice, especially when it's an older man. Ewan Ross has been on the phone asking me if I could help him and we've thrashed out a plan which could benefit us both. But it depends on you.'

'What do you mean?'

'Well, would you be willing to go up to Scarburn and do his testing say three days a week? Ewan and I would split the proceeds and you'd get a little cut too.'

I screwed a cork into the last bottle. 'It's all right with me. I'd enjoy a bit of fresh country. It's real wild up there – about twenty-five miles away isn't it?'

'Just about. It is a bit bleak, but it's beautiful in fine weather. And I'm sure you'll get on with Ewan.'

'I've heard quite a lot about him.' I laughed. 'They say he'd rather settle down with a bottle than work.'

Siegfried turned a level gaze on me. 'They say a lot things but he's a good friend of mine and just about the best veterinary surgeon I've ever seen.' He paused for a moment then went on. 'I want you to go up there tomorrow to meet him, then you can judge for yourself.'

As I drove out next morning I reflected on the snippets which had come through to me about Ewan Ross. I didn't know all that much about him; twenty-five miles was enough to make him remote from my own working area and in any case hard drinking and wild behaviour were the norm among the older members of the profession. The more recent graduates were a different type altogether; more scientifically orientated, more conscious of professional standards; but the men who had been on the go for twenty years or more, many of them ex-servicemen, were a hard-bitten, rugged lot of characters. Most of them had had a hell of a life, working single-handed through the years when times were hard, money short and the work at its roughest and I suppose they just had to erupt now and then.

Ewan Ross, it was said, would incarcerate himself in some village pub and go on a bender lasting days on end until his wife finally managed to winkle him out and entice him back to his practice. People said, too, that he liked to challenge big farm men in bars to 'take a hold' – to shake hands with him and have a test of grip which usually finished with the big man on the floor. There were tales, too, of brushes with the police – he'd lost his licence for a while for being drunk in charge of a car – and other things.

The scene beyond my car windows was changing all the time as I drove. The Dales country around Darrowby was softened by the trees which lined the valley floors and by the lush, level pastures by the rivers where they wandered among leisurely shallows. But this was the high Pennines, the harsh, wind-blown roof of England, almost treeless with only the endless miles of dry stone walls climbing and criss-crossing over the bald heights.

And, driving into Scarburn, it occurred to me that this was just the sort of place some seedy character would want to hole up. It was only too easy to picture the broken-down vet and his harassed, blowsy wife. I had always thought Darrowby was quiet and a bit rough-hewn but it was a sophisticated metropolis compared to Scarburn.

On this windy, sunless day the grey horse-shoe of buildings grouped around the steeply sloping market place seemed in danger of sliding down the high fell on which it was perched. I drove past the ironmonger's, the Methodist Chapel, a draper's with a few dowdy clothes in the window, the Temperance Hotel; there was no attempt at adornment or softness anywhere and apart from a few muffled women battling against the wind the streets were empty.

I found the veterinary surgeon's plate on a small modern house about two hundred yards beyond the market place and knocked at the door. I had a fairly clear mental image by now of my colleague within; needing a shave, running to fat, the smell of whisky about him, and as the door opened I drew in my breath in anticipation.

A tallish, heavy-shouldered man stood there. The face, ruddy and handsome with pale blue friendly eyes, could have been that of a young man but for the swathes of silver in the sandy hair above it. The suit of soft brown tweed hung gracefully on his lean frame. He held out his hand.

'You'll be James Herriot. Come away in.' The voice had the lilt of the Scottish Highlands with something else in it.

He led the way into the kitchen where a woman was standing by the stove. 'Ginny,' he called. 'Come and meet Siegfried's right hand man, young Mr Herriot.'

Virginia Ross turned her head and looked at me.

'Hello,' she said. 'You're just in time for coffee.' And she gave me a crooked smile with one eyebrow slightly raised which had an extraordinary effect. Over the years I knew her she always looked at me like that – as though I was a quite pleasant but amusing object – and it always did the same thing to me. It's difficult to put into words but perhaps I can best describe it by saying that if I had been a little dog I'd have gone leaping and gambolling around the room wagging my tail furiously.

She would be about ten years younger than Ewan – somewhere in her early forties – but she had the kind of attractiveness that was ageless. She filled three mugs with coffee and I sat down at the table with the feeling that I was with friends. I couldn't count the times I have sat in that kitchen since that first day, drinking tea or coffee or if I happened in around lunch time, eating Ginny's delectable food. She was a cook with the magic touch; in fact as time went on I found she could do just about anything. She spoke several languages, had read everything, she painted and embroidered and as I said, she could cook. How she could cook! She must have had to work on a very tight budget but she managed to make a poem out of the simplest materials.

Ewan pushed away his mug and stood up. 'I've got to operate on a colt for umbilical hernia. Would you care to come along?'

'Yes,' I said. 'I'd like that very much.'

We went out to a small building alongside the house which was the surgery and dispensary. There is a fascination in seeing another man's set-up and I browsed happily along the shelves and tables. There isn't nearly so much fun in doing this nowadays because vets all use the same drugs – a narrow variation in the range of antibiotics, sulphonamides and steroids – but back there in 1939 we were still using the countless mystical remedies of the dark ages.

And Ewan's selection was even more primitive than ours at Darrowby, Physic balls, electuaries, red blister, stimulant draught, ammonia powders, cooling lotions, alterative mixture, Donovan's solution; and a lot of Ewan's own pet ideas with a whiff of black magic about them; like his paste of arsenic and soft soap which you smeared on a length of twine and tied round the necks of tumours where it was supposed to eat its way through.

As I wandered round I watched him preparing for the operation. He didn't seem to have a steriliser but he was methodically boiling the instruments in a saucepan on a gas ring. Then he took them out with forceps and carefully wrapped them one by one in sheets of clean brown paper. He was a picture of unhurried calm.

It was the same when we got to the farm. Ewan paced about the field till he found a perfectly level spot where the grass was long and soft, then he pottered along, peering closely at the ground, throwing aside a few small stones which were lurking there. When he was satisfied he made a table out of a couple of straw bales, covered it with a clean sheet and laid out his instruments on it meticulously. Next to the bales he stationed a bucket of hot water, soap and towel and finally produced a beautiful soft white rope tied in a neat coil. Only then did he allow the colt to be led out.

I must have looked a bit open-mouthed because he grinned and said, 'I never start anything till I've set my stall out properly.'

What struck me was the difference from my boss in Darrowby. Siegfried would never have had the patience to go through all this procedure; his system was based on Napoleon's dictum of 'On s'engage et puis on voit' and it usually involved a lot of yelling and rushing about. I had to admit that this was more peaceful.

But I really saw what Ewan was made of when he started to do the job. He was using the old-fashioned method of casting the horse by sidelines and trussing him up before administering the chloroform but he did it as I'd never seen it done before.

The patient was a shaggy little animal with the beginnings of feathers round his hooves; he was typical of the hundreds of cart colts we had to deal with every year and he trembled nervously as he looked around him.

Ewan seemed to pacify him immediately with a few soft words as he placed the rope around his neck then between the hind legs and back through the neck loop; and when the farm men pulled on the rope he stood by the head still talking so that the colt collapsed easily on to his grassy bed.

It was an education for me to watch him then, deftly tugging and knotting till the animal was positioned on his back with his legs tied together fore to hind and the operation area exposed. Once more Ewan had set his stall out properly.

He gave me the job of looking after the chloroform muzzle while he incised the skin, tucked away the hernia and neatly sutured the wound. He did it all with the firm, almost rough movements of the expert surgeon and as I watched the strong fingers at work I was reminded again of the tales of 'take a hold'.

Even when he was finished and had thoroughly cleared away the last drop of blood and debris from the operation site he still was in no hurry. He washed and dried his instruments with great deliberation, wrapped them up again in the sheets of brown paper then sat down on the straw bales to wait for the colt to come round from the anaesthetic. As he sat there, perfectly relaxed, he pulled a cigarette paper from his pocket, tipped a stream of dark brown dusty tobacco into it from a little pouch, rolled the paper effortlessly with one hand, licked it, screwed up one end and thrust it into his mouth.

As the smoke curled round his ears he gave a few instructions in his soft Highland voice.

'Now just pull him on to his chest will you. That's right, put your knee behind his shoulder and let him rest there for a while. Don't hurry him, now, he'll get up when he's ready.'

He didn't leave for another twenty minutes when the colt gave a final effort and heaved himself to his feet where he stood shakily, looking around him in some bewilderment.

'Let him stand there awhile till he's steady on his legs,' Ewan said. 'Then you can walk him back to his box.'

He turned to me. 'Well now, there's not a bad little pub in this village. How about a beer before lunch?'

There was nobody but ourselves in the bar. Ewan took a contented sip of his half pint then pulled the small pouch again from his pocket. I watched him again as he rolled another cigarette with one hand.

I laughed. 'You know, I've only seen that done by cowboys on the pictures. Where did you learn the art?'

'Oh that?' Ewan gave his shy smile, 'In Canada, a long time ago. It was the only way I had of getting a smoke for years and I've never got out of the way of it.'

He obviously found difficulty in talking about himself but as we sat I was able to build a picture of his history. He was a farmer's son from West Sutherland and even as a small boy he had worked with horses and been fascinated by them. On leaving school he had, like many other restless Highlanders, sailed away to seek his fortune. First he tried Australia where he took a job riding the rabbit fences, then he moved to Canada and worked on a ranch for years, more or less living in the saddle. He came to England with the Canadian Expeditionary Force at the beginning of the war and served till 1918 in the cavalry. I suppose he must have recognised then that his life seemed to be inevitably bound up with horses so he enrolled with a lot of other ex-servicemen in the London Veterinary College. That was where he met Ginny.

He didn't go into details of how he had finally landed in Scarburn and I didn't press him. But it seemed such a waste. You don't often find a top class horseman and a veterinary surgeon combined. Siegfried was such a one and I never thought I'd see a better. But Ewan Ross could beat them all. The extraordinary thing was that he had settled in a cattle and sheep district where his equine skills were seldom exploited. Certainly there were numbers of racing stables in the Pennines but Ewan made not the slightest attempt to gain a footing there; a 'horse specialist' in a big Bentley used to travel around doing most of the racing work and making a packet of money in the process. He wasn't a bad chap, either, but Ewan had forgotten more about horses than he'd ever know.

I suppose the simple explanation was that Ewan was devoid of ambition. He didn't want a big successful practice, he wasn't interested in being rich or famous. Even this morning when I talked to him about our plans in Darrowby I could see he was listening with polite attention, but it didn't mean a thing to him. No, Ewan would do enough work to keep going and beyond that he just didn't give a damn.

We stayed for something like half an hour in the bar and we'd drunk three glasses of beer apiece. I looked at my watch.

'I'd better be getting back down the hill to Darrowby,' I said. 'I've got a few things fixed for this afternoon.'

Ewan smiled. 'Oh, there's no hurry. We'll just have one for the road.' His voice was soft as usual but it had a sleepy quality now and I was surprised to see a slight glassiness in the pale blue eyes. There was no doubt about it – that small amount of drink had affected him.

'No thanks,' I said. 'I've really got to go.'

And as I drove back along the narrow dry-walled road that crawled its slow way among the fells I pondered on the strange fact; Ewan Ross couldn't drink. Or he had a certain proportion of alcohol in his bloodstream so that he was easily topped up. But I didn't think it was that; he just had a low threshold for the stuff. I had a conviction that he would have stayed in that pub if I had been agreeable; and who knows when he might have come out? Ewan's famous benders could all have started as simply.

Anyway, I was only guessing and I never did find out, because I always said 'No thanks' when he said 'We'll just have one for the road.' All the years I knew him I never saw him drunk or anything like it so I can't say anything about that other side of his life.

Strangely enough, circumstances took me through Scarburn just a few days afterwards. It was Sunday and the church was turning out and from my car I saw Ewan and Ginny, dressed in their best, walking down the street ahead of me. I didn't catch them up – just watching them till the straight-backed easy striding man and the elegant woman turned the corner out of sight, and I thought as I was to think so often what marvellous-looking people were my two new friends.

Chapter Twelve

'You know, there's maybe something in this Raynes ghost business after all.' Tristan pushed his chair back from the breakfast table, stretched out his legs more comfortably and resumed his study of the *Darrowby and Houlton Times*. 'It says here they've got a historian looking into it and this man has unearthed some interesting facts.'

Siegfried didn't say anything, but his eyes narrowed as his brother took out a Woodbine and lit it. Siegfried had given up smoking a week ago and he didn't want to watch anybody lighting up; particularly somebody like Tristan who invested even the smallest action with quiet delight, rich fulfilment. My boss's mouth tightened to a grim line as the young man unhurriedly selected a cigarette, flicked his lighter and dragged the smoke deep with a kind of ecstatic gasp.

'Yes,' Tristan continued, thin outgoing wisps mingling with his words. 'This chap points out that several of the monks were murdered at Raynes Abbey in the fourteenth century.'

'Well, so what?' snapped Siegfried.

Tristan raised his eyebrows. 'This cowled figure that's been seen so often lately near the abbey – why shouldn't it be the spirit of one of those monks?'

'Whaat? What's that you say?'

'Well, after all it makes you think, doesn't it? Who knows what fell deeds might have been . . .?'

'What the hell are you talking about?' Siegfried barked.

Tristan looked hurt. 'That's all very well, and you may laugh, but remember what Shakespeare said.' He raised a solemn finger. 'There are more things in heaven and earth, Horatio, than are dreamt of in your . . .'

'Oh balls!' said Siegfried, bringing the discussion effectively to a close.

I took a last thankful swallow of coffee and put down my cup, I was pleased that the topic had petered out fairly peacefully because Siegfried was in an edgy condition. Up to last week he had been a dedicated puffer of pipe and cigarettes but he had also developed a classical smoker's cough and had suffered increasingly from violent stomach-ache. At times his long thin face had assumed the appearance of a skull, the cheeks deeply sunken, the eyes smouldering far down in their sockets. And the doctor had said he must give up smoking.

Siegfried had obeyed, felt immediately better and was instantly seized with the evangelical zeal of the convert. But he didn't just advise people to give up tobacco; I have seen him several times strike a cigarette from the trembling fingers of farm workers, push his face to within inches of theirs and grind out menacingly, 'Now don't ever let me see you with one of those bloody things in your mouth again, do you hear?'

Even now there are grizzled men who tell me with a shudder, 'Nay, ah've never had a fag sin' Mr Farnon told me to stop, thirty years back. Nay, bugger it, the way 'e looked at me I dursn't do it!'

However the uncomfortable fact remained that his crusade hadn't the slightest effect on his brother. Tristan smoked almost continually but he never coughed and his digestion was excellent.

Siegfried looked at him now as he contentedly tapped off a little ash and took another blissful suck. 'You smoke too many of those bloody cigarettes!'

'So do you.'

'No I don't!' Siegfried retorted. 'I'm a non-smoker and it's time you were, too! It's a filthy habit and you'll kill yourself the way you're going!'

Tristan gave him a benign look and again his words floated out on the fine Woodbine mist. 'Oh I'm sure you're wrong. Do you know, I think it rather agrees with me.'

Siegfried got up and left the room. I sympathised with him for he was in a difficult position. Being in loco parentis he was in a sense providing his brother with the noxious weeds and his innate sense of propriety prevented him from abusing his position by dashing the things from Tristan's hands as he did with others. He had to fall back on exhortation and it was getting him nowhere. And there was another thing – he probably wanted to avoid a row this morning as Tristan was leaving on one of his mysterious trips back to the Veterinary College; in fact my first job was to take him down to the Great North Road where he was going to hitch a lift.

After I had left him there I set off on my rounds and, as I drove, my thoughts kept going back to the conversation at breakfast. A fair number of people were prepared to swear that they had seen the Raynes ghost and though it was easy to dismiss some of them as sensation mongers or drunkards the fact remained that others were very solid citizens indeed.

The story was always the same. There was a hill beyond Raynes village and at the top a wood came right up to the roadside. Beyond lay the abbey. People driving up the hill late at night said they had seen the monk in their headlights – a monk in a brown habit just disappearing into the wood. They believed the figure had been walking across the road but they weren't sure because it was always a little too far away. But they were adamant about the other part; they had seen a cowled figure, head bowed, go into that wood. There must have been something uninviting about the apparition because nobody ever said they had gone into the wood after it.

It was strange that after my thoughts had been on Raynes during the day I should be called to the village at one o'clock the following morning. Crawling from bed and climbing wearily into my clothes I couldn't help thinking of Tristan curled up peacefully in his Edinburgh lodgings far away from the troubles of practice. But I didn't feel too bad about getting up; Raynes was only three miles away and the job held no prospect of hard labour – a colic in a little boy's Shetland pony. And it was a fine night – very cold with the first chill of autumn but with a glorious full moon to light my way along the road.

They were walking the pony round the yard when I got there. The owner was the accountant at my bank and he gave me a rueful smile.

'I'm very sorry to get you out of bed, Mr Herriot, but I was hoping this bit of bellyache would go off. We've been parading round here for two hours. When we stop he tries to roll.'

'You've done the right thing,' I said. 'Rolling can cause a twist in the bowel.' I examined the little animal and was reassured. He had a normal temperature, good strong pulse, and listening at his flank I could hear the typical abdominal sounds of spasmodic colic.

What he needed was a good evacuation of the bowel, but I had to think carefully when computing the dose of arecoline for this minute member of the equine species. I finally settled on an eighth of a grain and injected it into the neck muscles. The pony stood for a few moments in the typical colic position, knuckling over the sinking down on one hind leg then the other and occasionally trying to lie down.

'Walk him on again slowly will you?' I was watching for the next stage and I didn't have long to wait; the pony's jaws began to champ and his lips to slobber and soon long dribbles of saliva hung down from his mouth. All right so far but I had to wait another fifteen minutes before he finally cocked his tail and deposited a heap of faeces on the concrete of the yard.

'I think he'll be O.K. now,' I said. 'So I'll leave you to it. Give me another ring if he's still in pain.'

Beyond the village the road curved suddenly out of sight of the houses then began the long straight climb to the abbey. Just up there at the limits of my headlights would be where the ghost was always seen – walking across the road and into the black belt of trees. At the top of the hill, on an impulse, I drew in to the side of the road and got out of the car. This was the very place. At the edge of the wood, under the brilliant moon, the smooth boles of the beeches shone with an eerie radiance and, high above, the branches creaked as they swayed in the wind.

I walked into the wood, feeling my way carefully with an arm held before me till I came out on the other side. Raynes Abbey lay before me.

I had always associated the beautiful ruin with summer days with the sun warming the old stones of the graceful arches, the chatter of voices, children playing on the cropped turf; but this was 2.30 a.m. in an empty world and the cold breath of the coming winter on my face. I felt suddenly alone.

In the cold glare everything was uncannily distinct. But there was a look of unreality about the silent rows of columns reaching into the dark sky and throwing their long pale shadows over the grass. Away at the far end I could see the monks' cells – gloomy black caverns deep in shadow – and as I looked an owl hooted, accentuating the heavy, blanketing silence.

A prickling apprehension began to creep over me, a feeling that my living person had no place here among these brooding relics of dead centuries. I turned quickly and began to hurry through the wood, bumping into the trees, tripping over roots and bushes, and when I reached my car I was trembling and more out of breath than I should have been. It was good to slam the door, turn the ignition and hear the familiar roar of the engine.

I was home within ten minutes and trotted up the stairs, looking forward to catching up on my lost sleep. Opening my bedroom door I flicked on the switch and felt a momentary surprise when the room remained in darkness. Then I stood frozen in the doorway.

By the window, where the moonlight flooded in, making a pool of silver in the gloom, a monk was standing. A monk in a brown habit, motionless, arms folded, head bowed. His face was turned from the light towards me but I could see nothing under the drooping cowl but a horrid abyss of darkness.

I thought I would choke. My mouth opened but no sound came. And in my racing mind one thought pounded above the others – there were such things as ghosts after all.

Again my mouth opened and a hoarse shriek emerged.

'Who in the name of God is that?'

The reply came back immediately in a sepulchral bass.

'Tristaan.'

I don't think I actually swooned, but I did collapse limply across my bed and lay there gasping, the blood thundering in my ears. I was dimly aware of the monk standing on a chair and screwing in the light bulb, giggling helplessly the while. Then he flicked on the switch and sat on my bed. With his cowl pushed back on his shoulders he lit a Woodbine and looked down at me, still shaking with laughter.

'Oh God, Jim, that was marvellous – even better than I expected.'

I stared up at him and managed a whisper. 'But you're in Edinburgh . . .'

'Not me, old lad. There wasn't much doing so I concluded my business and hitched straight back, I'd just got in when I saw you coming up the garden. Barely had time to get the bulb out and climb into my outfit – I couldn't miss the opportunity.'

'Feel my heart,' I murmured.

Tristan rested his hand on my ribs for a moment and as he felt the fierce hammering a fleeting concern crossed his face.

'Hell, I'm sorry, Jim.' Then he patted my shoulder reassuringly. 'But don't worry. If it was going to be fatal you'd have dropped down dead on the spot. And anyway, a good fright is very beneficial – acts like a tonic. You won't need a holiday this year.'

'Thanks,' I said. 'Thanks very much.'

'I wish you could have heard yourself.' He began to laugh again. 'That scream of terror . . . oh dear, oh dear!'

I hoisted myself slowly into a sitting position, pulled out the pillow, propped it against the bed head and leaned back against it. I still felt very weak.

I eyed him coldly. 'So you're the Raynes ghost.'

Tristan grinned in reply but didn't speak.

'You young devil! I should have known. But tell me, why do you do it? What do you get out of it?'

'Oh I don't know.' The young man gazed dreamily at the ceiling through the cigarette smoke. 'I suppose it's just getting the timing right so that the drivers aren't quite sure whether they've seen me or not. And then I get a hell or a kick out of hearing them revving up like mad and roaring off for home. None of them ever slows down.'

'Well, somebody once told me your sense of humour was over-developed,' I said. 'And I'm telling you it'll land you in the cart one of these days.'

'Not a chance. I keep my bike behind a hedge about a hundred yards down the road so that I can make a quick getaway if necessary. There's no problem.'

'Well, please yourself.' I got off the bed and made shakily for the door. 'I'm going downstairs for a tot of whisky, and just remember this.' I turned and glared at him. 'If you try that trick on me again I'll strangle you.'

A few days later at about eight o'clock in the evening I was sitting reading by the fireside in the big room at Skeldale House when the door burst open and Siegfried burst into the room.

'James,' he rapped out. 'Old Horace Dawson's cow has split its teat. Sounds like a stitching job. The old chap won't be able to hold the cow and he has no near neighbours to help him so I wonder if you'd come and give me a hand.'

'Sure, glad to.' I marked the place in my book, stretched and yawned then got up from the chair. I noticed Siegfried's foot tapping on the carpet and it occurred to me, not for the first time, that the only thing that would satisfy him would be some kind of ejector seat on my chair which would hurl me straight through the door and into action on the word of command. I was being as quick as I could but I had the feeling as always – when I was writing something for him or operating under his eyes – that I wasn't going nearly fast enough. There were elements of tension in the knowledge that the mere fact of watching me rise from the chair and replace my book in the fireside alcove was an almost unbearable strain for him.

By the time I was half way across the carpet he had disappeared into the passage. I followed at a trot and just made it into the street as he was starting the car. Grabbing the door I made a dive for the interior and felt the road whip away from under my foot as we took off into the darkness.

Fifteen minutes later we screeched to a halt in the yard behind a little smallholding standing on its own across a couple of fields. The engine had barely stopped before my colleague was out of the car and striding briskly towards the cow house. He called to me over his shoulder as he went.

'Bring the suture materials, James, will you . . . and the local and syringe . . . and that bottle of wound lotion . . .'

I heard the brief murmur of conversation from within then Siegfried's voice again, raised this time in an impatient shout.

'James! What are you doing out there? Can't you find those things?'

I had hardly got the boot open and I rummaged frantically among the rows of tins and bottles. I found what he required, galloped across the yard and almost collided with him as he came out of the building.

He was in mid shout. 'James! What the hell's keeping you . . . oh, you're there. Right, let's have that stuff . . . what have you been doing all this time?'

He had been right about Horace Dawson, a tiny frail man of about eighty who couldn't be expected to do any strong-arm stuff. Despite his age he had stubbornly refused to give up milking the two fat shorthorn cows which stood in the little cobbled byre.

Our patient had badly damaged a teat; either she or her neighbour must have stood on it because there was a long tear running almost full length with the milk running from it.

'It's a bad one, Horace,' Siegfried said. 'You can see it goes right into the milk channel. But we'll do what we can for her – it'll need a good few stitches in there.'

He bathed and disinfected the teat then filled a syringe with local anaesthetic.

'Grab her nose, James,' he said, then spoke gently to the farmer. 'Horace, will you please hold her tail for me. Just catch it by the very end, that's the way . . . lovely.'

The little man squared his shoulders. 'Aye, ah can do that fine, Mr Farnon.'

'Good lad, Horace, that's splendid, thank you. Now stand well clear.' He bent over and as I gripped the animal's nose he inserted the needle above the top extremity of the wound.

There was an instant smacking sound as the cow registered her disapproval by kicking Siegfried briskly half way up his wellington boot. He made no sound but breathed deeply and flexed his knee a couple of times before crouching down again.

'Cush pet,' he murmured soothingly as he stuck the needle in again.

This time the cloven foot landed on his forearm, sending the syringe winging gracefully through the air till it came to rest by a piece of good fortune in the hay-rack. Siegfried straightened up, rubbed his arm thoughtfully, retrieved his syringe and approached the patient again.

For a few moments he scratched around the root of her tail and addressed her in the friendliest manner. 'All right, old lady, it isn't very nice, is it?'

When he got down again he adopted a new stance, burrowing with his head into the cow's flank and stretching his long arms high he managed despite a few more near misses to infiltrate the tissues round the wound with local. Then he proceeded to thread a needle unhurriedly, whistling tunelessly under his breath.

Mr Dawson watched him admiringly. 'Ah know why you're such a good feller wi' animals, Mr Farnon. It's because you're so patient – I reckon you're t'patientest man ah've ever seen.'

Siegfried inclined his head modestly and recommenced work. And it was more peaceful now. The cow couldn't feel a thing as my colleague put in a long, even row of stitches, pulling the lips of the wound firmly together.

When he had finished he put an arm round the old man's shoulders.

'Now, Horace, if that heals well the teat will be as good as new. But it won't heal if you pull at it, so I want you to use this tube to milk her.' He held up a bottle of spirit in which a teat syphon gleamed.

'Very good,' said Mr Dawson firmly. 'Ah'll use it.'

Siegfried wagged a playful finger in his face. 'But you've got to be careful, you know. You must boil the tube every time before use and keep it always in the bottle or you'll finish up with mastitis. Will you do that?'

'Mr Farnon,' the little man said, holding himself very erect. 'Ah'll do exackly as you say.'

'That's my boy, Horace.' Siegfried gave him a final pat on the back before starting to pick up his instruments. 'I'll pop back in about two weeks to take the stitches out.'

As we were leaving, the vast form of Claude Blenkiron loomed suddenly in the byre door. He was the village policeman, though obviously off duty judging by the smart check jacket and slacks.

'I saw you had summat on, Horace, and I wondered if you wanted a hand.'

'Nay, thank ye, Mr Blenkiron. It's good of ye but you're ower late. We've done t'job,' the old man replied.

Siegfried laughed. 'Wish you'd arrived half an hour ago, Claude. You could have tucked this cow under your arm while I stitched her.'

The big man nodded and a slow smile spread over his face. He looked the soul of geniality but I felt, as always, that there was a lot of iron behind that smile. Claude was a well-loved character in the district, a magnificent athlete who bestowed lavish help and friendship on all who needed it on his beat. But though he was a sturdy prop to the weak and the elderly he was also a merciless scourge of the ungodly.

I had no first hand knowledge but there were rumours that Claude preferred not to trouble the magistrates with trivialities but dispensed his own form of instant justice. It was said that he kept a stout stick handy and acts of hooliganism and vandalism were rapidly followed by a shrill yowling down some dark alley.

Second offenders were almost unknown and in fact his whole district was remarkably law-abiding. I looked again at the smiling face. He really was the most pleasant looking man but as I say there was something else there and nothing would ever have induced me to pick a fight with him.

'Right, then,' he said. 'I was just on me way into Darrowby so I'll say good night gentlemen.'

Siegfried put a hand on his arm. 'Just a moment, Claude, I want to go on to see another of my cases. I wonder if you'd give Mr Herriot a lift into the town.'

'I'll do that with pleasure, Mr Farnon,' the policeman replied and beckoned me to follow him.

In the darkness outside I got into the passenger seat of a little Morris Eight and waited for a few moments while Claude squeezed his bulk behind the wheel. As we set off he began to talk about his recent visit to Bradford where he had been taking part in a wrestling match.

We had to go through Raynes village on the way back and as we left the houses behind and began the ascent to the abbey he suddenly stopped talking. Then he startled me as he snapped upright in his seat and pointed ahead.

'Look, look there, it's that bloody monk!'

'Where? Where?' I feigned ignorance but I had seen it all right – the cowled, slow-pacing figure heading for the wood.

Claude's foot was on the boards and the car was screaming up the hill. At the top he swung savagely on to the roadside grass so that the headlights blazed into the depths of the wood and as he leapt from the car there was a fleeting moment when his quarry was in full view; a monk, skirts hitched high, legging it with desperate speed among the trees.

The big man reached into the back of the car and pulled out what looked like a heavy walking stick. 'After the bugger!' he shouted, plunging eagerly forward.

I panted after him. 'Wait a minute, what are you going to do if you catch him?'

'I'm goin' to come across his arse with me ash plant,' Claude said with chilling conviction and galloped ahead of me till he disappeared from the circle of light. He was making a tremendous noise, beating against the tree trunks and emitting a series of intimidating shouts.

My heart bled for the hapless spectre blundering in the darkness with the policeman's cries dinning in his ears. I waited with tingling horror for the final confrontation and the tension increased as time passed and I could still hear Claude in full cry; 'Come out of there, you can't get away! Come on, show yourself!' while his splintering blows echoed among the trees.

I did my own bit of searching but found nothing. The monk did indeed seem to have disappeared and when I finally returned to the car I found the big man already there.

'Well that's a rum 'un, Mr Herriot,' he said. 'I can't find 'im and I can't think where he's got to. I was hard on his heels when I first spotted him and he didn't get out of the wood because I can see over the fields in the moonlight. I've 'ad a scout round the abbey too, but he isn't there. He's just bloody vanished.'

I was going to say something like 'Well, what else would you expect from a ghost?' but the huge hand was still swinging that stick and I decided against it.

'Well I reckon we'd better get on to Darrowby,' the policeman grunted, stamping his feet on the frosty turf. I shivered. It was bitterly cold with an east wind getting up and I was glad to climb back into the car.

In Darrowby I had a few companionable beers with Claude at his favourite haunt, the Black Bull, and it was ten thirty when I got into Skeldale House. There was no sign of Tristan and I felt a twinge of anxiety.

It must have been after midnight when I was awakened by a faint scuffling from the next room. Tristan occupied what had been the long, narrow 'dressing room' in the grand days when the house was young. I jumped out of bed and opened the communicating door.

Tristan was in pyjamas and he cuddled two hot water bottles to his bosom. He turned his head and gave me a single haggard glance before pushing one of the bottles well down the bed. Then he crawled between the sheets and lay on his back with the second bottle clasped across his chest and his eyes fixed on the ceiling. I went over and looked down at him in some concern. He was shaking so much that the whole bed vibrated with him.

'How are you, Triss?' I whispered.

After a few moments a faint croak came up. 'Frozen to the bloody marrow, Jim.'

'But where the heck have you been?'

Again the croak. 'In a drainpipe.'

'A drainpipe!' I stared at him. 'Where?'

The head rolled feebly from side to side on the pillow. 'Up at the wood. Didn't you see those pipes by the roadside?'

A great light flashed. 'Of course, yes! They're going to put a new sewer into the village, aren't they?'

'That's right,' Tristan whispered. 'When I saw that big bloke pounding into the wood I cut straight back and dived into one of the pipes. God only knows how long I was in there.'

'But why didn't you come out after we left?'

A violent shudder shook the young man's frame and he closed his eyes briefly. 'I couldn't hear a thing in there. I was jammed tight with my cowl over my ears and there was a ninety mile a hour wind screaming down the pipe. I didn't hear the car start and I daren't come out in case that chap was still standing there with his bloody great shillelagh.' He took hold of the quilt with one hand and picked at it fitfully.

'Well never mind, Triss,' I said. 'You'll soon get warmed up and you'll be all right after a night's sleep.'

Tristan didn't appear to have heard. 'They're horrible things, drain-pipes, Jim.' He looked up at me with hunted eyes. 'They're full of muck and they stink of cats' pee.'

'I know, I know.' I put his hand back inside the quilt and pulled the sheets up round his chin. 'You'll be fine in the morning.' I switched off the light and tiptoed from the room. As I closed the door I could still hear his teeth chattering.

Clearly it wasn't only the cold that was bothering him; he was still in a state of shock. And no wonder. The poor fellow had been enjoying a little session of peaceful haunting with never a care in the world when without warning there was a scream of brakes a blaze of light and that giant bounding into the middle of it like the demon king. It had all been too much.

Next morning at the breakfast table Tristan was in poor shape. He looked very pale, he ate little and at intervals his body was racked by deep coughing spasms.

Siegfried looked at him quizzically. 'I know what's done this to you. I know why you're sitting there like a zombie, coughing your lungs up.'

His brother stiffened in his chair and a tremor crossed his face. 'You do?'

'Yes, I hate to say I told you so, but I did warn you, didn't I? It's all those bloody cigarettes!'

Tristan never did give up smoking but the Raynes ghost was seen no more and remains an unsolved mystery to this day.

Chapter Thirteen

The arrangement with Ewan Ross had worked out very well. It meant a lot of driving for me; twenty-five miles to Scarburn, then a full day round the farms in that area followed by the run back to Darrowby at night, but I enjoyed working up there on the airy summit of Yorkshire and meeting a fresh community of farmers who, like all hillmen, seemed to vie with each other in hospitality. In their rough, flagged kitchens I ate superb meals which belied their modest description of 'a bit o' dinner' and it was almost routine for me to bring home a parcel of butter, a few eggs, sometimes an exquisite piece of spare rib.

Of course I realise I was lucky. At the commencement of the Tuberculin Testing Scheme there was a nice incentive bonus on the milk or on the numbers of cattle and I appeared on the farms almost as a bringer of bounty. In later years when attestation became universal the stock owners came to regard the tests as a necessary nuisance, but, as I say, I was lucky – I was in on the honeymoon period.

The arrangement suited Siegfried, too. Certainly he had to work hard on the days when I was away but it brought in some welcome revenue to the practice.

And best of all it suited Ewan, because without doing a single thing or even thinking about it he had a Ministry cheque on his breakfast table every quarter. This was absolutely tailored to his personality because nothing would ever have induced him to spend hours in routine work, then go home and fill in forms with long columns of descriptions and ages and measurements.

When he had to do a job he did it magnificently. And he did it with such care – always boiling up before he left the house and wrapping syringes and instruments in his strips of clean brown paper of which he must have had an endless supply. But if he could get away with it he stayed at home. In fact, after lunch every day he took off his shoes, put on his slippers and got down by the fireside. Once he was there it took something spectacular to shift him.

I have seen him sitting there smoking while Ginny answered the phone to farmers who wanted his services.

'Och, it'll do tomorrow,' he would say.

Not for him the sweat of fighting the clock, the panic of urgent calls coming in from opposite directions, the tightening ball of tension in the stomach when the work began to pile up. No, no, he put on his slippers, rolled cigarettes, and let it all flow past him.

He had only a mild interest in the work we did in Darrowby but he was fascinated by the funny things that happened to us. He dearly loved to listen to my accounts of the various contretemps at Skeldale House and, strangely, he wanted to hear them again and again almost as a child would. Often, as he lay back in his chair with the smoke rising from his twisted little cigarette he would say suddenly in his soft Highland-Canadian voice.

'Tell me about the rubber suit.'

I must have told him that tale twenty times before but it made no difference. He would gaze fixedly at me as I went through the story again and though his expression hardly changed his shoulders would begin to shake silently and the pale blue eyes to brim with tears.

Looking back I often wonder who was right – Ewan or all the successful vets who gave themselves ulcers dashing round in circles. I do know that he enjoyed a deference from his clients which I never encountered elsewhere. Perhaps there is a lesson somewhere in the fact that he received grateful thanks if he went to an animal the same day he was called, whereas Siegfried and I who tried to get to a case within twenty minutes were greeted with 'what kept you?' if we took half an hour.

There was another advantage to Ewan in having me to do his testing; he was able to pass on occasional private jobs to me while I was on the farms and as the weeks passed he began to use me more and more as a general assistant. It became commonplace for the farmers to say, 'Oh, and Mr Ross said would you take some nanberries off a stirk's belly while you're here,' or 'Will you inject some calves for scour? Mr Ross rang and said you were coming.' One morning I was startled to find a couple of strapping two-year-old horses waiting for me to castrate standing before I commenced the day's work.

If the farmers had any objection to a young stranger doing their work they never voiced it. Whatever Ewan did or arranged was right with them; in fact there didn't seem to be much they wouldn't do for him.

This was brought home to me forcibly one night. I had had a particularly rough day in the Scarburn district. Herds which I thought had about twenty animals turned out to have fifty or sixty and these were scattered around in little buildings miles apart on the fell-sides. There was only one way to get to them – you walked; and while this might have been enjoyable in good weather it had been a lowering late autumn day with a gusting wind scouring the flattened grass and almost piercing my bones like the first quick gleam of winter's teeth. It had almost stupefied me.

And on top of that I had had a wider than usual selection of Ewan's private jobs; a couple of cleansings, a farrowing, a few pregnancy diagnoses; all jacket-off jobs which left my arms raw and painful. I must have tested about four hundred unyielding bovines, elbowing and squeezing between their craggy bodies, and it seemed almost too much that just when I was turning away from the very last cow of the day she should kick me resoundingly just behind the knee. This farewell gesture dropped me in a moaning heap on the byre floor and it was some minutes before I was able to hobble away.

The journey back to Darrowby had seemed interminable and it didn't help at all when I got home and found that Siegfried was out and there were a few more calls left for me in our own practice. When I finally crawled into bed I had nothing left to offer.

It was just after midnight when the bedside phone rang. With a feeling of disbelief I recognised Ewan's voice – what the devil could he possibly want with me at this hour?

'Hello, Jim, sorry to disturb you.' The words seemed to reach out and caress me.

'That's all right, Ewan, what can I do for you?' I said trying to sound casual but gripping the sheets tightly with my free hand.

Ewan paused for a moment. 'Well now I'm in a wee bit of bother here. It's a calving.'

The window rattled as the wind buffeted the glass. 'A calving?' I quavered.

'Yes, a big cow with a great long pelvis and the calf's head is back. I've been trying for an hour but I'm damned if I can reach it – my arm's not long enough.'

'Ah yes, I've a very short arm myself,' I babbled. 'I know just how you feel. I'm no good when it comes to jobs like that.'

A soft chuckle came over the line. 'Oh I don't want your arm, Jim, it's that embryotome I want.'

'Embryotome?'

'That's right. Remember you were telling me what a wonderful instrument it was.'

Why couldn't I keep my big mouth shut? My mind began to hunt round desperately for a way of escape.

'But Ewan, you'd kill the calf. An embryotome isn't indicated in a case like this.'

'This calf's dead and stinking, Jim. All I want is to get its head off to save the cow.'

I was trapped. I didn't say anything more but lay quivering, waiting for the terrible words which I knew were coming.

They came all right. 'Just slip out here and do it for me will you, Jim?'

As I tottered from my bed I became aware immediately that the knee where I had been kicked had stiffened up and I could hardly bend it. In the darkness of the garden the dead leaves crunched softly under my feet and when I reached the yard the wind roared in the elms, tearing the last leaves from the branches and hurling them past my face like driven snow flakes.

Huddled over the wheel, my head nodding with weariness, I drove out of the town. My destination was Hutton House, a farm about five miles on the other side of Scarburn, and I muttered feebly to myself as I peered through the windscreen.

'Just slip out here!' he says. 'Just slip out thirty bloody miles over narrow twisting roads and get down on your belly and knock your guts out!' Damn Ewan Ross, and damn his Highland charm and his Highland indolence. I was like a bloody little shuttlecock – back and forth, back and forth. And I was absolutely whacked and my arms were sore and my knee ached. Almost whimpering with self pity I bemoaned my lot. This country vetting was a mug's game. I should have been a doctor, my mother always wanted me to be a doctor, and I wouldn't have to drive thirty miles to a cold cow house but just pop round the corner into a nice warm bedroom and pat the hand of some sweet old lady and dole out a few pills then back within minutes to my bed – my deep, deep, soft, soft bed . . .

I lurched suddenly into wakefulness as the car careered straight for the roadside wall. Gripping the wheel tightly, feeling the wind pulling against the steering, I decided that the main thing was not to fall asleep. It wasn't easy; there was a numbing sameness about the miles of walls, the endless strip of road rolling out before me, but finally, after about an hour, I chugged into Scarburn and for a few moments my headlights swept across the unheeding tight-shut face of the little town. Then the last five miles with the engine fighting against the rising ground before I drew up outside the gate of Hutton House.

I should say the first gate because there were four along the track leading to the pin point of light high on the fellside. And at each gate the wind, whipping straight from the north, tugged fiercely at the car door as I got out and each time as I turned away from the headlights the fields were lost in the blackness and there was only the cold glitter of stars in a clean-swept sky.

At last the huddle of farm buildings lay before me and I drove up to the chink of brightness which came from the byre door. Even here in the yard the wind tore at me as I wrestled with the boot. Gasping, I lifted out my wellingtons, bottle of antiseptic and the accursed embryotome and hurried over to the low building.

Inside, all was peace; a delicious warmth rising from the long row of somnolent cows, my patient propped on her chest between two bales, Mr Hugill, the stooping, wrinkled farmer and Ewan sitting comfortably cross-legged, smoking one of his funny cigarettes. He was sitting in a chair, too – they had even brought a chair out here for him – and in the light of the big oil lamp he looked across at me without speaking for a moment then he gave me his shy smile.

'Jim, it's good of you to come. I've had a damn hard try but I know when I'm beat. I can tell you you're a sight for sore eyes walking in that door.'

Mr Hugill chuckled. 'Aye, we're badly in need of a bit o'young blood on t'job.'

Suddenly I stopped feeling sorry for myself. I didn't care about the long journey, about being winkled from my delectable bed. But I didn't feel much like young blood as I stripped off, knelt down gingerly on my stiff knee and thrust an arm, chaffed red and tingling from the antiseptic, into the cow.

I realised straight away what Ewan meant. This cow did have a hell of a long pelvis. The calf's feet were in the passage and the head was tucked away back along the ribs somewhere. I had to surmise this because at full stretch I could just reach the cleft made by the flexion of the neck. There was no chance of straightening it out, so my task was clear; I had to get an embryotomy wire down that cleft and round the neck so that I could cut off the head.

This was one of those calvings without the true savour; without the rewarding sight of a new living creature at the finish. But sometimes it happened like this. The calf I was feeling had been dead for about twenty-four hours judging by the sweetish smell and the emphysematous crackling under the skin, and had to be regarded simply as a piece of inanimate tissue which had to be removed or the mother would surely die of septicaemia or have to be slaughtered. As though divining my thoughts the cow laid her head along her side, looked at me and moaned softly. She had the bonny white face of the Hereford Cross and she looked sick; she wanted rid of that thing inside her more than anybody.

The usual procedure is to pass a cord round the part to be cut off and then pull the wire through; but it isn't as easy as that. It is one thing pushing it into a tight space but quite another thing finding it at the other side. Fortunately some intelligent chap who clearly knew what calving was all about had come up with a simple invention – a heavy lead weight with a small hole at one end for the cord and a bigger one at the other end for your finger.

I fished my weight out now and again pushed an arm alongside the dry legs and up to the cleft in the neck. By straining to the limit I managed to force the weight forward and felt it fall down into the cleft. I came out of the cow now and carefully soaped my arm. This was the moment of truth. If I could get hold of the weight on the underside of the neck and pull it through with the cord attached the rest was easy. The job was over in fact. If I couldn't reach it all was lost.

Again down on the cobbles and again the long reach between the calf's legs and the clinging vaginal wall right forward beneath the twisted neck where my lead weight just had to be. It wasn't there. Digging my toes between the stones on the floor I fought for another inch and managed to pass my fingers up into the cleft. Still nothing. The weight hadn't fallen through – it was stuck up there, probably a fraction above my groping fingers; and my hopes were stuck with it.

I went back to the bucket and soaped the other arm. Sometimes that worked. But the result was the same; a desperate fumbling at nothing. Not for the first time I cursed the accident of anatomy which had given me a short arm. Siegfried with his slender build and long reach would have been putting his jacket on by now, all ready to go home.

But there was nothing else for it but to fight on – and I wasn't in shape for fighting. Even a man in peak condition can't spend much time inside a cow

without having the blood squeezed relentlessly from his arm by the uterine
contractions, but when he starts as I did from a point of maximum fragility it
is really no contest. It took only about a minute for my arm to be reduced to
something like a stalk of asparagus with useless twitching fingers on the end.
I had to keep changing round faster and faster till I was flopping on the cobbles
like a stranded fish. And all the time it was getting worse in there; drier, more
clinging, everything closing down till I could hardly move, never mind get my
hand on that precious lead weight.

I must have gone on like this for the best part of an hour before the futility
of it became plain. I had to try something else. Hoisting myself on to my knees
I turned round.

'Mr Hugill, would you please bring me some warm water in another bucket.'
As the farmer hurried from the byre I turned to Ewan.

'It's that bloody weight,' I said. 'I expected it to fall straight down but it
hasn't. The bend in the neck must be so tight the thing can't get through. I'm
going to pump some water in to see if it'll open things up a bit.'

Ewan looked with compassion at my sweating face and sagging jaw, at the
caked dirt and slime and bits of straw sticking to my chest. 'Right, Jim,' he said.
'That sounds like a good idea.'

I didn't enjoy my visit out to the car. Standing stripped to the waist in total
darkness in the teeth of a north wind is an overrated pastime but it made a
change from the cobbles. I fumbled a pump and rubber tube from the boot and
returned to the byre at a trot.

Ewan operated the pump as I pushed the tube forward over the dried-out
legs, playing the water from side to side and especially into that bend in the
neck.

When I had finished I came out of the cow quickly, dropped the tube and,
slightly breathless, soaped my arm again. This was really it this time. That
water would give me more room, but only for a few seconds.

Lying down again I inserted my arm and it was like a different world – lots
of space, everything moist and moveable. My fingers trembled as they inched
forward under that neck and, hallelujah, the weight was there, the smooth,
metallic, beautiful edge of the thing just projecting from among the hair. I could
twiddle it with the end of my fingers and I felt it gradually coming down till the
hole was within reach and I thrust my finger through it with savage relief and
lay like that for a few moments smiling stupidly down at the wet stones and
knowing I had won.

The rest was routine. Joining the cord to the wire and pulling it round the
neck; threading the wire through the shining steel tubes of the embryotome
which protected the vaginal wall from the cutting edge; the few minutes of steady
sawing till the sudden lack of resistance told that the head was off and the
obstruction removed.

After that, Ewan and I took a leg apiece and delivered the calf without
difficulty, the head followed and the job was done. Swilling myself down with
the last of the water I looked at the cow; she had had a long tussle but nothing
to do her any harm; no hard pulling, no internal damage. She should be all
right. And as though trying to reassure me she hunched her hind legs under her,
gave a heave and got to her feet.

'By Gaw, that's a good sign,' Mr Hugill said.

The cow turned her fine white face towards me for a moment, straddled her
legs, strained a couple of times, and the placenta welled in multi-coloured
entirety from her vulva and plopped into the channel.

'And that's a better sign,' Ewan murmured. He looked at his watch. 'Nearly
three o'clock.' Then he turned to the farmer. 'Is your missus up, Mr Hugill?'

The old man didn't seem surprised at the question, in fact he seemed to be expecting it. 'Aye, she's up, right enough, Mr Ross?'

'And is the fire on?'

'Aye, there's a real good fire, Mr Ross,' he replied eagerly.

'Splendid!' Ewan said, rubbing his hands. 'Well, I think we'll have some boiled eggs.' He looked over at me. 'Boiled eggs all right for you, Jim?'

'Boiled eggs?' The concept was difficult to grasp at this hour.

'Yes, just the thing for you after your hard work.'

'Oh well, right, just as you say.'

Ewan became very brisk. 'Fine, we'll have boiled eggs, Mr Hugill, and some tea of course, and maybe a little toast.' He rubbed his chin thoughtfully like a diner at his favourite restaurant pondering over the menu. 'Oh and a few scones would be very nice.'

'Very good, Mr Ross, I'll go in and tell t'missus.' The farmer nodded happily and scuttled away.

Ten minutes later, walking into the farmhouse kitchen, I felt strangely disembodied. Maybe it was because my physical state had progressed from mere exhaustion to something like coma, but the whole thing seemed unreal. The brasses of hearth and mantelpiece glinting in the flames from a crackling wood fire, the table under a hissing tilly lamp laden with its burden of scones, crusty bread, ham and egg pie, curd tarts, fruit cake; it all looked like something from a dream. And it was funny, but the most incredible objects of all were the boiled eggs, brown and massive, top heavy in their china cradles, two for Ewan at the top of the table and two for me down the side.

Mrs Hugill, stout and beaming, poured our tea, then she and her husband sat down on either side of the fire and waited with evident interest for us to go into action. Ewan with total lack of self consciousness began busily to knock the tops off his eggs and slap butter on the toast. I followed mechanically, noting even through the mists that the eggs had a creamy savour which you maybe only found when the hens spent their lives pecking around a 1500 foot high farmyard, and that the tang of yeast was strong in the home made bread even though I mumbled it with a dry mouth and numb lips. The tea, too, would have been excellent but for the fact that I added salt to it instead of sugar; just sat and watched myself pouring salt from the little spoon first on to my egg plate then into my tea. It tasted different, but I don't recommend it.

All the time the call of home and bed was getting stronger but Ewan was in no hurry. Speaking through a mouthful of ham and egg pie he addressed his hostess.

'Mrs Hugill, now I know why you always win the prizes at Scarburn show with your baking.'

As the good lady giggled with pleasure I struggled to my feet. 'I second that, Mrs Hugill, I've really enjoyed it, but it's time I was away. I've a long way to go.'

Ewan swallowed, wiped his lips and smiled across the table. 'Well I can't thank you enough, Jim. You've saved the situation. I couldn't have done what you've done tonight even if I'd had your magic embryotome.'

'Oh that's all right, it's been a pleasure.' I made my way to the door and took a last look back at the scene which I still could scarcely believe; the farmer and his wife nodding and waving from the bright fireside, Ewan, in lordly state at the head of the table, hacking vigorously at a large Wensleydale cheese.

I hardly noticed the run back. In a comfortable state of suspended animation I sat with half closed eyes fixed on the road ahead. There was none of the apprehension of the journey out, none of the moaning and griping, just the warm satisfaction that a good cow would be pulling hay from its rack tomorrow instead of hanging from the butcher's hook. Only a little thing, nothing world-shaking about it, but good.

When I drove into the yard at Skeldale House the gale had blown itself out leaving a deep litter of leaves shining brilliant gold in the headlights and I scuffled my way through them, ankle deep, feeling the still air cool on my face in the darkness. Bed was an unbelievable haven and as I floated away my last emotion was a feeling of wonder at the things the farmers would do for Ewan Ross.

My clients had shown me many kindnesses in the past and I had a lot of future still ahead of me, but I doubted whether anybody would ever give me boiled eggs at three o'clock in the morning.

Chapter Fourteen

It was the chance to start my public speaking career; a definite opportunity which I knew I should grasp, yet I shrank from it.

'Oh I don't know,' I said to the curate, 'I've never done anything of the sort before. Maybe you'd better look for somebody else.'

The curate beamed on me. He was in his thirties and had always struck me as being a saintly man since he obviously saw no evil in anything or anybody.

'Oh come now, Mr Herriot. I'm sure you'd manage splendidly and the youth club are longing to hear you. A lot of my young people are from farming families and they'd be quite fascinated to have a vet speak to them.'

'Well it's very nice of you to say so, Mr Blenkinsopp.' But I had a mental image of the packed church hall, the rows of faces looking up at me, and I began to sweat at the very thought. 'I tell you what – if they want to hear a vet I'll get Mr Farnon to give them a talk. He's very good.'

The curate squeezed my arm. 'But Mr Herriot, it's you I want. You are very young and the boys and girls would have something in common with you from the start. And you'd only have to speak for about half and hour and then there would be questions and a lively discussion.'

'Oh I don't think I'd better,' I muttered though inwardly I writhed at the shame of being scared to get up in front of an audience. 'Maybe some other time, but I really don't feel I could do it just at present.'

Mr Blenkinsopp sighed. 'Ah well, just as you wish, but I know the club members will be disappointed. And Miss Alderson, too.'

'Miss Alderson?'

'Yes, Helen helps me run the club. In fact it was she who suggested you as a speaker.'

'She did?'

'Yes, indeed.'

'She attends all the meetings, I suppose?' I said.

'Oh of course. I'm sure she was looking forward to seeing you at our next get-together.'

'Mm . . . well . . . I wonder. Maybe I'd better have a bash at it.'

'Splendid!' The curate's face shone with pleasure. 'You have plenty of time – it's not till three weeks on Tuesday.'

'Well done, James.' Siegfried said at lunch. 'I'm glad you've grasped the nettle. All professional men have to get used to public speaking and the sooner you begin the better. And it helps our image – one has to wave the flag a little now and then.'

'I suppose so.' I fiddled with my napkin for a moment. 'But I haven't much idea about what to say. Have you any suggestions?'

'Thank you, Mrs Hall, that looks wonderful.' Siegfried said to our housekeeper as she impassively placed a large steak and kidney pie in front of him. Then he turned to me again. 'Well, James, you've been asked to speak as a vet so you've got to deal with veterinary matters. If they're farmers' sons and daughters they'll lap it up.'

'Yes, but that's a big subject. What exactly do you mean?'

My employer attacked the pie resolutely and a heavenly steam escaped as his knife pierced the crust. 'Pass your plate, James.' He mounded on meat and pastry then pushed a tureen of mashed potatoes towards me. 'I know it's a big subject so you've got to pick out some attractive and interesting aspects.'

'I don't think I'd know where to start,' I said. 'I wish you'd sort of sketch something out for me.'

Siegfried chewed thoughtfully for a few moments. 'Everybody has their own ideas about these things, of course, but if I were you I'd start off with something to catch their attention – some provocative remark or question – then I'd paint a broad tapestry of the profession, including its history, and in between I'd shove in some practical things, maybe about first aid in animals.'

'First aid, eh?'

'Yes, that's right.' My employer was warming to his subject. 'How to stop haemorrhage, how to deal with emergencies when the vet isn't available. How about puncturing the rumen in a bloated cow? That would make them sit up.'

'It would, wouldn't it? Yes, I think I'll do that.' I made a few mental notes. 'But how about the opening remark you mentioned? Any ideas about that?'

Siegfried carefully transported an extra boiled leek from its bed of white sauce on to his plate. For perhaps a minute he stared ahead of him in silence then without warning he crashed his fist down on the table, making me bite my tongue painfully.

'I've got it, James! Not a shadow of a doubt about it.' He held up a finger and intoned, 'WHAT DOES MRCVS MEAN TO YOU? There's your opening line – how about that?'

'Gosh, it's good!' I gazed at him admiringly. 'What does MRCVS mean to you? I really like that.'

'There you are, then,' he said, chewing smugly, 'and you must deliver it in loud, ringing tones. You'll have them on the edge of their seats right from the start, and gasping to hear more. A good beginning is vital.'

'Well thanks, Siegfried, you've been a big help. I think I can get the material together now but the only thing is, can I put it over? I've never spoken in public – what if I dry up as soon as I get on my feet? What if I can't remember a thing?'

'Oh there's no possibility of that, but I know how you feel and I'll give you one more piece of advice.' He pointed solemnly at me with his fork. 'Since it's your first time you ought to get the whole thing word perfect. Practise it day by day till you can recite it like poetry, then you'll be all right.'

'OK,' I said. 'I'll do that, too.'

Siegfried leaned back and laughed. 'Good lad! And in the meantime, stop worrying. You're going to knock 'em cold, James, I just know you are.'

I took his advice literally and over the next three weeks as I drove along the frost-bound roads my lips were continually moving as I harangued my imaginary audience. Several times I saw roadside workers look up in surprise as my declamations boomed out at them through the open windows, and I got to the stage where every syllable, every inflection tripped effortlessly off my tongue in perfect order.

In fact, it all began to sound so good to me that in a fearful sort of way I began to look forward to the big night. How many would be there to hear me? Fifty? Sixty? Maybe even a hundred? Well, let 'em all come. And Helen would be there. Maybe my stock wasn't so high in that direction but it wouldn't do any harm if she were to see me hold the mass of young people in my thrall, the youghful faces upturned eagerly to me, drinking in my every word.

My confidence grew steadily as the days passed and when the fateful Tuesday evening finally arrived I was in a state of pallid resolution. No panic. A certain tension and dryness of the mouth, but above all a cold determination to make good.

Before I left for the church hall I bathed, put on my best suit and inspected my face carefully in the mirror. It wouldn't do if I had a piece of cow muck sticking on an eyebrow in front of all that throng.

I was glad I didn't have far to walk because there had been a fall of snow that morning followed by a few hours of icy rain and the streets were deep in slush. As I opened the hall door and stepped inside, the curate met me with a radiant smile.

'Ah, Mr Herriot, here you are! So kind of you to come. Our young people can hardly wait to hear you.'

We were in a narrow lobby with doors on either side and from somewhere I could hear music and laughter. But I didn't pay much attention because Helen was coming down the stairs at the far end.

She laughed and for a moment her eyes held mine with that warm, interested, kind look which was part of her. It was a funny thing but whenever I met Helen she looked at me like that. I hadn't had a lot of luck in my contacts with her but afterwards there was no difference; it was always the same calm, friendly smile.

Of course she was a kind girl, Helen, that was it. This was probably the way she looked at everybody – with that soft flame kindling in her eyes' blue depths and the full lips parted over the white teeth. And there was the way her mouth went into little upturned folds in the corners . . . and how her dark hair fell softly across the white of her cheek . . .

But Mr Blenkinsopp was giving a series of little coughs. I dragged my attention back to him.

'Come in and see our club room before you start,' he said, opening one of the doors. 'I think you'll agree that it's a pleasant place for them to come on these wintry evenings.'

We went inside. A gramophone was playing and some pretty teenage girls were fox-trotting together to the music. A few lads lounged about while two others were playing billiards on a miniature table in the corner. The curate gazed fondly at the scene, the music stopped, the record was changed for a waltz and the dancing began again. It struck me as strange that it didn't seem to occur to any of the boys to dance with those attractive girls.

I looked at the two billiard players. They would be about fifteen or sixteen and were obviously devotees of the cinema. There was something of the Bowery pool room in their scowling attitude, the cigarettes dangling from their lips, the way they squinted through the smoke as they bent to play a shot, the tough, deadpan chalking of the cues, the contemptuous gangsterish disregard of the other occupants of the room.

The curate clapped his hands. 'Come now, boys and girls, it's time you joined the others in the hall. Mr Herriot is ready to talk to you now.'

The room emptied rapidly as the young people went through a door in the far corner. Soon there only remained the gangsters at the billiard table; they didn't appear to have heard. The curate called on them several times more but they took no notice. Finally Helen went over and whispered tensely at them and at length they threw down their cues and with a single malevolent glance in my direction they slouched from the room.

This then was the moment of truth when I would face my audience after the weeks of preparation. I took a deep breath and followed the others into the hall and on to the platform. Perched on a shaky chair between Helen and Mr Blenkinsopp I surveyed the scene.

It wasn't a big hall – it would probably have held a hundred if it had been full. But it wasn't full tonight, in fact the main feature about it was space. I made a quick count of the audience; there were twelve. They were disposed in little knots among the empty chairs. Half way up clustered the six teenage girls, then a few rows behind, a very fat boy holding a bag of potato crisps and near him a thin, dispirited-looking youth with sleepy eyes. Right on the back row, against the wall, the two gangsters lounged in attitudes of studied boredom. What surprised me most, however, was the sight of two tiny girls, mere tots of about four, right in the middle of the front row, a long way from anybody else. One sported a big pink bow in her hair while the other wore pigtails. Their little legs swinging, they looked up at me incuriously.

I turned to Helen. 'Who are those two?'

'Oh, they like to come with their big sisters now and again,' she replied. 'They love it and they're very good. They won't be any trouble.'

I nodded stupidly, still trying to adjust my mind to the fact that these were the people who were going to receive my searching exposition on veterinary science. None of them seemed to be showing the slightest interest in me except for one very pretty little thing in the centre of the teenage group who gazed up at me with shining eyes as though she couldn't wait for me to begin.

Mr Blenkinsopp stood up and made a charming introductory speech. As he spoke, the gangsters at the back giggled, wrestled and dug at each other's ribs; the girls, with the exception of the little darling in the centre peeped back at the fighting pair in admiration.

At last I heard the curate's final words. 'And now I have great pleasure in asking Mr Herriot to address you.'

I got slowly to my feet and gazed over the twelve. The gangsters were still wrestling, the fat boy put a crisp in his mouth and began to crunch it loudly, down in the front, tot number one was sucking her thumb while the other, rocking her head from side to side, appeared to be singing to herself.

I felt a moment of wild panic. Should I change the entire plan and just talk casually about a few trivial points? But I couldn't. I had the whole thing off parrot-like and I'd have to deliver it as I had learned it. There was no way out.

With an effort I steadied myself and cleared my throat. 'What does MRCVS mean to you?' I cried.

It seemed to startle Mr Blenkinsopp because he jumped slightly in his chair, but the audience remained totally unmoved. MRCVS appeared to mean not a thing to them. I ploughed ahead, sketching out the history of the Royal College, painstakingly illustrating its development from the early days of farriery. Nobody was listening except the little pet in the centre but I was in the groove and couldn't stop.

'A supplemental Royal Charter was granted in 1932,' I pronounced after about ten minutes' hard going and just then the thin boy yawned. I had labelled him as an ineffectual sort of lad but he certainly could yawn; it was a stretching, groaning, voluptuous paroxysm which drowned my words and it went on and on till he finally lay back, bleary and exhausted by the effort. His companion munched his crisps stolidly.

By the time I had been holding forth for twenty minutes I seemed to be standing listening to myself with a kind of wonder. 'After qualification,' I was saying, 'the main avenues open to the new graduate are general practice and work under the Ministry of Agriculture and Fisheries. The latter is mainly concerned with preventive medicine and with the implementation of the laws governing the notifiable diseases.'

The gangsters punched each other fiercely with stifled laughter, the fat boy had another crisp, tot one drew ecstatically on her thumb while her other hand fondled a lock of her hair. Tot two stuck her legs straight out and admired her little white socks and red shoes. Only the dear girl in the middle paid any attention.

I began to break out in a light perspiration. The thing was taking a lot longer than I had thought to get through, and I had the growing conviction that I must be looking more and more of a chump in Helen's eyes as time went on.

I had rehearsed a few light sallies designed to send my audience into convulsions of laughter as a contrast to the absorbing, serious stuff, but even those who were listening failed to change expression at my shafts of wit. Except, of course, for the little treasure in the middle who pealed back at me sweetly every time.

But I stuck to it grimly. Surely I'd get through to them when I came to the practical bit about first aid.

'All right,' I said, 'you've got a calf with a nasty cut on its leg. The blood is pouring out and you can't get hold of a vet. If you just leave it the blood will all run out and the calf will die. What are you going to do?'

Nobody seemed to care much either way except for tot two. She obviously didn't like the turn things were taking and she stared up at me, her lower lip protruding and trembling.

I went on to explain about tourniquets and pressure pads and then moved on to a discussion of bloat.

'This cow is blown up ready to burst,' I proceeded. 'You've got to do something or she could drop down dead any second.'

I glanced apprehensively at tot two. Her lip was sticking out more every second and was now like a soup plate, but it was no good, I had to go on.

'You must get a knife like a carving knife and stick it straight into the stomach,' I declaimed desperately. 'Now I'll tell you just where to stick it in ...'

But tot two had had enough. She threw back her head and bawled heartily till her big sister hurried down a few rows and led her away in floods of tears, her pigtails dangling forlornly. Tot one was undisturbed, utterly engrossed as she was with her thumb and the wisp of hair she was rub-rub-rubbing.

Anyway I was getting towards the last lap now.

'The future of the profession, I am convinced, will be less and less involved with the problems of the individual animal,' I went on, addressing myself now exclusively to the little sweetheart in the centre who kept her eyes fixed on me with open admiration. The thin boy went into another of his mighty yawns while his companion finished his last crisp and crumpled the bag noisily.

'We must also consider the emergence of small animal work in any of our plans for the future. Over the past few years the increase in this field has been ...'

But I had to pause as there was a major disturbance at the back. The jolly feud between the gangsters had flared into ugly warfare. Fists flew, blood streamed, a few ripe oaths rocketed over the company. After a couple of minutes the combatants drew apart and sat glaring and snarling at each other as they dabbed their wounds.

'Whatever the uncertainties and despite the depressed state of agriculture I feel there will always be a place for the veterinary surgeon in our national economy.' That was it. I sat down and Helen, the curate and the little charmer in the middle applauded enthusiastically.

Mr Blenkinsopp rose, beaming delightedly around him. He congratulated me on my splendid talk and said how much they'd all enjoyed it and finished by saying he would now throw the meeting open for questions.

I settled back in my chair. So this was to be the lively discussion he had talked about. I hunted around anxiously from face to face but my audience stared back, dead-eyed; for the first time all evening there was dead silence.

The minutes ticked away and I felt the tension building in me, but at last there was a stirring in the middle of the hall. It was my darling girl; God bless and keep her, she was going to say something. I felt a sudden glow at the knowledge that my words had stimulated a response in at least one young mind.

She sat up in her seat, moistened her lips and smiled at me, bright eyed. She was indeed going to ask a question and as it turned out it was the only one of the evening. I leaned forward expectantly as she began to speak.

'Mr Herriot, I 'ave a little dog what's moultin'. What can I do for 'im?'

Chapter Fifteen

Probably the most dramatic occurrence in the history of veterinary practice was the disappearance of the draught horse. It is an almost incredible fact that this glory and mainstay of the profession just melted quietly away within a few years. And I was one of those who were there to see it happen.

When I first came to Darrowby the tractor had already begun to take over, but tradition dies hard in the agricultural world and there were still a lot of horses around. Which was just as well because my veterinary education had been geared to things equine with everything else a poor second. It had been a good scientific education in many respects but at times I wondered if the people who designed it still had a mental picture of the horse doctor with his top hat and frock coat busying himself in a world of horse-drawn trams and brewers' drays.

We learned the anatomy of the horse in great detail then that of the other animals much more superficially. It was the same with the other subjects; from animal husbandry with such insistence on a thorough knowledge of shoeing that we developed into amateur blacksmiths – right up to medicine and surgery where it was much more important to know about glanders and strangles than canine distemper. Even as we were learning, we youngsters knew it was ridiculous, with the draught horse already cast as a museum piece and the obvious potential of cattle and small animal work.

Still, after we had absorbed a vast store of equine lore it was a certain comfort that there were still a lot of patients on which we could try it out. I should think in my first two years I treated farm horses nearly every day and though I never was and never will be an equine expert there was a strange thrill in meeting with the age-old conditions whose names rang down almost from mediaeval times. Quittor, fistulous withers, poll evil, thrush, shoulder slip – vets had been wrestling with them for hundreds of years using very much the same drugs and procedures as myself. Armed with my firing iron and box of blister I plunged determinedly into what had always been the surging mainstream of veterinary life.

And now, in less than three years the stream had dwindled, not exactly to a trickle but certainly to the stage where the final dry-up was in sight. This meant, in a way, a lessening of the pressures on the veterinary surgeon because there is no doubt that horse work was the roughest and most arduous part of our life.

So that today, as I looked at the three-year-old gelding, it occurred to me that this sort of thing wasn't happening as often as it did. He had a long tear in his flank where he had caught himself on barbed wire and it gaped open whenever he moved. There was no getting away from the fact that it had to be stitched.

The horse was tied by the head in his stall, his right side against the tall wooden partition. One of the farm men, a hefty six footer, took a tight hold of the head collar and leaned back against the manger as I puffed some iodoform into the wound. The horse didn't see to mind, which was a comfort because he was a massive animal emanating an almost tangible vitality and power. I threaded my needle with a length of silk, lifted one of the lips of the wound and passed it through. This was going to be no trouble, I thought as I lifted the flap at the other side and pierced it, but as I was drawing the needle through, the gelding made a convulsive leap and I felt as though a great wind had whistled across the front of my body. Then, strangely, he was standing there against the wooden boards as if nothing had happened.

On the occasions when I have been kicked I have never seen it coming. It is surprising how quickly those great muscular legs can whip out. But there was no doubt he had had a good go at me because my needle and silk was nowhere to be seen, the big man at the head was staring at me with wide eyes in a chalk white face and the front of my clothing was in an extraordinary state. I was wearing a gaberdine mac and it looked as if somebody had taken a razor blade and painstakingly cut the material into narrow strips which hung down in ragged strips to ground level. The great iron-shod hoof had missed my legs by an inch or two but my mac was a write-off.

I was standing there looking around me in a kind of stupor when I heard a cheerful hail from the doorway.

'Now then, Mr Herriot, what's he done at you?' Cliff Tyreman, the old horseman, looked me up and down with a mixture of amusement and asperity.

'He's nearly put me in hospital, Cliff,' I replied shakily. 'About the closest near miss I've ever had. I just felt the wind of it.'

'What were you tryin' to do?'

'Stitch that wound, but I'm not going to try any more. I'm off to the surgery to get a chloroform muzzle.'

The little man looked shocked. 'You don't need no choloform. I'll haud him and you'll have no trouble.'

'I'm sorry, Cliff.' I began to put away my suture materials, scissors and powder. 'You're a good bloke, I know, but he's had one go at me and he's not getting another chance. I don't want to be lame for the rest of my life.'

The horseman's small, wiry frame seemed to bunch into a ball of aggression. He thrust forward his head in a characteristic posture and glared at me. 'I've never heard owt as daft in me life.' Then he swung round on the big man who was still hanging on to the horse's head, the ghastly pallor of his face now tinged with a delicate green. 'Come on out o' there, Bob! You're that bloody scared you're upsetting t'oss. Come on out of it and let me have 'im!'

Bob gratefully left the head and, grinning sheepishly moved with care along the side of the horse. He passed Cliff on the way and the little man's head didn't reach his shoulder.

Cliff seemed thoroughly insulted by the whole business. He took hold of the head collar and regarded the big animal with the disapproving stare of a schoolmaster at a naughty child. The horse, still in the mood for trouble, laid back his ears and began to plunge about the stall, his huge feet clattering ominously on the stone floor, but he came to rest quickly as the little man uppercutted him furiously in the ribs.

'Get stood up straight there, ye big bugger. What's the matter with ye?' Cliff barked and again he planted his tiny fist against the swelling barrel of the chest, a puny blow which the animal could scarcely have felt but which reduced him to quivering submission. 'Try to kick, would you, eh? I'll bloody fettle you!' He shook the head collar and fixed the horse with a hypnotic stare as he spoke. Then he turned to me. 'You can come and do your job, Mr Herriot, he won't hurt tha.'

I looked irresolutely at the huge, lethal animal. Stepping open-eyed into dangerous situations is something vets are called upon regularly to do and I suppose we all react differently. I know there were times when an over-vivid imagination made me acutely aware of the dire possibilities and now my mind seemed to be dwelling voluptuously on the frightful power in those enormous shining quarters, on the unyielding flintiness of the spatulate feet with their rims of metal. Cliff's voice cut into my musings.

'Come on, Mr Herriot, I tell ye he won't hurt tha.'

I reopened my box and tremblingly threaded another needle. I didn't seem to have much option; the little man wasn't asking me, he was telling me. I'd have to try again.

I couldn't have been a very impressive sight as I shuffled forwards, almost tripping over the tattered hula-hula skirt which dangled in front of me, my shaking hands reaching out once more for the wound, my heart thundering in my ears. But I needn't have worried. It was just as the little man had said; he didn't hurt me. In fact he never moved. He seemed to be listening attentively to the muttering which Cliff was directing into his face from a few inches' range. I powdered and stitched and clipped as though working on an anatomical specimen. Chloroform couldn't have done it any better.

As I retreated thankfully from the stall and began again to put away my instruments the monologue at the horse's head began to change its character. The menacing growl was replaced by a wheedling, teasing chuckle.

'Well, ye see, you're just a daft awd bugger, getting yourself all airigated over nowt. You're a good lad, really, aren't ye, a real good lad.' Cliff's hand ran caressingly over the neck and the towering animal began to nuzzle his cheek, as completely in his sway as any Labrador puppy.

When he had finished he came slowly from the stall, stroking the back, ribs, belly and quarters, even giving a playful tweak at the tail on parting while what had been a few minutes ago an explosive mountain of bone and muscle submitted happily.

I pulled a packet of Gold Flake from my pocket. 'Cliff, you're a marvel. Will you have a cigarette?'

'It 'ud be like givin' a pig a strawberry,' the little man replied, then he thrust forth his tongue on which reposed a half-chewed gobbet of tobacco. 'It's allus there. Ah push it in fust thing every mornin' soon as I get out of bed and there it stays. You'd never know, would you?'

I must have looked comically surprised because the dark eyes gleamed and the rugged little face split into a delighted grin. I looked at that grin – boyish, invincible – and reflected on the phenomenon that was Cliff Tyreman.

In a community in which toughness and durability was the norm he stood out as something exceptional. When I had first seen him nearly three years ago barging among cattle, grabbing their noses and hanging on effortlessly, I had put him down as an unusually fit middle-aged man; but he was in fact nearly seventy. There wasn't much of him but he was formidable; with his long arms swinging, his stumping, pigeon-toed gait and his lowered head he seemed always to be butting his way through life.

'I didn't expect to see you today,' I said. 'I heard you had pneumonia.'

He shrugged. 'Aye, summat of t'sort. First time I've ever been off work since I was a lad.'

'And you should be in your bed now, I should say.' I looked at the heaving chest and partly open mouth. 'I could hear you wheezing away when you were at the horse's head.'

'Nay, I can't stick that nohow. I'll be right in a day or two.' He seized a shovel and began busily clearing away the heap of manure behind the horse, his breathing loud and stertorous in the silence.

Harland Grange was a large, mainly arable farm in the low country at the foot of the Dale, and there had been a time when this stable had had a horse standing in every one of the long row of stalls. There had been over twenty with at least twelve regularly at work, but now there were only two, the young horse I had been treating and an ancient grey called Badger.

Cliff had been head horseman and when the revolution came he turned to tractoring and other jobs around the farm with no fuss at all. This was typical of the reaction of thousands of other farm workers throughout the country; they didn't set up a howl at having to abandon the skills of a lifetime and start anew – they just got on with it. In fact, the younger men seized avidly upon the new machines and proved themselves natural mechanics.

But to the old experts like Cliff, something had gone. He would say: 'It's a bloody sight easier sitting on a tractor – it used to play 'ell with me feet walking up and down them fields all day.' But he couldn't lose his love of horses; the fellow feeling between working man and working beast which had grown in him since childhood and was in his blood forever.

My next visit to the farm was to see a fat bullock with a piece of turnip stuck in his throat but while I was there, the farmer, Mr Gilling, asked me to have a look at old Badger.

'He's had a bit of a cough lately. Maybe it's just his age, but see what you think.'

The old horse was the sole occupant of the stable now. 'I've sold the three year old,' Mr Gilling said. 'But I'll still keep the old 'un – he'll be useful for a bit of light carting.'

I glanced sideways at the farmer's granite features. He looked the least sentimental of men but I knew why he was keeping the old horse. It was for Cliff.

'Cliff will be pleased, anyway,' I said.

Mr Gilling nodded. 'Aye, I never knew such a feller for 'osses. He was never happier than when he was with them.' He gave a short laugh. 'Do you know, I can remember years ago when he used to fall out with his missus he'd come down to this stable of a night and sit among his 'osses. Just sit here for hours on end looking at 'em and smoking. That was before he started chewing tobacco.'

'And did you have Badger in those days?'

'Aye, we bred him. Cliff helped at his foaling – I remember the little beggar came arse first and we had a bit of a job pullin' him out.' He smiled again. 'Maybe that's why he was always Cliff's favourite. He always worked Badger himself – year in year out – and he was that proud of 'im that if he had to take him into the town for any reason he'd plait ribbons into his mane and hang all his brasses on him first.' He shook his head reminiscently.

The old horse looked round with mild interest as I went up to him. He was in his late twenties and everything about him suggested serene old age; the gaunt projection of the pelvic bones, the whiteness of face and muzzle, the sunken eye with its benign expression. As I was about to take his temperature he gave a sharp, barking cough and it gave me the first clue to his ailment. I watched the rise and fall of his breathing for a minute or two and the second clue was there to be seen; further examination was unnecessary.

'He's broken winded, Mr Gilling,' I said. 'Or he's got pulmonary emphysema to give it its proper name. Do you see that double lift of the abdomen as he breaths out? That's because his lungs have lost their elasticity and need an extra effort to force the air out.'

'What's caused it, then?'

'Well it's to do with his age, but he's got a bit of cold on him at the moment and that's brought it out.'

'Will he get rid of it in time?' the farmer asked.

'He'll be a bit better when he gets over his cold, but I'm afraid he'll never be quite right. I'll give you some medicine to put in his drinking water which will alleviate his symptoms.' I went out to the car for a bottle of the arsenical expectorant mixture which we used then.

It was about six weeks later that I heard from Mr Gilling again. He rang me about seven o'clock one evening.

'I'd like you to come out and have a look at old Badger,' he said.

'What's wrong? Is it his broken wind again?'

'No, it's not that. He's still got the cough but it doesn't seem to bother him much. No, I think he's got a touch of colic. I've got to go out but Cliff will attend to you.'

The little man was waiting for me in the yard. He was carrying an oil lamp. As I came up to him I exclaimed in horror.

'Good God, Cliff, what have you been doing to yourself?' His face was a patchwork of cuts and scratches and his nose, almost without skin, jutted from between two black eyes.

He grinned through the wounds, his eyes dancing with merriment. 'Came off me bike t'other day. Hit a stone and went right over handlebars, arse over tip.' He burst out laughing at the very thought.

'But damn it, man, haven't you been to a doctor? You're not fit to be out in that state.'

'Doctor? Nay, there's no need to bother them fellers. It's nowt much.' He fingered a gash on his jaw. 'Ah lapped me chin up for a day in a bit o' bandage, but it's right enough now.'

I shook my head as I followed him into the stable. He hung up the oil lamp then went over to the horse.

'Can't reckon t'awd feller up,' he said. 'You'd think there wasn't much ailing him but there's summat.'

There were no signs of violent pain but the animal kept transferring his weight from one hind foot to the other as if he did have a little abdominal discomfort. His temperature was normal and he didn't show symptoms of anything else.

I looked at him doubtfully. 'Maybe he has a bit of colic. There's nothing else to see, anyway. I'll give him an injection to settle him down.'

'Right you are, maister, that's good.' Cliff watched me get my syringe out then he looked around him into the shadows at the far end of the stable.

'Funny seeing only one 'oss standing here. I remember when there was a great row of 'em and the barfins and bridles hangin' there on the stalls and the rest of the harness behind them all shinin' on t'wall.' He transferred his plug of tobacco to the other side of his mouth and smiled. 'By gaw, I were in here at six o'clock every morning feedin' them and gettin' them ready for work and ah'll tell you it was a sight to see us all goin' off ploughing at the start o' the day. Maybe six pairs of 'osses setting off with their harness jinglin' and the ploughmen sittin' sideways on their backs. Like a regular procession it was.'

I smiled. 'It was an early start, Cliff.'

'Aye, by Gaw, and a late finish. We'd bring the 'osses home at night and give 'em a light feed and take their harness off, then we'd go and have our own teas and we'd be back 'ere again afterwards, curry-combing and dandy-brushin' all the sweat and dirt off 'em. Then we'd give them a right good stiff feed of chop and oats and hay to set 'em up for the next day.'

'There wouldn't be much left of the evening then, was there?'

'Nay, there wasn't. It was about like work and bed, I reckon, but it never bothered us.'

I stepped forward to give Badger the injection, then paused. The old horse had undergone a slight spasm, a barely perceptible stiffening of the muscles, and as I looked at him he cocked his tail for a second then lowered it.

'There's something else here,' I said. 'Will you bring him out of his stall, Cliff, and let me see him walk across the yard.'

And watching him clop over the cobbles I saw it again; the stiffness, the raising of the tail. Something clicked in my mind, I walked over and rapped him under the chin and as the membrana nictitans flicked across his eye then slid slowly back I knew.

I paused for a moment. My casual little visit had suddenly become charged with doom.

'Cliff,' I said. 'I'm afraid he's got tetanus.'

'Lockjaw, you mean?'

'That's right. I'm sorry, but there's no doubt about it. Has he had any wounds lately – especially in his feet?'

'Well he were dead lame about a fortnight ago and blacksmith let some matter out of his hoof. Made a right big 'ole.'

There it was. 'It's a pity he didn't get an anti-tetanus shot at the time,' I said. I put my hand into the animal's mouth and tried to prise it open but the jaws were clamped tightly together. 'I don't suppose he's been able to eat today.'

'He had a bit this morning but nowt tonight. What's the lookout for him, Mr Herriot?'

What indeed? If Cliff had asked me the same question today I would have been just as troubled to give him an answer. The facts are that seventy to eighty per cent of tetanus cases die and whatever you do to them in the way of treatment doesn't seem to make a whit of difference to those figures. But I didn't want to sound entirely defeatist.

'It's a very serious condition as you know, Cliff, but I'll do all I can. I've got some antitoxin in the car and I'll inject that into his vein and if the spasms get very bad I'll give him a sedative. As long as he can drink there's a chance for him because he'll have to live on fluids – gruel would be fine.'

For a few days Badger didn't get any worse and I began to hope. I've seen tetanus horses recover and it is a wonderful experience to come in one day and find that the jaws have relaxed and the hungry animal can once more draw food into its mouth.

But it didn't happen with Badger. They had got the old horse into a big loose box where he could move around in comfort and each day as I looked over the half door I felt myself willing him to show some little sign of improvement; but instead, after that first few days he began to deteriorate. A sudden movement or the approach of any person would throw him into a violent spasm so that he would stagger stiff-legged round the box like a big wooden toy, his eyes terrified, saliva drooling from between his fiercely clenched teeth. One morning I was sure he would fall and I suggested putting him in slings. I had to go back to the surgery for the slings and it was just as I was entering Skeldale House that the phone rang.

It was Mr Gilling. 'He's beat us to it, I'm afraid. He's flat out on the floor and I doubt it's a bad job, Mr Herriot. We'll have to put him down, won't we?'

'I'm afraid so.'

'There's just one thing. Mallock will be taking him away but old Cliff says he doesn't want Mallock to shoot 'im. Wants you to do it. Will you come?'

I got out the humane killer and drove back to the farm, wondering at the fact that the old man should find the idea of my bullet less repugnant than the knacker man's. Mr Gilling was waiting in the box and by his side Cliff, shoulders hunched, hands deep in his pockets. He turned to me with a strange smile.

'I was just saying to t'boss how grand t'awd lad used to look when I got 'im up for a show. By Gaw you should have seen him with 'is coat polished and the feathers on his legs scrubbed as white as snow and a big blue ribbon round his tail.'

'I can imagine it, Cliff,' I said. 'Nobody could have looked after him better.'

He took his hands from his pockets, crouched by the prostrate animal and for a few minutes stroked the white-flecked neck and pulled at the ears while the old sunken eye looked at him impassively.

He began to speak softly to the old horse but his voice was steady, almost conversational, as though he was chatting to a friend.

'Many's the thousand miles I've walked after you, awd lad, and many's the talk we've had together. But I didn't have to say much to tha, did I? I reckon you knew every move I made, everything I said. Just one little word and you always did what ah wanted you to do.'

He rose to his feet. 'I'll get on with me work now, boss,' he said firmly, and strode out of the box.

I waited awhile so that he would not hear the bang which signalled the end of Badger, the end of the horses of Harland Grange and the end of the sweet core of Cliff Tyreman's life.

As I was leaving I saw the little man again. He was mounting the iron seat of a roaring tractor and I shouted to him above the noise.

'The boss says he's going to get some sheep in and you'll be doing a bit of shepherding. I think you'll enjoy that.'

Cliff's undefeated grin flashed out as he called back to me.

'Aye, I don't mind learnin' summat new. I'm nobbut a lad yet!'

Chapter Sixteen

This was a different kind of ringing. I had gone to sleep as the great bells in the church tower down the street pealed for the Christmas midnight mass, but this was a sharper, shriller sound.

It was difficult at first to shake off the mantle of unreality in which I had wrapped myself last night. Last night – Christmas Eve. It had been like a culmination of all the ideas I had ever held about Christmas – a flowering of emotions I had never experienced before. It had been growing in me since the afternoon call to a tiny village where the snow lay deep on the single street and on the walls and on the ledges of the windows where the lights on the tinselled trees glowed red and blue and gold; and as I left it in the dusk I drove beneath the laden branches of a group of dark spruce as motionless as though they had been sketched against the white background of the fields. And when I reached Darrowby it was dark and around the market place the little shops were bright with decorations and the light from the windows fell in a soft yellow wash over the trodden snow of the cobbles. People, anonymously muffled, were hurrying about, doing their last minute shopping, their feet slithering over the rounded stones.

I had known many Christmases in Scotland but they had taken second place to the New Year celebrations; there had been none of this air of subdued excitement which started days before with folks shouting good wishes and coloured lights winking on the lonely fell-sides and the farmers' wives plucking the fat geese, the feathers piled deep around their feet. And for fully two weeks you heard the children piping carols in the street then knocking on the door for sixpences. And best of all, last night the Methodist choir and sung out there, filling the night air with rich, thrilling harmony.

Before going to bed and just as the church bells began, I closed the door of Skeldale House behind me and walked again into the market place. Nothing stirred now in the white square stretching smooth and cold and empty under the moon, and there was a Dickens look about the ring of houses and shops put together long before anybody thought of town plannng; tall and short, fat and thin, squashed in crazily around the cobbles, their snow-burdened roofs jagged and uneven against the frosty sky.

As I walked back, the snow crunching under my feet, the bells clanging, the sharp air tingling in my nostrils, the wonder and mystery of Christmas enveloped me in a great wave. Peace on earth, goodwill towards men; the words became meaningful as never before and I saw myself suddenly as a tiny particle in the scheme of things; Darrowby, the farmers, the animals and me seemed for the first time like a warm, comfortable entity. I hadn't been drinking but I almost floated up the stairs of Skeldale House to my bedroom.

The temperature up there was about the same as in the street. It was always like that and I had developed the habit of hurling off my clothes and leaping into bed before the freezing air could get at me, but tonight my movements were leisurely and when I finally crawled between the sheets I was still wallowing in my Yuletide euphoria. There wouldn't be much work tomorrow; I'd have a long lie – maybe till nine – and then a lazy day, a glorious hiatus in my busy life. As I drifted into sleep it was as though I was surrounded by the smiling faces of my clients looking down at me with an all-embracing benevolence; and strangely I fancied I could hear singing, sweet and haunting, just like the methodist choir – God Rest Ye Merry Gentlemen . . .

But now there was this other bell which wouldn't stop. Must be the alarm. But as I pawed at the clock the noise continued and I saw that it was six o'clock. It was the phone of course. I lifted the receiver.

A metallic voice, crisp and very wideawake, jarred in my ear. 'Is that the vet?'

'Yes, Herriot speaking,' I mumbled.

'This is Brown, Willet Hill. I've got a cow down with milk fever. I want you here quick.'

'Right, I'll see to it.'

'Don't take ower long.' Then a click at the far end.

I rolled on to my back and stared at the ceiling. So this was Christmas Day. The day when I was going to step out of the world for a spell and luxuriate in the seasonal spirit. I hadn't bargained for this fellow jerking me brutally back to reality. And not a word of regret or apology. No 'sorry to get you out of bed', or anything else, never mind 'Merry Christmas'. It was just a bit hard.

Mr Brown was waiting for me in the darkness of the farmyard. I had been to his place a few times before and as my headlights blazed on him I was struck, as always, by his appearance of perfect physical fitness. He was a gingery man of about forty with high cheekbones set in a sharp-featured clear-skinned face. Red hair peeped from under a check cap and a faint auburn down covered his cheeks, his neck, the backs of his hands. It made me a bit more sleepy just to look at him.

He didn't say good morning but nodded briefly then jerked his head in the direction of the byre. 'She's in there' was all he said.

He watched in silence as I gave the injections and it wasn't until I was putting the empty bottles into my pocket that he spoke.

'Don't suppose I'll have to milk her today?'

'No,' I replied. 'Better leave the bag full.'

'Anything special about feedin'?'

'No, she can have anything she likes when she wants it.' Mr Brown was very efficient. Always wanted to know every detail.

As we crossed the yard he halted suddenly and turned to face me. Could it be that he was going to ask me in for a nice hot cup of tea?

'You know,' he said, as I stood ankle deep in the snow, the frosty air nipping at my ears. 'I've had a few of these cases lately. Maybe there's summat wrong with my routine. Do you think I'm steaming up my cows too much?'

'It's quite possible.' I hurried towards the car. One thing I wasn't going to do was deliver a lecture on animal husbandry at this moment.

My hand was on the door handle when he said 'I'll give you another ring if she's not up by dinner time. And there's one other thing – that was a hell of a bill I had from you fellers last month, so tell your boss not to be so savage with 'is pen.' Then he turned and walked quickly towards the house.

Well that was nice, I thought as I drove away. Not even thanks or goodbye, just a complaint and a promise to haul me away from my roast goose if necessary. A sudden wave of anger surged in me. Bloody farmers! There were some miserable devils among them. Mr Brown had doused my festive feelings as effectively as if he had thrown a bucket of water over me.

As I mounted the steps of Skeldale House the darkness had paled to a shivery grey. Mrs Hall met me in the passage. She was carrying a tray.

'I'm sorry,' she said. 'There's another urgent job. Mr Farnon's had to go out, too. But I've got a cup of coffee and some fried bread for you. Come in and sit down – you've got time to eat it before you go.'

I sighed. It was going to be just another day after all. 'What's this about, Mrs Hall?' I asked, sipping the coffee.

'It's old Mr Kirby,' she replied. 'He's in a right state about his nanny goat.'

'Nanny goat!'

'Aye, he says she's choking.'

'Choking! How the heck can she be choking?' I shouted.

'I'm sure I don't know. And I wish you wouldn't shout at me, Mr Herriot. It's not my fault.'

'I'm sorry, Mrs Hall, I'm really sorry.' I finished the coffee sheepishly. My feeling of goodwill was at a very low ebb.

Mr Kirby was a retired farmer, but he had sensibly taken a cottage with a bit of land where he kept enough stock to occupy his time – a cow, a few pigs and his beloved goats. He had always had goats, even when he was running his dairy herd; he had a thing about them.

The cottage was in a village high up the Dale. Mr Kirby met me at the gate.

'Ee, lad,' he said. 'I'm right sorry to be bothering you this early in the morning and Christmas an' all, but I didn't have no choice. Dorothy's real bad.'

He led the way to a stone shed which had been converted into a row of pens. Behind the wire of one of them a large white Saanen goat peered out at us anxiously and as I watched her she gulped, gave a series of retching coughs, then stood trembling, saliva drooling from her mouth.

The farmer turned to me, wide-eyed. 'You see, I had to get you out, didn't I? If I left her till tomorrow she'd be a goner.'

'You're right, Mr Kirby,' I replied. 'You couldn't leave her. There's something in her throat.'

We went into the pen and as the old man held the goat against the wall I tried to open her mouth. She didn't like it very much and as I prised her jaws apart she startled me with a loud, long-drawn human-sounding cry. It wasn't a big mouth but I have a small hand and, as the sharp back teeth tried to nibble me, I poked a finger deep into the pharynx.

There was something there all right. I could just touch it but I couldn't get hold of it. Then the animal began to throw her head about and I had to come out; I stood there, saliva dripping from my hand, looking thoughtfully at Dorothy.

After a few moments I turned to the farmer. 'You know, this is a bit baffling. I can feel something in the back of her throat, but it's soft – like cloth. I'd been expecting to find a bit of twig, or something sharp sticking in there – it's funny what a goat will pick up when she's pottering around outside. But if it's cloth, what the heck is holding it there? Why hasn't she swallowed it down?'

'Aye, it's a rum 'un isn't it?' The old man ran a gentle hand along the animal's back. 'Do you think she'll get rid of it herself? Maybe it'll just slip down?'

'No, I don't. It's stuck fast, God knows how, but it is. And I've got to get it out soon because she's beginning to blow up. Look there.' I pointed to the goat's left side, bulged by the tympanitic rumen, and as I did so, Dorothy began another paroxysm of coughs which seemed almost to tear her apart.

Mr Kirby looked at me with a mute appeal, but just at that moment I didn't see what I could do. Then I opened the door of the pen. 'I'm going to get my torch from the car. Maybe I can see something to explain this.'

The old man held the torch as I once more pulled the goat's mouth open and again heard the curious child-like wailing. It was when the animal was in full cry that I noticed something under the tongue – a thin, dark band.

'I can see what's holding the thing now,' I cried. 'It's hooked round the tongue with string or something.' Carefully I pushed my forefinger under the band and began to pull.

It wasn't string. It began to stretch as I pulled carefully at it . . . like elastic. Then it stopped stretching and I felt a real resistance . . . whatever was in the throat was beginning to move. I kept up a gentle traction and very slowly the mysterious obstruction came sliding up over the back of the tongue and into the mouth, and when it came within reach I let go the elastic, grabbed the sodden mass and hauled it forth. It seemed as if there was no end to it – a long snake of dripping material nearly two feet long – but at last I had it out on to the straw of the pen.

Mr Kirby seized it and held it up and as he unravelled the mass wonderingly he gave a sudden cry.

'God 'elp us, it's me summer drawers!'

'Your what?'

'Me summer drawers. Ah don't like them long johns when weather gets warmer and I allus change into these little short 'uns. Missus was havin' a clearout afore the end of t'year and she didn't know whether to wash 'em or mek them into dusters. She washed them at t'finish and Dorothy must have got 'em off the line.' He held up the tattered shorts and regarded them ruefully. 'By gaw, they've seen better days, but I reckon Dorothy's fettled them this time.'

Then his body began to shake silently, a few low giggles escaped from him and finally he gave a great shout of laughter. It was an infectious laugh and I joined in as I watched him. He went on for quite a long time and when he had finished he was leaning weakly against the wire netting.

'Me poor awd drawers,' he gasped, then leaned over and patted the goat's head. 'But as long as you're all right, lass, I'm not worried.'

'Oh, she'll be O.K.' I pointed to her left flank. 'You can see her stomach's going down already.' As I spoke, Dorothy belched pleasurably and began to nose interestedly at her hay rack.

The farmer gazed at her fondly. 'Isn't that grand to see! She's ready for her grub again. And if she hadn't got her tongue round the elastic that lot would have gone right down and killed her.'

'I really don't think it would, you know', I said. 'It's amazing what ruminants can carry around in their stomachs. I once found a bicycle tyre inside a cow when I was operating for something else. The tyre didn't seem to be bothering her in the least.'

'I see.' Mr Kirby rubbed his chin. 'So Dorothy might have wandered around with me drawers inside her for years.'

'It's possible. You'd never have known what became of them.'

'By gaw, that's right.' Mr Kirby said, and for a moment I thought he was going to start giggling again, but he mastered himself and seized my arm. 'But I don't know what I'm keeping you out here for, lad. You must come in and have a bit o' Christmas cake.'

Inside the tiny living room of the cottage I was ushered to the best chair by the fireside where two rough logs blazed and crackled.

'Bring cake out for Mr Herriot, mother,' the farmer cried as he rummaged in the pantry. He reappeared with a bottle of whisky at the same time as his wife bustled in carrying a cake thickly laid with icing and ornamented with coloured spangles, toboggans, reindeers.

Mr Kirby unscrewed the stopper. 'You know, mother, we're lucky to have such men as this to come out on a Christmas mornin' to help us.'

'Aye, we are that.' The old lady cut a thick slice of the cake and placed it on a plate by the side of an enormous wedge of Wensleydale cheese.

Her husband meanwhile was pouring my drink. Yorkshiremen are amateurs with whisky and there was something delightfully untutored in the way he was sloshing it into the glass as if it was lemonade; he would have filled it to the brim if I hadn't stopped him.

Drink in hand, cake on knee, I looked across at the farmer and his wife who were sitting in upright kitchen chairs watching me with quiet benevolence. The two faces had something in common – a kind of beauty. You would find faces like that only in the country; deeply wrinkled and weathered, clear-eyed, alight with a cheerful serenity.

I raised my glass. 'A happy Christmas to you both.'

The old couple nodded and replied smilingly. 'And the same to you, Mr Herriot.'

'Aye, and thanks again, lad,' said Mr Kirby. 'We're right grateful to you for runnin' out here to save awd Dorothy. We've maybe mucked up your day for you but it would've mucked up ours if we'd lost the old lass, wouldn't it, mother?'

'Don't worry, you haven't spoiled anything for me.' I said. 'In fact you've made me realise again that it really is Christmas.' And as I looked around the little room with the decorations hanging from the low-beamed ceiling I could feel the emotions of last night surging slowly back, a warmth creeping through me that had nothing to do with the whisky.

I took a bit of the cake and followed it with a moist slice of cheese. When I had first come to Yorkshire I had been aghast when offered this unheard-of-combination, but time had brought wisdom and I had discovered that the mixture when chewed boldly together was exquisite; and, strangely, I had also found that there was nothing more suitable for washing it finally over the tonsils than a draught of raw whisky.

'You don't mind t'wireless, Mr Herriot?' Mrs Kirby asked. 'We always like to have it on Christmas morning to hear t'old hymns but I'll turn it off if you like.'

'No please leave it, it sounds grand.' I turned to look at the old radio with its chipped wooden veneer, the ornate scroll-work over the worn fabric; it must have been one of the earliest models and it gave off a tinny sound, but the singing of the church choir was none the less sweet . . . *Hark the Herald Angels Sing* – flooding the little room, mingling with the splutter of the logs and the soft voices of the old people.

They showed me a picture of their son, who was a policeman over in Houlton and their daughter who was married to a neighbouring farmer. They were bringing their grand-children up for Christmas dinner as they always did and Mrs Kirby opened a box and ran a hand over the long row of crackers. The choir started on *Once in Royal David's City*, I finished my whisky and put up only feeble resistance as the farmer plied the bottle again. Through the small window I could see the bright berries of a holly tree pushing through their covering of snow.

It was really a shame to have to leave here and it was sadly that I drained my glass for the second time and scooped up the last crumbs of cake and icing from my plate.

Mr Kirby came out with me and at the gate of the cottage he stopped and held out his hand.

'Thank ye lad, I'm right grateful,' he said. 'And all the very best to you.'

For a moment the rough dry palm rasped against mine, then I was in the car, starting the engine. I looked at my watch; it was still only half past nine but the first early sunshine was sparkling from a sky of palest blue.

Beyond the village the road climbed steeply then curved around the rim of the valley in a wide arc, and it was here that you came suddenly upon the whole great expanse of the Plain of York spread out almost at your feet. I always slowed down here and there was always something different to see, but today the vast chequerboard of fields and farms and woods stood out with a clarity I had never seen before. Maybe it was because this was a holiday and down there no factory chimney smoked, no lorries belched fumes, but the distance was magically foreshortened in the clear, frosty air and I felt I could reach out and touch the familiar landmarks far below.

I looked back at the enormous white billows and folds of the fells, crowding close, one upon another into the blue distance, every crevice uncannily defined, the highest summits glittering where the sun touched them. I could see the village with the Kirbys' cottage at the end. I had found Christmas and peace and goodwill and everything back there.

Farmers? They were the salt of the earth.'

Chapter Seventeen

Marmaduke Skelton was an object of interest to me long before our paths crossed. For one thing I hadn't thought people were ever called Marmaduke outside of books and for another he was a particularly well known member of the honourable profession of unqualified animal doctors.

Before the Veterinary Surgeons' Act of 1948 anybody who fancied his chance at it could dabble in the treatment of animal disease. Veterinary students could quite legally be sent out to cases while they were seeing practice, certain members of the lay public did a bit of veterinary work as a sideline while others did it as a full time job. These last were usually called 'quacks'.

The disparaging nature of the term was often unjust because, though some of them were a menace to the animal population, others were dedicated men who did their job with responsibility and humanity and after the Act were brought into the profession's fold as Veterinary Practitioners.

But long before all this there were all sorts and types among them. The one I knew best was Arthur Lumley, a charming little ex-plumber who ran a thriving small animal practice in Brawton, much to the chagrin of Mr Angus Grier MRCVS. Arthur used to drive around in a small van. He always wore a white coat and looked very clinical and efficient, and on the side of the van in foot-high letters which would have got a qualified man a severe dressing down from the Royal College was the legend, 'Arthur Lumley MKC, Canine and Feline Specialist.' The lack of 'letters' after their name was the one thing which differentiated these men from qualified vets in the eyes of the general public and I was interested to see that Arthur did have an academic attainment. However the degree of MKC was unfamiliar to me and he was somewhat cagey when I asked him about it; I did find out eventually what it stood for; Member of the Kennel Club.

Marmaduke Skelton was of a vastly different breed. I had been working long enough round the Scarburn district to become familiar with some of the local history and it seemed that when Mr and Mrs Skelton were producing a family in the early 1900s they must have thought their offspring were destined for great things; they named their four sons Mamaduke, Sebastian, Cornelius and, incredibly, Alonzo. The two middle brothers drove lorries for the Express Dairy and Alonzo was a small farmer; one of my vivid memories is the shock of surprise when I was filling up the forms after his tuberculin test and asked him for his first name. The exotic appellation pronounced in gruff Yorkshire was so incongruous that I thought he was pulling my leg; in fact I was going to make a light comment but something in his eye prompted me to leave it alone.

Marmaduke, or Duke as he was invariably called, was the colourful member of the family. I had heard a lot about him on my visits to the Scarburn farms; he was a 'right good hand' at calving, foaling and lambing, and 'as good as any vitnery' in the diagnosis and treatment of animals' ailments. He was also an expert castrator, docker and pig-killer. He made a nice living at his trade and, of course, in Ewan Ross he had the ideal professional opposition; a veterinary surgeon who worked only when he felt like it and who didn't bother to go to a case unless he was in the mood. Much as the farmers liked and in many cases revered Ewan, they were often forced to fall back on Duke's services.

If Duke had confined his activities to treating his patients I don't think Ewan would ever have spared him a thought; but Skelton liked to enliven his farm visits with sneers about the old Scotch vet who had never been much good and was definitely getting past it now. Maybe even that didn't get very far under Ewan's skin but at the mention of his rival's name his mouth would harden a little and a ruminative expression creep into the blue eyes.

And it wasn't easy to like Duke. There were the tales you heard about his savage brawls and about how he knocked his wife and children around when the mood was on him. I didn't find his appearance engaging either when I first saw him swaggering across Scarburn market place; a black bull of a man, a shaggy Heathcliffe with fierce, darting eyes and a hint of braggadocio in the bright red handkerchief tied round his neck.

But on this particular afternoon I wasn't thinking about Duke Skelton, in fact I wasn't thinking about anything much as I sprawled in a chair by the Rosses' fireside. I had just finished one of Ginny's lunches; something with the unassuming name of fish pie but in truth a magical concoction in which the humble haddock was elevated to unimagined heights by the admixture of potatoes, tomatoes, eggs, macaroni and things only Ginny knew. Then the apple crumble and the chair close to the fire with the heat from the flames beating on my face.

The thoughts I had were slumbrous ones; that this house and the people in it had come to have a magnetic attaction for me; that if this had been a big successful practice the phone would have been dinging and Ewan would be struggling into his coat as he chewed his last bite. And an unworthy thought as I glanced through the window at the white garden and the snow-burdened trees; that if I didn't hurry back to Darrowby. Siegfried might do double the work and finish the lot before I got home.

Playing with the soothing picture of the muffled figure of my boss battling round the farms I watched Ginny placing a coffee cup by her husband's elbow. Ewan smiled up into her face and just then the phone range.

Like most vets I am bell-happy and I jumped, but Ewan didn't. He began quietly to sip his coffee as Ginny picked up the receiver and he didn't change expression when his wife came over and said, 'It's Tommy Thwaite. One of his cows has put its calf bed out.'

These dread tidings would have sent me leaping round the room but Ewan took a long swallow at his coffee before replying.

'Thank you, dear. Will you tell him I'll have a look at her shortly.'

He turned to me and began to tell me something funny which had happened to him that morning and when he had finished he went into his characteristic laugh – showing nothing apart from a vibration of the shoulders and a slight popping of the eyes. Then he relaxed in his chair and recommenced his leisurely sipping.

Though it wasn't my case my feet were itching. A bovine prolapsed uterus was not only an urgent condition but it held such grim promise of hard labour that I could never get it over quickly enough. Some were worse than others and I was always in a hurry to find out what was in store.

Ewan, however, appeared to be totally incurious. In fact he closed his eyes and I thought for a moment he was settling down for a post prandial nap. But it was only a gesture of resignation at the wrecking of his afternoon's repose and he gave a final stretch and got up.

'Want to come with me, Jim?' he asked in his soft voice.

I hesitated for a moment then, callously abandoning Siegfried to his fate, I nodded eagerly and followed Ewan into the kitchen.

He sat down and pulled on a pair of thick woollen over-socks which Ginny had been warming by the stove, then he put on his Wellingtons, a short overcoat, yellow gloves and a check cap. As he strolled along the narrow track which had been dug through the garden snow he looked extraordinarily youthful and debonair.

He didn't go into his dispensary this time and I wondered what equipment he would use, thinking at the same time of Siegfried's words: 'Ewan has his own way of doing everything.'

At the farm Mr Thwaite trotted over to meet us. He was understandably agitated but there was something else; a nervous rubbing of the hands, an uneasy giggle as he watched my colleague opening the car boot.

'Mr Ross,' he blurted out at last, 'I don't want you to be upset, but I've summat to tell you.' He paused for a moment. 'Duke Skelton's in there with my cow.'

Ewan's expression did not flicker. 'Oh, right. Then you won't need me.' He closed the boot, opened the door and got back into the car.

'Hey, hey, I didn't mean you to go away!' Mr Thwaite ran round and cried through the glass. 'Duke just happened to be in t'village and he said he'd help me out.'

'Fine,' Ewan said, winding down the window, 'I don't mind in the least. I'm sure he'll do a good job for you.'

The farmer screwed up his face in misery. 'But you don't understand. He's been in there for about an hour and a half and he's no further forward. He's not doin' a bit o' good and he's about buggered an' all. I want you to take over, Mr Ross.'

'No, I'm sorry.' Ewan gave him a level stare. 'I couldn't possibly interfere. You know how it is, Tommy. He's begun the job – I've got to let him finish.' He started the engine.

'No, no, don't go!' shouted Mr Thwaite, beating the car roof with his hands. 'Duke's whacked, I tell ye. If you drive away now ah'm going to lose one of ma best cows. You've got to help me, Mr Ross!' He seemed on the verge of tears.

My colleague looked at him thoughtfully as the engine purred. Then he bent forward and turned off the ignition. 'All right, I'll tell you what – I'll go in there and see what he says. If he wants me to help, then I will.'

I followed him into the byre and as we paused just inside the door Duke Skelton looked up from his work. He had been standing head down, one hand resting on the rump of a massive cow, his mouth hanging open, his great barrel chest heaving. The thick hair over his shoulders and ribs was matted with blood from the huge everted uterus which dangled behind the animal. Blood and filth streaked his face and covered his arms and as he stared at us from under his shaggy brows he looked like something from the jungle.

'Well now, Mr Skelton,' Ewan murmured conversationally. 'How are you getting on?'

Duke gave him a quick malevolent glance. 'Ah'm doin' all right.' The words rumbled from deep down through his gaping lips.

Mr Thwaite stepped forward, smiling ingratiatingly. 'Come on, Duke, you've done your best. I think you should let Mr Ross give you a 'and now.'

'Well ah don't.' The big man's jaw jutted suddenly. 'If I was lookin' for help I wouldn't want 'IM.' He turned away and seized the uterus. Hoisting it in his arms he began to push at it with fierce concentration.

Mr Thwaite turned to us with an expression of despair and opened his mouth to lament again, but Ewan silenced him with a raised hand, pulling a milking stool from a corner and squatted down comfortably against a wall. Unhurriedly he produced his little pouch and, one-handed, began to make a cigarette; as he licked the paper, screwed up the end and applied a match he gazed with blank eyes at the sweating, struggling figure a few feet from him.

Duke had got the uterus about half way back. Grunting and gasping, legs straddled, he had worked the engorged mass inch by inch inside the vulva till he had just about enough cradled in his arms for one last push; and as he stood there taking a breather with the great muscles of his shoulders and arms rigid his immense strength was formidably displayed. But he wasn't as strong as that cow. No man is as strong as a cow and this cow was one of the biggest I had ever seen with a back like a table top and rolls of fat round her tailhead.

I had been in this position myself and I knew what was coming next. I didn't have to wait long. Duke took a long wheezing breath and made his assault, heaving desperately, pushing with arms and chest, and for a second or two he seemed to be winning as the mass disappeared steadily inside. Then the cow gave an almost casual strain and the whole thing welled out again till it hung down bumping against the animal's hocks.

As Duke almost collapsed against her pelvis in the same attitude as when we first came in I felt pity for the man. I found him uncharming but I felt for him. That could easily be me standing there; my jacket and shirt hanging on that nail, my strength ebbing, my sweat mingling with the blood. No man could do what he was trying to do. You could push back a calf bed with the aid of an epidural anaesthetic to stop the straining or you could sling the animal up to a beam with a block and tackle; you couldn't just stand there and do it from scratch as this chap was trying to do.

I was surprised Duke hadn't learned that with all his experience; but apparently it still hadn't dawned on him even now because he was going through all the motions of having another go. This time he got even further – a few more inches inside before the cow popped it out again. The animal appeared to have a sporting streak because there was something premeditated about the way she played her victim along before timing her thrust at the very last moment. Apart from that she seemed somewhat bored by the whole business; in fact with the possible exception of Ewan she was the calmest among us.

Duke was trying again. As he bent over wearily and picked up the gory organ I wondered how often he had done this since he arrived nearly two hours ago. He had guts, there was no doubt. But the end was near. There was a frantic urgency about his movements as though he knew himself it was his last throw and as he yet again neared his goal his grunts changed to an agonised whimpering, an almost tearful sound as though he were appealing to the recalcitrant mass, beseeching it to go away inside and stay away, just this once.

And when the inevitable happened and the poor fellow, panting and shaking, surveyed once more the ruin of his hopes I had the feeling that somebody had to do something.

Mr Thwaite did it. 'You've had enough, Duke,' he said. 'For God's sake come in the house and get cleaned up. Missus'll give you a bit o' dinner and while you're having it Mr Ross'll see what he can do.'

The big man, arms hanging limp by his sides, chest heaving, stared at the farmer for a few seconds then he turned abruptly and snatched his clothes from the wall.

'Aw right,' he said and began to walk slowly towards the door. He stopped opposite Ewan but didn't look at him. 'But ah'll tell you summat, Maister Thwaite. If ah can't put that calf bed back this awd bugger never will.'

Ewan drew on his cigarette and peered up at him impassively. He didn't follow him with his eyes as he left the byre but leaned back against the wall, puffed out a thin plume of smoke and watched it rise and disappear among the shadows in the roof.

Mr Thwaite was soon back. 'Now, Mr Ross,' he said a little breathlessly, 'I'm sorry about you havin' to wait but we can get on now. I expect you'll be needin' some fresh hot water and is there anything else you want?'

Ewan dropped his cigarette on the cobbles and ground it with his foot. 'Yes, you can bring me a pound of sugar.'

'What's that?'

'A pound of sugar.'

'A pound of . . . right, right . . . I'll get it.'

In no time at all the farmer returned with an unopened paper bag. Ewan split the top with his finger, walked over to the cow and began to dust the sugar all over the uterus. Then he turned to Mr Thwaite again.

'And I'll want a pig stool, too. I expect you have one.'

'Oh aye, we have one, but what the hangment . . . ?'

Ewan cocked a gentle eye at him. 'Bring it in, then. It's time we got this job done.'

As the farmer disappeared at a stiff gallop I went over to my colleague. 'What's going on, Ewan? What the devil are you chucking that sugar about for?'

'Oh it draws the serum out of the uterus. You can't beat it when the thing's engorged like that.'

'It does?' I glanced unbelievingly at the bloated organ. 'And aren't you going to give her an epidural . . . and some pituitrin . . . and a calcium injection?'

'Och no,' Ewan replied with his slow smile. 'I never bother about those things.'

I didn't get the chance to ask him what he wanted with the pig stool because just then Mr Thwaite trotted in with one under his arm.

Most farms used to have them. They were often called 'creels' and the sides of bacon were laid on them at pig-killing time. This was a typical specimen – like a long low table with four short legs and a slatted concave top. Ewan took hold of it and pushed it carefully under the cow just in front of the udder while I stared at it through narrowed eyes. I was getting out of my depth.

Ewan then walked unhurriedly out to his car and returned with a length of rope and two objects wrapped in the inevitable brown paper. As he draped the rope over the partition, pulled on a rubber parturition gown and began to open the parcels I realised I was once again watching Ewan setting out his stall.

From the first parcel he produced what looked like a beer tray but which I decided couldn't possibly be; but when he said, 'Here, hold this a minute, Jim,' and I read the emblazoned gold scroll, 'John Smith's Magnet Pale Ale' I had to change my mind. It was a beer tray.

He began to unfold the brown paper from the other object and my brain reeled a little as he fished out an empty whisky bottle and placed it on the tray. Standing there with my strange burden I felt like the stooge in a conjuring act and I wouldn't have been a bit surprised if my colleague had produced a live rabbit next.

But all he did was to fill the whisky bottle with some of the clean hot water from the bucket.

Next he looped the rope round the cow's horns, passed it round the body a couple of times then leaned back and pulled. Without protest the big animal collapsed gently on top of the pig stool and lay there with her rear end stuck high in the air.

'Right now, we can start,' Ewan murmured, and as I threw down my jacket and began to tear off my tie he turned to me in surprise.

'Here, here, what do you think you're doing?'

'Well I'm going to give you a hand, of course.'

One corner of his mouth twitched upwards. 'It's kind of you, Jim, but there's no need to get stripped off. This will only take a minute. I just want you and Mr Thwaite to keep the thing level for me.'

He gently hoisted the organ which to my fevered imagination had shrunk visibly since the sugar, on to the beer tray and gave the farmer and me an end each to hold.

Then he pushed the uterus back.

He did literally only take a minute or not much more. Without effort, without breaking sweat or exerting visible pressure he returned that vast mass to where it belonged while the cow, unable to strain or do a thing about it, just lay there with an aggrieved expression on her face. Then he took his whisky bottle, passed it carefully into the vagina and disappeared up to arm's length where he began to move his shoulder vigorously.

'What the hell are you doing now?' I whispered agitatedly into his ear from my position at the end of the beer tray.

'I'm rotating each horn to get it back into place and pouring a little hot water from the bottle into the ends of the horns to make sure they're completely involuted.'

'Oh, I see.' I watched as he removed the bottle, soaped his arms in the bucket and began to take off his overall.

'But aren't you going to stitch it in?' I blurted out.

Ewan shook his head. 'No, Jim. If you put it back properly it never comes out again.'

He was drying his hands when the byre door opened and Duke Skelton slouched in. He was washed and dressed, with his red handkerchief knotted again round his neck and he glared fierce-eyed at the cow which, tidied up and unperturbed, looked now just like all the other cows in the row. His lips moved once or twice before he finally found his voice.

'Aye, it's all right for some people,' he snarled. 'Some people with their bloody fancy injections and instruments! It's bloody easy that way, isn't it.' Then he swung round and was gone.

As I heard his heavy boots clattering across the yard it struck me that his words were singularly inapt. What was there even remotely fancy about a pig stool, a pound of sugar, a whisky bottle and a beer tray?

Chapter Eighteen

'I work for cats.'

That was how Mrs Bond introduced herself on my first visit, gripping my hand firmly and thrusting out her jaw defiantly as though challenging me to make something of it. She was a big woman with a strong, high-cheekboned face and a commanding presence and I wouldn't have argued with her anyway, so I nodded gravely as though I fully understood and agreed, and allowed her to lead me into the house.

I saw at once what she meant. The big kitchen-living room had been completely given over to cats. There were cats on the sofas and chairs and spilling in cascades on to the floor, cats sitting in rows along the window sills and right in the middle of it all, little Mr Bond, pallid, wispy-moustached, in his shirt sleeves reading a newspaper.

It was a scene which was going to become very familiar. A lot of the cats were obviously uncastrated Toms because the atmosphere was vibrant with their distinctive smell – a fierce pungency which overwhelmed even the sickly wisps from the big sauce-pans of nameless cat food bubbling on the stove. And Mr Bond was always there, always in his shirt sleeves and reading his paper, a lonely little island in a sea of cats.

I had heard of the Bonds, of course. They were Londoners who for some obscure reason had picked on North Yorkshire for their retirement. People said they had a 'bit o' brass' and they had bought an old house on the outskirts of Darrowby where they kept themselves to themselves – and the cats. I had heard that Mrs Bond was in the habit of taking in strays and feeding them and giving them a home if they wanted it and this had predisposed me in her favour, because in my experience the unfortunate feline species seemed to be fair game for every kind of cruelty and neglect. They shot cats, threw things at them, starved them and set their dogs on them for fun. It was good to see somebody taking their side.

My patient on this first visit was no more than a big kitten, a terrified little blob of black and white crouching in a corner.

'He's one of the outside cats,' Mrs Bond boomed.

'Outside cats?'

'Yes. All these you see here are the inside cats. The others are the really wild ones who simply refuse to enter the house. I feed them of course but the only time they come indoors is when they are ill.'

'I see.'

'I've had frightful trouble catching this one. I'm worried about his eyes – there seemed to be a skin growing over them, and I do hope you can do something for him. His name, by the way, is Alfred.'

'Alfred? Ah yes, quite.' I advanced cautiously on the little half-grown animal and was greeted by a waving set of claws and a series of open-mouthed spittings. He was trapped in his corner or he would have been off with the speed of light.

Examining him was going to be a problem. I turned to Mrs Bond. 'Could you let me have a sheet of some kind? An old ironing sheet would do. I'm going to have to wrap him up.'

'Wrap him up?' Mrs Bond looked very doubtful but she disappeared into another room and returned with a tattered sheet of cotton which looked just right.

I cleared the table of an amazing variety of cat feeding dishes, cat books, cat medicines and spread out the sheet, then I approached my patient again. You can't be in a hurry in a situation like this and it took me perhaps five minutes of wheedling and 'Puss-pussing' while I brought my hand nearer and nearer. When I got as far as being able to stroke his cheek I made a quick grab at the scruff of his neck and finally bore Alfred, protesting bitterly and lashing out in all directions, over to the table. There, still holding tightly to his scruff, I laid him on the sheet and started the wrapping operation.

This is something which as to be done quite often with obstreperous felines and, although I say it, I am rather good at it. The idea is to make a neat, tight roll, leaving the relevant piece of cat exposed; it may be an injured paw, perhaps the tail, and in this case of course the head. I think it was the beginning of Mrs Bond's unquestioning faith in me when she saw me quickly enveloping that cat till all you could see of him was a small black and white head protruding from an immovable cocoon of cloth. He and I were now facing each other, more or less eyeball to eyeball, and Alfred couldn't do a thing about it.

As I say, I rather pride myself on this little expertise and even today my veterinary colleagues have been known to remark: 'Old Herriot may be limited in many respects but by God he can wrap a cat.'

As it turned out, there wasn't a skin growing over Alfred's eyes. There never is.

'He's got a paralysis of the third eyelid, Mrs Bond. Animals have this membrane which flicks across the eye to protect it. In this case it hasn't gone back, probably because the cat is in low condition – maybe had a touch of cat flu or something else which has weakened him. I'll give him an injection of vitamins and leave you some powder to put in his food if you could keep him in for a few days. I think he'll be all right in a week or two.'

The injection presented no problems with Alfred furious but helpless inside his sheet and I had come to the end of my first visit to Mrs Bond's.

It was the first of many. The lady and I established an immediate rapport which was strengthened by the fact that I was always prepared to spend time over her assorted charges; crawling on my stomach under piles of logs in the outhouses to reach the outside cats, coaxing them down from trees, stalking them endlessly through the shrubbery. But from my point of view it was rewarding in many ways.

For instance there was the diversity of names she had for her cats. True to her London upbringing she had named many of the Toms after the great Arsenal team of those days. There was Eddie Hapgood, Cliff Bastin, Ted Drake, Wilf Copping, but she did slip up in one case because Alex James had kittens three times a year with unfailing regularity.

Then there was her way of calling them home. The first time I saw her at this was on a still summer evening. The two cats she wanted me to see were out in the garden somewhere and I walked with her to the back door where she halted, clasped her hands across her bosom, closed her eyes and gave tongue in a mellifluous contralto.

'Bates, Bates, Bates, Ba-hates.' She actually sang out the words in a reverent monotone except for a delightful little lilt on the 'Ba-hates'. Then once more she inflated her ample rib cage like an operatic prima donna and out it came again, delivered with the utmost feeling.

'Bates, Bates, Bates, Ba-hates.'

Anyway it worked, because Bates the cat came trotting from behind a clump of laurel. There remained the other patient and I watched Mrs Bond with interest.

She took up the same stance, breathed in, closed her eyes, composed her features into a sweet half-smile and started again.

'Seven-times-three, Seven-times-three, Seven-times-three-hee.' It was set to the same melody as Bates with the same dulcet rise and fall at the end. She didn't get the quick response this time, though, and had to go through the performance again and again, and as the notes lingered on the still evening air the effect was startlingly like a muezzin calling the faithful to prayer.

At length she was successful and a fat tortoiseshell slunk apologetically along the wall-side into the house.

'By the way, Mrs Bond,' I asked, making my voice casual. 'I didn't quite catch the name of that last cat.'

'Oh, Seven-times-three?' She smiled reminiscently. 'Yes, she is a dear. She's had three kittens seven times running, you see, so I thought it rather a good name for her, don't you?'

'Yes, yes, I do indeed. Splendid name, splendid.'

Another thing which warmed me towards Mrs Bond was her concern for my safety. I appreciated this because it is a rare trait among animal owners. I can think of the trainer after one of his racehorses had kicked me clean out of a loose box examining the animal anxiously to see if it had damaged its foot; the little old lady dwarfed by the bristling, teeth-bared Alsatian saying: 'You'll be gentle with him won't you and I hope you won't hurt him – he's very nervous'; the farmer, after an exhausting calving which I feel certain has knocked about two years off my life expectancy, grunting morosely: 'I doubt you've tired that cow out, young man.'

Mrs Bond was different. She used to meet me at the door with an enormous pair of gauntlets to protect my hands against scratches and it was an inexpressible relief to find that somebody cared. It became part of the pattern of my life; walking up the garden path among the innumerable slinking, wild-eyed little creatures which were the outside cats, the ceremonial acceptance of the gloves at the door, then the entry into the charged atmosphere of the kitchen with little Mr Bond and his newspaper just visible among the milling furry bodies of the inside cats. I was never able to ascertain Mr Bond's attitude to cats – come to think of it he hardly ever said anything – but I had the impression he could take them or leave them.

The gauntlets were a big help and at times they were a veritable godsend. As in the case of Boris. Boris was an enormous blue-black member of the outside cats and my bête noire in more senses than one. I always cherished a private conviction that he had escaped from a zoo; I had never seen a domestic cat with such sleek, writhing muscles, such dedicated ferocity. I'm sure there was a bit of puma in Boris somewhere.

It had been a sad day for the cat colony when he turned up. I have always found it difficult to dislike any animal; most of the ones which try to do us a mischief are activated by fear, but Boris was different; he was a malevolent bully and after his arrival the frequency of my visits increased because of his habit of regularly beating up his colleagues. I was forever stitching up tattered ears, dressing gnawed limbs.

We had one trial of strength fairly early. Mrs Bond wanted me to give him a worm dose and I had the little tablet all ready held in forceps. How I ever got hold of him I don't quite know, but I hustled him on to the table and did my wrapping act at lighting speed, swathing him in roll upon roll of stout material.

Just for a few seconds I thought I had him as he stared up at me, his great brilliant eyes full of hate. But as I pushed my loaded forceps into his mouth he clamped his teeth viciously down on them and I could feel .claws of amazing power tearing inside the sheet. It was all over in moments. A long leg shot out and ripped its way down my wrist, I let go my tight hold of the neck and in a flash Boris sank his teeth through the gauntlet into the ball of my thumb and was away. I was left standing there stupidly, holding the fragmented worm tablet in a bleeding hand and looking at the bunch of ribbons which had once been my wrapping sheet. From then on Boris loathed the very sight of me and the feeling was mutual.

But this was one of the few clouds in a serene sky. I continued to enjoy my visits there and life proceeded on a tranquil course except, perhaps, for some legpulling from my colleages. They could never understand my willingness to spend so much time over a lot of cats. And of course this fitted in with the general attitude because Siegfried didn't believe in people keeping pets of any kind. He just couldn't understand their mentality and propounded his views to anybody who cared to listen. He himself, of course, kept five dogs and two cats. The dogs, all of them, travelled everywhere with him in the car and he fed dogs and cats every day with his own hands – wouldn't allow anybody else to do the job. In the evening all seven animals would pile themselves round his feet as he sat in his chair by the fire. To this day he is still as vehemently anti-pet as ever, though another generation of waving dogs' tails almost obscures him as he drives around and he also has several cats, a few tanks of tropical fish and a couple of snakes.

Tristan saw me in action at Mrs Bond's on only one occasion. I was collecting some long forceps from the instrument cupboard when he came into the room.

'Anything interesting, Jim?' he asked.

'No, not really. I'm just off to see one of the Bond cats. It's got a bone stuck between its teeth.'

The young man eyed me ruminatively for a moment. 'Think I'll come with you. I haven't seen much small animal stuff lately.'

As we went down the garden at the cat establishment I felt a twinge of embarrassment. One of the things which had built up my happy relationship with Mrs Bond was my tender concern for her charges. Even with the wildest and the fiercest I exhibited only gentleness, patience and solicitude; it wasn't really an act, it came quite naturally to me. However I couldn't help wondering what Tristan would think of my cat bedside manner.

Mrs Bond in the doorway had summed up the situation in a flash and had two pairs of gauntlets waiting. Tristan looked a little surprised as he received his pair but thanked the lady with typical charm. He looked still more surprised when he entered the kitchen, sniffed the rich atmosphere and surveyed the masses of furry creatures occupying almost every available inch of space.

'Mr Herriot, I'm afraid it's Boris who has the bone in his teeth,' Mrs Bond said.

'Boris!' My stomach lurched. 'How on earth are we going to catch him?'

'Oh I've been rather clever,' she replied. 'I've managed to entice him with some of his favourite food into a cat basket.'

Tristan put his hand on a big wicker cage on the table. 'In here, is he?' he asked casually. He slipped back the catch and opened the lid. For something like a third of a second the coiled creature within and Tristan regarded each other tensely, then a sleek black body exploded silently from the basket past the young man's left ear on to the top of a tall cupboard.

'Christ!' said Tristan. 'What the hell was that?'

'That,' I said, 'was Boris, and now we've got to get hold of him again.' I climbed on to a chair, reached slowly on to the cupboard top and started 'Puss-puss-puss'ing in my most beguiling tone.

After about a minute Tristan appeared to think he had a better idea; he made a sudden leap and grabbed Boris's tail. But only briefly, because the big cat freed himself in an instant and set off on a whirlwind circuit of the room; along the tops of cupboards and dressers, across the curtains, careering round and round like a wall of death rider.

Tristan stationed himself at a strategic point and as Boris shot past he swiped at him with one of the gauntlets.

'Missed the bloody thing!' he shouted in chagrin. 'But here he comes again ... take that, you black sod! Damn it, I can't nail him!'

The docile little inside cats, startled by the scattering of plates and tins and pans and by Tristan's cries and arm wavings, began to run around in their turn, knocking over whatever Boris had missed. The noise and confusion even got through to Mr Bond because just for a moment he raised his head and looked around him in mild surprise at the hurtling bodies before returning to his newspaper.

Tristan, flushed with the excitement of the chase had really begun to enjoy himself. I cringed inwardly as he shouted over to me happily.

'Send him on, Jim, I'll get the bugger next time round!'

We never did catch Boris. We just had to leave the piece of bone to work its own way out, so it wasn't a successful veterinary visit. But Tristan as we got back into the car smiled contentedly.

'That was great, Jim. I didn't realise you had such fun with your pussies.'

Mrs Bond on the other hand, when I next saw her, was rather tight-lipped over the whole thing.

'Mr Herriot,' she said, 'I hope you aren't going to bring that young man with you again.'

Chapter Nineteen

I always liked having a student with us. These young men had to see at least six months' practice on their way through college and most of their vacations were spent going round with a vet.

We, of course, had our own resident student in Tristan but he was in a different category. I often envied him his remarkable brain because he didn't have to be taught anything – he seemed to know things, to absorb knowledge without apparent effort or indeed without showing interest. If you took Tristan to a case he usually spent his time on the farm sitting in the car reading his *Daily Mirror* and smoking Woodbines.

There were all types among the others – some from the country some from the towns, some dull-witted, some bright – but as I say, I liked having them.

For one thing they were good company in the car. A big part of a country vet's life consists of solitary driving and it was a relief to be able to talk to somebody. It was wonderful, too, to have a gate-opener. Some of the outlying farms were approached through long, gated roads – one which always struck terror into me had eight gates – and it is hard to convey the feeling of sheer luxury when somebody else leaped out and opened them.

And there was another little pleasure; asking the students questions. My own days of studying and examinations were still fresh in my memory and on top of that I had all the vast experience of nearly three years of practice. It gave me a feeling of power to drop casual little queries about the cases we saw and watch the lads squirm as I had so recently squirmed myself. I suppose that even in those early days I was forming a pattern for later life; unknown to myself I was falling in to the way of asking a series of my own pet questions as all examiners are liable to do and many years later I overhead one youngster asking another: 'Has he grilled you on the causes of fits in calves yet? Don't worry, he will.' That made me feel suddenly old but there was compensation on another occasion when a newly qualified ex-student rushed up to me and offered to buy me all the beer I could drink. 'You know what the examiner asked me in the final oral? The causes of fits in calves! By God I paralysed him – he had to beg me to stop talking.'

And students were useful in other ways. They ran and got things out of the car boot, they pulled a rope at calvings, they were skilled assistants at operations, they were a repository for my worries and doubts; it isn't too much to say that during their brief visits they revolutionised my life.

So this Easter I waited on the platform of Darrowby station with pleasant anticipation. This lad had been recommended by one of the Ministry officials. 'A really first class chap. Final year London – several times gold medallist. He's seen mixed and town practice and thought he ought to have a look at some of the real rural stuff. I said I'd give you a ring. His name is Richard Carmody.'

Veterinary students came in a variety of shapes and sizes but there were a few features most of them had in common and I already had a mental picture of an eager-faced lad in tweed jacket and rumpled slacks carrying a rucksack. He would probably jump on to the platform as soon as the train drew up. But this time there was no immediate sign of life and a porter had begun to load a stack of egg boxes into the guard's van before one of the compartment doors opened and a tall figure descended in leisurely manner.

I was doubtful about his identity but he seemed to place me on sight. He walked over, held out a hand and surveyed me with a level gaze.

'Mr Herriot?'

'Yes ... er ... yes. That's right.'

'My name is Carmody.'

'Ah yes, good. How are you?' We shook hands and I took in the fine check suit and tweedy hat, the shining brogues and pigskin case. This was a very superior student, in fact a highly impressive young man. About a couple of years younger than myself but with a mature air in the set of his broad shoulders and the assurance on his strong, high-coloured face.

I led him across the bridge out on to the station yard. He didn't actually raise his eyebrows when he saw my car but he shot a cold glance at the mud-spattered vehicle, at the cracked windscreen and smooth tyres; and when I opened the door for him I thought for a moment he was going to wipe the seat before sitting down.

At the surgery I showed him round. I was only the assistant but I was proud of our modest set-up and most people were impressed by their first sight of it. But Carmody said 'Hm', in the little operating room, 'Yes, I see,' in the dispensary, and 'Quite' at the instrument cupboard. In the stockroom he was more forthcoming. He reached out and touched a packet of our beloved Adrevan worm medicine for horses.

'Still using this stuff, eh?' he said with a faint smile.

He didn't go into any ecstasies but he did show signs of approval when I took him out through the french windows into the long, high-walled garden where the daffodils glowed among the unkempt tangle and the wisteria climbed high over the old bricks of the tall Georgian house. In the cobbled yard at the foot of the garden he looked up at the rooks making their din high in the overhanging elms and he gazed for a few moments through the trees to where you could see the bare ribs of the fells still showing the last white runnels of winter.

'Charming,' he murmured. 'Charming.'

I was glad enough to see him to his lodgings that evening. I felt I needed time to readjust my thinking.

When we started out next morning I saw he had discarded his check suit but was still very smart in a hacking jacket and flannels.

'Haven't you any protective clothing?' I asked.

'I've got these.' He indicated a spotless pair of Wellingtons in the back of the car.

'Yes, but I mean an oilskin or a coat of some kind. Some of our jobs are pretty dirty.'

He smiled indulgently. 'Oh, I'm sure I'll be all right. I've been round the farms before, you know.'

I shrugged my shoulders and left it at that.

Our first visit was to a lame calf. The little animal was limping round its pen, holding up a fore leg and looking very woebegone. The knee was visibly swollen and as I palpated it there seemed to be a lumpiness in the fluid within as if there might be a flocculus of pus among it. The temperature was a hundred and four.

I looked up at the farmer. 'This is joint ill. He probably got an infection through his navel soon after birth and it's settled in his knee. We'll have to take care of him because his internal organs such as the liver and lungs can be affected. I'll give him an injection and leave you some tablets for him.'

I went out to the car and when I came back Carmody was bending over the calf, feeling at the distended knee and inspecting the navel closely. I gave my injection and we left.

'You know,' Carmody said as we drove out of the yard, 'that wasn't joint ill.'

'Really?' I was a bit taken aback. I didn't mind students discussing the pros and cons of my diagnoses as long as they didn't do it in front of the farmer, but I had never had one tell me bluntly that I was wrong. I made a mental note to try to keep this fellow away from Siegfried; one remark like that and Siegfried would hurl him unhesitatingly out of the car, big as he was.

'How do you make that out, then?' I asked him.

'Well there was only the one joint involved and the navel was perfectly dry. No pain or swelling there. I should say he just sprained that knee.'

'You may be right, but wouldn't you say the temperature was a bit high for a sprain?'

Carmody grunted and shook his head slightly. Apparently he had no doubts.

A few gates cropped up in the course of our next batch of calls and Carmody got out and opened them just like any ordinary being except that he did it with a certain leisurely elegance. Watching his tall figure as he paced across, his head held high, the smart hat set at just the right angle, I had to admit again that he had enormous presence. It was remarkable at his age.

Shortly before lunch I saw a cow that the farmer had said on the phone might have TB. 'She's gone down t'nick ever since she calved, guvnor. I doubt she's a screw, but you'd better have a look at her, anyroad.'

As soon as I walked into the byre I knew what the trouble was. I have been blessed with an unusually sensitive nose and the sickly sweet smell of ketone hit me right away. It has always afforded me a childish pleasure to be able to say suddenly in the middle of a tuberculin test 'There's a cow in here about three weeks calved that isn't doing very well,' and watch the farmer scratch his head and ask me how I knew.

I had another little triumph today. 'Started going off her cake first didn't she?' and the farmer nodded assent. 'And the flesh has just melted off her since then?'

'That's right,' the farmer said, 'I've never seen a cow go down as quick.'

'Well you can stop worrying, Mr Smith. She hasn't got TB, she's got slow fever and we'll be able to put her right for you.'

Slow fever is the local term for acetonaemia and the farmer smiled in relief. 'Damn. I'm glad! I thowt she was dog meat. I nearly rang Mallock this morning.'

I couldn't reach for the steroids which we use today, but I injected six ounces of glucose and 100 units of insulin intravenously – it was one of my pet remedies and might make modern vets laugh But it used to work. The cow, dead-eyed and gaunt, was too weak to struggle as the farmer held her nose.

When I had finished I ran my hand over the jutting bones, covered, it seemed, only by skin.

'She'll soon fatten up now,' I said. 'But cut her down to once a day milking – that's half the battle. And if that doesn't work, stop milking her entirely for two or three days.'

'Yes, I reckon she's putting it in t'bucket instead of on her back.'

'That's it exactly, Mr Smith.'

Carmody didn't seem to appreciate this interchange of home-spun wisdom and fidgeted impatiently. I took my cue and headed for the car.

'I'll see her in a couple of days,' I cried as we drove away, and waved to Mrs Smith who was looking out from the farmhouse doorway. Carmody however raised his hat gravely and held it a few inches above his head till we had left the yard, which was definitely better. I had noticed him doing this at every place we had visited and it looked so good that I was playing with the idea of starting to wear a hat so that I could try it too.

I glanced sideways at my companion. Most of a morning's work done and I hadn't asked him any questions. I cleared my throat.

'By the way, talking about that cow we've just seen, can you tell me something about the causes of acetonaemia?'

Carmody regarded me impassively. 'As a matter of fact I can't make up my mind which theory I endorse at the moment. Stevens maintains it is the incomplete oxidation of fatty acids, Sjollema leans towards liver intoxication and Janssen implicates one of the centres of the autonomic nervous system. My own view is that if we could only pin-point the exact cause of the production of diacetic acid and beta-oxybutyric acid in the metabolism we'd be well on the way to understanding the problem. Don't you agree?'

I closed my mouth which had begun to hang open.

'Oh yes, I do indeed . . . it's that oxy . . . that old beta-oxy . . . yes, that's what it is, without a doubt.' I slumped lower in my seat and decided not to ask Carmody any more questions; and as the stone walls flipped past the windows I began to face up to the gradually filtering perception that this was a superior being next to me. It was depressing to ponder on the fact that not only was he big, good-looking, completely sure of himself but brilliant as well. Also, I thought bitterly, he had every appearance of being rich.

We rounded the corner of a lane and came up to a low huddle of stone buildings. It was the last call before lunch and the gate into the yard was closed.

'We might as well go through,' I murmured. 'Do you mind?'

The student heaved himself from the car, unlatched the gate and began to bring it round. And he did it as he seemed to do everything; coolly, unhurriedly, with natural grace. As he passed the front of the car I was studying him afresh, wondering again at his style, his massive composure, when, apparently from nowhere, an evil looking little black cur dog glided silently out, sank its teeth with dedicated venom into Carmody's left buttock and slunk away.

Not even the most monolithic dignity can survive being bitten deeply and without warning in the backside. Carmody screamed, leaped in the air clutching his rear, then swarmed to the top of the gate with the agility of a monkey. Squatting on the top spar, his natty hat tipped over one eye, he glared about him wildly.

'What the hell?' he yelled. 'What the bloody hell?'

'It's all right,' I said, hurrying towards him and resisting the impulse to throw myself on the ground and roll about. 'It was just a dog.'

'Dog? What dog? Where?' Carmody's cries took on a frantic note.

'It's gone – disappeared. I only saw it for a couple of seconds.' And indeed, as I looked around it was difficult to believe that that flitting little black shadow had ever existed.

Carmody took a bit of coaxing down from the top of the gate and when he finally did reach ground level he limped over and sat down in the car instead of seeing the case. And when I saw the tattered cloth on his bottom I couldn't blame him for not risking a further attack. If it had been anybody else I'd have told him to drop his pants so that I could slap on some iodine but in this instance I somehow couldn't bring myself to do it. I left him sitting there.

Chapter Twenty

When Carmody turned up for the afternoon round he had completely recovered his poise. He had changed his flannels and adopted a somewhat lopsided sitting position in the car but apart from that the dog episode might never have happened. In fact we had hardly got under way when he addressed me with a touch of arrogance.

'Look, I'm not going to learn much just watching you do things. Do you think I could carry out injections and the like? I want actual experience with the animals themselves.'

I didn't answer for a moment but stared ahead through the maze of fine cracks on the windscreen. I couldn't very well tell him that I was still trying to establish myself with the farmers and that some of them had definite reservations about my capabilities. Then I turned to him.

'OK. I'll have to do the diagnosing but whenever possible you can carry on from there.'

He soon had his first taste of action. I decided that a litter of ten week old pigs might benefit from an injection of E coli antiserum and handed him the bottle and syringe. And as he moved purposefully among the little animals I thought with gloomy satisfaction that though I may not be au fait with all the small print in the text books I did know better than to chase pigs into the dirty end of the pen to catch them. Because with Carmody in close pursuit the squealing creatures leaped from their straw bed and charged in a body towards a stagnant lake of urine against the far wall. And as the student grabbed at their hind legs the pigs scrabbled among the filth, kicking it back over him in a steady shower. He did finally get them all injected but at the end his smart outfit was liberally spattered and I had to open the windows wide to tolerate his presence in the car.

The next visit was to a big arable farm in the low country, and it was one of the few places where they had hung on to their horses; the long stable had several stalls in use and the names of the horses on the wall above; Boxer, Captain, Bobby, Tommy, and the mares Bonny and Daisy. It was Tommy the old cart horse we had to see and his trouble was a 'stoppage'.

Tommy was an old friend of mine; he kept having mild bouts of colic with constipation and I often wondered if he had a faecolith lurking about in his bowels somewhere. Anyway, six drachms of Istin in a pint of water invariably restored him to normal health and I began automatically to shake up the yellow powder in a drenching bottle. Meanwhile the farmer and his man turned the horse round in his stall, ran a rope under his nose band, threw it over a beam in the stable roof and pulled the head upwards.

I handed the bottle to Carmody and stepped back. The student looked up and hesitated. Tommy was a big horse and the head, pulled high, was far beyond reach; but the farm man pushed a ramshackle kitchen chair wordlessly forward and Carmody mounted it and stood swaying precariously.

I watched with interest. Horses are awkward things to drench at any time and Tommy didn't like Istin, even though it was good for him. On my last visit I had noticed that he was becoming very clever at holding the bitter mixture at the back of his throat instead of swallowing it. I had managed to foil him by tapping him under the chin just as he was toying with the idea of coughing it out and he had gulped it down with an offended look. But it was more and more becoming a battle of wits.

Carmody never really had a chance. He started off well enough by grasping the horse's tongue and thrusting the bottle past the teeth, but Tommy outwitted him effortlessly by inclining his head and allowing the liquid to flow from the far side of his mouth.

'It's coming out t'other side, young man!' the farmer cried with some asperity.

The student gasped and tried to direct the flow down the throat but Tommy had summed him up immediately as an amateur and was now in complete command of the situation. By judicious rolling of the tongue and a series of little coughs and snorts he kept ridding himself of most of the medicine and I felt a pang of pity at the sight of Carmody weaving about on the creaking chair as the yellow fluid cascaded over his clothes.

At the end, the farmer squinted into the empty bottle.

'Well I reckon t'oss got SOME of it,' he muttered sourly.

Carmody eyed him impassively for a moment, shook a few ounces of Istin solution from somewhere up his sleeve and strode out of the stable.

At the next farm I was surprised to detect a vein of sadism in my makeup. The owner, a breeder of pedigree Large Whits pigs, was exporting a sow abroad and it had to be subjected to various tests including a blood sample for Brucellosis. Extracting a few c.c.'s of blood from the ear vein of a struggling pig is a job which makes most vets shudder and it was clearly a dirty trick to ask a student to do it, but the memory of his coldly confident request at the beginning of the afternoon seemed to have stilled my conscience. I handed him the syringe with scarcely a qualm.

The pigman slipped a noose into the sow's mouth and drew it tight over the snout and behind the canine teeth. This common method of restraint isn't at all painful but the sow was one of those who didn't like any form of mucking about. She was a huge animal and as soon as she felt the rope she opened her mouth wide in a long-drawn, resentful scream. The volume of sound was incredible and she kept it up effortlessly without any apparent need to draw breath. Conversation from then on was out of the question and I watched in the appalling din as Carmody put an elastic tourniquet at the base of the sow's ear, swabbed the surface with spirit and then poked with his needle at the small blood vessel. Nothing happened. He tried again but the syringe remained obstinately empty. He had a few more attempts then, as I felt the top of my head was going to come loose I wandered from the pen into the peace of the yard.

I took a leisurely stroll round the outside of the piggery, pausing for a minute or two to look at the view at the far end where the noise was comparatively faint. When I returned to the pen the screaming hit me again like a pneumatic drill and Carmody, sweating and slightly pop-eyed, looked up from the ear where he was still jabbing fruitlessly. It seemed to me that everybody had had enough. Using sign language I indicated to the student that I'd like to have a go and by a happy chance my first effort brought a dark welling of blood into the syringe. I waved to the pigman to remove the rope and the moment he did so the big sow switched off the noise magically and began to nose, quite unperturbed, among the straw.

'Nothing very exciting at the next place,' I kept the triumph out of my voice as we drove away. 'Just a bullock with a tumour on its jaw. But it's an interesting herd – all Galloways, and this group we're going to see have been wintered outside. They're the toughest animals in the district.'

Carmody nodded. Nothing I said seemed to rouse much enthusiasm in him. For myself this herd of untamed black cattle always held a certain fascination; contacts with them were always coloured by a degree of uncertainty – sometimes you could catch them to examine them, sometimes you couldn't.

As we approached the farm I could see a bunch of about thirty bullocks streaming down the scrubby hillside on our right. The farm men were driving them down through the scattered gorse bushes and the sparse groups of trees to where the stone walls met in a rough V at the front.

One of them waved to me. 'We're going to try to get a rope on 'im down in the corner while he's among his mates. He's a wick bugger – you'd never get near him in t'field.'

After a lot of shouting and waving and running about the bullocks were finally cornered and they stood in a tight, uneasy pack, their shaggy black polls bobbing among the steam rising from their bodies.

'There he is! You can see the thing on his face.' A man pointed to a big beast about the middle of the bunch and began to push his way towards him. My admiration for the Yorkshire farm worker rose another notch as I watched him squeezing between the plunging, kicking animals. 'When I get the rope on his head you'll all have to get on t'other end – one man'll never hold 'im.' He gasped as he fought his way forward.

He was obviously an expert because as soon as he got within reach he dropped the halter on to the bullock's head with practised skill. 'Right!' he shouted. 'Give me a hand with him. We have 'im now.'

But as he spoke the beast gave a great bellow and began to charge from the pack. The man cried out despairingly and disappeared among the hairy bodies. The rope whipped free out of reach of everybody. Except Carmody. As the bullock shot past him he grabbed the trailing rope with a reflex action and hung on.

I watched, fascinated, as man and beast careered across the field. They were travelling away from me towards the far slope, the animal head down, legs pistoning, going like a racehorse, the student also at full speed but very upright, both hands on the rope in front of him, a picture of resolution.

The men and I were helpless spectators and we stood in a silent group as the beast turned left suddenly and disappeared behind a clump of low trees. It was gone for only a few moments but it seemed a long time and when it reappeared it was going faster than ever, hurtling over the turf like a black thunderbolt. Carmody, incredibly, was still there on the end of the rope and still very upright but his strides had increased to an impossible length till he seemed to be touching the ground only every twenty feet or so.

I marvelled at his tenacity but obviously the end was near. He took a last few soaring, swooping steps then he was down on his face. But he didn't let go. The bullock, going better than ever, had turned towards us now, dragging the inert form apparently without effort, and I winced as I saw it was headed straight for a long row of cow pats.

It was when Carmody was skidding face down through the third heap of muck that I suddenly began to like him. And when he finally did have to release his hold and lay for a moment motionless on the grass I hurried over to help him up. He thanked me briefly then looked calmly across the field at a sight which is familiar to every veterinary surgeon – his patient thundering out of sight across the far horizon.

The student was almost unrecognisable. His clothes and face were plastered with filth except where the saffron streaks of the Istin showed up like war paint, he smelt abominably, he had been bitten in the backside, nothing had really gone right for him all day yet he was curiously undefeated. I smiled to myself. It was no good judging this bloke by ordinary standards; I could recognise the seeds of greatness when I saw them.

Carmody stayed with us for two weeks and after that first day I got on with him not so badly. Of course it wasn't the same relationship as with other students; there was always a barrier of reserve. He spent a lot of time squinting down the practice microscope at blood films, skin scrapings, milk smears, and by the end of each day he had collected a fresh supply of samples from the cases he had seen. He would come and drink a polite beer with me after an evening call but there was none of the giggling over the day's events as with the other young lads. I had the feeling always that he would rather have been writing up his case book and working out his findings.

But I didn't mind. I found an interest in being in contact with a truly scientific mind. He was as far removed as he could be from the traditional studious swot – his was a cold, superior intellect and there was something rewarding in watching him at work.

I didn't see Carmody again for over twenty years. I picked out his name in the Record when he qualified with top marks then he disappeared into the great world of research for a while to emerge with a Ph.D. and over the years he added a string of further degrees and qualifications. Every now and then an unintelligible article would appear in the professional journals under his name and it became commonplace when reading scientific papers to see references to what Dr Carmody had said on the subject.

When I finally did see him he was the guest of honour at a professional banquet, an international celebrity heavy with honours. From where I was sitting at the far end of one of the side tables I listened to his masterly speech with a feeling of inevitability; the wide grasp of his subject, the brilliant exposition – I had seen it all coming those many years ago.

Afterwards when we had left the tables he moved among us and I gazed with something like awe at the majestic figure approaching. Carmody had always been big, but with the tail coat tight across the massive shoulders and the vast expanse of gleaming shirt front stretched over the curving abdomen he was almost overpowering. As he passed he stopped and looked at me.

'It's Herriot, isn't it?' the handsome, high-coloured face still had that look of calm power.

'Yes, it is. It's good to see you again.'

We shook hands. 'And how is the practice at Darrowby?'

'Oh, as usual,' I replied. 'Bit too busy at times. We could do with some help if ever you felt like it.'

Carmody nodded gravely. 'I'd like that very much. It would be good for me.' He was about to move on when he paused. 'Perhaps you'd let me know any time you want a pig bled.' For a moment we looked into each other's eyes and I saw a small flame flicker briefly in the frosty blue. Then he was gone.

As I looked at the retreating back a hand gripped my arm. It was Brian Miller, a happily obscure practitioner like myself.

'Come on, Jim, I'll buy you a drink,' he said.

We went into the bar and ordered two beers.

'That Carmody!' Brian said. 'The man's got a tremendous brain, but by God he's a cold fish.'

I sipped at the beer and looked thoughtfully into my glass for a few seconds.

'Oh I don't know,' I said. 'He certainly gives that impression, but Carmody's all right.'

Chapter Twenty-one

The big room at Skeldale House was full. It seemed to me that this room with its graceful alcoves, high, carved ceiling and french windows lay at the centre of our life in Darrowby. It was where Siegfried, Tristan and I gathered when the day's work was done, toasting our feet by the white wood fireplace with the glass-fronted cupboard on top, talking over the day's events. It was the heart of our bachelor existence, sitting there in a happy stupor, reading, listening to the radio, Tristan usually flipping effortlessly through the *Daily Telegraph* crossword.

It was where Siegfried entertained his friends and there was a constant stream of them – old and young, male and female. But tonight it was Tristan's turn and the pack of young people with drinks in their hands were there at his invitation. And they wouldn't need much persuasion. Though just about the opposite of his brother in many ways he had the same attractiveness which brought the friends running at the crook of a finger.

The occasion was the Daffodil Ball at the Drovers' Arms and we were dressed in our best. This was a different kind of function from the usual village institute hop with the farm lads in their big boots and music from a scraping fiddle and piano. It was a proper dance with a popular local band – Lenny Butterfield and his Hot Shots – and was an annual affair to herald the arrival of spring.

I watched Tristan dispensing the drinks. The bottles of whisky, gin and sherry which Siegfried kept in the fireplace cupboard had taken some severe punishment but Tristan himself had been abstemious. An occasional sip from a glass of light ale perhaps, but nothing more. Drinking, to him, meant the bulk intake of draught bitter; all else was mere vanity and folly. Dainty little glasses were anathema and even now when I see him at a party where everybody is holding small drinks Tristan somehow contrives to have a pint in his hand.

'Nice little gathering, Jim,' he said, appearing at my elbow. 'A few more blokes than girls but that won't matter much.'

I eyed him coldly. I knew why there were extra men. It was so that Tristan wouldn't have to take the floor too often. It fitted in with his general dislike of squandering energy that he was an unenthusiastic dancer; he didn't mind walking a girl round the floor now and again during the evening but he preferred to spend most of the time in the bar.

So, in fact, did a lot of the Darrowby folk. When we arrived at the Drovers the bar was congested while only a dedicated few circled round the ballroom. But as time went on more and more couples ventured out and by ten o'clock the dance floor was truly packed.

And I soon found I was enjoying myself. Tristan's friends were an effervescent bunch; likable young men and attractive girls; I just couldn't help having a good time.

Butterfield's famed band in their short red jackets added greatly to the general merriment. Lenny himself looked about fifty-five and indeed all four of the Hot Shots ensemble were rather elderly, but they made up for their grey hairs by sheer vivacity. Not that Lenny's hair was grey; it was dyed a determined black and he thumped the piano with dynamic energy, beaming out at the company through his horn-rimmed glasses, occasionally bawling a chorus into the microphone by his side, announcing the dances, making throaty wisecracks. He gave value for money.

There was no pairing off in our party and I danced with all the girls in turn. At the peak of the evening I was jockeying my way around the floor with Daphne and the way she was constructed made it a rewarding experience. I never have been one for skinny women but I suppose you could say that Daphne's development had strayed a little too far in the other direction. She wasn't fat, just lavishly endowed.

Battling through the crush, colliding with exuberant neighbours, bouncing deliciously off Daphne, with everybody singing as they danced and the Hot Shots pouring out an insistent boom-boom beat, I felt I hadn't a care in the world. And then I saw Helen.

She was dancing with the inevitable Richard Edmundson, his shining gold head floating above the company like an emblem of doom. And it was uncanny how in an instant my cosy little world disintegrated leaving a chill gnawing emptiness.

When the music stopped I returned Daphne to her friends and went to find Tristan. The comfortable little bar in the Drovers was overflowing and the temperature like an oven. Through an almost impenetrable fog of cigarette smoke I discerned my colleague on a high stool holding court with a group of perspiring revellers. Tristan himself looked cool and, as always, profoundly content. He drained his glass, smacked his lips gently as though it had been the best pint of beer he'd ever tasted, then, as he reached across the counter and courteously requested a refill he spotted me struggling towards him.

When I reached his stool he laid an affable hand on my shoulder, 'Ah, Jim, nice to see you. Splendid dance, this, don't you think.'

I didn't bring up the fact that I hadn't seen him on the floor yet, but making my voice casual I mentioned that Helen was there.

Tristan nodded benignly. 'Yes, saw her come in. Why don't you go and dance with her?'

'I can't do that. She's with a partner – young Edmundson.'

'Not at all.' Tristan surveyed his fresh pint with a critical eye and took an exploratory sip. 'She's with a party, like us. No partner.'

'How do you know that?'

'I watched all the fellows hang their coats out there while the girls went upstairs. No reason at all why you shouldn't have a dance with her.'

'I see.' I hesitated for a few moments then made my way back to the ballroom. But it wasn't as easy as that. I had to keep doing my duty with the girls in our group and whenever I headed for Helen she was whisked away by one of her men friends before I got near her. At times I fancied she was looking over at me but I couldn't be sure; the only thing I knew for certain was that I wasn't enjoying myself any more; the magic and gaiety had gone and I felt a rising misery at the thought that this was going to be another of my frustrating contacts with Helen when all I could do was look at her hopelessly. Only this time was worse – I hadn't even spoken to her.

I was almost relieved when the manager came up and told me there was a call for me. I went to the phone and spoke to Mrs Hall. There was a bitch in trouble whelping and I had to go. I looked at my watch – after midnight, so that was the end of the dance for me.

I stood for a moment listening to the muffled thudding from the dance floor then slowly pulled on my coat before going in to say goodbye to Tristan's friends. I exchanged a few words with them, waved, then turned back and pushed the swing door open.

Helen was standing there, about a foot away from me. Her hand was on the door, too. I didn't wonder whether she was going in or out but stared dumbly into her smiling blue eyes.

'Leaving already, Jim?' she said.

'Yes, I've got a call, I'm afraid.'

'Oh what a shame. I hope it's nothing very serious.'

I opened my mouth to speak, but her dark beauty and the very nearness of her suddenly filled my world and a wave of hopeless longing swept over and submerged me. I slid my hand a few inches down the door and gripped hers as a drowning man might, and wonderingly I felt her fingers come round and entwine themselves tightly in mine.

And in an instant there was no band, no noise, no people, just the two of us standing very close in the doorway.

'Come with me,' I said.

Helen's eyes were very large as she smiled that smile I knew so well.

'I'll get my coat,' she murmured.

This wasn't really me, I thought, standing on the hall carpet watching Helen trotting quickly up the stairs, but I had to believe it as she reappeared on the landing pulling on her coat. Outside, on the cobbles of the market place my car, too, appeared to be taken by surprise because it roared into life at the first touch of the starter.

I had to go back to the surgery for my whelping instruments and in the silent moonlit street we got out and I opened the big white door to Skeldale House.

And once in the passage it was the most natural thing in the world to take her in my arms and kiss her gratefully and unhurriedly. I had waited a long time for this and the minutes flowed past unnoticed as we stood there, our feet on the black and red eighteenth-century tiles, our heads almost touching the vast picture of the Death of Nelson which dominated the entrance.

We kissed again at the first bend of the passage under the companion picture of the Meeting of Wellington and Blucher at Waterloo. We kissed at the second bend by the tall cupboard where Siegfried kept his riding coats and boots. We kissed in the dispensary in between searching for my instruments. Then we tried it out in the garden and this was the best of all with the flowers still and expectant in the moonlight and the fragrance of the moist earth and grass rising about us.

I have never driven so slowly to a case. About ten miles an hour with Helen's head on my shoulder and all the scents of spring drifting in through the open window. And it was like sailing from stormy seas into a sweet, safe harbour, like coming home.

The light in the cottage window was the only one showing in the sleeping village, and when I knocked at the door Bert Chapman answered. Bert was a council roadman – one of the breed for whom I felt an abiding affinity.

The council men were my brethren of the roads. Like me they spent most of their lives on the lonely by-ways around Darrowby and I saw them most days of the week, repairing the tarmac, cutting back the grass verges in the summer, gritting and snow ploughing in the winter. And when they spotted me driving past they would grin cheerfully and wave as if the very sight of me had made their day. I don't know whether they were specially picked for good nature but I don't think I have ever met a more equable body of men.

One old farmer remarked sourly to me once. 'There's no wonder the buggers are 'appy, they've got nowt to do.' An exaggeration, of course, but I knew how he felt; compared with farming every other job was easy.

I had seen Bert Chapman just a day or two ago, sitting on a grassy bank, his shovel by his side, a vast sandwich in his hand. He had raised a corded forearm in salute, a broad smile bisecting his round, sun-reddened face. He had looked eternally carefree but tonight his smile was strained.

'I'm sorry to bother you this late, Mr Herriot,' he said as he ushered us into the house, 'but I'm gettin' a bit worried about Susie. Her pups are due and she's been making a bed for them and messing about all day but nowt's happened. I was goin' to leave her till morning but about midnight she started panting like 'ell – I don't like the look of her.'

Susie was one of my regular patients. Her big, burly master was always bringing her to the surgery, a little shame-faced at his solicitude, and when I saw him sitting in the waiting room looking strangely out of place among the ladies with their pets, he usually said 'T'missus asked me to bring Susie.' But it was a transparent excuse.

'She's nobbut a little mongrel, but very faithful,' Bert said, still apologetic, but I could understand how he felt about Susie, a shaggy little ragamuffin whose only wile was to put her paws on my knees and laugh up into my face with her tail lashing. I found her irresistible.

But she was a very different character tonight. As we went into the living room of the cottage the little animal crept from her basket, gave a single indeterminate wag of her tail then stood miserably in the middle of the floor, her ribs heaving. As I bent to examine her she turned a wide panting mouth and anxious eyes up to me.

I ran my hands over her abdomen. I don't think I have ever felt a more bloated little dog; she was as round as a football, absolutely bulging with pups, ready to pop, but nothing was happening.

'What do you think?' Bert's face was haggard under his sunburn and he touched the dog's head briefly with a big calloused hand.

'I don't know yet, Bert,' I said. 'I'll have to have a feel inside. Bring me some hot water, will you?'

I added some antiseptic to the water, soaped my hand and with one finger carefully explored the vagina. There was a pup there, all right; my finger tip brushed across the nostrils, the tiny mouth and tongue; but he was jammed in that passage like a cork in a bottle.

Squatting back on my heels I turned to the Chapmans.

'I'm afraid there's a big pup stuck fast. I have a feeling that if she could get rid of this chap the others would come away. They'd probably be smaller.'

'Is there any way of shiftin' him, Mr Herriot?' Bert asked.

I paused for a moment. 'I'm going to put forceps on his head and see if he'll move. I don't like using forceps but I'm going to have one careful try and if it doesn't work I'll have to take her back to the surgery for a caesarian.'

'An operation?' Bert said hollowly. He gulped and glanced fearfully at his wife. Like many big men he had married a tiny woman and at this moment Mrs Chapman looked even smaller than her four foot eleven inches as she huddled in her chair and stared at me with wide eyes.

'Oh I wish we'd never had her mated,' she wailed, wringing her hands. 'I told Bert five year old was too late for a first litter but he wouldn't listen. And now we're maybe going to lose 'er.'

I hastened to reassure her. 'No, she isn't too old, and everything may be all right. Let's just see how we get on.'

I boiled the instrument for a few minutes on the stove then kneeled behind my patient again. I poised the forceps for a moment and at the flash of steel a grey tinge crept under Bert's sunburn and his wife coiled herself into a ball in her chair. Obviously they were non-starters as assistants so Helen held Susie's head while I once more reached in towards the pup. There was desperately little room but I managed to direct the forceps along my finger till they touched the nose. Then very gingerly I opened the jaws and pushed them forward with the very gentlest pressure until I was able to clamp them on either side of the head.

I'd soon know now. In a situation like this you can't do any pulling, you can only try to ease the thing along. This I did and I fancied I felt just a bit of movement; I tried again and there was no doubt about it, the pup was coming towards me. Susie, too, appeared to sense that things were taking a turn for the better. She cast off her apathy and began to strain lustily.

It was no trouble after that and I was able to draw the pup forth almost without resistance.

'I'm afraid this one'll be dead,' I said, and as the tiny creature lay across my palm there was no sign of breathing. But, pinching the chest between thumb and forefinger I could feel the heart pulsing steadily and I quickly opened his mouth and blew softly down into his lungs.

I repeated this a few times then laid the pup on his side in the basket. I was just thinking it was going to be no good when the little rib cage gave a sudden lift, then another and another.

'He's off!' Bert exclaimed happily. 'That's champion! We want these puppies alive tha knows. They're by Jack Dennison's terrier and he's a grand 'un.'

'That's right,' Mrs Chapman put in. 'No matter how many she has, they're all spoken for. Everybody wants a pup out of Susie.'

'I can believe that,' I said. But I smiled to myself. Jack Dennison's terrier was another hound of uncertain ancestry, so this lot would be a right mixture. But none the worse for that.

I gave Susie half a c.c. of pituitrin. 'I think she needs it after pushing against that fellow for hours. We'll wait and see what happens now.'

And it was nice waiting. Mrs Chapman brewed a pot of tea and began to slap butter on to home-made scones. Susie, partly aided by my pituitrin, pushed out a pup in a self-satisfied manner about every fifteen minutes. The pups themselves soon set up a bawling of surprising volume for such minute creatures. Bert, relaxing visibly with every minute, filled his pipe and regarded the fast-growing family with a grin of increasing width.

'Ee, it is kind of you young folks to stay with us like this.' Mrs Chapman put her head on one side and looked at us worriedly. 'I should think you've been dying to get back to your dance all this time.'

I thought of the crush at the Drovers. The smoke, the heat, the nonstop boom-boom of the Hot Shots and I looked around the peaceful little room with the old-fashioned black grate, the low, varnished beams, Mrs Chapman's sewing box, the row of Bert's pipes on the wall. I took a firmer grasp of Helen's hand which I had been holding under the table for the last hour.

'Not at all, Mrs Chapman,' I said. 'We haven't missed it in the least.' And I have never been more sincere.

It must have been about half past two when I finally decided that Susie had finished. She had six fine pups which was a good score for a little thing like her and the noise had abated as the family settled down to feast on her abundant udder.

I lifted the pups out one by one and examined them. Susie didn't mind in the least but appeared to be smiling with modest pride as I handled her brood. When I put them back with her she inspected them and sniffed them over busily before rolling on to her side again.

'Three dogs and three bitches,' I said. 'Nice even litter.'

Before leaving I took Susie from her basket and palpated her abdomen. The degree of deflation was almost unbelievable; a pricked balloon could not have altered its shape more spectacularly and she had made a remarkable metamorphosis to the lean, scruffy little extrovert I knew so well.

When I released her she scurried back and curled herself round her new family who were soon sucking away with total absorption.

Bert laughed. 'She's fair capped wi' them pups.' He bent over and prodded the first arrival with a horny forefinger. 'I like the look o' this big dog pup. I reckon we'll keep this 'un for ourselves, mother. He'll be company for t'awd lass.'

It was time to go. Helen and I moved over to the door and little Mrs Chapman with her fingers on the handle looked up at me.

'Well, Mr Herriot,' she said, 'I can't thank you enough for comin' out and putting our minds at rest. I don't know what I've done wi' this man of mine if anything had happened to his little dog.'

Bert grinned sheepishly. 'Nay,' he muttered. 'Ah was never really worried.'

His wife laughed and opened the door and as we stepped out into the silent scented night she gripped my arm and looked up at me roguishly.

'I suppose this is your young lady,' she said.

I put my arm round Helen's shoulders.

'Yes,' I said firmly, 'this is my young lady.'

Chapter Twenty-two

It was almost as though I were looking at my own cows because as I stood in the little new byre and looked along the row of red and roan backs I felt a kind of pride.

'Frank,' I said. 'They look marvellous. You wouldn't think they were the same animals.'

Frank Metcalfe grinned. 'Just what I was thinking meself. It's wonderful what a change of setting'll do for livestock.'

It was the cows' first day in the new byre. Previously I had seen them only in the old place – a typical Dales cowhouse, centuries old with a broken cobbled floor and gaping holes where the muck and urine lay in pools, rotting wooden partitions between the stalls and slit windows as though the place had been built as a fortress. I could remember Frank sitting in it milking, almost invisible in the gloom, the cobwebs hanging in thick fronds from the low roof above him.

In there, the ten cows had looked what they were – a motley assortment of ordinary milkers – but today they had acquired a new dignity and style.

'You must feel it's been worth all your hard work,' I said, and the young farmer nodded and smiled. There was a grim touch about the smile as though he was reliving for a moment the hours and weeks and months of back-breaking labour he had put in there. Because Frank Metcalfe had done it all himself. The rows of neat, concreted standings, the clean, level sweep of floor, the whitewashed, cement-rendered walls all bathed in light from the spacious windows had been put there by his own two hands.

'I'll show you the dairy,' Frank said.

We went into a small room which he had built at one end and I looked admiringly at the gleaming milk cooler, the spotless sinks and buckets, the strainer with its neat pile of filter pads.

'You know,' I said. 'This is how milk should be produced. All those mucky old places I see every day on my rounds – they nearly make my hair stand on end.'

Frank leaned over and drew a jet of water from one of the taps. 'Aye, you're right. It'll all be like this and better one day and it'll pay the farmers better too. I've got me TT licence now and the extra fourpence a gallon will make a hell of a difference. I feel I'm ready to start.'

And when he did start, I thought, he'd go places. He seemed to have all the things it took to succeed at the hard trade of farming – intelligence, physical toughness, a love of the land and animals and the ability to go slogging on endlessly when other people were enjoying their leisure. I felt these qualities would overcome his biggest handicap which was simply that he didn't have any money.

Frank wasn't a farmer at all to start with. He was a steel worker from Middlesbrough. When he had first arrived less than a year ago with his young wife to take over the isolated small holding at Bransett I had been surprised to learn that he hailed from the city because he had the dark, sinewy look of the typical Dalesman – and he was called Metcalfe.

He had laughed when I mentioned this. 'Oh, my great grandfather came from these parts and I've always had a hankering to come back.'

As I came to know him better I was able to fill in the gaps in that simple statement. He had spent all his holidays up here as a small boy and though his father was a foreman in the steelworks and he himself had served his time at the trade the pull of the Dales had been like a siren song welling stronger till he had been unable to resist it any longer. He had worked on farms in his spare time, read all he could about agriculture and finally had thrown up his old life and rented the little place high in the fells at the end of a long, stony track.

With its primitive house and tumbledown buildings it seemed an unpromising place to make a living and in any case I hadn't much faith in the ability of townspeople to suddenly turn to farming and make a go of it; in my short experience I had seen quite a few try and fail. But Frank Metcalfe had gone about the job as though he had been at it all his life, repairing the broken walls, improving the grassland, judiciously buying stock on his shoe-string budget; there was no sign of the bewilderment and despair I had seen in so many others.

I had mentioned this to a retired farmer in Darrowby and the old man chuckled. 'Aye, you've got to have farmin' inside you. There's very few people as can succeed at it unless it's in their blood. It matters nowt that young Metcalfe's been brought up in a town, he's still got it in 'im – he's got it through the titty, don't you see, through the titty.'

Maybe he was right, but whether Frank had it through the titty or through study and brains he had transformed the holding in a short time. When he wasn't milking, feeding, mucking out, he was slaving at that little byre, chipping stones, mixing cement, sand and dust clinging to the sweat on his face. And now, as he said, he was ready to start.

As we came out of the dairy he pointed to another old building across the yard. 'When I'm straightened out I aim to convert that into another byre. I've had to borrow a good bit but now I'm TT I should be able to clear it off in a couple of years. Sometime in the future if all goes well I might be able to get a bigger place altogether.'

He was about my own age and a natural friendship had sprung up between us. We used to sit under the low beams of his cramped living room with its single small window and sparse furniture and as his young wife poured cups of tea he liked to talk of his plans. And, listening to him, I always felt that a man like him would do well not only for himself but for farming in general.

I looked at him now as he turned his head and gazed for a few moments round his domain. He didn't have to say: 'I love this place, I feel I belong here.' It was all there in his face, in the softening of his eyes as they moved over the huddle of grass fields cupped in a hollow of the fells. These fields, clawed by past generations from the rough hillside and fighting their age-old battle with heather and bracken, ran up to a ragged hem of cliff and scree and above you could just see the lip of the moor – a wild land of bog and peat hag. Below, the farm track disappeared round the bend of a wooded hill. The pastures were poor and knuckles of rock pushed out in places through the thin soil, but the clean, turf-scented air and the silence must have been like a deliverance after the roar and smoke of the steel-works.

'Well we'd better see that cow, Frank,' I said. 'The new byre nearly made me forget what I came for.'

'Aye, it's this red and white 'un. My latest purchase and she's never been right since I got her. Hasn't come on to her milk properly and she seems dosy, somehow.'

The temperature was a hundred and three and as I put the thermometer away I sniffed. 'She smells a bit, doesn't she?'

'Aye,' Frank said. 'I've noticed that myself.'

'Better bring me some hot water, then. I'll have a feel inside.'

The uterus was filled with a stinking exudate and as I withdrew my arm there was a gush of yellowish, necrotic material. 'Surely she must have had a bit of a discharge,' I said.

Frank nodded. 'Yes, she has had, but I didn't pay much attention – a lot of them do it when they're clearing up after calving.'

I drained the uterus by means of a rubber tube and irrigated it with antiseptic, then I pushed in a few acriflavine pessaries. 'That'll help to clean her up, and I think she'll soon be a lot better in herself, but I'm going to take a blood sample from her.'

'Why's that?'

'Well it may be nothing, but I don't like the look of that yellow stuff. It consists of decayed cotyledones – you know, the berries on the calf bed – and when they're that colour it's a bit suspicious of Brucellosis.'

'Abortion, you mean?'

'It's possible, Frank. She may have calved before her time or she may have calved normally but still been infected. Anyway the blood will tell us. Keep her isolated in the meantime.'

A few days later at breakfast time in Skeldale House I felt a quick stab of anxiety as I opened the lab report and read that the agglutination test on the blood had given a positive result. I hurried out to the farm.

'How long have you had this cow?' I asked.

'Just over three weeks,' the young farmer replied.

'And she's been running in the same field as your other cows and the in-calf heifers?'

'Yes, all the time.'

I paused for a moment. 'Frank, I'd better tell you the implications. I know you'll want to know what might happen. The source of infection in Brucellosis is the discharges of an infected cow and I'm afraid this animal of yours will have thoroughly contaminated that pasture. Any or all of your animals may have picked up the bug.'

'Does that mean they'll abort?'

'Not necessarily. It varies tremendously. Many cows carry their calves through despite infection.' I was doing my best to sound optimistic.

Frank dug his hands deep into his pockets. His thin, dark-complexioned face was serious. 'Damn, I wish I'd never seen the thing. I bought her at Houlton market – God knows where she came from, but it's too late to talk like that now. What can we do about the job?'

'The main thing is to keep her isolated and away from the other stock. I wish there was some way to protect the others but there isn't much we can do. There are only two types of vaccine – live ones which can only be given to empty cows and yours are all in-calf, and dead ones which aren't reckoned to be of much use.'

'Well I'm the sort that doesn't like to just sit back and wait. The dead vaccine won't do any harm if it doesn't do any good, will it?'

'No.'

'Right, let's do 'em all with it and we'll hope for the best.'

Hoping for the best was something vets did a lot of in the thirties. I vaccinated the entire herd and we waited.

Nothing happened for a full eight weeks. Summer lengthened into autumn and the cattle were brought inside. The infected cow improved, her discharge cleared up and she began to milk a bit better. Then Frank rang early one morning.

'I've found a dead calf laid in the channel when I went in to milk. Will you come?'

It was a thinly-haired seven months foetus that I found. The cow looked sick and behind her dangled the inevitable retained placenta. Her udder which, if she had calved normally would have been distended with milk, the precious milk Frank depended on for his livelihood, was almost empty.

Obsessed by a feeling of helplessness I could only offer the same old advice; isolate, disinfect – and hope.

A fortnight later one of the in-calf heifers did it – she was a pretty little Jersey cross which Frank had hoped would push up his butter fat percentage – and a week after that one of the cows slipped a calf in her sixth month of pregnancy.

It was when I was visiting this third case that I met Mr Bagley. Frank introduced him somewhat apologetically. 'He says he has a cure for this trouble, Jim. He wants to talk to you about it.'

In every sticky situation there is always somebody who knows better than the vet. Subconsciously I suppose I had been waiting for a Mr Bagley to turn up and I listened patiently.

He was very short with bandy legs in cloth leggings, and he looked up at me intently. 'Young man, I've been through this on ma own farm and ah wouldn't be here today if I hadn't found the remedy.'

'I see, and what was that, Mr Bagley?'

'I have it 'ere.' The little man pulled a bottle from his jacket pocket. 'It's a bit mucky – it's been stood in t'cow house window for a year or two.'

I read the label. 'Professor Driscoll's Abortion Cure. Give two table-spoonsful to each cow in the herd in a pint of water and repeat on the following day.' The professor's face took up most of the label. He was an aggressive-looking, profusely whiskered man in a high Victorian collar and he glared out at me belligerently through a thick layer of dust. He wasn't so daft, either, because lower down the bottle I read. 'If an animal has aborted a dose of this mixture will prevent further trouble.' He knew as well as I did that they didn't often do it more than once.

'Yes,' Mr Bagley said. 'That's the stuff. Most of my cows did it on me but I kept goin' with the medicine and they were right as a bobbin next time round.'

'But they would be in any case. They develop an immunity you see.'

Mr Bagley put his head on one side and gave a gentle unbelieving smile. And who was I to argue, anyway? I hadn't a thing to offer.

'OK, Frank,' I said wearily. 'Go ahead – like my vaccine, I don't suppose it can do any harm.'

A fresh bottle of Driscoll's cure was purchased and little Mr Bagley supervised the dosing of the herd. He was cock-a-hoop when, three weeks later, one of the cows calved bang on time.

'Now then, what do you say, young man? Ma stuff's working already, isn't it?'

'Well I expected some of them to calve normally,' I replied and the little man pursed his lips as though he considered me a bad loser.

But I wasn't really worried about what he thought; all I felt was an unhappy resignation. Because this sort of thing was always happening in those days before the modern drugs appeared. Quack medicines abounded on the farms and the vets couldn't say a lot about them because their own range of pharmaceuticals was pitifully inadequate.

And in those diseases like abortion which had so far defeated all the efforts of the profession at control the harvest for the quack men was particularly rich. The farming press and country newspapers were filled with confident advertisements of red drenches, black draughts, pink powders which were positively guaranteed to produce results. Professor Driscoll had plenty of competition.

When shortly afterwards another cow calved to time Mr Bagley was very nice about it. 'We all 'ave to learn, young man, and you haven't had much practical experience. You just hadn't heard of my medicine and I'm not blaming you, but I think we're on top of t'job now.'

I didn't say anything. Frank was beginning to look like a man who could see a gleam of hope and I wasn't going to extinguish it by voicing my doubts. Maybe the outbreak had run its course – these things were unpredictable.

But the next time I heard Frank on the phone all my gloomy forebodings were realised. 'I want you to come out and cleanse three cows.'

'Three!'

'Aye, they did it one after the other – bang, bang, bang. And all before time. It's an absolute bugger, Jim – I don't know what I'm going to do.'

He met me as I got out of the car at the top of the track. He looked ten years older, his face pale and haggard as though he hadn't slept. Mr Bagley was there, too, digging a hole in front of the byre door.

'What's he doing?' I asked.

Frank looked down at his boots expressionlessly. 'He's burying one of the calves. He says it does a lot of good if you put it in front of the door.' He looked at me with an attempt at a smile. 'Science can do nowt for me so we might as well try a bit of black magic.'

I felt a few years older myself as I picked my way round the deep grave Mr Bagley was digging. The little man looked up at me as I passed. 'This is a very old remedy,' he explained. 'Ma medicine seems to be losing its power so we'll have to try summat stronger. The trouble is,' he added with some asperity. 'I was called in on this case far too late.'

I removed the putrefying afterbirths from the three cows and got off the place as soon as possible. I felt such a deep sense of shame that I could hardly meet Frank's eye. And it was even worse on my next visit a fortnight later because as I walked across the yard I was conscious of a strange smell polluting the sweet hill air. It was a penetrating, acrid stink and though it rang a bell somewhere I couldn't quite identify it. As Frank came out of the house he saw me sniffing and looking round.

'Not very nice is it?' he said with a tired smile. 'I don't believe you've met our goat.'

'You've got a goat?'

'Well, we've got the loan of one – an old Billy. I don't see him around right now but by God you can always smell him. Mr Bagley dug 'im up somewhere – says he did one of his neighbours a world of good when he was having my trouble. Burying the calves wasn't doing any good so he thought he'd better bring on the goat. It's the smell that does the trick, he says.'

'Frank, I'm sorry,' I said. 'It's still going on, then?'

He shrugged his shoulders. 'Aye, two more since I saw you. But I'm past worrying now, Jim, and for God's sake stop looking so bloody miserable yourself. You can't do anything, I know that. Nobody can do anything.'

Driving home, I brooded on his words. Contagious Bovine Abortion has been recognised for centuries and I had read in old books of the filthy scourge which ravaged and ruined the ancient farmers just as it was doing to Frank Metcalfe today. The experts of those days said it was due to impure water, improper feeding, lack of exercise, sudden frights. They did note, however, that other cows which were allowed to sniff at the foetuses and afterbirths were likely to suffer the same fate themselves. But beyond that it was a black tunnel of ignorance.

We modern vets, on the other hand, knew all about it. We knew it was caused by a Gram negative bacillus called Brucella abortus whose habits and attributes we had studied till we knew its every secret; but when it came to helping a farmer in Frank's situation we were about as much use as our colleagues of old who wrote those quaint books. True, dedicated researchers were working to find a strain of the bacillus which would form a safe and efficient vaccine to immunise cattle in calfhood and as far back as 1930 a certain strain 19 had been developed from which much was hoped. But even now it was still in the experimental stage. If Frank had had the luck to be born twenty years later the chances are that those cows he bought would have all been vaccinated and protected by that same strain 19. Nowadays we even have an efficient dead vaccine for the pregnant cows.

Best of all there is now a scheme under way for the complete eradication of Brucellosis and this has brought the disease to the notice of the general public. People are naturally interested mainly in the public health aspect and they have learned about the vast spectrum of illnesses which the infected milk can cause in humans. But few townsmen know what Brucellosis can do to farmers.

The end of Frank's story was not far away. Autumn was reaching into winter and the frost was sparkling on the steps of Skeldale House when he called one night to see me. We went into the big room and I opened a couple of bottles of beer.

'I thought I'd come and tell you, Jim,' he said in a matter of fact tone. 'I'm having to pack up.'

'Pack up?' Something in me refused to accept what he was saying.

'Aye, I'm going back to me old job in Middlesbrough. There's nowt else to do.'

I looked at him helplessly. 'It's as bad as that, is it?'

'Well just think.' He smiled grimly. 'I have three cows which calved normally out of the whole herd. The rest are a mucky, discharging, sickly lot with no milk worth talking about. I've got no calves to sell or keep as replacements. I've got nowt.'

I hesitated. 'There's no hope of raising the wind to get you over this?'

'No, Jim. If I sell up now I'll just about be able to pay the bank what I owe them. The rest I borrowed from my old man and I'm not goin' back to him for more. I promised him I'd return to the steelworks if this didn't work out and that's what I'm goin' to do.'

'Oh hell, Frank,' I said. 'I can't tell you how sorry I am. You haven't had a scrap of luck all the way through.'

He looked at me and smiled with no trace of self pity. 'Aye well,' he said. 'These things happen.'

I almost jumped at the words. 'These things happen!' That's what farmers always said after a disaster. That old man in Darrowby had been right. Frank really did have it through the titty.

And in truth he wasn't the only man to be bankrupted in this way. What had hit Frank was called an 'abortion storm' and the same sort of thing had driven a legion of good men to the wall. Some of them hung on, tightened their belts, spent their life savings and half starved till the storm abated and they could start again. But Frank had no savings to see him through; his venture had been a gamble from the beginning and he had lost.

I never heard of him again. At first I thought he might write, but then I realised that once the agonising break had been made it had to be complete.

From some parts of the northern Pennines you can see away over the great sprawl of Teesside and when the fierce glow from the blast furnaces set the night sky alight I used to think of Frank down there and wonder how he was getting on. He'd make a go of it all right, but how often did his mind turn to the high-blown green hollow where he had hoped to build something worth while and to live and bring up his children?

Some people called Peters bought the little farm at Bransett after he left. Strangely enough they were from Teesside, too, but Mr Peters was a wealthy director of the ICI and used the place only as a weekend retreat. It was ideal for the purpose because he had a young family all keen on riding and the fields were soon being grazed by an assortment of horses and ponies. In the summer Mrs Peters used to spend months on end up there with the children. They were nice people who cared for their animals and I was a frequent visitor.

The dwelling house was renovated almost out of recognition and I drank coffee instead of tea in the living room which had become a place of grace and charm with an antique table, chintz covers and pictures on the walls. The old outbuildings were converted into loose boxes with shining, freshly painted doors.

The only thing which got no attention was Frank's little new byre; it was used as a storage place for corn and bedding for the horses.

I always felt a tug at my heart when I looked in there at the thick dust on the floor, the windows almost opaque with dirt, the cobwebs everywhere, the rusting water bowls, the litter of straw bales, peat moss and sacks of oats where once Frank's cows had stood so proudly.

It was all that was left of a man's dream.

Chapter Twenty-three

After the night of the Daffodil Ball I just seemed to drift naturally into the habit of dropping in to see Helen on an occasional evening. And before I knew what was happening I had developed a pattern; around eight o'clock my feet began to make of their own accord for Heston Grange. Of course I fought the impulse – I didn't go every night; there was my work which often occupied me round the clock, there was a feeling of propriety, and there was Mr Alderson.

Helen's father was a vague little man who had withdrawn into himself to a great extent since his wife's death a few years ago. He was an expert stocksman and his farm could compare with the best, but a good part of his mind often seemed to be elsewhere. And he had acquired some little peculiarities; when things weren't going well he carried on long muttered conversations with himself but when he was particularly pleased about something he was inclined to break into a loud, tuneless humming. It was a penetrating sound and on my professional visits I could often locate him by tracking down this characteristic droning among the farm buildings.

At first when I came to see Helen I'm sure he never even noticed me – I was just one of the crowd of young men who hung around his daughter; but as time went on and my visits became more frequent he suddenly seemed to become conscious of me and began to regard me with an interest which deepened rapidly into alarm. I couldn't blame him, really. He was devoted to Helen and it was natural that he should desire a grand match for her. Richard Edmundson represented just that. His family were rich, powerful people and Richard was very keen indeed. Compared to him, an unknown, impecunious young vet was a poor bargain.

When Mr Alderson was around, my visits were uncomfortable affairs, and it was a pity because I instinctively liked him. He had an amiable, completely inoffensive nature which was very appealing and under other conditions we would have got along very well. But there was no getting round the fact that he resented me. And it wasn't because he wanted to hang on to Helen – he was an unselfish man and anyway, he had an excellent housekeeper in his sister who had been recently widowed and had come to live with the Aldersons. Auntie Lucy was a redoubtable character and was perfectly capable of running the household and looking after the two younger children. It was just that he had got used to the comfortable assumption that one day his daughter would marry the son of his old friend and have a life of untroubled affluence; and he had a stubborn streak which rebelled fiercely against any prospect of change.

So it was always a relief when I got out of the house with Helen. Everything was right then; we went to the little dances in the village institutes, we walked for miles along the old grassy mine tracks among the hills, or sometimes she came on my evening calls with me. There wasn't anything spectacular to do in Darrowby but there was a complete lack of strain, a feeling of being self-sufficient in a warm existence of our own that made everything meaningful and worthwhile.

Things might have gone on like this indefinitely but for a conversation I had with Siegfried. We were sitting in the big room at Skeldale House as we often did before bedtime, talking over the day's events when he laughed and slapped his knee.

'I had old Harry Forster in tonight paying his bill. He was really funny – sat looking round the room and saying "It's a nice little nest you have here, Mr Farnon, a nice little nest" and then, very sly "It's time there was a bird in this nest, you know, there should be a little bird in here." '

I laughed too. 'Well, you should be used to it by now. You're the most eligible bachelor in Darrowby. People are always having a dig at you – they won't be happy till they've got you married off.'

'Wait a minute, not so fast.' Siegfried eyed me thoughtfully. 'I don't think for a moment that Harry was talking about me, it was you he had in mind.'

'What do you mean?'

'Well just think. Didn't you say you had run into the old boy one night when you were walking over his land with Helen. He'd be on to a thing like that in a flash. He thinks it's time you were hitched up, that's all.'

I lay back in my chair and gave myself over to laughter. 'Me! Married! That'll be the day. Can you imagine it? Poor old Harry.'

Siegfried leaned forward. 'What are you laughing at, James? He's quite right – it's time you were married.'

'What's that?' I looked at him incredulously. 'What are you on about now?'

'It's quite simple,' he said. 'I'm saying you ought to get married, and soon.'

'Oh come on Siegfried, you're joking!'

'Why should I be?'

'Well damn it, I'm only starting my career, I've no money, no nothing, I've never even thought about it.'

'You've never even . . . well tell me this, are you courting Helen Alderson or aren't you?'

'Well I'm . . . I've been . . . oh I suppose you could call it that.'

Siegfried settled back comfortably on his chair, put his finger tips together and assumed a judicial expression. 'Good, good. You admit you're courting the girl. Now let us take it a step further. She is, from my own observation, extremely attractive – in fact she nearly causes a traffic pile-up when she walks across the cobbles on market day. It's common knowledge that she is intelligent, equable and an excellent cook. Perhaps you would agree with this?'

'Of course I would,' I said, nettled at his superior air. 'But what's this all about? Why are you going on like a High Court judge?'

'I'm only trying to establish my point, James, which is that you seem to have an ideal wife lined up and you are doing nothing about it. In fact, not to put a too fine point on it, I wish you'd stop playing around and let us see a little action.'

'But it's not as simple as that,' I said, my voice rising, 'I've told you already I'd have to be a lot better off, and anyway, give me a chance, I've only been going to the house for a few weeks – surely you don't start thinking of getting married as soon as that. And there's another thing – her old man doesn't like me.'

Siegfried put his head on one side and I gritted my teeth as a saintly expression began to settle on his face. 'Now my dear chap, don't get angry, but there's something I have to tell you for your own good. Caution is often a virtue, but in your case you carry it too far. It's a little flaw in your character and it shows in a multitude of ways. In your wary approach to problems in your work, for instance – you are always too apprehensive, proceeding fearfully step by step when you should be plunging boldly ahead. You keep seeing dangers when there aren't any – you've got to learn to take a chance, to lash out a bit. As it is, you are confined to a narrow range of activity by your own doubts.'

'The original stick-in-the-mud in fact, eh?'

'Oh come now, James, I didn't say that, but while we're talking, there's another small point I want to bring up. I know you won't mind my saying this. Until you get married I'm afraid I shall fail to get the full benefit of your assistance in the practice because frankly you are becoming increasingly besotted and bemused to the extent that I'm sure you don't know what you're doing half the time.'

'What the devil are you talking about? I've never heard such . . .'

'Kindly hear me out, James. What I'm saying is perfectly true – you're walking about like a man in a dream and you've developed a disturbing habit of staring into space when I'm talking to you. There's only one cure, my boy.'

'And it's a simple little cure, isn't it!' I shouted. 'No money, no home, but leap into matrimony with a happy cry. There's not a thing to worry about!'

'Ah-ah, you see, there you go again, looking for difficulties.' He gave a little laugh and gazed at me with pitying affection. 'No money you say. Well one of these days you'll be a partner here. Your plate will be out on those railings in front of the house, so you'll never be short of your daily bread. And as regards a home – look at all the empty rooms in this house. You could set up a private suite upstairs without any trouble. So that's just a piffling little detail.'

I ran my hand distractedly through my hair. My head was beginning to swim. 'You make it all sound easy.'

'But it IS easy!' Siegfried shot upright in his chair. 'Go out and ask that girl without further delay and get her into church before the month is out!' He wagged a finger at me. 'Learn to grasp the nettle of life, James. Throw off your hesitant ways and remember': He clenched his fist and struck an attitude. 'There is a tide in the affairs of men which, taken at the flood . . .'

'O.K., O.K.,' I said, rising wearily from my chair, 'that's enough, I get the message. I'm going to bed now.'

And I don't suppose I am the first person to have had his life fundamentally influenced by one of Siegfried's chance outbursts. I thought his opinions ridiculous at the time but he planted a seed which germinated and flowered almost overnight. There is no doubt he is responsible for the fact that I was the father of a grown-up family while I was still a young man, because when I brought the subject up with Helen she said yes she'd like to marry me and we set our eyes on an early date. She seemed surprised at first – maybe she had the same opinion of me as Siegfried and expected it would take me a few years to get off the ground.

Anyway, before I had time to think much more about it everything was neatly settled and I found I had made a magical transition from jeering at the whole idea to making plans for furnishing our prospective bedsitter at Skeldale House.

It was a blissful time with only one cloud on the horizon; but that cloud bulked large and forbidding. As I walked hand in hand with Helen, my thoughts in the air, she kept bringing me back to earth with an appealing look.

'You know, Jim, you'll really have to speak to Dad. It's time he knew.'

Chapter Twenty-four

I had been warned long before I qualified that country practice was a dirty, stinking job. I had accepted the fact and adjusted myself to it but there were times when this side of my life obtruded itself and became almost insupportable. Like now, when even after a long hot bath I still smelt.

As I hoisted myself from the steaming water I sniffed at my arm and there it was; the malodorous memory of that horrible cleansing at Tommy Dearlove's striking triumphantly through all the soap and antiseptic almost as fresh and pungent as it had been at four o'clock this afternoon. Nothing but time would move it.

But something in me rebelled at the idea of crawling into bed in this state and I looked with something like desperation along the row of bottles on the bathroom shelf. I stopped at Mrs Hall's bath salts, shining violent pink in their big glass jar. This was something I'd never tried before and I tipped a small handful into the water round my feet. For a moment my head swam as the rising steam was suddenly charged with an aggressive sweetness then on an impulse I shook most of the jar's contents into the bath and lowered myself once more under the surface.

For a long time I lay there smiling to myself in triumph as the oily liquid lapped around me. Not even Tommy Dearlove's cleansing could survive this treatment.

The whole process had a stupefying effect on me and I was half asleep even as I sank back on the pillow. There followed a few moments of blissful floating before a delicious slumber claimed me. And when the bedside phone boomed in my ear the sense of injustice and personal affront was even stronger than usual. Blinking sleepily at the clock which said 1.15 a.m. I lifted the receiver and mumbled into it, but I was jerked suddenly wide awake when I recognised Mr Alderson's voice. Candy was calving and something was wrong. Would I come right away.

There has always been a 'this is where I came in' feeling about a night call. And as my lights swept the cobbles of the deserted market place it was there again; a sense of returning to fundamentals, of really being me. The silent houses, the tight drawn curtains, the long, empty street giving way to the stone walls of the country road flipping endlessly past on either side. At these times I was usually in a state of suspended animation, just sufficiently awake to steer the car in the right direction, but tonight I was fully alert, my mind ticking over anxiously.

Because Candy was something special. She was the house cow, a pretty little Jersey and Mr Alderson's particular pet. She was the sole member of her breed in the herd but whereas the milk from the Shorthorns went into the churns to be collected by the big dairy, Candy's rich yellow offering found its way on to the family porridge every morning or appeared heaped up on trifles and fruit pies or was made into butter, a golden creamy butter to make you dream.

But apart from all that, Mr Alderson just liked the animal. He usually stopped opposite her on his way down the byre and began to hum to himself and gave her tail head a brief scratch as he passed. And I couldn't blame him because I sometimes wish all cows were Jerseys; small, gentle, doe-eyed creatures you could push around without any trouble; with padded corners and fragile limbs. Even if they kicked you it was like a love tap compared with the clump from a craggy Friesian.

I just hoped it would be something simple with Candy, because my stock wasn't high with Mr Alderson and I had a nervous conviction that he wouldn't react favourably if I started to make a ham-fisted job of calving his little favourite. I shrugged away my fears; obstetrics in the Jersey were usually easy.

Helen's father was an efficient farmer. As I pulled up in the yard I could see into the lighted loose box where two buckets of water were steaming in readiness for me. A towel was draped over the half door and Stan and Bert, the two long-serving cowmen, were standing alongside their boss. Candy was lying comfortably in deep straw. She wasn't straining and there was nothing visible at the vulva but the cow had a preoccupied, inward look as though all was not well with her.

I closed the door behind me. 'Have you had a feel inside her, Mr Alderson?'

'Aye, I've had me hand in and there's nowt there.'

'Nothing at all?'

'Not a thing. She'd been on for a few hours and not showing so I popped me hand in and there's no head, no legs, nowt. And not much room, either. That's when I rang you.'

This sounded very strange. I hung my jacket on a nail and began thoughtfully to unbutton my shirt. It was when I was pulling it over my head that I noticed Mr Alderson's nose wrinkling. The farm men, too, began to sniff and look at each other wonderingly. Mrs Hall's bath salts, imprisoned under my clothing had burst from their bondage in a sickly wave, filling the enclosed space with their strident message. Hurriedly I began to wash my arms in the hope that the alien odour might pass away but it seemed to get worse, welling from my warm skin, competing incongruously with the honest smells of cow, hay and straw. Nobody said anything. These men weren't the type to make the ribald remark which would have enabled me to laugh the thing off. There was no ambiguity about this scent; it was voluptuously feminine and Bert and Stan stared at me open mouthed. Mr Alderson, his mouth turned down at the corners, his nostrils still twitching, kept his eyes fixed on the far wall.

Cringing inwardly I knelt behind the cow and in a moment my embarrassment was forgotten. The vagina was empty; a smooth passage narrowing rapidly to a small, ridged opening just wide enough to admit my hand. Beyond I could feel the feet and head of a calf. My spirits plummeted. Torsion of the uterus. There was going to be no easy victory for me here.

I sat back on my heels and turned to the farmers. 'She's got a twisted calf bed. There's a live calf in there all right but there's no way out for it – I can barely get my hand through.'

'Aye, I thought it was something peculiar.' Mr Alderson rubbed his chin and looked at me doubtfully. 'What can we do about it, then?'

'We'll have to try to correct the twist by rolling the cow over while I keep hold of the calf. It's a good job there's plenty of us here.'

'And that'll put everything right, will it?'

I swallowed. I didn't like these jobs. Sometimes rolling worked and sometimes it didn't and in those days we hadn't quite got round to performing caesarians on cows. If I was unsuccessful I had the prospect of telling Mr Alderson to send Candy to the butcher. I banished the thought quickly.

'It'll put everything right,' I said. It had to. I stationed Bert at the front legs, Stan at the hind and the farmer holding the cow's head on the floor. Then I stretched myself on the hard concrete, pushed in a hand and grasped the calf's foot.

'Now roll her,' I gasped, and the men pulled the legs round in a clockwise direction. I held fiercely to the little feet as the cow flopped on to her other side. Nothing seemed to be happening inside.

'Push her on to her chest,' I panted.

Stan and Bert expertly tucked the legs under the cow and rolled her on to her brisket and as she settled there I gave a yell of pain.

'Get her back, quick! We're going the wrong way!' The smooth band of tissue had tightened on my wrist in a numbing grip of frightening power. For a moment I had the panicky impression that I'd never get out of there again.

But the men worked like lightning. Within seconds Candy was stretched out on her original side, the pressure was off my arm and we were back where we started.

I gritted my teeth and took a fresh grip on the calf's foot. 'O.K., try her the other way.'

This time the roll was anti-clockwise and we went through 180 degrees without anything happening. I only just kept my grasp on the foot – the resistance this time was tremendous. Taking a breather for a few seconds I lay face down while the sweat sprang out on my back, sending out fresh exotic vapours from the bath salts.

'Right. One more go!' I cried and the men hauled the cow further over.

And oh it was beautiful to feel everything magically unravelling and my arm lying free in a wide uterus with all the room in the world and the calf already beginning to slide towards me.

Candy summed up the situation immediately and for the first time gave a determined heaving strain. Sensing victory just round the corner she followed up with another prolonged effort which popped the calf wet and wriggling into my arms.

'By gum, it was quick at t'finish,' Mr Alderson murmured wonderingly. He seized a wisp of hay and began to dry off the little creature.

Thankfully I soaped my arms in one of the buckets. After every delivery there is a feeling of relief but in this case it was overwhelming. It no longer mattered that the loose box smelt like a ladies' hairdressing salon, I just felt good. I said good night to Bert and Stan as they returned to their beds, giving a final incredulous sniff as they passed me. Mr Alderson was pottering about, having a word with Candy then starting again on the calf which he had already rubbed down several times. He seemed fascinated by it. And I couldn't blame him because it was like something out of Disney; a pale gold faun, unbelievably tiny with large dark limpid eyes and an expression of trusting innocence. It was a heifer, too.

The farmer lifted it as if it were a whippet dog and laid it by the mother's head. Candy nosed the little animal over, rumbling happily in her throat, then she began to lick it. I watched Mr Alderson. He was standing, hands clasped behind him, rocking backwards and forwards on his heels, obviously enchanted by the scene. Any time now, I thought. And I was right; the tuneless humming broke out, even louder than usual, like a joyful paean.

I stiffened in my Wellingtons. There would never be a better time. After a nervous cough I spoke up firmly.

'Mr Alderson,' I said and he half turned his head. 'I would like to marry your daughter.'

The humming was switched off abruptly and he turned slowly till he was facing me. He didn't speak but his eyes searched my face unhappily. Then he bent stiffly, picked up the buckets one by one, tipped out the water and made for the door.

'You'd better come in the house,' he said.

The farmhouse kitchen looked lost and forsaken with the family abed. I sat in a high backed wooden chair by the side of the empty hearth while Mr Alderson put away his buckets, hung up the towel and washed his hands methodically at the sink, then he pottered through to the parlour and I heard him bumping and clinking about in the sideboard. When he reappeared he bore a tray in front of him on which a bottle of whisky and two glasses rattled gently. The tray lent the simple procedure an air of formality which was accentuated by the heavy cut crystal of the glasses and the virgin, unopened state of the bottle.

Mr Alderson set the tray down on the kitchen table which he dragged nearer to us before settling in the chair at the other side of the fireplace. Nobody said anything. I waited in the lengthening silence while he peered at the cap of the bottle like a man who had never seen one before then unscrewed it with slow apprehension as though he feared it might blow up in his face.

Finally he poured out two measures with the utmost gravity and precision, ducking his head frequently to compare the levels in the two glasses, and with a last touch of ceremony proffered the laden tray.

I took my drink and waited expectantly.

Mr Alderson looked into the lifeless fireplace for a minute or two then he directed his gaze upwards at the oil painting of the paddling cows which hung above the mantelpiece. He pursed his lips as though about to whistle but appeared to change his mind and without salutation took a gulp of his whisky which sent him into a paroxysm of coughing from which it took him some time to recover. When his breathing had returned to normal he sat up straight and fixed me with streaming eyes. He cleared his throat and I felt a certain tension.

'Aye well,' he said, 'it's grand hay weather.'

I agreed with him and he looked round the kitchen with the interested stare of a total stranger. Having completed his inspection he took another copious swallow from his glass, grimaced, closed his eyes, shook his head violently a few times, then leaned forward.

'Mind you,' he said, 'a night's rain would do a lot o' good.'

I gave my opinion that it undoubtedly would and the silence fell again. It lasted even longer this time and my host kept drinking his whisky as though he was getting used to it. And I could see that it was having a relaxing effect; the strained lines on his face were beginning to smooth out and his eyes were losing their hunted look.

Nothing more was said until he had replenished our glasses, balancing the amounts meticulously again. He took a sip at his second measure then he looked down at the rug and spoke in a small voice.

'James,' he said, 'I had a wife in a thousand.'

I was so surprised I hardly knew what to say. 'Yes, I know,' I murmured. 'I've heard a lot about her.'

Mr Alderson went on, still looking down, his voice full of gentle yearning.

'Yes, she was the grandest lass for miles around and the bonniest.' He looked up at me suddenly with the ghost of a smile. 'Nobody thought she'd ever have a feller like me, you know. But she did.' He paused and looked away. 'Aye, she did.'

He began to tell me about his dead wife. He told me calmly, without self pity, but with a wistful gratitude for the happiness he had known. And I discovered that Mr Alderson was different from a lot of the farmers of his generation because he said nothing about her being a 'good worker'. So many of the women of those times seemed to be judged mainly on their working ability and when I had first come to Darrowby I had been shocked when I commiserated with a newly widowed old man. He had brushed a tear from his eye and said, 'Aye, she was a grand worker.'

But Mr Alderson said only that his wife had been beautiful, that she had been kind, and that he had loved her very much. He talked about Helen, too, about the things she had said and done when she was a little girl, about how very like her mother she was in every way. He never said anything about me but I had the feeling all the time that he meant it to concern me; and the very fact that he was talking freely seemed a sign that the barriers were coming down.

Actually he was talking a little too freely. He was half way down his third huge whisky and in my experience Yorkshiremen just couldn't take the stuff. I had seen burly ten pint men from the local pub keel over after a mere sniff at the amber fluid and little Mr Alderson hardly drank at all. I was getting worried.

But there was nothing I could do, so I let him ramble on happily. He was lying right back in his chair now, completely at ease, his eyes, alight with his memories, gazing somewhere above my head. In fact I am convinced he had forgotten I was there because after one long passage he dropped his eyes, caught sight of me and stared for a moment without recognition. When he did manage to place me it seemed to remind him of his duties as a host. But as he reached again for the bottles he caught sight of the clock on the wall.

'Well dang it, it's four o'clock. We've been here long enough. It's hardly worth goin' to bed, but I suppose we'd better have an hour or two's sleep.' He tipped the last of the whisky down his throat, jumped briskly to his feet, looked around him for a few moments in a business-like sort of way then pitched head first with a sickening clatter among the fire irons.

Frozen with horror, I started forward to help the small figure scrabbling on the hearth but I needn't have worried because he bounced back to his feet in a second or two and looked me in the eye as if nothing had happened.

'Well, I'd better be off,' I said. 'Thanks for the drink.' There was no point in staying longer as I realised that the chances of Mr Alderson saying 'Bless you, my son' or anything like that were remote. But I had a comforting impression that all was going to be well.

As I made my way to the door the farmer made a creditable attempt to usher me out but his direction was faulty and he tacked helplessly away from me across the kitchen floor before collapsing against a tall dresser. From under a row of willow pattern dinner plates his face looked at me with simple bewilderment.

I hesitated then turned back. 'I'll just walk up the stairs with you, Mr Alderson,' I said in a matter of fact voice and the little man made no resistance as I took his arm and guided him towards the door in the far corner.

As we creaked our way upstairs he stumbled and would have gone down again had I not grabbed him round the waist. As I caught him he looked up at me and grunted 'Thanks, lad,' and we grinned at each other for a moment before restarting the climb.

I supported him across the landing to his bedroom door and he stood hesitating as though about to say something. But finally he just nodded to me a couple of times before ducking inside.

I waited outside the door, listening in some anxiety to the bumps and thumps from within; but I relaxed as a loud, tuneless humming came through the panels. Everything most certainly was going to be all right.

Chapter Twenty-five

'Well, do'you want t'job or don't you?'

Walt Barnett towered over me in the surgery doorway and his eyes flickered from my head to my feet and up again without expression. The cigarette dangling from his lower lip seemed to be a part of him as did the brown trilby hat and the shining navy blue serge suit stretched tightly over his bulky form. He must have weighed nearly twenty stones and with his red beefy brutal mouth and overbearing manner he was undeniably formidable.

'Well, er . . . yes. Of course we want the job,' I replied. 'I was just wondering when we could fit it in.' I went over to the desk and began to look through the appointment book. 'We're pretty full this week and I don't know what Mr Farnon has fixed for the week after. Maybe we'd better give you a ring.'

The big man had burst in on me without warning or greeting and barked, 'I 'ave a fine big blood 'oss to geld. When can you do 'im?'

I had looked at him hesitantly for a few moments, taken aback partly by the arrogance of his approach, partly by his request. This wasn't good news to me; I didn't like castrating fine big blood 'osses – I much preferred the ordinary cart colts and if you came right down to it I had a particular preference for Shetland ponies. But it was all part of living and if it had to be done it had to be done.

'You can give me a ring if you like, but don't be ower long about it.' The hard unsmiling stare still held me. 'And I want a good job doin', think on!'

'We always try to do a good job, Mr Barnett,' I said, fighting a rising prickle of resentment at his attitude.

'Aye well I've heard that afore and I've had some bloody balls-ups,' he said. He gave me a final truculent nod, turned and walked out, leaving the door open.

I was still standing in the middle of the room seething and muttering to myself when Siegfried walked in. I hardly saw him at first and when he finally came into focus I found I was glowering into his face.

'What's the trouble, James?' he asked. 'A little touch of indigestion, perhaps?'

'Indigestion? No . . . no . . . Why do you say that?'

'Well you seemed to be in some sort of pain, standing there on one leg with your face screwed up.'

'Did I look like that? Oh it was just our old friend Walt Barnett. He wants us to cut a horse for him and he made the request in his usual charming way – he really gets under my skin, that man.'

Tristan came in from the passage. 'Yes, I was out there and I heard him. He's a bloody big lout.'

Siegfried rounded on him. 'That's enough! I don't want to hear that kind of talk in here.' Then he turned back to me. 'And really, James, even if you were upset I don't think it's an excuse for profanity.'

'What do you mean?'

'Well, some of the expletives I heard you muttering there were unworthy of you.' He spread his hands in a gesture of disarming frankness, 'Heaven knows I'm no prude but I don't like to hear such language within these walls.' He paused and his features assumed an expression of deep gravity. 'After all, the people who come in here provide us with our bread and butter and they should be referred to with respect.'

'Yes, but . . .'

'Oh I know some are not as nice as others but you must never let them irritate you. You've heard the old saying, "The customer is always right." Well I think it's a good working axiom and I always abide by it myself.' He gazed solemnly at Tristan and me in turn. 'So I hope I make myself clear. No swearing in the surgery – particularly when it concerns the clients.'

'It's all right for you!' I burst out heatedly. 'But you didn't hear Barnett. I'll stand so much, but . . .'

Siegfried put his head on one side and a smile of ethereal beauty crept over his face. 'My dear old chap, there you go again, letting little things disturb you. I've had to speak to you about this before, haven't I? I wish I could help you, I wish I could pass on my own gift of remaining calm at all times.'

'What's that you said?'

'I said I wanted to help you, James, and I will.' He held up a forefinger. 'You've probably often wondered why I never get angry or excited.'

'Eh?'

'Oh I know you have – you must have. Well I'll let you into a little secret.' His smile took on a roguish quality. 'If a client is rude to me I simply charge him a little more. Instead of getting all steamed up like you do I tell myself that I'm putting ten bob extra on the bill and it works like magic.'

'Is that so?'

'Yes indeed, my boy.' He thumped my shoulder then became very serious. 'Of course I realise that I have an advantage right at the start – I have been blessed with a naturally even temperament while you are blown about in all directions by every little wind of circumstance. But I do think that this is something you could cultivate, so work at it, James, work at it. All this fretting and fuming is bad for you – your whole life would change if you could just acquire my own tranquil outlook.'

I swallowed hard. 'Well thank you, Siegfried,' I said. 'I'll try.'

Walt Barnett was a bit of a mystery man in Darrowby. He wasn't a farmer, he was a scrap merchant, a haulier, a dealer in everything from linoleum to second hand cars, and there was only one thing the local people could say for certain about him – he had brass, lots of brass. They said everything he touched turned to money.

He had bought a decaying mansion a few miles outside the town where he lived with a downtrodden little wife and where he kept a floating population of livestock; a few bullocks, some pigs and always a horse or two. He employed all the vets in the district in turn, probably because he didn't think much of any of us; a feeling which, I may say, was mutual. He never seemed to do any physical work and could be seen most days of the week shambling around the streets of Darrowby, hands in pockets, cigarette dangling, his brown trilby on the back of his head, his huge body threatening to burst through that shiny navy suit.

After my meeting with him we had a busy few days and it was on the following Thursday that the phone rang in the surgery. Siegfried lifted it and immediately his expression changed. From across the floor I could clearly hear the loud hectoring tones coming through the receiver and as my colleague listened a slow flush spread over his cheeks and his mouth hardened. Several times he tried to put in a word but the torrent of sound from the far end was unceasing. Finally he raised his voice and broke in but instantly there was a click and he found himself speaking to a dead line.

Siegfried crashed the receiver into its rest and swung round. 'That was Barnett – playing hell because we haven't rung him.' He stood staring at me for a few moments, his face dark with anger.

'The bloody bastard!' he shouted. 'Who the hell does he think he is? Abusing me like that, then hanging up on me when I try to speak!'

For a moment he was silent then he turned to me. 'I'll tell you this, James, he wouldn't have spoken to me like that if he'd been in this room with me.' He came over to me and held out his hands, fingers crooked menacingly. 'I'd have wrung his bloody neck, big as he is! I would have, I tell you, I'd have strangled the bugger!'

'But Siegfried,' I said. 'What about your system?'

'System? What system?'

'Well, you know the trick you have when people are unpleasant – you put something on the bill, don't you?'

Siegfried let his hands fall to his sides and stared at me for some time, his chest rising and falling with his emotion. Then he patted me on the shoulder and turned away towards the window where he stood looking out at the quiet street.

When he turned back to me he looked grim but calmer. 'By God, James, you're right. That's the answer. I'll cut Barnett's horse for him but I'll charge him a tenner.'

I laughed heartily. In those days the average charge for castrating a horse was a pound, or if you wanted to be more professional, a guinea.

'What are you laughing at?' my employer enquired sourly.

'Well . . . at your joke. I mean, ten pounds . . . ha-ha-ha!'

'I'm not joking, I'm going to charge him a tenner.'

'Oh come on, Siegfried, you can't do that.'

'You just watch me,' he said. 'I'm going to sort that bugger.'

Two mornings later I was going through the familiar motions of preparing for a castration; boiling up the emasculator and laying it on the enamel tray along with the scalpel, the roll of cotton wool, the artery forceps, the tincture of iodine, the suture materials, the tetanus antitoxin and syringes. For the last five minutes Siegfried had been shouting at me to hurry.

'What the hell are you doing through there, James? Don't forget to put in an extra bottle of chloroform. And bring the sidelines in case he doesn't go down. Where have you hidden those spare scalpel blades, James?'

The sunshine streamed across the laden tray, filtering through the green tangle of the wistaria which fell untidily across the surgery window. Reminding me that it was May and that there was nowhere a May morning came with such golden magic as to the long garden at Skeldale House; the high brick walls with their crumbling mortar and ancient stone copings enfolding the sunlight in a warm clasp and spilling it over the untrimmed lawns, the banks of lupins and bluebells, the masses of fruit blossom. And right at the top the rooks cawing in the highest branches of the elms.

Siegfried, chloroform muzzle looped over one shoulder, made a final check of the items on the tray then we set off. In less than half an hour we were driving through the lodge gates of the old mansion then along a mossy avenue which wandered among pine and birch trees up to the house which looked out from its wooded background over the rolling miles of fell and moor.

Nobody could have asked for a more perfect place for the operation; a high-walled paddock deep in lush grass. The two-year-old, a magnificent chestnut, was led in by two characters who struck me as typical henchmen for Mr Barnett. I don't know where he had dug them up but you didn't see faces like that among the citizens of Darrowby. One was a brown goblin who, as he conversed with his companion, repeatedly jerked his head and winked one eye as though they were sharing some disreputable secret. The other had a head covered with ginger stubble surmounting a countenance of a bright scrofulous red which looked as though a piece would fall off if you touched it; and deep in the livid flesh two tiny eyes darted.

The two of them regarded us unsmilingly and the dark one spat luxuriously as we approached.

'It's a nice morning,' I said.

Ginger just stared at me while Winker nodded knowingly and closed one eye as if I had uttered some craftiness which appealed to him.

The vast hunched figure of Mr Barnett hovered in the background, cigarette drooping, the bright sunshine striking brilliant shafts of light from the tight sheen of the navy suit.

I couldn't help comparing the aspect of the trio of humans with the natural beauty and dignity of the horse. The big chestnut tossed his head then stood looking calmly across the paddock, the large fine eyes alight with intelligence, the noble lines of the face and neck blending gently into the grace and power of the body. Observations I had heard about the higher and lower animals floated about in my mind.

Siegfried walked around the horse, patting him and talking to him, his eyes shining with the delight of the fanatic.

'He's a grand sort, Mr Barnett,' he said.

The big man glowered at him. 'Aye well, don't spoil 'im, that's all. I've paid a lot o'money for that 'oss.'

Siegfried gave him a thoughtful look then turned to me.

'Well, let's get on. We'll drop him over there on that long grass. Are you ready, James?'

I was ready, but I'd be a lot more at ease if Siegfried would just leave me alone. In horse work I was the anaesthetist and my colleague was the surgeon. And he was good; quick, deft, successful. I had no quarrel with the arrangement; he could get on with his job and let me do mine. But there was the rub; he would keep butting into my territory and I found it wearing.

Anaesthesia in the large animals has a dual purpose; it abolishes pain and acts as a means of restraint. It is obvious that you can't do much with these potentially dangerous creatures unless they are controlled.

That was my job. I had to produce a sleeping patient ready for the knife and very often I thought it was the most difficult part. Until the animal was properly under I always felt a certain tension and Siegfried didn't help in this respect. He would hover at my elbow, offering advice as to the quantity of chloroform and he could never bear to wait until the anaesthetic had taken effect. He invariably said, 'He isn't going to go down, James.' Then, 'Don't you think you should strap a fore leg up?'

Even now, thirty years later, when I am using such intravenous drugs as thiopentone he is still at it. Stamping around impatiently as I fill my syringe, poking over my shoulder with a long fore-finger into the jugular furrow. 'I'd shove it in just there, James.'

I stood there irresolute, my employer by my side, the chloroform bottle in my pocket, the muzzle dangling from my hand. It would be wonderful, I thought, if just once I could be on my own to get on with it. And, after all, I had worked for him for nearly three years – surely I knew him well enough to be able to put it to him.

I cleared my throat. 'Siegfried, I was just wondering. Would you care to go and sit down over there for a few minutes till I get him down?'

'What's that?'

'Well I thought it would be a good idea if you left me to it. There's a bit of a crowd round the horse's head – I don't want him excited. So why don't you relax for a while. I'll give you a shout when he's down?'

Siegfried raised a hand. 'My dear chap, anything you say. I don't know what I'm hanging around here for anyway. I never interfere with your end as you well know.' He turned about and, tray under arm, marched off to where he had parked his car on the grass about fifty yards away. He strode round behind the Rover and sat down on the turf, his back against the metal. He was out of sight.

Peace descended. I became suddenly aware of the soft warmth of the sun on my forehead, of the bird song echoing among the nearby trees. Unhurriedly I fastened on the muzzle under the head collar and produced my little glass measure.

This once I had plenty of time. I'd start him off with just a couple of drachms to get him used to the smell of it without frightening him. I poured the clear fluid on to the sponge.

'Walk him slowly round in a circle,' I said to Ginger and Winker. 'I'm going to give him a little bit at a time, there's no hurry. But keep a good hold of that halter shank in case he plays up.'

There was no need for my warning. The two-year-old paced round calmly and fearlessly and every minute or so I trickled a little extra on to the sponge. After a while his steps became laboured and he began to sway drunkenly as he walked. I watched him happily; this was the way I liked to do it. Another little dollop would just about do the trick. I measured out another half ounce and walked over to the big animal.

His head nodded sleepily as I gave it to him. 'You're just about ready aren't you, old lad,' I was murmuring when the peace was suddenly shattered.

'He isn't going to go down, you know, James!' It was a booming roar from the direction of the car and as I whipped round in consternation I saw a head just showing over the bonnet. There was another cry.

'Why don't you strap up a . . .?'

At that moment the horse lurched and collapsed quietly on the grass and Siegfried came bounding knife in hand from his hiding place like a greyhound.

'Sit on his head!' he yelled. 'What are you waiting for, he'll be up in a minute! And get that rope round that hind leg! And bring my tray! And fetch the hot water!' He panted up to the horse then turned and bawled into Ginger's face, 'Come on, I'm talking to you. MOVE!'

Ginger went off at a bow-legged gallop and cannoned into Winker who was rushing forward with the bucket. Then they had a brief but frenzied tug of war with the rope before they got round the pastern.

'Pull the leg forward,' cried my employer, bending over the operation site, then a full blooded bellow, 'Get the bloody foot out of my eye, will you! What's the matter with you, you wouldn't pull a hen off its nest the way you're going.'

I knelt quietly at the head, my knee on the neck. There was no need to hold him down; he was beautifully out, his eyes blissfully closed as Siegfried worked with his usual lightning expertise. There was a mere few seconds of silence broken only by the tinkling of instruments as they fell back on the tray, then my colleague glanced along the horse's back. 'Open the muzzle, James.'

The operation was over.

I don't think I've ever seen an easier job. By the time we had washed our instruments in the bucket the two-year-old was on his feet, cropping gently at the grass.

'Splendid anaesthetic, James,' said Siegfried, drying off the emasculator. 'Just right. And what a grand sort of horse.'

We had put our gear back in the boot and were ready to leave when Walt Barnett heaved his massive bulk over towards us. He faced Siegfried across the bonnet of the car.

'Well that were nowt of a job,' he grunted, slapping a cheque book down on the shining metal, 'How much do you want?'

There was an arrogant challenge in the words and, faced with the dynamic force, the sheer brutal presence of the man, most people who were about to charge a guinea would have changed their minds and said a pound.

'Well, I'm askin' yer,' he repeated. 'How much do you want?'

'Ah yes,' said Siegfried lightly. 'That'll be a tenner.'

The big man put a meaty hand on the cheque book and stared at my colleague. 'What?'

'That'll be a tenner,' Siegfried said again.

'Ten pounds?' Mr Barnett's eyes opened wider.

'Yes,' said Siegfried, smiling pleasantly. 'That's right. Ten pounds.'

There was a silence as the two men faced each other across the bonnet. The bird song and the noises from the wood seemed abnormally loud as the seconds ticked away and nobody moved. Mr Barnett was glaring furiously and I looked from the huge fleshy face which seemed to have swollen even larger across to the lean, strong-jawed, high-cheekboned profile of my employer. Siegfried still wore the remains of a lazy smile but down in the grey depths of his eye a dangerous light glinted.

Just when I was at screaming point the big man dropped his head suddenly and began to write. When he handed the cheque over he was shaking so much that the slip of paper fluttered as though in a high wind.

'Here y'are, then' he said hoarsely.

'Thank you so much.' Siegfried read the cheque briefly then stuffed it carelessly into a side pocket. 'Isn't it grand to have some real May weather, Mr Barnett. Does us all good. I'm sure.'

Walt Barnett mumbled something and turned away. As I got into the car I could see the great expanse of navy blue back moving ponderously towards the house.

'He won't have us back, anyway,' I said.

Siegfried started the engine and we moved away. 'No, James, I should think he'd get his twelve bore out if we ventured down this drive again. But that suits me – I think I can manage to get through the rest of my life without Mr Barnett.'

Our road took us through the little village of Baldon and Siegfried slowed down outside the pub, a yellow-washed building standing a few yards back from the road with a wooden sign reading The Cross Keys and a large black dog sleeping on the sunny front step.

My boss looked at his watch. 'Twelve fifteen – they'll just have opened. A cool beer would be rather nice wouldn't it. I don't think I've been in this place before.'

After the brightness outside, the shaded interior was restful, with only stray splinters of sunshine filtering through the curtains on to the flagged floor, the fissured oak tables, the big fireplace with its high settle.

'Good morning to you, landlord,' boomed my employer, striding over to the bar. He was in his most ducal mood and I felt it was a pity he didn't have a silver-knobbed stick to rap on the counter.

The man behind the counter smiled and knuckled a forelock in the approved manner. 'Good morning to you, sir, and what can I get for you gentlemen?'

I half expected Siegfried to say, 'Two stoups of your choicest brew, honest fellow,' but instead he just turned to me and murmured 'I think two halves of bitter, eh James?'

The man began to draw the beer.

'Won't you join us?' Siegfried enquired.

'Thank ye sir, I'll 'ave a brown ale with you.'

'And possibly your good lady, too?' Siegfried smiled over at the landlord's wife who was stacking glasses at the end of the counter.

'That's very kind of you, I will.' She looked up, gulped, and an expression of wonder crept over her face. Siegfried hadn't stared at her – it had only been a five second burst from the grey eyes – but the bottle rattled against the glass as she poured her small port and she spent the rest of the time gazing at him dreamily.

'That'll be five and sixpence,' the landlord said.

'Right.' My employer plunged a hand into his bulging side pocket and crashed down on the counter an extraordinary mixture of crumpled bank notes, coins, veterinary instruments, thermometers, bits of string. He stirred the mass with a forefinger, flicking out a half crown and two florins across the woodwork.

'Wait a minute!' I exclaimed. 'Aren't those my curved scissors? I lost them a few days . . .'

Siegfried swept the pile out of sight into his pocket.

'Nonsense! What makes you think that?'

'Well, they look exactly like mine. Unusual shape – lovely long, flat blades. I've been looking everywhere . . .'

'James!' He drew himself up and faced me with frozen hauteur. 'I think you've said enough. I may be capable of stooping to some pretty low actions but I'd like to believe that certain things are beneath me. And stealing a colleague's curved scissors is one of them.'

I relapsed into silence. I'd have to bide my time and take my chance later. I was fairly sure I'd recognised a pair of my dressing forceps in there too.

In any case, something else was occupying Siegfried's mind. He narrowed his eyes in intense thought then delved into his other pocket and produced a similar collection which he proceeded to push around the counter anxiously.

'What's the matter?' I asked.

'That cheque I've just taken. Did I give it to you?'

'No, you put it in that pocket. I saw you.'

'That's what I thought. Well it's gone.'

'Gone?'

'I've lost the bloody thing!'

I laughed. 'Oh you can't have. Go through your other pockets – it must be on you somewhere.'

Siegfried made a systematic search but it was in vain.

'Well James,' he said at length. 'I really have lost it, but I've just thought of a simple solution. I will stay here and have one more beer while you slip back to Walt Barnett and ask him for another cheque.'

Chapter Twenty-six

Considering we spent our honeymoon tuberculin testing it was a big success. It compared favourably, at any rate, with the experiences of a lot of people I know who celebrated this milestone in their lives by cruising for a month on sunny seas and still wrote it off as a dead loss. For Helen and me it had all the ingredients; laughter, fulfilment and camaraderie, and yet it only lasted a week. And, as I say, we spent it tuberculin testing.

The situation had its origins one morning at the breakfast table when Siegfried, red-eyed after a bad night with a colicky mare, was opening the morning mail. He drew his breath in sharply as a thick roll of forms fell from an official envelope.

'God almighty! Look at all that testing!' He smoothed out the forms on the table cloth and read feverishly down the long list of farm premises. 'And they want us to start this lot around Ellerthorpe next week without fail – it's very urgent.' He glanced at me for a moment. 'That's when you're getting married, isn't it?'

I shifted uncomfortably in my chair. 'Yes, I'm afraid it is.'

Siegfried snatched a piece of toast from the rack and began to slap butter on it. 'Well this is just great isn't it? The practice going mad, a week's testing right at the top of the Dale, away in the back of beyond, and your wedding smack in the middle of it. You'll be drifting gaily off on your honeymoon without a care in the world while I'm rushing around here nearly disappearing up my own backside!' He bit a piece from the toast and began to chew it worriedly.

'I'm sorry, Siegfried,' I said. 'I didn't mean to land you in the cart like this. I couldn't know the practice was going to get so busy right now and I never expected them to throw all this testing at us.'

Siegfried paused in his chewing and pointed a finger at me. 'That's just it, James, that's your trouble – you don't look ahead. You just go belting straight on without a thought. Even when it comes to a bloody wedding you're not worried – oh no, let's get on with it, to hell with the consequences.' He paused to cough up a few crumbs which he had inhaled in his agitation. 'In fact I can't see what all the hurry is – you've got all the time in the world to get married, you're just a boy. And another thing – you hardly know this girl, you've only been seeing her regularly for a few weeks.'

'But wait a minute, you said . . .'

'No, let me finish, James. Marriage is a very serious step, not to be embarked upon without long and serious thought. Why in God's name does it have to be next week? Next year would have been soon enough and you could have enjoyed a nice long engagement. But no, you've got to rush in and tie the knot and it isn't so easily untied you know.'

'Oh hell, Siegfried, this is too bad! You know perfectly well it was you who . . .'

'One moment more. Your precipitate marital arrangements are going to cause me a considerable headache but believe me I wish you well. I hope all turns out for the best despite your complete lack of foresight, but at the same time I must remind you of the old saying. "Marry in haste, repent at leisure." '

I could stand no more. I leaped to my feet, thumped a fist on the table and yelled at him.

'But damn it, it was your idea! I was all for leaving it for a bit but you . . .'

Siegfried wasn't listening. He had been cooling off all the time and now his face broke into a seraphic smile. 'Now, now, now, James, you're getting excited again. Sit down and calm yourself. You mustn't mind my speaking to you like this – you are very young and it's my duty. You haven't done anything wrong at all; I suppose it's the most natural thing in the world for people of your age to act without thinking ahead, to jump into things with never a thought of the morrow. It's just the improvidence of youth.' Siegfried was about six years older than me but he had donned the mantle of the omniscient grey-beard without effort.

I dug my fingers into my knees and decided not to pursue the matter. I had no chance anyway, and besides, I was beginning to feel a bit worried about clearing off and leaving him snowed under with work. I got up and walked to the window where I watched old Will Varley pushing a bicycle up the street with a sack of potatoes balanced on the handlebars as I had watched him a hundred times before. Then I turned back to my employer. I had had one of my infrequent ideas.

'Look, Siegfried, I wouldn't mind spending my honeymoon round Ellerthorpe. It's wonderful up there at this time of the year and we could stay at the Wheat Sheaf. I could do the testing from there.'

He looked at me in astonishment. 'Spend it at Ellerthorpe? And testing? It's impossible – what would Helen say?'

'She wouldn't mind. In fact she could do the writing for me. We were only going off touring in the car so we haven't made any plans, and anyway it's funny, but Helen and I have often said we'd like to stay at the Wheat Sheaf some time – there's something about that little pub.'

Siegfried shook his head decisively. 'No, James I won't hear of it. In fact you're beginning to make me feel guilty. I'll get through the work all right so forget about it and go away and have a good time.'

'No, I've made up my mind. I'm really beginning to like the idea.' I scanned the list quickly. 'I can start testing at Allen's and do all those smaller ones around there on Tuesday, get married on Wednesday and go back for the second injection and readings on Thursday and Friday. I can knock hell out of that list by the end of the week.'

Siegfried looked at me as though he was seeing me for the first time. He argued and protested but for once I got my way. I fished the Ministry notification cards from the desk drawer and began to make the arrangements for my honeymoon.

On Tuesday at 12 noon I had finished testing the Allens' huge herd scattered for miles over the stark fells at the top of the Dale and was settling down with the hospitable folk for the inevitable 'bit o' dinner'. Mr Allen was at the head of the scrubbed table and facing me were his two sons, Jack, aged about twenty and Robbie, about seventeen. The young men were superbly fit and tough and I had been watching all morning in something like awe as they man-handled the wild, scattered beasts, chasing and catching tirelessly hour after hour. I had stared incredulously as Jack had run down a galloping heifer on the open moor, seized its horns and bore it slowly to the ground for me to inject; it struck me more than once that it was a pity that an Olympic selector was unlikely to stray into this remote corner of high Yorkshire – he would have found some world-beating material.

I always had to stand a bit of legpulling from Mrs Allen, a jolly talkative woman; on previous visits she had ribbed me mercilessly about being a slowcoach with the girls, the disgrace of having nothing better than a housekeeper to look after me. I knew she would start on me again today but I bided my time; I had a devastating riposte up my sleeve. She had just opened the oven door, filling the room with a delectable fragrance, and as she dumped a huge slab of roast ham on the table she looked down at me with a smile.

'Now then, Mr Herriot, when are we going to get you married off? It's time you found a nice girl, you know I'm always at you but you take not a bit o' notice.' She giggled as she bustled back to the cooking range for a bowl of mashed potatoes.

I waited until she returned before I dropped my bombshell. 'Well, as a matter of fact, Mrs Allen,' I said airily, 'I've decided to accept your advice. I'm getting married tomorrow.'

The good woman, mounding mashed potatoes on to my plate, stopped with her spoon in mid-air. 'Married tomorrow?' Her face was a study in blank astonishment.

'That's right. I thought you'd be pleased.'

'But . . . but . . . you're coming back here to read the test on Thursday and Friday.'

'Well of course. I have to finish the test, haven't I? I'll be bringing my wife with me – I'm looking forward to introducing her to you.'

There was a silence. The young men stared at me, Mr Allen stopped sawing at the ham and regarded me stolidly, then his wife gave an uncertain laugh.

'Oh come on, I don't believe it. You're kidding us. You'd be off on your honeymoon if you were getting married tomorrow.'

'Mrs Allen,' I said with dignity. 'I wouldn't joke about a serious matter like that. Let me repeat – tomorrow is my wedding day and I'll be bringing my wife along on Thursday to see you.'

Completely deflated, she heaped our plates and we all fell to in silence. But I knew she was in agony; she kept darting little glances at me and it was obvious she was dying to ask me more. The boys too, seemed intrigued; only Mr Allen, a tall, quiet man who, I'm sure wouldn't have cared if I'd been going to rob a bank tomorrow, ploughed calmly through his food.

Nothing more was said until I was about to leave, then Mrs Allen put a hand on my arm.

'You really don't mean it, do you?' Her face was haggard with strain.

I got into the car and called out through the window. 'Goodbye and thank you, Mrs Allen. Mrs Herriot and I will be along first thing on Thursday.'

I can't remember much about the wedding. It was a 'quiet do' and my main recollection is of desiring to get it all over with as soon as possible. I have only one vivid memory; of Siegfried, just behind me in the church booming 'Amen' at regular intervals throughout the ceremony – the only time I have ever heard a best man do this.

It was an incredible relief when Helen and I were ready to drive away and when we were passing Skeldale House Helen grasped my hand.

'Look!' she cried excitedly. 'Look over there!'

Underneath Siegfried's brass plate which always hung slightly askew on the iron railings was a brand new one. It was of the modern bakelite type with a black background and bold white letters which read 'J. Herriot MRCVS Veterinary Surgeon', and it was screwed very straight and level on the metal.

Siegfried had said something about 'You'll see my wedding present on the way out.' And here it was. Not many people got a partnership as a gift, but it had happened to me and was the crowning point of three years of magnanimity.

I looked back down the street to try to see Siegfried but we had said our goodbyes and I would have to thank him later. So I drove out of Darrowby with a feeling of swelling pride because I knew what the plate meant – I was a man with a real place in the world. The thought made me slightly breathless. In fact we were both a little dizzy and we cruised for hours around the countryside, getting out when we felt like it, walking among the hills, taking no account of time. It must have been nine o'clock in the evening and darkness coming in fast when we realised we had gone far out of our way.

We had to drive ten miles over a desolate moor on the fell top and it was very dark when we rattled down the steep, narrow road into Ellerthorpe. The Wheat Sheaf was an unostentatious part of the single long village street, a low grey stone building with no light over the door, and as we went into the slightly musty-smelling hallway the gentle clink of glasses came from the public bar on our left. Mrs Burn, the elderly widow who owned the place, appeared from a back room and scrutinised us unemotionally.

'We've met before, Mrs Burn,' I said and she nodded. I apologised for our lateness and was wondering whether I dare ask for a few sandwiches at this time of night when the old lady spoke up, quite unperturbed.

'Nay,' she said, 'it's right. We've been expecting you and your supper's waiting.' She led us to the dining room where her niece, Beryl, served a hot meal in no time. Thick lentil soup, followed by what would probably be called a goulash these days but which was in fact simply a delicious stew with mushrooms and vegetables obviously concocted by a culinary genius. We had to say no to the gooseberry pie and cream.

It was like that all the time at the Wheat Sheaf. The whole place was aggressively unfashionable; needing a lick of paint, crammed with hideous Victorian furniture, but it was easy to see how it had won its reputation. It didn't have stylish guests, but fat, comfortable men from the industrial West Riding brought their wives at the week-ends and did a bit of fishing or just took in the incomparable air between the mealtimes which were the big moments of the day. There was only one guest while we were there and he was a permanent one – a retired draper from Darlington who was always at the table in good time, a huge white napkin tucked under his chin, his eyes gleaming as he watched Beryl bring in the food.

But it wasn't just the home-fed ham, the Wensleydale cheese, the succulent steak and kidney pies, the bilberry tarts and mountainous Yorkshire puddings which captivated Helen and me. There was a peace, a sleepy insinuating charm about the old pub which we always recall with happiness. I still often pass the Wheat Sheaf, and as I look at its ancient stone frontage, quite unaltered by the passage of a mere thirty years, the memories are still fresh and warm; our footsteps echoing in the empty street when we took our last walk at night, the old brass bedstead almost filling the little room, the dark rim of the fells bulking against the night sky beyond our window, faint bursts of laughter from the farmers in the bar downstairs.

I particularly enjoyed too, our very first morning when I took Helen to do the test at Allen's. As I got out of the car I could see Mrs Allen peeping round the curtains in the kitchen window. She was soon out in the yard and her eyes popped when I brought my bride over to her. Helen was one of the pioneers of slacks in the Dales and she was wearing a bright purple pair this morning which would in modern parlance knock your eye out. The farmer's wife was partly shocked, partly fascinated but she soon found that Helen was of the same stock as herself and within seconds the two women were chattering busily. I judged from Mrs Allen's vigorous head-nodding and her ever widening smile that Helen was putting her out of her pain by explaining all the circumstances. It took a long time and finally Mr Allen had to break into the conversation.

'If we're goin', we'll have to go,' he said gruffly and we set off to start the second day of the test.

We began on a sunny hillside where a group of young animals had been penned. Jack and Robbie plunged in among the beasts while Mr Allen took off his cap and courteously dusted the top of the wall.

'Your missus can sit 'ere,' he said.

I paused as I was about to start measuring. My missus! It was the first time anybody had said that to me. I looked over at Helen as she sat cross-legged on the rough stones, her notebook on her knee, pencil at the ready, and as she pushed back the shining dark hair from her forehead she caught my eye and smiled; and as I smiled back at her I became aware suddenly of the vast, swelling glory of the Dales around us, and of the Dales scent of clover and warm grass, more intoxicating than any wine. And it seemed that my first three years at Darrowby had been leading up to this moment; that the first big step of my life was being completed right here with Helen smiling at me and the memory, fresh in my mind, of my new plate hanging in front of Skeldale House.

I might have stood there indefinitely, in a sort of trance, but Mr Allen cleared his throat in a marked manner and I turned back to the job in hand.

'Right,' I said, placing my calipers against the beast's neck. 'Number thirty-eight, seven millimetres and circumscribed,' I called out to Helen. 'Number thirty-eight, seven, C.'

'Thirty-eight, seven, C,' my wife repeated as she bent over her book and started to write.

Vet in Harness

Vet in Harness

With love To
MY MOTHER
In dear old Glasgow town

Chapter One

As I crawled into bed and put my arm around Helen it occurred to me, not for the first time, that there are few pleasures in this world to compare with snuggling up to a nice woman when you are half frozen.

There weren't any electric blankets in the thirties. Which was a pity because nobody needed the things more than country vets. It is surprising how deeply bone-marrow cold a man can get when he is dragged from his bed in the small hours and made to strip off in farm buildings when his metabolism is at a low ebb. Often the worst part was coming back to bed; I often lay exhausted for over an hour, longing for sleep but kept awake until my icy limbs and feet had thawed out.

But since my marriage such things were but a dark memory. Helen stirred in her sleep – she had got used to her husband leaving her in the night and returning like a blast from the North Pole – and instinctively moved nearer to me. With a sigh of thankfulness I felt the blissful warmth envelop me and almost immediately the events of the last two hours began to recede into unreality.

It had started with the aggressive shrilling of the bedside phone at one a.m. And it was Sunday morning, a not unusual time for some farmers after a late Saturday night to have a look round their stock and decide to send for the vet.

This time it was Harold Ingledew. And it struck me right away that he would have just about had time to get back to his farm after his ten pints at the Four Horse Shoes where they weren't too fussy about closing time.

And there was a significant slurr in the thin croak of his voice.

'I 'ave a ewe amiss. Will you come?'

'Is she very bad?' In my semi-conscious state I always clung to the faint hope that one night somebody would say it would wait till morning. It had never happened yet and it didn't happen now: Mr Ingledew was not to be denied.

'Aye, she's in a bad way. She'll have to have summat done for 'er soon.'

Not a minute to lose, I thought bitterly. But she had probably been in a bad way all the evening when Harold was out carousing.

Still, there were compensations. A sick sheep didn't present any great threat. It was worst when you had to get out of bed facing the prospect of a spell of sheer hard labour in your enfeebled state. But in this case I was confident that I would be able to adopt my half-awake technique; which meant simply that I would be able to go out there and deal with the emergency and return between the sheets while still enjoying many of the benefits of sleep.

There was so much night work in country practice that I had been compelled to perfect this system as, I suspect, had many of my fellow practitioners. I had done some sterling work while in a somnambulistic limbo.

So, eyes closed, I tiptoed across the carpet and pulled on my working clothes. I effortlessly accomplished the journey down the long flights of stairs but when I opened the side door the system began to crumble, because even in the shelter of the high-walled garden the wind struck at me with savage force. It was difficult to stay asleep. In the yard as I backed out of the garage the high branches of the elms groaned in the darkness as they bent before the blast.

Driving from the town I managed to slip back into my trance and my mind played lazily with the phenomenon of Harold Ingledew. This drinking of his was so out of character. He was a tiny mouse of a man about seventy years old and when he came into the surgery on an occasional market day it was difficult to extract more than a few muttered words from him. Dressed in his best suit, his scrawny neck protruding from a shirt collar several sizes too big for him, he was the very picture of a meek and solid citizen; the watery blue eyes and fleshless cheeks added to the effect and only the brilliant red colouration of the tip of his nose gave any hint of other possibilities.

His fellow smallholders in Therby village were all steady characters and did not indulge beyond a social glass of beer now and then, and his next door neighbour had been somewhat bitter when he spoke to me a few weeks ago.

'He's nowt but a bloody nuisance is awd Harold.'

'How do you mean?'

'Well, every Saturday night and every market night he's up roarin' and singin' till four o'clock in the mornin'.'

'Harold Ingledew? Surely not! He's such a quiet little chap.'

'Aye, he is for the rest of t'week.'

'But I can't imagine him singing!'

'You should live next door to 'im, Mr Herriot. He makes a 'ell of a racket. There's no sleep for anybody till he settles down.'

Since then I had heard from another source that this was perfectly true and that Mrs Ingledew tolerated it because her husband was entirely submissive at all other times.

The road to Therby had a few sharp little switchbacks before it dipped to the village and looking down I could see the long row of silent houses curving away to the base of the fell which by day hung in peaceful green majesty over the huddle of roofs but now bulked black and menacing under the moon.

As I stepped from the car and hurried round to the back of the house the wind caught at me again, jerking me to wakefulness as though somebody had thrown a bucket of water over me. But for a moment I forgot the cold in the feeling of shock as the noise struck me. Singing . . . loud raucous singing echoing around the old stones of the yard.

It was coming from the lighted kitchen window.

'JUST A SONG AT TWILIGHT, WHEN THE LIGHTS ARE LOW!'

I looked inside and saw little Harold sitting with his stockinged feet extended towards the dying embers of the fire while one hand clutched a bottle of brown ale.

'AND THE FLICKERING SHADOWS SOFTLY COME AND GO!' He was really letting it rip, head back, mouth wide.

I thumped on the kitchen door.

'THOUGH THE HEART BE WEARY, SAD THE DAY AND LONG!' replied Harold's reedy tenor and I banged impatiently at the woodwork again.

The noise ceased and I waited an unbelievably long time till I heard the key turning and the bolt rattling back. The little man pushed his nose out and gave me a questioning look.

'I've come to see your sheep,' I said.

'Oh aye.' He nodded curtly with none of his usual diffidence. 'Ah'll put me boots on.' He banged the door in my face and I heard the bolt shooting home.

Taken aback as I was I realised that he wasn't being deliberately rude. Bolting the door was proof that he was doing everything mechanically. But for all that he had left me standing in an uncharitable spot. Vets will tell you that there are corners in farmyards which are colder than any hill top and I was in one now. Just beyond the kitchen door was a stone archway leading to the open fields and through this black opening there whistled a Siberian draught which cut effortlessly through my clothes.

I had begun to hop from one foot to the other when the singing started again. 'THERE'S AN OLD MILL BY THE STREAM, NELLIE DEAN!'

Horrified, I rushed back to the window. Harold was back in his chair, pulling on a vast boot and taking his time about it. As he bellowed he poked owlishly at the lace holes and occasionally refreshed himself from the bottle of brown ale.

I tapped on the window. 'Please hurry, Mr Ingledew.'

'WHERE WE USED TO SIT AND DREAM, NELLIE DEAN!' bawled Harold in response.

My teeth had begun to chatter before he got both boots on but at last he reappeared in the doorway.

'Come on then,' I gasped. 'Where is this ewe? Have you got her in one of these boxes?'

The old man raised his eyebrows. 'Oh, she's not 'ere.'

'Not here?'

'Nay, she's up at t'top buildings.'

'Right back up the road, you mean?'

'Aye, ah stopped off on t'way home and had a look at 'er.'

I stamped and rubbed my hands. 'Well, we'll have to drive back up. But there's no water, is there? You'd better bring a bucket of warm water, some soap and a towel.'

'Very good.' He nodded solemnly and before I knew what was happening the door was slammed shut and bolted and I was alone again in the darkness. I trotted immediately to the window and was not surprised to see Harold seated comfortably again. He leaned forward and lifted the kettle from the hearth and for a dreadful moment I thought he was going to start heating the water on the ashes of the fire. But with a gush of relief I saw him take hold of a ladle and reach into the primitive boiler in the old black grate.

'AND THE WATERS AS THEY FLOW SEEM TO MURMUR SWEET AND LOW!' he warbled, happy at his work, as he unhurriedly filled a bucket.

I think he had forgotten I was there when he finally came out because he looked at me blankly as he sang.

'YOU'RE MY HEART'S DESIRE, I LOVE YOU, NELLIE DEAN!' he informed me at the top of his voice.

'All right, all right,' I grunted. 'Let's go.' I hurried him into the car and we set off on the way I had come.

Harold held the bucket at an angle on his lap, and as we went over the switchbacks the water slopped gently on to my knee. The atmosphere in the car soon became so highly charged with beer fumes that I began to feel lightheaded.

'In 'ere!' the old man barked suddenly as a gate appeared in the headlights. I pulled on to the grass verge and stood on one leg for a few moments till I had shaken a surplus pint or two of water from my trousers. We went through the gate and I began to hurry towards the dark bulk of the hillside barn, but I noticed that Harold wasn't following me. He was walking aimlessly around the field.

'What are you doing, Mr Ingledew?'

'Lookin' for t'ewe.'

'You mean she's outside?' I repressed an impulse to scream.

'Aye, she lambed this afternoon and ah thowt she'd be right enough out 'ere.' He produced a torch, a typical farmer's torch – tiny and with a moribund battery – and projected a fitful beam into the darkness. It made not the slightest difference.

As I stumbled across the field a sense of hopelessness assailed me. Above, the ragged clouds scurried across the face of the moon but down here I could see

nothing. And it was so cold. The recent frosts had turned the ground to iron and
the crisp grass cowered under the piercing wind. I had just decided that there
was no way of finding an animal in this black waste land when Harold piped
up.

'She's over 'ere.'

And sure enough when I groped my way towards the sound of his voice he
was standing by an unhappy looking ewe. I don't know what instinct had
brought him to her but there she was. And she was obviously in trouble; her
head hung down miserably and when I put my hand on her fleece she took only
a few faltering steps instead of galloping off as a healthy sheep would. Beside
her, a tiny lamb huddled close to her flank.

I lifted her tail and took her temperature. It was normal. There were no signs
of the usual post-lambing ailments; no staggering to indicate a deficiency, no
discharge or accelerated respirations. But there was something very far wrong.

I looked again at the lamb. He was an unusually early arrival in this high
country and it seemed unfair to bring the little creature into the inhospitable
world of a Yorkshire March. And he was so small ... yes ... yes ... it was
beginning to filter through to me. He was too damn small for a single lamb.

'Bring me that bucket, Mr Ingledew!' I cried. I could hardly wait to see if I
was right. But as I balanced the receptacle on the grass the full horror of the
situation smote me. I was going to have to strip off.

They don't give vets medals for bravery but as I pulled off my overcoat and
jacket and stood shivering in my shirt sleeves on that black hillside I felt I
deserved one.

'Hold her head,' I gasped and soaped my arm quickly. By the light of the
torch I felt my way into the vagina and I didn't have to go very far before I
found what I had expected; a woolly little skull. It was bent downwards with
the nose under the pelvis and the legs were back.

'There's another lamb in here,' I said. 'It's laid wrong or it would have been
born with its mate this afternoon.'

Even as I spoke my fingers had righted the presentation and I drew the little
creature gently out and deposited him on the grass. I hadn't expected him to be
alive after his delayed entry but as he made contact with the cold ground his
limbs gave a convulsive twitch and almost immediately I felt his ribs heaving
under my hand.

For a moment I forgot the knife-like wind in the thrill which I always found
in new life, the thrill that was always fresh, always warm. The ewe, too, seemed
stimulated because in the darkness I felt her nose pushing interestedly at the
new arrival.

But my pleasant ruminations were cut short by a scuffling from behind me
and some muffled words.

'Bugger it!' mumbled Harold.

'What's the matter?'

'Ah've kicked bucket ower.'

'Oh no! Is the water all gone?'

'Aye, nowt left.'

Well this was great. My arm was smeared with mucus after being inside the
ewe. I couldn't possibly put my jacket on without a wash.

Harold's voice issued again from the darkness. 'There's some watter ower at
building.'

'Oh good. We've got to get this ewe and lambs over there anyway.' I threw
my clothes over my shoulder, tucked a lamb under each arm and began to
blunder over the tussocks of grass to where I thought the barn lay. The ewe,
clearly feeling better without her uncomfortable burden, trotted behind me.

It was Harold again who had to give me directions.

'Ower 'ere!' he shouted.

When I reached the barn I cowered thankfully behind the massive stones. It was no night for a stroll in shirt sleeves. Shaking uncontrollably I peered at the old man. I could just see his form in the last faint radiance of the torch and I wasn't quite sure what he was doing. He had lifted a stone from the pasture and was bashing something with it; then I realised he was bending over the water trough, breaking the ice.

When he had finished he plunged the bucket into the trough and handed it to me.

'There's your watter,' he said triumphantly.

I thought I had reached the ultimate in frigidity but when I plunged my hands into the black liquid with its floating icebergs I changed my mind. The torch had finally expired and I lost the soap very quickly. When I found I was trying to work up a lather with one of the pieces of ice I gave it up and dried my arms.

Somewhere nearby I could hear Harold humming under his breath, as comfortable as if he was by his own fireside. The vast amount of alcohol surging through his bloodstream must have made him impervious to the cold.

We pushed the ewe and lambs into the barn which was piled high with hay and before leaving I struck a match and looked down at the little sheep and her new family settled comfortably among the fragrant clover. They would be safe and warm in there till morning.

My journey back to the village was less hazardous because the bucket on Harold's knee was empty. I dropped him outside his house then I had to drive to the bottom of the village to turn; and as I came past the house again the sound forced its way into the car.

'IF YOU WERE THE ONLY GIRL IN THE WORLD AND I WERE THE ONLY BOY!'

I stopped, wound the window down and listened in wonder. It was incredible how the noise reverberated around the quiet street and if it went on till four o'clock in the morning as the neighbours said, then they had my sympathy.

'NOTHING ELSE WOULD MATTER IN THE WORLD TODAY!'

It struck me suddenly that I could soon get tired of Harold's singing. His volume was impressive but for all that he would never be in great demand at Covent Garden; he constantly wavered off key and there was a grating quality in his top notes which set my teeth on edge.

'WE WOULD GO ON LOVING IN THE SAME OLD WAY!'

Hurriedly I wound the window up and drove off. As the heaterless car picked its way between the endless flitting pattern of walls I crouched in frozen immobility behind the wheel. I had now reached the state of total numbness and I can't remember much about my return to the yard at Skeldale House, nor my automatic actions of putting away the car, swinging shut the creaking doors of what had once been the old coach house, and trailing slowly down the long garden.

But a realisation of my blessings began to return when I slid into bed and Helen, instead of shrinking away from me as it would have been natural to do, deliberately draped her feet and legs over the human ice block that was her husband. The bliss was unbelievable. It was worth getting out just to come back to this.

I glanced at the luminous dial of the alarm clock. It was three o'clock and as the warmth flowed over me and I drifted away, my mind went back to the ewe and lambs, snug in their scented barn. They would be asleep now, I would soon be asleep, everybody would be asleep.

Except, that is, Harold Ingledew's neighbours. They still had an hour to go.

Chapter Two

I had only to sit up in bed to look right across Darrowby to the hills beyond.

I got up and walked to the window. It was going to be a fine morning and the early sun glanced over the weathered reds and greys of the jumbled roofs, some of them sagging under their burden of ancient tiles, and brightened the tufts of green where trees pushed upwards from the gardens among the bristle of chimney pots. And behind everthing the calm bulk of the fells.

It was my good fortune that this was the first thing I saw every morning; after Helen, of course, which was better still.

Following our unorthodox tuberculin testing honeymoon we had set up our first home on the top of Skeldale House. Siegfried, my boss up to my wedding and now my partner, had offered us free use of these empty rooms on the third storey and we had gratefully accepted; and though it was a makeshift arrangement there was an airy charm, an exhilaration in our high perch that many would have envied.

It was makeshift because everything at that time had a temporary complexion and we had no idea how long we would be there. Siegfried and I had both volunteered for the RAF and were on deferred service but that is all I am going to say about the war. This book is not about such things which in any case were so very far from Darrowby; it is the story of the months I had with Helen between our marriage and my call-up and is about the ordinary things which have always made up our lives; my work, the animals, the Dales.

This front room was our bed-sitter and though it was not luxuriously furnished it did have an excellent bed, a carpet, a handsome side table which had belonged to Helen's mother and two armchairs. It had an ancient wardrobe, too, but the lock didn't work and the only way we kept the door closed was by jamming one of my socks in it. The toe always dangled outside but it never seemed of any importance.

I went out and across a few feet of landing to our kitchen-dining room at the back. This apartment was definitely spartan. I clumped over bare boards to a bench we had rigged against the wall by the window. This held a gas ring and our crockery and cutlery. I seized a tall jug and began my long descent to the main kitchen downstairs because one minor snag was that there was no water at the top of the house. Down two flights to the three rooms on the first storey then down two more and a final gallop along the passage to the big stone-flagged kitchen at the end.

I filled the jug and returned to our eyrie two steps at a time. I wouldn't like to do this now whenever I needed water but at that time I didn't find it the least inconvenience.

Helen soon had the kettle boiling and we drank our first cup of tea by the window looking down on the long garden. From up here we had an aerial view of the unkempt lawns, the fruit trees, the wistaria climbing the weathered brick towards our window, and the high walls with their old stone copings stretching away to the cobbled yard under the elms. Every day I went up and down that path to the garage in the yard but it looked so different from above.

'Wait a minute, Helen,' I said. 'Let me sit on that chair.'

She had laid the breakfast on the bench where we ate and this was where the difficulty arose. Because it was a tall bench and our recently acquired high stool fitted it but our chair didn't.

'No, I'm all right, Jim, really I am.' She smiled at me reassuringly from her absurd position, almost at eye level with her plate.

'You can't be all right,' I retorted. 'Your chin's nearly in among your cornflakes. Please let me sit there.'

She patted the seat of the stool. 'Come on, stop arguing. Sit down and have your breakfast.'

This, I felt, just wouldn't do. I tried a different tack.

'Helen!' I said severely. 'Get off that chair!'

'No!' she replied without looking at me, her lips pushed forward in a characteristic pout which I always found enchanting but which also meant she wasn't kidding.

I was at a loss. I toyed with the idea of pulling her off the chair, but she was a big girl. We had had a previous physical try-out when a minor disagreement had escalated into a wrestling match and though I thoroughly enjoyed the contest and actually won in the end I had been surprised by her sheer strength. At this time in the morning I didn't feel up to it. I sat on the stool.

After breakfast Helen began to boil water for the washing-up, the next stage in our routine. Meanwhile I went downstairs, collected my gear, including suture material for a foal which had cut its leg and went out the side door into the garden. Just about opposite the rockery I turned and looked up at our window. It was open at the bottom and an arm emerged holding a dishcloth. I waved and the dishcloth waved back furiously. It was the start to every day.

And, driving from the yard, it seemed a good start. In fact everything was good. The raucous cawing of the rooks in the elms above as I closed the double doors, the clean fragrance of the air which greeted me every morning, and the challenge and interest of my job.

The injured foal was at Robert Corner's farm and I hadn't been there long before I spotted Jock, his sheepdog. And I began to watch the dog because behind a vet's daily chore of treating his patients there is always the fascinating kaleidoscope of animal personality and Jock was an interesting case.

A lot of farm dogs are partial to a little light relief from their work. They like to play and one of their favourite games is chasing cars off the premises. Often I drove off with a hairy form galloping alongside and the dog would usually give a final defiant bark after a few hundred yards to speed me on my way. But Jock was different.

He was really dedicated. Car chasing to him was a deadly serious art which he practised daily without a trace of levity. Corner's farm was at the end of a long track, twisting for nearly a mile between its stone walls down through the gently sloping fields to the road below and Jock didn't consider he had done his job properly until he had escorted his chosen vehicle right to the very foot. So his hobby was an exacting one.

I watched him now as I finished stitching the foal's leg and began to tie on a bandage. He was slinking about the buildings, a skinny little creature who, without his mass of black and white hair would have been an almost invisible mite, and he was playing out a transparent charade of pretending he was taking no notice of me – wasn't the least bit interested in my presence, in fact. But his furtive glances in the direction of the stable, his repeated criss-crossing of my line of vision gave him away. He was waiting for his big moment.

When I was putting on my shoes and throwing my Wellingtons into the boot I saw him again. Or rather part of him; just a long nose and one eye protruding from beneath a broken door. It wasn't till I had started the engine and begun to move off that he finally declared himself, stealing out from his hiding place, body low, tail trailing, eyes fixed intently on the car's front wheels, and as I gathered speed and headed down the track he broke into an effortless lope.

I had been through this before and was always afraid he might run in front of me so I put my foot down and began to hurtle downhill. This was where Jock came into his own. I often wondered how he'd fare against a racing greyhound because by golly he could run. That sparse frame housed a perfect physical machine and the slender limbs reached and flew again and again, devouring the stony ground beneath, keeping up with the speeding car with joyful ease.

There was a sharp bend about half way down and here Jock invariably sailed over the wall and streaked across the turf, a little dark blur against the green, and having craftily cut off the corner he reappeared like a missile zooming over the grey stones lower down. This put him into a nice position for the run to the road and when he finally saw me on to the tarmac my last view of him was of a happy panting face looking after me. Clearly he considered it was a job well done and he would wander contentedly back up to the farm to await the next session, perhaps with the postman or the baker's van.

And there was another side to Jock. He was an outstanding performer at the sheepdog trials and Mr Corner had won many trophies with him. In fact the farmer could have sold the little animal for a lot of money but couldn't be persuaded to part with him. Instead he purchased a bitch, a scrawny little female counterpart of Jock and a trial winner in her own right. With this combination Mr Corner thought he could breed some world-beating types for sale. On my visits to the farm the bitch joined in the car-chasing but it seemed as though she was doing it more or less to humour her new mate and she always gave up at the first bend leaving Jock in command. You could see her heart wasn't in it.

When the pups arrived, seven fluffy black balls tumbling about the yard and getting under everybody's feet. Jock watched indulgently as they tried to follow him in his pursuit of my vehicle and you could almost see him laughing as they fell over their feet and were left trailing far behind.

It happened that I didn't have to go there for about ten months but I saw Robert Corner in the market occasionally and he told me he was training the pups and they were shaping well. Not that they needed much training; it was in their blood and he said they had tried to round up the cattle and sheep nearly as soon as they could walk. When I finally saw them they were like seven Jocks – meagre, darting little creatures flitting noiselessly about the buildings – and it didn't take me long to find out that they had learned more than sheep herding from their father. There was something very evocative about the way they began to prowl around in the background as I prepared to get into my car, peeping furtively from behind straw bales, slinking with elaborate nonchalance into favourable positions for a quick getaway. And as I settled in my seat I could sense they were all crouched in readiness for the off.

I revved my engine, let in the clutch with a bump and shot across the yard and in a second the immediate vicinity erupted in a mass of hairy forms. I roared on to the track and put my foot down and on either side of me the little animals pelted along shoulder to shoulder, their faces all wearing the intent fanatical expression I knew so well. When Jock cleared the wall the seven pups went with him and when they reappeared and entered the home straight I noticed something different. On past occasions Jock had always had one eye on the car – this was what he considered his opponent; but now on that last quarter mile as he hurtled along at the head of a shaggy phalanx he was glancing at the pups on either side as though they were the main opposition.

And there was no doubt he was in trouble. Superbly fit though he was, these stringy bundles of bone and sinew which he had fathered had all his speed plus the newly minted energy of youth and it was taking every shred of his power to keep up with them. Indeed there was one terrible moment when he stumbled and was engulfed by the bounding creatures around him; it seemed that all was lost but there was a core of steel in Jock. Eyes popping, nostrils dilated, he fought his way through the pack until by the time we reached the road he was once more in the lead.

But it had taken its toll. I slowed down before driving away and looked down at the little animal standing with lolling tongue and heaving flanks on the grass verge. It must have been like this with all the other vehicles and it wasn't a merry game any more. I suppose it sounds silly to say you could read a dog's thoughts but everything in his posture betrayed the mounting apprehension that his days of supremacy were numbered. Just round the corner lay the unthinkable ignominy of being left trailing in the rear of that litter of young up-starts and as I drew away Jock looked after me and his expression was eloquent.

'How long can I keep this up?'

I felt for the little dog and on my next visit to the farm about two months later I wasn't looking forward to witnessing the final degradation which I felt was inevitable. But when I drove into the yard I found the place strangely unpopulated.

Robert Corner was forking hay into the cow's racks in the byre. He turned as I came in.

'Where are all your dogs?' I asked.

He put down his fork. 'All gone. By gaw, there's a market for good workin' sheepdogs. I've done right well out of t'job.'

'But you've still got Jock?'

'Oh aye, ah couldn't part with t'awd lad. He's over there.'

And so he was, creeping around as of old, pretending he wasn't watching me. And when the happy time finally arrived and I drove away it was like it used to be with the lean little animal haring along by the side of the car, but relaxed, enjoying the game, winging effortlessly over the wall and beating the car down to the tarmac with no trouble at all.

I think I was as relieved as he was that he was left alone with his supremacy unchallenged; that he was still top dog.

Chapter Three

You could hardly expect to find a more unlikely character in Darrowby than Roland Partridge. The thought came to me for the hundredth time as I saw him peering through the window which looked on to Trengate just a little way up the other side of the street from our surgery.

He was tapping the glass and beckoning to me and the eyes behind the thick spectacles were wide with concern. I waited and when he opened the door I stepped straight from the street into his living room because these were tiny dwellings with only a kitchen in the rear and a single small bedroom overlooking the street above. But when I went in I had the familiar feeling of surprise.

Because most of the other occupants of the row were farmworkers and their furnishings were orthodox; but this place was a studio.

An easel stood in the light from the window and the walls were covered from floor to ceiling with paintings. Unframed canvases were stacked everywhere and the few ornate chairs and the table with its load of painted china and other bric-à-brac added to the artistic atmosphere.

The simple explanation was, of course, that Mr Partridge was in fact an artist. But the unlikely aspect came into it when you learned that this middle-aged velvet-jacketed aesthete was the son of a small farmer, a man whose forebears had been steeped in the soil for generations.

'I happened to see you passing there, Mr Herriot,' he said. 'Are you terribly busy?'

'Not too busy, Mr Partridge. Can I help you?'

He nodded gravely. 'I wonder whether you could spare a moment to look at Percy. I'd be most grateful.'

'Of course,' I replied. 'Where is he?'

He was ushering me towards the kitchen when there was a bang on the outer door and Bert Hardisty the postman burst in. Bert was a rough-hewn character and he dumped a parcel unceremoniously on the table.

'There y'are, Rolie!' he shouted and turned to go.

Mr Partridge gazed with unruffled dignity at the retreating back. 'Thank you very much indeed, Bertram, good day to you.'

Here was another thing. The postman and the artist were both Darrowby born and bred, had the same social background, had gone to the same school, yet their voices were quite different. Roland Partridge, in fact, spoke with the precise, well-modulated syllables of a barrister-at-law.

We went into the kitchen. This was where he cooked for himself in his bachelor state. When his father died many years ago he had sold the farm immediately. Apparently his whole nature was appalled by the earthy farming scene and he could not get out quickly enough. At any rate he had got sufficient money from the sale to indulge his interests and he had taken up painting and lived ever since in this humble cottage, resolutely doing his own thing. This had all happened long before I came to Darrowby and the dangling lank hair was silver now. I always had the feeling that he was happy in his way because I couldn't imagine that small, rather exquisite figure plodding round a muddy farmyard.

It was probably in keeping with his nature that he had never married. There was a touch of asceticism in the thin cheeks and pale blue eyes and it was possible that his self-contained imperturbable personality might denote a lack of warmth. But that didn't hold good with regard to his dog, Percy.

He loved Percy with a fierce protective passion and as the little animal trotted towards him he bent over him, his face alight with tenderness.

'He looks pretty bright to me,' I said. 'He's not sick, is he?'

'No . . . no . . .' Mr Partridge seemed strangely ill at ease. 'He's perfectly well in himself, but I want you to look at him and see if you notice anything.'

I looked. And I saw only what I had always seen, the snow-white, shaggy-haired little object regarded by local dog breeders and other *cognoscenti* as a negligible mongrel but nevertheless one of my favourite patients. Mr Partridge, looking through the window of a pet shop in Brawton about five years ago had succumbed immediately to the charms of two soulful eyes gazing up at him from a six-week-old tangle of white hair and had put down his five bob and rushed the little creature home. Percy had been described in the shop somewhat vaguely as a 'terrier' and Mr Partridge had flirted fearfully with the idea of having his tail docked; but such was his infatuation that he couldn't bring himself to cause such a mutilation and the tail had grown in a great fringed curve almost full circle over the back.

To me, the tail nicely balanced the head which was undoubtedly a little too big for the body but Mr Partridge had been made to suffer for it. His old friends in Darrowby who, like all country folks, considered themselves experts with animals, were free with their comments. I had heard them at it. When Percy was young it was:

'Time ye had that tail off, Rolie. Ah'll bite it off for ye if ye like.' And later, again and again. 'Hey Rolie, you should've had that dog's tail off when he were a pup. He looks bloody daft like that.'

When asked Percy's breed Mr Partridge always replied haughtily, 'Sealyham Cross', but it wasn't as simple as that; the tiny body with its luxuriant bristling coat, the large, rather noble head with high, pricked ears, the short, knock-kneed legs and that tail made him a baffling mixture.

Mr Partridge's friends again were merciless, referring to Percy as a 'tripe-'ound' or a 'mouse-'ound' and though the little artist received these railleries with a thin smile I knew they bit deep. He had a high regard for me based simply on the fact that the first time I saw Percy I exclaimed quite spontaneously, 'What a beautiful little dog!' And since I have never had much time for the points and fads of dog breeding I really meant it.

'Just what is wrong, Mr Partridge?' I asked. 'I can't see anything unusual.'

Again the little man appeared to be uneasy. 'Well now, watch as he walks across the floor. Come, Percy my dear.' He moved away from me and the dog followed him.

'No ... no ... I don't quite understand what you mean.'

'Watch again.' He set off once more. 'It's at his ... his er ... back end.'

I crouched down. 'Ah now, yes, wait a minute. Just hold him there, will you?'

I went over and had a close look. 'I see it now. One of his testicles is slightly enlarged.'

'Yes ... yes ... quite.' Mr Partridge's face turned a shade pinker. 'That is ... er ... what I thought.'

'Hang on to him a second while I examine it.' I lifted the scrotum and palpated gently. 'Yes, the left one is definitely bigger and it is harder too.'

'Is it ... anything serious?'

I paused. 'No, I shouldn't think so. Tumours of the testicles are not uncommon in dogs and fortunately they aren't inclined to metastasise – spread through the body – very readily. So I shouldn't worry too much.'

I added the last bit hastily because at the mention of the word 'tumour' the colour had drained from his face alarmingly.

'That's a growth, isn't it?' he stammered.

'Yes, but there are all kinds and a lot of them are not malignant. So don't worry but please keep an eye on him. It may not grow much but if it does you must let me know immediately.'

'I see ... and if it does grow?'

'Well the only thing would be to remove the testicle.'

'An operation?' The little man stared at me and for a moment I thought he would faint.

'Yes, but not a serious one. Quite straightforward, really.' I bent down and felt the enlargement again. It was very slight. From the front end, Percy kept up a continuous musical growling. I grinned. He always did that – when I took his temperature, cut his nails, anything; a nonstop grumble and it didn't mean a thing. I knew him well enough to realise there was no viciousness in him; he was merely asserting his virility, reminding me what a tough fellow he was, and it was not idle boasting because for all his lack of size he was a proud, mettlesome little dog, absolutely crammed with character.

After I had left the house I looked back and saw Mr Partridge standing there watching me. He was clasping and unclasping his hands.

And even when I was back in the surgery half of me was still in that odd little studio. I had to admire Mr Partridge for doing exactly what he wanted to do because in Darrowby he would never get any credit for it. A good horseman or cricketer would be revered in the town but an artist . . . never. Not even if he became famous, and Mr Partridge would never be famous. A few people bought his paintings but he could not have lived on the proceeds. I had one of them hanging in our bed-sitter and to my mind he had a definite gift. In fact I would have tried to afford more of them but for the fact that he obviously shrank from that aspect of the Yorkshire Dales which I loved most.

If I had been able to paint I would have wanted to show how the walls climbed everywhere over the stark fell-sides. I would have tried to capture the magic of the endless empty moors with the reeds trembling over the black bog pools. But Mr Partridge went only for the cosy things; willows hanging by a rustic bridge, village churches, rose-covered cottages.

Since Percy was a near neighbour I saw him nearly every day, either from our bed-sitter at the top of the house or from the surgery below. His master exercised him with great zeal and regularity and it was a common sight to see the artist passing on the other side of the road with the little animal trotting proudly beside him. But from that distance it was impossible to see if the tumour was progressing, and since I heard nothing from Mr Partridge I assumed that all was well. Maybe that thing had grown no more. Sometimes it happened that way.

Keeping a close watch on the little dog reminded me of other incidents connected with him, particularly the number of times he was involved in a fight. Not that Percy ever started a brawl – at ten inches high he wasn't stupid enough for that – but somehow big dogs when they saw that dainty white figure prancing along were inclined to go for him on sight. I witnessed some of these attacks from our windows and the same thing happened every time; a quick flurry of limbs, a snarling and yelping and then the big dog retreated bleeding.

Percy never had a mark on him – that tremendous thick coat gave him complete protection – but he always got a nip in from underneath. I had stitched up several of the local street fighters after Percy had finished with them.

It must have been about six weeks later when Mr Partridge came in again. He looked tense.

'I'd like you to have a look at Percy again, Mr Herriot.'

I lifted the dog on to the surgery table and I didn't need to examine him very closely.

'It's quite a lot bigger, I'm afraid.' I looked across the table at the little man.

'Yes, I know.' He hesitated. 'What do you suggest?'

'Oh there's no doubt at all he'll have to come in for an operation. That thing must come off.'

Horror and despair flickered behind the thick spectacles.

'An operation!' He leaned on the table with both hands.

'I hate the idea, I just can't bear the thought of it!'

I smiled reassuringly. 'I know how you feel, but honestly there's nothing to worry about. As I told you before, it's quite a simple procedure.'

'Oh I know, I know,' he moaned. 'But I don't want him to be . . . cut about, you understand . . . it's just the idea of it.'

And I couldn't persuade him. He remained adamant and marched resolutely from the surgery with his pet. I watched him crossing the road to his house and I knew he had let himself in for a load of worry, but I didn't realise just how bad it was going to be.

It was to be a kind of martyrdom.

Chapter Four

I do not think martyrdom is too strong a word for what Mr Partridge went through over the next few weeks, because with the passage of time that testicle became more and more massive and due to the way Percy carried his tail the thing was lamentably conspicuous.

People used to turn and stare as man and dog made their way down the street, Percy trotting bravely, his master, eyes rigidly to the front, putting up a magnificent pretence of being quite unaware of anything unusual. It really hurt me to see them and I found the sight of the smart little dog's disfigurement particularly hard to bear.

Mr Partridge's superior facade had always made him a natural target for a certain amount of legpulling which he bore stoically; but the fact that it now involved his pet pierced him to the soul.

One afternoon he brought him over to the surgery and I could see that the little man was almost in tears. Gloomily I examined the offending organ which was now about six inches long; gross, pendulous, undeniably ludicrous.

'You know, Mr Herriot,' the artist gasped. 'Some boys chalked on my window, "Roll up and see the famous Chinese dog, Wun Hung Lo." I've just been wiping it off.'

I rubbed my chin. 'Well that's an ancient joke, Mr Partridge. I shouldn't worry about that.'

'But I do worry! I can't sleep because of the thing!'

'For heaven's sake, then, why don't you let me operate? I could put the whole business right for you.'

'No! No! I can't do that!' His head rolled on his shoulders; he was the very picture of misery as he stared at me. 'I'm frightened, that's what it is. I'm frightened he'll die under the anaesthetic.'

'Oh come now! He's a strong little animal. There's no reason at all for such fears.'

'But there is a risk isn't there?'

I looked at him helplessly. 'Well there's a slight risk in all operations if you come right down to it, but honestly in this case . . .'

'No! That's enough. I won't hear of it,' he burst out and seizing Percy's lead he strode away.

Things went from bad to worse after that. The tumour grew steadily, easily visible now from my vantage point in the surgery window as the dog went by on the other side of the street, and I could see too that the stares and occasional ridicule were beginning to tell on Mr Partridge. His cheeks had hollowed and he had lost some of his high colour.

But I didn't have words with him till one market day several weeks later. It was early afternoon – the time the farmers often came in to pay their bills. I was showing one of them out when I saw Percy and his master coming out of the house. And I noticed immediately that the little animal now had to swing one hind leg slightly to clear the massive obstruction.

On an impulse I called out and beckoned to Mr Partridge.

'Look,' I said as he came across to me. 'You've just got to let me take that thing off. It's interfering with his walking – making him lame. He can't go on like this.'

The artist didn't say anything but stared back at me with hunted eyes. We were standing there in silence when Bill Dalton came round the corner and marched up to the surgery steps, cheque book in hand. Bill was a large beefy farmer who spent most of market day in the bar of the Black Swan and he was preceded by an almost palpable wave of beer fumes.

'Nah then, Rolie lad, how ista?' he roared, slapping the little man violently on the back.

'I am quite well, William, thank you, and how are you?'

But Bill didn't answer. His attention was all on Percy who had strolled a few paces along the pavement. He watched him intently for a few moments, then, repressing a giggle, he turned to Mr Partridge with a mock-serious expression.

'Tha knows, Rolie,' he said, 'that blood 'ound of your reminds me of the young man of Devizes, whose balls were of different sizes. The one was so small it was no ball at all, but the other one won several prizes.' He finished with a shout of laughter which went on and on till he collapsed weakly against the iron railings.

For a moment I thought Mr Partridge was going to strike him. He glared up at the big man and his chin and mouth trembled with rage, then he seemed to gain control of himself and turned to me.

'Can I have a word with you, Mr Herriot?'

'Certainly.' I walked a few yards with him down the street.

'You're right,' he said. 'Percy will have to have that operation. When can you do him?'

'Tomorrow,' I replied. 'Don't give him any more food and bring him in at two in the afternoon.'

It was with a feeling of intense relief that I saw the little dog stretched on the table the next day. With Tristan as anaesthetist I quickly removed the huge testicle, going well up the spermatic cord to ensure the complete excision of all tumour tissue. The only thing which troubled me was that the scrotum itself had become involved due to the long delay in operating. This is the sort of thing that can lead to a recurrence and as I carefully cut away the affected parts of the scrotal wall I cursed Mr Partridge's procrastination. I put in the last stitch with my fingers crossed.

The little man was in such transports of joy at seeing his pet alive after my efforts and rid of that horrid excrescence that I didn't want to spoil everything by voicing my doubts; but I wasn't entirely happy. If the tumour did recur I wasn't sure just what I could do about it.

But in the meantime I enjoyed my own share of pleasure at my patient's return to normality. I felt a warm rush of satisfaction whenever I saw him tripping along, perky as ever and free from the disfigurement which had bulked so large in his master's life. Occasionally I used to stroll casually behind him on the way down Trengate into the market place, saying nothing to Mr Partridge but shooting some sharp glances at the region beneath Percy's tail.

In the meantime I had sent the removed organ off to the pathology department of Glasgow Veterinary College and their report told me that it was a Sertoli Cell Tumour. They also added the comforting information that this type was usually benign and that metastasis into the internal organs occurred in only a very small proportion of cases. Maybe this lulled me into a deeper security than was warranted because I stopped following Percy around and in fact, in the nonstop rush of new cases, forgot all about his spell of trouble.

So that when Mr Partridge brought him round to the surgery I thought it was for something else and when his master lifted him on to the table and turned him round to show his rear end I stared uncomprehendingly for a moment. But I leaned forward anxiously when I spotted the ugly swelling on the left side of the scrotum. I palpated quickly, with Percy's growls and grousings providing an irritable obligato, and there was no doubt about it, the tumour was growing again. It meant business, too, because it was red, angry-looking, painful; a dangerously active growth if ever I had seen one.

'It's come up quite quickly, has it?' I asked.

Mr Partridge nodded. 'Yes, indeed. I can almost see it getting bigger every day.'

We were in trouble. There was no hope of trying to cut this lot away; it was a great diffuse mass without clear boundaries and I wouldn't have known where to start. Anyway, if I began any more poking about it would be just what was needed to start a spread into the internal organs, and that would be the end of Percy.

'It's worse this time, isn't it?' The little man looked at me and gulped.

'Yes . . . yes . . . I'm afraid so.'

'Is there anything at all you can do about it?' he asked.

I was trying to think of a painless way of telling him that there wasn't when I remembered something I had read in the Veterinary Record a week ago. It was about a new drug, Stilboestrol, which had just come out and was supposed to be useful for hormonal therapy in animals; but the bit I was thinking about was a small print extract which said it had been useful in cancer of the prostate in men. I wondered . . .

'There's one thing I'd like to try,' I said, suddenly brisk, 'I can't guarantee anything, of course, because it's something new. But we'll see what a week or two's course does.'

'Oh good, good,' Mr Partridge breathed, snatching gratefully at the straw.

I rang May and Baker's and they sent the Stilboestrol to me immediately.

I injected Percy with 10 mg of the oily suspension and put him on to 10 mg tablets daily. They were big doses for a little dog but in a desperate situation I felt they were justified. Then I sat back and waited.

For about a week the tumour continued to grow and I nearly stopped the treatment, then there was a spell lasting several days during which I couldn't be sure; but then with a surge of relief I realised there could be no further doubt – the thing wasn't getting any bigger. I wasn't going to throw my hat in the air and I knew anything could still happen but I had done something with my treatment; I had halted that fateful progress.

The artist's step acquired a fresh spring as he passed on his daily walk and then as the ugly mass actually began to diminish he would wave towards the surgery window and point happily at the little white animal trotting by his side.

Poor Mr Partridge. He was on the crest of the wave but just ahead of him was the second and more bizarre phase of his martyrdom.

At first neither I nor anybody else realised what was going on. All we knew was there suddenly seemed to be a lot of dogs in Trengate – dogs we didn't usually see, from other parts of the town; big ones, small ones, shaggy mongrels and sleek aristocrats all hanging round apparently aimlessly, but then it was noticed that there was a focal point of attraction. It was Mr Partridge's house.

And it hit me blindingly one morning as I looked out of our bedroom window.

They were after Percy. For some reason he had taken on the attributes of a bitch in heat. I hurried downstairs and got out my pathology book. Yes, there is was. The Sertoli Cell tumour occasionally made dogs attractive to other male dogs. But why should it be happening now when the thing was reducing and not when it was at its height? Or could it be the Stilboestrol? The new drug was said to have a feminising effect, but surely not to that extent.

Anyway, whatever the cause, the undeniable fact remained that Percy was under siege, and as the word got around the pack increased, being augmented by several of the nearby farm dogs, a Great Dane who had made the journey from Houlton, and Magnus, the little dachschund from the Drovers' Arms. The queue started forming almost at first light and by ten o'clock there would be a milling throng almost blocking the street. Apart from the regulars the odd canine visitor passing through would join the company, and no matter what his breed or size he was readily accepted into the club, adding one more to the assortment of stupid expressions, lolling tongues and waving tails; because, motley crew though they were, they were all happily united in the roisterous, bawdy camaraderie of lust.

The strain on Mr Partridge must have been almost intolerable. At times I noticed the thick spectacles glinting balefully at the mob through his window but most of the time he kept himself in hand, working calmly at his easel as though he were oblivious that every one of the creatures outside had evil designs on his treasure.

Only rarely did his control snap. I witnessed one of these occasions when he rushed screaming from his doorway, laying about him with a walking stick; and I noticed that the polished veneer slipped from him and his cries rang out in broadest Yorkshire.

'Gerrout, ye bloody rotten buggers! Gerrout of it!'

He might as well have saved his energy because the pack scattered only for a few seconds before taking up their stations again.

I felt for the little man but there was nothing I could do about it. My main feeling was of relief that the tumour was going down but I had to admit to a certain morbid fascination at the train of events across the street.

Percy's walks were fraught with peril. Mr Partridge always armed himself with his stick before venturing from the house and kept Percy on a short lead, but his precautions were unavailing as the wave of dogs swept down on him. The besotted creatures, mad with passion, leapt on top of the little animal as the artist beat vainly on the shaggy backs and yelled at them; and the humiliating procession usually continued right across the market place to the great amusement of the inhabitants.

At lunch time most of the dogs took a break and at nightfall they all went home to bed, but there was one little brown spaniel type who, with the greatest dedication, never left his post. I think he must have gone almost without food for about two weeks because he dwindled practically to a skeleton and I think he might have died if Helen hadn't taken pieces of meat over to him when she saw him huddled trembling in the doorway in the cold darkness of the evening. I know he stayed there all night because every now and then a shrill yelping wakened me in the small hours and I deduced that Mr Partridge had got home on him with some missile from his bedroom window. But it made no difference; he continued his vigil undaunted.

I don't quite know how Mr Partridge would have survived if this state of affairs had continued indefinitely; I think his reason might have given way. But mercifully signs began to appear that the nightmare was on the wane. The mob began to thin as Percy's condition improved and one day even the little brown dog reluctantly left his beat and slunk away to his unknown home.

That was the very day I had Percy on the table for the last time. I felt a thrill of satisfaction as I ran a fold of the scrotal skin between my fingers.

'There's nothing there now, Mr Partridge. No thickening, even. Not a thing.'

The little man nodded. 'Yes, it's a miracle, isn't it! I'm very grateful to you for all you've done. I've been so terribly worried.'

'Oh, I can imagine. You've been through a bad time. But I'm really as pleased as you are yourself – it's one of the most satisfying things in practice when an experiment like this comes off.'

But often over the subsequent years, as I watched dog and master pass our window, Mr Partridge with all his dignity restored, Percy as trim and proud as ever, I wondered about that strange interlude.

Did the Stilboestrol really reduce that tumour or did it regress naturally? And were the extraordinary events caused by the treatment or the condition or both?

I could never be quite sure of the answer, but of the outcome I could be happily certain. That unpleasant growth never came back . . . and neither did all those dogs.

Chapter Five

This was the real Yorkshire with the clean limestone wall riding the hill's edge and the path cutting brilliant green through the crowding heather. And, walking face on to the scented breeze I felt the old tingle of wonder at being alone on the wide moorland where nothing stirred and the spreading miles of purple blossom and green turf reached away till it met the hazy blue of the sky.

But I wasn't really alone. There was Sam, and he made all the difference. Helen had brought a lot of things into my life and Sam was one of the most precious; he was a Beagle and her own personal pet. He would be about two years old when I first saw him and I had no way of knowing that he was to be my faithful companion, my car dog, my friend who sat by my side through the lonely hours of driving till his life ended at the age of fourteen. He was the first of a series of cherished dogs whose comradeship have warmed and lightened my working life.

Sam adopted me on sight. It was as though he had read the *Faithful Hound Manual* because he was always near me; paws on the dash as he gazed eagerly through the windscreen on my rounds, head resting on my foot in our bed-sitting room, trotting just behind me wherever I moved. If I had a beer in a pub he would be under my chair and even when I was having a haircut you only had to lift the white sheet to see Sam crouching beneath my legs. The only place I didn't dare take him was to the cinema and on these occasions he crawled under the bed and sulked.

Most dogs love car riding but to Sam it was a passion which never waned – even in the night hours; he would gladly leave his basket when the world was asleep, stretch a couple of times and follow me out into the cold. He would be on to the seat before I got the car door fully open and this action became so much a part of my life that for a long time after his death I still held the door

open unthinkingly, waiting for him. And I still remember the pain I felt when
he did not bound inside.

And having him with me added so much to the intermissions I granted myself
on my daily rounds. Whereas in offices and factories they had tea breaks I just
stopped the car and stepped out into the splendour which was always at hand
and walked for a spell down hidden lanes, through woods, or as today, along
one of the grassy tracks which ran over the high tops.

This thing which I had always done had a new meaning now. Anybody who
has ever walked a dog knows the abiding satisfaction which comes from giving
pleasure to a loved animal, and the sight of the little form trotting ahead of me
lent a depth which had been missing before.

Round the curve of the path I came to where the tide of heather lapped thickly
down the hillside on a little slope facing invitingly into the sun. It was a call I
could never resist. I looked at my watch; oh I had a few minutes to spare and
there was nothing urgent ahead, just Mr Dacre's tuberculin test. In a moment
I was stretched out on the springy stems, the most wonderful natural mattress
in the world.

Lying there, eyes half closed against the sun's glare, the heavy heather
fragrance around me, I could see the cloud shadows racing across the flanks of
the fells, throwing the gulleys and crevices into momentary gloom but trailing
a fresh flaring green in their wake.

Those were the days when I was most grateful I was in country practice; the
shirt sleeve days when the bleak menace of the bald heights melted into
friendliness, when I felt at one with all the airy life and growth about me and
was glad that I had become what I never thought I would be, a doctor of farm
animals.

My partner, Siegfried would be somewhere out there, thrashing round the
practice and Tristan his student brother would probably be studying in Skeldale
House. This latter was quite a thought because I had never seen Tristan open
a text book until lately. He had been blessed with the kind of brain which made
swotting irrelevant but he would take his finals this year and even he had to get
down to it. I had little doubt he would soon be a qualified man and in a way
it seemed a shame that his free spirit should be shackled by the realities of
veterinary practice. It would be the end of a luminous chapter.

A long-eared head blotted out the sunshine as Sam came and sat on my chest.
He looked at me questioningly. He didn't hold with this laziness but I knew if
I didn't move after a few minutes he would curl up philosophically on my ribs
and have a sleep until I was ready to go. But this time I answered the unspoken
appeal by sitting up and he leaped around me in delight as I rose and began to
make my way back to the car and Mr Dacre's test.

'Move over, Bill!' Mr Dacre cried some time later as he tweaked the big bull's
tail.

Nearly every farmer kept a bull in those days and they were all called Billy
or Bill. I suppose it was because this was a very mature animal that he received
the adult version. Being a docile beast he responded to the touch on his tail by
shuffling his great bulk to one side, leaving me enough space to push in between
him and the wooden partition against which he was tied by a chain.

I was reading a tuberculin test and all I wanted to do was to measure the
intradermal reaction. I had to open my calipers very wide to take in the thickness
of the skin on the enormous neck.

'Thirty,' I called out to the farmer.

He wrote the figure down on the testing book and laughed.

'By heck, he's got some pelt on 'im.'

'Yes,' I said, beginning to squeeze my way out. 'But he's a big fellow, isn't he?'

Just how big he was was brought home to me immediately because the bull suddenly swung round, pinning me against the partition. Cows did this regularly and I moved them by bracing my back against whatever was behind me and pushing them away. But it was different with Bill.

Gasping, I pushed with all my strength against the rolls of fat which covered the vast roan-coloured flank, but I might as well have tried to shift a house.

The farmer dropped his book and seized the tail again but this time the bull showed no response. There was no malice in his behaviour – he was simply having a comfortable lean against the boards and I don't suppose he even noticed the morsel of puny humanity wriggling frantically against his rib-cage.

Still, whether he meant it or not, the end result was the same; I was having the life crushed out of me. Pop-eyed, groaning, scarcely able to breathe, I struggled with everything I had, but I couldn't move an inch. And just when I thought things couldn't get any worse, Bill started to rub himself up and down against the partition. So that was what he had come round for; he had an itch and he just wanted to scratch it.

The effect on me was catastrophic. I was certain my internal organs were being steadily ground to pulp and as I thrashed about in complete panic the huge animal leaned even more heavily.

I don't like to think what would have happened if the wood behind me had not been old and rotten, but just as I felt my senses leaving me there was a cracking and splintering and I fell through into the next stall. Lying there like a stranded fish on a bed of shattered timbers I looked up at Mr Dacre, waiting till my lungs started to work again.

The farmer, having got over his first alarm, was rubbing his upper lip vigorously in a polite attempt to stop himself laughing. His little girl who had watched the whole thing from her vantage point in one of the hay racks had no such inhibitions. Screaming with delight, she pointed at me.

'Ooo, Dad, Dad, look at that man! Did you see him, Dad, did you see him? Ooo what a funny man!' She went into helpless convulsions. She was only about five but I had a feeling she would remember my performance all her life.

At length I picked myself up and managed to brush the matter off lightly, but after I had driven a mile or so from the farm I stopped the car and looked myself over. My ribs ached pretty uniformly as though a light road roller had passed over them and there was a tender area on my left buttock where I had landed on my calipers but otherwise I seemed to have escaped damage. I removed a few spicules of wood from my trousers, got back into the car and consulted my list of visits.

And when I read my next call a gentle smile of relief spread over my face. 'Mrs Tompkin, 14, Jasmine Terrace. Clip budgie's beak.'

Thank heaven for the infinite variety of veterinary practice. After that bull I needed something small and weak and harmless and really you can't ask for much better in that line than a budgie.

Number 14 was one of a row of small mean houses built of the cheap bricks so beloved of the jerry builders after the First World War. I armed myself with a pair of clippers and stepped on to the narrow strip of pavement which separated the door from the road. A pleasant looking red-haired woman answered my knock.

'I'm Mrs Dodds from next door,' she said. 'I keep an eye on t'old lady. She's over eighty and lives alone. I've just been out gettin' her pension for her.'

She led me into the cramped little room. 'Here y'are, love,' she said to the old woman who sat in a corner. She put the pension book and money on the mantelpiece. 'And here's Mr Herriot come to see Peter for you.'

Mrs Tompkin nodded and smiled. 'Oh that's good. Poor little feller can't hardly eat with 'is long beak and I'm worried about him. He's me only companion, you know.'

'Yes, I understand, Mrs Tompkin.' I looked at the cage by the window with the green budgie perched inside. 'These little birds can be wonderful company when they start chattering.'

She laughed. 'Aye, but it's a funny thing. Peter never has said owt much. I think he's lazy! But I just like havin' him with me.'

'Of course you do,' I said. 'But he certainly needs attention now.'

The beak was greatly overgrown, curving away down till it touched the feathers of the breast. I would be able to revolutionise his life with one quick snip from my clippers. The way I was feeling this job was right up my street.

I opened the cage door and slowly inserted my hand.

'Come on, Peter,' I wheedled as the bird fluttered away from me. And I soon cornered him and enclosed him gently in my fingers. As I lifted him out I felt in my pocket with the other hand for the clippers, but as I poised them I stopped.

The tiny head was no longer poking cheekily from my fingers but had fallen loosely to one side. The eyes were closed. I stared at the bird uncomprehendingly for a moment then opened my hand. He lay quite motionless on my palm. He was dead.

Dry mouthed, I continued to stare; at the beautiful iridescence of the plumage, the long beak which I didn't have to cut now, but mostly at the head dropping down over my forefinger. I hadn't squeezed him or been rough with him in any way but he was dead. It must have been sheer fright.

Mrs Dodds and I looked at each other in horror and I hardly dared turn my head towards Mrs Tompkin. When I did, I was surprised to see that she was still nodding and smiling.

I drew her neighbour to one side. 'Mrs Dodds, how much does she see?'

'Oh she's very short-sighted but she's right vain despite her age. Never would wear glasses. She's hard of hearin', too.'

'Well look,' I said. My heart still pounding. 'I just don't know what to do. If I tell her about this the shock will be terrible. Anything could happen.'

Mrs Dodds nodded, stricken-faced. 'Aye, you're right. She's that attached to the little thing.'

'I can only think of one alternative,' I whispered. 'Do you know where I can get another budgie?'

Mrs Dodds thought for a moment. 'You could try Jack Almond at t'town end. I think he keeps birds.'

I cleared my throat but even then my voice came out in a dry croak. 'Mrs Tompkin, I'm just going to take Peter along to the surgery to do this job. I won't be long.'

I left her still nodding and smiling and, cage in hand, fled into the street. I was at the town end and knocking at Jack Almond's door within three minutes.

'Mr Almond?' I asked of the stout, shirtsleeved man who answered.

'That's right, young man.' He gave me a slow, placid smile.

'Do you keep birds?'

He drew himself up with dignity. 'I do, and I'm t'president of the Darrowby and Houlton Cage Bird Society.'

'Fine,' I said breathlessly. 'Have you got a green budgie?'

'Ah've got Canaries, Budgies, Parrots, Parakeets, Cockatoos . . .'

'I just want a budgie.'

'Well ah've got Albinos, Blue-greens, Barreds, Litinos . . .'

'I just want a green one.'

A slightly pained expression flitted across the man's face as though he found my attitude of haste somewhat unseemly.

'Aye . . . well, we'll go and have a look,' he said.

I followed him as he paced unhurriedly through the house into the back yard which was largely given over to a long shed containing a bewildering variety of birds.

Mr Almond gazed at them with gentle pride and his mouth opened as though he was about to launch into a dissertation then he seemed to remember that he had an impatient chap to deal with and dragged himself back to the job in hand.

'There's a nice little green 'un here. But he's a bit older than t'others. Matter of fact I've got 'im talkin'.'

'All the better, just the thing. How much do you want for him?'

'But . . . there's some nice 'uns along here. Just let me show you . . .'

I put a hand on his arm. 'I want that one. How much?'

He pursed his lips in frustration then shrugged his shoulders.

'Ten bob.'

'Right. Bung him in this cage.'

As I sped back up the road I looked in the driving mirror and could see the poor man regarding me sadly from his doorway.

Mrs Dodds was waiting for me back at Jasmine Terrace.

'Do you think I'm doing the right thing?' I asked her in a whisper.

'I'm sure you are,' she replied. 'Poor awd thing, she hasn't much to think about and I'm sure she'd fret over Peter.'

'That's what I thought.' I made my way into the living room.

Mrs Tompkin smiled at me as I went in. 'That wasn't a long job, Mr Herriot.'

'No,' I said, hanging the cage with the new bird up in its place by the window. 'I think you'll find all is well now.'

It was months before I had the courage to put my hand into a budgie's cage again. In fact to this day I prefer it if the owners will lift the birds out for me. People look at me strangely when I ask them to do this; I believe they think I am scared the little things might bite me.

It was a long time, too, before I dared go back to Mrs Tompkin's but I was driving down Jasmine Terrace one day and on an impulse I stopped outside Number 14.

The old lady herself came to the door.

'How . . .' I said. 'How is . . . er . . .?'

She peered at me closely for a moment then laughed. 'Oh I see who it is now. You mean Peter, don't you, Mr Herriot. Oh 'e's just grand. Come in and see 'im.'

In the little room the cage still hung by the window and Peter the Second took a quick look at me then put on a little act for my benefit; he hopped around the bars of the cage, ran up and down his ladder and rang his little bell a couple of times before returning to his perch.

His mistress reached up, tapped the metal and looked lovingly at him.

'You know, you wouldn't believe it,' she said. 'He's like a different bird.'

I swallowed. 'Is that so? In what way?'

'Well he's so active now. Lively as can be. You know 'e chatters to me all day long. It's wonderful what cuttin' a beak can do.'

Chapter Six

This was one for Granville Bennett. I liked a bit of small animal surgery and was gradually doing more as time went on but this one frightened me. A twelve-year-old spaniel bitch in the last stages of pyometritis, pus dripping from her vulva on to the surgery table, temperature a hundred and four, panting, trembling, and, as I held my stethoscope against her chest I could hear the classical signs of valvular insufficiency. A dicky heart was just what I needed on top of everything else.

'Drinking a lot of water, is she?' I asked.

Old Mrs Barker twisted the strings of her shopping bag anxiously. 'Aye, she never seems to be away from the water bowl. But she won't eat – hasn't had a bite for the last four days.'

'Well I don't know,' I took off my stethoscope and stuffed it in my pocket. 'You should have brought her in long ago. She must have been ill for weeks.'

'Not rightly ill, but a bit off it. I thought there was nothing to worry about as long as she was eating.'

I didn't say anything for a few moments. I had no desire to upset the old girl but she had to be told.

'I'm afraid this is rather serious, Mrs Barker. The condition has been building up for a long time. It's in her womb, you see, a bad infection, and the only cure is an operation.'

'Well will you do it, please?' The old lady's lips quivered.

I came round the table and put my hand on her shoulder.

'I'd like to, but there are snags. She's in poor shape and twelve years old. Really a poor operation risk. I'd like to take her through to the Veterinary Hospital at Hartington and let Mr Bennett operate on her.'

'All right,' she said, nodding eagerly. 'I don't care what it costs.'

'Oh we'll keep it down as much as possible.' I walked along the passage with her and showed her out of the door. 'Leave her with me – I'll look after her, don't worry. What's her name, by the way?'

'Dinah,' she replied huskily, still peering past me down the passage.

I went through and lifted the phone. Thirty years ago country practitioners had to turn to the small animal experts when anything unusual cropped up in that line. It is different nowadays when our practices are more mixed. In Darrowby now we have the staff and equipment to tackle any type of small animal surgery but it was different then. I had heard it said that sooner or later every large animal man had to scream for help from Granville Bennett and now it was my turn.

'Hello, is that Mr Bennett?'

'It is indeed.' A big voice, friendly, full of give.

'Herriot here. I'm with Farnon in Darrowby.'

'Of course! Heard of you, laddie, heard of you.'

'Oh . . . er . . . thanks. Look, I've got a bit of a sticky job here. I wonder if you'd take it on for me.'

'Delighted, laddie, what is it?'

'A real stinking pyo.'

'Oh lovely!'

'The bitch is twelve years old.'

'Splendid!'

'And toxic as hell.'

'Excellent!'

'And one of the worst hearts I've heard for a long time.'

'Fine, fine! When are you coming through?'

'This evening, if it's O.K. with you. About eight.'

'Couldn't be better, laddie. See you.'

Hartington was a fair-sized town – about 200,000 inhabitants – but as I drove into the centre the traffic had thinned and only a few cars rolled past the rows of shop fronts. I hoped my twenty-five mile journey had been worth it. Dinah, stretched out on a blanket in the back looked as if she didn't care either way. I glanced behind me at the head drooping over the edge of the seat, at the white muzzle and the cataracts in her eyes gleaming palely in the light from the dash. She looked so old. Maybe I was wasting my time, placing too much faith in this man's reputation.

There was do doubt Granville Bennett had become something of a legend in northern England. In those days when specialisation was almost unknown he had gone all out for small animal work – never looked at farm stock – and had set a new standard by the modern procedures in his animal hospital which was run as nearly as possible on human lines. It was, in fact, fashionable for veterinary surgeons of that era to belittle dog and cat work; a lot of the older men who had spent their lives among the teeming thousands of draught horses in city and agriculture would sneer, 'Oh I've no time to bother with those damn things.' Bennet had gone dead in the opposite direction.

I had never met him but I knew he was a young man in his early thirties. I had heard a lot about his skill, his business acumen, and about his reputation as a *bon viveur*. He was, they said, a dedicated devotee of the work-hard-play-hard school.

The Veterinary Hospital was a long low building near the top of a busy street. I drove into a yard and knocked at a door in the corner. I was looking with some awe at a gleaming Bentley dwarfing my own battered little Austin when the door was opened by a pretty receptionist.

'Good evening,' she murmured with a dazzling smile which I thought must be worth another half crown on the bill for a start. 'Do come in, Mr Bennett is expecting you.'

I was shown into a waiting room with magazines and flowers on a corner table and many impressive photographs of dogs and cats on the walls – taken, I learned later, by the principal himself. I was looking closely at a superb study of two white poodles when I heard a footstep behind me. I turned and had my first view of Granville Bennett.

He seemed to fill the room. Not over tall but of tremendous bulk. Fat, I thought at first, but as he came nearer it seemed to me that the tissue of which he was composed wasn't distributed like fat. He wasn't flabby, he didn't stick out in any particular place, he was just a big wide, solid, hard-looking man. From the middle of a pleasant blunt-featured face the most magnificent pipe I had ever seen stuck forth shining and glorious, giving out delicious wisps of expensive smoke. It was an enormous pipe, in fact it would have looked downright silly with a smaller man, but on him it was a thing of beauty. I had a final impression of a beautifully cut dark suit and sparkling shirt cuffs as he held out a hand.

'James Herriot!' He said it as somebody else might have said 'Winston Churchill', or 'Stanley Matthews'.

'That's right.'

'Well, this is grand. Jim, is it?'

'Well yes, usually.'

'Lovely. We've got everything laid on for you, Jim. The girls are waiting in the theatre.'

'That's very kind of you, Mr Bennett.'

'Granville, Granville please!' He put his arm through mine and led me to the operating room.

Dinah was already there, looking very woebegone. She had had a sedative injection and her head nodded wearily. Bennett went over to her and gave her a swift examination.

'Mm, yes, let's get on, then.'

The two girls went into action like cogs in a smooth machine. Bennett kept a large lay staff and these animal nurses, both attractive, clearly knew what they were about. While one of them pulled up the anaesthetic and instrument trolleys the other seized Dinah's foreleg expertly above the elbow, raised the radial vein by pressure and quickly clipped and disinfected the area.

The big man strolled up with a loaded needle and effortlessly slipped the needle into the vein.

'Pentothal,' he said as Dinah slowly collapsed and lay unconscious on the table. It was one of the new short-acting anaesthetics which I had never seen used.

While Bennett scrubbed up and donned sterilised gown and cap the girls rolled Dinah on her back and secured her there with ties to loops on the operating table. They applied the ether and oxygen mask to her face then shaved and swabbed the operation site. The big man returned in time to have a scalpel placed in his hand.

With almost casual speed he incised skin and muscle layers and when he went through the peritoneum the horns of the uterus which in normal health would have been two slim pink ribbons now welled into the wound like twin balloons, swollen and turgid with pus. No wonder Dinah had felt ill, carrying that lot around with her.

The stubby fingers tenderly worked round the mass, ligated the ovarian vessels and uterine body then removed the whole thing and dropped it into an enamel bowl. It wasn't till he had begun to stitch that I realised that the operation was nearly over though he had been at the table for only a few minutes. It would all have looked childishly easy except that his total involvement showed in occasional explosive commands to the nurses.

And as I watched him working under the shadowless lamp with the white tiled walls around him and the rows of instruments gleaming by his side it came to me with a rush of mixed emotions that this was what I had always wanted to do myself. My dreams when I had first decided on veterinary work had been precisely of this. Yet here I was, a somewhat shaggy cow doctor; or perhaps more correctly a farm physician, but certainly something very different. The scene before me was a far cry from my routine of kicks and buffets, of muck and sweat. And yet I had no regrets; the life which had been forced on me by circumstances had turned out to be a thing of magical fulfilment. It came to me with a flooding certainty that I would rather spend my days driving over the unfenced roads of the high country than stooping over that operating table.

And anyway I couldn't have been a Bennett. I don't think I could have matched his technique and this whole set up was eloquent of a lot of things like business sense, foresight and driving ambition which I just didn't possess.

My colleague was finished now and was fitting up an intravenous saline drip. He taped the needle down in the vein then turned to me.

'That's it, then, Jim. It's up to the old girl now.' He began to lead me from the room and it struck me how very pleasant it must be to finish your job and walk away from it like this. In Darrowby I'd have been starting now to wash the instruments, scrub the table, and the final scene would have been of Herriot the great surgeon swilling the floor with mop and bucket. This was a better way.

Back in the waiting room Bennett pulled on his jacket and extracted from a side pocket the immense pipe which he inspected with a touch of anxiety as if he feared mice had been nibbling at it in his absence. He wasn't satisfied with his examination because he brought forth a soft yellow cloth and began to polish the briar with intense absorption. Then he held the pipe high, moving it slightly from side to side, his eyes softening at the play of the light on the exquisite grain. Finally he produced a pouch of mammoth proportions, filled the bowl, applied a match with a touch of reverence and closed his eyes as a fragrant mist drifted from his lips.

'That baccy smells marvellous,' I said. 'What is it?'

'Navy Cut De Luxe.' He closed his eyes again. 'You know, I could eat the smoke.'

I laughed. 'I use the ordinary Navy Cut myself.'

He gazed at me like a sorrowing Buddha, 'Oh you mustn't, laddie, you mustn't. This is the only stuff. Rich ... fruity ...' His hand made languid motions in the air. 'Here, you can take some away with you.'

He pulled open a drawer. I had a brief view of a stock which wouldn't have disgraced a fair-sized tobacconist's shop; innumerable tins, pipes, cleaners, reamers, cloths.

'Try this,' he said, 'and tell me if I'm not right.'

I looked down at the first container in my hand. 'Oh but I can't take all this. It's a four ounce tin!'

'Rubbish, my boy. Put it in your pocket.' He became suddenly brisk. 'Now I expect you'll want to hang around till old Dinah comes out of the anaesthetic so why don't we have a quick beer? I'm a member of a nice little club just across the road.'

'Well fine, sounds great.'

He moved lightly and swiftly for a big man and I had to hurry to keep up with him as he left the surgery and crossed to a building on the other side of the street.

Chapter Seven

Inside the club was masculine comfort, hails of welcome from some prosperous looking members and a friendly greeting from the man behind the bar.

'Two pints, Fred,' murmured Bennett absently, and the drinks appeared with amazing speed. My colleague poured his down apparently without swallowing and turned to me.

'Another Jim?'

I had just tried a sip at mine and began to gulp anxiously at the bitter ale.
'Right, but let me get this one.'

'No can do, laddie.' He glanced at me with mild severity. 'Only members can
buy drinks. Same again, Fred.'

I found I had two glasses at my elbow and with a tremendous effort I got the
first one down. Gasping slightly I was surveying the second one timidly when
I noticed that Bennett was threequarters down his. As I watched he drained it
effortlessly.

'You're slow, Jim,' he said, smiling indulgently. 'Just set them up again will
you, Fred.'

In some alarm I watched the barman ply his handle and attacked my second
pint resolutely. I surprised myself by forcing it over my tonsils then, breathing
heavily, I got hold of the third one just as Bennet spoke again.

'We'll just have one for the road, Jim,' he said pleasantly. 'Would you be so
kind, Fred?'

This was ridiculous but I didn't want to appear a piker at our first meeting.
With something akin to desperation I raised the third and began to suck feebly
at it. When my glass was empty I almost collapsed against the counter. My
stomach was agonisingly distended and a light perspiration had broken out on
my brow. As I almost lay there I saw my colleague moving across the carpet
towards the door.

'Time we were off, Jim,' he said. 'Drink up.'

It's wonderful what the human frame can tolerate when put to the test. I
would have taken bets that it was impossible for me to drink that fourth pint
without at least half an hour's rest, preferably in the prone position, but as
Bennett's shoe tapped impatiently I tipped the beer a little at a time into my
mouth, feeling it wash around my back teeth before incredibly disappearing
down my gullet. I believe the water torture was a favourite with the Spanish
Inquisition and as the pressure inside me increased I knew just how their victims
felt.

When I at last blindly replaced my glass and splashed my way from the bar
the big man was holding the door open. Outside in the street he placed an arm
across my shoulder.

'The old Spaniel won't be out of it yet,' he said. 'We'll just slip to my house
and have a bite – I'm a little peckish.'

Sunk in the deep unholstery of the Bentley, cradling my swollen abdomen in
my arms I watched the shop fronts flicker past the windows and give way to the
darkness of the open countryside. We drew up outside a fine grey stone house
in a typical Yorkshire village and Bennett ushered me inside.

He pushed me towards a leather armchair. 'Make yourself at home, laddie.
Zoe's out at the moment but I'll get some grub.' He bustled through to the
kitchen and reappeared in seconds with a deep bowl which he placed on a table
by my side.

'You know, Jim,' he said, rubbing his hands. 'There's nothing better after
beer than a few pickled onions.'

I cast a timorous glance into the bowl. Everthing in this man's life seemed to
be larger than life, even the onions. They were bigger than golf balls,
brownish-white, glistening.

'Well thanks Mr Ben . . . Granville.' I took one of them, held it between
finger and thumb and stared at it helplessly. The beer hadn't even begun to sort
itself out inside me; the idea of starting on this potent-looking vegetable was
unthinkable.

Granville reached into the bowl, popped an onion into his mouth, crunched
it quickly, swallowed and sank his teeth into a second. 'By God, that's good.

You know, my little wife's a marvellous cook. She even makes pickled onions better than anyone.'

Munching happily he moved over to the sideboard and clinked around for a few moments before placing in my hand a heavy cut glass tumbler about two thirds full of neat whisky. I couldn't say anything because I had taken the plunge and put the onion in my mouth; and as I bit boldly into it the fumes rolled in a volatile wave into my nasal passages, making me splutter. I took a gulp at the whisky and looked up at Granville with watering eyes.

He was holding out the onion bowl again and when I declined he regarded it for a moment with hurt in his eyes. 'It's funny you don't like them, I always thought Zoe did them marvellously.'

'Oh you're wrong, Granville, they're delicious. I just haven't finished this one.'

He didn't reply but continued to look at the bowl with gentle sorrow. I realised there was nothing else for it; I took another onion.

Immensely gratified, Granville hurried through to the kitchen again. This time when he came back he bore a tray with an enormous cold roast, a loaf of bread, butter and mustard.

'I think a beef sandwich would go down rather nicely, Jim,' he murmured, as he stropped his carving knife on a steel. Then he noticed my glass of whisky still half full.

'C'mon, c'mon, c'mon!' he said with some asperity. 'You're not touching your drink.' He watched me benevolently as I drained the glass then he refilled it to its old level. 'That's better. And have another onion.'

I stretched my legs out and rested my head on the back of the chair in an attempt to ease my internal turmoil. My stomach was a lake of volcanic lava bubbling and popping fiercely in its crater with each additional piece of onion, every sip of whisky setting up a fresh violent reaction. Watching Granville at work, a great wave of nausea swept over me. He was sawing busily at the roast, carving off slices which looked to be an inch thick, slapping mustard on them and enclosing them in the bread. He hummed with contentment as the pile grew. Every now and then he had another onion.

'Now then, laddie,' he cried at length, putting a heaped plate at my elbow. 'Get yourself round that lot.' He took his own supply and collapsed with a sigh into another chair.

He took a gargantuan bite and spoke as he chewed. 'You know, Jim, this is something I enjoy – a nice little snack. Zoe always leaves me plenty to go at when she pops out.' He engulfed a further few inches of sandwich. 'And I'll tell you something, though I say it myself, these are bloody good, don't you think so?'

'Yes indeed.' Squaring my shoulders I bit, swallowed and held my breath as another unwanted foreign body slid down to the ferment below.

Just then I heard the front door open.

'Ah, that'll be Zoe,' Granville said, and was about to rise when a disgracefully fat Staffordshire Bull Terrier burst into the room, waddled across the carpet and leapt into his lap.

'Phoebles, my dear, come to daddykins!' he shouted. 'Have you had nice walkies with mummy?'

The Staffordshire was closely followed by a Yorkshire Terrier which was also enthusiastically greeted by Granville.

'Yoo-hoo, Victoria, Yoo-hoo!'

The Yorkie, an obvious smiler, did not jump up but contented herself with sitting at her master's feet, baring her teeth ingratiatingly every few seconds.

I smiled through my pain. Another myth exploded; the one about these specialist small animal vets not being fond of dogs themselves. The big man crooned over the two little animals. The fact that he called Phoebe 'Phoebles' was symptomatic.

I heard light footsteps in the hall and looked up expectantly. I had Granville's wife taped neatly in my mind; domesticated, devoted, homely; many of these dynamic types had wives like that, willing slaves content to lurk in the background. I waited confidently for the entrance of a plain little hausfrau.

When the door opened I almost let my vast sandwich fall. Zoe Bennett was a glowing warm beauty who would make any man alive stop for another look. A lot of soft brown hair, large grey-green friendly eyes, a tweed suit sitting sweetly on a slim but not too slim figure; and something else, a wholesomeness, an inner light which made me wish suddenly that I was a better man or at least that I looked better than I did.

In an instant I was acutely conscious of the fact that my shoes were dirty, that my old jacket and corduroy trousers were out of place here. I hadn't troubled to change but had rushed straight out in my working clothes, and they were different from Granville's because I couldn't go round the farms in a suit like his.

'My love, my love!' he carolled joyously as his wife bent over and kissed him fondly. 'Let me introduce Jim Herriot from Darrowby.'

The beautiful eyes turned on me.

'How d'you do, Mr Herriot!' She looked as pleased to see me as her husband had done and again I had the desperate wish that I was more presentable; that my hair was combed, that I didn't have this mounting conviction that I was going to explode into a thousand pieces at any moment.

'I'm going to have a cup of tea, Mr Herriot. Would you like one?'

'No-no, no no, thank you very much but no, no, not at the moment.' I backed away slightly.

'Ah well, I see you've got one of Granville's little sandwiches.' She giggled and went to get her tea.

When she came back she handed a parcel to her husband. 'I've been shopping today, darling. Picked up some of those shirts you like so much.'

'My sweet! how kind of you!' He began to tear at the brown paper like a schoolboy and produced three elegant shirts in cellophane covers. 'They're marvellous, my pet, you spoil me.' He looked up at me. 'Jim! These are the most wonderful shirts, you must have one.' He flicked a shining package across the room on to my lap.

I looked down at it in amazement. 'No, really I can't . . .'

'Of course you can. You keep it.'

'But Granville, not a shirt . . . it's too . . .'

'It's a very good shirt.' He was beginning to look hurt again.

I subsided.

They were both so kind. Zoe sat right by me with her tea cup, chatting pleasantly, while Granville beamed at me from his chair as he finished the last of the sandwiches and started again on the onions.

The proximity of the attractive woman was agreeable but embarrassing. My corduroys in the warmth of the room had begun to give off the unmistakable bouquet of the farmyard where they spent most of their time. And though it was one of my favourite scents there was no doubt it didn't go with these elegant surroundings.

And worse still, I had started a series of internal rumblings and musical tinklings which resounded only too audibly during every lull in the conversation. The only other time I have heard such sounds was in a cow with an advanced case of displacement of the abomasum. My companions delicately feigned deafness even when I produced a shameful, explosive belch which made the little fat dog start up in alarm, but when another of these mighty borborygmi escaped me and almost made the windows rattle I thought it time to go.

In any case I wasn't contributing much else. The alcohol had taken hold and I was increasingly conscious that I was just sitting there with a stupid leer on my face. In striking contrast to Granville who looked just the same as when I first met him back at the surgery. He was cool and possessed, his massive urbanity unimpaired. It was a little hard.

So, with the tin of tobacco bumping against my hip and the shirt tucked under my arm I took my leave.

Back at the hospital I looked down at Dinah. The old dog had come through wonderfully well and she lifted her head and gazed at me sleepily. Her colour was good and her pulse strong. The operative shock had been dramatically minimised by my colleague's skilful speedy technique and by the intravenous drip.

I knelt down and stroked her ears. 'You know, I'm sure she's going to make it, Granville.'

Above me the great pipe nodded with majestic confidence.

'Of course, laddie, of course.'

And he was right. Dinah was rejuvenated by her hysterectomy and lived to delight her mistress for many more years.

On the way home that night she lay by my side on the passenger seat, her nose poking from a blanket. Now and then she rested her chin on my hand as it gripped the gear lever and occasionally she licked me lazily.

I could see she felt better than I did.

Chapter Eight

As I looked at the group of sick young cattle on the hillside a mixture of apprehension and disbelief flooded through me. Surely not more trouble for the Dalbys.

The old saw 'It never rains but it pours' seems to apply with particular force to farming. The husk outbreak last year and now this. It had all started with the death of Billy Dalby; big, slow-smiling, slow-talking Billy. He was as strong and tough as any of the shaggy beasts which ranged his fields but he had just melted away in a few weeks. Cancer of the pancreas they said it was and Billy was gone before anybody could realise it and there was only his picture smiling down from the kitchen mantelpiece on his wife and three young children.

The general opinion was that Mrs Dalby should sell up and get out. You needed a man to run this place and anyway Prospect House was a bad farm. Neighbouring farmers would stick out their lower lips and shake their heads when they looked at the boggy pastures on the low side of the house with the tufts of spiky grass sticking from the sour soil or at the rocky outcrops and scattered stones on the hillside fields. No, it was a poor place and a woman would never make a go of it.

Everybody thought the same thing except Mrs Dalby herself. There wasn't much of her, in fact she must have been one of the smallest women I have ever seen – around five feet high – but there was a core of steel in her. She had her own mind and her own way of doing things.

I remember when Billy was still alive I had been injecting some sheep up there and Mrs Dalby called me into the house.

'You'll have a cup of tea, Mr Herriot?' She said it in a gracious way, not casually, her head slightly on one side and a dignified little smile on her face.

And when I went into the kitchen I knew what I would find; the inevitable tray. It was always a tray with Mrs Dalby. The hospitable Dales people were continually asking me in for some kind of refreshment – a 'bit o' dinner' perhaps, but if it wasn't midday there was usually a mug of tea and a scone or a hunk of thick-crusted apple pie – but Mrs Dalby invariably set out a special tray. And there it was today with a clean cloth and the best china cup and saucer and side plates with sliced buttered scones and iced cakes and malt bread and biscuits. It was on its own table away from the big kitchen table.

'Do sit down, Mr Herriot,' she said in her precise manner. 'I hope that tea isn't too strong for you.'

Her speech was what the farmers would call 'very proper' but it went with her personality which to me embodied a determination to do everything as correctly as possible.

'Looks perfect to me, Mrs Dalby.' I sat down, feeling somewhat exposed, in the middle of the kitchen with Billy smiling comfortably from an old armchair by the fire and his wife standing by my side.

She never sat down with us but stood there, very erect, hands clasped in front of her, head inclined, ceremoniously attending to my every wish. 'Let me fill your cup, Mr Herriot,' or 'Won't you try some of this custard tart?'

She wasn't what you would call pretty; it was a rough-skinned red little face with tiny, very dark eyes but there was a sweet expression and a quiet dignity. And as I say, there was strength.

Billy died in the spring and as everybody waited for Mrs Dalby to make arrangement for the sale she went right on with the running of the farm. She did it with the help of a big farm worker called Charlie who had helped Billy occasionally but now came full time. During the summer I was called out a few times for trivial ailments among the cattle and I could see that Mrs Dalby was managing to hang on; she looked a bit haggard because she was now helping in the fields and buildings as well as coping with her housework and young family, but she was still fighting.

It was half way through September when she asked me to call to see some young cattle – stirks of around nine months – which were coughing.

'They were really fit when they were turned out in May,' she said, as we walked across the grass to the gate in the corner. 'But they've gone down badly this last week or two.'

I held the gate open, we walked through, and as I approached the group of animals I grew progressively uneasy. Even at this distance I could see that something was far wrong; they were not moving around or grazing as they should have been but were curiously immobile. There would be about thirty of them and many had their necks extended forward as if seeking air. And from the bunch a barking cough was carried to us on the soft breeze of late summer.

By the time we reached the cattle my uneasiness had been replaced by a dry-mouthed dread. They didn't seem to care as I moved in among them and I had to shout and wave my arms to get them moving; and they had barely begun to stir before the coughing broke out throughout the group; not just an occasional bark but a hacking chorus which seemed almost to be tearing the little animals apart. And they weren't just coughing; most of them were panting, standing straddle-legged, ribs heaving in a desperate fight for breath. A few showed bubbles of saliva at their lips and from here and there among the pack groans of agony sounded as the lungs laboured.

I turned as in a dream to Mrs Dalby.

'They've got husk.' Even as I said it it sounded a grimly inadequate description of the tragedy I was witnessing. Because this was neglected husk, a terrible doom-laden thing.

'Husk?' the little woman said brightly. 'What causes it?'

I looked at her for a moment then tried to make my voice casual.

'Well it's a parasite. A tiny worm which infests the bronchial tubes and sets up bronchitis – in fact that's the proper name, parasitic bronchitis. The larvae climb up the blades of grass and the cattle eat them as they graze. Some pastures are badly affected with it.' I broke off. A lecture was out of place at a time like this.

What I felt like saying was why in God's name hadn't I been called in weeks ago. Because this wasn't only bronchitis now; it was pneumonia, pleurisy, emphysema and any other lung condition you cared to name with not merely a few of the hair-like worms irritating the tubes, but great seething masses of them crawling everywhere, balling up and blocking the vital air passages. I had opened up a lot of calves like these and I knew how it looked.

I took a deep breath. 'They're pretty bad, Mrs Dalby. A mild attack isn't so bad if you can get them off the grass right away, but this has gone a long way beyond that. You can see for yourself, can't you – they're like a lot of little skeletons. I wish I'd seen them sooner.'

She looked up at me apprehensively and I decided not to belabour the point. It would be like rubbing it in; saying what her neighbours had said all along, that her inexperience would land her in trouble sooner or later. If Billy had been here he probably would never have turned his young cattle on to this marshy field; or he would have spotted the trouble right at the start and brought them inside. Charlie would be no help in a situation like this; he was a good willing chap but lived up to the Yorkshire saying, 'Strong in t'arm and thick in t'head.' Farming is a skilful business and Billy, the planner, the stocksman, the experienced agriculturist who knew his own farm inside out, just wasn't there.

Mrs Dalby drew herself up with that familiar gesture.

'Well what can we do about it, Mr Herriot?'

An honest reply in those days would have been, 'Medicinally nothing.' But I didn't say that.

'We've got to get them all inside immediately. Every mouthful of this grass is adding to the worm burden. Is Charlie around to give us a hand?'

'Yes, he's in the next field, mending a wall.' She trotted across the turf and in a minute or two returned with the big man ambling by her side.

'Aye, ah thought it were a touch of husk,' he said amiably, then with a hint of eagerness. 'Are ye goin' to give them the throat injection?'

'Yes ... yes ... but let's get them up to the buildings.' As we drove the cattle slowly up the green slope I marvelled ruefully at this further example of faith in the intratracheal injection for husk. There was really no treatment for the condition and it would be another twenty years before one appeared in the shape of diethylcarbamazine, but the accepted procedure was to inject a mixture of chloroform, turpentine and creosote into the windpipe. Modern vets may raise their eyebrows at the idea of introducing this barbaric concoction directly into the delicate lung tissue and we old ones didn't think much of it either. But the farmers loved it.

When we had finally got the stirks into the fold yard I looked round them with something like despair. The short journey had exacerbated their symptoms tremendously and I stood in the middle of a symphony of coughs, grunts and groans while the cattle, tongues protruding, ribs pumping, gasped for breath.

I got a bottle of the wonderful injection from the car, and with Charlie holding the head and little Mrs Dalby hanging on to the tail I began to go through the motions. Seizing the trachea in my left hand I inserted the needle between the cartilaginous rings and squirted a few c.c.'s into the lumen and, as always, the stirk gave a reflex cough, sending up the distinctive aroma of the medicaments into our faces.

'By gaw, you can smell it straight off, guvnor,' Charlie said with deep satisfaction. 'Ye can tell it's gettin' right to t'spot.'

Most of the farmers said something like that. And they had faith. The books spoke comfortably about the chloroform stupefying the worms, the turpentine killing them and the creosote causing increased coughing which expelled them. But I didn't believe a word of it. The good results which followed were in my opinion due entirely to bringing the animals in from the infected pasture.

But I knew I had to do it and we injected every animal in the yard. There were thirty-two of them and Mrs Dalby's tiny figure was involved in the catching of all of them; clutching vainly at their necks, grabbing their tails, pushing them up against the wall. William, the eldest son, aged eight, came in from school and plunged into the fray by his mother's side.

My repeated 'Be careful, Mrs Dalby!' or Charlie's gruff 'Watch thissen, Missis, or you'll get lamed!' had no effect. During the mêlée both she and the little boy were kicked, trodden on and knocked down but they never showed the slightest sign of being discouraged.

At the end, the little woman turned to me, her face flushed to an even deeper hue. Panting, she looked up, 'Is there anything else we can do, Mr Herriot?'

'Yes there is.' In fact the two things I was going to tell her were the only things which ever did any good. 'First, I'm going to leave you some medicine for the worms which are in the stomach. We can get at them there, so Charlie must give every stirk a dose. Secondly, you'll have to start giving them the best possible food – good hay and high protein cake.'

Her eyes widened. 'Cake? That's expensive stuff. And hay . . .'

I knew what she was thinking. The precious hay safely garnered for next winter's feed; to have to start using it now was a cruel blow, especially with all that beautiful grass out there; grass, the most natural, most perfect food for cattle but every blade carrying its own load of death.

'Can't they go out again . . . ever?' she asked in a small voice.

'No, I'm sorry. If they had just had a mild attack you could have kept them in at nights and turned them out after the dew had left the grass in the mornings. The larvae climb up the grass mainly when it's wet. But your cattle have got too far. We daren't risk them picking up any more worms.'

'Right . . . thank you, Mr Herriot. We know where we are, anyway.' She paused. 'Do you think we'll lose any of them?'

My stomach contracted into a tight ball. I had already told her to buy cake she couldn't afford and it was a certainty she would have to lay out more precious cash for hay in the winter. How was I going to tell her that nothing in the world was going to stop this batch of beasts dying like flies? When animals with husk started blowing bubbles it was nearly hopeless and the ones which were groaning with every breath were quite simply doomed. Nearly half of them were in these two categories and what about the rest? The pathetic barking other half? Well, they had a chance.

'Mrs Dalby,' I said, 'it would be wrong of me to make light of this. Some of them are going to die, in fact unless there's a miracle you are going to lose quite a few of them.' At the sight of her stricken face I made an attempt to be encouraging. 'However, where there's life there's hope and sometimes you get pleasant surprises at this job.' I held up a finger. 'Worm them and get some good grub into them! That's your hope – to help them to fight it off themselves.'

'I see.' She lifted her chin in her characteristic way. 'And now you must come in for a wash.'

And of course there it was in its usual place in the kitchen; the tray with all the trimmings.

'Really, Mrs Dalby. You shouldn't have bothered. You have enough to do without this.'

'Nonsense,' she said, the smile back on her face. 'You take one spoonful of sugar don't you?'

As I sat there she stood in her habitual position, hands clasped in front of her, watching me while the middle boy, Dennis, who was five, looked up at me solemnly and Michael, a mere toddler of two, fell over the coal scuttle and started to bawl lustily.

The usual procedure was to repeat the intratracheal injection in four days so I had to go through with it. Anyway, it gave me a chance to see how the cattle were faring.

When I drew up in the yard my first sight was of a long sack-covered mound on the cobbles. A row of hooves protruded from beneath the sacks. I had expected something of the sort but the reality was still like a blow in the face. It was still quite early in the morning and perhaps I wasn't feeling quite strong enough to have the evidence of my failure thrust before my eyes. Because failure it undoubtedly was; even though I had been in a hopeless position from the start there was something damning in those motionless hooves jutting from their rough blanket.

I made a quick count. There were four dead cattle under there. Wearily I made my way into the fold yard; I had no cheerful expectation of what I would find inside. Two of the stirks were down and unable to rise from the deep straw, the rest were still panting, but I noticed with a faint lifting of my gloom that several of them were doggedly munching at the cubes of cake in the troughs and others were pulling an occasional wisp of hay from the racks. It was incredible how animals with advanced respiratory symptoms would still eat; and it provided the only gleam of hope.

I walked over to the house. Mrs Dalby greeted me cheerfully as though those carcases outside didn't exist.

'It's time for the second injection,' I said, and then after some hesitation, 'I see you've lost four of them . . . I'm sorry.'

'Well you told me, Mr Herriot.' She smiled through the tired lines on her face. 'You said I had to expect it so it wasn't as big a shock as it might have been.' She finished washing the youngest child's face, seized a towel in her work-roughened hands and rubbed him briskly, then she straightened up. It was Saturday and William was at home and I noticed not for the first time that there was something about the little boy which suggested that even at his age he had decided he was going to be the man about the house. He pulled on his little Wellingtons and marched resolutely with us across the yard to do his bit as he saw it. I rested my hand on his shoulder as he walked beside me; he would have to grow up a lot more rapidly than most youngsters but I had the feeling that the realities of life wouldn't bowl him over very easily.

We gave the animals their second injection with the two little Dalbys again throwing themselves fearlessly into the rough and tumble and that was about the last practical thing I did in the husk outbreak.

Looking back, there is a macabre fascination in recalling situations like this when we veterinary surgeons were utterly helpless in the face of inevitable disaster. Nowadays, thank heavens, the young members of the profession do not have to stand among a group of gasping, groaning creatures with the sick knowledge that they can't do a thing about it; they have an excellent oral vaccine to prevent husk and efficient therapeutic agents to treat it.

But with the Dalbys who needed my help so desperately I had nothing to offer; my memories are of repeated comfortless visits, of death, and of an all-pervading reek of chloroform, creosote and turpentine. When the business had finally come to an end a dozen of the stirks had died, about five were alive but blowing hard and would probably be stunted and unthrifty for the rest of their lives. The rest, thanks to the good feeding and not to my treatment, had recovered.

It was a crushing blow for any farmer to take but for a widow struggling to survive it could have been fatal. But on my last visit little Mrs Dalby, hovering as usual, hands clasped, above the tea tray, was undefeated.

'Only them as has them can lose them,' she said firmly, her head tilted as always.

I had heard that said many times and they were brave Yorkshire words. But I wondered . . . did she have enough to be able to lose so many?

She went on, 'I know you've told me not to turn the young beasts on to that field next year but isn't there anything we can give them to stop them getting husk?'

'No, Mrs Dalby, I'm sorry.' I put down my cup. 'I don't think there's anything country vets need and want more than a husk vaccine. People keep asking us that question and we have to keep on saying no.'

We had to keep on saying no for another twenty years as we watched disasters like I had just seen at the Dalbys', and the strange thing is that now we have a first rate vaccine it is taken completely for granted.

Driving away I stopped to open the gate at the end of the track and looked back at the old stone farmhouse crouching against the lower slopes. It was a perfect autumn day with mellow golden sunshine softening the harsh sweep of fell and moor with their striding walls and the air so still and windless that the whirring of a pigeon's wings overhead was loud in the silence. Across the valley on the hilltop a frieze of sparse trees stood as motionless as though they had been painted across the blue canvas of sky.

It seemed wrong that in the midst of this beauty was worry and anxiety, grinding struggle and the threat of ruin. I closed the gate and got back into the car. That little woman over there may have weathered this calamity but as I started the engine the thought was strong in my mind that another such thing would finish her.

Chapter Nine

I was vastly relieved when winter came and spring followed and I saw virtually nothing of Mrs Dalby. It was one market day in mid-summer that she came to the surgery. I was just going to open the door when Siegfried beat me to it. More than most people he appreciated the hospitality we were shown on the farms and he had sampled Mrs Dalby's tray as often as I had. On top of that he had the deepest admiration for her indomitable battle to keep the farm going for her children, so that whenever she appeared at Skeldale House he received her like royalty. His manners, always impeccable, became those of a Spanish grandee.

I watched him now as he threw the door wide and hurried to the top step.

'Why, Mrs Dalby! How very nice to see you! Do come inside.' He extended his hand towards the house.

The little woman, dignified as ever, inclined her head, smiled and walked past him while Siegfried hastened to her side; and as they negotiated the passage he kept up a running fire of enquiries. 'And how is William . . . and Dennis . . . and little Michael? Good, good, splendid.'

At the sitting-room door there was the same ceremonious opening and courteous gestures and once inside a tremendous scraping of armchairs as he hauled them around to make sure she was comfortable and in the right position.

Next he galloped through to the kitchen to organise some refreshment and when Mrs Hall appeared with the tray he raked it with an anxious glance as though he feared it might fall below the standard of Mrs Dalby's. Apparently reassured, he poured the tea, hovered around solicitously for a moment or two then sat down opposite, the very picture of rapt attention.

The little woman thanked him and sipped at her cup.

'Mr Farnon, I have called to see you about some young beasts. I turned a batch of thirty-five out this spring and they looked in good condition but now they're losing ground fast – all of them.'

My heart gave a great thump and something must have shown in my face because she smiled across at me.

'Oh don't worry, Mr Herriot, it's not husk again. There's not a cough among the lot of them. But they are going thin and they're badly scoured.'

'I think I know what that will be,' Siegfried said, leaning across to push a plate of Mrs Hall's flapjack towards her. 'They'll have picked up a few worms. Not lungworms but the stomach and intestinal kind. They probably just need a good dose of medicine to clear them out.'

She nodded and took a piece of the flapjack. 'Yes, that's what Charlie thought and we've dosed the lot of them. But it doesn't seem to have made any difference.'

'That's funny.' Siegfried rubbed his chin. 'Mind you they sometimes need a repeat but you should have seen some improvement. Perhaps we'd better have a look at them.'

'That's what I would like,' she said. 'It would set my mind at rest.'

Siegfried opened the appointment book. 'Right, and the sooner the better. Tomorrow morning all right? Splendid.' He made a quick note then looked up at her. 'By the way I'm going off for a week's holiday starting this evening so Mr Herriot will be coming.'

'That will be fine,' she replied, turning to me and smiling without a trace of doubt or misgiving. If she was thinking 'This is the fellow who supervised the deaths of nearly half of my young stock last year' she certainly didn't show it. In fact when she finally finished her tea and left she waved and smiled again as though she could hardly wait to see me again.

And when I walked across the fields with Mrs Dalby next day it was like turning the clock back to last year, except that we were going in the other direction; not down towards the marshy ground below the house but up to the stony pastures which climbed in an uneven checkerboard between their stone walls over the lower slopes of the hill.

The similarity persisted as we approached, too. These young beasts – roans, reds, red and whites – were an almost exact counterpart of last year's batch; shaggy little creatures, little more than calves, they stood spindly-legged and knock-kneed regarding us apathetically as we came up the rise. And though their symptoms were entirely different from the previous lot there was one thing I could say for sure; they were very ill.

As I watched I could see the dark watery diarrhoea flowing from them without any lifting of the tails as though there was nothing they could do to control it. And every one of them was painfully thin, the skin stretched over the jutting pelvic bones and the protruding rows of ribs.

'I haven't neglected them this time,' Mrs Dalby said.

'I know they look dreadful but this seems to have happened within a few days.'

'Yes ... yes ... I see ... ' My eyes were hunting desperately among the little animals trying to find some sort of clue. I had seen unthriftiness from parasitism but nothing like this.

'Have you kept a lot of cattle in these fields over the last year or two?' I asked.

She paused in thought for a moment. 'No ... no ... I don't think so. Billy used to let the milk cows graze up here now and then but that's all.'

The grass wouldn't be likely to be 'sick' with worms, then. In any case it didn't look like that. What it did look like was Johne's disease, but how in God's name could thirty-five young things like this get Johne's at the same time? Salmonella ...? Coccidiosis ...? Some form of poisoning, perhaps ... this was the time of year when cattle ate strange plants. I walked slowly round the field, but there was nothing unusual to be seen; it took even the grass all its time to grow on these wind-blown hillsides and there was no great range of other herbage. I could see bracken higher up the fell but none down here; Billy would have cleared it years ago.

'Mrs Dalby,' I said. 'I think you'd better give these stirks another dose of the worm medicine just to be sure and in the meantime I'm going to take some samples of the manure for examination at the laboratory.'

I brought up some sterile jars from the car and went painstakingly round the pasture scooping up as wide a range as possible from the pools of faeces.

I took them to the lab myself and asked them to phone the results through. The call came within twenty-four hours; negative for everything. I resisted the impulse to dash out to the farm immediately; there was nothing I could think of doing and it wouldn't look so good for me to stand there gawping at the beasts and scratching my head. Better to wait till tomorrow to see if the second dose of worm medicine did any good. There was no reason why it should, because none of the samples showed a pathogenic worm burden.

In these cases I always hope that inspiration will come to me as I am driving around or even when I am examining other animals but this time as I climbed from the car outside Prospect House I was barren of ideas.

The young beasts were slightly worse. I had decided that if I still couldn't think of anything I would give the worst ones vitamin injections more or less for the sake of doing something; so with Charlie holding the heads I inserted the hypodermic under the taut skins of ten of the little creatures, trying at the same time to put away the feeling of utter futility. We didn't have to drive them inside; they were easily caught in the open field and that was a bad sign in itself.

'Well you'll let me know, Mrs Dalby,' I said hoarsely as I got back into the car. 'If that injection improves them I'll do the lot.' I gave what I hoped was a confident wave and drove off.

I felt so bad that it had a numbing effect on me and over the next few days my mind seemed to shy away from the subject of the Dalby stirks as though by not thinking about them they would just go away. I was reminded that they were still very much there by a phone call from Mrs Dalby.

'I'm afraid my cattle aren't doing any good, Mr Herriot.' Her voice was strained.

I grimaced into the receiver. 'And the ones I injected . . .?'

'Just the same as the others.'

I had to face up to reality now and drove out to Prospect House immediately; but the felling of cold emptiness, of having nothing to offer, made the journey a misery. I hadn't the courage to go to the farmhouse and face Mrs Dalby but hurried straight up through the fields to where the young beasts were gathered.

And when I walked among them and studied them at close range the apprehension I had felt on the journey was nothing to the sick horror which rushed through me now. Another catastrophe was imminent here. The big follow-up blow which was all that was needed to knock the Dalby family out once and for all was on its way. These animals were going to die. Not just half of them like last year but all of them, because there was hardly any variation in their symptoms; there didn't seem to be a single one of them which was fighting off the disease.

But what disease? God almighty, I was a veterinary surgeon! Maybe not steeped in experience but I wasn't a new beginner any more. I should surely have some small inkling why a whole great batch of young beasts was sinking towards the knacker yard in front of my eyes.

I could see Mrs Dalby coming up the field with little William, striding in his tough, arm-swinging way by her side, and Charlie following behind.

What the hell was I going to say to them? Shrug my shoulders with a light laugh and say I hadn't a single clue in my head and that it would probably be best to phone Mallock now and ask them to shoot the lot of them straight away for dog meat? They wouldn't have any cattle to bring on for next year but that wouldn't matter because they would no longer be farming.

Stumbling among the stricken creatures I gazed at them in turn, almost choking as I looked at the drooping, sunken-eyed heads, the gaunt little bodies, the eternal trickle of that deadly scour. There was a curious immobility about the group, probably because they were too weak to walk about; in fact as I watched, one of them took a few steps, swayed and almost fell.

Charlie was pushing open the gate into the field just a hundred yards away. I turned and stared at the nearest animal, almost beseeching it to tell me what was wrong with it, where it felt the pain, how this thing had all started. But I got no response. The stirk, one of the smallest, only calf-size, with a very dark roan-coloured head showed not the slightest interest but gazed back at me incuriously through its spectacles. What was that . . . what was I thinking about . . . spectacles? Was my reason toppling . . .? But yes, by God, he did have spectacles . . . a ring of lighter hair surrounding each eye. And that other beast over there . . . he was the same. Oh glory be, now I knew! At last I knew!

Mrs Dalby, panting slightly, had reached me.

'Good morning, Mr Herriot,' she said, trying to smile. 'What do you think, then?' She looked around the cattle with anxious eyes

'Ah, good morning to you, Mrs Dalby,' I replied expansively, fighting down the impulse to leap in the air and laugh and shout and perhaps do a few cartwheels. 'Yes, I've had a look at them and it is pretty clear now what the trouble is.'

'Really? Then what . . .?'

'It's copper deficiency.' I said it casually as though I had been turning such a thing over in my mind right from the beginning. 'You can tell by the loss of the pigment in the coat, especially around the eyes. In fact when you look at them you can see that a lot of them are a bit paler than normal.' I waved an airy hand in the general direction of the stirks.

Charlie nodded. 'Aye, by gaw, you're right. Ah thowt they'd gone a funny colour.'

'Can we cure it?' Mrs Dalby asked the inevitable question.

'Oh yes, I'm going straight back to the surgery now to make up a copper mixture and we'll dose the lot. And you'll have to repeat that every fortnight while they are out at grass. It's a bit of a nuisance, I'm afraid, but there's no other way. Can you do it?'

'Oh aye, we'll do it,' Charlie said.

And 'Oh aye, we'll do it,' little William echoed, sticking out his chest and strutting around aggressively as though he wanted to start catching the beasts right away.

The treatment had a spectacular effect. I didn't have the modern long-lasting copper injections at my disposal but the solution of copper sulphate which I concocted under the surgery tap at Skeldale House worked like magic. Within a few weeks that batch of stirks was capering, lively and fully fleshed, over those hillside fields. Not a single death, no lingering unthriftiness. It was as though the whole thing had never happened, as though the hand of doom had never hovered over not only the cattle but the little family of humans.

It had been a close thing and, I realised, only a respite. That little woman had a long hard fight ahead of her still.

I have always abhorred change of any kind but it pleases me to come forward twenty years and spectate at another morning in the kitchen at Prospect House. I was seated at the same little table picking a buttered scone from the same tray and wondering whether I should follow it with a piece of malt bread or one of the jam tarts.

Billy still smiled down from the mantelpiece and Mrs Dalby, hands clasped in front of her, was watching me, her head a little on one side, the same half smile curving her lips. The years had not altered her much; there was some grey in her hair but the little red, weathered face and the bright eyes were as I had always known them.

I sipped my tea and looked across at the vast bulk of William sprawled in his father's old chair, smiling his father's smile at me. There were about fifteen stones of William and I had just been watching him in action as he held a fully grown bullock's hind foot while I examined it. The animal had made a few attempts to kick but the discouragement on its face had been obvious as William's great hands effortlessly engulfed its fetlock and a corner of his wide shoulder span dug into its abdomen.

No, I couldn't expect William to be the same, nor Dennis and Michael clattering into the kitchen now in their heavy boots and moving over to the sink to wash their hands. They were six footers too with their father's high-shouldered easy slouching walk but without William's sheer bulk.

Their tiny mother glanced at them then up at the picture on the mantelpiece. 'It would have been our thirtieth anniversary today,' she said conversationally.

I looked up at her, surprised. She never spoke of such things and I didn't know how to answer. I couldn't very well say 'congratulations' when she had spent twenty of those years alone. She had never said a word about her long fight; and it had been a winning fight. She had bought the neighbouring farm lower down the Dale when old Mr Mason retired; it was a good farm with better land and William had lived there after his marriage and they ran the two places as one. Things were pretty good now with her three expert stocksmen sons eliminating the need for outside labour except old Charlie who still pottered around doing odd jobs.

'Yes, thirty years,' Mrs Dalby said, looking slowly round the room as though she was seeing it for the first time. Then she turned back and bent over me, her face serious.

'Mr Herriot,' she said, and I was sure that at last, on this special day, she was going to say something about the years of struggle, the nights of worry and tears, the grinding toil.

For a moment she rested her hand lightly on my shoulder and her eyes looked into mine.

'Mr Herriot, are you quite sure that tea is to your liking?'

Chapter Ten

Every professional visit has its beginning in a call, a summons from the client which can take varying forms. . . .

'This is Joe Bentley speaking,' said the figure on the surgery doorstep. It was an odd manner of address, made stranger by the fact that Joe was holding his clenched fist up by his jaw and staring vacantly past me.

' 'ello, 'ello,' Joe continued as though into space, and suddenly everything became clear. That was an imaginary telephone he was holding and he was doing his best to communicate with the vet; and not doing badly considering the innumerable pints of beer that were washing around inside him.

On market days the pubs stayed open from ten o'clock till five and Joe was one of the now extinct breed who took their chance to drink themselves almost insensible. The modern farmer may have a few drinks on market day but the old reckless intake is rare now.

In Darrowby it was confined to a group of hard-bitten characters, all of them elderly, so even then the custom was on the wane. But it wasn't uncommon to see them when they came to pay their bills, leaning helplessly against the surgery wall and pushing their cheque books wordlessly at us. Some of them still used a pony and trap and the old joke about the horse taking them home was illustrated regularly. One old chap kept an enormously powerful ancient car simply for the purpose of getting him home; even if he engaged top gear by mistake when he collapsed into the driver's seat the vehicle would still take off. Some didn't go home at all on market day but spent the night carousing and playing cards till dawn.

As I looked at Joe Bentley swaying on the step I wondered what his programme might be for the rest of the evening. He closed his eyes, held his fist close to his face, and spoke again.

'Hellow, who's there?' he asked in an affected telephone voice.

'Herriot speaking,' I replied. Clearly Joe wasn't trying to be funny. He was just a little confused. It was only right to cooperate with him. 'How are you, Mr Bentley?'

'Nicely, thank ye,' Joe answered solemnly, eyes still tightly closed. 'Are you very well?'

'I'm fine, thanks. Now what can I do for you?'

This seemed to floor him temporarily because he remained silent for several seconds, opening his eyes occasionally and squinting somewhere over my left shoulder with intense concentration. Then something seemed to click; he closed his eyes again, cleared his throat and recommenced.

'Will you come up to ma place? I've a cow wants cleansin'.'

'Do you want me to come tonight?'

Joe gave this serious thought, pursing his lips and scratching his ear with his free hand before answering.

'Nay, morning'll do. Goodbye and thank ye.' He replaced the phantom telephone carefully in its rest, swung round and made his way down the street with great dignity. He hardly staggered at all and there was something purposeful in his bearing which convinced me that he was heading back to the Red Bear. For a moment I thought he would fall outside Johnson's the ironmongers but by the time he rounded the corner into the market place he was going so well that I felt sure he'd make it.

And I can remember Mr Biggins standing by the desk in our office, hands deep in his pockets, chin thrust forward stubbornly.

'I 'ave a cow gruntin' a bit.'

'Oh, right, we'll have a look at her.' I reached for a pen to write the visit in the book.

He shuffled his feet. 'Well ah don't know. She's maybe not as bad as all that.'

'Well, whatever you say . . .'

'No,' he said, 'It's what you say – you're t'vet.'

'It's a bit difficult.' I replied. 'After all, I haven't seen her. Maybe I'd better pay you a visit.'

'Aye, that's all very fine, but it's a big expense. It's ten bob every time you fellers walk on to ma place and that's before you start. There's all t'medicines and everything on top.'

'Yes, I understand, Mr Biggins. Well, would you like to take something away with you? A tin of stomach powder, perhaps?'

'How do you know it's t'stomach?'

'Well I don't actually . . .'

'It might be summat else.'

'That's very true, but . . .'

'She's a right good cow, this,' he said with a touch of aggression. 'Paid fifty pun for her at Scarburn Market.'

'Yes, I'm sure she is. And consequently I really think she'd be worth a visit. I could come out this afternoon.'

There was a long silence. 'Aye, but it wouldn't be just one visit, would it? You'd be comin' again next day and maybe the one after that and before we knew we'd 'ave a clonkin' great bill.'

'Yes, I'm sorry, Mr Biggins, everything is so expensive these days.'

'Yes, by gaw!' He nodded vigorously. 'Sometimes it ud be cheaper to give you t'cow at t'end of it.'

'Well now, hardly that . . . but I do see your point.'

I spent a few moments in thought. 'How about taking a fever drink as well as the stomach powder? That would be safer.'

He gave me a long blank stare. 'But you still wouldn't be sure, would you?'

'No, not quite sure, not absolutely . . .'

'She could even 'ave a wire in 'er'.

'True, very true.'

'Well then, shoving medicines down her neck isn't goin' to do no good is it?'

'It isn't, you're right.'

'Ah don't want to lose this cow, tha knows!' he burst out truculently. 'Ah can't afford to lose 'er!'

'I realise that, Mr Biggins. That's why I feel I should see her – I did suggest that if you remember.'

He did not reply immediately and only the strain in his eyes and a faint twitching of a cheek muscle betrayed the inner struggle which was raging. When he finally spoke it was in a hoarse croak.

'Aye, well, it might be best ... but ... er we could mebbes leave 'er till mornin' and see how she is then.'

'That's a good idea.' I smiled in relief. 'You have a look at her first thing in the morning and give me a ring before nine if she's no better.'

My words seemed to deepen his gloom. 'But what if she doesn't last till mornin'?'

'Well of course there is that risk.'

'Not much good ringin' you if she's dead, is it?'

'That's true, of course.'

'Ah'd be ringin' Mallock the knacker man, wouldn't I?'

'Afraid so, yes ...'

'Well that's no bloody use to me, gettin' five quid from Mallock for a good cow!'

'Mm, no ... I can see how you feel.'

'Ah think a lot about this cow!'

'I'm sure you do.'

'It ud be a big loss for me.'

'Quite.'

Mr Biggins hunched his shoulders and glared at me belligerently. 'Well then what are you goin' to do about 'er?'

'Let's see.' I ran my fingers through my hair. 'Perhaps you could wait till tonight and see if she recovers and if she isn't right by say, eight o'clock you could let me know and I'd come out.'

'You'd come out then, would you?' he said slowly, narrowing his eyes.

I gave him a bright smile. 'That's right.'

'Aye, but last time you came out at night you charged extra, ah'm sure you did.'

'Well, probably,' I said, spreading my hands. 'That's usual in veterinary practices.'

'So we're worse off than afore, aren't we?'

'When you look at it like that ... I suppose so ...'

'Ah'm not a rich man, tha knows.'

'I realise that.'

'Takes me all ma time to pay t'ordinary bill without extras.'

'Oh I'm sure ...'

'So that idea's a bad egg, ain't it?'

'Seems like it ... yes ...' I lay back in my chair, feeling suddenly tired.

Mr Biggins glowered at me morosely but I wasn't going to be tempted into any further gambits. I gave him what I fancied was a neutral stare and I hoped it conveyed the message that I was open to suggestions but wasn't going to make any myself.

The silence which now blanketed the room seemed to be of a durable nature. Down at the end of the street the church clock tolled the quarter hour, far off in the market place a dog barked, Miss Dobson, the grocer's daughter, glided past the window on her bicycle but no word was uttered.

Mr Biggins, biting his lower lip, darting his eyes desperately from his feet to me and back again, was clearly at the end of his resources, and it came to me at last that I had to take a firm initiative.

'Mr Biggins,' I said. 'I've got to be on my way. I have a lot of calls and one of them is within a mile of your farm, so I shall see your cow around three o'clock.' I stood up to indicate that the interview was over.

The farmer gave me a hunted look. I had the feeling that he had been resigned to a long period of stalemate and this sudden attack had taken him out of his stride. He opened his mouth as though to speak then appeared to change his mind and turned to go. At the door he paused, raised his hand and looked at me beseechingly for a moment, then he sank his chin on his chest and left the room.

I watched him through the window and as he crossed the road he stopped half way in the street in the same indeterminate way, muttering to himself and glancing back at the surgery; and as he lingered there I grew anxious that he might be struck by a passing car, but at length he squared his shoulders and trailed slowly out of sight.

And sometimes it isn't easy to get a clear picture over the telephone . . .

'This is Bob Fryer.'

'Good morning, Herriot here.'

'Now then, one of me sows is bad.'

'Oh right, what's the trouble?'

A throaty chuckle. 'Ah, that's what ah want *you* to tell *me!*'

'Oh, I see.'

'Aye, ah wouldn't be ringin' you up if I knew what the trouble was, would I? Heh, heh, heh, heh!'

The fact that I had heard this joke about two thousand times interfered with my full participation in the merriment but I managed a cracked laugh in return.

'That's perfectly true, Mr Fryer. Well, why have you rung me?'

'Damn, I've told ye – to find out what the trouble is.'

'Yes, I understand that, but I'd like some details. What do you mean when you say she's bad?'

'Well, she's just a bit off it.'

'Quite, but could you tell me a little more?'

A pause. 'She's dowly, like.'

'Anything else?'

'No . . . no . . . she's a right poorly pig, though.'

I spent a few moments in thought. 'Is she doing anything funny?'

'Funny? Funny? Nay, there's nowt funny about t'job, I'll tell tha! It's no laughin' matter.'

'Well . . . er . . . let me put it this way. Why are you calling me out?'

'I'm calling ye out because you're a vet. That's your job, isn't it?'

I tried again. 'It would help if I knew what to bring with me. What are her symptoms?'

'Symptoms? Well, she's just off colour, like.'

'Yes, but what is she doing?'

'She's doin' nowt. That's what bothers me.'

'Let's see.' I scratched my head. 'Is she very ill?'

'I reckon she's in bad fettle.'

'But would you say it was an urgent matter?'

Another long pause. 'Well, she's nobbut middlin'. She's not framin' at all.'

'Yes . . . yes . . . and how long has she been like this?'

'Oh, for a bit.'

'But how long exactly?'

'For a good bit.'

'But Mr Fryer, I want to know when she started these symptoms. How long has she been affected?'

'Oh . . . ever since we got 'er.'

'Ah, and when was that?'

'Well, she came wi' the others . . .'

Chapter Eleven

It was going to take a definite effort of will to get out of the car. I had driven about ten miles from Darrowby, thinking all the time that the Dales always looked their coldest, not when they were covered with snow, but as now, when the first sprinkling streaked the bare flanks of the fells in bars of black and white like the ribs of a crouching beast. And now in front of me was the farm gate rattling on its hinges as the wind shook it.

The car, heaterless and draughty as it was, seemed like a haven in an uncharitable world and I gripped the wheel tightly with my woollen-gloved hands for a few moments before opening the door. The wind almost tore the handle from my fingers as I got out but I managed to crash the door shut before stumbling over the frozen mud to the gate. Muffled as I was in heavy coat and scarf pulled up to my ears I could feel the icy gusts biting at my face, whipping up my nose and hammering painfully into the air spaces in my head.

I had driven through and, streaming-eyed, was about to get back into the car when I noticed something unusual. There was a frozen pond just off the path and among the rime-covered rushes which fringed the dead opacity of the surface a small object stood out, shiny black.

I went over and looked closer. It was a tiny kitten, probably about six weeks old, huddled and immobile, eyes tightly closed. Bending down I poked gently at the furry body. It must be dead; a morsel like this couldn't possibly survive in such cold . . . but no, there was a spark of life because the mouth opened soundlessly for a second then closed.

Quickly I lifted the little creature and tucked it inside my coat. As I drove into the farmyard I called to the farmer who was carrying two buckets out of the calf house. 'I've got one of your kittens here, Mr Butler. It must have strayed outside.'

Mr Butler put down his buckets and looked blank. 'Kitten? We haven't got no kittens at present.'

I showed him my find and he looked more puzzled.

'Well that's a rum 'un, there's no black cats on this spot. We've all sorts o' colours but no black 'uns.'

'Well he must have come from somewhere else,' I said. 'Though I can't imagine anything so small travelling very far. It's rather mysterious.'

I held the kitten out and he engulfed it with his big, work-roughened hand.

'Poor little beggar, he's only just alive. I'll take him into t'house and see if the missus can do owt for him.'

In the farm kitchen Mrs Butler was all concern. 'Oh what a shame!' She smoothed back the bedraggled hair with one finger. 'And it's got such a pretty face.' She looked up at me. 'What is it, anyway, a him or a her?'

I took a quick look behind the hind legs. 'It's a Tom.'

'Right,' she said. 'I'll get some warm milk into him but first of all we'll give him the old cure.'

She went over to the fireside oven on the big black kitchen range, opened the door and popped him inside.

I smiled. It was the classical procedure when new-born lambs were found suffering from cold and exposure; into the oven they went and the results were often dramatic. Mrs Butler left the door partly open and I could just see the little black figure inside; he didn't seem to care much what was happening to him.

The next hour I spent in the byre wrestling with the hind feet of a cow. The cleats were overgrown and grossly misshapen and upturned, causing the animal to hobble along on her heels. My job was to pare and hack away the excess horn and my long held opinion that the hind feet of a cow were never meant to be handled by man was thoroughly confirmed. We had a rope round the hock and the leg pulled up over a beam in the roof but the leg still pistoned back and forth while I hung on till my teeth rattled. By the time I had finished the sweat was running into my eyes and I had quite forgotten the cold day outside.

Still, I thought, as I eased the kinks from my spine when I had finished, there were compensations. There was a satisfaction in the sight of the cow standing comfortably on two almost normal looking feet.

'Well that's summat like,' Mr Butler grunted. 'Come in the house and wash your hands.'

In the kitchen as I bent over the brown earthenware sink I kept glancing across at the oven.

Mrs Butler laughed. 'Oh he's still with us. Come and have a look.'

It was difficult to see the kitten in the dark interior but when I spotted him I put out my hand and touched him and he turned his head towards me.

'He's coming round,' I said. 'That hour in there has worked wonders.'

'Doesn't often fail.' The farmers wife lifted him out. 'I think he's a little tough 'un.' She began to spoon warm milk into the tiny mouth. 'I reckon we'll have him lappin' in a day or two.'

'You're going to keep him, then?'

'Too true we are. I'm going to call him Moses.'

'Moses?'

'Aye, you found him among the rushes, didn't you?'

I laughed. 'That's right. It's a good name.'

I was on the Butler farm about a fortnight later for the ever recurring job of 'cleansing' a cow and I kept looking around for Moses. Farmers rarely have their cats indoors and I thought that if the black kitten had survived he would have joined the feline colony around the buildings.

Farm cats have a pretty good time. They may not be petted or cosseted but it has always seemed to me that they lead a free, natural life. They are expected to catch mice but if they are not so inclined there is abundant food at hand; bowls of milk here and there and the dogs' dishes to be raided if anything interesting is left over. I had seen plenty of cats around today, some flitting nervously away, others friendly and purring. There was a tabby loping gracefully across the cobbles and a big tortoiseshell was curled on a bed of straw at the warm end of the byre; cats are connoisseurs of comfort. When Mr Butler went to fetch the hot water I had a quick look in the bullock house and a white Tom regarded me placidly from between the bars of a hay rack where he had been taking a siesta. But there was no sign of Moses.

I finished drying my arms and was about to make a casual reference to the kitten when Mr Butler handed me my jacket.

'Come round here with me if you've got a minute,' he said. 'I've got summat to show you.'

I followed him through the door at the end and across a passage into the long, low-roofed piggery. He stopped at a pen about half way down and pointed inside.

'Look 'ere,' he said.

I leaned over the wall and my face must have shown my astonishment because the farmer burst into a shout of laughter.

'That's summat new for you, isn't it?'

I stared unbelievingly down at a large sow stretched comfortably on her side, suckling a litter of about twelve piglets and right in the middle of the long pink row, furry black and incongruous, was Moses. He had a teat in his mouth and was absorbing his nourishment with the same rapt enjoyment as his smooth-skinned fellows on either side.

'What the devil . . .?' I gasped.

Mr Butler was still laughing. 'I thought you'd never have seen anything like that before, I never have, any road.'

'But how did it happen?' I still couldn't drag my eyes away.

'It was the Missus's idea,' he replied. 'When she'd got the little youth lappin' milk she took him out to find a right warm spot for him in the buildings. She settled on this pen because the sow, Bertha, had just had a litter and I had a heater in and it was grand and cosy.'

I nodded. 'Sounds just right.'

'Well she put Moses and a bowl of milk in here,' the farmer went on, 'but the little feller didn't stay by the heater very long – next time I looked in he was round at t'milk bar.'

I shrugged my shoulders. 'They say you see something new every day at this game, but this is something I've never even heard of. Anyway, he looks well on it – does he actually live on the sow's milk or does he still drink from his bowl?'

'A bit of both, I reckon. It's hard to say.'

Anyway, whatever mixture Moses was getting he grew rapidly into a sleek, handsome animal with an unusually high gloss to his coat which may or may not have been due to the porcine element of his diet. I never went to the Butlers' without having a look in the pig pen. Bertha, his foster mother, seemed to find nothing unusual in this hairy intruder and pushed him around casually with pleased grunts just as she did with the rest of her brood.

Moses for his part appeared to find the society of the pigs very congenial. When the piglets curled up together and settled down for a sleep Moses would be somewhere in the heap and when his young colleagues were weaned at eight weeks he showed his attachment to Bertha by spending most of his time with her.

And it stayed that way over the years. Often he would be right inside the pen, rubbing himself happily along the comforting bulk of the sow, but I remember him best in his favourite place; crouching on the wall looking down perhaps meditatively on what had been his first warm home.

Chapter Twelve

I was beginning to learn a few tricks of my own.

In my bachelor days those early morning rings at the doorbell used to start me galloping downstairs into the freezing passage in my pyjamas full of enthusiasm, in fact almost bursting with impatience to learn what the immediate future held for me. But marriage had maybe softened me. At any rate, a long run of sessions in my bare feet on the doorstep with the bracing Yorkshire air whistling round my ankles had persuaded me that this was an overrated pastime.

The trouble was that in those days there were very few telephones on the farms and many of the farmers used to cycle in to the surgery when they wanted the vet; and of course farmers are inclined to rise rather early; a lot of them seemed to think that around 7 a.m. was a good time.

I just had to alter my system and now when I heard that long jangling downstairs I crawled out from beside Helen, tiptoed over to the window and opened it. Our bed-sitter being at the front of the house I was able to push my head through a few inches of space and carry on long conversations while most of me stayed warmly inside.

But on this Sunday morning something was wrong. I had heard the ring, taken up my kneeling position on the floor and got my head through the window. But I couldn't see anybody.

'Hello!' I called.

' 'ellow!' came back the reply immediately. But there was nobody on the step.

'Hello!' I shouted.

' 'ellow!' a hearty bellow responded.

'Hello!' I bawled at the top of my voice. I still couldn't see a soul.

' 'ellow, 'ellow, 'ellow!' echoed a full-throated yell with just a touch of asperity in it.

This was ridiculous. I didn't feel up to another effort – my head was beginning to throb – so I pushed the sash up a few inches more and leaned further out into the street.

And as I gazed down over the long stretch of ivy-covered brick it became clear why I had been unable to see anybody on the step. A man with very bandy legs encased in brown leggings was leaning against the wall of the house; he was bent double and apparently hollering straight down at the ground. I was baffled at first then I realised that he was directing his cries down through the small iron grating which led to the cellar. There was a chute there where the coalman used to tip his bags.

From my new vantage point I was able to attract the man's attention and when he looked up I saw it was Mr Dawson of Highstones.

He grinned cheerfully, quite unabashed. 'Oh, you're there are you? I have a cow with a touch o' felon. Give us a call some time this morning will you?' He waved and was gone.

I returned thoughtfully to Helen's side. And as I tried to drop off to sleep again the strong impression kept pushing into my consciousness that Mr Dawson wouldn't have been at all surprised if I had popped my head up through the grating instead of the window. It seemed to me that he had accepted the fact that I dwelt somewhere in the grimy darkness at the bottom of that cleft. It lent weight to an idea that had been growing in my mind for some time; that farmers looked on vets as different beings. We weren't really people at all.

There was Mr Coates last week. He had got me out of bed at 3 a.m. to a farrowing and when I stumbled, eyes half closed, from the car he was standing outside the piggery holding a lamp.

'Well now, Mr Herriot,' he said brightly, 'were you in bed when ah phoned?'

I stared at the man. 'In bed? Where the heck do you think I'd be at three o'clock in the morning?'

'Well ah don't know.' Mr Coates looked a little confused. 'Ah thought you might be up studyin'.'

There it was again. Up studyin'! Did they really think a vet was a creature apart – a kind of troglodyte who lived in a cell with only his text books and instruments for company? He didn't have a social life, he required no sleep, he didn't even have to eat. This last point was a very real one; I have often noticed a certain puzzlement in a farmer's face when I said I'd be as quick as I could but I'd have to finish my dinner first; or a pregnant silence at the end of the phone when I said I was just starting my breakfast.

But the man who most blatantly ignored my nutritional requirements and actually seemed to be trying to sabotage them was Mr Grainger of Beckton. He was a fierce man in his sixties and he called to see me every Saturday evening at six o'clock. What made this particularly wearing was that Helen chose each Saturday to put on a sumptuous high tea. Maybe she wanted to remind me of my Scottish upbringing but she used to set before me things like herrings in oatmeal with mustard sauce or sole and chips or ham and eggs and fill in the spaces on the table with new-baked scones, pancakes, curd tarts, cherry cakes.

It was usually when I was half way through the first course that the bell rang and there, sure enough, was Mr Grainger glaring belligerently through the glass door. He would never come into the house. All he wanted was a ten minutes' discussion on the doorstep. At first I used to say, 'I'm just at my tea,' or something like that, or I'd go on chewing in an exaggerated manner and keep wiping my lips on a napkin until I realised I was wasting my time. Mr Grainger was only interested in me as an object to talk at.

I said he wanted a discussion but that was the wrong word; he just wanted to air his views. An insight into his character could be gained from the remarks of one of his neighbours who told me that the Beckton Farmers' Discussion Group had folded up because whenever Mr Grainger got up to speak all the other farmers walked out.

In any case it seemed to enliven his Saturday evening to hold me trapped there while he described the symptoms displayed by his livestock during the previous week. He never asked me for advice; he made it quite clear that he knew a lot better than me how to treat his animals, but he did want to tell me about it. And he told me at great length, his hands clasped over his stick in front of him, his eyes fixed on mine in a hostile stare.

But nothing is wholly bad and I did reap some small recompense from observing his antics as he tried to illustrate his case histories with actions.

I can recall one Saturday when he was complaining bitterly that he had been swindled over a carthorse he had just purchased. He was a particularly stiff-jointed man and not cut out for portraying the lameness of horses, but he managed to give an astounding impression of stringhalt. I diagnosed it instantly as he strutted up and down the pavement in front of Skeldale House, jerking one leg up behind him at every step. Then he stopped abruptly and held the offending limb out, quivering, behind him . . . good heavens, maybe he was a shiverer, too! The farmer kept his eyes on me and seemed oblivious of the interest of the passers-by. There were quite a few people in the street, probably bound for the early show at the cinema, but for the moment they appeared to find Mr Grainger more entertaining.

'And that's not all,' he cried. 'There's summat wrang with his watterworks.'

'Really? How do you mean?'

'Why 'e can't stale properly. Has a 'ell of a job. Gets himself all wraxed up like this.'

Mr Grainger went into another of his impersonations – that of a horse having difficulty in passing urine – and I had to admit it was probably his best yet. He planted his stick firmly on the pavement and holding the top with both hands he backed away from it till his body was parallel with the ground. Then he began to straddle his legs further and further apart. The knot of people on the other side of the road had increased to a fair-sized crowd and they stared, fascinated, at the extraordinary sight. Mr Grainger was indeed the very picture of equine suffering and as he hollowed his back and paddled his wide-spaced feet I could almost share the desperate battle for release. When he finally raised his head and groaned the effect was harrowing.

When all was finished Mr Grainger did as he always did – gave me a cold nod and stumped off without a word. There was no need for him to say, 'See you next Saturday'. I knew he'd be back.

Then there was Mr Grimsdale. His attitude towards me was something I couldn't quite make out, but I did know that he always had a depressing effect on me. He did this by the simple expedient of telling me that I didn't look very well.

I thought back to the visit to his farm yesterday when he had called me to a cow with a cut teat. He was a tall cadaverous man with sunken cheeks and a mournful expression – he would have made a wonderful undertaker – and he looked at me in his own particular way as I got out of the car.

I wondered what it would be today. My own conviction is that you should never tell anybody they don't look well, no matter what you think. And Mr Grimsdale's little sallies bit especially deeply because he always referred to me in agricultural terms as though I were one of his bullocks.

'You've lost a bit o' ground lately, young man,' he would say, directing a piercing glance from my face down to my feet and down again. 'Aye, you're losin' ground fast – it's plain to see.'

Or another time it might be, 'You've run off a bit, Mr Herriot. There's no doubt you've run off.' And his stick would twitch in his hand as if he would have liked to give me an exploratory poke.

But today he didn't say anything until I had finished stitching the teat and was washing my hands in a bucket of water. Then as I straightened up he adopted his usual stance; throwing up his head and jutting his chin he appraised me gloomily.

'You've failed since ah last saw you, young man. Soon as you walked across t'yard this morning ah thought to meself, aye that lad's failed over t'last week or two.'

And as the sharp eyes bored into me from behind the long pointed nose his viewpoint was plain. He, at any rate, could contemplate the prospect of my early demise with some compassion but without going to pieces.

I worked up a sickly smile as I always did.

'Oh, I'm fine, Mr Grimsdale, never felt better.' But the voice had an uncertain quaver and I knew by my sinking stomach that his shaft had gone home again. And then there was the usual humiliating business when I had driven away. I always stopped the car just round the corner where a high curve of wall hid me from the farm.

Staring into the car mirror I put out my tongue, pulled down my eyelids to have a look at my mucous membranes and muttered desperately as though Mr Grimsdale was still there.

'I feel fine, really I do . . . fine . . . fine . . .'

Talking of farmers' attitudes to their vets, I think it is fair to say that in Robert Hewison's cheerful household, though Siegfried's prowess as an animal doctor was highly regarded, his main claim to fame was as a judge of Christmas cake.

Mrs Hewison was a baker of great repute and when she started long before the festive season to stir up vast quantities of fruit and candied peel and butter and all the other things that went into her peerless cakes it was a very serious business. Not that there was any question of a failure – her cakes varied from excellent to superb – but once the long process had been completed and the last piece of marzipan and icing applied she dearly loved to have the accolade from an expert. And in her eyes Siegfried was number one.

Robert Hewison confided in me once: 'Tha knows, my missus is never content till your guvnor's had a taste.'

I was privileged to be present on one of these occasions. It was a few days before Christmas and Siegfried and I had gone together to Robert's farm to lift a horse which had got cast in its stall. We did the job successfully with the aid of slings and a block and tackle and Robert, as always, asked us into the house.

The farmer's wife, her dark, rather solemn face illumined by friendly eyes, ushered us to the two tall wooden chairs by the fireside.

'Come and get warmed up, gentlemen,' she said. 'And you'll have a drink and a bit o' cake, won't you?'

'You're very kind, Mrs Hewison,' replied Siegfried. 'That would be lovely.'

He sat down, but I went through to the offshoot of the kitchen to wash my hands at the sink. The farmer's wife was cutting at a large cake on a table nearby. She nudged me and whispered conspiratorially.

'This isn't me own cake. It's one me sister baked, but I'm not telling Mr Farnon that. We'll just see what he says.'

I stared at her. 'But is that quite fair? Hadn't you better tell him?'

'No, I want to have his true judgement, so I'm not sayin' a word.'

I went back to the kitchen with some misgiving. It was unlike this lady to play jokes, but maybe after years of unqualified approbation she wanted to put my colleague's sincerity to the test. Anyway, I hoped nothing unfortunate would happen.

As I took my place by the fire Robert and his three sons came in and sat around in a circle. I was given a piece of cake, too, but nobody paid any attention to me; all eyes were on Siegfried.

'I'd like to know what you think of t'cake this year, Mr Farnon,' our hostess said.

My colleague toasted the family gracefully, sipped at his whisky then lifted the plate with its slice of cake. Silence fell upon the company. Holding the plate in the palm of his hand he studied the cake carefully from various angles before breaking off a fair-sized piece. This he massaged gently between thumb and forefinger for a few moments, his eyes half closed. Then after sniffing at it a couple of times he put it in his mouth.

I could feel the tension building in the room as he chewed gravely, his face quite expressionless. When he had finally swallowed the portion he smacked his lips once or twice meditatively then turned his head and looked full at Mrs Hewison. Amid a deathly hush they gazed into each other's eyes for several long seconds but Siegfried still didn't say anything. Instead he reached for his glass again and took another drink of whisky which he seemed to wash around his mouth before breaking off another portion of cake.

He took a long time over this piece, chewing in a slow motion, his eyes, deadly serious, staring sightlessly in front of him. Robert, the boys, all of us, leaned a little forward in our chairs, as he finally swallowed the last crumb, wiped his lips and sat immobile, apparently wrapped in thought. Then as he clearly came to a decision he sat upright in his chair, straightened his shoulders and turned resolutely towards the lady of the house once more.

Siegfried was and is a man of the highest principle. Over the years I have known him he has always given his opinions truthfully, fearlessly and with a total disregard of the consequences; and though this trait ruffled the stream of his life on occassion, there were times, as now, when it stood him in good stead.

'Mrs Hewison,' he said, his eyes steady and unwavering. 'This is a good cake.' He paused. 'A very good cake indeed.' He hesitated again and I could see the real iron in the man coming out. 'But if you will permit me, I'm bound to say that it is not up to your usual standard.'

Mrs Hewison, usually an undemonstrative person, burst into a loud cry of delight and Robert and his sons, who were obviously in on the joke, roared and clapped their hands.

Siegfried looked around in some surprise at the sudden tumult which went on and on as though somebody had scored a goal in the cup final. He was obviously puzzled and of course there was no way he could know that his previous exalted position in the household was now utterly impregnable.

Chapter Thirteen

I was back at Granville Bennett's again. Back in the tiled operating theatre with the great lamp pouring its harsh light over my colleague's bowed head, over the animal nurses, the rows of instruments, the little animal stretched on the table.

Until late this afternoon I had no idea that another visit to Hartington was in store for me; not until the doorbell rang as I was finishing a cup of tea and I went along the passage and opened the door and saw Colonel Bosworth on the step. He was holding a wicker cat basket.

'Can I trouble you for a moment, Mr Herriot?' he said.

His voice sounded different and I looked up at him questioningly. Most people had to look up at Colonel Bosworth with his lean six feet three inches and his tough soldier's face which matched the DSO and MC which he had brought out of the war. I saw quite a lot of him, not only when he came to the surgery but out in the country where he spent most of his time hacking along the quiet roads around Darrowby on a big hunter with two Cairn terriers trotting behind. I liked him. He was a formidable man but he was unfailingly courteous and there was a gentleness in him which showed in his attitude to his animals.

'No trouble,' I replied. 'Please come inside.'

In the waiting room he held out the basket. His eyes were strained and there was shock and hurt in his face.

'It's little Maudie,' he said.

'Maudie . . . your black cat?' When I had been to his house the little creature had usually been in evidence, rubbing down the colonel's ankles, jumping on his knee competing assiduously with the terriers for his attention.

'What's the matter, is she ill?'

'No . . . no . . .' He swallowed and spoke carefully. 'She's had an accident, I'm afraid.'

'What kind of accident?'

'A car struck her. She never goes out into the road in front of the house but for some reason she did this afternoon.'

'I see.' I took the basket from him. 'Did the wheel go over her?'

'No, I don't think it can have done that because she ran back into the house afterwards.'

'Oh well,' I said. 'That sounds hopeful. It probably isn't anything very much.'

The colonel paused for a moment. 'Mr Herriot, I wish you were right but it's . . . rather frightful. It's her face you see. Must have been a glancing blow but I . . . really don't see how she can live.'

'Oh . . . as bad as that . . . I'm sorry. Anyway come through with me and I'll have a look.'

He shook his head. 'No, I'll stay here if you don't mind. And there's just one thing.' He laid his hand briefly on the basket. 'If you think, as I do, that it's hopeless, please put her to sleep immediately. She must not suffer any more.'

I stared at him uncomprehendingly for a moment then hurried along the passage to the operating room. I put the basket on the table, slid the wooden rod from its loops and opened the lid. I could see the sleek little black form crouched in the depths and as I stretched my hand out gingerly towards it the head rose slowly and turned towards me with a long, open-mouthed wail of agony.

And it wasn't just an open mouth. The whole lower jaw was dangling uselessly, the mandible shattered and splintered, and as another chilling cry issued from the basket I had a horrific glimpse of jagged ends of bone gleaming from the froth of blood and saliva.

I closed the basket quickly and leaned on the lid.

'Christ!' I gasped. 'Oh Christ!'

I closed my eyes but couldn't dispel the memory of the grotesque face, the terrible sound of pain and worst of all the eyes filled with the terrified bewilderment which makes animal suffering so unbearable.

With trembling haste I reached behind me to the trolley for the bottle of Nembutal. This was the one thing vets could do, at any rate; cut short this agony with merciful speed. I pulled 5 c.c.'s into the syringe; more than enough – she'd drift into sleep and never wake up again. Opening the basket I reached down and underneath the cat and slipped the needle through the abdominal skin; an intraperitoneal injection would have to do. But as I depressed the plunger it was as though a calmer and less involved person was tapping me on the shoulder and saying, 'Just a minute, Herriot, take it easy. Why don't you think about this for a bit?'

I stopped after injecting 1 c.c. That would be enough to anaesthetise Maudie. In a few minutes she would feel nothing. Then I closed the lid and began to walk about the room. I had repaired a lot of cats' broken jaws in my time; they seemed to be prone to this trouble and I had gained much satisfaction from wiring up symphyseal fractures and watching their uneventful healing. But this was different.

After five minutes I opened the basket and lifted the little cat, sound asleep and as limp as a rag doll, on to the table.

I swabbed out the mouth and explored with careful fingers, trying to piece the grisly jigsaw together. The symphysis had separated right enough and that could be fastened together with wire, but how about those mandibular rami, smashed clean through on both sides – in fact there were two fractures on the left. And some of the teeth had been knocked out and others slackened; there was nothing to get hold of. Could they be held together by metal plates screwed into the bone? Maybe ... and was there a man with the skill and equipment to do such a job ...? I thought I just might know one.

I went over the sleeping animal carefully; there wasn't a thing amiss except that pathetic drooping jaw. Meditatively I stroked the smooth, shining fur. She was only a young cat with years of life in front of her and as I stood there the decision came to me with a surge of relief and I trotted back along the passage to ask the colonel if I could take Maudie through to Granville Bennett.

It had started to snow heavily when I set out and I was glad it was downhill all the way to Hartington; many of the roads higher up the Dale would soon be impassable on a night like this.

In the Veterinary Hospital I watched the big man drilling, screwing, stitching. It wasn't the sort of job which could be hurried but it was remarkable how quickly those stubby fingers could work. Even so, we had been in the theatre for nearly an hour and Granville's complete absorption showed in the long silences broken only by the tinkling of instruments, occasional barking commands and now and then a sudden flare of exasperation. And it wasn't only the nurses who suffered; I had scrubbed up and had been pressed into service and when I failed to hold the jaw exactly as my colleague desired he exploded in my face.

'Not that bloody way, Jim! ... What the hell are you playing at? ... No, no, no, no, *no*! ..... Oh God Almighty!'

But at last all was finished and Granville threw off his cap and turned away from the table with that air of finality which had made me envy him the first time. He was sweating. In his office he washed his hands, towelled his brow, and pulled on an elegant grey jacket from the pocket of which he produced a pipe. It was a different pipe from last time; I learned in time that all Granville's pipes were not only beautiful but big and this one had a bowl like a fair-sized coffee cup. He rubbed it gently along the side of his nose, gave it a polish with the yellow cloth he always seemed to carry and held it lovingly against the light.

'Straight grain, Jim. Superb, isn't it?'

He contentedly scooped tobacco from his vast pouch, ignited it and puffed a cloud of delectable smoke at me before taking me by the arm. 'Come on, laddie. I'll show you round while they're clearing up in there.'

We did a tour of the hospital, taking in the waiting and consulting rooms, X-ray room, dispensary and, of course, the office with its impressive card index system with case histories of all patients, but the bit I enjoyed most was walking along the row of heated cubicles where an assortment of animals were recovering from their operations.

Granville stabbed his pipe at them as we went along. 'Spay, enterotomy, aural haematoma, entropion.' Then he bent suddenly, put a finger through the wire front and adopted a wheedling tone. 'Come now, George, come on little fellow, don't be frightened, it's only Uncle Granville.'

A small West Highland with a leg in a cast hobbled to the front and my colleague tickled his nose through the wire.

'That's George Wills-Fentham,' he said in explanation. 'Old Lady Wills-Fentham's pride and joy. Nasty compound fracture but he's doing very nicely. He's a bit shy is George but a nice little chap when you get to know him, aren't you, old lad?' He continued his tickling and in the dim light I could see the short white tail wagging furiously.

Maudie was lying in the very last of the recovery pens, a tiny, trembling figure. That trembling meant she was coming out of the anaesthetic and I opened the door and stretched my hand out to her. She still couldn't raise her head but she was looking at me and as I gently stroked her side, her mouth opened in a faint rusty miaow. And with a thrill of deep pleasure I saw that her lower jaw belonged to her again; she could open and close it; that hideous dangling tatter of flesh and bone was only a bad memory.

'Marvellous, Granville,' I murmured. 'Absolutely bloody marvellous.'

Smoke plumed in quiet triumph from the noble pipe. 'Yes, it's not bad, is it laddie. A week or two on fluids and she'll be as good as new. No problems there.'

I stood up. 'Great! I can't wait to tell Colonel Bosworth. Can I take her home tonight?'

'No, Jim, no. Not this time. I just want to keep an eye on her for a couple of days then maybe the colonel can collect her himself.' He led me back into the brightly lit office where he eyed me for a moment.

'You must come and have a word with Zoe while you're here,' he said. 'But first, just a suggestion. I wonder if you'd care to slip over with me to . . .'

I took a rapid step backward. 'Well . . . er . . . really. I don't think so,' I gabbled. 'I enjoyed my visit to the club that other night but . . . er . . . perhaps not this evening.'

'Hold on, laddie, hold on,' Granville said soothingly. 'Who said anything about the club? No, I just wondered if you'd like to come to a meeting with me?'

'Meeting?'

'Yes, Professor Milligan's come through from Edinburgh to speak to the Northern Veterinary Society about metabolic diseases. I think you'd enjoy it.'

'You mean milk fever, acetonaemia and all that.'

'Correct. Right up your street, old son.'

'Well it is, isn't it? I wonder . . .' I stood for a few moments deep in thought, and one of the thoughts was why an exclusively small animal man like Granville wanted to hear about cow complaints. But I was maybe doing him an injustice; he probably wanted to maintain a broad, liberal view of veterinary knowledge.

It must have been obvious that I was dithering because he prodded me a little further.

'I'd like to have your company, Jim, and anyway I see you're all dressed and ready for anything. Matter of fact when you walked in tonight I couldn't help thinking what a smart lad you looked.'

He was right there. I hadn't dashed through in my farm clothes this time. With the memory of my last visit still painfully fresh in my mind I was determined that if I was going to meet the charming Zoe again I was going to be: (a) Properly dressed, (b) Sober (c) in a normal state of health and not bloated and belching like an impacted bullock. Helen, agreeing that my image needed refurbishing, had rigged me out in my best suit.

Granville ran his hand along my lapel. 'Fine piece of serge if I may say so.'

I made up my mind. 'Right, I'd like to come with you. Just let me ring Helen to say I won't be straight back and then I'm your man.'

Chapter Fourteen

Outside it was still snowing; city snow drifting down in a wet curtain which soon lost itself in the dirty churned-up slush in the streets. I pulled my coat higher round my neck and huddled deeper in the Bentley's leather luxury. As we swept past dark buildings and shops I kept expecting Granville to turn up some side street and stop, but within a few minutes we were speeding through the suburbs up towards the North Road. This meeting, I thought, must be out in one of the country institutes, and I didn't say anything until we had reached Scotch Corner and the big car had turned on to the old Roman Road at Bowes.

I stretched and yawned. 'By the way, Granville, where are they holding this meeting?'

'Appleby,' my colleague replied calmly.

I came bolt upright in my seat then I began to laugh.

'What's the joke, old son?' Granville enquired.

'Well ... Appleby ... ha-ha-ha! Come on, where are we really heading?'

'I've told you, laddie, the Pemberton Arms, Appleby, to be exact.'

'Do you mean it?'

'Of course.'

'But hell, Granville, that's on the other side of the Pennines.'

'Quite right. Always has been, laddie.'

I ran a hand through my hair. 'Wait a minute. Surely it isn't worth going about forty miles in weather like this. We'll never get over Bowes Moor you know – in fact I heard yesterday it was blocked. Anyway, it's nearly eight o'clock – we'd be too late.'

The big man reached across and patted my knee.

'Stop worrying, Jim. We'll get there and we'll be in plenty of time. You've got to remember you're sitting in a proper motor car now. A drop of snow is nothing.'

As if determined to prove his word he put his foot down and the great car hurtled along the dead straight stretch of road. We skidded a bit on the corner at Greta Bridge then roared through Bowes and up to the highest country. I couldn't see much. In fact on the moor top I couldn't see anything, because up there it was the real country snow; big dry flakes driving straight into the headlights and settling comfortably with millions of their neighbours on the already deep white carpet on the road. I just didn't know how Granville was able to see, never mind drive fast; I had no idea how we were going to get back over here in a few hours time when the wind had drifted the snow across the road. But I kept my mouth shut. It was becoming increasingly obvious that I emerged as a sort of maiden aunt in Granville's company, so I held my peace and prayed.

I followed this policy through Brough and along the lower road where the going was easier until I climbed out with a feeling of disbelief in the yard of the Pemberton Arms. It was nine o'clock.

We slipped into the back of the room and I settled into my chair, prepared to improve my mind a little. There was a man on the platform holding forth and at first I had difficulty in picking up the substance of his words; he wasn't mentioning anything about animal diseases but suddenly everything clicked into place.

'We are indeed grateful,' the man was saying, 'to Professor Milligan for coming all this way and for giving us a most interesting and instructive talk. I know I speak for the entire audience when I say we have enjoyed it thoroughly, so may I ask you to show your appreciation in the usual manner. There was a long round of applause then an outburst of talk and a pushing back of chairs.

I turned to Granville in some dismay. 'That was the vote of thanks. It's finished.'

'So it is, laddie.' My colleague didn't seem unduly disappointed or even surprised. 'But come with me – there are compensations.'

We joined the throng of vets and moved across the richly carpeted hall to another room where bright lights shone down on a row of tables laden with food. Then I recognised Bill Warrington the Burroughs Wellcome representative and all became clear.

This was a commercially sponsored evening and the real action, in Granville's estimation, began right here. I remembered then that Siegfried had once told me that Granville hated to miss any of these occasions. Though the most generous of men there was some piquancy in the gratis food and drink which attracted him irresistibly.

Even now he was guiding me purposefully towards the bar. But our progress was slow due to a phenomenon peculiar to Granville; everybody seemed to know him. Since those days I have been with him to restaurants, pubs, dances and it has been just the same. In fact I have often thought that if I took him to visit some lost tribe in the jungles of the Amazon one of them would jump and say, 'Well hello, Granville old boy!' and slap him on the back.

Finally however he fought his way through his fellow vets and we reached the bar where two dark little men in white coats were already under pressure; they were working with the impersonal concentration of people who knew that the whisky always took a hammering on veterinary evenings, but they paused and smiled as my colleague's massive presence hovered at the counter.

'Now then, Mr Bennett. How are you, Mr Bennett?'

'Good evening, Bob. Nice to see you, Reg.' Granville responded majestically.

I noticed that Bob put down his bottle of ordinary whisky and reached down for a bottle of Glenlivet Malt to charge Granville's glass. The big man sniffed the fine spirit appreciatively.

'And one for my friend, Mr Herriot,' he said.

The barmen's respectful expressions made me feel suddenly important and I found myself in possession of my own vast measure of Glenlivet. I had to get it down quickly followed by a few speedy refills since the barmen took their cue from my companion's consumption.

Then I followed in Granville's regal wake as he made his way among the tables with the air of a man in his natural environment. Messrs Burroughs Wellcome had done us proud and we worked our way through a variety of canapes, savouries and cold meats. Now and again we revisited the bar for more of the Glenlivet then back to the tables.

I knew I had drunk too much and now I was eating too much. But the difficulty with Granville was that if I ever declined anything he took it as a personal insult.

'Try one of those prawn things,' he would say, sinking his teeth into a mushroom vol au vent and if I hesitated a wounded look would come into his eyes.

But I was enjoying myself. Veterinary surgeons are my favourite people and

I revelled as I always did in their tales of successes and failures. Especially the failures; they were particular soothing. Whenever the thought of how we were going to get home stole into my mind I banished it quickly.

Granville seemed to have no qualms because he showed no signs of moving when the company began to thin out; in fact we were the last to leave, our departure being accorded a touch of ceremony by a final substantial stirrup cup from Bob and Reg.

As we left the hotel I felt fine; a little light-headed perhaps and with the merest hint of regret at being pressed to a second helping of trifle and cream, but otherwise in excellent shape. As we settled once more into the Bentley Granville was at his most expansive.

'Excellent meeting that, Jim. I told you it would be worth the journey.'

We were the only members of the company who were headed eastward and were alone on the road. In fact it occurred to me that we hadn't seen a single car on the road to Appleby and now there was something uncomfortable in our total isolation. The snow had stopped and the brilliant moon flooded its cold light over a white empty world. Empty, that is, except for us, and our solitary state was stressed by the smooth, virgin state of the glistening carpet ahead.

I was conscious of an increasing disquiet as the great gaunt spine of the Pennines bulked before us and as we drew nearer it reared up like an angry white monster.

Past the snow-burdened roofs of Brough then the long climb with the big car slipping from side to side as it fought its way up the bending, twisting hill, engine bellowing. I thought I'd feel better when we reached the top but the first glimpse of the Bowes Moor road sent my stomach into a lurch of apprehension; miles and miles of it coiling its way across the most desolate stretch of country in all England. And even from this distance you could see the drifts, satin smooth and beautiful, pushing their deadly way across our path.

On either side of the road a vast white desert rolled and dipped endlessly toward the black horizon; there was not a light, not a movement, not a sign of life anywhere.

The pipe jutted aggressively as Granville roared forward to do battle. We hit the first drift, slewed sideways for a tense few seconds then we were on the other side, speeding into the unbroken surface. Then the next drift and the next and the next. Often I thought we were stuck but always, wheels churning, engine screaming we emerged. I had had plenty of experience of snow driving and I could appreciate Granville's expertise as, without slackening speed he picked out the shallowest, narrowest part of each obstruction for his attack. He had this heavy powerful car to help him but he could drive all right.

However, my trepidation at being stranded in this waste land was gradually being overshadowed by another uneasiness. When I had left the hotel I was pretty well topped up with food and drink and if I had been handled gently for the next few hours I'd have been all right. But on the bumpy journey to Brough I had been increasingly aware of a rising queasiness; my mind kept flitting back unhappily to that exotic cocktail, Reg's speciality, which Granville had said I must try; he had prevailed on me too, to wash down the whiskies with occasional beers which, he said, were essential to maintain a balanced intake of fluids and solids. And that final trifle – it had been a mistake.

And now I wasn't just being bumped, I was being thrown around like a pea in a drum as the Bentley lurched and skidded and occasionally took off altogether. Soon I began to feel very ill indeed. And like a seasick man who didn't care if the ship foundered I lost all interest in our progress; I closed my eyes, braced my feet on the floor and shrunk into an inner misery.

I hardly noticed as, after an age of violent motion, we finally began to go downhill and thundered through Bowes. After that there was little danger of having to spend the night in the car but Granville kept his foot down and we rocked over the frozen ground while I felt steadily worse.

I would dearly have loved to ask my colleague to stop and allow me to be quietly sick by the roadside but how do you say such a thing to a man who never seemed to be in the least affected by over indulgence and who, even at that moment was chatting gaily as he refilled his pipe with his free hand. The internal pounding seemed to have forced extra alcohol into my bloodstream because on top of my other discomforts my vision was blurred, I was dizzy and had the strong conviction that if I tried to stand up I would fall flat on my face.

I was busy with these preoccupations when the car stopped.

'We'll just pop in and say hello to Zoe,' Granville said.

'Wha's that?' I slurred.

'We'll go inside for a few minutes.'

I looked around. 'Where are we?'

Granville laughed. 'Home, old son. I can see a light, so Zoe's still up. You must come and have a quick cup of coffee.'

I crawled laboriously from the seat and stood leaning on the car. My colleague tripped lightly to the door and rang the bell. He was as fit as a fiddle I thought bitterly as I reeled after him. I was slumped against the porch breathing heavily when the door opened and there was Zoe Bennett, bright eyed, glowing, beautiful as ever.

'Why Mr Herriot!' she cried. 'How nice to see you again!'

Slack-jawed, green-faced, rumple-suited, I stared into her eyes, gave a gentle hiccup and staggered past her into the house.

Next morning Granville rang to say all was going to be well because Maudie had been able to lap a little milk. It was kind of him to let me know and I didn't want to sound churlish by saying that was all I had managed to do, too.

It happened that morning by a coincidence that I had a far outlying visit and had to pass the Scotch Corner turning on the North Road. I stopped the car and sat gazing at the long snow-covered road stretching towards the Pennines. I was starting my engine when an AA man came over and spoke at my window.

'You're not thinking of trying the Bowes Moor road, are you?' he said.

'No, no. I was just looking.'

He nodded in satisfaction.

'I'm glad to hear that. It's blocked you know. There hasn't been a car over there for two days.'

Chapter Fifteen

One of the things Helen and I had to do was furnish our bedsitter and kitchen. And when I say 'furnish' I use the word in its most austere sense. We had no high-flown ideas about luxury; it was, after all, a temporary arrangement and anyway we had no money to throw around.

My present to Helen at the time of our marriage was a modest gold watch and this had depleted my capital to the extent that a bank statement at the commencement of our married life revealed the sum of twenty-five shillings standing to my credit. Admittedly I was a partner now but when you start from scratch it takes a long time to get your head above water.

But we did need the essentials like a table, chairs, cutlery, crockery, the odd rug and carpet, and Helen and I decided that it would be most sensible to pick up these things at house sales. Since I was constantly going round the district I was able to drop in at these events and the duty of acquiring our necessities had been delegated to me. But after a few weeks it was clear that I was falling down on the job.

I had never realised it before but I had a blind spot in these matters. I would go to a sale and come away with a pair of brass candlesticks and a stuffed owl. On another occasion I acquired an ornate inkwell with a carved metal figure of a dog on it together with a polished wooden box with innumerable fascinating little drawers and compartments for keeping homeopathic prescriptions. I could go on for a long time about the things I bought but they were nearly all useless.

Helen was very nice about it.

'Jim,' she said one day when I was proudly showing her a model of a fully rigged sailing ship in a bottle which I had been lucky enough to pick up, 'it's lovely, but I don't think we need it right now.'

I must have been a big disappointment to the poor girl and also to the local auctioneers who ran the sales. These gentlemen, when they saw me hovering around the back of the crowd would cheer up visibly. They, in common with most country folk, thought all vets were rich and that I would be bidding for some of the more expensive items. When a nice baby grand piano came up they would look over the heads at me with an expectant smile and their disappointment was evident when I finally went away with a cracked-faced barometer or a glove stretcher.

A sense of my failure began to seep through to me and when I had to take a sample through to the Leeds laboratory I saw a chance to atone.

'Helen,' I said, 'there's a huge saleroom right in the city centre. I'll take an hour off and go in there. I'm bound to see something we need.'

'Oh good!' my wife replied. 'That's a great idea! There'll be lots to choose from there. You haven't had much chance to find anything at those country sales.' Helen was always kind.

After my visit to the Leeds lab I asked the way to the salerooms.

'Leave your car here,' one of the locals advised me. 'You'll never park in the main street and you can get a tram right to the door.'

I was glad I listened to him because when I arrived the traffic was surging both ways in a nonstop stream. The saleroom was at the top of an extraordinarily long flight of smooth stone steps leading right to the top of the building. When I arrived, slightly out of breath, I thought immediately I had come to the right place, a vast enclosure strewn with furniture, cookers, gramophones, carpets – everything you could possibly want in a house.

I wandered around fascinated for quite a long time then my attention centred on two tall piles of books quite near to where the auctioneer was selling. I lifted one of them. It was *The Geography of the World*. I had never seen such beautiful books; as big as encyclopaedias and with thick embossed covers and gold lettering. The pages, too, were edged with gold and the paper was of a delightfully smooth texture. Quite enthralled I turned the pages, marvelling at the handsome illustrations, the coloured pictures each with its covering transparent sheet. They were a little old-fashioned, no doubt, and when I looked at the front I saw they were printed in 1858; but they were things of beauty.

Looking back, I feel that fate took a hand here because I had just reluctantly turned away when I heard the auctioneer's voice.

'Now then, here's a lovely set of books. *The Geography of the World in Twenty Four Volumes.* Just look at them. You don't find books like them today. Who'll give me a bid?'

I agreed with him. They were unique. But they must be worth pounds. I looked round the company but nobody said a word.

'Come on, ladies and gentlemen, surely somebody wants this wonderful addition to their library. Now what do I hear?'

Again the silence then a seedy looking man in a soiled mackintosh spoke up. 'Arf a crown,' he said morosely.

I looked around expecting a burst of laughter at this sally, but nobody was amused. In fact the auctioneer didn't seem surprised.

'I have a half a crown bid.' He glanced about him and raised his hammer. With a thudding of the heart I realised he was going to sell.

I heard my own voice, slightly breathless. 'Three shillings.'

'I have a bid of three shillings for *The Geography of the World in Twenty Four Volumes.* Are you all done?' Bang went the hammer. 'Sold to the gentleman over there.'

They were mine! I couldn't believe my luck. This surely was the bargain to end all bargains. I paid my three shillings while one of the men tied a length of rough string round each pile. The first pause in my elation came when I tried to lift my purchases. Books are heavy things and these were massive specimens; and there were twenty-four of them.

With a hand under each string I heaved like a weight-lifter and, pop-eyed, veins standing out on my forehead, I managed to get them off the ground and began to stagger shakily to the exit.

The first string broke on the top step and twelve of my volumes cascaded downwards over the smooth stone. After the first moment of panic I decided that the best way was to transport the intact set down to the bottom and come back for the others. I did this but it took me some time and I began to perspire before I was all tied up again and poised on the kerb ready to cross the road.

The second string broke right in the middle of the tramlines as I attempted a stiff-legged dash through a break in the traffic. For about a year I scrabbled there in the middle of the road while horns hooted, tram bells clanged and an interested crowd watched from the sidewalks. I had just got the escaped volumes in a column and was reknotting the string when the other lot burst from their binding and slithered gently along the metal rails; and it was when I was retrieving them that I noticed a large policeman, attracted by the din and the long line of vehicles, walking with measured strides in my direction.

In my mental turmoil I saw myself for the first time in the hands of the law. I could be done on several charges – Breach of the Peace, Obstructing Traffic to name only two – but I perceived that the officer was approaching very slowly and rightly or wrongly I feel that when a policeman strolls towards you like that he is a decent chap and is giving you a chance to get away. I took my chance. He was still several yards off when I had my two piles reassembled and I thrust my hands under the strings, tottered to the far kerb and lost myself in the crowd.

When I finally decided there was no longer any fear of feeling the dread grip on my shoulder I stopped in my headlong flight and rested in a shop doorway. I was puffing like a broken-winded horse and my hands hurt abominably. The saleroom string was coarse, hairy and abrasive and already it threatened to take the skin off my fingers.

Anyway, I thought, the worst was over. The tram stop was just at the end of the block there. I joined the queue and when the tram arrived, shuffled forward with the others. I had one foot on the step when a large hand was thrust before my eyes.

'Just a minute, brother, just a minute! Where d'you think you're goin'?' The face under the conductor's hat was the meaty, heavy jowled, pop-eyed kind which seems to take a mournful pleasure in imparting bad news.

'You're not bringin' that bloody lot on 'ere, brother. I'll tell tha now!'

I looked up at him in dismay. 'But . . . it's just a few books . . .'

'Few books! You want a bloody delivery van for that lot. You're not usin' my tram – passengers couldn't stir inside!' His mouth turned down aggressively.

'Oh but really,' I said with a ghastly attempt at an ingratiating smile, 'I'm just going as far as . . .'

'You're not goin' anywhere in 'ere, brother! Ah've no time to argue – move your foot, ah'm off!'

The bell ding-dinged and the tram began to move. As I hopped off backwards one of the strings broke again.

After I had got myself sorted out I surveyed my situation and it appeared fairly desperate. My car must be over a mile away, mostly uphill, and I would defy the most stalwart Nepalese Sherpa to transport these books that far. I could of course just abandon the things; lean them against this wall and take to my heels . . . But no, that would be anti-social and anyway they were beautiful. If only I could get them home all would be well.

Another tram rumbled up to the stop and again I hefted my burden and joined the in-going passengers, hoping nobody would notice.

It was a female voice this time.

'Sorry, you can't come on, luv.' She was middle-aged, motherly and her plump figure bulged her uniform tightly.

'We don't 'ave delivery men on our trams. It's against t'rules.'

I repressed a scream. 'But I'm not a . . . these are my own books. I've just bought them.'

'Bought 'em?' Her eyebrows went up as she stared at the dusty columns.

'Yes . . . and I've got to get them home somehow.'

'Well somebody'll tek 'em home for you luv. Hasta got far to go?'

'Darrowby.'

'Eee, by gum, that's a long way. Right out in t'country.' She peered into the tram's interior. 'But there isn't no room in there, luv.'

The passengers had all filed in and I was left alone standing between my twin edifices; and the conductress must have seen a desperate light in my eyes because she made a sudden gesture.

'Come on then, luv! You can stand out 'ere on the platform wi' me. I'm not supposed to, but ah can't see you stuck there.'

I didn't know whether to kiss her or burst into tears. In the end I did neither but stacked the books in a corner of the platform and stood swaying over them till we arrived at the park where I had left my car.

The relief at my deliverance was such that I laughed off the few extra contretemps on my way to the car. There were in fact several more spills before I had the books tucked away on the back seat but when I finally drove away I felt like singing.

It was when I was threading my way through the traffic that I began to rejoice that I lived in the country, because the car was filled with an acrid reek which I thought could only come from the conglomeration of petrol fumes and industrial smoke. But even when the city had been left behind and I was climbing into the swelling green of the Pennines the aroma was still with me.

I wound down the window and gulped greedily as the sweet grassy air flowed in but when I closed it the strange pungency returned immediately. I stopped, learned over and sniffed at the region of the back seat. And there was no doubt about it; it was the books.

Ah well, they must have been kept in a damp place or something like that. I was sure it would soon pass off. But in the meantime it certainly was powerful; it nearly made my eyes water.

I had never really noticed the long climb to our eyrie on top of Skeldale House but it was different today. I suppose my arms and shoulders were finally beginning to feel the strain and that string, bristly but fragile, was digging into my hands harder than ever, but it was true that every step was an effort and when I at last gained the top landing I almost collapsed against the door of our bed-sitter.

When, perspiring and dishevelled, I entered, Helen was on her knees, dusting the hearth. She looked up at me expectantly.

'Any luck, Jim?'

'Yes, I think so,' I replied with a trace of smugness. 'I think I got a bargain.'

Helen rose and looked at me eagerly. 'Really?'

'Yes.' I decided to play my trump card. 'I only had to spend three shillings!'

'Three shillings! What . . . where . . .?'

'Wait there a minute.' I went out to the landing and put my hand under those strings. This, thank heaven, would be the last time I would have to do this. A lunge and a heave and I had my prizes through the doorway and displayed for my wife's inspection.

She stared at the two piles. 'What have you got there?'

'*The Geography of the World in Twenty Four Volumes*,' I replied triumphantly.

'The Geography of the . . . and is that all?'

'Yes, couldn't manage anything else, I'm afraid. But look – aren't they magnificent books!'

My wife's level gaze had something of disbelief, a little of wonder. For a moment one corner of her mouth turned up then she coughed and became suddenly brisk.

'Ah well, we'll have to see about getting some shelves for them. Anyway, leave them there for now.' She went over and kneeled again by the hearth. But after a minute or two she paused in her dusting.

'Can you smell anything funny?'

'Well, er . . . I think it's the books, Helen. They're just a bit musty . . . I don't think it'll last long.'

But the peculiar exhalation was very pervasive and it was redolent of extreme age. Very soon the atmosphere in our room was that of a freshly opened mausoleum.

I could see Helen didn't want to hurt my feelings but she kept darting looks of growing alarm at my purchases. I decided to say it for her.

'Maybe I'd better take them downstairs just for now.'

She nodded gratefully.

The descent was torture, made worse by the fact that I had thought I was finished with such things. I finally staggered into the office and parked the books behind the desk. I was panting and rubbing my hands when Siegfried came in.

'Ah, James, had a nice run through to Leeds?'

'Yes, they said at the lab that they'd give us a ring about those sheep as soon as they've cultured the organisms.'

'Splendid!' My colleague opened the door of the cupboard and put some forms inside then he paused and began to sniff the air.

'James, there's a bloody awful stink in here.'

I cleared my throat. 'Well yes, Siegfried, I bought a few books while I was in Leeds. They seem a little damp.' I pointed behind the desk.

Siegfried's eyes widened as he looked at the twin edifices. 'What the devil are they?'

I hesitated. '*The Geography of the World in Twenty Four Volumes.*'

He didn't say anything but looked from me to the books and back again. And he kept sniffing. There was no doubt that only his innate good manners were preventing him from telling me to get the damn things out of here.

'I'll find a place for them,' I said, and with a great weariness pushed my hands yet again under the strings. My mind was in a ferment as I shuffled along the passage. What in heaven's name was I going to do with them? But as I passed the cellar door on my right it seemed to provide the answer.

There were great vaulted chambers beneath Skeldale House, a proper wine cellar in the grand days. The man who went down there to read the gas meter always described them as 'The Cattycombs' and as I descended into the murky, dank-smelling depths I thought sadly that it was a fitting resting place for my books. We kept only coal and wood down here now and from the muffled thuds I judged that Tristan was chopping logs.

He was a great log chopper and when I rounded the corner he was whirling his axe expertly round his head. He stopped when he saw me with my burden and asked the inevitable question.

I answered for, I hoped, the last time. '*The Geography of the World in Twenty Four Volumes.*' And I followed with a blow by blow account of my story.

As he listened he opened one tome after another, sniffed at it and replaced it hurriedly. And he didn't have to tell me, I knew already. My cherished books were down here to stay.

But the compassion which has always been and still is uppermost among the many facets of Tristan's character came to the fore now.

'Tell you what, Jim,' he said. 'We can put them in there.' He pointed to a dusty wine bin just visible in the dim light which filtered through the iron grating at the top of the coal chute which led from the street.

'It's just like a proper book shelf.'

He began to lift the volumes into the bin and when he had arranged them in a long row he ran his finger along the faded opulence of the bindings.

'There now, they look a treat in there, Jim.' He paused and rubbed his chin. 'Now all you want is somewhere to sit. Let's see now . . . ah, yes!' He retreated into the gloom and reappeared with an armful of the biggest logs. He made a few more journeys and in no time had rigged up a seat for me within arm's reach of the books.

'That'll do fine,' he said with deep satisfaction. 'You can come down here and have a read whenever you feel like it.'

And that is how it turned out. The books never came up those steps again but quite frequently when I had a few minutes to spare and wanted to improve my mind I went down and sat on Tristan's seat in the twilight under the grating and renewed my acquaintance with *The Geography of the World in Twenty Four Volumes.*

Chapter Sixteen

I was sitting at the desk in the office at Skeldale House, writing up tuberculin testing forms when a young woman tapped on the door and walked in.

'I think I'm pregnant,' she murmured shyly.

I looked up at her in some surprise. It was an unusual opening to a conversation and I didn't quite know how to reply. She was about my own age and her demure attractiveness and rather prim style of dress didn't seem to belong to one so outspoken.

A furtive glance at her left hand did not help. She was wearing gloves so I was unable to use the presence or absence of a wedding ring to say either 'Congratulations' or 'Bad luck'.

'Really?' I replied lamely and followed it up with what I hoped was a non-committal smile.

'Yes, I think so.' She looked down and smoothed a finger along the strap of her handbag. Then she faced me again with an expectant expression as though she was waiting for me to make a move or say something helpful.

I dredged my mind desperately. There ought to be a fitting rejoinder somewhere but at the moment it escaped me. The silence was becoming embarrassing when the girl spoke again.

'Will you be able to examine me tonight?'

My face must have registered extreme emotion because she continued hastily.

'If it isn't suitable . . . I could come tomorrow night, doctor.'

Suddenly all was clear and I began to relax. The fact that our surgery was right next door to that of the local medicos gave rise to various contretemps but this was something new. Usually it was somebody wandering aimlessly along the passage, 'Looking for t'doctor', and they invariably left hastily when they discovered our identity. People often say to me, 'Vets must know just as much as doctors' but when it comes to the crunch they are never very keen to let me treat them.

There were notable exceptions to this rule among the older breed of farmers. Quite a few of these tough old men came to consult us about their rheumatism or their indigestion because 'them fellers next door never do me any bloody good.'

But usually it was just the accidental visitor and the doctors in their turn occasionally had their surgery hour enlivened by a lady marching in with a shaggy creature on a lead and asking them to squeeze out its anal glands.

I stood up and gave the girl a reassuring smile, while my mind ticked over busily. It seemed to me that in her delicate condition the sudden revelation that she was in the presence of a veterinary surgeon might have disastrous effects. So I took her gently by the arm, steered her from the room and along the passage to the front door. Still preserving a discreet silence I escorted her over the few yards of pavement to where our medical colleagues' plates hung by their entrance. I opened the door, led her inside, ushered her into the waiting room among the patient rows of country folk sitting there, gave her a final smile and nod, and fled.

There was another night when Tristan and I were tidying up after a cat spay. The sound of heavy boots echoed on the passage tiles then the door burst open and a stocky man in a cloth cap and collarless shirt strode in.

'I'm not goin' to be waitin' along there!' he said belligerently in the rich tones of Erin.

'Is that so?' I replied.

'Yiss, it is so. I haven't the time to be sittin' waitin'!'

'I see. Well what can we do for you?'

He grabbed a chair, pulled it up to the table, sat down, leaned his elbow on the freshly washed surface and looked up at me with a truculent eye.

'It's me ear!' He cocked the offending organ in my direction.

I realised he was one of the many Irish labourers who came to the district every year to help with the turnip hoeing. I could understand his entering the wrong door but was surprised at his aggressiveness; most of his compatriots were noted for their charm.

I was about to redirect him when Tristan, loth as always to pass up the slightest chance of a giggle, broke in.

'Your ear, eh?' he murmured sympathetically. 'Is it very painful?'

'Oh aye, it hurts bad. I think I've got a little bile startin' in there.'

Tristan tut-tutted. 'Too bad, too bad, let's have a look at it.' He moved over to the instrument cupboard and produced the auroscope which we used for examining dogs with ear canker. Taking it from its case he switched on the light and bent over the man.

'Just bend your head over a little, will you? Fine, fine.' He sounded very professional.

He inserted the auroscope and peered into the depths of the ear. 'Hmm . . . hmm . . . yes, yes, I see. Oh that's rather nasty.' At last he nodded gently. 'You are quite right. You have a little infected spot in there.'

'That's what I thought,' the man grunted. 'What are you going to do, then?'

Tristan rested his chin on his hand for a moment.

'I really think I ought to give you an injection. It would be the quickest way of clearing the thing up.' He spoke seriously but confidently with the hint of a grave smile at the corner of his lips. Like me he was wearing a white coat and would have passed without a quibble as a Harley Street specialist.

The man seemed similarly impressed. He squared his shoulders and nodded. 'Right then, let's be havin' it. You ought to know.'

As I watched wonderingly Tristan laid our white enamel tray on the table and on it he deposited a roll of cotton wool, a bottle of iodine and a row of enormous needles. They were the big, wide-bored needles for running calcium under a cow's skin and lying there they looked like items from a plumber's kit.

Next he rummaged in a cupboard for some time then emerged bearing the only 100 c.c. syringe in the practice. This was very rarely used – occasionally for giving sodium iodide injections to bullocks – and it was a fearsome object. Unlike its modern plastic counterparts it was made of glass and with its massive mounting of stainless steel and great metal plunger it looked much bigger.

The Irishman had been shifting uneasily in his seat as Tristan set out his stall but as the syringe clattered down on the enamel his eyes widened and he swallowed a couple of times.

My colleague, however, was wonderfully composed. He whistled softly as he fitted one of the huge needles to the nozzle of the syringe, then hummed a light tune while he hoisted a jar of acrivlavine solution on to the table. Carefully, almost lovingly, he drew up the full 100 c.c.'s then stood with the syringe poised against the light, giving off iridescent gleams as he rocked it gently to and fro.

The man had lost a lot of his bluster. His mouth hung slightly open.

'Just a minute,' he said a trifle breathlessly. 'Phwhaat doctors are you?'

'I beg your pardon,' enquired Tristan, still juggling with his dreadful instrument.

'Phwhaat's your names? Phwhaat do you call you doctors?'

Tristan gave a light laugh. 'Oh we're not doctors. We're vets.'

'Vits!' the chair grated on the floor as the man pushed back from the table.

'Yes, that's right,' Tristan said innocently, advancing with the loaded syringe. 'But you needn't worry. I assure you . . .'

I don't think I have ever seen anybody leave a room as quickly as that man His chair overturned, there was a scurry, a scraping of hobnails, the clattering of fleeing feet in the passage then the banging of the outside door.

He was gone, never to return . . .

I don't think there is much doubt that we held an earthy fascination for our medical colleagues. They were constantly drifting in to watch us at work, particularly my own doctor, Harry Allinson, whose bald head often hovered over me as I operated on the small animals.

'I've got to hand it to you boys,' he used to say. 'When we come up against a surgical case we write a note to the hospital but you just switch on the steriliser.'

He was interested, too, in our work with the microscope. It intrigued him that we should spend so much time peering down at skin scrapings for mange, blood films for anthrax milk and sputum smears for tuberculosis.

'Sometimes I think you are a really scientific chap, Jim,' he would laugh. 'Then I see you with your instruments.'

He was referring to the occasions when he met me coming out of the surgery in the morning carrying my kit for the round; the grisly docking knives, firing tools, tooth forceps and dehorning shears which are now mercifully consigned to the museum. He would lift them from my arms and examine them wonderingly. 'You put the horse's tail in there, do you? And you bring the blade down like this . . . bang . . . just like a guillotine . . . my God!'

I felt the same way myself.

Harry Allinson's towering, wide-shouldered frame was part of the scenery of Darrowby. He was a Scot, like so many of the doctors in Yorkshire, a great athlete in his youth, a scratch golfer and an ebullient personality. One of his main characteristics was sheer noisiness and it was his habit to march into his patients' homes shouting and banging about. He was to deliver both my children and years later when one or the other was ill I have heard him come hollering into the house . . . 'Anybody in? Who's there? Come on, let's be having you!' And it was wonderful how the little measles-ridden form revived and began to shout back at him.

It was rewarding, too, to discover the gentleness and understanding behind the uproar. Those qualities were always there when people needed them.

Although he saw so much of my own work I was unable, naturally enough, to see him in action apart from when he was attending my own family. There was one time, however, when I did have a peep behind the curtain.

I was called to see a lame cart horse and as I walked on to the farm I was surprised to see the vast form of Gobber Newhouse almost obscuring the view. The entire twenty stones of him was leaning on a shovel and he appeared to be part of a gang of building workers putting up a new barn.

'Nah then, Herriot,' he said affably, 'what've ye been killin' this morning'?' He followed this typical sally with a throaty chuckle and looked round at his colleagues for applause.

I gave him a nod and passed by. Fortunately I didn't often see Gobber but

when I did he always addressed me as 'Herriot' and he invariably got in some
little dig. And incidentally this was the first time I had ever observed him going
through the motions of work; the Labour Exchange must have put some pressure
on him because normally his life consisted of drinking, gambling, fighting and
knocking his long-suffering little wife about.

I spent some time with the horse's hind foot resting on my knee as I pared
away at the sole. But there was no sign of pus and the only abnormality was
a smelly disintegration of the horn around the frog.

'He's got thrush,' I said to the farmer. 'This doesn't often make them lame
but he has shed quite a lot of horn and some of the sensitive tissues are exposed.
I'll leave you some lotion for him.'

I was walking back to get the bottle from the car when I saw there was some
kind of commotion among the builder's men. They were standing in a group
around Gobber who was seated on an upturned milk pail. He had his boot off
and was anxiously examining his foot.

The foreman called over to me. 'Are you going straight back to Darrowby,
Mr Herriot?'

'Yes, I am.'

'Well maybe you wouldn't mind givin' this feller a lift. He's stood on a nail
– went clean through his boot. Could you take him to a doctor?'

'Yes, of course.' I went over and viewed the fat man whose mates seemed to
be enjoying the situation.

'Here's the vet come to see ye, Gobber,' one of them cried. 'He'll soon fix you
up. He's been doctorin' t'oss's foot, now he can do yours. Will we haud 'im
down for ye, Mr Herriot?'

Another peered gloomily at the punctured wound on the foot. 'By Gaw, this
is a 'ell of a farm for lockjaw, Gobber. Ah'm afraid ye'll die a 'orrible death.'

The big man was not amused. His face was a tragic mask and the effort of
hauling his foot into view above his enormous belly made him shake
uncontrollably.

I opened the car door and, supported by a man on either side, he limped with
many facial contortions across the farmyard. At first I thought we'd never be
able to get him into the little vehicle and he groaned piteously as we pushed,
pulled and finally wedged him into the passenger seat.

As we headed along the road to Darrowby he cleared his throat nervously.

'Mr Herriot,' he said. It was the first time he had ever accorded me a 'Mister'.
'Is it true that where there's a lot of 'osses there's more lockjaw?'

'Yes, I should say so,' I replied.

He swallowed. 'There's allus been a lot of 'osses at that farm, hasn't there?'

'There has indeed.'

'And what ...' He passed a hand across his forehead. 'What kind of ... er
... cuts gets lockjaw in them?'

I saw no reason to be merciful. 'Oh, deep punctured wounds like you have.
Especially in the feet.'

'Oh bloody 'ell!' moaned Gobber. Like many bullies he was a big baby when
his own hide was in danger.

Watching him sweating there I relented a little.

'Don't worry,' I said. 'The doctor will give you a little shot and you'll have
nothing to worry about.'

The big man squirmed and wrung his hands. 'Ah but I don't like t'needle.'

'It's nothing, really,' I said, with only the slightest touch of sadism. 'Just a
quick jab.'

'Oh bloody 'ell!'

At the surgery Harry Allinson gave us a cold look as we staggered in. He had attended a few of Mrs Newhouse's black eyes and he didn't approve of Gobber.

'Right, Jim,' he grunted. 'Leave him to me.'

I was about to go when Gobber caught at my sleeve.

'Stay with me, Mr Herriot!' he whimpered. The man was in a pitiable state of fright and I looked questioningly at the doctor.

Harry shrugged. 'OK, you can stay and hold his hand if that's what he wants.' He produced a phial of tetanus antitoxin and a syringe.

'Drop your trousers and bend over, Newhouse,' he ordered curtly.

Gobber complied, exposing flaccid acres of the biggest backside, horses included, which I had ever seen.

'You know, Newhouse,' Harry said conversationally as he filled the syringe before the big man's terrified eyes. 'Your wife tells me you have no feelings.' He laughed gently. 'Yes, that's what she says . . . you have absolutely no feelings.'

He stepped quickly to the rear, rammed the needle deep into the quivering buttock, then, as a shrill howl shook the windows, he looked into Gobber's face with a wolfish grin.

'But you bloody well felt that, didn't you!'

Chapter Seventeen

You often see dogs running along a road but there was something about this one which made me slow down and take a second look.

It was a small brown animal and it was approaching on the other side; and it wasn't just ambling by the grass verge but galloping all out on its short legs, head extended forward as though in desperate pursuit of something unseen beyond the long empty curve of tarmac ahead. As the dog passed I had a brief glimpse of two staring eyes and a lolling tongue, then he was gone.

My car stalled and lurched to a halt but I sat unheeding, still gazing into the mirror at the small form receding rapidly until it was almost invisible against the browns and greens of the surrounding moor. As I switched on the engine I had difficulty in dragging my thoughts back to the job in hand; because I had seen something chilling there, a momentary but vivid impression of frantic effort, despair, blind terror. And driving away, the image stayed with me. Where had that dog come from? There were no roadside farms on this high, lonely by-way, not a parked car anywhere. And in any case he wasn't just casually going somewhere; there was a frenzied urgency in his every movement.

It was no good I had to find out. I backed off the unfenced road among the spare tufts of heather and turned back in the direction I had come. I had to drive a surprisingly long way before I saw the little animal, still beating his solitary way, and at the sound of the approaching car he halted, stared for a moment then trotted on again. But his labouring limbs told me he was near exhaustion and I pulled up twenty yards ahead of him, got out and waited.

He made no protest as I knelt on the roadside turf and caught him gently as he came up to me. He was a Border terrier and after another quick glance at the car his eyes took on their terrified light as he looked again at the empty road ahead.

He wasn't wearing a collar but there was a ring of flattened hair on his neck as though one had recently been removed. I opened his mouth and looked at his teeth; he wasn't very old – probably around two or three. There were rolls of fat along his ribs so he hadn't been starved. I was examining his skin when suddenly the wide panting mouth closed and the whole body stiffened as another car approached. For a moment he stared at it with fierce hope but when the vehicle flashed by he sagged and began to pant again.

So that was it. He had been dumped. Some time ago the humans he had loved and trusted had opened their car door, hurled him out into an unknown world and driven merrily away. I began to feel sick – physically sick – and a murderous rage flowed through me. Had they laughed, I wondered, these people at the idea of the bewildered little creature toiling vainly behind them?

I passed my hand over the rough hairs of the head. I could forgive anybody for robbing a bank but never for this, 'Come on, fella,' I said, lifting him gently, 'you're coming home with me.'

Sam was used to strange dogs in the car and he sniffed incuriously at the newcomer. The terrier huddled on the passenger seat trembling violently and I kept my hand on him as I drove.

Back in our bed-sitter Helen pushed a bowl of meat and biscuit under his nose but the little animal showed no interest.

'How could anybody do this?' she murmured. 'And anyway, why? What reason could they have?'

I stroked the head again. 'Oh you'd be surprised at some of the reasons. Sometimes they do it because a dog turns savage, but that can't be so in this case.' I had seen enough of dogs to interpret the warm friendly light behind the fear in those eyes. And the way the terrier had submitted unquestioningly as I had prised his mouth open, lifted him, handled him, all pointed to one thing; he was a docile little creature.

'Or sometimes,' I continued, 'they dump dogs just because they're tired of them. They got them when they were charming puppies and have no interest in them when they grow up. Or maybe the licence is due to be paid – that's a good enough reason for some people to take a drive into the country and push their pets out into the unknown.'

I didn't say any more. There was quite a long list and why should I depress Helen with tales of the other times when I had seen it happen? People moving to another house where they couldn't keep a dog. A baby arriving and claiming all the attention and affection. And dogs were occasionally abandoned when a more glamorous pet superseded them.

I looked at the little terrier. This was the sort of thing which could have happened to him. A big dashing Alsatian, an eye-catching Saluki – anything like that would take over effortlessly from a rather roly-poly Border terrier with some people. I had seen it in the past. The little fellow was definitely running to fat despite his comparative youth; in fact when he had been running back there his legs had splayed out from his shoulders. That was another clue; it was possible he had spent most of his time indoors without exercise.

Anyway I was only guessing. I rang the police. No reports of a lost dog in the district. I hadn't really expected any.

During the evening we did our best to comfort the terrier but he lay trembling, his head on his paws, his eyes closed. The only time he showed interest was when a car passed along the street outside, then he would raise his head and listen, ears pricked, for a few seconds till the sound died away. Helen hoisted him on to her lap and held him there for over an hour, but he was too deeply sunk in his misery to respond to her caresses and soft words.

I finally decided it would be the best thing to sedate him and gave him a shot of morphine. When we went to bed he was stretched out sound asleep in Sam's basket with Sam himself curled up philosophically on the rug by his side.

Next morning he was still unhappy but sufficiently recovered to look around him and take stock. When I went up and spoke to him he rolled over on his back, not playfully but almost automatically as though it was a normal mannerism. I bent and rubbed his chest while he looked up at me non-committally. I liked dogs which rolled over like this; they were usually good-natured and it was a gesture of trust.

'That's better, old lad,' I said. 'Come on, cheer up!'

For a moment his mouth opened wide. He had a comical little monkey face and briefly it seemed to be split in two by a huge grin, making him look extraordinarily attractive.

Helen spoke over my shoulder. 'He's a lovely little dog, Jim! He's so appealing – I could get really fond of him.'

Yes, that was the trouble. So could I. I could get too fond of all the unwanted animals which passed through our hands; not just the abandoned ones but the dogs which came in for euthanasia with the traumatic addendum 'unless you can find him a home'. That put the pressure on me. Putting an animal to sleep when he was incurably ill, in pain, or so old that life had lost its savour was something I could tolerate. In fact often it seemed as though I were doing the suffering creature a favour. But when a young, healthy, charming animal was involved then it was a harrowing business.

What does a vet do in these circumstances. Refuse and send the owner away with the lurking knowledge that the man might go round to the chemist and buy a dose of posion? That was far worse than our humane, painless barbiturate. One thing a vet can't do is take in all those animals himself. If I had given way to all my impulses I would have accumulated a positive menagerie by now.

It was a hell of a problem which had always troubled me and now I had a soft hearted wife which made the pull twice as strong.

I turned to her now and voiced my thoughts.

'Helen, we can't keep him, you know. One dog in a bed-sitter is enough.' I didn't add that we ourselves probably would not be in the bed-sitter much longer; that was another thing I didn't want to bring up.

She nodded. 'I suppose so. But I have the feeling that this is one of the sweetest little dogs I've seen for a long time. When he gets over his fear, I mean. What on earth can we do with him?'

'Well, he's a stray.' I bent again and rubbed the rough hair over the chest. 'So he should really go to the kennels at the police station. But if he isn't claimed in ten days we are back where we started.' I put my hand under the terrier's body and lifted him, limp and unresisting, into the crook of my arm. He liked people, this one; liked and trusted them. 'I could ask around the practice, of course, but nobody seems to want a dog when there's one going spare.' I thought for a moment or two. 'Maybe an advert in the local paper.'

'Wait a minute,' Helen said. 'Talking about the paper – didn't I read something about an animal shelter last week?'

I looked at her uncomprehendingly then I remembered.

'That's right. Sister Rose from the Topley Banks hospital. They were interviewing her about the stray animals she had taken in. It would be worth a try.' I replaced the terrier in Sam's basket. 'We'll keep this little chap today and I'll ring Sister Rose when I finish work tonight.'

At teatime I could see that things were getting out of hand. When I came in the little dog was on Helen's knee and it looked as though he had been there for a long time. She was stroking his head and looking definitely broody.

Not only that, but as I looked down at him I could feel myself weakening.

Little phrases were creeping unbidden into my mind . . . 'I wonder if we could find room for him . . .' . . . 'Not much extra trouble . . .' . . . 'Perhaps if we . . .'

I had to act quickly or I was sunk. Reaching for the phone I dialled the hospital number. They soon found Sister Rose and I listened to a cheerful, businesslike voice. She didn't seem to find anything unusual in the situation and the matter-of fact way she asked questions about the terrier's age, appearance, temperament etc. gave the impression that she had seen a lot of unwanted animals through her hands.

I could hear the firm pencilling sounds as she took notes then, 'Well now that sounds fine. He's the sort we can usually find a home for. When can you bring him along?'

'Now,' I replied.

The misty look in Helen's eyes as I marched out with the dog under my arm told me I was only just in time. And as I drove along the road I couldn't put away the thought that if things had been different – the future settled and a proper home – this little brown creature rolling on his back on the passenger seat with his wide mouth half open and the friendly eyes fixed questioningly on mine would never have got away from me. Only when the occasional car flashed by did he spring upright and look from the window with the old despairing expression. Would he ever forget?

Sister Louisa Rose was a rather handsome woman in her late forties with the sort of healthy smiling face I had imagined at the other end of the phone. She reached out and took the terrier from me with the eager gesture of the animal lover.

'Oh, he looks rather a dear, doesn't he?' she murmured.

Behind her house, a modern bungalow in the open country near the hospital, she led me to a row of kennels with outside runs. Some of them housed single dogs but there was one large one with an assortment of mixed breeds playing happily together on the grass.

'I think we'll put him in here,' she said. 'It'll cheer him up quicker than anything and I'm sure he'll mix in well.' She opened a door in the wire netting surround and pushed the little animal in. The other dogs surrounded him and there was the usual ceremonious sniffing and leg-cocking.

Sister Rose cupped her chin with her hand and looked down thoughtfully through the wire. 'A name, we must have a name . . . let me see . . . no . . . no . . . yes . . . Pip! We'll call him Pip!'

She looked at me with raised eyebrows and I nodded vigorously. 'Yes, definitely – just right. He looks like a Pip.'

She smiled impishly. 'I think so, too, but I've had a lot of practice, you know. I've become rather good at it.'

'I'll bet you have. I suppose you've named all this lot?'

'Of course.' She began to point them out one by one. 'There's Bingo – he was a badly neglected puppy. And Fergus – just lost. That bigger retriever is Griff – he was the survivor of a car crash where his owners were killed. And Tessa, badly injured when she was thrown from a fast-moving vehicle. Behind her over there is Sally Anne who really started me in the business of Animal Sheltering. She was found heavily pregnant with her paws bleeding so she must have run for many miles. I took her in and managed to find homes for all her puppies and she's still here. Placing those pups got me into contact with a lot of pet owners and before I knew what was happening everybody had the idea that I regularly took in stray animals. So I started and you can see the result. I shall have to expand these premises soon.'

Pip didn't look so lonely now and after the preliminary courtesies he joined a group watching interestedly a fierce tug-of-war on a stick between a Collie and a crossed Labrador.

I laughed. 'You know I had no idea you had all these dogs. How long do you keep them?'

'Till I can find a home for them. Some are only here a day, others stay for weeks or months. And there are one or two like Sally Anne who seem to be permanent boarders now.'

'But how on earth do you feed them all? It must be an expensive business.'

She nodded and smiled. 'Oh I run little dog shows, coffee mornings, raffles, jumble sales, anything, but whatever my efforts I'm afraid the strays keep munching their way into the red. But I manage.'

She managed, I guessed, by dipping deeply into her own pocket. Around me the abandoned and rejected dogs barked and ran around happily. I had often thought when I encountered cruelty and neglect that there was a whole army of people who did these unspeakable things, a great unheeding horde who never spared a thought for the feelings of the helpless creatures who depended on them. It was frightening in a way, but thank heavens there was another army ranged on the other side, an army who fought for the animals with everything they had – with their energy, their time, their money.

I looked at Sister Rose, at the steady eyes in the clear-skinned, scrubbed, nurse's face. I would have thought her profession of dedication to the human race would have filled her life utterly with no room for anything else, but it was not so.

'Well, I'm very grateful to you, Sister,' I said. 'I hope somebody will take Pip off your hands soon and if there's anything else I can do, please let me know.'

She smiled. 'Oh don't worry, I have a feeling this little chap won't be here very long.'

Before leaving I leaned on the wire and took another look at the Border terrier. He seemed to be settling all right but every now and then he stopped and looked up at me with those questioning eyes which pulled so hard. I had the nasty feeling that I, too, was letting him down. His owners, then me, then Sister Rose, all in a couple of days . . . I hoped it would work out for him.

Chapter Eighteen

I found it difficult to get that dog out of my mind and I lasted only a week before dropping in at the Animal Shelter. Sister Rose in an old mackintosh and Wellingtons was filling the feed bowls in one of the kennels.

'You've come about Pip, I expect,' she said, putting down her bucket. 'Well he went yesterday. I thought I'd have no trouble. A very nice couple called round. They wanted to give a home to a stray and they picked him out straight away.' She pushed the hair back from her forehead. 'In fact I've had a good week. I've found excellent homes for Griff and Fergus too.'

'Fine, fine. That's great.' I paused for a moment. 'I was wondering . . . er . . . about Pip. Has he gone out of the district?'

Oh, no, he's right here in Darrowby. The people are called Plenderleith – he's a retired civil servant, quite high up I believe and he gave a generous donation to the centre though I didn't expect one. They've bought one of those nice little houses on the Houlton Road and there's a lovely garden for Pip to play. I gave them your name, by the way, so no doubt they'll be coming round to see you.'

A wave of totally irrational pleasure swept over me.

'Ah well, I'm glad to hear that. I'll be able to see how he's getting on.'

I didn't have long to wait. It was less than a week later that I opened the waiting-room door and saw an elderly couple sitting there with Pip on the end of a very new lead. He adopted his usual gambit of rolling on to his back as soon as he saw me, but this time there was no helpless appeal in his expression but sheer joyous abandon with the comical little face split across by a wide panting grin. As I went through the ritual of chest rubbing I noticed he was wearing a new collar, too; expensive looking, with a shining medallion bearing his name, address and telephone number. I lifted him and we all went through to the consulting room.

'Well now, what's the trouble?' I asked.

'No trouble, really,' the man replied. He was plump, and the pink face, grave eyes and immaculate dark suit accorded perfectly with my idea of a top civil servant.

'I have recently acquired this small animal and should be grateful for your advice about him. By the way, my name is Plenderleith and may I introduce my wife.'

Mrs Plenderleith was plump too, but it was a giggly plumpness. She didn't look such a solid citizen as her husband.

'Firstly,' he continued, 'I should like you to give him a thorough check-up.'

I had already done this, but went through it again, though Pip made things difficult by rolling over every time I got the stethoscope on his chest. And as I took his temperature I noticed that Mr Plenderleith ran his hand repeatedly over the brown hair of the back while his wife, looking over his shoulder, made encouraging noises and nodded reassuringly at the little dog.

'Absolutely sound in wind and limb,' I pronounced as I finished.

'Splendid,' the man said. 'Er ... there was this little brown mark on his abdomen ...' A touch of anxiety showed in his eyes.

'Just a patch of pigment. Nothing, I assure you.'

'Ah yes, good, good.' Mr Plenderleith cleared his throat. 'I have to confess, Mr Herriot, that my wife and I have never owned an animal before. Now I believe in doing things thoroughly, so in order to give him proper care and attention I have decided to study the matter. With this in view I have purchased some books on the subject.' He produced some shiny volumes from under his arm. *Care of the Dog, The Dog in Sickness and Health*, and finally *The Border Terrier*.

'Good idea,' I replied. Normally I would have shied away from this imposing battery but in this case I liked the way things were going. I had the growing conviction that Pip was on a good wicket here.

'I have already gleaned a considerable amount from my reading,' Mr Plenderleith went on, 'and I believe it is desirable that he be inoculated against distemper. As you know, he is a stray so there is no means of ascertaining whether or not this has been done.'

I nodded. 'Quite right. In fact I was going to suggest that.' I produced a phial of the vaccine and began to fill a syringe.

Pip was much less concerned than his owners as I gently injected the contents under his skin. Mr Plenderleith, his face rigid with apprehension, kept patting the dog's head while his wife at the other end stroked the hind limbs and adjured her pet to be brave.

After I had put the syringe away. Mr Plenderleith, visibly relieved, recommenced his investigations. 'Let me see now.' He put on his spectacles, produced a gold pencil and snapped open a leather bound pad where I could see a long list of neatly written notes. 'I have one or two queries here.'

And he had indeed. He grilled me at length on feeding, housing, exercise, the relative values of wicker dog baskets and metal frame beds, the salient features of the common ailments, often referring to his shiny books. 'I have a note here concerning page 143, line 9. It says . . .'

I answered him patiently, leaning across the table. I had a waiting list of farm visits including several fairly urgent jobs but I listened with growing contentment. I had hoped for concerned and responsible persons to take this little animal over and these people were right out of the blueprint.

When at length Mr Plenderleith had finished he put away his note-book and pencil and removed his spectacles with the firm precise movements which seemed part of him.

'One of the reasons I desired a dog, Mr Herriot,' he went on, 'was to provide myself with exercise. Don't you think that is a good idea?'

'It certainly is. One of the surest ways to keep fit is to own an active little animal like this. You simply *have* to take him out and just think of all the lovely grassy tracks over the hills around here. On Sunday afternoons when other people are lying asleep in their chairs under their newspapers you'll be out there striding the fells, rain, hail or snow.'

Mr Plenderleith squared his shoulders and his jaw jutted as though he already saw himself battling through a blizzard.

'And another thing,' his wife giggled, 'it'll take some of this off.' She thumped him irreverently on his bulging waistline.

'Now now, my dear,' he admonished her gravely, but I had seen the makings of a sheepish grin which completely belied his stuffed shirt image. Mr Plenderleith, I felt, was all right.

He put his books under his arm and reached out for the little dog. 'Come, Pip, we mustn't delay Mr Herriot any longer.' But his wife was too quick for him. She gathered the terrier into her arms and as we walked along the passage she held the rough face against her own.

Outside the surgery door I saw them installed in a spotless little family saloon and as they drove away Mr Plenderleith inclined his head gravely, his wife gave a gay wave, but Pip, his hind legs on her knee, feet on the dashboard, gazing eagerly through the windscreen was too busy and interested to look at me.

As they rounded the corner I had the impression of a little cycle coming to a happy end. And of course the main cog in the sequence of events had been Sister Rose. This was just one of the helpless creatures she had salvaged. Her Animal Shelter would grow and expand and daily she would work harder without gain to herself. There were other people like her all over the country, other Shelters; and I felt I had been given a privileged glimpse of that selfless army which battled ceaselessly and untiringly on the side of the great throng of dependent animals.

But right now I was concerned only with one thing. Pip had come home for good.

Chapter Nineteen

'Double Bezique!' Helen said, laying out the two queens of spades and the jacks of diamonds. And she looked across at me with a grin of triumph.

She had the right kind of mouth, wide and generous, for such a grin and there was no doubt she had cause for jubilation.

'Well that's torn it,' I grunted moodily. 'I've been wondering where those cards were and now I know. But why didn't you declare them separately?'

'It's better fun this way,' my wife replied with a callous laugh. 'I wanted to see your face when I put them all out at once.'

'O.K., O.K.,' I said. 'Gloat all you want. I didn't realise I had married a sadist.'

With a sinking heart I saw her move her little peg five hundred points up the board. It was a body blow and one from which I knew I would never recover. She had already won two games tonight – I was being thrashed.

Still, there were compensations. There was a subdued excitement in just sitting there by our fireside on a black winter's night like this and listening to the wind buffeting the tall old house. I think it was the nearness of the wild that made the coals burn brighter and the room seem cosier, the awareness of the towering bare hills close by and the night wind shrieking over the high tops and over the vast white emptiness of the moors where it was cold, cold, and a man could quite easily lose himself and die.

I dealt the next hand and looked with disgust at the rubbish I had given myself. I stole a glance at Helen. The faintest trace of smugness showed in her face as she viewed her hand. This wasn't going to be my night.

We played a lot of Bezique on those dark evenings. There wasn't much to do in Darrowby but boredom was never a problem. At the beginning, in the summer days, we walked every day along the grassy tracks in the hills which make Yorkshire the finest walking country in England. We started to cultivate a piece of the long garden behind the house for our own use and I discovered an undreamed-of fascination in peas and broad beans. We picked mushrooms which may not sound very exciting but I have warm memories of the two of us wandering around sunlit fields with carrier bags and stopping now and then to look at the beauty nearby. In those days before the old permanent pastures were ploughed up and artificial fertilisers were scarcely used mushrooms grew abundantly; and they were marvellous to eat. There was tennis, too, and at weekends Helen came with me on my rounds.

But when the winter closed in Bezique was the thing. I studied my cards again and listened to the wind. It made a soft whistling noise down in the tiled passage far below. It was always as cold as the street in that passage and not much warmer in the graceful sitting room where the wind would tug at the heavy curtains over the french windows and perhaps send fugitive gusts up the stairs to Siegfried's and Tristan's rooms and then up to us on the top.

And the wind would push its fingers up under the tiles into the two empty silent rooms which lay even higher than us. Rooms where the dust lay thick beneath their tiny windows and the wind would stir the cobwebs among the rafters and pull at the little bell hanging from the great coiled spring. I could hear the faint tinkling which in the days of the old house's glory would summon a little maidservant from her high nest.

But now the bell went unheeded in the empty darkness. There was nobody to answer it. The six servants who used to look after the Georgian elegance of Skeldale House were only a memory among the older folk of Darrowby and there was only Mrs Hall the housekeeper in her room at the end of the offshoot.

'Royal marriage,' I said stiffly, putting out the king and queen of trumps and advancing my peg a paltry forty points.

Helen nodded and I could see she was trying not to look condescending. She hadn't declared anything for some time now and I had a nasty feeling she was building up to something big. She bent over and poked the fire. There was too much coal on it because I had laid the fire this evening.

We had a system that whoever was first home did that job. We had to arrange something like this because Helen was a working girl now. There wasn't much to do in our two rooms and our finances were at a low ebb so she had taken a job as secretary to the local millers. The mill was on the roadside down by the river and passers-by could see the big mill wheel turning in the water and hear the great stones grinding the corn in the room upstairs with the opening on to the road where the lorries came to collect the loaded bags.

Helen's office was behind the mill shop, a floury, dusty, mealy place stacked tightly with sacks of cow cake, sheep nuts, hen pellets and drums of black treacle and when I slowed down outside I could often catch a glimpse of her red-sweatered back as she bent over her books.

Tonight I had been first home and Helen had come in as I was lighting my pile of sticks and coal. Girls used to wear things called 'pixie hoods' in those days and I can see her now in a blue pixie hood, her face flushed with the long climb up the stairs looking round that door at me busy with my chores.

But tonight my worst fears were being realised. My wife gave a long contented sigh and laid out one by one the dread ace, king, queen, jack and ten.

'Sequence,' she murmured in a matter of fact tone and moved her peg up another two hundred and fifty.

It wasn't a defeat, it was a massacre. It was obvious I hadn't long to live. But as I scanned the board anxiously the front door bell echoed along the passage downstairs.

Maybe I was going to be saved. I leapt to my feet and began the familiar descent.

A bulky figure loomed beyond the glass door at the end of the passage and as I turned the handle a waft of beer fumes blew in.

'Ah want a cleansing drink,' the figure said.

I opened the door wide. 'Come inside for a minute, it's a cold night.'

It was Reg Mallaby, a member of the large body of farmers who liked to drop in at the surgery on the way home after a night in the pub or the cinema, just to pick up some medicaments for the livestock.

We went into the office and he stood leaning on the desk, breathing heavily. 'A cleansing drink, eh?' I said. 'Right, I'll bring one through.'

Of course there was no such thing as a cleansing drink – there never has been – and when I first came to Darrowby and didn't know any better I used to waste a lot of time telling the farmers so. I went out of my way to explain as lucidly as I could that nothing you poured down a cow's throat could possibly influence the separation of the afterbirth and that they shouldn't throw their money away on something which was useless. The farmers listened with growing disbelief then left, offended, to purchase a cleansing drink at the chemist's shop.

I took a more practical view now and went through to the stockroom. There was quite a pile of the square packets there. They were wrapped in bright red paper with lettering in confident black capitals and we did a brisk trade in them at half a crown a time. We bought them by the gross from a wholesaler and though I never had them analysed I had a strong suspicion that they consisted of a pound of Epsom salts flavoured with aromatic powder.

'Here you are, Mr Mallaby,' I said. 'That's what you want, isn't it?'

'Aye, that's it, young man.' The farmer handled the packet almost lovingly. 'They're champion things, these, tha knows. Ah've never known 'em fail. Must have some wonderful stuff in 'em.'

He handed over his half crown then looked at me benevolently. 'I 'ope I haven't disturbed you, lad. Maybe you were doing summat important like?'

'No, that's quite all right, Mr Mallaby.' I looked at him with mingled surprise and gratitude. He was the first of the nocturnal callers who had shown any interest or concern. It had always been another symptom of the general opinion that vets have no private life. 'No, you needn't worry about that. I was just playing cards with my wife.'

The farmer nodded and a slow seraphic smile crept over his face. There was no doubt he had been indulging to the full. Then he narrowed his eyes suddenly. 'Is your Missus t'lass that works at t'mill?'

'Yes, that's right. She's in the office there.'

His face became very solemn. 'Aye well, I 'ave a complaint to make.'

'A complaint? What do you mean?'

I must have looked astonished because he held up a placatory hand.

'Now then, young man, she's a grand lass, I'm not sayin' nowt about that. But she sent me a wrong bill.'

'A wrong bill? In what way?'

'There was a mistake in it. She charged me for a lot o' things I never 'ad.'

'Well that's very strange. Are you absolutely sure?' I could easily imagine myself making clerical errors but in my experience Helen was a model of efficiency in that line.

'Aye, ah'm sure,' he replied. 'Haud on a minute and I'll show you. I 'ave it in my pocket here.'

He put his cleansing drink on the desk and began a laborious search of his pockets. He tracked down the offending account among a huge wad of envelopes which he extracted from inside his coat.

'There y'are, young man,' he said importantly. 'Just have a look at that.'

I studied the paper carefully. Opposite a date at the top there was an entry 'Two bags pig meal' and underneath on dates when the order had obviously been repeated Helen had put dittos by writing 'do ... do ... do ... do'.

'Well what's wrong with it, Mr Mallaby?'

The farmer pursed his lips. 'Ah'll tell ye. Ye see that about pig meal?'

I nodded.

'Well,' he went on, 'ah've had a few bags o' that, I'm not denyin' and I expect to pay for't. But ...' and here he raised a portentous forefinger, 'there's one thing I'm certain of. Ah've never 'ad none o' them bloody doo-doo's.'

Chapter Twenty

No vet likes to have his job made more difficult and as I worked inside the ewe I fought a rising tide of irritation.

'You know, Mr Kitson,' I said testily, 'you should have got me out sooner. How long have you been trying to lamb this ewe?'

The big man grunted and shrugged his shoulders. 'Oh, for a bit – not ower long.'

'Half an hour – an hour?'

'Nay, nay, nobbut a few minutes.' Mr Kitson regarded me gloomily along his pointed nose. It was his habitual expression; in fact I had never seen him smile and the idea of a laugh ever disturbing those pendulous cheeks was unthinkable.

I gritted my teeth and decided to say no more about it, but I knew it had taken more than a few minutes to cause the swelling of the vaginal wall, this sandpaper dryness of the little creature's inside. And it was a simple enough presentation – biggish twins, one anterior the other posterior, but of course as often happens the hind legs of one were laid alongside the head of the other giving the illusion that they belonged to the same lamb. I'd like to bet that Mr Kitson had been guddling for ages inside her with his big rough hands in a dogged attempt to bring that head and those legs out together.

If I had been there at the start it would have been the work of a few moments but instead here I was without an inch of space, trying to push things around with one finger instead of my full hand and getting nowhere.

Fortunately the present day farmer doesn't often play this trick on us. The usual thing I hear at a lambing is, 'Nay, I just had a quick feel and I knew it wasn't a job for me,' or something I heard from a farmer the other day, 'Two men at one ewe's no good,' and I think that says it very well.

But Mr Kitson was of the old school. He didn't believe in getting the vet out until every other avenue had been explored and when he did finally have to fall back on our services he was usually dissatisfied with the result.

'This is no good,' he said, withdrawing my hand and swilling it quickly in the bucket. 'I'll have to do something about this dryness.'

I walked the length of the old stable which had been converted into temporary lambing pens and lifted a tube of lubricating cream from the car boot. Coming in again I heard a faint sound from my left. The stable was dimly lit and an ancient door had been placed across the darkest corner to make a small enclosure. I looked inside and in the gloom could just discern a ewe lying on her chest, head outstretched. Her ribs rose and fell with the typical quick distressed respirations of a sheep in pain. Occasionally she moaned softly.

'What's the trouble here?' I asked.

Mr Kitson regarded me impassively from the other end of the building. 'She 'ad a roughish time lambin' yesterday.'

'How do you mean, roughish?'

'Well . . . a big single lamb wi' a leg back and I couldn't fetch it round.'

'So you just pulled it out as it was . . . with the leg back?'

'Aye, nowt else ah could do.'

I leaned over the door and lifted the ewe's tail, filthy with faeces and discharge. I winced as I saw the tumefied, discoloured vulva and perineum.

'She could do with a bit of attention, Mr Kitson.'

The farmer looked startled. 'Nay, nay, I don't want none o' that. It's ower with her – there's nowt you can do.'

'You mean she's dying?'

'That's right.'

I put my hand on the sheep's head, feeling the coldness of the ears and lips. He could be right.

'Well have you rung Mallock to come and pick her up? She really should be put out of her pain as soon as possible.'

'Aye . . . ah'll do that.' Mr Kitson shuffled his feet and looked away.

I knew what the situation was. He was going to let the ewe 'take her chance'. The lambing season was always a rewarding and fulfilling time for me but this was the other side of the coin. It was a hectic time in the farming year, a sudden onslaught of extra work on top of the routine jobs and in some ways it overwhelmed the resources of farmers and vets alike. The flood of new life left a pathetic debris behind it; a flotsam and jetsam of broken creatures; ewes too old to stand a further pregnancy, some debilitated by diseases like liver fluke and toxaemia, others with infected arthritic joints and others who had just had a 'roughish time'. You were inclined to find them lying half forgotten in dark corners like the one in this stable. They had been left there to 'take their chance'.

I returned in silence to my original patient. My lubricating cream made a great difference and I was able to use more than one finger to explore. I had to make up my mind whether to repel the posterior or anterior presentation and since the head was well into the vagina I decided to bring out the anterior first.

With the farmer's help I raised the ewe's hindquarters till they were resting on a straw bale. I could work downhill now and gently pushed the two hind limbs away into the depths of the uterus. In the space which this left I was able to hook a finger round the fore limbs which were laid back along the ribs of the anterior lamb and bring them into the passage. I only needed another application of the cream and a few moments' careful traction and the lamb was delivered.

But it was all too late. The tiny creature was quite dead and the knell of disappointment sounded in me as it always did at the sight of a perfectly formed body which lacked only the spark of life.

Hurriedly I greased my arm again and felt inside for the repelled lamb. There was plenty of room now and I was able to loop my hand round the hocks and draw the lamb out without effort. This time I had little hope of life and my effort were solely to relieve the ewe's discomfort but as the lamb came into the cold outside air I felt the convulsive jerk and wriggle of the woolly little form in my hands which told me all was well.

It was funny how often this happened; you got a dead lamb – sometimes even a decomposed one – with a live one lurking behind it. Anyway it was a bonus and with a surge of pleasure I wiped the mucus from its mouth and pushed it forward for its mother to lick. A further exploration of the uterus revealed nothing more and I got to my feet.

'Well she's come to no harm, and I think she'll be all right now,' I said. 'And could I have some fresh water, Mr Kitson, please?'

The big man wordlessly emptied the bucket on to the stable floor and went off towards the house. In the silence I could faintly hear the panting of the ewe in the far corner. I tried not to think of what lay in front of her. Soon I would drive off and see other cases, then I would have lunch and start my afternoon round while hidden in this cheerless place a helpless animal was gasping her life away. How long would it take her to die? A day? Two days.

It was no good. I had to do something about it. I ran out to my car, grabbed the bottle of nembutal and my big fifty c.c. syringe and hurried back into the stable. I vaulted over the rotting timbers of the door, drew out forty c.c.'s from the bottle and plunged the whole dose into the sheep's peritoneal cavity. Then I leapt back, galloped the length of the stable and when Mr Kitson returned I was standing innocently where he had left me.

I towelled myself, put on my jacket and gathered up my bottle of antiseptic and the tube of cream which had served me so well.

Mr Kitson preceded me along the stable and on the way out he glanced over the door in the corner.

'By gaw, she's goin' fast,' he grunted.

I looked over his shoulder into the gloom. The panting had stopped and was replaced by slow, even respirations. The eyes were closed. The sheep was anaesthetised. She would die in peace.

'Yes,' I said. 'She's definitely sinking. I don't think it will be very long now.' I couldn't resist a parting shaft. 'You've lost this ewe and that lamb back there. I think I could have saved both of them for you if you'd given me a chance.'

Maybe my words got through to Mr Kitson, because I was surprised to be called back to the farm a few days later to a ewe which had obviously suffered very little interference.

The animal was in a field close to the house and she was clearly bursting with lambs; so round and fat she could hardly waddle. But she looked bright and healthy.

'There's a bloody mix-up in there,' Mr Kitson said morosely. 'Ah could feel two heads and God only knows how many feet. Didn't know where the 'ell I was.'

'But you didn't try very hard?'

'Nay, never tried at all.'

Well, we were making progress. As the farmer gripped the sheep round the neck I knelt behind her and dipped my hands in the bucket. For once it was a warm morning. Looking back, my memories of lambing times have been of bitter winds searing the grass of the hill pastures, of chapped hands, chafed arms, gloves, scarves and cold-nipped ears. For years after I left Glasgow I kept waiting for the balmy early springs of western Scotland. After thirty years I am still waiting and it has begun to dawn on me that it doesn't happen that way in Yorkshire.

But this morning was one of the exceptions. The sun blazed from a sky of soft blue, there was no wind but a gentle movement of the air rolled the fragrance of the moorland flowers and warm grass over and around me as I knelt there.

And I had my favourite job in front of me. I almost chuckled as I fished around inside the ewe. There was all the room in the world, everything was moist and fresh and unspoiled, and it was child's play to fit the various jigsaws together. In about thirty seconds I had a lamb wriggling on the grass, in a few moments more a second, then a third and finally to my delight I reached away forward and found another little cloven foot and whisked it out into the world.

'Quadruplets!' I cried happily, but the farmer didn't share my enthusiasm.

'Nowt but a bloody nuisance,' he muttered. 'She'd be far better wi' just two.' He paused and gave me a sour look. 'Any road, ah reckon there wasn't no need to call ye. I could've done that job meself.'

I looked at him sadly from my squatting position. Sometimes in our job you feel you just can't win. If you take too long, you're no good, if you're too quick the visit wasn't necessary. I have never quite subscribed to the views of a cynical old colleague who once adjured me: 'Never make a lambing look easy. Hold the buggers in for a few minutes if necessary.' But at times I felt he had a point.

Anyway, I had my own satisfaction in watching the four lambs. So often I had pitied these tiny creatures in their entry into an uncharitable world, sometimes even of snow and ice, but today it was a joy to see them trying to struggle to their feet under the friendly sun, their woolly coats already drying rapidly. Their mother, magically deflated, was moving among them in a bemused manner as though she couldn't quite believe what she saw. As she nosed and licked them her deep-throated chuckles were answered by the first treble quaverings of her family. I was listening, enchanted, to this conversation when Mr Kitson spoke up.

'There's t'ewe you lambed t'other day.'

I looked up and there indeed she was, trotting proudly past, her lamb close at her flank.

'Ah yes, she looks fine,' I said. That was good to see but my attention was caught by something else. I pointed across the grass.

'That ewe away over there ...' As a rule all sheep look alike to me but there was something about this one I recognised ... a loss of wool from her back, a bare strip of skin stretched over the jutting ridge of her spinal column ... surely I couldn't be mistaken.

The farmer followed my pointing finger. 'Aye, that's t'awd lass that was laid in the stable last time you were here.' He turned an expressionless gaze on me. 'The one you told me to get Mallock to fetch.'

'But ... but ... she was dying!' I blurted out.

The corner of Mr Kitson's mouth twitched upwards in what must have been the nearest possible approach to a smile. 'Well, that's what you tellt me, young feller.' He hunched his shoulders. 'Said she 'adn't long to go, didn't you?'

I had no words to offer. I just gaped at him. I must have been the picture of bewilderment and it seemed the farmer was puzzled too because he went on.

'But I'll tell tha summat. Ah've been among sheep all me life but ah've never seen owt like it. That ewe just went to sleep.'

'Is that so?'

'Aye, went to sleep, ah tell you and she stayed sleepin' for two days!'

'She slept for two days?'

'She did, ah'm not jokin', nor jestin'. Ah kept goin' into t'stable but she never altered. Lay there peaceful as you like all t'first day, then all t'second, then when I went in on t'third morning she was standin' there lookin' at me and ready for some grub.'

'Amazing!' I got to my feet. 'I must have a look at her.'

I really wanted to see what had become of that mass of inflammation and tumefaction under her tail and I approached her carefully, jockeying her bit by bit into the bottom corner of the field. There we faced each other for a few tense moments as I tried a few feints and she responded with nimble side-steps; then as I made my final swoop to catch her fleece she eluded me effortlessly and shot past me with a thundering of hooves. I gave chase for twenty yards but it was too hot and wellingtons aren't the ideal gear for running. In any case I have long held the notion that if a vet can't catch his patient there's nothing much to worry about.

And as I walked back up the field a message was tapping in my brain. I had discovered something, discovered something by accident. That ewe's life had been saved not by medicinal therapy but simply by stopping her pain and allowing nature to do its own job of healing. It was a lesson I have never forgotten; that animals confronted with severe continuous pain and the terror and shock that goes with it will often retreat even into death, and if you can remove that pain amazing things can happen. It is difficult to explain rationally but I know that it is so.

By the time I had got back to Mr Kitson the sun was scorching the back of my neck and I could feel a trickle of sweat under my shirt. The big man was still watching the ewe which had finished its gallop and was cropping the grass contentedly.

'Ah can't get over it,' he murmured, scratching the thin bristle on his jaw. 'Two whole days and never a move.' He turned to me and his eyes widened.

'Ah'll tell tha, young man, you'd just think she'd been drugged!'

Chapter Twenty-one

I found it difficult to get Mr Kitson's ewe out of my mind but I had to make the effort because while all the sheep work was going on the rest of the practice problems rolled along unabated. One of these concerned the Flaxtons' Poodle, Penny.

Penny's first visit to the surgery was made notable by the attractiveness of her mistress. When I stuck my head round the waiting-room door and said, 'Next please,' Mrs Flaxton's little round face with its shining tight cap of blue-black hair seemed to illumine the place like a beacon. It is possible that the effect was heightened by the fact that she was sitting between fifteen stone Mrs Barmby, who had brought her canary to have its claws clipped, and old Mr Spence who was nearly ninety and had called round for some flea powder for his cat, but there was no doubt she was good to look at.

And it wasn't just that she was pretty; there was a round-eyed, innocent appeal about her and she smiled all the time. Penny, sitting on her knee, seemed to be smiling from under the mound of brown curls on her forehead.

In the consulting room I lifted the little dog on to the table. 'Well now, what's the trouble?'

'She has a touch of sickness and diarrhoea,' Mrs Flaxton replied. 'It started yesterday.'

'I see.' I turned and lifted the thermometer from the trolley. 'Has she had a change of food?'

'No, nothing like that.'

'Is she inclined to eat rubbish when she's out?'

Mrs Flaxton shook her head. 'No, not as a rule. But I suppose even the nicest dog will have a nibble at a dead bird or something horrid like that now and then.' She laughed and Penny laughed back at her.

'Well, she has a slightly raised temperature but she seems bright enough.' I put my hand round the dog's middle. 'Let's have a feel at your tummy, Penny.'

The little animal winced as I gently palpated the abdomen, and there was a tenderness throughout the stomach and intestines.

'She has gastroenteritis,' I said. 'But it seems fairly mild and I think it should clear up quite soon. I'll give you some medicine for her and you'd better keep her on a light diet for a few days.'

'Yes, I'll do that. Thank you very much.' Mrs Flaxton's smile deepened as she patted her dog's head. She was about twenty-three and she and her young husband had only recently come to Darrowby. He was a representative of one of the big agricultural firms which supplied meal and cattle cake to the farms and I saw him occasionally on my rounds. Like his wife, and indeed his dog, he gave off an ambience of eager friendliness.

I sent Mrs Flaxton off with a bottle of bismuth, kaolin and chlorodyne mixture which was one of our cherished treatments. The little dog trotted down the surgery steps, tail wagging, and I really didn't expect any more trouble.

Three days later, however, Penny was in the surgery again. She was still vomiting and the diarrhoea had not taken up in the least.

I got the dog on the table again and carried out a further examination but there was nothing significant to see. She had now had five days of this weakening condition but though she had lost a bit of her perkiness she still looked remarkably bright. The Toy Poodle is small but tough and very game and this one wasn't going to let anything get her down easily.

But I still didn't like it. She couldn't go on like this. I decided to alter the treatment to a mixture of carbon and astringents which had served me well in the past.

'This stuff looks a bit messy,' I said, as I gave Mrs Flaxton a powder box full of the black granules. 'But I have had good results with it. She's still eating, isn't she, so I should mix it in her food.'

'Oh thank you.' She gave me one of her marvellous smiles as she put the box in her bag and I walked along the passage with her to the door. She had left her pram at the foot of the steps and I knew before I looked under the hood what kind of baby I would find. Sure enough the chubby face on the pillow gazed at me with round friendly eyes and then split into a delighted grin.

They were the kind of people I liked to see but as they moved off down the street I hoped for Penny's sake that I wouldn't be seeing them for a long time. However, it was not to be. A couple of days later they were back and this time the Poodle was showing signs of strain. As I examined her she stood motionless and dead-eyed with only the occasional twitch of her tail as I stroked her head and spoke to her.

'I'm afraid she's just the same, Mr Herriot,' her mistress said. 'She's not eating much now and whatever she does goes straight through her. And she has a terrific thirst – always at her water bowl and then she brings it back.'

I nodded. 'I know. This inflammation inside her gives her a raging desire for water and of course the more she drinks the more she vomits. And this is terribly weakening.'

Again I changed the treatment. In fact over the next few days I ran through just about the entire range of available drugs. I look back with a wry smile at the things I gave that little dog, powdered epicacuanha and opium, sodium salicylate and tincture of camphor, even way-out exotics like decoction of haematoxylin and infusion of caryophyllum which thank heavens have been long forgotten. I might have done a bit of good if I had had access to a gut-active antibiotic like neomycin but as it was I got nowhere.

I was visiting Penny daily as she was unfit to bring to the surgery. I had her on a diet of arrowroot and boiled milk but that, like my medical treatment, achieved nothing. And all the time the little dog was slipping away.

The climax came about three o'clock one morning. As I lifted the bedside phone Mr Flaxton's voice, with a tremor in it, came over the line.

'I'm terribly sorry to get you out of your bed at this hour, Mr Herriot, but I wish you'd come round to see Penny.'

'Why, is she worse?'

'Yes, and she's . . . well . . . she's suffering now, I'm afraid. You saw her this afternoon didn't you? Well since then she's been drinking and vomiting and this diarrhoea running away from her all the time till she's about at the far end. She's just lying in her basket crying. I'm sure she's in great pain.'

'Right, I'll be there in a few minutes.'

'Oh thank you.' He paused for a moment. 'And Mr Herriot . . . you'll come prepared to put her down won't you?'

My spirits, never very high at that time in the morning, plummeted to the depths. 'As bad as that, is it?'

'Well honestly we can't bear to see her. My wife is so upset . . . I don't think she can stand any more.'

'I see.' I hung up the phone and threw the bedclothes back with a violence which brought Helen wide awake. Being disturbed in the small hours was one of the crosses a vet's wife has to bear, but normally I crept out as quietly as I could. This time, however, I stamped about the bedroom, dragging on my clothes and muttering to myself; and though she must have wondered what this latest crisis meant she wisely watched me in silence until I turned out the light and left.

I had not far to go. The Flaxtons lived in one of the new bungalows on the Brawton Road less than a mile away. The young couple, in their dressing gowns, led me into the kitchen and before I reached the dog basket in the corner I could hear Penny's whimperings. She was not lying comfortably curled up, but on her chest, head forward, obviously acutely distressed. I put my hands under her and lifted her and she was almost weightless. A Toy Poodle in its prime is fairly insubstantial but after her long illness Penny was like a bedraggled little piece of thistledown, her curly brown coat wet and soiled by vomit and diarrhoea.

Mrs Flaxton's smile for once was absent. I could see she was keeping back the tears as she spoke.

'It really would be the kindest thing . . .'

'Yes . . . yes . . .' I replaced the tiny animal in her basket and crouched over her, chin in hand. 'Yes, I suppose you're right.'

But still I didn't move but stayed, squatting there, staring down in disbelief at the evidence of my failure. This dog was only two years old – a lifetime of running and jumping and barking in front of her; all she was suffering from was gastroenteritis and now I was going to extinguish the final spark in her. It was a bitter thought that this would be just about the only positive thing I had done right from the start.

A weariness swept over me that was not just due to the fact that I had been snatched from sleep. I got to my feet with the slow stiff movements of an old man and was about to turn away when I noticed something about the little animal. She was on her chest again, head extended, mouth open, tongue lolling as she panted. There was something there I had seen before somewhere . . . that posture . . . and the exhaustion, pain and shock . . . it slid almost imperceptibly into my sleepy brain that she looked exactly like Mr Kitson's ewe in its dark corner. A different species, yes, but all the other things were there.

'Mrs Flaxton,' I said, 'I want to put Penny to sleep. Not the way you think, but to anaesthetise her. Maybe if she has a rest from this nonstop drinking and vomiting and straining it will give nature a chance.'

The young couple looked at me doubtfully for a few moments then it was the husband who spoke.

'Don't you think she has been through enough, Mr Herriot?'

'She has, yes she has.' I ran a hand through my rumpled uncombed hair. 'But this won't cause her any more distress. She won't know a thing about it.'

When they still hesitated I went on. 'I would very much like to try it – it's just an idea I've got.'

They looked at each other, then Mrs Flaxton nodded. 'All right, go ahead, but this will be the last, won't it?'

Out into the night air to my car for the same bottle of nembutal and a very small dose for the little creature. I went back to my bed with the same feeling I had had about the ewe; come what may there would be no more suffering.

Next morning Penny was still stretched peacefully on her side and when, about four o'clock in the afternoon, she showed signs of awakening I repeated the injection.

Like the ewe she slept for forty-eight hours and when she finally did stagger to her feet she did not head immediately for her water bowl as she had done for so many days. Instead she made her feeble way outside and had a walk round the garden.

From then on, recovery, as they say in the case histories, was uneventful. Or as I would rather write it, she wonderfully and miraculously just got better and never ailed another thing throughout her long life.

Helen and I used to play tennis on the grass courts near the Darrowby cricket ground. So did the Flaxtons and they always brought Penny along with them. I used to look through the wire at her romping with other dogs and later with the Flaxtons' fast growing young son and I marvelled.

I do not wish to give the impression that I advocate wholesale anaesthesia for all animal ailments but I do know that sedation has a definite place. Nowadays we have a sophisticated range of sedatives and tranquillisers to choose from and when I come up against an acute case of gastroenteritis in dogs I use one of them as an adjunct to the normal treatment; because it puts a brake on the deadly exhausting cycle and blots out the pain and fear which go with it.

And over the years, whenever I saw Penny running around, barking, bright-eyed, full of the devil, I felt a renewed welling of thankfulness for the cure which I discovered in a dark corner of a stable by accident.

Chapter Twenty-two

The name was on the garden gate – Lilac Cottage. I pulled out my list of visits and checked the entry again. 'Cook, Lilac Cottage, Marston Hall. Bitch overdue for whelping.' This was the place all right, standing in the grounds of the Hall, a nineteenth-century mansion house whose rounded turrets reared above the fringe of pine trees less than half a mile away.

The door was opened by a heavy featured dark woman of about sixty who regarded me unsmilingly.

'Good morning, Mrs Cook,' I said. 'I've come to see your bitch.'

She still didn't smile. 'Oh, very well. You'd better come in.'

She led me into the small living room and as a little Yorkshire Terrier jumped down from an armchair her manner changed.

'Come here, Cindy my darlin',' she cooed. 'This gentleman's come to make you better.' She bent down and stroked the little animal, her face radiant with affection.

I sat down in another armchair. 'Well what's the trouble, Mrs Cook?'

'Oh, I'm worried to death.' She clasped her hands anxiously. 'She should have had her pups yesterday and there's nothing happenin'. Ah couldn't sleep all night – I'd die if anything happened to this dog.'

I looked at the terrier, tail wagging, gazing up, bright-eyed under her mistress' caress. 'She doesn't seem distressed at all. Has she shown any signs of labour?'

'What d'you mean?'

'Well, has she been panting or uneasy in any way? Is there any discharge?'

'No, nothing like that.'

I beckoned to Cindy and spoke to her and she came timidly across the lino till I was able to lift her on to my lap. I palpated the distended abdomen; there was a lot of pups in there but everything appeared normal. I took her temperature – normal again.

'Bring me some warm water and soap, Mrs Cook, will you please?' I said. The terrier was so small that I had to use my little finger, soaped and disinfected, to examine her, and as I felt carefully forward the walls of the vagina were dry and clinging and the cervix, when I reached it, tightly closed.

I washed and dried my hands. 'This little bitch isn't anywhere near whelping, Mrs Cook. Are you sure you haven't got your dates wrong?'

'No, I 'aven't, it was sixty-three days yesterday.' She paused in thought for a moment. 'Now ah'd better tell you this, young man. Cindy's had pups before and she did self and same thing – wouldn't get on with t'job. That was two years ago when I was livin' over in Listondale. I got Mr Broomfield the vet to her and he just gave her an injection. It was wonderful – she had the pups half an hour after it.'

I smiled. 'Yes, that would be pituitrin. She must have been actually whelping when Mr Broomfield saw her.'

'Well whatever it was, young man, I wish you'd give her some now. Ah can't stand all this suspense.'

'I'm sorry.' I lifted Cindy from my lap and stood up. 'I can't do that. It would be very harmful at this stage.'

She stared at me and it struck me that that dark face could look very forbidding. 'So you're not goin' to do anything at all?'

'Well . . .' There are times when it is a soothing procedure to give a client something to do even if it is unnecessary. 'Yes, I've got some tablets in the car. They'll help to keep the little dog fit until she whelps.'

'But I'd far rather have that injection. It was just a little prick. Didn't take Mr Broomfield more than a second to do.'

'I assure you, Mrs Cook, it can't be done at the moment. I'll get the tablets from the car.'

Her mouth tightened. I could see she was grievously disappointed in me. 'Oh well if you won't you won't, so you'd better get them things.' She paused: 'And me name isn't Cook!'

'It isn't?'

'No it isn't, young man.' She didn't seem disposed to offer further information so I left in some bewilderment.

Out in the road, a few yards from my car, a farm man was trying to start a tractor. I called over to him.

'Hey, the lady in there says her name isn't Cook.'

'She's right an' all. She's the cook over at the Hall. You've gotten a bit mixed up.' He laughed heartily.

It all became suddenly clear; the entry in the day book, everything. 'What's her right name, then?'

'Booby,' he shouted just as the tractor roared into life.

Funny name, I thought, as I produced my harmless vitamin tablets from the boot and returned to the cottage. Once inside I did my best to put things right with plenty of 'Yes, Mrs Booby' and 'No, Mrs Booby' but the lady didn't thaw. I told her not to worry and that I was sure nothing would happen for several days but I could tell I wasn't impressing her.

I waved cheerfully as I went down the path.

'Goodbye, Mrs Booby,' I cried. 'Don't hesitate to ring me if you're in doubt about anything.'

She didn't appear to have heard.

'Oh I wish you'd do as I say,' she wailed. 'It was just a little prick.'

The good lady certainly didn't hesitate to ring. She was at me again the next day and I had to rush out to her cottage. Her message was the same as before; she wanted the wonderful injection which would make those pups pop out and she wanted it right away. Mr Broomfield hadn't messed about and wasted time like I had. And on the third and fourth and fifth mornings she had me out at Marston examining the little bitch and reciting the same explanations. Things came to a head on the sixth day.

In the room at Lilac Cottage the dark eyes held a desperate light as they stared into mine. 'I'm about at the end of my tether, young man. I tell you I'll die if anything happens to this dog. I'll die. Don't you understand?'

'Of course I know how you feel about her, Mrs Booby. Believe me, I fully understand.'

'Then why don't you do something?' she snapped.

I dug my nails into my palms. 'Look, I've told you. A pituitrin injection works by contracting the muscular walls of the uterus so it can only be given when labour has started and the cervix is open. If I find it is indicated I will do it, but if I give this injection now it could cause rupture of the uterus. It could cause death.' I stopped because I fancied little bubbles were beginning to collect at the corners of my mouth.

But I don't think she had listened to a word. She sunk her head in her hands. 'All this time, I can't stand it.'

I was wondering if I could stand much more of it myself. Bulging Yorkshire Terriers had begun to prance through my dreams at night and I greeted each new day with a silent prayer that the pups had arrived. I held out my hand to Cindy and she crept reluctantly towards me. She was heartily sick of this strange man who came every day and squeezed her and stuck fingers into her and she submitted again with trembling limbs and frightened eyes to the indignity.

'Mrs Booby,' I said, 'are you absolutely sure that dog didn't have access to Cindy after the service date you gave me?'

She sniffed. 'You keep askin' me that and ah've been thinking about it. Maybe he did come a week after, now I think on.'

'Well, that's it, then!' I spread my hands. 'She's held to the second mating, so she should be due tomorrow.'

'Ah would still far rather you would get it over with today like Mr Broomfield did . . . it was just a little prick.'

'But Mrs Booby . . .!'

'And let me tell you another thing, me name's not Booby!'

I clutched at the back of the chair. 'It's not?'

'Naw!'

'Well . . . what is it, then?'

'It's Dooley . . . Dooley!' She looked very cross.

'Right . . . right . . .' I stumbled down the garden path and drove away. It was not a happy departure.

Next morning I could hardly believe it when there was no call from Marston.

Maybe all was well at last. But I turned cold when an urgent call to go to Lilac Cottage was passed on to one of the farms on my round. I was right at the far end of the practice area and was in the middle of a tough calving and it was well over three hours before I got out at the now familiar garden gate. The cottage door was open and as I ventured up the path a little brown missile hurtled out at me. It was Cindy, but a transformed Cindy, a snarling, barking little bundle of ferocity; and though I recoiled she fastened her teeth in my trouser cuff and hung on grimly.

I was hopping around on one leg trying to shake off the growling little creature when a peal of almost girlish laughter made me look round.

Mrs Dooley, vastly amused, was watching me from the doorway. 'My word, she's different since she had them pups. Just shows what a good little mother she is, guarding them like that.' She gazed fondly at the tiny animal dangling from my ankle.

'Had the pups. . .?'

'Aye, when they said you'd be a long time I rang Mr Farnon. He came right away and d'you know he gave Cindy that injection I've wanted all along. And I tell you 'e wasn't right out of t'garden gate before the pups started. She's had seven – beauties they are.'

'Ah well that's fine, Mrs Dooley . . . splendid.' Siegfried had obviously felt a pup in the passage. I finally managed to rid myself of Cindy and when her mistress lifted her up I went into the kitchen to inspect the family.

They certainly were grand pups and I lifted the squawking little morsels one by one from their basket while their mother snarled from Mrs Dooley's arms like a starving wolfhound.

'They're lovely, Mrs Dooley,' I murmured.

She looked at me pityingly. 'I told you what to do, didn't I, but you wouldn't 'ave it. It only needed a little prick. Ooo, that Mr Farnon's a lovely man – just like Mr Broomfield.'

This was a bit much. 'But you must realise, Mrs Dooley, he just happened to arrive at the right time. If I had come . . .'

'Now, now, young man, be fair. Ah'm not blamin' you, but some people have had more experience. We all 'ave to learn.' She sighed reminiscently. 'It was just a little prick – Mr Farnon'll have to show you how to do it. I tell you he wasn't right out of t'garden gate . . .'

Enough is enough. I drew myself up to my full height. 'Mrs Dooley, madam,' I said frigidly, 'let me repeat once and for all . . .'

'Oh, hoity toity, hoity toity, don't get on your high horse wi' me!' she exclaimed. 'We've managed very nicely without you so don't complain.' Her expression became very severe. 'And one more thing – me name's not Mrs Dooley.'

My brain reeled for a moment. The world seemed to be crumbling about me. 'What did you say?'

'I said me name's not Mrs Dooley.'

'It isn't?'

'Naw!' She lifted her left hand and as I gazed at it dully I realised it must have been all the mental stress which have prevented me from noticing the total absence of rings.

'Naw!' she said. 'It's Miss!'

Chapter Twenty-three

I had never been married before so there was nothing in my past experience to go by but it was beginning to dawn on me that I was very nicely fixed.

I am talking, of course, of material things. It would have been enough for me or anybody else to be paired with a beautiful girl whom I loved and who loved me. I hadn't reckoned on the other aspects.

This business of studying my comfort, for instance. I thought such things had gone out of fashion, but not so with Helen. It was brought home to me again as I walked in to breakfast this morning. We had at last acquired a table – I had bought it at a farm sale and brought it home in triumph tied to the roof of my car – and now Helen had vacated the chair on which she used to sit at the bench and had taken over the high stool. She was perched away up there now, transporting her food from far below, while I was expected to sit comfortably in the chair. I don't think I am a selfish swine by nature but there was nothing I could do about it.

And there were other little things. The neat pile of clothing laid out for me each morning; the clean, folded shirt and handkerchief and socks so different from the jumble of my bachelor days. And when I was late for meals, which was often, she served me with my food but instead of going off and doing something else she would down tools and sit watching me while I ate. It made me feel like a sultan.

It was this last trait which gave me a clue to her behaviour. I suddenly remembered that I had seen her sitting by Mr Alderson while he had a late meal; sitting in the same pose, one arm on the table, quietly watching him. And I realised I was reaping the benefit of her lifetime attitude to her father. Mild little man though he was she had catered gladly to his every wish in the happy acceptance that the man of the house was number one; and the whole pattern was rubbing off on me now.

In fact it set me thinking about the big question of how girls might be expected to behave after marriage. One old farmer giving me advice about choosing a wife once said; 'Have a bloody good look at the mother first, lad', and I am sure he had a point. But if I may throw in my own little word of counsel it would be to have a passing glance at how she acts towards her father.

Watching her now as she got down and started to serve my breakfast the warm knowledge flowed through me as it did so often that my wife was the sort who just liked looking after a man and that I was so very lucky.

And I was certainly blooming under the treatment. A bit too much, in fact, and I was aware I shouldn't be attacking this plateful of porridge and cream; especially with all that material sizzling in the frying pan. Helen had brought with her to Skeldale House a delicious dowry in the shape of half a pig and there hung from the beams of the topmost attic a side of bacon and a majestic ham; a constant temptation. Some samples were in the pan now and though I had never been one for large breakfasts I did not demur when she threw in a couple of big brown eggs to keep them company. And I put up only feeble resistance when she added some particularly tasty smoked sausage which she used to buy in a shop in the market place.

When I had got through it all I rose rather deliberately from the table and as I put on my coat I noticed it wasn't so easy to button as it used to be.

'Here are your sandwiches, Jim,' Helen said, putting a parcel in my hand. I was spending a day in the Scarburn district, tuberculin testing for Ewan Ross, and my wife was always concerned lest I grow faint from lack of nourishment on the long journey.

I kissed her, made a somewhat ponderous descent of the long flights of stairs and went out the side door. Half way up the garden I stopped as always and looked up at the window under the tiles. An arm appeared and brandished a dishcloth vigorously. I waved back and continued my walk to the yard. I found I was puffing a little as I got the car out and I laid my parcel almost guiltily on the back seat. I knew what it would contain; not just sandwiches but meat and onion pie, buttered scones, ginger cake to lead me into further indiscretions.

There is no doubt that in those early days I would have grown exceedingly gross under Helen's treatment. But my job saved me; the endless walking between the stone barns scattered along the hillsides, the climbing in and out of calf pens, pushing cows around, and regular outbursts of hard physical effort in calving and foaling. So I escaped with only a slight tightening of my collar and the occasional farmer's remark, 'By gaw, you've been on a good pasture, young man!'

Driving away, I marvelled at the way she indulged my little whims, too. I have always had a pathological loathing of fat, so Helen carefully trimmed every morsel from my meat. This feeling about fat, which almost amounted to terror, had been intensified since coming to Yorkshire, because back in the thirties the farmers seemed to live on the stuff. One old man, noticing my pop-eyed expression as I viewed him relishing his lunch of roast fat bacon, told me he had never touched lean meat in his life.

'Ah like to feel t'grease runnin' down ma chin!' he chuckled. He pronounced it 'grayus' which made it sound even worse. But he was a ruddy-faced octogenarian, so it hadn't done him any harm; and this held good for hundreds of others just like him. I used to think that the day in day out hard labour of farming burned it up in their systems but if I had to eat the stuff it would kill me very rapidly.

The latter was, of course, a fanciful notion as was proved to me one day.

It was when I was torn from my bed one morning at 6 a.m. to attend a calving heifer at old Mr Horner's small farm and when I got there I found there was no malpresentation of the calf but that it was simply too big. I don't like a lot of pulling but the heifer, lying on her bed of straw, was obviously in need of assistance. Every few seconds she strained to the utmost and a pair of feet came into view momentarily then disappeared as she relaxed.

'Is she getting those feet out any further?' I asked.

'Nay, there's been no change for over an hour,' the old man replied.

'And when did the water bag burst?'

'Two hours since.'

There was no doubt the calf was well and truly stuck and getting drier all the time, and if the labouring mother had been able to speak I think she would have said: 'For Pete's sake get this thing away from me!'

I could have done with a big strong man to help me but Mr Horner, apart from his advanced age, was a rather shaky lightweight. And since the farm was perched on a lonely eminence miles from the nearest village there was no chance of calling in a neighbour. I would have to do the job myself.

It took me nearly an hour. With a thin rope behind the calf's ears and through his mouth to stop the neck from telescoping I eased the little creature inch by inch into the world. Not so much pulling but rather leaning back and helping the heifer as she strained. She was a rather undersized little animal and she lay patiently on her side, accepting the situation with the resignation of her kind. She could never have calved without help and all the time I had the warm conviction that I was doing what she wanted and needed. I felt I should be as patient as she was so I didn't hurry but let things come in their normal sequence; the little nose with the nostrils twitching reassuringly, then the eyes wearing a preoccupied light during the tight squeeze, then the ears and with a final rush the rest of the calf.

The young mother was obviously none the worse because she rolled on to her chest almost immediately and began to sniff with the utmost interest at the new arrival. She was in better shape than myself because I discovered with some surprise that I was sweating and breathless and my arms and shoulders were aching.

The farmer, highly pleased, rubbed my back briskly with the towel as I bent over the bucket, then he helped me on with my shirt.

'Well that's champion, lad. You'll come in and have a cup of tea now, won't you?'

In the kitchen Mrs Horner placed a steaming mug on the table and smiled across at me.

'Will you sit down along o' my husband and have a bit o' breakfast?' she asked.

There is nothing like an early calving to whet the appetite and I nodded readily. 'That's very kind of you, I'd love to.'

It is always a good feeling after a successful delivery and I sighed contentedly as I sank into a chair and watched the old lady set out bread, butter and jam in front of me. I sipped my tea and as I exchanged a word with the farmer I didn't see what she was doing next. Then my toes curled into a tight ball as I found two huge slices of pure white fat lying on my plate.

Shrinking back in my seat I saw Mrs Horner sawing at a great hunk of cold boiled bacon. But it wasn't ordinary bacon, it was one hundred per cent fat without a strip of lean anywhere. Even in my shocked state I could see it was a work of art; cooked to a turn, beautifully encrusted with golden crumbs and resting on a spotless serving dish . . . but fat.

She dropped two similar slices on her husband's plate and looked at me expectantly.

My position was desperate. I could not possibly offend this sweet old person but on the other hand I knew beyond all doubt that there was no way I could eat what lay in front of me. Maybe I could have managed a tiny piece if it had been hot and fried crisp, but cold, boiled and clammy . . . never. And there was an enormous quantity; two slices about six inches by four and at least half an inch thick with the golden border of crumbs down one side. The thing was impossible.

Mrs Horner sat down opposite me. She was wearing a flowered mob cap over her white hair and for a moment she reached out, bent her head to one side and turned the dish with the slab of bacon a little to the left to show it off better. Then she turned to me and smiled. It was a kind, proud smile.

There have been times in my life when, confronted by black and hopeless circumstances, I have discovered in myself undreamed-of resources of courage and resolution. I took a deep breath, seized knife and fork and made a bold incision in one of the slices, but as I began to transport the greasy white segment to my mouth I began to shudder and my hand stayed frozen in space. It was at that moment I spotted the jar of piccalilli.

Feverishly I scooped a mound of it on to my plate. It seemed to contain just about everything; onions, apples, cucumber and other assorted vegetables jostling each other in a powerful mustard-vinegar sauce. It was the work of a moment to smother my loaded fork with the mass, then I popped it into my mouth, gave a couple of quick chews and swallowed. It was a start and I hadn't tasted a thing except the piccalilli.

'Nice bit of bacon,' Mr Horner murmured.

'Delicious!' I replied, munching desperately at the second forkful. 'Absolutely delicious!'

'And you like ma piccalilli too!' The old lady beamed at me. 'Ah can tell by the way you're slappin' it on!' She gave a peal of delighted laughter.

'Yes, indeed.' I looked at her with streaming eyes. 'Some of the best I've ever tasted.'

Looking back, I realise it was one of the bravest things I have ever done. I stuck to my task unwaveringly, dipping again and again into the jar, keeping my mind a blank, refusing grimly to think of the horrible thing that was happening to me. There was only one bad moment, when the piccalilli, which packed a tremendous punch and was never meant to be consumed in large mouthfuls, completely took my breath away and I went into a long coughing spasm. But at last I came to the end. A final heroic crunch and swallow, a long gulp at my tea and the plate was empty. The thing was accomplished.

And there was no doubt it had been worth it. I had been a tremendous success with the old folks. Mr Horner slapped my shoulder.

'By gaw, it's good to see a young feller enjoyin' his food! When I were a lad I used to put it away sharpish, like that, but ah can't do it now.' Chuckling to himself, he continued with his breakfast.

His wife showed me the door. 'Aye, it was a real compliment to me.' She looked at the table and giggled. 'You've nearly finished the jar!'

'Yes, I'm sorry, Mrs Horner,' I said, smiling through my tears and trying to ignore the churning in my stomach. 'But I just couldn't resist it.'

Contrary to my expectations I didn't drop down dead soon afterwards but for a week I was oppressed by a feeling of nausea which I am prepared to believe was purely psychosomatic.

At any rate, since that little episode I have never knowingly eaten fat again. My hatred was transformed into something like an obsession from then on.

And I haven't been all that crazy about piccalilli either.

Chapter Twenty-four

I wondered how long this feeling of novelty at being a married man would last. Maybe it went on for years and years. At any rate I did feel an entirely different person from the old Herriot as I paced with my wife among the stalls at the garden fête.

It was an annual affair in aid of the Society for the Prevention of Cruelty to Children and it was held on the big lawn behind the Darrowby vicarage with the weathered brick of the old house showing mellow red beyond the trees. The hot June sunshine bathed the typically English scene; the women in their

flowered dresses, the men perspiring in their best suits, laughing children
running from the tombola to the coconut shy or the ice-cream kiosk. In a little
tent at one end, Mrs Newbould, the butcher's wife, thinly disguised as Madame
Claire the fortune teller, was doing a brisk trade. It all seemed a long way from
Glasgow.

And the solid citizen feeling was heightened by the pressure of Helen's hand
on my arm and the friendly nods of the passers-by. One of these was the curate.
Mr Blenkinsopp. He came up to us, exuding, as always, a charm that was
completely unworldly.

'Ah, James,' he murmured. 'And Helen!' He beamed on us with the benevolence he felt for the entire human race. 'How nice to see you here!'

He walked along with us as the scent from the flower beds and the trodden
grass rose in the warm air.

'You know, James, I was just thinking about you the other day. I was in
Rainby – you know I take the service there every second week – and they were
telling me they were having great difficulty in finding young men for the cricket
team. I wondered if you would care to turn out for them.'

'Me? Play cricket?'

'Yes, of course.'

I laughed. 'I'm afraid I'm no cricketer. I'm interested in the game and I like
to watch it, but where I come from they don't play it very much.'

'Oh, but surely you must have played at some time or other.'

'A bit at school, but they go more for tennis in Scotland. And anyway it was
a long time ago.'

'Oh well, there you are.' Mr Blenkinsopp spread his hands. 'It will come
back to you easily.'

'I don't know about that,' I said. 'But another thing, I don't live in Rainby,
doesn't that matter?'

'Not really,' the curate replied. 'It is such a problem finding eleven players
in these tiny villages that they often call on outsiders. Nobody minds.'

I stopped my stroll over the grass and turned to Helen. She was giving me
an encouraging smile and I began to think, well . . . why not? It looked as
though I had settled in Yorkshire. I had married a Yorkshire girl. I might as
well start doing the Yorkshire things, like playing cricket – there wasn't anything
more Yorkshire than that.

'All right then, Mr Blenkinsopp,' I said. 'You're not getting any bargain but
I don't mind having a go.'

'Splendid! The next match is on Tuesday evening – against Hedwick. I am
playing so I'll pick you up at six o'clock. His face radiated happiness as though
I had done him the greatest favour.

'Well, thanks,' I replied. 'I'll have to fix it with my partner to be off that
night, but I'm sure it will be O.K.'

The weather was still fine on Tuesday and, going round my visits, I found it
difficult to assimilate the fact that for the first time in my life I was going to
perform in a real genuine cricket match.

It was funny the way I felt about cricket. All my experience of the game was
based on the long-range impressions I had gained during my Glasgow boyhood.
Gleaned from newspapers, from boys' magazines, from occasional glimpses of
Hobbs and Sutcliffe and Woolley on the cinema newsreels, they had built up
a strangely glamorous picture in my mind. The whole thing, it seemed to me,
was so deeply and completely English; the gentle clunk of bat on ball, the
white-clad figures on the wide sweep of smooth turf; there was a softness a
graciousness about cricket which you found nowhere else; nobody ever got

excited or upset at this leisurely pursuit. There was no doubt at all that I looked on cricket with a romanticism and nostalgia which would have been incomprehensible to people who had played the game all their lives.

Promptly at six Mr Blenkinsopp tooted the horn of his little car outside the surgery. Helen had advised me to dress ready for action and she had clearly been right because the curate, too, was resplendent in white flannels and blazer. The three young farmers crammed in the back were, however, wearing open-necked shirts with their ordinary clothes.

'Hello, James!' said Mr Blenkinsopp.

'Now then, Jim,' said two of the young men in the back. But 'Good afternoon, Mr Herriot,' said the one in the middle.

He was Tom Willis, the captain of the Rainby team and in my opinion, one of nature's gentlemen. He was about my own age and he and his father ran the kind of impoverished small-holding which just about kept them alive. But there was a sensitivity and refinement about him and a courtesy which never varied. I never cared how people addressed me and a lot of the farmers used my first name, but to Tom and his father I was always Mr Herriot. They considered it was the correct way to address the vet and that was that.

Tom leaned from the back seat now, his lean face set in its usual serious expression.

'It's good of you to give up your time, Mr Herriot. I know you're a busy man but we're allus short o' players at Rainby.'

'I'm looking forward to it, Tom, but I'm no cricketer, I'll tell you now.'

He gazed at me with gentle disbelief and I had an uncomfortable feeling that everybody had the impression that because I had been to college I was bound to have a blue.

Hedwick was at the top end of Allerdale, a smaller offshoot of the main Dale, and as we drove up the deep ever-narrowing cleft in the moorland I wound down the window. It was the sort of country I saw every day but I wasn't used to being a passenger and there was no doubt you could see more this way. From the overlapping fringe of heather far above, the walls ran in spidery lines down the bare green flanks to the softness of the valley floor where grey farmhouses crouched; and the heavy scent of the new cut hay lying in golden swathes in the meadows drifted deliciously into the car. There were trees, too, down here, not the stunted dwarfs of the high country above us, but giants in the exultant foliage of high summer.

We stopped at Hedwick because we could go no further. This was the head of the Dale, a cluster of cottages, a farm and a pub. Where the road curved a few cars were drawn up by the side of a solid-looking wall on which leaned a long row of cloth-capped men, a few women and chattering groups of children.

'Ah,' said Mr Blenkinsopp. 'A good turn-out of spectators. Hedwick always support their team well. They must have come from all over the Dale.'

I looked around in surprise. 'Spectators?'

'Yes, of course. They've come to see the match.'

Again I gazed about me. 'But I can't see the pitch.'

'It's there,' Tom said. 'Just over t'wall.'

I leaned across the rough stones and stared in some bewilderment at a wildly undulating field almost knee deep in rough grass among which a cow, some sheep and a few hens wandered contentedly. 'Is this it?'

'Aye, that's it. If you stand on t'wall you can see the square.'

I did as he said and could just discern a five foot wide strip of bright green cut from the crowding herbage. The stumps stood expectantly at either end. A massive oak tree sprouted from somewhere around mid-on.

The strip stood on the only level part of the field, and that was a small part.

Within twenty yards it swept up steeply to a thick wood which climbed over the lower slopes of the fell. On the other side it fell away to a sort of ravine where the rank grass ended only in a rocky stream. The wall bordering the near side ran up to a group of farm buildings.

There was no clubhouse but the visiting team were seated on a form on the grass while nearby, a little metal score board about four feet high stood near its pile of hooked number plates.

The rest of our team had arrived, too, and with a pang of alarm I noticed that there was not a single pair of white flannels among them. Only the curate and I were properly attired and the immediate and obvious snag was that he could play and I couldn't.

Tom and the home captain tossed a coin. Hedwick won and elected to bat. The umpires, two tousle-haired, sunburnt young fellows in grubby white coats strolled to the wicket, our team followed and the Hedwick batsmen appeared. Under their pads they both wore navy blue serge trousers (a popular colour among both teams) and one of them sported a bright yellow sweater.

Tom Willis with the air of authority and responsibility which was natural to him began to dispose the field. No doubt convinced that I was a lynx-eyed catcher he stationed me quite close to the bat on the off side then after a grave consultation with Mr Blenkinsopp he gave him the ball and the game was on.

And Mr Blenkinsopp was a revelation. In his university sweater, gleaming flannels and brightly coloured cap he really looked good. And indeed it was soon very clear that he was good. He handed his cap to the umpire, retreated about twenty yards into the undergrowth, then turned and, ploughing his way back at ever increasing speed, delivered the ball with remarkable velocity bang on the wicket. The chap in yellow met it respectfully with a dead bat and did the same with the next but then he uncoiled himself and belted the third one high over the fielders on to the slope beneath the wood. As one of our men galloped after it the row of heads above the wall broke into a babel of noise.

They cheered every hit, not with the decorous ripple of applause I had always imagined, but with raucous yells. And they had plenty to shout about. The Hedwick lads, obviously accustomed to the peculiarities of their pitch wasted no time on classical strokes; they just gave a great hoick at the ball and when they connected it travelled immense distances. Occasionally they missed and Mr Blenkinsopp or one of our other bowlers shattered their stumps but the next man started cheerfully where they left off.

It was exhilarating stuff but I was unable to enjoy it. Everything I did, in fact my every movement proclaimed my ignorance to the knowledgeable people around me. I threw the ball in to the wrong end, I left the ball when I should have chased it and sped after it when I should have stayed in my place. I couldn't understand half the jargon which was being bandied around. No, there was not a shadow of a doubt about it; here in this cricket mad corner of a cricket mad county I was a foreigner.

Five wickets had gone down when a very fat lad came out to bat. His appearance of almost perfect rotundity was accentuated by the Fair Isle sweater stretched tightly over his bulging abdomen and judging by the barrage of witticisms which came from the heads along the wall it seemed he was a local character. He made a violent cross-batted swish at the first delivery, missed, and the ball sank with a thud into his midriff. Howls of laughter arose from players, spectators and umpires alike as he collapsed slowly at the crease and massaged himself ruefully. He slashed at the next one and it flew off the edge of his bat like a bullet, struck my shinbone a fearful crack and dropped into the grass. Resisting the impulse to scream and hop around in my agony I gritted my teeth, grabbed the ball and threw it in.

'Oh well stopped, Mr Herriot,' Tom Willis called from his position at mid on. He clapped his hands a few times in encouragement.

Despite his girth the fat lad smote lustily and was finally caught in the outfield for fifteen.

The next batsman seemed to be taking a long time to reach the wicket. He was shuffling, bent-kneed, through the clover like a very old man, trailing his bat wearily behind him, and when he finally arrived at the crease I saw that he was indeed fairly advanced in years. He wore only one pad, strapped over baggy grey trousers which came almost up to his armpits and were suspended by braces. A cloth cap surmounted a face shrunken like a sour apple. From one corner of the downturned mouth a cigarette dangled.

He took guard and looked at the umpire.

'Middle and leg,' he grunted.

'Aye, that's about it, Len,' the umpire replied.

Len pursed his little mouth.

'About it . . . about it . . .? Well is it or bloody isn't it?' he enquired peevishly.

The young man in white grinned indulgently. 'Aye it is, Len, that's it.'

The old man removed his cigarette, flicked it on to the grass and took up his guard again. His appearance suggested that he might be out first ball or in fact that he had no right to be there at all, but as the delivery came down he stepped forward and with a scything sweep thumped the ball past the bowler and just a few inches above the rear end of the cow which had wandered into the line of fire. The animal looked round in some surprise as the ball whizzed along its backbone and the old man's crabbed features relaxed into the semblance of a smile.

'By gaw, vitnery,' he said, looking over at me, 'ah damn near made a bit of work for tha there.' He eyed me impassively for a moment. 'Ah reckon tha's never took a cricket ball out of a cow's arse afore, eh?'

Len returned to the job in hand and proved a difficult man to dislodge. But it was the batsman at the other end who was worrying Tom Willis. He had come in first wicket down, a ruddy faced lad of about nineteen wearing a blue shirt and he was still there piling on the runs.

At the end of the over, Tom came up to me. 'Fancy turning your arm over, Mr Herriot?' he enquired gravely.

'Huh?'

'Would you like a bowl? A fresh man might just unsettle this feller.'

'Well . . . er . . .' I didn't know what to say. The idea of me bowling in a real match was unthinkable. Tom made up my mind by throwing me the ball.

Clasping it in a clammy hand I trotted up to the wicket while the lad in the blue shirt crouched intently over his bat. All the other bowlers had hurled their missiles down at top speed but as I ambled forward it burst on me that if I tried that I would be miles off my target. Accuracy, I decided, must be my watchword and I sent a gentle lob in the direction of the wicket. The batsman, obviously convinced that such a slow ball must be laden with hidden malice followed its course with deep suspicion and smothered it as soon as it arrived. He did the same with the second but that was enough for him to divine that I wasn't bowling off breaks, leg breaks or googlies but simply little dollies and he struck the third ball smartly into the ravine.

There was a universal cry of *'Maurice!'* from our team because Maurice Briggs, the Rainby blacksmith was fielding down there and since he couldn't see the wicket he had to be warned. In due course the ball soared back from the depths, propelled no doubt by Maurice's strong right arm, and I recommenced my attack. The lad in blue thumped my remaining three deliveries effortlessly for six. The first flew straight over the wall and the row of cars into the adjoining field, the next landed in the farmyard and the third climbed in a tremendous arc away above the ravine and I heard it splash into the beck whence it was retrieved with a certain amount of profanity by the invisible Maurice.

An old farm man once said to me when describing a moment of embarrassment. 'Ah could've got down a mouse 'ole.' And as I returned to my place in the field I knew just what he meant. In fact the bowler at the other end got through his over almost without my noticing it and I was still shrunk in my cocoon of shame when I saw Tom Willis signalling to me.

I couldn't believe it. He was throwing me the ball again. It was a typically magnanimous gesture, a generous attempt to assure me that I had done well enough to have another go.

Again I shambled forward and the blue-shirted lad awaited me, almost licking his lips. He had never come across anyone like me before and it seemed too good to be true that I should be given another over; but there I was, and he climbed gratefully into each ball I sent down and laid into it in a kind of ecstasy with the full meat of the bat.

I would rather not go into details. Sufficient to say that I have a vivid memory of his red face and blue shirt and of the ball whistling back over my head after each delivery and of the almost berserk yells of the spectators. But he didn't hit every ball for six. In fact there were two moments of light relief in my torment; one when the ball smashed into the oak tree, ricocheted and almost decapitated old Len at the other end; the other when a ball snicked off the edge of the bat and ploughed through a very large cow pat, sending up a noisome spray along its course. It finished at the feet of Mr Blenkinsopp and the poor man was clearly in a dilemma. For the last hour he had been swooping on everything that came near him with the grace of the born cricketer.

But now he hovered over the unclean object, gingerly extending a hand then withdrawing it as his earthier colleagues in the team watched in wonder. The batsmen were galloping up and down, the crowd was roaring but the curate made no move. Finally he picked the thing up with the utmost daintiness in two fingers, regarded it distastefully for a few moments and carried it to the wicketkeeper who was ready with a handful of grass in his big gloves.

At the end of the over Tom came up to me. 'Thank ye, Mr Herriot, but I'm afraid I'll have to take you off now. This wicket's not suited to your type of bowling – not takin' spin at all.' He shook his head in his solemn way.

I nodded thankfully and Tom went on. 'Tell ye what, go down and relieve that man in the outfield. We could do wi' a safe pair of hands down there.'

Chapter Twenty-five

I obeyed my skipper's orders and descended to the ravine and when Maurice had clambered up the small grassy cliff which separated me from the rest of the field I felt strangely alone. It was a dank, garlic-smelling region, perceptively colder than the land above and silent except for the gurgle of the beck behind me. There was a little hen house down here with several hens pecking around and some sheep who obviously felt it was safer than the higher ground.

I could see nothing of the pitch, only occasional glimpses of the heads of players so I had no idea of what was going on. In fact it was difficult to believe I was still taking part in a cricket match but for the spectators. From their position along the wall they had a grandstand view of everything and in fact were looking down at me from short range. They appeared to find me quite interesting, too, because a lot of them kept their eyes on me, puffing their pipes and making remarks which I couldn't hear but which caused considerable hilarity.

It was a pity about the spectators because it was rather peaceful in the ravine. It took a very big hit to get down there and I was more or less left to ruminate. Occasionally the warning cries would ring out from above and a ball would come bounding over the top. Once a skied drive landed with a thud in a patch of deep grass and with an enraged squawking a Rhode Island cockerel emerged at top speed and legged it irascibly to a safer haven.

Now and then I clawed my way up the bank and had a look at the progress of the game. Len had gone but the lad in blue was still there. After another dismissal I was surprised to see one of the umpires give his coat to the outgoing batsman, seize the bat and start laying about him. Both umpires were in fact members of the team.

It was after a long spell of inaction and when I was admiring the long splash of gold which the declining sun was throwing down the side of the fell when I heard the frantic yells. '*Jim! James! Mr Herriot!*' The whole team was giving tongue and, as I learned later, the lad in the blue shirt had made a catchable shot.

But I knew anyway. Nobody but he could have struck the blow which sent that little speck climbing higher and higher into the pale evening sky above me; and as it began with terrifying slowness to fall in my direction time came to a halt. I was aware of several of my team mates breasting the cliff and watching me breathlessly, of the long row of heads above the wall, and suddenly I was gripped by a cold resolve. I was going to catch this fellow out. He had humiliated me up there but it was my turn now.

The speck was coming down faster now as I stumbled about in the tangled vegetation trying to get into position. I nearly fell over a ewe with two big fat lambs sucking at her then I was right under the ball, hands cupped, waiting.

It fell, at the end, like a cannon ball, heavy and unyielding, on the end of my right thumb, bounded over my shoulder and thumped mournfully on the turf.

A storm of derision broke from the heads, peals of delighted laughter, volleys of candid comment.

'Get a basket!' advised one worthy.

'Fetch 'im a bucket!' suggested another.

As I scrabbled for the ball among the herbage I didn't know which was worse – the physical pain which was excruciating, or the mental anguish. After I had finally hurled the thing up the cliff I cradled the throbbing thumb in my other hand and rocked back and forth on my heels, moaning softly.

My team mates returned sadly to their tasks but Tom Willis, I noticed, lingered on, looking down at me.

'Hard luck, Mr Herriot. Very easy to lose t'ball against them trees.' He nodded encouragingly then was gone.

I was not troubled further in the innings. We never did get blueshirt out and he had an unbeaten sixty-two at the close. The Hedwick score was a hundred and fifty-four, a very useful total in village cricket.

There was a ten minute interval while two of our players donned the umpires' coats and our openers strapped on their pads. Tom Willis showed me the batting list he had drawn up and I saw without surprise that I was last man in.

'Our team's packed with batting, Mr Herriot,' he said seriously. 'I couldn't find a place for you higher up the order.'

Mr Blenkinsopp, preparing to receive the first ball, really looked the part, gay cap pulled well down, college colours bright on the broad V of his sweater. But in this particular situation he had one big disadvantage; he was too good.

All the coaching he had received had been aimed at keeping the ball down. An 'uppish' stroke was to be deplored. But everything had to be uppish on this pitch.

As I watched from my place on the form he stepped out and executed a flawless cover drive. At Headingley the ball would have rattled against the boards for four but here it travelled approximately two and a half feet and the fat lad stooped carelessly, lifted it from the dense vegetation and threw it back to the bowler. The next one the curate picked beautifully off his toes and flicked it to square leg for what would certainly have been another four anywhere else. This one went for about a yard before the jungle claimed it.

It saddened me to watch him having to resort to swiping tactics which were clearly foreign to him. He did manage to get in a few telling blows but was caught on the boundary for twelve.

It was a bad start for Rainby with that large total facing them and the two Hedwick fast bowlers looked very formidable. One of them in particular, a gangling youth with great long arms and a shock of red hair seemed to fire his missiles with the speed of light, making the batsmen duck and dodge as the ball flew around their ears.

'That's Tagger Hird,' explained my nearest team mate on the bench. 'By gaw 'e does chuck 'em down. It's a bugger facin' him when the light's getting bad.'

I nodded in silence. I wasn't looking forward to facing him at all, in any kind of light. In fact I was dreading any further display of my shortcomings and I had the feeling that walking out there to the middle was going to be the worst part of all.

But meanwhile I couldn't help responding to the gallant fight Rainby were putting up. As the match went on I found we had some stalwarts in our ranks. Bert Chapman the council roadman and an old acquaintance of mine strode out with his ever present wide grin splitting his brick-red face and began to hoist the ball all over the field. At the other end Maurice Briggs the blacksmith, sleeves rolled high over his mighty biceps and the bat looking like a Woolworths toy in his huge hands, clouted six after six, showing a marked preference for the ravine where there now lurked some hapless member of the other team. I felt for him, whoever it was down there; the sun had gone behind the hills and the light was fading and it must have been desperately gloomy in those humid depths.

And then when Tom came in he showed the true strategical sense of a captain. When Hedwick were batting it had not escaped his notice that they aimed a lot of their shots at a broad patch of particularly impenetrable vegetation, a mato grosso of rank verdure containing not only tangled grasses but nettles, thistles and an abundance of nameless flora. The memory of the Hedwick batsmen running up and down while his fielders thrashed about in there was fresh in his mind as he batted, and at every opportunity he popped one with the greatest accuracy into the jungle himself.

It was the kind of innings you would expect from him; not spectacular, but thoughtful and methodical. After one well-placed drive he ran seventeen while the fielders clawed at the undergrowth and the yells from the wall took on a frantic note.

And all the time we were creeping nearer to the total. When eight wickets had fallen we had reached a hundred and forty and our batsmen were running whether they hit the ball or not. It was too dark by now, to see, in any case, with great black banks of cloud driving over the fell top and the beginnings of a faint drizzle in the air.

In the gathering gloom I watched as the batsman swung, but only managed to push the ball a few yards up the pitch. Nevertheless he broke into a full gallop and collided with his partner who was roaring up from the other end. They fell in a heap with the ball underneath and the wicketkeeper, in an attempt at a run-out, dived among the bodies and scrabbled desperately for the ball. Animal cries broke out from the heads on the wall, the players were all bellowing at each other and at that moment I think the last of my romantic illusions about cricket slipped quietly away.

But soon I had no more time to think about such things. There was an eldritch scream from the bowler and our man was out L.B.W. It was my turn to bat.

Our score was a hundred and forty-five and as, dry-mouthed, I buckled on my pads, the lines of the poem came back to me. 'Ten to win and the last man in.' But I had never dreamed that my first innings in a cricket match would be like this, with the rain pattering steadily on the grass and the oil lamps on the farm winking through the darkness.

Pacing my way to the wicket I passed close by Tagger Hird who eyed me expressionlessly, tossing the ball from one meaty hand to another and whistling softly to himself. As I took guard he began his pounding run up and I braced myself. He had already dropped two of our batsmen in groaning heaps and I realised I had small hope of even seeing the ball.

But I had decided on one thing! I wasn't going to just stand there and take it. I wasn't a cricketer but I was going to try to hit the ball. And as Tagger arrived at full gallop and brought his arm over I stepped out and aimed a violent lunge at where I thought the thing might be. Nothing happened. I heard the smack on the sodden turf and the thud into the wicketkeeper's gloves, that was all.

The same thing happened with the next two deliveries. Great flailing blows which nearly swung me off my feet but nothing besides the smack and the thud. As Tagger ran up the fourth time I was breathless and my heart was thumping. I was playing a whirlwind innings except that I hadn't managed to make contact so far.

Again the arm came over and again I leapt out. And this time there was a sharp crack. I had got a touch but I had no idea where the ball had gone. I was standing gazing stupidly around me when I heard a bellowed *'Come on!'* and saw my partner thundering towards me. At the same time I spotted a couple of fielders running after something away down on my left and then the umpire made a signal. I had scored a four.

With the fifth ball I did the same thing and heard another crack, but this time, as I glared wildly about me I saw there was activity somewhere behind me on my right. We ran three and I had made seven.

There had been a no-ball somewhere and with the extra delivery Tagger scattered my partner's stumps and the match was over. We had lost by two runs.

'A merry knock, Mr Herriot,' Tom said, as I marched from the arena. 'Just for a minute I was beginnin' to think you were goin' to pull it off for us there.'

There was a pie and pea supper for both teams in the pub and as I settled down with a frothing pint of beer the thought kept coming back to me. Seven not out! After the humiliations of the evening it was an ultimate respectability. I had not at any time seen the ball during my innings and I had no idea how it had arrived in those two places but I had made seven not out. And as the meal arrived in front of me – delicious home-made steak and kidney pie with mounds of mushy peas – and I looked around at the roomful of laughing sunburnt men I began to feel good.

Tom sat on one side of me and Mr Blenkinsopp on the other. I had been interested to see that the curate could sink a pint with the best of them and he smiled as he put down his glass.

'Well done indeed, James. Nearly a story book ending. And you know, I'm quite sure you'd have clinched it if your partner had been able to keep going.'

I felt myself blushing. 'Well it's very kind of you, but I was a bit lucky.'

'Lucky? Not a bit of it!' said Mr Blenkinsopp. 'You played two beautiful strokes – I don't know how you did it in the conditions.'

'Beautiful strokes?'

'Most certainly. A delightful leg glance followed by a late cut of the greatest delicacy. Don't you agree, Tom?'

Tom sprinkled a little salt on his peas and turned to me. 'Ah do agree. And the best bit was how you got 'em up in the air to clear t'long grass. That was clever that was.' He conveyed a forkful of pie to his mouth and began to munch stolidly.

I looked at him narrowly. Tom was always serious so there was nothing to be learned from his expression. He was always kind, too, he had been kind all evening.

But I really think he meant it this time.

Chapter Twenty-six

'Is this the thing you've been telling me about?' I asked.

Mr Wilkin nodded. 'Aye, that's it, it's always like that.'

I looked down at the helpless convulsions of the big dog lying at my feet; at the staring eyes, the wildly pedalling limbs. The farmer had told me about the periodic attacks which had begun to affect his sheepdog, Gyp, but it was coincidence that one should occur when I was on the farm for another reason.

'And he's all right afterwards, you say?'

'Right as a bobbin. Seems a bit dazed, maybe, for about an hour then he's back to normal.' The farmer shrugged. 'I've had lots o' dogs through my hands as you know and I've seen plenty of dogs with fits. I thought I knew all the causes – worms, wrong feeding, distemper – but this has me beat. I've tried everything.'

'Well you can stop trying, Mr Wilkin,' I said. 'You won't be able to do much for Gyp. He's got epilepsy.'

'Epilepsy? But he's a grand, normal dog most of t'time.'

'Yes, I know. That's how it goes. There's nothing actually wrong with his brain – it's a mysterious condition. The cause is unknown but it's almost certainly hereditary.'

Mr Wilkin raised his eyebrows. 'Well that's a rum 'un. If it's hereditary why hasn't it shown up before now? He's nearly two years old and he didn't start this till a few weeks ago.'

'That's typical,' I replied. 'Eighteen months to two years is about the time it usually appears.'

Gyp interrupted us by getting up and staggering towards his master, wagging his tail. He seemed untroubled by his experience. In fact the whole thing had lasted less than two minutes.

Mr Wilkin bent and stroked the rough head briefly. His craggy features were set in a thoughtful cast. He was a big powerful man in his forties and now as the eyes narrowed in that face which rarely smiled he looked almost menacing. I had heard more than one man say he wouldn't like to get on the wrong side of Sep Wilkin and I could see what they meant. But he had always treated me right and since he farmed nearly a thousand acres I saw quite a lot of him.

His passion was sheepdogs. A lot of farmers liked to run dogs at the trials but Mr Wilkin was one of the top men. He bred and trained dogs which regularly won at the local events and occasionally at the national trials. And what was troubling me was that Gyp was his main hope.

He had picked out the two best pups from a litter – Gyp and Sweep – and had trained them with the dedication that had made him a winner. I don't think I have ever seen two dogs enjoy each other quite as much; whenever I was on the farm I would see them together, sometimes peeping nose by nose over the half door of the loose box where they slept, occasionally slinking devotedly round the feet of their master but usually just playing together. They must have spent hours rolling about in ecstatic wrestling matches, growling and panting, gnawing gently at each other's limbs.

A few months ago George Crossley, one of Mr Wilkin's oldest friends and a keen trial man, had lost his best dog with nephritis and Mr Wilkin had let him have Sweep. I was surprised at the time because Sweep was shaping better than Gyp in his training and looked like turning out a real champion. But it was Gyp who remained. He must have missed his friend but there were other dogs on the farm and if they didn't quite make up for Sweep he was never really lonely.

As I watched, I could see the dog recovering rapidly. It was extraordinary how soon normality was restored after that frightening convulsion. And I waited with some apprehension to hear what his master would say.

The cold, logical decision for him to make would be to have Gyp put down and, looking at the friendly, tail-wagging animal I didn't like the idea at all. There was something very attractive about him. The big-boned, well-marked body was handsome but his most distinctive feature was his head where one ear somehow contrived to stick up while the other lay flat, giving him a lop-sided, comic appeal. Gyp, in fact, looked a bit of a clown. But a clown who radiated goodwill and camaraderie.

Mr Wilkin spoke at last. 'Will he get any better as he grows older?'

'Almost certainly not,' I replied.

'Then he'll always 'ave these fits?'

'I'm afraid so. You say he has them every two or three weeks – well it will probably carry on more or less like that with occasional variations.'

'But he could have one any time?'

'Yes.'

'In the middle of a trial, like.' The farmer sunk his head on his chest and his voice rumbled deep. 'That's it, then.'

In the long silence which followed, the fateful words became more and more inevitable. Sep Wilkin wasn't the man to hesitate in a matter which concerned his ruling passion. Ruthless culling of any animal which didn't come up to standard would be his policy. When he finally cleared his throat I had a sinking premonition of what he was going to say.

But I was wrong.

'If I kept him, could you do anything for him?' he asked.

'Well I could give you some pills for him. They might decrease the frequency of the fits.' I tried to keep the eagerness out of my voice.

'Right . . . right . . . I'll come into t'surgery and get some,' he muttered.

'Fine. But . . . er . . . you won't ever breed from him, will you?' I said.

'Naw, naw, naw,' the farmer grunted with a touch of irritability as though he didn't want to pursue the matter further.

And I held my peace because I felt intuitively that he did not want to be detected in a weakness; that he was prepared to keep the dog simply as a pet. It was funny how events began to slot into place and suddenly make sense. That was why he had let Sweep, the superior trial dog, go. He just liked Gyp. In fact Sep Wilkin, hard man though he may be, had succumbed to that off-beat charm.

So I shifted to some light chatter about the weather as I walked back to the car, but when I was about to drive off the farmer returned to the main subject.

'There's one thing about Gyp I never mentioned,' he said, bending to the window. 'I don't know whether it has owt to do with the job or not. He has never barked in his life.'

I looked at him in surprise. 'You mean never, ever?'

'That's right. Not a single bark. T'other dogs make a noise when strangers come on the farm but I've never heard Gyp utter a sound since he was born.'

'Well that's very strange,' I said. 'But I can't see that it is connected with his condition in any way.'

And as I switched on the engine I noticed for the first time that while a bitch and two half grown pups gave tongue to see me on my way Gyp merely regarded me in his comradely way, mouth open, tongue lolling, but made no noise. A silent dog.

The thing intrigued me. So much so that whenever I was on the farm over the next few months I made a point of watching the big sheepdog at whatever he was doing. But there was never any change. Between the convulsions which had settled down to around three week intervals he was a normal active happy animal. But soundless.

I saw him, too, in Darrowby when his master came in to market. Gyp was often seated comfortably in the back of the car, but if I happened to speak to Mr Wilkin on these occasions I kept off the subject because, as I said, I had the feeling that he more than most farmers would hate to be exposed in keeping a dog for other than working purposes.

And yet I have always entertained a suspicion that most farm dogs were more or less pets. The dogs on sheep farms were of course indispensable working animals and on other establishments they no doubt performed a function in helping to bring in the cows. But watching them on my daily rounds I often wondered. I saw them rocking along on carts at haytime, chasing rats among the stooks at harvest, pottering around the buildings or roaming the fields at the side of the farmer; and I wondered . . . what did they really do?

My suspicions were strengthened at other times – as when I was trying to round up some cattle into a corner and the dog tried to get into the act by nipping at a hock or tail. There was invariably a hoarse yell of 'Siddown, dog!' or 'Gerrout, dog!'

So right up to the present day I still stick to my theory; most farm dogs are pets and they are there mainly because the farmer just likes to have them around. You would have to put a farmer on the rack to get him to admit it but I think I am right. And in the process those dogs have a wonderful time. They don't have to beg for walks, they are out all day long, and in the company of their masters. If I want to find a man on a farm I look for his dog, knowing the man won't be far away. I try to give my own dogs a good life but it cannot compare with the life of the average farm dog.

There was a long spell when Sep Wilkin's stock stayed healthy and I didn't see either him or Gyp, then I came across them both by accident at a sheepdog trial. It was a local event run in conjunction with the Mellerton Agricultural Show and since I was in the district I decided to steal an hour off.

I took Helen with me, too, because these trials have always fascinated us. The wonderful control of the owners over their animals, the intense involvement of the dogs themselves, the sheer skill of the whole operation always held us spellbound.

She put her arm through mine as we went in at the entrance gate to where a crescent of cars was drawn up at one end of a long field. The field was on the river's edge and through a fringe of trees the afternoon sunshine glinted on the tumbling water of the shallows and turned the long beach of bleached stones to a dazzling white. Groups of men, mainly competitors, stood around chatting as they watched. They were quiet, easy, bronzed men and as they seemed to be drawn from all social strata from prosperous farmers to working men their garb was varied; cloth caps, trilbies, deerstalkers or no hat at all; tweed jackets, stiff best suits, open-necked shirts, fancy ties, sometimes neither collar nor tie. Nearly all of them leaned on long crooks with the handles fashioned from rams' horns.

Snatches of talk reached us as we walked among them.

'You got 'ere, then, Fred.' 'That's a good gather.' 'Nay, 'e's missed one, 'e'll get nowt for that.' 'Them sheep's a bit flighty.' 'Aye they're buggers.' And above it all the whistles of the man running a dog; every conceivable level and pitch of whistle with now and then a shout. 'Sit!' 'Get by!' Every man had his own way with his dog.

The dogs waiting their turn were tied up to a fence with a hedge growing over it. There were about seventy of them and it was rather wonderful to see that long row of waving tails and friendly expressions. They were mostly strangers to each other but there wasn't even the semblance of disagreement, never mind a fight. It seemed that the natural obedience of these little creatures was linked to an amicable disposition.

This appeared to be common to their owners, too. There was no animosity, no resentment at defeat, no unseemly display of triumph in victory. If a man overran his time he ushered his group of sheep quietly in the corner and returned with a philosophical grin to his colleagues. There was a little quiet leg-pulling but that was all.

We came across Sep Wilkin leaning against his car at the best vantage point about thirty yards away from the final pen. Gyp, tied to the bumper, turned and gave me his crooked grin while Mrs Wilkin on a camp stool by his side rested a hand on his shoulder. Gyp, it seemed, had got under her skin too.

Helen went over to speak to her and I turned to her husband. 'Are you running a dog today, Mr Wilkin?'

'No, not this time, just come to watch. I know a lot o' the dogs.'

I stood near him for a while watching the competitors in action, breathing in the clean smell of trampled grass and plug tobacco. In front of us next to the pen the judge stood by his post.

I had been there for about ten minutes when Mr Wilkin lifted a pointing finger. 'Look who's there!'

George Crossley with Sweep trotting at his heels was making his way unhurriedly to the post. Gyp suddenly stiffened and sat up very straight, his cocked ears accentuating the lop-sided look. It was many months since he had seen his brother and companion; it seemed unlikely I thought, that he would remember him. But his interest was clearly intense, and as the judge waved his white handkerchief and the three sheep were released from the far corner he rose slowly to his feet.

A gesture from Mr Crossley sent Sweep winging round the perimeter of the field in a wide, joyous gallop and as he neared the sheep a whistle dropped him on his belly. From then on it was an object lesson in the cooperation of man and dog. Sep Wilkin had always said Sweep would be a champion and he looked the part, darting and falling at his master's commands. Short piercing whistles, shrill plaintive whistles; he was in tune with them all.

No dog all day had brought his sheep through the three lots of gates as effortlessly as Sweep did now and as he approached the pen near us it was obvious that he would win the cup unless some disaster struck. But this was the touchy bit; more than once with other dogs the sheep had broken free and gone bounding away within feet of the wooden rails.

George Crossley held the gate wide and extended his crook. You could see now why they all carried those long sticks. His commands to Sweep, huddled flat along the turf, were now almost inaudible but the quiet words brought the dog inching first one way then the other. The sheep were in the entrance to the pen now but they still looked around them irresolutely and the game was not over yet. But as Sweep wriggled towards them almost imperceptibly they turned and entered and Mr Crossley crashed the gate behind them.

As he did so he turned to Sweep with a happy cry of *'Good lad!'* and the dog responded with a quick jerking wag of his tail.

At that, Gyp, who had been standing very tall, watching every move with the most intense concentration raised his head and emitted a single resounding bark.

'Woof!' went Gyp as we all stared at him in astonishment.

'Did you hear that?' gasped Mrs Wilkin.

'Well, by gaw!' her husband burst out, looking open-mouthed at his dog.

Gyp didn't seem to be aware that he had done anything unusual. He was too preoccupied by the reunion with his brother and within seconds the two dogs were rolling around, chewing playfully at each other as of old.

I suppose the Wilkins as well as myself had the feeling that this event might start Gyp barking like any other dog, but it was not to be.

Six years later I was on the farm and went to the house to get some hot water. As Mrs Wilkin handed me the bucket she looked down at Gyp who was basking in the sunshine outside the kitchen window.

'There you are, then, funny fellow,' she said to the dog.

I laughed. 'Has he ever barked since that day?'

Mrs Wilkin shook her head. 'No he hasn't, not a sound. I waited a long time but I know he's not going to do it now.'

'Ah well, it's not important. But still, I'll never forget that afternoon at the trial,' I said.

'Nor will I!' She looked at Gyp again and her eyes softened in reminiscence. 'Poor old lad, eight years old and only one woof!'

Chapter Twenty-seven

A full surgery! But the ripple of satisfaction as I surveyed the packed rows of heads waned quickly as realisation dawned. It was only the Dimmocks again.

I first encountered the Dimmocks one evening when I had a call to a dog which had been knocked down by a car. The address was down in the old part of the town and I was cruising slowly along the row of decaying cottages looking for the number when a door burst open and three shock-headed little children ran into the street and waved me down frantically.

'He's in 'ere, Mister!' they gasped in unison as I got out, and then began immediately to put me in the picture.

'It's Bonzo!' 'Aye, a car 'it 'im!' 'We 'ad to carry 'im in, Mister!' They all got their words in as I opened the garden gate and struggled up the path with the three of them hanging on to my arms and tugging at my coat; and en route I gazed in wonder at the window of the house where a mass of other young faces mouthed at me and a tangle of arms gesticulated.

Once through the door which opened directly into the living room I was swamped by a rush of bodies and borne over to the corner where I saw my patient.

Bonzo was sitting upright on a ragged blanket. He was a large shaggy animal of indeterminate breed and though at a glance there didn't seem to be much ailing him he wore a pathetic expression of self pity. Since everybody was talking at once I decided to ignore them and carry out my examination. I worked my way over legs, pelvis, ribs and spine; no fractures. His mucous membranes were a good colour, there was no evidence of internal injury. In fact the only thing I could find was slight bruising over the left shoulder. Bonzo had sat like a statue as I felt over him, but as I finished he toppled over on to his side and lay looking up at me apologetically, his tail thumping on the blanket.

'You're a big soft dog, that's what you are,' I said and the tail thumped faster.

I turned and viewed the throng and after a moment or two managed to pick out the parents. Mum was fighting her way to the front while at the rear, Dad, a diminutive figure, was beaming at me over the heads. I did a bit of shushing and when the babel died down I addressed myself to Mrs Dimmock.

'I think he's been lucky,' I said. 'I can't find any serious injury. I think the car must have bowled him over and knocked the wind out of him for a minute, or he may have been suffering from shock.'

The uproar broke out again. 'Will 'e die, Mister?' 'What's the matter with 'im?' 'What are you going to do?'

I gave Bonzo an injection of a mild sedative while he lay rigid, a picture of canine suffering, with the tousled heads looking down at him with deep concern and innumerable little hands poking out and caressing him.

Mrs Dimmock produced a basin of hot water and while I washed my hands I was able to make a rough assessment of the household. I counted eleven little Dimmocks from a boy in his early teens down to a grubby faced infant crawling around the floor; and judging by the significant bulge in Mum's midriff the number was soon to be augmented. They were clad in a motley selection of hand-me downs; darned pullovers, patched trousers, tattered dresses, yet the general atmosphere in the house was of unconfined *joie de vivre*.

Bonzo wasn't the only animal and I stared in disbelief as another biggish dog and a cat with two half grown kittens appeared from among the crowding legs and feet. I would have thought that the problem of filling the human mouths would have been difficult enough without importing several animals.

But the Dimmocks didn't worry about such things; they did what they wanted to do, and they got by. Dad, I learned later, had never done any work within living memory. He had a 'bad back' and lived what seemed to me a reasonably gracious life, roaming interestedly around the town by day and enjoying a quiet beer and a game of dominoes in a corner of the Four Horse Shoes by night.

I saw him quite often; he was easy to pick out because he invariably carried a walking stick which gave him an air of dignity and he always walked briskly and purposefully as though he were going somewhere important.

I took a final look at Bonzo, still stretched on the blanket, looking up at me with soulful eyes then I struggled towards the door.

'I don't think there's anything to worry about,' I shouted above the chattering which had speedily broken out again, 'but I'll look in tomorrow and make sure.'

When I drew up outside the house next morning I could see Bonzo lolloping around the garden with several of the children. They were passing a ball from one to the other and he was leaping ecstatically high in the air to try to intercept it.

He was clearly none the worse for his accident but when he saw me opening the gate his tail went down and he dropped almost to his knees and slunk into the house. The children received me rapturously.

'You've made 'im better, Mister!' 'He's all right now, isn't he?' 'He's 'ad a right big breakfast this mornin', Mister!'

I went inside with little hands clutching at my coat. Bonzo was sitting bolt upright on his blanket in the same attitude as the previous evening, but as I approached he slowly collapsed on to his side and lay looking up at me with a martyred expression.

I laughed as I knelt by him. 'You're the original old soldier, Bonzo, but you can't fool me. I saw you out there.'

I gently touched the bruised shoulder and the big dog tremblingly closed his eyes as he resigned himself to his fate. Then when I stood up and he realised he wasn't going to have another injection he leapt to his feet and bounded away into the garden.

There was a chorus of delighted cries from the Dimmocks and they turned and looked at me with undisguised admiration. Clearly they considered that I had plucked Bonzo from the jaws of death. Mr Dimmock stepped forward from the mass.

'You'll send me a bill, won't you,' he said, with the dignity that was peculiar to him.

My first glance last night had decided me that this was a no-charging job and I hadn't even written it in the book, but I nodded solemnly.

'Very well, Mr Dimmock, I'll do that.'

And throughout our long association, though no money ever changed hands, he always said the same thing – 'You'll send me a bill, won't you.'

This was the beginning of my close relationship with the Dimmocks. Obviously they had taken a fancy to me and wanted to see as much as possible of me. Over the succeeding weeks and months they brought in a varied selection of dogs, cats, budgies, rabbits at frequent intervals, and when they found that my services were free they stepped up the number of visits; and when one came they all came. I was anxiously trying to expand the small animal side of the practice and increasingly my hopes were raised momentarily then dashed when I opened the door and saw a packed waiting room.

And it increased the congestion when they started bringing their auntie, Mrs Pounder, from down the road with them to see what a nice chap I was. Mrs Pounder, a fat lady who always wore a greasy velour hat perched on an untidy mound of hair, evidently shared the family tendency to fertility and usually brought a few of her own ample brood with her.

That is how it was this particular morning. I swept the assembled company with my eye but could discern only beaming Dimmocks and Pounders; and this time I couldn't even pick out my patient. Then the assembly parted and spread out as though by a prearranged signal and I saw little Nellie Dimmock with a tiny puppy on her knee.

Nellie was my favourite. Mind you, I liked all the family; in fact they were such nice people that I always enjoyed their visits after that first disappointment. Mum and Dad were always courteous and cheerful and the children, though boisterous, were never ill-mannered; they were happy and friendly and if they saw me in the street they would wave madly and go on waving till I was out of sight. And I saw them often because they were continually scurrying around the town doing odd jobs – delivering milk or papers. Best of all, they loved their animals and were kind to them.

But as I say, Nellie was my favourite. She was about nine and had suffered an attack of 'infantile paralysis', as it used to be called, when very young. It had left her with a pronounced limp and a frailty which set her apart from her robust brothers and sisters. Her painfully thin legs seemed almost too fragile to carry her around but above the pinched face her hair, the colour of ripe corn, flowed to her shoulders and her eyes, though slightly crossed, gazed out calm and limpid blue through steel-rimmed spectacles.

'What's that you've got, Nellie?' I asked.

'It's a little dog,' she almost whispered. ' 'e's mine.'

'You mean he's your very own?'

She nodded proudly. 'Aye, 'e's mine.'

'He doesn't belong to your brothers and sisters, too?'

'Naw, 'e's mine.'

Rows of Dimmock and Pounder heads nodded in eager acquiescence as Nellie lifted the puppy to her cheek and looked up at me with a smile of a strange sweetness. It was a smile that always tugged at my heart; full of a child's artless happiness and trust but with something else which was poignant and maybe had to do with the way Nellie was.

'Well, he looks a fine dog to me,' I said. 'He's a Spaniel, isn't he?'

She ran a hand over the little head. 'Aye, a Cocker. Mr Brown said 'e was a Cocker.'

There was a slight disturbance at the back and Mr Dimmock appeared from the crush. He gave a respectful cough.

'He's a proper pure bred, Mr Herriot,' he said. 'Mr Brown from the bank's bitch had a litter and 'e gave this 'un to Nellie.' He tucked his stick under his arm and pulled a long envelope from an inside pocket. He handed it to me with a flourish. 'That's 'is pedigree.'

I read it through and whistled softly. 'He's a real blue-blooded hound, all right, and I see he's got a big long name. Darrowby Tobias the third. My word, that sounds great.'

I looked down at the little girl again. 'And what do *you* call him Nellie?'

'Toby,' she said softly. 'I calls 'im Toby.'

I laughed. 'All right, then. What's the matter with Toby anyway. Why have you brought him?'

'He's been sick, Mr Herriot.' Mrs Dimmock spoke from somewhere among the heads. 'He can't keep nothin' down.'

'Well I know what that'll be. Has he been wormed?'

'No, don't think so.'

'I should think he just needs a pill,' I said. 'But bring him through and I'll have a look at him.'

Other clients were usually content to send one representative through with their animals but the Dimmocks all had to come. I marched along with the crowd behind me filling the passage from wall to wall. Our consulting-cum-operating room was quite small and I watched with some apprehension as the procession filed in after me. But they all got in, Mrs Pounder, her velour hat slightly askew, squeezing herself in with some difficulty at the rear.

My examination of the puppy took longer than usual as I had to fight my way to the thermometer on the trolley then struggle in the other direction to get the stethoscope from its hook on the wall. But I finished at last.

'Well I can't find anything wrong with him,' I said. 'So I'm pretty sure he just has a tummy full of worms. I'll give you a pill now and you must give it to him first thing tomorrow morning.'

Like a football match turning out, the mass of people surged along the passage and into the street and another Dimmock visit had come to an end.

I forgot the incident immediately because there was nothing unusual about it. The pot-bellied appearance of the puppy made my diagnosis a formality; I didn't expect to see him again.

But I was wrong. A week later my surgery was once more overflowing and I had another squashed-in session with Toby in the little back room. My pill had evacuated a few worms but he was still vomiting, still distended.

'Are you giving him five very small meals a day as I told you?' I asked.

I received emphatic affirmative and I believed them. The Dimmocks really took care of their animals. There was something else here, yet I couldn't find it. Temperature normal, lungs clear, abdomen negative on palpation; I couldn't make it out. I dispensed a bottle of our antacid mixture with a feeling of defeat. A young puppy like this shouldn't need such a thing.

This was the beginning of a frustrating period. There would be a span of two or three weeks when I would think the trouble had righted itself then without warning the place would be full of Dimmocks and Pounders and I'd be back where I started.

And all the time Toby was growing thinner.

I tried everything; gastric sedatives, variations of diet, quack remedies. I interrogated the Dimmocks repeatedly about the character of the vomiting – how long after eating, what were the intervals between, and I received varying replies. Sometimes he brought his food straight back, at others he retained it for several hours. I got nowhere.

It must have been over eight weeks later – Toby would be about four months old – when I again viewed the assembled Dimmocks with a sinking heart. Their visits had become depressing affairs and I could not foresee anything better today as I opened the waiting-room door and allowed myself to be almost carried along the passage. This time it was Dad who was the last to wedge himself into the consulting room then Nellie placed the little dog on the table.

I felt an inward lurch of sheer misery. Toby had grown despite his disability and was now a grim caricature of a Cocker Spaniel, the long silky ears drooping from an almost fleshless skull, the spindly legs pathetically feathered. I had thought Nellie was thin but her pet had outdone her. And he wasn't just thin, he was trembling slightly as he stood arch-backed on the smooth surface, and his face had the dull inward look of an animal which has lost interest.

The little girl ran her hand along the jutting ribs and the pale, squinting eyes looked up at me through the steel spectacles with that smile which pulled at me more painfully than ever before. She didn't seem worried. Probably she had no idea how things were, but whether she had or not I knew I'd never be able to tell her that her dog was slowly dying.

I rubbed my eyes wearily. 'What has he had to eat today?'

Nellie answered herself. 'He's 'ad some bread and milk.'

'How long ago was that?' I asked, but before anybody could reply the little dog vomited, sending the half digested stomach contents soaring in a graceful arc to land two feet away on the table.

I swung round on Mrs Dimmock. 'Does he always do it like that?'

'Aye he mostly does – sends it flying out, like.'

'But why didn't you tell me?'

The poor lady looked flustered. 'Well . . . I don't know . . . I . . .'

I held up a hand. 'That's all right, Mrs Dimmock, never mind.' It occurred to me that all the way through my totally ineffectual treatment of this dog not a single Dimmock or Pounder had uttered a word of criticism so why should I start to complain now?

But I knew what Toby's trouble was now. At last, at long last, I knew.

And in case my present day colleagues reading this may think I had been more than usually thick-headed in my handling of the case I would like to offer in my defence that such limited text books as there were in those days made only a cursory reference to pyloric stenosis (narrowing of the exit of the stomach where it joins the small intestine) and if they did they said nothing about treatment.

But surely, I thought, somebody in England was ahead of the books. There must be people who were actually doing this operation . . . and if there were I had a feeling one might not be too far away . . .

I worked my way through the crush and trotted along the passage to the phone.

'Is that you Granville?'

'*Jim!*' A bellow of pure unalloyed joy. 'How are you laddie?'

'Very well, how are you?'

'Ab-so-lutely tip top, old son! Never better!'

'Granville, I've got a four-month-old spaniel pup I'd like to bring through to you. It's got pyloric stenosis.'

'Oh lovely!'

'I'm afraid the little thing's just about on its last legs – a bag of bones.'

'Splendid, splendid!'

'This is because I've been mucking about for four weeks in ignorance.'

'Fine, just fine!'

'And the owners are a very poor family. They can't pay anything I'm afraid.'

'Wonderful!'

I hesitated a moment. 'Granville, you do . . . er . . . you have . . . operated on these cases before?'

'Did five yesterday.'

'What!'

A deep rumble of laughter. 'I do but jest, old son, but you needn't worry, I've done a few. And it isn't such a bad job.'

'Well that's great.' I looked at my watch. 'It's half past nine now, I'll get Siegfried to take over my morning round and I'll see you before eleven.'

Chapter Twenty-eight

Granville had been called out when I arrived and I hung around his surgery till I heard the expensive sound of the Bentley purring into the yard. Through the window I saw yet another magnificent pipe glinting behind the wheel then my colleague, in an impeccable pin-striped suit which made him look like the Director of the Bank of England, paced majestically towards the side door.

'Good to see you, Jim!' he exclaimed, wringing my hand warmly. Then before removing his jacket he took his pipe from his mouth and regarded it with a trace of anxiety for a second before giving it a polish with his yellow cloth and placing it tenderly in a drawer.

It wasn't long before I was under the lamp in the operating room bending over Toby's small outstretched form while Granville – the other Granville Bennett – worked with fierce concentration inside the abdomen of the little animal.

'You see the gross gastric dilatation,' he murmured. 'Classical lesion.' He gripped the pylorus and poised his scalpel. 'Now I'm going through the serous coat.' A quick deft incision. 'A bit of blunt dissection here for the muscle fibres ... down ... down ... a little more ... ah, there it is, you can see it – the mucosa bulging into the cleft. Yes ... yes ... just right. That's what you've got to arrive at.'

I peered down at the tiny tube which had been the site of all Toby's troubles. 'Is that all, then?'

'That's all, laddie.' He stepped back with a grin. 'The obstruction is relieved now and you can take bets that this little chap will start to put weight on now.'

'That's wonderful, Granville. I'm really grateful.'

'Nonsense, Jim, it was a pleasure. You can do the next one yourself now, eh?' He laughed, seized needle and sutures and sewed up the abdominal muscles and skin at an impossible pace.

A few minutes later he was in his office pulling on his jacket, then as he filled his pipe he turned to me.

'I've got a little plan for the rest of the morning, laddie.'

I shrank away from him and threw up a protective hand. 'Well now, er ... it's kind of you, Granville, but I really ... I honestly must get back ... we're very busy, you know ... can't leave Siegfried too long ... work'll be piling up ...' I stopped because I felt I was beginning to gibber.

My colleague looked wounded. 'All I meant, old son, was that we want you to come to lunch. Zoe is expecting you.'

'Oh ... oh, I see. Well that's very kind. We're not going ... anywhere else, then?'

'Anywhere else?' He blew out his cheeks and spread his arms wide. 'Of course not. I just have to call in at my branch surgery on the way.'

'Branch surgery? I didn't know you had one.'

'Oh yes, just a stone's throw from my house.' He put an arm round my shoulders. 'Well let's go, shall we?'

As I lay back, cradled in the Bentley's luxury, I dwelt happily on the thought that at last I was going to meet Zoe Bennett when I was my normal self. She would learn this time that I wasn't a perpetually drunken oaf. In fact the next hour or two seemed full of rosy promise; an excellent lunch illumined by my witty conversation and polished manners, then back with Toby, magically resuscitated, to Darrowby.

I smiled to myself when I thought of Nellie's face when I told her her pet was going to be able to eat and grow strong and playful like any other pup. I was still smiling when the car pulled up on the outskirts of Granville's home village. I glanced idly through the window at a low stone building with leaded panes and a wooden sign dangling over the entrance. It read 'Old Oak Tree Inn'. I turned quickly to my companion.

'I thought we were going to your branch surgery?'

Granville gave me a smile of childish innocence. 'Oh that's what I call this place. It's so near home and I transact quite a lot of business here.' He patted my knee. 'We'll just pop in for an appetiser, eh?'

'Now wait a minute,' I stammered, gripping the sides of my seat tightly. 'I just can't be late today. I'd much rather . . .'

Granville raised a hand. 'Jim, laddie, we won't be in for long.' He looked at his watch. 'It's exactly twelve thirty and I promised Zoe we'd be home by one o'clock. She's cooking roast beef and Yorkshire pudding and it would take a braver man than me to let her pudding go flat. I guarantee we'll be in that house at one o'clock on the dot – O.K.?'

I hesitated. I couldn't come to much harm in half an hour. I climbed out of the car.

As we went into the pub a large man, who had been leaning on the counter, turned and exchanged enthusiastic greetings with my colleague.

'Albert!' cried Granville. 'Meet Jim Herriot from Darrowby. Jim, this is Albert Wainright, the landlord of the Wagon and Horses over in Matherley. In fact he's president of the Licensed Victuallers' Association this year, aren't you Albert?'

The big man grinned and nodded and for a moment I felt overwhelmed by the two figures on either side of me. It was difficult to describe the hard, bulky tissue of Granville's construction but Mr Wainright was unequivocally fat. A checked jacket hung open to display an enormous expanse of striped shirted abdomen overflowing the waistband of his trousers. Above a gay bow tie cheerful eyes twinkled at me from a red face and when he spoke his tone was rich and fruity. He embodied the rich ambience of the term 'Licensed Victualler'.

I began to sip at the half pint of beer I had ordered but when another appeared in two minutes I saw I was going to fall hopelessly behind and switched to the whiskies and sodas which the others were drinking. And my undoing was that both my companions appeared to have a standing account here; they downed their drinks, tapped softly on the counter and said, 'Yes please, Jack,' whereupon three more glasses appeared with magical speed. I never had a chance to buy a round. In fact no money ever changed hands.

It was a quiet, friendly little session with Albert and Granville carrying on a conversation of the utmost good humour punctuated by the almost soundless taps on the bar. And as I fought to keep up with the two virtuosos the taps came more and more frequently till I seemed to hear them every few seconds.

Granville was as good as his word. When it was nearly one o'clock he looked at his watch.

'Got to be off now, Albert. Zoe's expecting us right now.'

And as the car rolled to a stop outside the house dead on time I realised with a dull despair that it had happened to me again. Within me a witch's brew was beginning to bubble, sending choking fumes into my brain. I felt terrible and I knew for sure I would get rapidly worse.

Granville, fresh and debonair as ever, leaped out and lead me into the house.

'Zoe, my love!' he warbled, embracing his wife as she came through from the kitchen.

When she disengaged herself she came over to me. She was wearing a flowered apron which made her look if possible even more attractive.

'Hel-*lo!*' she cried and gave me that look which she shared with her husband as though meeting James Herriot was an unbelievable boon. 'Lovely to see you again. I'll get lunch now.' I replied with a foolish grin and she skipped away.

Flopping into an armchair I listened to Granville pouring steadily over at the sideboard. He put a glass in my hand and sat in another chair. Immediately the obese Staffordshire Terrier bounded on to his lap.

'Phoebles, my little pet!' he sang joyfully. 'Daddykins is home again'. And he pointed playfully at the tiny Yorkie who was sitting at his feet, baring her teeth repeatedly in a series of ecstatic smiles. 'And I see you, my little Victoria, I see you!'

By the time I was ushered to the table I was like a man in a dream, moving sluggishly, speaking with slurred deliberation. Granville poised himself over a vast sirloin, stropped his knife briskly then began to hack away ruthlessly. He was a prodigal server and piled about two pounds of meat on my plate then he started on the Yorkshire puddings. Instead of a single big one, Zoe had made a large number of little round ones as the farmers' wives often did, delicious golden cups, crisply brown round the sides. Granville heaped about six of these by the side of the meat as I watched stupidly. Then Zoe passed me the gravy boat.

With an effort I took a careful grip on the handle, closed one eye and began to pour. For some reason I felt I had to fill up each of the little puddings with gravy and owlishly directed the stream into one then another till they were all overflowing. Once I missed and spilled a few drops of the fragrant liquid on the tablecloth. I looked up guiltily at Zoe and giggled.

Zoe giggled back, and I had the impression that she felt that though I was a peculiar individual there was no harm in me. I just had this terrible weakness that I was never sober day or night, but I wasn't such a bad fellow at heart.

It usually took me a few days to recover from a visit to Granville and by the following Saturday I was convalescing nicely. It happened that I was in the market place and saw a large concourse of people crossing the cobbles. At first I thought from the mixture of children and adults that it must be a school outing but on closer inspection I realised it was only the Dimmocks and Pounders going shopping.

When they saw me they diverted their course and I was engulfed by a human wave.

'Look at 'im now, Mister!' 'He's eatin' like a 'oss now!' 'He's goin' to get fat soon, Mister!' The delighted cries rang around me.

Nellie had Toby on a lead and as I bent over the little animal I could hardly believe how a few days had altered him. He was still skinny but the hopeless look had gone; he was perky, ready to play. It was just a matter of time now.

His little mistress ran her hand again and again over the smooth brown coat.

'You are proud of your little dog, aren't you Nellie,' I said, and the gentle squinting eyes turned on me.

'Yes, I am.' She smiled that smile again. 'Because 'e's mine.'

Chapter Twenty-nine

There is plenty of time for thinking during the long hours of driving and now as I headed home from a late call my mind was idly assessing my abilities as a planner.

I had to admit that planning was not one of my strong points. Shortly after we were married I told Helen that I didn't think we should have children just at present. I pointed out that I would soon be going away, we did not have a proper home, our financial state was precarious and it would be far better to wait till after the war.

I had propounded my opinions weightily, sitting back in my chair and puffing my pipe like a sage, but I don't think I was really surprised when Helen's pregnancy was positively confirmed.

From the warm darkness the grass smell of the Dales stole through the open window and as I drove through a silent village it was mingled briefly with the mysterious sweetness of wood smoke. Beyond the houses the road curved smooth and empty between the black enclosing fells. No ... I hadn't organised things very well. Leaving Darrowby and maybe England for an indefinite period, no home, no money and a pregnant wife. It was an untidy situation. But I was beginning to realise that life was not a tidy little parcel at any time.

The clock tower showed 11 p.m. as I rolled through the market place and, turning into Trengate, I saw that the light had been turned off in our room. Helen had gone to bed. I drove round the yard at the back, put away the car and walked down the long garden. It was the end to every day, this walk; sometimes stumbling over frozen snow but tonight moving easily through the summer darkness under the branches of the apple trees to where the house stood tall and silent against the stars.

In the passage I almost bumped into Siegfried.

'Just getting back from Allenby's, James?' he asked. 'I saw on the book that you had a colic.'

I nodded. 'Yes, but it wasn't a bad one. Just a bit of spasm. Their grey horse had been feasting on some of the hard pears lying around the orchard.'

Siegfried laughed. 'Well I've just beaten you in by a few minutes. I've been round at old Mrs Dewar's for the last hour holding her cat's paw while it had kittens.'

We reached the corner of the passage and he hesitated. 'Care for a nightcap, James?'

'I would, thanks,' I replied, and we went into the sitting room. But there was a constraint between us because Siegfried was off to London early next morning to enter the Air Force – he'd be gone before I got up – and we both knew that this was a farewell drink.

I dropped into my usual armchair while Siegfried reached into the glass-fronted cupboard above the mantelpiece and fished out the whisky bottle and glasses. He carelessly tipped out two prodigal measures and sat down opposite.

We had done a lot of this over the years, often yarning till dawn, but naturally enough it had faded since my marriage. It was like turning back the clock to sip the whisky and look at him on the other side of the fireplace and to feel, as though it were a living presence, the charm of the beautiful room with its high ceiling, graceful alcoves and french window.

We didn't talk about his departure but about the things we had always talked about and still do; the miraculous recovery of that cow, what old Mr Jenks said yesterday, the patient that knocked us flat, leapt the fence and disappeared for good. Then Siegfried raised a finger.

'Oh, James, I nearly forgot. I was tidying up the books and I find I owe you some money.'

'You do?'

'Yes, and I feel rather bad about it. It goes back to your pre-partnership days when you used to get a cut from Ewan Ross's testing. There was a slip-up somewhere and you were underpaid. Anyway, you've got fifty pounds to come.'

'Fifty pounds! Are you sure?'

'Quite sure, James, and I do apologise.'

'No need to apologise, Siegfried. It'll come in very handy right now.'

'Good, good . . . anyway, the cheque's in the top drawer of the desk if you'll have a look tomorrow.' He waved a languid hand and started to talk about some sheep he had seen that afternoon.

But for a few minutes I hardly heard him. Fifty pounds! It was a lot of money in those days, especially when I would soon be earning three shillings a day as an AC2 during my initial training. It didn't solve my financial problem but it would be a nice little cushion to fall back on.

My nearest and dearest are pretty unanimous that I am a bit slow on the uptake and maybe they are right because it was many years later before it got through to me that there never was any fifty pounds owing. Siegfried knew I needed a bit of help at that time and when it all became clear long afterwards I realised that this was exactly how he would do it. No embarrassment to me. He hadn't even handed me the cheque. . . .

As the level in the bottle went down the conversation became more and more effortless. At one point some hours later my mind seemed to have taken on an uncanny clarity and it was as if I was disembodied and looking down at the pair of us. We had slid very low in our chairs, our heads well down the backs, legs extended far across the rug. My partner's face seemed to stand out in relief and it struck me that though he was only in his early thirties he looked a lot older. It was an attractive face, lean, strong-boned with steady humorous eyes, but not young. In fact, Siegfried, in the time I had known him, had never looked young, but he has the last laugh now because he has hardly altered with the years and is one of those who will never look old.

At that moment of the night when everything was warm and easy and I felt omniscient it seemed a pity that Tristan wasn't there to make up the familiar threesome. As we talked, the memories marched through the room like a strip of bright pictures; of November days on the hillsides with the icy rain driving into our faces, of digging the cars out of snow drifts, of the spring sunshine warming the hard countryside. And the thought recurred that Tristan had been part of it all and that I was going to miss him as much as I would miss his brother.

I could hardly believe it when Siegfried rose, threw back the curtains, and the grey light of morning streamed in. I got up and stood beside him as he looked at his watch.

'Five o'clock, James,' he said, and smiled. 'We've done it again.'

He opened the french window and we stepped into the hushed stillness of the garden. I was taking grateful gulps of the sweet air when a single bird call broke the silence.

'Did you hear that blackbird?' I said.

He nodded and I wondered if he was thinking the same thing as myself; that it sounded just like the same blackbird which had greeted the early daylight when we talked over my first case those years ago.

We went up the stairs together in silence. Siegfried stopped at his door.

'Well, James . . .' he held out his hand and his mouth twitched up at one corner.

I gripped the hand for a moment then he turned and went into his room. And as I trailed dumbly up the next flight it seemed strange that we had never said goodbye. We didn't know when, if ever, we would see each other again yet neither of us had said a word. I don't know if Siegfried wanted to say anything but there was a lot trying to burst from me.

I wanted to thank him for being a friend as well as a boss, for teaching me so much, for never letting me down. There were other things, too, but I never said them.

Come to think of it, I've never even thanked him for that fifty pounds . . . until now.

Chapter Thirty

'Look, Jim,' Helen said, 'this is one engagement we can't be late for. Old Mrs Hodgson is an absolute pet – she'd be terribly hurt if we let her supper spoil.'

I nodded. 'You're right, my girl, that mustn't happen. But I've got only three calls this afternoon and Tristan's doing the evening. I can't see anything going wrong.'

This nervousness about a simple action like going out for a meal might be incomprehensible to the layman but to vets and their wives it was very real, particularly in those days of one or two-man practices. The idea of somebody preparing a meal for me then waiting in vain for me to turn up was singularly horrifying but it happened to all of us occasionally.

It remained a gnawing worry whenever Helen and I were asked out; especially to somebody like the Hodgsons. Mr Hodgson was a particularly likeable old farmer, short-sighted to the point of semi-blindness, but the eyes which peered through the thick glasses were always friendly. His wife was just as kind and she had looked at me quizzically when I had visited the farm two days ago.

'Does it make you feel hungry, Mr Herriot?'

'It does indeed, Mrs Hodgson. It's a marvellous sight.'

I was washing my hands in the farm kitchen and stealing a glance at a nearby table where all the paraphernalia of the family pig-killing lay in their full glory. Golden rows of pork pies, spareribs, a mound of newly made sausages, jars of brawn. Great pots were being filled with lard, newly rendered in the fireside oven.

She looked at me thoughtfully. 'Why don't you bring Mrs Herriot round one night and help us eat it?'

'Well that's most kind of you and I'd love to, but . . .'

'Now then, no buts!' She laughed. 'You know there's far too much stuff here – we have to give so much away.'

This was quite true. In the days when every farmer and many of the townsfolk of Darrowby kept pigs for home consumption, killing time was an occasion for feasting. The hams and sides were cured and hung up but the masses of offal and miscellaneous pieces had to be eaten at the time; and though farmers with big families could tackle it, others usually passed delicious parcels round their friends in the happy knowledge that there would be a reciprocation in due course.

'Well, thanks, Mrs Hodgson,' I said. 'Tuesday evening, then, seven o'clock.'

And here I was on Tuesday afternoon heading confidently into the country with the image of Mrs Hodgson's supper hanging before me like a vision of the promised land. I knew what it would be; a glorious mixed grill of spareribs, onions, liver and pork fillet garlanded with those divine farm sausages which are seen no more. It was something to dream about.

In fact I was still thinking about it when I drew into Edward Wiggin's farmyard. I walked over to the covered barn and looked in at my patients – a dozen half grown bullocks resting on the deep straw. I had to inject these fellows with Blackleg vaccine. If I didn't it was a fair bet that one or more of them would be found dead due to infection with the deadly Clostridium which dwelt in the pastures of that particular farm.

It was a common enough disease and stockholders had recognised it for generations and had resorted to some strange practices to prevent it; such as running a seton – a piece of twine or bandage – through the dewlap of the animal. But now we had an efficient vaccine.

I was thinking I'd be here for only a few minutes because Mr Wiggin's man, Wilf, was an expert beast catcher; then I saw the farmer coming across the yard and my spirits sank. He was carrying his lasso. Wilf, by his side, rolled his eyes briefly heavenwards when he saw me. He too clearly feared the worst.

We went into the barn and Mr Wiggin began the painstaking process of arranging his long, white rope, while we watched him gloomily. He was a frail little man in his sixties and had spent some years of his youth in America. He didn't talk a lot about it but everybody in time gained the impression that he had been a sort of cowboy over there and indeed he talked in a soft Texan drawl and seemed obsessed with the mystique of the ranch and the open range. Anything to do with the Wild West was near to his heart and nearest of all was his lasso.

You could insult Mr Wiggin with many things and he wouldn't turn a hair but question his ability to snare the wildest bovine with a single twirl of his rope and the mild little man could explode into anger. And the unfortunate thing was that he was no good at it.

Mr Wiggin had now got a long loop dangling from his hand and he began to whirl it round his head as he crept towards the nearest bullock. When he finally made his cast the result was as expected; the rope fell limply half way along the animal's back and dropped on to the straw.

'Tarnation!' said Mr Wiggin and started again. He was a man of deliberate movements and there was something maddening in the way he methodically assembled his rope again. It seemed an age before he once more advanced on a bullock with the rope whirring round his head.

'Bugger it!' Wilf grunted as the loop end lashed him across the face.

His boss turned on him. 'Keep out of the dadblasted road, Wilf,' he said querulously. 'I gotta start again now.'

This time he didn't even make contact with the animal and as he retrieved his lasso from the straw Wilf and I leaned wearily against the wall of the barn.

Yet again the whizz of the rope and a particularly ambitious throw which sent it high into the criss-cross of beams in the roof where it stuck. The farmer tugged at it several times in vain.

'Goldurn it, it's got round a nail up there. Slip across the yard and fetch a ladder, Wilf.'

As I waited for the ladder then watched Wilf climbing into the shadowy heights of the barn I pondered on Mr Wiggin. The way he spoke, the expressions he used were familiar to most Yorkshire folk since they filtered continually across the Atlantic in films and books. In fact there were dark mutterings that Mr Wiggin had learned them that way and had never been near a ranch in his life. There was no way of knowing.

At last the rope was retrieved, the ladder put away, and the little man went into action once more. He missed again but one of the bullocks got its foot in the loop and for a few moments the farmer hung on with fierce determination as the animal produced a series of piston-like kicks to rid itself of the distraction. And as I watched the man's lined face set grimly, the thin shoulders jerking, it came to me that Mr Wiggin wasn't just catching a beast for injection; he was roping a steer, the smell of the prairie was in his nostrils, the cry of the coyote in his ears.

It didn't take long for the bullock to free itself and with a grunt of 'Ornery crittur!' Mr Wiggin started again. And as he kept on throwing his rope ineffectually I was uncomfortably aware that time was passing and that our chances of doing our job were rapidly diminishing. When you have to handle a bunch of young beasts the main thing is not to upset them. If Mr Wiggin hadn't been there we would have penned them quietly in a corner and Wilf would have moved among them and caught their noses in his powerful fingers.

They were thoroughly upset. They had been peacefully chewing the cud or having a mouthful of hay from the rack but now, goaded by the teasing rope, were charging around like racehorses. Wilf and I watched in growing despair as Mr Wiggin for once managed to get a loop round one of them, but it was too wide and slipped down and round the body. The bullock shook it off with an angry bellow then went off at full gallop, bucking and kicking. I looked at the throng of frenzied creatures milling past; it was getting more like a rodeo every minute.

And it was a disastrous start to the afternoon. I had seen a couple of dogs at the surgery after lunch and it had been nearly two thirty when I set out. It was now nearly four o'clock and I hadn't done a thing.

And I don't think I ever would have if fate hadn't stepped in. By an amazing fluke Mr Wiggin cast his loop squarely over the horns of a shaggy projectile as it thundered past him, the rope tightened on the neck and Mr Wiggin on the other end flew gracefully through the air for about twenty feet till he crashed into a wooden feeding trough.

We rushed to him and helped him to his feet. Badly shaken but uninjured he looked at us.

'Doggone, I jest couldn't hold the blame thing,' he murmured. 'Reckon I'd better sit down in the house for a while. You'll have to catch that pesky lot yourselves.'

Back in the barn, Wilf whispered to me, 'By gaw it's an ill wind, guvnor. We can get on now. And maybe it'll make 'im forget that bloody lasso for a bit.'

The bullocks were too excited to be caught by the nose but instead Wilf treated me to an exhibition of roping, Yorkshire style. Like many of the local stocksmen he was an expert with a halter and it fascinated me to see him dropping it on the head of a moving animal so that one loop fell behind the ears and the other snared the nose.

With a gush of relief I pulled the syringe and bottle of vaccine from my pocket and had the whole batch inoculated within twenty minutes.

Driving off I glanced at my watch and my pulse quickened as I saw it was a quarter to five. The afternoon had almost slipped away and there were still two more calls. But I had till seven o'clock and surely I wouldn't come across any more Mr Wiggin's. And as the stone walls flipped past I ruminated again on that mysterious little man. Had he once been a genuine cowboy or was the whole thing fantasy?

I recalled that one Thursday evening Helen and I were leaving the Brawton cinema where we usually finished our half day; the picture had been a Western and just before leaving the dark interior I glanced along the back row and right at the far end I saw Mr Wiggin all on his own, huddled in the corner and looking strangely furtive.

Ever since then I have wondered. . . .

Five o'clock saw me hurrying into the smallholding belonging to the Misses Dunn. Their pig had cut its neck on a nail and my previous experience of this establishment suggested that it wouldn't be anything very serious.

These two maiden ladies farmed a few acres just outside Dollingsford village. They were objects of interest because they did most of the work themselves and in the process they lavished such affection on their livestock that they had become like domestic pets. The little byre held four cows and whenever I had to examine one of them I could feel the rough tongue of her neighbour licking at my back; their few sheep ran up to people in the fields and sniffed round their legs like dogs; calves sucked at your fingers, an ancient pony wandered around wearing a benign expression and nuzzling anyone within reach. The only exception among the amiable colony was the pig, Prudence, who was thoroughly spoiled.

I looked at her now as she nosed around the straw in her pen. She was a vast sow and the four-inch laceration in her neck muscles was obviously posing no threat to her life; but it was gaping and couldn't be left like that.

'I'll have to put a few stitches in there,' I said, and the big Miss Dunn gasped and put a hand to her mouth.

'Oh dear! Will it hurt her? I shan't be able to look, I'm afraid.'

She was a tall muscular lady in her fifties with a bright red face and often as I looked at her wide shoulders and the great arms with their bulging biceps I had the feeling that she could flatten me effortlessly with one blow if she so desired. But strangely she was nervous and squeamish about the realities of animal doctoring and it was always her little wisp of a sister who helped at lambings, calvings and the rest.

'Oh you needn't worry, Miss Dunn,' I replied. 'It'll be all over before she knows what's happening.' I climbed into the pen, went up to Prudence, and touched her gently on the neck.

Immediately the sow unleashed a petulant scream as though she had been stabbed with a hot iron and when I tried to give her back a friendly scratch the huge mouth opened again and the deafening sound blasted out. And this time she advanced on me threateningly. I stood my ground till the yawning cavern with its yellowed teeth was almost touching my leg then I put a hand on the rail and vaulted out of the pen.

'We'll have to get her into a smaller space,' I said. 'I'll never be able to stitch her in that big pen. She has too much room to move around and she's too big to hold.'

Little Miss Dunn held up her hand. 'We have the very place. In the calf house across the yard. If we got her into one of those narrow stalls she wouldn't be able to turn round.'

'Fine!' I rubbed my hands. 'And I'll be able to do the stitching over the top from the passage. Let's get her over there.'

I opened the door and after a bit of poking and pushing Prudence ambled majestically out on to the cobbles of the yard. But there she stood, grunting sulkily, a stubborn glint in her little eyes, and when I leaned my weight against her back end it was like trying to move an elephant. She had no intention of moving any further; and that calf house was twenty yards away.

I stole a look at my watch. Five fifteen, and I didn't seem to be getting anywhere.

The little Miss Dunn broke into my thoughts. 'Mr Herriot, I know how we can get her across the yard.'

'You do?'

'Oh yes, Prudence has been naughty before and we have found a way of persuading her to move.'

I managed a smile. 'Great! How do you do it?'

'Well now,' and both sisters giggled, 'she is very fond of digestive biscuits.'

'What's that?'

'She simply loves digestive biscuits.'

'She does?'

'Adores them!'

'Well, that's very nice,' I said. 'But I don't quite see . . .'

The big Miss Dunn laughed. 'Just you wait and I'll show you.'

She began to stroll towards the house and it seemed to me that though those ladies were by no means typical Dales' farmers they did share the general attitude that time was of no consequence. The door closed behind her and I waited . . . and as the minutes ticked away I began to think she was brewing herself a cup of tea. In my mounting tension I turned away and gazed down over the hillside fields to where the grey roofs and old church tower of Dollingsford showed above the riverside trees. The quiet peace of the scene was in direct contrast to my mental state.

Just when I was giving up hope, big Miss Dunn reappeared carrying a long round paper container. She gave me a roguish smile as she held it up to me.

'These are what she likes. Now just watch.'

She produced a biscuit and threw it down on the cobbles a few feet in front of the sow. Prudence eyed it impassively for a few moments then without haste strolled forward, examined it carefully, and began to eat it.

When she had finished, big Miss Dunn glanced at me conspiratorially and threw another biscuit in front of her. The pig again moved on unhurriedly and started on the second course. This was gradually leading her towards the buildings across the yard but it was going to take a long time. I reckoned that each biscuit was advancing her about ten feet and the calf house would be all of twenty yards away, so allowing three minutes a biscuit it was going to take nearly twenty minutes to get there.

I broke out in a sweat at the thought, and my fears were justified because nobody was in the slightest hurry. Especially Prudence who slowly munched each titbit then snuffled around picking up every crumb while the ladies smiled down at her fondly.

'Look,' I stammered. 'Do you think you could throw the biscuits a bit further ahead of her . . . just to save time, I mean?'

Little Miss Dunn laughed gaily. 'Oh we've tried that, but she's such a clever old darling. She knows she'll get less that way.'

To demonstrate she threw the next biscuit about fifteen feet away from the pig but the massive animal surveyed it with a cynical expression and didn't budge until it was kicked back to the required spot. Miss Dunn was right; Prudence wasn't so daft.

So I just had to wait, gritting my teeth as I watched the agonising progress. I was almost at screaming point at the end though the others were thoroughly enjoying themselves. But at last the final biscuit was cast into the calf pen, the pig made her leisurely way inside and the ladies, with triumphant giggles, closed the door behind her.

I leapt forward with my needle and suture silk and of course as soon as I laid a finger on her skin Prudence set up an almost unbearable nonstop squeal of rage. Big Miss Dunn put her hands over her ears and fled in terror but her little sister stayed with me bravely and passed me my scissors and dusting powder whenever I asked in sign language above the din.

My head was still ringing as I drove away, but that didn't worry me as much as the time. It was six o'clock.

Chapter Thirty-one

Tensely I assessed my position. The next and final visit was only a couple of miles away – I could make it in ten minutes. Then say twenty minutes on the farm, fifteen minutes back to Darrowby, a lightning wash and change and I could still be pushing my knees under Mrs Hodgson's table by seven o'clock.

And the next job wasn't a long one; just a bull to ring. Nowadays, since the advent of Artificial Insemination, there aren't many bulls about – only the big dairy men and pedigree breeders keep them – but in the thirties nearly every farmer had one, and inserting rings in their noses was a regular job. The rings were put in when they were about a year old and were necessary to restrain the big animals when they had to be led around.

I was immensely relieved when I arrived to find the gaunt figure of old Ted Buckle the farmer and his two men waiting for me in the yard. A classical way for a vet to waste time is to go hollering around the empty buildings then do more of the same out in the empty fields, waving madly, trying to catch the eye of a dot on the far horizon.

'Now then, young man,' Ted said, and even that short phrase took a fair time to come out. To me, the old man was a constant delight; speaking the real old Yorkshire – which you seldom hear now and which I won't try to reproduce here – with slow deliberation as though he were savouring every syllable as much as I was enjoying listening to him. 'You've come, then.'

'Yes, Mr Buckle, and I'm glad to see you're ready and waiting for me.'

'Aye, ah doan't like keepin' you fellers hangin' about.' He turned to his men. 'Now then, lads, go into that box and get haud'n that big lubber for Mr Herriot.'

The 'lads', Ernest and Herbert, who were both in their sixties, shuffled into the bull's loose box and closed the door after them. There was a few seconds of muffled banging against the wood, a couple of bellows and the occasional Anglo-Saxon expression from the men, then silence.

'Ah think they have 'im now,' Ted murmured and, not for the first time, I looked wonderingly at his wearing apparel. I had never seen him in anything else but that hat and coat in the time I had known him. With regard to the coat, which countless years ago must have been some kind of mackintosh, two things puzzled me: why he put it on and how he put it on. The long tatter of unrelated ribbons tied round the middle with binder twine could not possibly afford him any protection from the elements and how on earth did he know which were the sleeve holes among all the other apertures? And the hat, an almost crownless trilby from the early days of the century whose brim drooped vertically in sad folds over ears and eyebrows; it seemed incredible that he actually hung the thing up on a peg each night and donned it again in the morning.

Maybe the answer was to be found in the utterly serene humorous eyes which looked out from the skeleton-thin face. Nothing changed for Ted and the passage of a decade was a fleeting thing. I remember him showing me the old-fashioned 'reckon' which held the pans and kettles over the fire on his farm kitchen. He pointed out the row of holes where you could adjust it for large pans or small as though it were some modern invention.

'Aye, it's a wonderful thing, and t'lad that put it in for me made a grand job!'

'When was that, Mr Buckle?'

'It were eighteen ninety-seven. Ah remember it well. He was a right good workman was t'lad.'

But the men had reappeared with the young bull on a halter and they soon had him held in the accepted position for ringing.

There was a ritual about this job, a set pattern as unvarying as a classical ballet. Ernest and Herbert pulled the bull's head over the half door and held it there by pulling on a shank on either side of the halter. The portable crush had not yet been invented and this arrangement with the bull inside the box and the men outside was adopted for safety's sake. The next step was to make a hole through the tough tissue at the extremity of the nasal septum with the special punch which I had ready in its box.

But first there was a little refinement which I had introduced myself. Though it was the general custom to punch the hole without any preliminaries I always had the feeling that the bull might not like it very much; so I used to inject a couple of c.c.'s of local anaesthetic into the nose before I started. I poised my syringe now and Ernest, holding the left shank, huddled back apprehensively against the door.

'Tha's standin' middlin' to t'side, Ernest,' Ted drawled. 'Doesta think he's goin' to jump on top o' tha?'

'Naw, naw.' The man grinned sheepishly and took a shorter hold of the rope.

But he jumped back to his former position when I pushed the needle into the gristle just inside the nostril because the bull let loose a sudden deep-throated bellow of anger and reared up above the door. Ted had delayed ringing this animal; he was nearly eighteen months and very big.

'Haud 'im, lads,' Ted murmured as the two men clung to the ropes. 'That's right – he'll settle down shortly.'

And he did. With his chin resting on the top of the door, held by the ropes on either side, he was ready for the next act. I pushed my punch into the nose, gripped the handles and squeezed. I never felt much like a professional gentleman when I did this, but at least my local had worked and the big animal didn't stir as the jaws of the instrument clicked together, puncturing a small round hole in the hard tissue.

The next stage in the solemn rite was unfolded as I unwrapped the bronze ring from its paper covering, took out the screw and opened the rind wide on its hinge. I waited for the inevitable words.

Ted supplied them. 'Take tha cap off, Herbert. Tha woan't catch caud just for a minute.'

It was always a cap. A big bucket, a basin would have been more practical to hold that stupid, tiny screw and equally foolish little screwdriver, but it was always a cap. And a greasy old cap such as Herbert now removed from his polished pate.

My next step would be to slip the ring through the hole I had made, close it, insert the screw and tighten it up. That was where the cap came in; it was held under the ring to guard against sudden movements, because if the screw fell and was lost in the dirt and straw then all was lost. Then Ted would hand me the long rasp or file which every farmer had around somewhere and I would carefully smooth off the rim of the screw whether it needed it or not.

But this time there was to be a modification of the stereotyped little drama. As I stepped forward with my ring the young bull and I stood face to face and for a moment the wide set eyes under the stubby horns looked into mine. And as I reached out he must have moved slightly because the sharp end of the ring pricked him a little on the muzzle; the merest touch, but he seemed to take it as a personal insult because his mouth opened in an exasperated bawl and again he reared on his hind legs.

He was a well grown animal and in that position he looked very large indeed; and when his fore feet clumped down on the half door and the great rib cage loomed above us he was definitely formidable.

'The bugger's comin' over!' Ernest gasped and released his hold on the halter shank. He had never had much enthusiasm for the job and he abandoned it now without regret. Herbert was made of sterner stuff and he hung on grimly to his end as the bull thrashed above him, but after a cloven hoof had whizzed past his ear and another whistled just over his gleaming dome he too let go and fled.

Ted, untroubled as always, was well out of range and there remained only myself dancing in front of the door and gesticulating frantically at the bull in the vain hope that I might frighten him back whence he came; and the only thing that kept me there was the knowledge that every inch he scrambled out was taking me further from Mrs Hodgson's glorious supper.

I stood my ground until the snorting, bellowing creature was two thirds over, hanging grotesquely with the top of the door digging deep into his abdomen, then with a final plunge he was into the yard and I ran for cover. But the bull was not bent on mischief; he took one look at the open gate into the field and thundered through it like an express train.

From behind a stack of milk churns I watched sadly as he curveted joyously over the grass, revelling in his new found freedom. Bucking and kicking, tail in the air he headed for the far horizon where the wide pasture dipped to a beck which wandered along the floor of a shallow depression. And as he disappeared over the brow of the hill the last hope of my spareribs went with him.

'It'll tek us an hour to catch that bugger,' grunted Ernest gloomily.

I looked at my watch. Half past six. The bitter injustice of the whole thing overwhelmed me and I set up a wail of lamentation.

'Yes, dammit, and I've got an appointment in Darrowby at seven o'clock!' I stamped over the cobbles for a moment or two then swung round on old Ted. 'I'll never make it now . . . I'll have to ring my wife . . . have you got a phone?'

Ted's drawl was lazier than ever. 'Nay, we 'aven't got no phone. Ah don't believe in them things.' He fished out a tobacco tin from his pocket, unscrewed the lid and produced a battered timepiece which he scrutinised without haste. 'Any road, there's nowt to stop ye bein' back i' Darrowby by seven.'

'But . . . but . . . that's impossible . . . and I can't keep these people waiting . . . I must get to a phone.'

'Doan't get s'flustered, young man.' The old man's long face creased into a soothing smile. 'Ah tell ye you won't be late.'

I waved my arms around. 'But he's just said it'll take an hour to catch that bull!'

'Fiddlesticks! Ernest allus talks like that ... 'e's never 'appy unless 'e's miserable. Ah'll get bull in i' five minutes.'

'Five minutes! That's ridiculous! I'll ... I'll drive down the road to the nearest phone box while you're catching him.'

'You'll do nowt of t'sort, lad.' Ted pointed to a stone water trough against the wall. 'Go and sit thissen down and think of summat else ... ah'll only be five minutes.'

Wearily I sank on to the rough surface and buried my face in my hands. When I looked up the old man was coming out of the byre and in front of him ambled a venerable cow. By the number of rings on the long curving horns she must have been well into her teens; the gaunt pelvic bones stood out like a hatstand and underneath her a pendulous udder almost touched the ground.

'Get out there awd lass,' Ted said and the old cow trotted into the field, her udder swinging gently at each step. I watched her until she had disappeared over the hill, then turned to see Ted throwing cattle cake into a bucket.

He strolled through the gate and as I gazed uncomprehendingly he began to beat the bucket with a stick. At the same time he raised his voice in a reedy tenor and called out across the long stretch of green.

'Cush, cush!' he cried. 'Cush, pet, cush!'

Almost immediately the cow reappeared over the brow and just behind her the bull. I looked with wonder as Ted banged on his bucket and the cow broke into a stiff gallop with my patient close by her side. When she reached the old man she plunged her head in among the cake while the bull, though he was as big as she, pushed his nose underneath her and seized one of her teats in his great mouth. It was an absurd sight but she didn't seem to mind as the big animal, almost on his knees, sucked away placidly.

In fact it was like a soothing potion because when the cow was led inside he followed; and he made no complaint as I slipped the ring in his nose and fastened it with the screw which mercifully had survived inside Herbert's cap.

'Quarter to seven!' I panted happily as I jumped into the driving seat. 'I'll get there in time now.' I could see Helen and me standing on the Hodgson's step and the door opening and the heavenly scent of the spareribs and onions drifting out from the kitchen.

I looked again at the scarecrow figure with that hat brim drooping over the calm eyes. 'You did a wonderful job there, Mr Buckle. I wouldn't have believed it if I hadn't seen it. It was amazing how that bull followed the cow in like that.'

The old man smiled and I had a sudden surging impression of the wisdom in that quiet mind.

'There's nowt amazin' about it, lad, it's most nat'ral thing in t'world. That's 'is mother.'

Chapter Thirty-two

I slowed down and gazed along the farm lane. That was Tristan's car parked against the byre and inside, behind that green door, he was calving a cow. Because Tristan's student days were over. He was a fully fledged veterinary surgeon now and the great world of animal doctoring with all its realities stretched ahead.

Not for long, though, because like many others he was bound for the army and would leave soon after myself. But it wouldn't be so bad for Tristan because at least he would be doing his own job. When Siegfried and I had volunteered for service there had been no need for our profession in the army so we had gone into RAF aircrew which was the only branch open to our 'reserved occupation'. But when it came to Tristan's turn the fighting had escalated in the far east and they were crying out for vets to doctor the horses, mules, cattle, camels.

The timing suggested that the Gods were looking after him as usual. In fact I think the Gods love people like Tristan who sway effortlessly before the winds of fate and spring back with a smile, looking on life always with blithe optimism. Anyway it seemed natural and inevitable that whereas Siegfried and I as second class aircraftmen pounded the parade ground for weary hours Captain Tristan Farnon sailed off to the war in style.

But in the meantime I was glad of his help. After my departure he would run things with the aid of an assistant, then, when he left, the practice would be in the hands of two strangers till we returned. It seemed strange but everything was impermanent at that time.

I drew up and looked thoughtfully at the car. This was Mark Dowson's place and when I had rung the surgery from out in the country Helen told me about this calving. I didn't want to butt in and fuss but I couldn't help wondering how Tristan was getting on, because Mr Dowson was a dour, taciturn character who wouldn't hesitate to come down on a young man if things went wrong.

Still, I hadn't anything to worry about because since he qualified Tristan was doing fine. The farmers had always liked him during his sporadic visits as a student but now that he was on the job regularly the good reports were coming in thick and fast.

'I'll tell tha, that young feller does work! Doesn't spare 'imself,' or 'Ah've never seen a lad put his 'eart and soul into his job like this 'un.' And one man drew me to one side and muttered, 'He meks some queer noises but he does try. I think he'd kill 'isself afore he'd give up.'

That last remark made me think. Tristan's forte was certainly not brute effort and I had been a bit bewildered at some of the comments till I began to remember some of my experiences with him in his student days. He had always applied his acute intelligence to any situation in his own particular way and the way he reacted to the little accidents of country practice led me to believe he was operating a system.

The first time I saw this in action was when he was standing by the side of a cow watching me pulling milk from a teat. Without warning the animal swung round and brought an unyielding cloven hoof down on his foot. This is a common and fairly agonising experience and before the days of steel-tipped wellingtons I have frequently had the skin removed from my toes in neat parchment-like rolls. When it happened to me I was inclined to hop around and swear a bit and my performance was usually greeted with appreciative laughter from the farmers. Tristan, however, handled it differently.

He gasped, leaned with bowed head against the cow's pelvic bone for a moment then opened his mouth wide and emitted a long groan. Then, as the cowman and I stared at him, he reeled over the cobbles dragging a damaged limb uselessly behind him. Arrived at the far wall he collapsed against it, face on the stone, still moaning pitifully.

Thoroughly alarmed, I rushed to his aid. This must be a fracture and already my mind was busy with plans to get him to hospital with all possible speed. But he revived rapidly and when we left the byre ten minutes later he was tripping along with no trace of a limp. And I did notice one thing; nobody had laughed at him, he had received only sympathy and commiseration.

This sort of thing happened on other places. He sustained a few mild kicks, he was crushed between cows, he met with many of the discomforts which are part of our life and he reacted in the same histrionic way. And how it paid off! To a man, the farmers exhibited the deepest concern when he went into his act and there was something more; it actually improved his image. I was pleased about that because impressing Yorkshire farmers isn't the easiest task and if Tristan's method worked it was all right with me.

But I smiled to myself as I sat outside the farm. I couldn't see Mr Dowson being affected by any sign of suffering. I had had my knocks there in the past and he obviously hadn't cared a damn.

On an impulse I drove down the lane and walked into the byre. Tristan, stripped off and soaped, was just inserting an arm into a large red cow while the farmer, pipe in hand, was holding the tail. My colleague greeted me with a pleasant smile but Mr Dowson just nodded curtly.

'What have you got, Triss?' I asked.

'Both legs back,' he replied. 'And they're a long way in. Look at the length of her pelvis.'

I knew what he meant. It wasn't a difficult presentation but it could be uncomfortable in these long cows. I leaned back against the wall; I might as well see how he fared.

He braced himself and reached as far forward as he could, and just then the cow's flanks bulged as she strained hard against him. This is never very nice; the powerful contractions of the uterus squeeze the arm relentlessly between calf and pelvis and you have to grit your teeth till it passes off.

Tristan, however, went a little further.

'Ooh! Aah! Ouch!' he cried. Then as the animal still kept up the pressure he went into a gasping groan. When she finally relaxed he stood there quite motionless for a few seconds, his head hanging down as though the experience had drained him of all his strength.

The farmer drew on his pipe and regarded him impassively. Throughout the years I had known Mr Dowson I had never seen any particular emotion portrayed in those hard eyes and craggy features. In fact it had always seemed to me that I could have dropped down dead in front of him and he wouldn't even blink.

My colleague continued his struggle and the cow, entering into the spirit of the game, fought back with a will. Some animals will stand quietly and submit to all kinds of internal interference but this was a strainer; every movement of the arm within her was answered by a violent expulsive effort. I had been through it a hundred times and I could almost feel the grinding pressure on the wrist, the helpless numbing of the fingers.

Tristan showed what he thought about it all by a series of heartrending sounds. His repertoire was truly astounding and he ranged from long harrowing moans through shrill squeals to an almost tearful whimpering.

At first Mr Dowson appeared oblivious to the whole business, puffing smoke, glancing occasionally through the byre door, scratching at the bristle on his chin. But as the minutes passed his eyes were dragged more and more to the suffering creature before him until his whole attention was riveted on the young man.

And in truth he was worth watching because Tristan added to his vocal performance an extraordinary display of facial contortions. He sucked in his cheeks, rolled his eyes, twisted his lips, did everything in fact but wiggle his ears. And there was no doubt he was getting through to Mr Dowson. As the noises and grimaces became more extravagant the farmer showed signs of growing uneasiness; he darted anxious glances at my colleague and occasionally his pipe trembled violently. Like me, he clearly thought some dreadful climax was at hand.

As if trying to bring matters to a head the cow started to build up to a supreme effort. She straddled her legs wide, grunted deeply and went into a prolonged heave. As her back arched Tristan opened his mouth wide in a soundless protest then little panting cries began to escape him. This, I thought, was his most effective ploy yet; a long drawn 'Aah ... aah ... aah ...' creeping gradually up the scale and building increasing tension in his audience. My toes were curling with apprehension when, with superb timing, he released a sudden piercing scream.

That was when Mr Dowson cracked. His pipe had almost wobbled from his mouth but now he stuffed it into his pocket and rushed to Tristan's side.

'Ista all right, young man?' he enquired hoarsely.

My colleague, his face a mask of anguish, did not reply.

The farmer tried again. 'Will ah get you a cup o' tea?'

For a moment Tristan made no response, then, eyes closed, he nodded dumbly.

Mr Dowson scampered eagerly from the byre and within minutes returned with a steaming mug. After that I had to shake my head to dispel the feeling of unreality. It couldn't be true, this vision of the hard-bitten farmer feeding the tea to the young man in sips, cradling the lolling head in a horny hand. Tristan was still inside the cow, still apparently semi-conscious with pain but submitting helplessly to the farmer's ministrations.

With a sudden lunge he produced one of the calf's legs and as he flopped against the cow's rump he was rewarded with another long gulp of tea. After the first leg the rest wasn't so bad and the second leg and the calf itself soon followed.

As the little creature landed wriggling on the floor, Tristan collapsed on his knees beside it and extended a trembling hand towards a pile of hay, prepared to give the new arrival a rub down.

Mr Dowson would have none of it.

'George!' he bellowed to one of his men in the yard. 'Get in 'ere and wisp this calf!' Then solicitously to Tristan, 'You maun come into t'house, lad, and have a drop o' brandy. You're about all in.'

The dream continued in the farm kitchen and I watched disbelievingly as my colleague fought his way back to health and strength with the aid of several stiff measures of Martell Three Star. I had never had treatment like this and a wave of envy swept over me as I wondered whether it was worth adopting Tristan's system.

But I still have never found the courage to try it.

Chapter Thirty-three

It was strange, but somehow the labels on the calves' backs made them look even more pathetic; the auction mart labels stuck roughly with paste on the hairy rumps, stressing the little creatures' role as helpless merchandise.

As I lifted one sodden tail and inserted the thermometer a thin whitish diarrhoea trickled from the rectum and streamed down the thighs and hocks.

'It's the old story, I'm afraid Mr Clark,' I said.

The farmer shrugged and dug his thumbs under his braces. In the blue overalls and peaked porter's cap he always wore he didn't look much like a farmer and for that matter this place did not greatly resemble a farm; the calves were in a converted railway wagon and all around lay a weird conglomeration of rusting agricultural implements, pieces of derelict cars, broken chairs. 'Aye, it's a beggar isn't it? I wish I didn't have to buy calves in markets but you can't always find 'em on t'farms when you want them. This lot looked all right when I got them two days since.'

'I'm sure they did.' I looked at the five calves, arch-backed, trembling, miserable. 'But they've had a tough time and it's showing now. Taken from their mothers at a week old, carted for miles in a draughty wagon, standing for most of the day at the mart then the final journey here on a cold afternoon. They didn't have a chance.'

'Well ah gave them a good bellyful of milk as soon as they came. They looked a bit starved and ah thought it would warm them up.'

'Yes, you'd think it would, Mr Clark, but really their stomachs weren't in a fit state to accept rich food like that when they were cold and tired. Next time if I were you I'd just give them a drink of warm water with maybe a little glucose and make them comfortable till next day.'

'White scour' they called it. It killed countless thousands of calves every year and the name always sent a chill through me because the mortality rate was depressingly high.

I gave each of them a shot of E coli antiserum. Most authorities said it did no good and I was inclined to agree with them. Then I rummaged in my car boot and produced a packet of our astringent powders of chalk, opium and catechu.

'Here, give them one of these three times a day, Mr Clark,' I said. I tried to sound cheerful but I'm sure my tone lacked conviction. Whiskered veterinary surgeons in top hats and tail coats had been prescribing chalk, opium and catechu a hundred years ago and though it might have been helpful in mild diarrhoea it was almost useless against the lethal bacterial enteritis of white scour. It was a waste of time just trying to dry up the diarrhoea; what was wanted was a drug which would knock out the vicious bugs which caused it, but there wasn't such a thing around.

However there was one thing which we vets of those days used to do which is sometimes neglected since the arrival of the modern drugs; we attended to the comfort and nursing of the animals. The farmer and I wrapped each calf in a big sack which went right round its body and was fastened with binder twine round the ribs, in front of the brisket and under the tail. Then I fussed round the shed, plugging up draught holes, putting up a screen of straw bales between the calves and the door.

Before I left I took a last look at them; there was no doubt they were warm and sheltered now. They would need every bit of help with only my astringent powders fighting for them.

I didn't see them again until the following afternoon. Mr Clark was nowhere around so I went over to the railway wagon and opened the half door.

This, to me, is the thing that lies at the very heart of veterinary practice; the wondering and worrying about how your patient is progressing then the long moment when you open that door and find out. I rested my elbows on the timbers and looked inside. The calves were lying quite motionless on their sides, in fact I had to look closely to make sure they were not dead. I banged the door behind me with deliberate force but not a head was raised.

Walking through the deep straw and looking down at the outstretched animals, each in his rough sacking jacket, I swore to myself. It looked as though the whole lot was going to perish. Great, great, I thought as I kicked among the straw – not just one or two but a hundred per cent death rate this time.

'Well you don't look very 'opeful, young man.' Mr Clark's head and shoulders loomed over the half door.

I dug my hands into my pockets. 'No, damn it, I'm not. They've gone down really fast, haven't they?'

'Aye, it's ower wi' them all right. I've just been in t'house ringing Mallock.'

The knacker man's name was like the pealing of a mournful bell. 'But they're not dead yet,' I said.

'No, but it won't be long. Mallock allus gives a bob or two more if he can get a beast alive. Makes fresher dog meat, he says.'

I didn't say anything and I must have looked despondent because the farmer gave a wry smile and came over to me.

'It isn't your fault, lad. I know all about this dang white scour. If you get the right bad sort there's nothing anybody can do. And you can't blame me for tryin' to get a bit back – I've got to make the best of a bad job.'

'Oh I know,' I said. 'I'm just disappointed I can't have a go at them with this new medicine.'

'What's that, then?'

I took the tin from my pocket and read the label. 'It's called M and B 693, or sulphapyridine, to give it it's scientific name. Just came in the post this morning. It's one of a completely new range of drugs – they're called the sulphonamides and we've never had anything like them before. They're supposed to actually kill certain germs, such as the organisms which cause scour.'

Mr Clark took the tin from me and removed the lid. 'A lot of little blue tablets, eh? Well ah've seen a few wonder cures for this ailment but none of 'em's much good – this'll be another, I'll bet.'

'Could be,' I said. 'But there's been a lot of discussion about these sulphonamides in our veterinary journals. They're not quack remedies, they're a completely fresh field. I wish I could have tried them on your calves.'

'Well look at them.' The farmer gazed gloomily over the five still bodies. 'Their eyes are goin' back in their heads. Have you ever seen calves like that get better?'

'No, I haven't, but I'd still like to have a go.'

As I spoke a tall-sided wagon rumbled into the yard. A sprightly, stocky man descended from the driver's seat and came over to us.

'By gaw, Jeff,' said Mr Clark. 'You 'aven't been long.'

'Naw, they got me on t'phone at Jenkinson's, just down t'road.' He gave me a smile of peculiar sweetness.

I studied Jeff Mallock as I always did with a kind of wonder. He had spent the greater part of his forty odd years delving in decomposing carcases, slashing nonchalantly with his knife at tuberculous abscesses, wallowing in infected blood and filthy uterine exudates yet he remained a model of health and fitness. He had the clear eyes and the smooth pink skin of a twenty-year-old and the effect was heightened by the untroubled serenity of his expression. To the best of my knowledge Jeff never took any hygienic precautions such as washing his hands and I have seen him enjoying a snack on his premises, seated on a heap of bones and gripping a cheese and onion sandwich with greasy fingers.

He peered over the door at the calves. 'Yes, yes, a clear case of stagnation of t'lungs. There's a lot of it about right now.'

Mr Clark looked at me narrowly. 'Lungs? You never said owt about lungs, young man.' Like all farmers he had complete faith in Jeff's instant diagnosis.

I mumbled something. I had found it useless to argue this point. The knacker man's amazing ability to tell at a glance the cause of an animal's illness or death was a frequent source of embarrassment to me. No examination was necessary – he just knew, and of all his weird catalogue of diseases stagnation of t'lungs was the favourite.

He turned to the farmer. 'Well, ah'd better shift 'em now, Willie. Reckon they won't last much longer.'

I bent down and lifted the head of the nearest calf. They were all shorthorns, three roans, a red and this one which was pure white. I passed my fingers over the hard little skull, feeling the tiny horn buds under the rough hair. When I withdrew my hand the head dropped limply on to the straw and it seemed to me that there was something of finality and resignation in the movement.

My thoughts were interrupted by the roar of Jeff's engine. He was backing his wagon round to the door of the calf house and as the high unpainted boards darkened the entrance the atmosphere of gloom deepened. These little animals had suffered two traumatic journeys in their short lives. This was to be the last, the most fateful and the most sordid.

When the knacker man came in he stood by the farmer, looking at me as I squatted in the straw among the prostrate creatures. They were both waiting for me to quit the place, leaving my failure behind me.

'You know, Mr Clark,' I said, 'even if we could save one of them it would help to reduce your loss.'

The farmer regarded me expressionlessly. 'But they're all dyin', lad. You said so yourself.'

'Yes, I did, I know, but the circumstances could be a bit different today.'

'Ah know what it is.' He laughed suddenly. 'You've got your heart set on havin' a go with them little tablets, haven't you?'

I didn't answer but looked up at him with a mute appeal.

He was silent for a few moments then he put a hand on Mallock's shoulder. 'Jeff, if this young feller is that concerned about ma stock I'll 'ave to humour 'im. You're not bothered, are you?'

'Nay, Willie, nay,' replied Jeff, completely unruffled, 'I can pick 'em up tomorrow, just as easy.'

'Right,' I said. 'Let's have a look at the instructions.' I fished out the pamphlet from the tin and read rapidly, working out the dose for the weight of the calves. 'We'll have to give them a loading dose first. I think twelve tablets per calf then six every eight hours after that.'

'How do you get 'em down their necks?' the farmer asked.

'We'll have to crush them and shake them up in water. Can we go into the house to do that?'

In the farm kitchen we borrowed Mrs Clark's potato masher and pounded the tablets until we had five initial doses measured out. Then we returned to the shed and began to administer them to the calves. We had to go carefully as the little creatures were so weak they had difficulty in swallowing, but the farmer held each head while I trickled the medicine into the side of the mouth.

Jeff enjoyed every minute of it. He showed no desire to leave but produced a pipe richly decorated with nameless tissues, leaned on the top of the half door and, puffing happily, watched us with tranquil eyes. He was quite unperturbed by his wasted journey and when we had finished he climbed into his wagon and waved to us cordially.

'I'll be back to pick 'em up in t'mornin', Willie,' he cried, quite without malice I'm sure. 'There's no cure for stagnation of t'lungs.'

I thought of his words next day as I drove back to the farm. He was just stating the fact; his supply of dog meat was merely being postponed for another twenty-four hours. But at least, I told myself, I had the satisfaction of having tried, and since I expected nothing I wasn't going to be disappointed.

As I pulled up in the yard Mr Clark walked over and spoke through the window. 'There's no need for you to get out of the car.' His face was a grim mask.

'Oh,' I said, the sudden lurch in my stomach belying my calm facade. 'Like that, is it?'

'Aye, come and look 'ere.' He turned and I followed him over to the shed. By the time the door creaked open a slow misery had begun to seep into me.

Unwillingly I gazed into the interior.

Four of the calves were standing in a row looking up at us with interest. Four shaggy, rough-jacketed figures, bright-eyed and alert. The fifth was resting on the straw, chewing absently at one of the strings which held his sack.

The farmer's weathered face split into a delighted grin. 'Well ah told you there was no need to get out of your car, didn't I? They don't need no vitnery, they're back to normal.'

I didn't say anything. This was something which my mind, as yet, could not comprehend. As I stared unbelievingly the fifth calf rose from the straw and stretched luxuriously.

'He's wraxin', d'you see?' cried Mr Clark. 'There's nowt much wrong wi' them when they do that.'

We went inside and I begun to examine the little animals. Temperatures were normal, the diarrhoea had dried up, it was uncanny. As if in celebration the white calf which had been all but dead yesterday began to caper about the shed, kicking up his legs like a mustang.

'Look at that little bugger!' burst out the farmer. 'By gaw I wish I was as fit meself!'

I put the thermometer back in its tube and dropped it into my side pocket. 'Well, Mr Clark,' I said slowly, 'I've never seen anything like this. I still feel stunned.'

'Beats hen-racin', doesn't it,' the farmer said, wide-eyed, then he turned towards the gate as a wagon appeared from the lane. It was the familiar doom-burdened vehicle of Jeff Mallock.

The knacker man showed no emotion as he looked into the shed. In fact it was difficult to imagine anything disturbing those pink cheeks and placid eyes, but I fancied the puffs of blue smoke from his pipe came a little faster as he took in the scene. The pipe itself showed some fresh deposits on its bowl – some fragments of liver, I fancied, since yesterday.

When he had looked his fill he turned and strolled towards his wagon. On the way he gazed expansively around him and then at the dark clouds piling in the western sky.

'Ah think it'll turn to rain afore t'day's out, Willie,' he murmured.

I didn't know it at the time but I had witnessed the beginning of the revolution. It was my first glimpse of the tremendous therapeutic breakthrough which was to sweep the old remedies into oblivion. The long rows of ornate glass bottles with their carved stoppers and Latin inscriptions would not stand on the dispensary shelves much longer and their names, dearly familiar for many generations – Sweet Spirits of Nitre, Sal ammoniac, Tincture of Camphor – would be lost and vanish for ever.

This was the beginning and just around the corner a new wonder was waiting – Penicillin and the other antibiotics. At last we had something to work with, at last we could use drugs which we knew were going to do something.

All over the country, probably all over the world at that time, vets were having these first spectacular results, going through the same experience as myself; some with cows, some with dogs and cats, others with valuable racehorses, sheep, pigs in all kinds of environments. But for me it happened in that old converted railway wagon among the jumble of rusting junk on Willie Clark's farm.

Of course it didn't last – not the miraculous part of it anyway. What I had seen at Willie Clark's was the impact of something new on an entirely unsophisticated bacterial population, but it didn't go on like that. In time the organisms developed a certain amount of resistance and new and stronger sulphonamides and antibiotics had to be produced. And so the battle has continued. We have good results now but no miracles, and I feel I was lucky to be one of the generation which was in at the beginning when the wonderful things did happen.

Those five calves never looked behind them and the memory of them gives me a warm glow even now. Willie, of course, was overjoyed and even Jeff Mallock gave the occasion his particular accolade. As he drove away he called back at us:

'Them little blue tablets must have good stuff in 'em. They're fust things I've ever seen could cure stagnation of t'lungs.'

Chapter Thirty-four

There was one marvellous thing about the set-up in Darrowby. I had the inestimable advantage of being a large animal practitioner with a passion for dogs and cats. So that although I spent most of my time in the wide outdoors of Yorkshire there was always the captivating background of the household pets to make a contrast.

I treated some of them every day and it made an extra interest in my life; interest of a different kind, based on sentiment instead of commerce and because of the way things were it was something I could linger over and enjoy. I suppose with a very intensive small animal practice it would be easy to regard the thing as a huge sausage machine, an endless procession of hairy forms to prod with hypodermic needles. But in Darrowby we got to know them all as individual entities.

Driving through the town I was able to identify my ex-patients without difficulty; Rover Johnson, recovered from his ear canker, coming out of the ironmongers with his mistress, Patch Walker, whose broken leg had healed beautifully, balanced happily on the back of his owner's coal wagon, or Spot Briggs who was a bit of a rake anyway and would soon be tearing himself again on barbed wire, ambling all alone across the market place cobbles in seach of adventure. I got quite a kick out of recalling their ailments and mulling over their characteristics. Because they all had their own personalities and they were manifested in different ways.

One of these was their personal reaction to me and my treatment. Most dogs and cats appeared to bear me not the slightest ill will despite the fact that I usually had to do something disagreeable to them.

But there were exceptions and one of these was Magnus, the Miniature Dachshund from the Drovers' Arms.

He was in my mind now as I leaned across the bar counter.

'A pint of Smiths, please, Danny,' I whispered.

The barman grinned. 'Coming up, Mr Herriot.' He pulled at the lever and the beer hissed gently into the glass and as he passed it over the froth stood high and firm on the surface.

'That ale looks really fit tonight,' I breathed almost inaudibly.

'Fit? It's beautiful!' Danny looked fondly at the brimming glass. 'In fact it's a shame to sell it.'

I laughed, but pianissimo. 'Well it's nice of you to spare me a drop.' I took a deep pull and turned to old Mr Fairburn who was as always sitting at the far corner of the bar with his own fancy flower-painted glass in his hand.

'It's been a grand day, Mr Fairburn,' I murmured *sotto voce*.

The old man put his hand to his ear. 'What's that you say?'

'Nice warm day it's been.' My voice was like a soft breeze sighing over the marshes.

I felt a violent dig at my back. 'What the heck's the matter with you, Jim? Have you got laryngitis?'

I turned and saw the tall bald-headed figure of Dr Allinson, my medical adviser and friend. 'Hello, Harry,' I cried. 'Nice to see you.' Then I put my hand to my mouth.

But it was too late. A furious yapping issued from the manager's office. It was loud and penetrating and it went on and on.

'Damn, I forgot,' I said wearily. 'There goes Magnus again.'

'Magnus? What are you talking about?'

'Well, it's a long story.' I took another sip at my beer as the din continued from the office. It really shattered the peace of the comfortable bar and I could see the regulars fidgeting and looking out into the hallway.

Would that little dog ever forget? It seemed a long time now since Mr Beckwith, the new young manager at the Drovers, had brought Magnus in to the surgery. He had looked a little apprehensive.

'You'll have to watch him, Mr Herriot.'

'What do you mean?'

'Well, be careful. He's very vicious.'

I looked at the sleek little form, a mere brown dot on the table. He would probably turn the scale at around six pounds. And I couldn't help laughing.

'Vicious? He's not big enough, surely.'

'Don't you worry!' Mr Beckwith raised a warning finger. 'I took him to the vet in Bradford where I used to manage the White Swan and he sank his teeth into the poor chap's finger.'

'He did?'

'He certainly did! Right down to the bone! By God I've never heard such language but I couldn't blame the man. There was blood all over the place. I had to help him to put a bandage on.'

'Mm, I see.' It was nice to be told before you had been bitten and not after. 'And what was he trying to do to the dog? Must have been something pretty major.'

'It wasn't you know. All I wanted was his nails clipping.'

'Is that all? And why have you brought him today?'

'Same thing.'

'Well honestly, Mr Beckwith,' I said, 'I think we can manage to cut his nails without bloodshed. If he'd been a Bull Mastiff or an Alsatian we might have had a problem, but I think that you and I between us can control a Miniature Dachshund.'

The manager shook his head. 'Don't bring me into it. I'm sorry, but I'd rather not hold him, if you don't mind.'

'Why not?'

'Well, he'd never forgive me. He's a funny little dog.'

I rubbed my chin. 'But if he's as difficult as you say and you can't hold him, what do you expect me to do?'

'I don't know, really . . . maybe you could sort of dope him . . . knock him out?'

'You mean a general anaesthetic? To cut his claws . . .?'

'It'll be the only way, I'm afraid.' Mr Beckwith stared gloomily at the tiny animal. 'You don't know him.'

It was difficult to believe but it seemed pretty obvious that this canine morsel was the boss in the Beckwith home. In my experience many dogs had occupied this position but none as small as this one. Anyway, I had no more time to waste on this nonsense.

'Look,' I said, 'I'll put a tape muzzle on his nose and I'll have this job done in a couple of minutes.' I reached behind me for the nail clippers and laid them on the table, then I unrolled a length of bandage and tied it in a loop.

'Good boy, Magnus,' I said ingratiatingly as I advanced towards him.

The little dog eyed the bandage unwinkingly until it was almost touching his nose then, with a surprising outburst of ferocity, he made a snarling leap at my hand. I felt the draught on my fingers as a row of sparkling teeth snapped shut half an inch away, but as he turned to have another go my free hand clamped on the scruff of his neck.

'Right, Mr Beckwith,' I said calmly, 'I have him now. Just pass me that bandage again and I won't be long.'

But the young man had had enough. 'Not me!' he gasped. 'I'm off!' He turned the door handle and I heard his feet scurrying along the passage.

Ah well, I thought, it was probably best. With boss dogs my primary move was usually to get the owner out of the way. It was surprising how quickly these tough guys calmed down when they found themselves alone with a no-nonsense stranger who knew how to handle them. I could recite a list who were raving tearaways in their own homes but apologetic tail-waggers once they crossed the surgery threshold. And they were all bigger than Magnus.

Retaining my firm grip on his neck I unwound another foot of bandage and as he fought furiously, mouth gaping, lips retracted like a scaled-down Siberian wolf, I slipped the loop over his nose, tightened it and tied the knot behind his ears. His mouth was now clamped shut and just to make sure, I applied a second bandage so that he was well and truly trussed.

This was when they usually packed in and I looked confidently at the dog for signs of submission. But above the encircling white coils the eyes glared furiously and from within the little frame an enraged growling issued, rising and falling like the distant droning of a thousand bees.

Sometimes a stern word or two had the effect of showing them who was boss. 'Magnus!' I barked at him. 'That's enough! Behave yourself!' I gave his neck a shake to make it clear that I wasn't kidding but the only response was a sidelong squint of pure defiance from the slightly bulging eyes.

I lifted the clippers. 'All right,' I said wearily, 'if you won't have it one way you'll have it the other.' And I tucked him under one arm, seized a paw and began to clip.

He couldn't do a thing about it. He fought and wriggled but I had him as in a vice. And as I methodically trimmed the overgrown nails, wrathful bubbles escaped on either side of the bandage along with his splutterings. If dogs could swear I was getting the biggest cursing in history.

I did my job with particular care, taking pains to keep well away from the sensitive core of the claw so that he felt nothing, but it made no difference. The indignity of being mastered for once in his life was insupportable.

Towards the conclusion of the operation I began to change my tone. I had found in the past that once dominance has been established it is quite easy to work up a friendly relationship, so I started to introduce a wheedling note.

'Good little chap,' I cooed. 'That wasn't so bad, was it?'

I laid down the clippers and stroked his head as a few more resentful bubbles forced their way round the bandage. 'All right, Magnus, we'll take your muzzle off now.' I began to loosen the knot. 'You'll feel a lot better then, won't you?'

So often it happened that when I finally removed the restraint the dog would apparently decide to let bygones be bygones and in some cases would even lick my hand. But not so with Magnus. As the last turn of bandage fell from his nose he made another very creditable attempt to bite me.

'All right, Mr Beckwith,' I called along the passage, 'you can come and get him now.'

My final memory of the visit was of the little dog turning at the top of the surgery steps and giving me a last dirty look before his master led him down the street.

It said very clearly, 'Right, mate, I won't forget you.'

That had been weeks ago but ever since that day the very sound of my voice was enough to set Magnus yapping his disapproval. At first the regulars treated it as a big joke but now they had started to look at me strangely. Maybe they thought I had been cruel to the animal or something. It was all very embarrassing because I didn't want to abandon the Drovers; the bar was always cosy even on the coldest night and the beer very consistent.

Anyway if I had gone to another pub I would probably have started to do my talking in whispers and people would have looked at me even more strangely then.

How different it was with Mrs Hammond's Irish Setter. This started with an urgent phone call one night when I was in the bath. Helen knocked on the bathroom door and I dried off quickly and threw on my dressing gown. I ran upstairs and as soon as I lifted the receiver an anxious voice burst in my ear.

'Mr Herriot, it's Rock! He's been missing for two days and a man has just brought him back now. He found him in a wood with his foot in a gin trap. He must . . .' I heard a half sob at the end of the line. 'He must have been caught there all this time.'

'Oh, I'm sorry! Is it very bad?'

'Yes it is.' Mrs Hammond was the wife of one of the local bank managers and a capable, sensible woman. There was a pause and I imagined her determinedly gaining control of herself. When she spoke her voice was calm.

'Yes, I'm afraid it looks as though he'll have to have his foot amputated.'

'Oh, I'm terribly sorry to hear that.' But I wasn't really surprised. A limb compressed in one of those barbarous instruments for forty-eight hours would be in a critical state. These traps are now mercifully illegal but in those days they often provided me with the kind of jobs I didn't want and the kind of decisions I hated to make. Did you take a limb from an uncomprehending animal to keep it alive or did you bring down the merciful but final curtain of euthanasia? I was responsible for the fact that there were several three-legged dogs and cats running around Darrowby and though they seemed happy enough and their owners still had the pleasure of their pets, the thing, for me, was clouded with sorrow.

Anyway, I would do what had to be done.

'Bring him straight round, Mrs Hammond,' I said.

Rock was a big dog but he was the lean type of Setter and seemed very light as I lifted him on to the surgery table. As my arms encircled the unresisting body I could feel the rib cage sharply ridged under the skin.

'He's lost a lot of weight,' I said.

His mistress nodded. 'It's a long time to go without food. He ate ravenously when he came in, despite his pain.'

I put a hand beneath the dog's elbow and gently lifted the leg. The vicious teeth of the trap had been clamped on the radius and ulna but what worried me was the grossly swollen state of the foot. It was at least twice its normal size.

'What do you think, Mr Herriot?' Mrs Hammond's hands twisted anxiously at the handbag which every woman seemed to bring to the surgery irrespective of the circumstances.

I stroked the dog's head. Under the light, the rich sheen of the coat glowed red and gold. 'This terrific swelling of the foot. It's partly due to inflammation but also to the fact that the circulation was pretty well cut off for the time he was in the trap. The danger is gangrene – that's when the tissue dies and decomposes.'

'I know,' she replied. 'I did a bit of nursing before I married.'

Carefully I lifted the enormous foot. Rock gazed calmly in front of him as I felt around the metacarpals and phalanges, working my way up to the dreadful wound.

'Well, it's a mess,' I said, 'but there are two good things. First, the leg isn't broken. The trap has gone right down to the bone but there is no fracture. And second and more important, the foot is still warm.'

'That's a good sign?'

'Oh yes. It means there's still some circulation. If the foot had been cold and clammy the thing would have been hopeless. I would have had to amputate.'

'You think you can save his foot, then?'

I held up my hand. 'I don't know, Mrs Hammond. As I say, he still has some circulation but the question is how much. Some of this tissue is bound to slough off and things could look very nasty in a few days. But I'd like to try.'

I flushed out the wound with a mild antiseptic in warm water and gingerly explored the grisly depths. As I snipped away the pieces of damaged muscle and cut off the shreds and flaps of dead skin the thought was uppermost that it must be extremely unpleasant for the dog; but Rock held his head high and scarcely flinched. Once or twice he turned his head towards me enquiringly as I probed deeply and at times I felt his moist nose softly brushing my face as I bent over the foot, but that was all.

The injury seemed a desecration. There are few more beautiful dogs than an Irish Setter and Rock was a picture; sleek coated and graceful with silky feathers on legs and tail and a noble, gentle-eyed head. As the thought of how he would look without a foot drove into my mind I shook my head and turned quickly to lift the sulphanilamide powder from the trolley behind me. Thank heavens this was now available, one of the new revolutionary drugs, and I packed it deep into the wound with the confidence that it would really do something to keep down the infection. I applied a layer of gauze then a light bandage with a feeling of fatalism. There was nothing else I could do.

Rock was brought in to me every day. And every day he endured the same procedure; the removal of the dressing which was usually adhering to the wound to some degree, then the inevitable trimming of the dying tissues and the rebandaging. Yet, incredibly, he never showed any reluctance to come. Most of my patients came in very slowly and left at top speed, dragging their owners on the end of the leads; in fact some turned tail at the door, slipping their collar and sped down Trengate with their owners in hot pursuit. Dogs aren't so daft and there is doubtless a dentist's chair type of association about a vet's surgery.

Rock, however, always marched in happily with a gentle waving of his tail. In fact when I went into the waiting room and saw him sitting there he usually offered me his paw. This had always been a characteristic gesture of his but there seemed something uncanny about it when I bent over him and saw the white-swathed limb outstretched towards me.

After a week the outlook was grim. All the time the dead tissue had been sloughing and one night when I removed the dressing Mrs Hammond gasped and turned away. With her nursing training she had been very helpful, holding the foot this way and that intuitively as I worked, but tonight she didn't want to look.

I couldn't blame her. In places the white bones of the metacarpals could be seen like the fingers of a human hand with only random strands of skin covering them.

'Is it hopeless, do you think?' She whispered, still looking away.

I didn't answer for a moment as I felt my way underneath the foot. 'It does look awful, but do you know, I think we have reached the end of the road and are going to turn the corner soon.'

'How do you mean?'

'Well, all the under surface is sound and warm. His pads are perfectly intact. And do you notice, there's no smell tonight? That's because there is no more dead stuff to cut away. I really think this foot is going to start granulating.'

She stole a look. 'And do you think those . . . bones . . . will be covered over?'

'Yes, I do.' I dusted on the faithful sulphanilamide. 'It won't be exactly the same foot as before but it will do.'

And it turned out just that way. It took a long time but the new healthy tissue worked its way upwards as though determined to prove me right and when, many months later, Rock came into the surgery with a mild attack of conjunctivitis he proffered a courteous paw as was his wont. I accepted the civility and as we shook hands I looked at the upper surface of the foot. It was hairless, smooth and shining, but it was completely healed.

'You'd hardly notice it, would you?' Mrs Hammond said.

'That's right, it's marvellous. Just this little bare patch. And he walked in without a limp.'

Mrs Hammond laughed. 'Oh, he's quite sound on that leg now. And do you know, I really think he's grateful to you – look at him.'

I suppose the animal psychologists would say it was ridiculous even to think that the big dog realised I had done him a bit of good; that lolling-tongued open mouth, warm eyes and outstretched paw didn't mean anything like that.

Maybe they are right, but what I do know and cherish is the certainty that after all the discomforts I had put him through Rock didn't hold a thing against me.

I have to turn back to the other side of the coin to discuss Timmy Butterworth. He was a wire-haired Fox Terrier who resided in Gimber's yard, one of the little cobbled alleys off Trengate, and the only time I had to treat him was one lunch time.

I had just got out of the car and was climbing the surgery steps when I saw a little girl running along the street, waving frantically as she approached. I waited for her and when she panted up to me her eyes were wide with fright.

'Ah'm Wendy Butterworth,' she gasped. 'Me mam sent me. Will you come to our dog?'

'What's wrong with him?'

'Me mam says he's et summat!'

'Poison?'

'Ah think so?'

It was less than a hundred yards away, not worth taking the car. I broke into a trot with Wendy by my side and within seconds we were turning into the narrow archway of the 'yard'. Our feet clattered along the tunnel-like passage then we emerged into one of the unlikely scenes which had surprised me so much when I first came to Darrowby; the miniature street with its tiny crowded houses, strips of garden, bow windows looking into each other across a few feet of cobbles. But I had no time to gaze around me today because Mrs Butterworth, stout, red-faced and very flustered was waiting for me.

'He's in 'ere, Mr Herriot!' she cried and threw wide the door of one of the cottages. It opened straight into the living room and I saw my patient sitting on the hearth rug looking somewhat thoughtful.

'What's happened, then?' I asked.

The lady clasped and unclasped her hands. 'I saw a big rat run down across t'yard yesterday and I got some poison to put down for 'im.' She gulped agitatedly. 'I mixed it in a saucer full o' porridge then somebody came to t'door and when ah came back, Timmy was just finishin' it off!'

The terrier's thoughtful expression had deepened and he ran his tongue slowly round his lips with the obvious reflection that that was the strangest porridge he had ever tasted.

I turned to Mrs Butterworth. 'Have you got the poison tin there?'

'Yes, here it is.' With a violently trembling hand she passed it to me.

I read the label. It was a well known name and the very look of it sounded a knell in my mind recalling the many dead and dying animals with which it was associated. Its active ingredient was zinc phosphide and even today with our modern drugs we are usually helpless once a dog has absorbed it.

I thumped the tin down on the table. 'We've got to make him vomit immediately! I don't want to waste time going back to the surgery – have you got any washing soda? If I push a few crystals down it'll do the trick.'

'Oh dear!' Mrs Butterworth bit her lip. 'We 'aven't such a thing in the house ... is there anything else we could ...'

'Wait a minute!' I looked across the table, past the piece of cold mutton, the tureen of potatoes and a jar of pickles. 'Is there any mustard in that pot?'

'Aye, it's full.'

Quickly I grabbed the pot, ran to the tap and diluted the mustard to the consistency of milk.

'Come on!' I shouted. 'Let's have him outside.'

I seized the astonished Timmy, whisked him from the rug, shot through the door and dumped him on the cobbles. Holding his body clamped tightly between my knees and his jaws close together with my left hand I poured the liquid mustard into the side of his mouth whence it trickled down to the back of his throat. There was nothing he could do about it, he had swallowed the disgusting stuff, and when about a tablespoon had gone down I released him.

After a single affronted glare at me the terrier began to retch then to lurch across the smooth stones. Within seconds he had deposited his stolen meal in a quiet corner.

'Do you think that's the lot?' I asked.

'That's it,' Mrs Butterworth replied firmly. 'I'll fetch a brush and shovel.'

Timmy, his short tail tucked down, slunk back into the house and I watched him as he took up his favourite position on the hearthrug. He coughed, snorted, pawed at his mouth, but he just couldn't rid himself of that dreadful taste; and increasingly it was obvious that he had me firmly tagged as the cause of all the trouble. As I left he flashed me a glance which said quite plainly, 'You rotten swine!'

There was something in that look which reminded me of Magnus from the Drovers, but the first sign that Timmy, unlike Magnus, wasn't going to be satisfied with vocal disapproval come within a few days. I was strolling meditatively down Trengate when a white missile issued from Gimber's Yard, nipped me on the ankle and disappeared as silently as he had come. I caught only a glimpse of the little form speeding on its short legs down the passage.

I laughed. Fancy his remembering! But it happened again and again and I realised that the little dog was indeed lying in wait for me. He never actually sank his teeth into me – it was a gesture more than anything – but it seemed to satisfy him to see me jump as he snatched briefly at my calf or trouser leg. I was a sitting bird because I was usually deep in thought as I walked down the street.

And when I thought about it, I couldn't blame Timmy. Looking at it from his point of view he had been sitting by his fireside digesting an unusual meal and minding his own business when a total stranger had pounced on him, hustled him from the comfort of his rug and poured mustard into him. It was outrageous and he just wasn't prepared to let the matter rest there.

For my part there was a certain satisfaction in being the object of a vendetta waged by an animal who would have been dead without my services. And unpleasantly dead because the victims of phosphorus poisoning had to endure long days and sometimes weeks of jaundice, misery and creeping debility before the inevitable end.

So I suffered the attacks with good grace. But when I remembered I crossed to the other side of the street to avoid the hazard of Gimber's Yard; and from there I could often see the little white dog peeping round the corner waiting for the moment when he would make me pay for that indignity.

Timmy, I knew, was one who would never forget.

Chapter Thirty-five

I suppose there was a wry humour in the fact that my call-up papers arrived on my birthday, but I didn't see the joke at the time.

The event is preserved in my memory in a picture which is as clear to me today as when I walked into our 'dining room' that morning. Helen perched away up on her high stool at the end of the table, very still, eyes downcast. By the side of my plate my birthday present, a tin of Dobie's Blue Square tobacco, and next to it a long envelope. I didn't have to ask what it contained.

I had been expecting it for some time but it still gave me a jolt to find I had only a week before presenting myself at Lord's Cricket Ground, St John's Wood, London. And that week went by at frightening speed as I made my final plans, tidying up the loose ends in the practice, getting my Ministry of Agriculture forms sent off, arranging for our few possessions to be taken to Helen's old home where she would stay while I was away.

Having decided that I would finish work at teatime on Friday I had a call from old Arnold Summergill at about three o'clock that afternoon; and I knew that would be my very last job because it was always an expedition rather than a visit to his smallholding which clung to a bracken strewn slope in the depths of the hills. I didn't speak directly to Arnold but to Miss Thompson the postmistress in Hainby village.

'Mr Summergill wants you to come and see his dog,' she said over the phone.

'What's the trouble?' I asked.

I heard a muttered consulation at the far end.

'He says its leg's gone funny.'

'Funny? What d'you mean, funny?'

Again the quick babble of voices. 'He says it's kind of stickin' out.'

'All right,' I said. 'I'll be along very soon.'

It was no good asking for the dog to be brought in. Arnold had never owned a car. Nor had he ever spoken on a telephone – all our conversations had been carried on through the medium of Miss Thompson. Arnold would mount his rusty bicycle, pedal to Hainby and tell his troubles to the postmistress. And the symptoms; they were typically vague and I didn't suppose there would be anything either 'funny' or 'sticking out' about that leg when I saw it.

Anyway, I thought, as I drove out of Darrowby, I wouldn't mind having a last look at Benjamin. It was a fanciful name for a small farmer's dog and I never really found out how he had acquired it. But after all he was an unlikely breed for such a setting, a massive Old English Sheep Dog who would have looked more in place decorating the lawns of a stately home than following his master round Arnold's stony pastures. He was a classical example of the walking hearthrug and it took a second look to decide which end of him was which. But when you did manage to locate his head you found two of the most benevolent eyes imaginable glinting through the thick fringe of hair.

Benjamin was in fact too friendly at times, especially in winter when he had been strolling in the farmyard mud and showed his delight at my arrival by planting his huge feet on my chest. He did the same thing to my car, too, usually just after I had washed it, smearing clay lavishly over windows and bodywork while exchanging pleasantries with Sam inside. When Benjamin made a mess of anything he did it right.

But I had to interrupt my musings when I reached the last stage of my journey. And as I hung on to the kicking, jerking wheel and listened to the creaking and groaning of springs and shock absorbers, the thought forced its way into my mind as it always did around here that it cost us money to come to Mr Summergill's farm. There could be no profit from the visit because this vicious track must knock at least five pounds off the value of the car on every trip. Since Arnold did not have a car himself he saw no reason why he should interfere with the primeval state of his road.

It was simply a six foot strip of earth and rock and it wound and twisted for an awful long way. The trouble was that to get to the farm you had to descend into a deep valley before climbing through a wood towards the house. I think going down was worse because the vehicle hovered agonisingly on the top of each ridge before plunging into the yawning ruts beyond; and each time, listening to the unyielding stone grating on sump and exhaust I tried to stop myself working out the damage in pounds, shillings and pence.

And when at last, mouth gaping, eyes popping, tyres sending the sharp pebbles flying, I ground my way upwards in bottom gear over the last few yards leading to the house I was surprised to see Arnold waiting for me there alone. It was unusual to see him without Benjamin.

He must have read my questioning look because he jerked his thumb over his shoulder.

'He's in t'house,' he grunted, and his eyes were anxious.

I got out of the car and looked at him for a moment as he stood there in a typical attitude, wide shoulders back, head high. I have called him 'old' and indeed he was over seventy, but the features beneath the woollen tammy which he always wore pulled down over his ears were clean and regular and the tall figure lean and straight. He was a fine looking man and must have been handsome in his youth, yet he had never married. I often felt there was a story there but he seemed content to live here alone, a 'bit of a 'ermit' as they said in the village. Alone, that is, except for Benjamin.

As I followed him into the kitchen he casually shooed out a couple of hens who had been perching on a dusty dresser. Then I saw Benjamin and pulled up with a jerk.

The big dog was sitting quite motionless by the side of the table and this time the eyes behind the overhanging hair were big and liquid with fright. He appeared to be too terrified to move and when I saw his left fore leg I couldn't blame him. Arnold had been right after all; it was indeed sticking out with a vengeance, at an angle which made my heart give a quick double thud; a complete lateral dislocation of the elbow, the radius projecting away out from the humerus at an almost impossible obliquity.

I swallowed carefully. 'When did this happen, Mr Summergill?'

'Just an hour since.' He tugged worriedly at his strange headgear. 'I was changing the cows into another field and awd Benjamin likes to have a nip at their heels when he's behind 'em. Well he did it once ower often and one of them lashed lashed out and got 'im on the leg.'

'I see.' My mind was racing. This thing was grotesque. I had never seen anything like it, in fact thirty years later I still haven't seen anything like it. How on earth was I going to reduce the thing away up here in the hills? By the look of it I would need general anaesthesia and a skilled assistant.

'Poor old lad,' I said, resting my hand on the shaggy head as I tried to think. 'What are we going to do with you?'

The tail whisked along the flags in reply and the mouth opened in a nervous panting, giving a glimpse of flawlessly white teeth.

Arnold cleared his throat. 'Can you put 'im right?'

Well it was a good question. An airy answer might give the wrong impression yet I didn't want to worry him with my doubts. It would be a mammoth task to get the enormous dog down to Darrowby; he nearly filled the kitchen, never mind my little car. And with that leg sticking out and with Sam already in residence. And would I be able to get the joint back in place when I got him there? And even if I did manage it I would still have to bring him all the way back up here. It would just about take care of the rest of the day.

Gently I passed my fingers over the dislocated joint and searched my memory for details of the anatomy of the elbow. For the leg to be in this position the processus anconeus must have been completely disengaged from the supracondyloid fossa where it normally lay; and to get it back the joint would have to be flexed until the anconeus was clear of the epicondyles.

'Now let's see,' I murmured to myself. 'If I had this dog anaesthetised and on the table I would have to get hold of him like this.' I grasped the leg just above the elbow and began to move the radius slowly upwards. Benjamin gave me a quick glance then turned his head away, a gesture typical of good-natured dogs, conveying the message that he was going to put up with whatever I thought it necessary to do.

I flexed the joint still further until I was sure the anconeus was clear, then carefully rotated the radius and ulna inwards.

'Yes . . . yes . . . ' I muttered again. 'This must be about the right position . . .' But my soliloquy was interrupted by a sudden movement of the bones under my hand; a springing, flicking sensation.

I looked incredulously at the leg. It was perfectly straight.

Benjamin, too, seemed unable to take it in right away, because he peered cautiously round through his shaggy curtain before lowering his nose and sniffing around the elbow. Then he seemed to realise all was well and ambled over to his master.

And he was perfectly sound. Not a trace of a limp.

A slow smile spread over Arnold's face. 'You've mended him, then.'

'Looks like it, Mr Summergill.' I tried to keep my voice casual, but I felt like cheering or bursting into hysterical laughter. I had only been making an examination, feeling things out a little, and the joint had popped back into place. A glorious accident.

'Aye well, that's grand,' the farmer said. 'Isn't it, awd lad?' He bent and tickled Benjamin's ear.

I could have been disappointed by this laconic reception of my performance, but I realised it was a compliment to me that he wasn't surprised that I, James Herriot, his vet, should effortlessly produce a miracle when it was required.

A theatre-full of cheering students would have rounded off the incident or it would be nice to do this kind of thing to some millionaire's animal in a crowded drawing room, but it never happened that way. I looked around the kitchen, at the cluttered table, the pile of unwashed crockery in the sink, a couple of Arnold's ragged shirts drying before the fire, and I smiled to myself. This was the sort of setting in which I usually pulled off my spectacular cures. The only spectators here, apart from Arnold, were the two hens who had made their way back on to the dresser and they didn't seem particularly impressed.

'Well, I'll be getting back down the hill,' I said. And Arnold walked with me across the yard to the car.

'I hear you're off to join up,' he said as I put my hand on the door.

'Yes, I'm away tomorrow, Mr Summergill.'

'Tomorrow, eh?' he raised his eyebrows.

'Yes, to London. Ever been there?'

'Nay, nay, be damned!' The woollen cap quivered as he shook his head. 'That'd be no good to me.'

I laughed. 'Why do you say that?'

'Well now, I'll tell ye.' He scratched his chin ruminatively. 'Ah nobbut went once to Brawton and that was enough. Ah couldn't walk on t'street!'

'Couldn't walk?'

'Nay. There were that many people about. I 'ad to take big steps and little 'uns, then big steps and little 'uns again. Couldn't get goin'.'

I had often seen Arnold stalking over his fields with the long, even stride of the hillman with nothing in his way and I knew exactly what he meant. 'Big steps and little 'uns.' That put it perfectly.

I started the engine and waved and as I moved away the old man raised a hand.

'Tek care, lad,' he murmured.

I spotted Benjamin's nose just peeping round the kitchen door. Any other time he would have been out with his master to see me off the premises but it had been a strange day for him culminating with my descending on him and mauling his leg about. He wasn't taking any more chances.

I drove gingerly down through the wood and before starting up the track on the other side I stopped the car and got out with Sam leaping eagerly after me.

This was a little lost valley in the hills, a green cleft cut off from the wild country above. One of the bonuses in a country vet's life is that he sees these hidden places. Apart from old Arnold nobody ever came down here, not even the postman who left the infrequent mail in a box at the top of the track and nobody saw the blazing scarlets and golds of the autumn trees nor heard the busy clucking and murmuring of the beck among its clean-washed stones.

I walked along the water's edge watching the little fish darting and flitting in the cool depths. In the spring these banks were bright with primroses and in May a great sea of bluebells flowed among the trees but today, though the sky was an untroubled blue, the clean air was touched with the sweetness of the dying year.

I climbed a little way up the hillside and sat down among the bracken now fast turning to bronze. Sam, as was his way, flopped by my side and I ran a hand over the silky hair of his ears. The far side of the valley rose steeply to where, above the gleaming ridge of limestone cliffs, I could just see the sunlit rim of the moor.

I looked back to where the farm chimney sent a thin tendril of smoke from behind the brow of the hill, and it seemed that the episode with Benjamin, my last job in veterinary practice before I left Darrowby, was a fitting epilogue. A little triumph, intensely satisfying but by no means world shaking; like all the other little triumphs and disasters which make up a veterinary surgeon's life but go unnoticed by the world.

Last night, after Helen had packed my bag I had pushed Black's Veterinary Dictionary in among the shirts and socks. It was a bulky volume but I had been gripped momentarily by a fear that I might forget the things I had learned, and conceived on an impulse the scheme of reading a page or two each day to keep my memory fresh. And here among the bracken the thought came back to me; that it was the greatest good fortune not only to be fascinated by animals but to know about them. Suddenly the knowing became a precious thing.

I went back and opened the car door. Sam jumped on to the seat and before I got in I looked away down in the other direction from the house to the valley's mouth where the hills parted to give a glimpse of the plain below. And the endless wash of pale tints, the gold of the stubble, the dark smudges of wood, the mottled greens of the pasture land were like a perfect water colour. I found myself staring greedily as if for the first time at the scene which had so often lifted my heart, the great wide clean-blown face of Yorkshire.

I would come back to it all, I thought as I drove away; back to my work . . . how was it that book had described it . . . my hard, honest and fine profession.

Chapter Thirty-six

I had to catch the early train and Bob Cooper was at the door with his ancient taxi before eight o'clock next morning.

Sam followed me across the room expectantly as he always did but I closed the door gently against his puzzled face. Clattering down the long flight of stairs I caught a glimpse through the landing window of the garden with the sunshine beginning to pierce the autumn mist, turning the dewy grass into a glittering coverlet, glinting on the bright colours of the apples and the last roses.

In the passage I paused at the side door where I had started my day's work so many times since coming to Darrowby, but then I hurried past. This was one time I went out the front.

Bob pushed open the taxi door and I threw my bag in before looking up over the ivy-covered brick of the old house to our little room under the tiles. Helen was in the window. She was crying. When she saw me she waved gaily and smiled, but it was a twisted smile as the tears flowed. And as we drove round the corner and I swallowed the biggest ever lump in my throat a fierce resolve welled in me; men all over the country were leaving their wives and I had to leave Helen now, but nothing, nothing, nothing would ever get me away from her again.

The shops were still closed and nothing stirred in the market place. As we left I turned and looked back at the cobbled square with the old clock tower and the row of irregular roofs with the green fells quiet and peaceful behind, and it seemed that I was losing something for ever.

I wish I had known then that it was not the end of everything. I wish I had known it was only the beginning. But at that moment I knew only that soon I would be far from here; in London, pushing my way through the crowds. Taking big steps and little 'uns.

Vets Might
Fly

Vets Might Fly

To
my dogs, HECTOR and DAN
Faithful companions of the daily round.

The four lines from 'If I Only Had Wings' are reproduced by permission of The Peter Maurice Music Co. Ltd., 138–140 Charing Cross Road, London WC2H 0LD, England.

Chapter One

'Move!' bawled the drill corporal. 'Come on, speed it up!' He sprinted effortlessly to the rear of the gasping, panting column of men and urged us on from there.

I was somewhere in the middle, jog-trotting laboriously with the rest and wondering how much longer I could keep going. And as my ribs heaved agonisingly and my leg muscles protested I tried to work out just how many miles we had run.

I had suspected nothing when we lined up outside our billets. We weren't clad in PT kit but in woollen pullovers and regulation slacks and it seemed unlikely that anything violent was imminent. The corporal, too, a cheerful little cockney, appeared to regard us as his brothers. He had a kind face.

'Awright, lads,' he had cried, smiling over the fifty new airmen. 'We're just going to trot round to the park, so follow me. Le-eft turn! At the double, qui-ick march! 'eft-ight, 'eft-ight, 'eft-ight!'

That had been a long, long time ago and we were still reeling through the London streets with never a sign of a park anywhere. The thought hammered in my brain that I had been under the impression that I was fit. A country vet, especially in the Yorkshire Dales, never had the chance to get out of condition; he was always on the move, wrestling with the big animals, walking for miles between the fell-side barns; he was hard and tough. That's what I thought.

But now other reflections began to creep in. My few months of married life with Helen had been so much lotus eating. She was too good a cook and I was too faithful a disciple of her art. Just lounging by our bed-sitter's fireside was the sweetest of all occupations. I had tried to ignore the disappearance of my abdominal muscles, the sagging of my pectorals, but it was all coming home to me now.

'It's not far now, lads,' the corporal chirped from the rear, but he struck no responsive chords in the toiling group. He had said it several times before and we had stopped believing him.

But this time it seemed he really meant it, because as we turned into yet another street I could see iron railings and trees at the far end. The relief was inexpressible. I would just about have the strength to make it through the gates – to the rest and smoke which I badly needed because my legs were beginning to seize up.

We passed under an arch of branches which still bore a few autumn leaves and stopped as one man, but the corporal was waving us on.

'Come on, lads, round the track!' he shouted and pointed to a broad earthen path which circled the park.

We stared at him. He couldn't be serious! A storm of protest broke out.

'Aw no, corp . . . !' 'Have a heart, corp . . . !'

The smile vanished from the little man's face. 'Get movin', I said! Faster, faster . . . one-two, one-two.'

As I stumbled forward over the black earth, between borders of sooty rhododendrons and tired grass, I just couldn't believe it. It was all too sudden. Three days ago I was in Darrowby and half of me was still back there, back with Helen. And another part was still looking out of the rear window of the taxi at the green hills receding behind the tiled roofs into the morning sunshine; still standing in the corridor of the train as the flat terrain of southern England slid past and a great weight built up steadily in my chest.

My first introduction to the RAF was at Lord's cricket ground. Masses of forms to fill, medicals, then the issue of an enormous pile of kit. I was billeted in a block of flats in St John's Wood – luxurious before the lush fittings had been removed. But they couldn't take away the heavy bathroom ware and one of our blessings was the unlimited hot water gushing at our touch into the expensive surroundings.

After that first crowded day I retired to one of those green-tiled sanctuaries and lathered myself with a new bar of a famous toilet soap which Helen had put in my bag. I have never been able to use that soap since. Scents are too evocative and the merest whiff jerks me back to that first night away from my wife, and to the feeling I had then. It was a dull, empty ache which never really went away.

On the second day we marched endlessly; lectures, meals, inoculations. I was used to syringes but the very sight of them was too much for many of my friends. Especially when the doctor took the blood samples; one look at the dark fluid flowing from their veins and the young men toppled quietly from their chairs, often four or five in a row while the orderlies, grinning cheerfully, bore them away.

We ate in the London Zoo and our meals were made interesting by the chatter of monkeys and the roar of lions in the background. But in between it was march, march, march, with our new boots giving us hell.

And on this third day the whole thing was still a blur. We had been wakened as on my first morning by the hideous 6 a.m. clattering of dustbin lids; I hadn't really expected a bugle but I found this noise intolerable. However, at the moment my only concern was that we had completed the circuit of the park. The gates were only a few yards ahead and I staggered up to them and halted among my groaning comrades.

'Round again, lads!' the corporal yelled, and as we stared at him aghast he smiled affectionately. 'You think this is tough? Wait till they get hold of you at ITW. I'm just kinda breakin' you in gently. You'll thank me for this later. Right, at the double! One-two, one-two!'

Bitter thoughts assailed me as I lurched forward once more. Another round of the park would kill me – there was not a shadow of a doubt about that. You left a loving wife and a happy home to serve king and country and this was how they treated you. It wasn't fair.

The night before I had dreamed of Darrowby. I was back in old Mr Dakin's cow byre. The farmer's patient eyes in the long, drooping-moustached face looked down at me from his stooping height.

'It looks as though it's over wi' awd Blossom, then,' he said, and rested his hand briefly on the old cow's back. It was an enormous, work-swollen hand. Mr Dakin's gaunt frame carried little flesh but the grossly thickened fingers bore testimony to a life of toil.

I dried off the needle and dropped it into the metal box where I carried my suture materials, scalpels and blades. 'Well, it's up to you of course, Mr Dakin, but this is the third time I've had to stitch her teats and I'm afraid it's going to keep on happening.'

'Aye, it's just the shape she is.' The farmer bent and examined the row of knots along the four-inch scar. 'By gaw, you wouldn't believe it could mek such a mess – just another cow standin' on it.'

'A cow's hoof is sharp,' I said. 'It's nearly like a knife coming down.'

That was the worst of very old cows. Their udders dropped and their teats became larger and more pendulous so that when they lay down in their stalls the vital milk-producing organ was pushed away to one side into the path of the neighbouring animals. If it wasn't Mabel on the right standing on it, it was Buttercup on the other side.

There were only six cows in the little cobbled byre with its low roof and wooden partitions and they all had names. You don't find cows with names any more and there aren't any farmers like Mr Dakin, who somehow scratched a living from a herd of six milkers plus a few calves, pigs and hens.

'Aye, well,' he said. 'Ah reckon t'awd lass doesn't owe me anythin'. Ah remember the night she was born, twelve years ago. She was out of awd Daisy and ah carried her out of this very byre on a sack and the snow was comin' down hard. Sin' then ah wouldn't like to count how many thousand gallons o' milk she's turned out – she's still givin' four a day. Naw, she doesn't owe me a thing.'

As if she knew she was the topic of conversation Blossom turned her head and looked at him. She was the classical picture of an ancient bovine; as fleshless as her owner, with jutting pelvic bones, splayed, overgrown feet and horns with a multitude of rings along their curving length. Beneath her, the udder, once high and tight, drooped forlornly almost to the floor.

She resembled her owner, too, in her quiet, patient demeanour. I had infiltrated her teat with a local anaesthetic before stitching but I don't think she would have moved if I hadn't used any. Stitching teats puts a vet in the ideal position to be kicked, with his head low down in front of the hind feet, but there was no danger with Blossom. She had never kicked anybody in her life.

Mr Dakin blew out his cheeks. 'Well, there's nowt else for it. She'll have to go. I'll tell Jack Dodson to pick 'er up for the fatstock market on Thursday. She'll be a bit tough for eatin' but ah reckon she'll make a few steak pies.'

He was trying to joke but he was unable to smile as he looked at the old cow. Behind him, beyond the open door, the green hillside ran down to the river and the spring sunshine touched the broad sweep of the shallows with a million dancing lights. A beach of bleached stones gleamed bone-white against the long stretch of grassy bank which rolled up to the pastures lining the valley floor.

I had often felt that this smallholding would be an ideal place to live; only a mile outside Darrowby, but secluded, and with this heart-lifting vista of river and fell. I remarked on this once to Mr Dakin and the old man turned to me with a wry smile.

'Aye, but the view's not very sustainin',' he said.

It happened that I was called back to the farm on the following Thursday to 'cleanse' a cow and was in the byre when Dodson the drover called to pick up Blossom. He had collected a group of fat bullocks and cows from other farms and they stood, watched by one of his men, on the road high above.

'Nah then, Mr Dakin,' he cried as he bustled in. 'It's easy to see which one you want me to tek. It's that awd screw over there.'

He pointed at Blossom, and in truth the unkind description seemed to fit the bony creature standing between her sleek neighbours.

The farmer did not reply for a moment, then he went up between the cows and gently rubbed Blossom's forehead. 'Aye, this is the one, Jack.' He hesitated, then undid the chain round her neck. 'Off ye go, awd lass,' he murmured, and the old animal turned and made her way placidly from the stall.

'Aye, come on with ye!' shouted the dealer, poking his stick against the cow's rump.

'Doan't hit 'er!' barked Mr Dakin.

Dodson looked at him in surprise. 'Ah never 'it 'em, you know that. Just send 'em on, like.'

'Ah knaw, ah knaw, Jack, but you won't need your stick for this 'un. She'll go wherever ye want – allus has done.'

Blossom confirmed his words as she ambled through the door and, at a gesture from the farmer, turned along the track.

The old man and I stood watching as the cow made her way unhurriedly up the hill, Jack Dodson in his long khaki smock sauntering behind her. As the path wound behind a clump of sparse trees man and beast disappeared but Mr Dakin still gazed after them, listening to the clip-clop of the hooves on the hard ground.

When the sound died away he turned to me quickly. 'Right, Mr Herriot, we'll get on wi' our job, then. I'll bring your hot watter.'

The farmer was silent as I soaped my arm and inserted it into the cow. If there is one thing more disagreeable than removing the bovine afterbirth it is watching somebody else doing it, and I always try to maintain a conversation as I grope around inside. But this time it was hard work. Mr Dakin responded to my sallies on the weather, cricket and the price of milk with a series of grunts.

Holding the cow's tail he leaned on the hairy back and, empty-eyed, blew smoke from the pipe which like most farmers at a cleansing he had prudently lit at the outset. And of course, since the going was heavy, it just would happen that the job took much longer than usual. Sometimes a placenta simply lifted out but I had to peel this one away from the cotyledons one by one, returning every few minutes to the hot water and antiseptic to re-soap my aching arms.

But at last it was finished. I pushed in a couple of pessaries, untied the sack from my middle and pulled my shirt over my head. The conversation had died and the silence was almost oppressive as we opened the byre door.

Mr Dakin paused, his hand on the latch. 'What's that?' he said softly.

From somewhere on the hillside I could hear the clip-clop of a cow's feet. There were two ways to the farm and the sound came from a narrow track which joined the main road half a mile beyond the other entrance. As we listened a cow rounded a rocky outcrop and came towards us.

It was Blossom, moving at a brisk trot, great udder swinging, eyes fixed purposefully on the open door behind us.

'What the hangment . . . ?' Mr Dakin burst out, but the old cow brushed past us and marched without hesitation into the stall which she had occupied for all those years. She sniffed enquiringly at the empty hay rack and looked round at her owner.

Mr Dakin stared back at her. The eyes in the weathered face were expressionless but the smoke rose from his pipe in a series of rapid puffs.

Heavy boots clattered suddenly outside and Jack Dodson panted his way through the door.

'Oh, you're there, ye awd beggar!' he gasped. 'Ah thought I'd lost ye!'

He turned to the farmer. 'By gaw, I'm sorry, Mr Dakin. She must 'ave turned off at t'top of your other path. Ah never saw her go.'

The farmer shrugged. 'It's awright, Jack. It's not your fault, ah should've told ye.'

'That's soon mended anyway.' The drover grinned and moved towards Blossom. 'Come on, lass, let's have ye out of there again.'

But he halted as Mr Dakin held an arm in front of him.

There was a long silence as Dodson and I looked in surprise at the farmer who continued to gaze fixedly at the cow. There was a pathetic dignity about the old animal as she stood there against the mouldering timber of the partition, her eyes patient and undemanding. It was a dignity which triumphed over the unsightliness of the long upturned hooves, the fleshless ribs, the broken-down udder almost brushing the cobbles.

Then, still without speaking, Mr Dakin moved unhurriedly between the cows and a faint chink of metal sounded as he fastened the chain around Blossom's neck. Then he strolled to the end of the byre and returned with a forkful of hay which he tossed expertly into the rack.

This was what Blossom was waiting for. She jerked a mouthful from between the spars and began to chew with quiet satisfaction.

'What's to do, Mr Dakin?' the drover cried in bewilderment. 'They're waiting for me at t'mart!'

The farmer tapped out his pipe on the half door and began to fill it with black shag from a battered tin. 'Ah'm sorry to waste your time, Jack, but you'll have to go without 'er.'

'Without 'er . . . ? But . . . ?'

'Aye, ye'll think I'm daft, but that's how it is. T'awd lass has come 'ome and she's stoppin' 'ome.' He directed a look of flat finality at the drover.

Dodson nodded a couple of times then shuffled from the byre. Mr Dakin followed and called after him,

'Ah'll pay ye for your time, Jack. Put it down on ma bill.'

He returned, applied a match to his pipe and drew deeply.

'Mr Herriot,' he said as the smoke rose around his ears, 'do you ever feel when summat happens that it was meant to happen and that it was for t'best?'

'Yes, I do, Mr Dakin. I often feel that.'

'Aye well, that's how I felt when Blossom came down that hill.' He reached out and scratched the root of the cow's tail. 'She's allus been a favourite and by gaw I'm glad she's back.'

'But how about those teats? I'm willing to keep stitching them up, but . . .'

'Nay, lad, ah've had an idea. Just came to me when you were tekkin' away that cleansin' and I thowt I was ower late.'

'An idea?'

'Aye.' The old man nodded and tamped down the tobacco with his thumb. 'I can put two or three calves on to 'er instead of milkin' 'er. The old stable is empty – she can live in there where there's nobody to stand on 'er awd tits.'

I laughed. 'You're right, Mr Dakin. She'd be safe in the stable and she'd suckle three calves easily. She could pay her way.'

'Well, as ah said, it's matterless. After all them years she doesn't owe me a thing.' A gentle smile spread over the seamed face. 'Main thing is, she's come 'ome.'

My eyes were shut most of the time now as I blundered round the park and when I opened them a red mist swirled. But it is incredible what the human frame will stand and I blinked in disbelief as the iron gates appeared once more under their arch of sooty branches.

I had survived the second lap but an ordinary rest would be inadequate now. This time I would have to lie down. I felt sick.

'Good lads!' the corporal called out, cheerful as ever. 'You're doin' fine. Now we're just going to 'ave a little hoppin' on the spot.'

Incredulous wails rose from our demoralised band but the corporal was unabashed.

'Feet together now. Up! Up! Up! That's no good, come on, get some height into it! Up! Up!'

This was the final absurdity. My chest was a flaming cavern of agony. These people were supposed to be making us fit and instead they were doing irreparable damage to my heart and lungs.

'You'll thank me for this later, lads. Take my word for it. GET YOURSELVES OFF THE GROUND. UP! UP!'

Through my pain I could see the corporal's laughing face. The man was clearly a sadist. It was no good appealing to him.

And as, with the last of my strength, I launched myself into the air it came to me suddenly why I had dreamed about Blossom last night.

I wanted to go home, too.

Chapter Two

The fog swirled over the heads of the marching men; a London fog, thick, yellow, metallic on the tongue. I couldn't see the head of the column, only the swinging lantern carried by the leader.

This 6.30 a.m. walk to breakfast was just about the worst part of the day, when my morale was low and thoughts of home rose painfully.

We used to have fogs in Darrowby, but they were country fogs, different from this. One morning I drove out on my rounds with the headlights blazing against the grey curtain ahead, seeing nothing from my tight-shut box. But I was heading up the Dale, climbing steadily with the engine pulling against the rising ground, then quite suddenly the fog thinned to a shimmering silvery mist and was gone.

And there, above the pall, the sun was dazzling and the long green line of the fells rose before me, thrusting exultantly into a sky of summer blue.

Spellbound, I drove upwards into the bright splendour, staring through the windscreen as though I had never seen it all before; the bronze of the dead bracken spilling down the grassy flanks of the hills, the dark smudges of trees, the grey farmhouses and the endless pattern of walls creeping to the heather above.

I was in a rush as usual but I had to stop. I pulled up in a gateway, Sam jumped out and we went through into a field; and as the beagle scampered over the glittering turf I stood in the warm sunshine amid the melting frost and looked back at the dark damp blanket which blotted out the low country but left this jewelled world above it.

And, gulping the sweet air, I gazed about me gratefully at the clean green land where I worked and made my living.

I could have stayed there, wandering round, watching Sam exploring with waving tail, nosing into the shady corners where the sun had not reached and the ground was iron hard and the rime thick and crisp on the grass. But I had an appointment to keep, and no ordinary one – it was with a peer of the realm. Reluctantly I got back into the car.

I was due to start Lord Hulton's tuberculin test at 9.30 a.m. and as I drove round the back of the Elizabethan mansion to the farm buildings nearby I felt a pang of misgiving; there were no animals in sight. There was only a man in tattered blue dungarees hammering busily at a makeshift crush at the exit to the fold yard.

He turned round when he saw me and waved his hammer. As I approached I looked wonderingly at the slight figure with the soft fairish hair falling over his brow, at the holed cardigan and muck-encrusted wellingtons. You would have expected him to say, 'Nah then, Mr Herriot, how ista this mornin'?'

But he didn't, he said, 'Herriot, my dear chap, I'm most frightfully sorry, but I'm very much afraid we're not quite ready for you.' And he began to fumble with his tobacco pouch.

William George Henry Augustus, Eleventh Marquis of Hulton, always had a pipe in his mouth and he was invariably either filling it, cleaning it out with a metal reaming tool or trying to light it. I had never seen him actually smoking it. And at times of stress he attempted to do everything at once. He was obviously embarrassed at his lack of preparedness and when he saw me glance involuntarily at my watch he grew more agitated, pulling his pipe from his mouth and putting it back in again, tucking the hammer under his arm, rummaging in a large box of matches.

I gazed across to the rising ground beyond the farm buildings. Far off on the horizon I could make out tiny figures: galloping beasts, scurrying men; and faint sounds came down to me of barking dogs, irritated bellowings and shrill cries of 'Haow, haow!' 'Gerraway by!' 'Siddown, dog!'

I sighed. It was the old story. Even the Yorkshire aristocracy seemed to share this carefree attitude to time.

His lordship clearly sensed my feelings because his discomfort increased.

'It's too bad of me, old chap,' he said, spraying a few matchsticks around and dropping flakes of tobacco on the stone flags. 'I did promise to be ready for nine thirty but those blasted animals just won't cooperate.'

I managed a smile. 'Oh never mind, Lord Hulton, they seem to be getting them down the hill now and I'm not in such a panic this morning, anyway.'

'Oh splendid, splendid!' He attempted to ignite a towering mound of dark flake which spluttered feebly then toppled over the edge of his pipe. 'And come and see this! I've been rigging up a crush. We'll drive them in here and we'll really have 'em. Remember we had a spot of bother last time, what?'

I nodded. I did remember. Lord Hulton had only about thirty suckling cows but it had taken a three-hour rodeo to test them. I looked doubtfully at the rickety structure of planks and corrugated iron. It would be interesting to see how it coped with the moorland cattle.

I didn't mean to rub it in, but again I glanced unthinkingly at my watch and the little man winced as though he had received a blow.

'Dammit!' he burst out. 'What are they doing over there? Tell you what, I'll go and give them a hand!' Distractedly, he began to change hammer, pouch, pipe and matches from hand to hand, dropping them and picking them up, before finally deciding to put the hammer down and stuff the rest into his pockets. He went off at a steady trot and I thought as I had done so often that there couldn't be many noblemen in England like him.

If I had been a marquis, I felt, I would still have been in bed or perhaps just parting the curtains and peering out to see what kind of day it was. But Lord Hulton worked all the time, just about as hard as any of his men. One morning I arrived to find him at the supremely mundane task of 'plugging muck', standing on a manure heap, hurling steaming forkfuls on to a cart. And he always dressed in rags. I suppose he must have had more orthodox items in his wardrobe but I never saw them. Even his tobacco was the great smoke of the ordinary farmer – Redbreast Flake.

My musings were interrupted by the thunder of hooves and wild cries; the Hulton herd was approaching. Within minutes the fold yard was filled with milling creatures, steam rising in rolling clouds from their bodies.

The marquis appeared round the corner of the building at a gallop.

'Right, Charlie!' he yelled. 'Let the first one into the crush!'

Panting with anticipation he stood by the nailed boards as the men inside opened the yard gate. He didn't have to wait long. A shaggy red monster catapulted from the interior, appeared briefly in the narrow passage then emerged at about fifty miles an hour from the other end with portions of his lordship's creation dangling from its horns and neck. The rest of the herd pounded close behind.

'Stop them! Stop them!' screamed the little peer, but it was of no avail. A hairy torrent flooded through the opening and in no time at all the herd was legging it back to the high land in a wild stampede. The men followed them and within a few moments Lord Hulton and I were standing there just as before watching the tiny figures on the skyline, listening to the distant 'Haow, haow!' 'Gerraway by!'

'I say,' he murmured despondently. 'It didn't work terribly well, did it!'

But he was made of stern stuff. Seizing his hammer he began to bang away with undiminished enthusiasm and by the time the beasts returned the crush was rebuilt and a stout iron bar pushed across the front to prevent further break-outs.

It seemed to solve the problem because the first cow, confronted by the bar, stood quietly and I was able to clip the hair on her neck through an opening between the planks. Lord Hulton, in high good humour, settled down on an upturned oil drum with my testing book on his knee.

'I'll do the writing for you,' he cried. 'Fire away, old chap!'

I poised my calipers. 'Eight, eight.' He wrote it down and the next cow came in.

'Eight, eight,' I said, and he bowed his head again.

The third cow arrived: 'Eight, eight.' And the fourth, 'Eight, eight.'

His lordship looked up from the book and passed a weary hand across his forehead.

'Herriot, dear boy, can't you vary it a bit? I'm beginning to lose interest.'

All went well until we saw the cow which had originally smashed the crush. She had sustained a slight scratch on her neck.

'I say, look at that!' cried the peer. 'Will it be all right?'

'Oh yes, it's nothing. Superficial.'

'Ah, good, but don't you think we should have something to put on it? Some of that . . .'

I waited for it. Lord Hulton was a devotee of May and Baker's Propamidine Cream and used it for all minor cuts and grazes in his cattle. He loved the stuff. But unfortunately he couldn't say 'Propamidine'. In fact nobody on the entire establishment could say it except Charlie the farm foreman and he only thought he could say it. He called it 'Propopamide' but his lordship had the utmost faith in him.

'Charlie!' he bawled. 'Are you there, Charlie?'

The foreman appeared from the pack in the yard and touched his cap. 'Yes, m'lord.'

'Charlie, that wonderful stuff we get from Mr Herriot – you know, for cut teats and things. Pro . . . Pero . . . what the hell do you call it again?'

Charlie paused. It was one of his big moments. 'Propopamide, m'lord.'

The marquis, intensely gratified, slapped the knee of his dungarees. 'That's it, Propopamide! Damned if I can get my tongue round it. Well done, Charlie!'

Charlie inclined his head modestly.

The whole test was a vast improvement on last time and we were finished within an hour and a half. There was just one tragedy. About half way through, one of the cows dropped down dead with an attack of hypomagnesaemia, a condition which often plagues sucklers. It was a sudden, painless collapse and I had no chance to do anything.

Lord Hulton looked down at the animal which had just stopped breathing. 'Do you think we could salvage her for meat if we bled her?'

'Well, it's typical hypomag. Nothing to harm anybody . . . you could try. It would depend on what the meat inspector says.'

The cow was bled, pulled into a van and the peer drove off to the abattoir. He came back just as we were finishing the test.

'How did you get on?' I asked him. 'Did they accept her?'

He hesitated. 'No . . . no, old chap,' he said sadly. 'I'm afraid they didn't.'

'Why? Did the meat inspector condemn the carcass?'

'Well . . . I never got as far as the meat inspector, actually . . . just saw one of the slaughtermen.'

'And what did he say?'

'Just two words, Herriot.'

'Two words . . . ?'

'Yes . . . "Bugger off!"'

I nodded. 'I see.' It was easy to imagine the scene. The tough slaughterman viewing the small, unimpressive figure and deciding that he wasn't going to be put out of his routine by some ragged farm man.

'Well, never mind, sir,' I said. 'You can only try.'

'True . . . true, old chap.' He dropped a few matches as he fumbled disconsolately with his smoking equipment.

As I was getting into the car I remembered about the Propamidine. 'Don't forget to call down for that cream, will you?'

'By Jove, yes! I'll come down for it after lunch. I have great faith in that Prom . . . Pram . . . Charlie! Damn and blast, what is it?'

Charlie drew himself up proudly. 'Propopamide, m'lord.'

'Ah yes, Propopamide!' The little man laughed, his good humour quite restored. 'Good lad, Charlie, you're a marvel!'

'Thank you, m'lord.' The foreman wore the smug expression of the expert as he drove the cattle back into the field.

It's a funny thing, but when you see a client about something you very often see him soon again about something else. It was only a week later, with the district still in the iron grip of winter, that my bedside 'phone jangled me from slumber.

After that first palpitation of the heart which I feel does vets no good at all I reached a sleepy hand from under the sheets.

'Yes?' I grunted.

'Herriot . . . I say, Herriot . . . is that you, Herriot?' The voice was laden with tension.

'Yes, it is, Lord Hulton.'

'Oh good . . . good . . . dash it, I do apologise. Frightfully bad show, waking you up like this . . . but I've got something damn peculiar here.' A soft pattering followed which I took to be matches falling around the receiver.

'Really?' I yawned and my eyes closed involuntarily. 'In what way, exactly?'

'Well, I've been sitting up with one of my best sows. Been farrowing and produced twelve nice piglets, but there's something very odd.'

'How do you mean?'

'Difficult to describe, old chap . . . but you know the . . . er . . . bottom aperture . . . there's a bloody great long red thing hanging from it.'

My eyes snapped open and my mouth gaped in a soundless scream. Prolapsed uterus! Hard labour in cows, a pleasant exercise in ewes, impossible in sows.

'Long red . . . ! When . . . ? How . . . ?' I was stammering pointlessly. I didn't have to ask.

'Just popped it out, dear boy. I was waiting for another piglet and whoops, there it was. Gave me a nasty turn.'

My toes curled tightly beneath the blankets. It was no good telling him that I had seen five prolapsed uteri in pigs in my limited experience and had failed in every case. I had come to the conclusion that there was no way of putting them back.

But I had to try. 'I'll be right out,' I muttered.

I looked at the alarm clock. It was five thirty. A horrible time, truncating the night's slumber yet eliminating any chance of a soothing return to bed for an hour before the day's work. And I hated turning out even more since my marriage. Helen was lovely to come back to, but by the same token it was a bigger wrench to leave her soft warm presence and venture into the inhospitable world outside.

And the journey to the Hulton farm was not enlivened by my memories of those five other sows. I had tried everything; full anaesthesia, lifting them upside down with pulleys, directing a jet from a hose on the everted organ, and all the time pushing, straining, sweating over the great mass of flesh which refused to go back through that absurdly small hole. The result in each case had been the conversion of my patient into pork pies and a drastic plummeting of my self-esteem.

There was no moon and the soft glow from the piggery door made the only light among the black outlines of the buildings. Lord Hulton was waiting at the entrance and I thought I had better warn him.

'I have to tell you, sir, that this is a very serious condition. It's only fair that you should know that the sow very often has to be slaughtered.'

The little man's eyes widened and the corners of his mouth drooped.

'Oh, I say! That's rather a bore . . . one of my best animals. I . . . I'm rather attached to that pig.' He was wearing a polo-necked sweater of such advanced dilapidation that the hem hung in long woollen fronds almost to his knees, and as he tremblingly attempted to light his pipe he looked very vulnerable.

'But I'll do my very best,' I added hastily. 'There's always a chance.'

'Oh, good man!' In his relief, he dropped his pouch and as he stooped the open box of matches spilled around his feet. It was some time before we retrieved them and went into the piggery.

The reality was as bad as my imaginings. Under the single weak electric bulb of the pen an unbelievable length of very solid-looking red tissue stretched from the rear end of a massive white sow lying immobile on her side. The twelve pink piglets fought and worried along the row of teats; they didn't seem to be getting much.

As I stripped off and dipped my arms into the steaming bucket I wished with all my heart that the porcine uterus was a little short thing and not this horrible awkward shape. And it was a disquieting thought that tonight I had no artificial aids. People used all sorts of tricks and various types of equipment but here in this silent building there was just the pig, Lord Hulton and me. His lordship, I knew, was willing and eager, but he had helped me at jobs before and his usefulness was impaired by the fact that his hands were always filled with his smoking items and he kept dropping things.

I got down on my knees behind the animal with the feeling that I was on my own. And as soon as I cradled the mass in my arms the conviction flooded through me that this was going to be the same as all the others. The very idea of this lot going back whence it came was ridiculous and the impression was reinforced as I began to push. Nothing happened.

I had sedated the sow heavily and she wasn't straining much against me; it was just that the thing was so huge. By a supreme effort I managed to feed a few inches back into the vaginal opening but as soon as I relaxed it popped quietly out again. My strongest instinct was to call the whole thing off without delay; the end result would be the same and anyway I wasn't feeling very strong. In fact my whole being was permeated by the leaden-armed pervading weakness one feels when forced to work in the small hours.

I would try just once more. Lying flat, my naked chest against the cold concrete I fought with the thing till my eyes popped and my breath gave out, but it had not the slightest effect and it made my mind up; I had to tell him.

Rolling over on my back I looked up at him, panting, waiting till I had the wind to speak. I would say, 'Lord Hulton, we are really wasting our time here. This is an impossible case. I am going back home now and I'll ring the slaughterhouse first thing in the morning.' The prospect of escape was beguiling; I might even be able to crawl in beside Helen for an hour. But as my mouth framed the words the little man looked down at me appealingly as though he knew what I was going to say. He tried to smile but darted anxious glances at me, at the pig and back again. From the other end of the animal a soft uncomplaining grunt reminded me that I wasn't the only one involved.

I didn't say anything. I turned back on to my chest, braced my feet against the wall of the pen and began again. I don't know how long I lay there, pushing, relaxing, pushing again as I gasped and groaned and the sweat ran steadily down my back. The peer was silent but I knew he was following my progress intently because every now and then I had to brush matches from the surface of the uterus.

Then for no particular reason the heap of flesh in my arms felt suddenly smaller. I glared desperately at the thing. There was no doubt about it, it was only half the size. I had to take a breather and a hoarse croak escaped me.

'God! I think it's going back!'

I must have startled Lord Hulton in mid fill because I heard a stifled 'What . . . what . . . oh I say, how absolutely splendid!' and a fragrant shower of tobacco cascaded from above.

This was it, then. Summoning the last of my energy for one big effort I blew half an ounce or so of Redbreast Flake from the uterine mucosa and heaved forward. And, miraculously there was little resistance and I stared in disbelief as the great organ disappeared gloriously and wonderfully from sight. I was right behind it with my arm, probing frantically away up to the shoulder as I rotated my wrist again and again till both uterine cornua were fully involuted. When I was certain beyond doubt that everything was back in place I lay there for a few moments, my arm still deep inside the sow, my forehead resting on the floor. Dimly, through the mist of exhaustion I heard Lord Hulton's cries.

'Stout fella! Dash it, how marvellous! Oh stout fella!' He was almost dancing with joy.

One last terror assailed me. What if it came out again? Quickly I seized needle and thread and began to insert a few sutures in the vulva.

'Here, hold this!' I barked, giving him the scissors.

Stitching with the help of Lord Hulton wasn't easy. I kept pushing needle or scissors into his hands then demanding them back peremptorily, and it caused a certain amount of panic. Twice he passed me his pipe to cut the ends of my suture and on one occasion I found myself trying in the dim light to thread the silk through his reaming tool. His lordship suffered too, in his turn, because I heard the occasional stifled oath as he impaled a finger on the needle.

But at last it was done. I rose wearily to my feet and leaned against the wall, my mouth hanging open, sweat trickling into my eyes. The little man's eyes were full of concern as they roved over my limply hanging arms and the caked blood and filth on my chest.

'Herriot, my dear old chap, you're all in! And you'll catch pneumonia or something if you stand around half naked. You need a hot drink. Tell you what – get yourself cleaned up and dressed and I'll run down to the house for something.' He scurried swiftly away.

My aching muscles were slow to obey as I soaped and towelled myself and pulled on my shirt. Fastening my watch round my wrist I saw that it was after seven and I could hear the farm men clattering in the yard outside as they began their morning tasks.

I was buttoning my jacket when the little peer returned. He bore a tray with a pint mug of steaming coffee and two thick slices of bread and honey. He placed it on a bale of straw and pulled up an upturned bucket as a chair before hopping on to a meal bin where he sat like a pixie on a toadstool with his arms around his knees, regarding me with keen anticipation.

'The servants are still abed, old chap,' he said. 'So I made this little bite for you myself.'

I sank on to the bucket and took a long pull at the coffee. It was black and scalding with a kick like a Galloway bullock and it spread like fire through my tired frame. Then I bit into the first slice of bread; home made, plastered thickly with farm butter and topped by a lavish layer of heather honey from the long row of hives I had often seen on the edge of the moor above. I closed my eyes in reverence as I chewed, then as I reached for the pint pot again I looked up at the small figure on the bin.

'May I say, sir, that this isn't a bite, it's a feast. It is all absolutely delicious.'

His face lit up with impish glee. 'Well, dash it . . . do you really think so? I'm so pleased. And you've done nobly, dear boy. Can't tell you how grateful I am.'

As I continued to eat ecstatically, feeling the strength ebbing back, he glanced uneasily into the pen.

'Herriot . . . those stitches. Don't like the look of them much . . .'

'Oh yes,' I said. 'They're just a precaution. You can nick them out in a couple of days.'

'Splendid! But won't they leave a wound? We'd better put something on there.'

I paused in mid chew. Here it was again. He only needed his Propamidine to complete his happiness.

'Yes, old chap, we must apply some of that Prip . . . Prom . . . oh hell and blast, it's no good!' He threw back his head and bellowed, 'Charlie!'

The foreman appeared in the entrance, touching his cap. 'Morning, m'lord.'

'Morning, Charlie. See that this sow gets some of that wonderful cream on her. What the blazes d'you call it again?'

Charlie swallowed and squared his shoulders. 'Propopamide, m'lord.'

The little man threw his arms high in delight. 'Of course, of course! Propopamide! I wonder if I'll ever be able to get that word out?' He looked admiringly at his foreman. 'Charlie, you never fail – I don't know how you do it.'

Charlie bowed gravely in acknowledgement.

Lord Hulton turned to me. 'You'll let us have some more Propopamide, won't you, Herriot?'

'Certainly,' I replied. 'I think I have some in the car.'

Sitting there on the bucket amid the mixed aroma of pig and barley meal and coffee I could almost feel the waves of pleasure beating on me. His lordship was clearly enchanted by the whole business, Charlie was wearing the superior smile which always accompanied his demonstrations of lingual dexterity, and as for myself I was experiencing a mounting euphoria.

I could see into the pen and the sight was rewarding. The little pigs who had been sheltered in a large box during the operation were back with their mother, side by side in a long pink row as their tiny mouths enclosed the teats. The sow seemed to be letting her milk down, too, because there was no frantic scramble for position, just a rapt concentration.

She was a fine pedigree pig and instead of lying on the butcher's slab today she would be starting to bring up her family. As though reading my thoughts she gave a series of contented grunts and the old feeling began to bubble in me, the deep sense of fulfilment and satisfaction that comes from even the smallest triumph and makes our lives worth while.

And there was something else. A new thought stealing into my consciousness with a delicious fresh tingle about it. At this moment, who else in the length and breadth of Britain was eating a breakfast personally prepared and served by a marquis?

Chapter Three

I am afraid of dentists.

I am particularly afraid of strange dentists, so before I went into the RAF I made sure my teeth were in order. Everybody told me they were very strict about the aircrews' teeth and I didn't want some unknown prodding around in my mouth. There had to be no holes anywhere or they would start to ache away up there in the sky, so they said.

So before my call-up I went to old Mr Grover in Darrowby and he painstakingly did all that was necessary. He was good at his job and was always gentle and careful and didn't strike the same terror into me as other dentists. All I felt when I went to his surgery was a dryness of the throat and a quivering at the knees, and providing I kept my eyes tightly shut all the time I managed to get through the visit fairly easily.

My fear of dentists dates back to my earliest experiences in the twenties. As a child I was taken to the dread Hector McDarroch in Glasgow and he did my dental work right up to my teens. Friends of my youth tell me that he inspired a similar lasting fear in them, too, and in fact there must be a whole generation of Glaswegians who feel the same.

Of course you couldn't blame Hector entirely. The equipment in those days was primitive and a visit to any dental practitioner was an ordeal. But Hector, with his booming laugh, was so large and overpowering that he made it worse. Actually he was a very nice man, cheerful and good-natured, but the other side of him blotted it all out.

The electric drill had not yet been invented or if it had, it hadn't reached Scotland, and Hector bored holes in teeth with a fearsome foot-operated machine. There was a great wheel driven by a leather belt and this powered the drill, and as you lay in the chair two things dominated the outlook; the wheel whirring by your ear and Hector's huge knee pistoning almost into your face as he pedalled furiously.

He came from the far north and at the Highland games he used to array himself in kilt and sporran and throw cabers around like matchsticks. He was so big and strong that I always felt hopelessly trapped in that chair with his bulk over me and the wheel grinding and the pedal thumping. He didn't exactly put his foot on my chest but he had me all right.

And it didn't worry him when he got into the sensitive parts with his drill; my strangled cries were of no avail and he carried on remorselessly to the end. I had the impression that Hector thought it was cissy to feel pain, or maybe he was of the opinion that suffering was good for the soul.

Anyway, since those days I've had a marked preference for small frail soft-spoken dentists like Mr Grover. I like to feel that if it came to a stand-up fight I would have a good chance of victory and escape. Also, Mr Grover understood that people were afraid, and that helped. I remember him chuckling when he told me about the big farm men who came to have their teeth extracted. Many a time, he said, he had gone across the room for his instruments and turned back to find the chair empty.

I still don't enjoy going to the dentist but I have to admit that the modern men are wonderful. I hardly see mine when I go. Just a brief glimpse of a white coat then all is done from behind. Fingers come round, things go in and out of my mouth but even when I venture to open my eyes I see nothing.

Hector McDarroch, on the other hand, seemed to take a pleasure in showing off his grisly implements, filling the long-needled syringe right in front of my eyes and squirting the cocaine ceilingwards a few times before he started on me. And worse, before an extraction he used to clank about in a tin box, producing a series of hideous forceps and examining them, whistling softly, till he found the right one.

So with all this in mind, as I sat in a long queue of airmen for the preliminary examination, I was thankful I had been to Mr Grover for a complete check-up. A dentist stood by a chair at the end of the long room and he examined the young men in blue one by one before calling out his findings to an orderly at a desk.

I derived considerable entertainment from watching the expressions on the lads' faces when the call went out. 'Three fillings, two extractions!' 'Eight fillings!' Most of them looked stunned, some thunderstruck, others almost tearful. Now and again one would try to expostulate with the man in white but it was no good; nobody was listening. At times I could have laughed out loud. Mind you, I felt a bit mean at being amused, but after all they had only themselves to blame. If only they had shown my foresight they would have had nothing to worry about.

When my name was called I strolled across, humming a little tune, and dropped nonchalantly into the chair. It didn't take the man long. He poked his way swiftly along my teeth then rapped out, 'Five fillings and one extraction!'

I sat bolt upright and stared at him in amazement.

'But . . . but . . .' I began to yammer, 'I had a check up by my own . . .'

'Next, please,' murmured the dentist.

'But Mr Grover said . . .'

'Next man! Move along!' bawled the orderly, and as I shuffled away I gazed appealingly at the white-coated figure. But he was reciting a list of my premolars and incisors and showed no interest.

I was still trembling when I was handed the details of my fate.

'Report at Regent Lodge tomorrow morning for the extraction,' the WAAF girl said.

Tomorrow morning! By God, they didn't mess about! And what the heck did it all mean, anyway? My teeth were perfectly sound. There was only that one with the bit of enamel chipped off. Mr Grover had pointed it out and said it wouldn't give any trouble. It was the tooth that held my pipe – surely it couldn't be that one.

But there came the disquieting thought that my opinion didn't matter. When my feeble protests were ignored back there it hit me for the first time that I wasn't a civilian any more.

Next morning the din from the dustbin lids had hardly subsided when the grim realisation drove into my brain. I was going to have a tooth out today! And very soon, too. I passed the intervening hours in growing apprehension; morning parade, the march through the darkness to breakfast. The dried egg and fried bread were less attractive than ever and the grey day had hardly got under way before I was approaching the forbidding façade of Regent Lodge.

As I climbed the steps my palms began to sweat. I didn't like having my teeth drilled but extractions were infinitely worse. Something in me recoiled from the idea of having a part of myself torn away by force, even if it didn't hurt. But of course, I told myself as I walked along an echoing corridor, it never did hurt nowadays. Just a little prick, then nothing.

I was nurturing this comforting thought when I turned into a large assembly room with numbered doors leading from it. About thirty airmen sat around wearing a variety of expressions from sickly smiles to tough bravado. A chilling smell of antiseptic hung on the air. I chose a chair and settled down to wait. I had been in the armed forces long enough to know that you waited a long time for everything and I saw no reason why a dental appointment should be any different.

As I sat down the man on my left gave me a brief nod. He was fat, and greasy black hair fell over his pimpled brow. Though engrossed in picking his teeth with a match he gave me a long appraising stare before addressing me in rich cockney.

'What room you goin' in, mate?'

I looked at my card. 'Room four.'

'Blimey, mate, you've 'ad it!' He removed his matchstick and grinned wolfishly.

'Had it . . . ? What do you mean?'

'Well, haven't you 'eard? That's The Butcher in there.'

'The . . . The . . . Butcher?' I quavered.

'Yeh, that's what they call the dental officer in there.' He gave an expansive smile. 'He's a right killer, that bloke, I'll tell yer.'

I swallowed. 'Butcher . . . ? Killer . . . ? Oh come on. They'll all be the same, I'm sure.'

'Don't you believe it, mate. There's good an' there's bad, and that bloke's pure murder. It shouldn't be allowed.'

'How do you know, anyway?'

He waved an airy hand. 'Oh I've been 'ere a few times and I've heard some bleedin' awful screams comin' out of that room. Spoken to some of the chaps afterwards, too. They all call 'im The Butcher.'

I rubbed my hands on the rough blue of my trousers. 'Oh you hear these tales. I'm sure they're exaggerated.'

'Well, you'll find out, mate.' He resumed his tooth picking. 'But don't say I didn't tell you.'

He went on about various things but I only half heard him. His name, it seemed, was Simkin, and he was not an aircrew cadet like the rest of us but a regular and a member of the groundstaff; he worked in the kitchens. He spoke scornfully of us raw recruits and pointed out that we would have to 'get some service in' before we were fit to associate with the real members of the Royal

Air Force. I noticed, however, that despite his own years of alleigance he was still an AC2 like myself.

Almost an hour passed with my heart thumping every time the door of number four opened. I had to admit that the young men leaving that room all looked a bit shattered and one almost reeled out, holding his mouth with both hands.

'Cor! Look at that poor bugger!' Simkin drawled with ill-concealed satisfaction. 'Strike me! He's been through it, poor bleeder. I'm glad I'm not in your shoes, mate.'

I could feel the tension mounting in me. 'What room are you going into, anyway?' I asked.

He did a bit of deep exploration with his match. 'Room two, mate. I've been in there before. He's a grand bloke, one of the best. Never 'urts you.'

'Well you're lucky, aren't you?'

'Not lucky, mate.' He paused and stabbed his match at me. 'I know my way around, that's all. There's ways and means.' He allowed one eyelid to drop briefly.

The conversation was abruptly terminated as the dread door opened and a WAAF came out.

'AC2 Herriot!' she called.

I got up on shaking limbs and took a deep breath. As I set off I had a fleeting glimpse of the leer of pure delight on Simkin's face. He was really enjoying himself.

As I passed the portals my feeling of doom increased. The Butcher was another Hector McDarroch; about six feet two with rugby forward shoulders bulging his white coat. My flesh crept as he unleashed a hearty laugh and motioned me towards the chair.

As I sat down I decided to have one last try.

'Is this the tooth?' I asked, tapping the only possible suspect.

'It is indeed!' boomed The Butcher. 'That's the one.'

'Ah well,' I said with a light laugh. 'I'm sure I can explain. There's been some mistake . . .'

'Yes . . . yes . . .' he murmured, filling the syringe before my eyes and sending a few playful spurts into the air.

'There's just a bit of enamel off it, and Mr Grover said . . .'

The WAAF suddenly wound the chair back and I found myself in the semi-prone position with the white bulk looming over me.

'You see,' I gasped desperately. 'I need that tooth. It's the one that holds my . . .'

A strong finger was on my gum and I felt the needle going in. I resigned myself to my fate.

When he had inserted the local the big man put the syringe down. 'We'll just give that a minute or two,' he said, and left the room.

As soon as the door closed behind him the WAAF tiptoed over to me.

'This feller's loopy!' she whispered.

Half lying, I stared at her.

'Loopy . . . ? What d'you mean?'

'Crackers! Round the bend! No idea how to pull teeth!'

'But . . . but . . . he's a dentist isn't he . . . ?'

She pulled a wry face, 'Thinks he is! But he hasn't a clue!'

I had no time to explore this cheering information further because the door opened and the big man returned.

He seized a horrible pair of forceps and I closed my eyes as he started flexing his muscles.

I must admit I felt nothing. I knew he was twisting and tugging away up there but the local had mercifully done its job. I was telling myself that it would soon be over when I heard a sharp crack.

I opened my eyes. The Butcher was gazing disappointedly at my broken-off tooth in his forceps. The root was still in my gum.

Behind him the WAAF gave me a long 'I told you so' nod. She was a pretty little thing, but I fear the libido of the young men she encountered in here would be at a low ebb.

'Oh!' The Butcher grunted and began to rummage in a metal box. It took me right back to the McDarroch days as he fished out one forceps after another, opened and shut them a few times then tried them on me.

But it was of no avail, and as the time passed I was the unwilling witness of the gradual transition from heartiness to silence, then to something like panic. The man was clearly whacked. He had no idea how to shift that root.

He must have been gouging for half an hour when an idea seemed to strike him. Pushing all the forceps to one side he almost ran from the room and reappeared shortly with a tray on which reposed a long chisel and a metal mallet.

At a sign from him the WAAF wound the chair back till I was completely horizontal. Seemingly familiar with the routine, she cradled my head in her arms in a practised manner and stood waiting.

This couldn't be true, I thought, as the man inserted the chisel into my mouth and poised the mallet; but all doubts were erased as the metal rod thudded against the remnants of my tooth and my head in turn shot back into the little WAAF's bosom. And that was how it went on. I lost count of time as The Butcher banged away and the girl hung on grimly to my jerking skull.

The thought uppermost in my mind was that I had always wondered how young horses felt when I knocked wolf teeth out of them. Now I knew.

When it finally stopped I opened my eyes, and though by this time I was prepared for anything I still felt slightly surprised to see The Butcher threading a needle with a length of suture silk. He was sweating and looking just a little desperate as he bent over me yet again.

'Just a couple of stitches,' he muttered hoarsely, and I closed my eyes again.

When I left the chair I felt very strange indeed. The assault on my cranium had made me dizzy and the sensation of the long ends of the stitches tickling my tongue was distinctly odd. I'm sure that when I came out of the room I was staggering, and instinctively I pawed at my mouth.

The first man I saw was Simkin. He was there where I had left him but he looked different as he beckoned excitedly to me. I went over and he caught at my tunic with one hand.

'What d'yer think, mate?' he gasped. 'They've changed me round and I've got to go into room four.' He gulped. 'You looked bloody awful comin' out there. What was it like?'

I looked at him. Maybe there was going to be a gleam of light this morning. I sank into the chair next to him and groaned.

'By God, you weren't kidding! I've never met anybody like that – he's half killed me. They don't call him The Butcher for nothing!'

'Why ... what ... what did 'e do?'

'Nothing much. Just knocked my tooth out with a hammer and chisel, that's all.'

'Garn! You're 'avin' me on!' Simkin made a ghastly attempt to smile.

'Word of honour,' I said. 'Anyway, there's the tray coming out now. Look for yourself.'

He stared at the WAAF carrying the dreadful implements and turned very pale.

'Oh blimey! What . . . what else did 'e do?'

I held my jaw for a moment. 'Well he did something I've never seen before. He made such a great hole in my gum that he had to stitch me up afterwards.'

Simkin shook his head violently. 'Naow, I'm not 'avin' that! I don't believe yer!'

'All right,' I said. 'What do you think of this?'

I leaned forward, put my thumb under my lip and jerked it up to give him a close-up view of the long gash and the trailing blood-stained ends of the stitches.

He shrank away from me, lips trembling, eyes wide.

'Gawd!' he moaned. 'Oh Gawd . . . !'

It was unfortunate that the WAAF chose that particular moment to call out 'AC2 Simkin' piercingly from the doorway, because the poor fellow leaped as though a powerful electric current had passed through him. Then, head down, he trailed across the room. At the door he turned and gave me a last despairing look and I saw him no more.

This experience deepened my dread of the five fillings which awaited me. But I needn't have worried; they were trivial things and were efficiently and painlessly dealt with by RAF dentists very different from The Butcher.

And yet, many years after the war had ended, the man from room four stretched out a long arm from the past and touched me on the shoulder. I began to feel something sharp coming through the roof of my mouth and went to Mr Grover, who X-rayed me and showed me a pretty picture of that fateful root still there despite the hammer and chisel. He extracted it and the saga was ended.

The Butcher remained a vivid memory because, apart from my ordeal, I was constantly reminded of him by the dangerous wobbling of my pipe at the edge of that needless gap in my mouth.

But I did have a small solace. I finished my visit to room four with a parting shaft which gave me a little comfort. As I tottered away I paused and addressed the big man's back as he prepared for his next victim.

'By the way,' I said. 'I've knocked out a lot of teeth just like you did there.'

He turned and stared at me. 'Really? Are you a dentist?'

'No,' I replied over my shoulder as I left. 'I'm a vet!'

Chapter Four

I like women better than men.

Mind you, I have nothing against men – after all, I am one myself – but in the RAF there were too many of them. Literally thousands, jostling, shouting, swearing; you couldn't get away from them. Some of them became my friends and have remained so until the present day, but the sheer earthy mass of them made me realise how my few months of married life had changed me.

Women are gentler, softer, cleaner, altogether nicer things and I, who always considered myself one of the boys, had come to the surprising conclusion that the companion I wanted most was a woman.

My impression that I had been hurled into a coarser world was heightened at the beginning of each day, particularly one morning when I was on fire picket duty and had the sadistic pleasure of rattling the dustbin lids and shouting 'Wakey-wakey!' along the corridors. It wasn't the cursing and the obscene remarks which struck deepest, it was the extraordinary abdominal noises issuing from the dark rooms. They reminded me of my patient, Cedric, and in an instant I was back in Darrowby answering the telephone.

The voice at the other end was oddly hesitant.

'Mr Herriot . . . I should be grateful if you would come and see my dog.' It was a woman, obviously upper class.

'Certainly. What's the trouble?'

'Well . . . he . . . er . . . he seems to suffer from . . . a certain amount of flatus.'

'I beg your pardon?'

There was a long pause. 'He has. . . . excessive flatus.'

'In what way, exactly?'

'Well . . . I suppose you'd describe it as . . . windiness.' The voice had begun to tremble.

I thought I could see a gleam of light. 'You mean his stomach . . .?'

'No, not his stomach. He passes . . . er . . . a considerable quantity of . . . wind from his . . . his . . .' A note of desperation had crept in.

'Ah, yes!' All became suddenly clear. 'I quite understand. But that doesn't sound very serious. Is he ill?'

'No, he's very fit in other ways.'

'Well then, do you think it's necessary for me to see him?'

'Oh yes, indeed, Mr Herriot. I wish you would come as soon as possible. It has become quite . . . quite a problem.'

'All right,' I said. 'I'll look in this morning. Can I have your name and address, please?'

'It's Mrs Rumney, The Laurels.'

The Laurels was a very nice house on the edge of the town standing back from the road in a large garden. Mrs Rumney herself let me in and I felt a shock of surprise at my first sight of her. It wasn't just that she was strikingly beautiful; there was an unworldly air about her. She would be around forty but had the appearance of a heroine in a Victorian novel – tall, willowy, ethereal. And I could understand immediately her hesitation on the 'phone. Everything about her suggested fastidiousness and delicacy.

'Cedric is in the kitchen,' she said. 'I'll take you through.'

I had another surprise when I saw Cedric. An enormous Boxer hurled himself on me in delight, clawing at my chest with the biggest, horniest feet I had seen for a long time. I tried to fight him off but he kept at me, panting ecstatically into my face and wagging his entire rear end.

'Sit down, boy!' the lady said sharply, then, as Cedric took absolutely no notice, she turned to me nervously. 'He's so friendly.'

'Yes,' I said breathlessly, 'I can see that.' I finally managed to push the huge animal away and backed into a corner for safety. 'How often does this . . . excessive flatus occur?'

As if in reply an almost palpable sulphurous wave arose from the dog and eddied around me. It appeared that the excitement of seeing me had activated Cedric's weakness. I was up against the wall and unable to obey my first instinct to run for cover so I held my hand over my face for a few moments before speaking.

'Is that what you meant?'

Mrs Rumney waved a lace handkerchief under her nose and the faintest flush crept into the pallor of her cheeks.

'Yes,' she replied almost inaudibly 'Yes . . . that is it.'

'Oh well,' I said briskly. 'There's nothing to worry about. Let's go into the other room and we'll have a word about his diet and a few other things.'

It turned out that Cedric was getting rather a lot of meat and I drew up a little chart cutting down the protein and adding extra carbohydrates. I prescribed a kaolin antacid mixture to be given night and morning and left the house in a confident frame of mind.

It was one of those trivial things and I had entirely forgotten it when Mrs Rumney 'phoned again.

'I'm afraid Cedric is no better, Mr Herriot.'

'Oh I'm sorry to hear that. He's still . . . er . . . still . . . yes . . . yes . . .' I spent a few moments in thought. 'I tell you what – I don't think I can do any more by seeing him at the moment, but I think you should cut out his meat completely for a week or two. Keep him on biscuits and brown bread rusked in the oven. Try him with that and vegetables and I'll give you some powder to mix in his food. Perhaps you'd call round for it.'

The powder was a pretty strong absorbent mixture and I felt sure it would do the trick, but a week later Mrs Rumney was on the 'phone again.

'There's absolutely no improvement, Mr Herriot.' The tremble was back in her voice. 'I . . . I do wish you'd come and see him again.'

I couldn't see much point in viewing this perfectly healthy animal again but I promised to call. I had a busy day and it was after six o'clock before I got round to The Laurels. There were several cars in the drive and when I went into the house I saw that Mrs Rumney had a few people in for drinks; people like herself – upper class and of obvious refinement. In fact I felt rather a lout in my working clothes among the elegant gathering.

Mrs Rumney was about to lead me through to the kitchen when the door burst open and Cedric bounded delightedly into the midst of the company. Within seconds an aesthetic-looking gentleman was frantically beating off the attack as the great feet ripped down his waistcoat. He got away at the cost of a couple of buttons and the Boxer turned his attention to one of the ladies. She was in imminent danger of losing her dress when I pulled the dog off her.

Pandemonium broke out in the graceful room. The hostess's plaintive appeals rang out above the cries of alarm as the big dog charged around, but very soon I realised that a more insidious element had crept into the situation. The atmosphere in the room became rapidly charged with an unmistakable effluvium and it was clear that Cedric's unfortunate malady had reasserted itself.

I did my best to shepherd the animal out of the room but he didn't seem to know the meaning of obedience and I chased him in vain. And as the embarrassing minutes ticked away I began to realise for the first time the enormity of the problem which confronted Mrs Rumney. Most dogs break wind occasionally but Cedric was different; he did it all the time. And while his silent emanations were perhaps more treacherous there was no doubt that the audible ones were painfully distressing in a company like this.

Cedric made it worse, because at each rasping expulsion he would look round enquiringly at his back end then gambol about the room as though the fugitive zephyr was clearly visible to him and he was determined to corner it.

It seemed a year before I got him out of there. Mrs Rumney held the door wide as I finally managed to steer him towards it but the big dog wasn't finished yet. On his way out he cocked a leg swiftly and directed a powerful jet against an immaculate trouser leg.

After that night I threw myself into the struggle on Mrs Rumney's behalf.

I felt she desperately needed my help, and I made frequent visits and tried innumerable remedies. I consulted my colleague Siegfried on the problem and he suggested a diet of charcoal biscuits. Cedric ate them in vast quantities and with evident enjoyment but they, like everything else, made not the slightest difference to his condition.

And all the time I pondered upon the enigma of Mrs Rumney. She had lived in Darrowby for several years but the townsfolk knew little about her. It was a matter of debate whether she was a widow or separated from her husband. But I was not interested in such things; the biggest mystery to me was how she ever got involved with a dog like Cedric.

It was difficult to think of any animal less suited to her personality. Apart from his regrettable affliction he was in every way the opposite to herself; a great thick-headed rumbustious extrovert totally out of place in her gracious menage. I never did find out how they came together but on my visits I found that Cedric had one admirer at least.

He was Con Fenton, a retired farm worker who did a bit of jobbing gardening and spent an average of three days a week at The Laurels. The Boxer romped down the drive after me as I was leaving and the old man looked at him with undisguised admiration.

'By gaw,' he said. 'He's a fine dog, is that!'

'Yes, he is, Con, he's a good chap really.' And I meant it. You couldn't help liking Cedric when you got to know him. He was utterly amiable and without vice and he gave off a constant aura not merely of noxious vapours but of bonhomie. When he tore off people's buttons or sprinkled their trousers he did it in a spirit of the purest amity.

'Just look at them limbs!' breathed Con, staring rapturously at the dog's muscular thighs. 'By heck, 'e can jump ower that gate as if it weren't there. He's what ah call a dog!'

As he spoke it struck me that Cedric would be likely to appeal to him because he was very like the Boxer himself; not over-burdened with brains, built like an ox with powerful shoulders and a big constantly-grinning face – they were two of a kind.

'Aye, ah allus likes it when t'missus lets him out in t'garden.' Con went on. He always spoke in a peculiar snuffling manner. 'He's grand company.'

I looked at him narrowly. No, he wouldn't be likely to notice Cedric's complaint since he always saw him out of doors.

On my way back to the surgery I brooded on the fact that I was achieving absolutely nothing with my treatment. And though it seemed ridiculous to worry about a case like this, there was no doubt the thing had begun to prey on my mind. In fact I began to transmit my anxieties to Siegfried. As I got out of the car he was coming down the steps of Skeldale House and he put a hand on my arm.

'You've been to The Laurels, James? Tell me,' he enquired solicitously, 'how is your farting Boxer today?'

'Still at it, I'm afraid,' I replied, and my colleague shook his head in commiseration.

We were both defeated. Maybe if chlorophyll tablets had been available in those days they might have helped but as it was I had tried everything. It seemed certain that nothing would alter the situation. And it wouldn't have been so bad if the owner had been anybody else but Mrs Rumney; I found that even discussing the thing with her had become almost unbearable.

Siegfried's student brother Tristan didn't help, either. When seeing practice he was very selective in the cases he wished to observe, but he was immediately attracted to Cedric's symptoms and insisted on coming with me on one occasion.

I never took him again because as we went in the big dog bounded from his mistress' side and produced a particularly sonorous blast as if in greeting.

Tristan immediately threw out a hand in a dramatic gesture and declaimed: 'Speak on, sweet lips that never told a lie!' That was his only visit. I had enough trouble without that.

I didn't know it at the time but a greater blow awaited me. A few days later Mrs Rumney was on the 'phone again.

'Mr Herriot, a friend of mine has such a sweet little Boxer bitch. She wants to bring her along to be mated with Cedric.'

'Eh?'

'She wants to mate her bitch with my dog.'

'With Cedric . . .?' I clutched at the edge of the desk. It couldn't be true! 'And . . . and are you agreeable?'

'Yes, of course.'

I shook my head to dispel the feeling of unreality. I found it incomprehensible that anyone should want to reproduce Cedric, and as I gaped into the receiver a frightening vision floated before me of eight little Cedrics all with his complaint. But of course such a thing wasn't hereditary. I took a grip of myself and cleared my throat.

'Very well, then, Mrs Rumney, you'd better go ahead.'

There was a pause. 'But Mr Herriot, I want you to supervise the mating.'

'Oh really, I don't think that's necessary.' I dug my nails into my palm. 'I think you'll be all right without me.'

'Oh but I would be much happier if you were there. Please come,' she said appealingly.

Instead of emitting a long-drawn groan I took a deep breath.

'Right,' I said. 'I'll be along in the morning.'

All that evening I was obsessed by a feeling of dread. Another acutely embarrassing session was in store with this exquisite woman. Why was it I always had to share things like this with her? And I really feared the worst. Even the daftest dog, when confronted with a bitch in heat, knows instinctively how to proceed, but with a really ivory-skulled animal like Cedric I wondered . . .

And next morning all my fears were realised. The bitch, Trudy, was a trim little creature and showed every sign of willingness to cooperate. Cedric, on the other hand, though obviously delighted to meet her, gave no hint of doing his part. After sniffing her over, he danced around her a few times, goofy-faced, tongue lolling. Then he had a roll on the lawn before charging at her and coming to a full stop, big feet outsplayed, head down, ready to play. I sighed. It was as I thought. The big chump didn't know what to do.

This pantomime went on for some time and, inevitably, the emotional strain brought on a resurgence of his symptoms. Frequently he paused to inspect his tail as though he had never heard noises like that before.

He varied his dancing routine with occasional headlong gallops round the lawn and it was after he had done about ten successive laps that he seemed to decide he ought to do something about the bitch. I held my breath as he approached her but unfortunately he chose the wrong end to commence operations. Trudy had put up with his nonsense with great patience but when she found him busily working away in the region of her left ear it was too much. With a shrill yelp she nipped him in the hind leg and he shot away in alarm.

After that whenever he came near she warned him off with bared teeth. Clearly she was disenchanted with her bridegroom and I couldn't blame her.

'I think she's had enough, Mrs Rumney,' I said.

I certainly had had enough and so had the poor lady, judging by her slight breathlessness, flushed cheeks and waving handkerchief.

'Yes ... yes ... I suppose you're right,' she replied.

So Trudy was taken home and that was the end of Cedric's career as a stud dog.

This last episode decided me. I had to have a talk with Mrs Rumney and a few days later I called in at The Laurels.

'Maybe you'll think it's none of my business,' I said. 'But I honestly don't think Cedric is the dog for you. In fact he's so wrong for you that he is upsetting your life.'

Mrs Rumney's eyes widened. 'Well ... he is a problem in some ways ... but what do you suggest?'

'I think you should get another dog in his place. Maybe a poodle or a corgi – something smaller, something you could control.'

'But Mr Herriot, I couldn't possibly have Cedric put down.' Her eyes filled quickly with tears. 'I really am fond of him despite his ... despite everything.'

'No, no, of course not!' I said. 'I like him too. He has no malice in him. But I think I have a good idea. Why not let Con Fenton have him?'

'Con ...?'

'Yes, he admires Cedric tremendously and the big fellow would have a good life with the old man. He has a couple of fields behind his cottage and keeps a few beasts. Cedric could run to his heart's content out there and Con would be able to bring him along when he does the garden. You'd still see him three times a week.'

Mrs Rumney looked at me in silence for a few moments and I saw in her face the dawning of relief and hope.

'You know, Mr Herriot, I think that could work very well. But are you sure Con would take him?'

'I'd like to bet on it. An old bachelor like him must be lonely. There's only one thing worries me. Normally they only meet outside and I wonder how it would be when they were indoors and Cedric started to ... when the old trouble ...'

'Oh, I think that would be all right,' Mrs Rumney broke in quickly. 'When I go on holiday Con always takes him for a week or two and he has never mentioned any ... anything unusual ... in that way.'

I got up to go. 'Well, that's fine. I should put it to the old man right away.'

Mrs Rumney rang within a few days. Con had jumped at the chance of taking on Cedric and the pair had apparently settled in happily together. She had also taken my advice and acquired a poodle puppy.

I didn't see the new dog till it was nearly six months old and its mistress asked me to call to treat it for a slight attack of eczema. As I sat in the graceful room looking at Mrs Rumney, cool, poised, tranquil, with the little white creature resting on her knee I wouldn't help feeling how right and fitting the whole scene was. The lush carpet, the trailing velvet curtains, the fragile tables with their load of expensive china and framed miniatures. It was no place for Cedric.

Con Fenton's cottage was less than half a mile away and on my way back to the surgery, on an impulse I pulled up at the door. The old man answered my knock and his big face split into a delighted grin when he saw me.

'Come in, young man!' he cried in his strange snuffly voice. 'I'm right glad to see tha!'

I had hardly stepped into the tiny living room when a hairy form hurled itself upon me. Cedric hadn't changed a bit and I had to battle my way to the broken

armchair by the fireside. Con settled down opposite and when the Boxer leaped
to lick his face he clumped him companionably on the head with his fist.

'Siddown, ye great daft bugger,' he murmured with affection. Cedric sank
happily on to the tattered hearthrug at his feet and gazed up adoringly at his
new master.

'Well, Mr Herriot,' Con went on as he cut up some villainous-looking plug
tobacco and began to stuff it into his pipe. 'I'm right grateful to ye for gettin'
me this grand dog. By gaw, he's a topper and ah wouldn't sell 'im for any
money. No man could ask for a better friend.'

'Well that's great, Con,' I said. 'And I can see that the big chap is really
happy here.'

The old man ignited his pipe and a cloud of acrid smoke rose to the low,
blackened beams. 'Aye, he's 'ardly ever inside. A gurt strong dog like 'im wants
to work 'is energy off, like.'

But just at that moment Cedric was obviously working something else off
because the familiar pungency rose from him even above the billowings from the
pipe. Con seemed oblivious of it but in the enclosed space I found it overpowering.

'Ah well,' I gasped. 'I just looked in for a moment to see how you were getting
on together. I must be on my way.' I rose hurriedly and stumbled towards the
door but the redolence followed me in a wave. As I passed the table with the
remains of the old man's meal I saw what seemed to be the only form of
ornament in the cottage, a cracked vase holding a magnificent bouquet of
carnations. It was a way of escape and I buried my nose in their fragrance.

Con watched me approvingly. 'Aye, they're lovely flowers aren't they?
T'missus at Laurels lets me bring 'ome what I want and I reckon them carnations
is me favourite.'

'Yes, they're a credit to you.' I still kept my nose among the blooms.

'There's only one thing,' the old man said pensively. 'Ah don't get t'full benefit
of 'em.'

'How's that, Con?'

He pulled at his pipe a couple of times, 'Well, you can hear ah speak a bit
funny, like?'

'No . . . no . . . not really.'

'Oh aye, ye know ah do. I've been like it since I were a lad I 'ad a operation
for adenoids and summat went wrong.'

'Oh, I'm sorry to hear that,' I said.

'Well, it's nowt serious, but it's left me lackin' in one way.'

'You mean . . .?' A light was beginning to dawn in my mind, an elucidation
of how man and dog had found each other, of why their relationship was so
perfect, of the certainty of their happy future together. It seemed like fate.

'Aye,' the old man went on sadly. 'I 'ave no sense of smell.'

Chapter Five

I think it was when I saw the London policeman wagging a finger at a scowling
urchin that I thought of Wesley Binks and the time he put the firework through
the surgery letter box.

It was what they used to call a 'banger' and it exploded at my feet as I hurried along the dark passage in answer to the door bell's ring, making me leap into the air in terror.

I threw open the front door and looked into the street. It was empty, but at the corner where the lamplight was reflected in Robson's shop window I had a brief impression of a fleeing form and a faint echo of laughter. I couldn't do anything about it but I knew Wes was out there somewhere.

Wearily I trailed back into the house. Why did this lad persecute me? What could a ten-year-old boy possibly have against me? I had never done him any harm, yet I seemed to be the object of a deliberate campaign.

Or maybe it wasn't personal. It could be that he felt I represented authority or the establishment in some way, or perhaps I was just convenient.

I was certainly the ideal subject for his little tricks of ringing the door bell and running away, because I dared not ignore the summons in case it might be a client, and also the consulting and operating rooms were such a long way from the front of the house. Sometimes I was dragged down from our bed-sitter under the tiles. Every trip to the door was an expedition and it was acutely exasperating to arrive there and see only a little figure in the distance dancing about and grimacing at me.

He varied this routine by pushing rubbish through the letter box, pulling the flowers from the tiny strip of garden we tried to cultivate between the flagstones and chalking rude messages on my car.

I knew I wasn't the only victim because I had heard complaints from others; the fruiterer who saw his apples disappear from the box in front of the shop, the grocer who unwillingly supplied him with free biscuits.

He was the town naughty boy all right, and it was incongruous that he should have been named Wesley. There was not the slightest sign in his behaviour of any strict methodist upbringing. In fact I knew nothing of his family life – only that he came from the poorest part of the town, a row of 'yards' containing tumbledown cottages, some of them evacuated because of their condition.

I often saw him wandering about in the fields and lanes or fishing in quiet reaches of the river when he should have been in school. When he spotted me on these occasions he invariably called out some mocking remark and if he happened to be with some of his cronies they all joined in the laughter at my expense. It was annoying but I used to tell myself that there was nothing personal in it. I was an adult and that was enough to make me a target.

Wes's greatest triumph was undoubtedly the time he removed the grating from the coal cellar outside Skeldale House. It was on the left of the front steps and underneath it was a steep ramp down which the coalmen tipped their bags.

I don't know whether it was inspired intuition but he pinched the grating on the day of the Darrowby Gala. The festivities started with a parade through the town led by the Houlton Silver Band and as I looked down from the windows of our bed-sitter I could see them all gathering in the street below.

'Look, Helen,' I said. 'They must be starting the march from Trengate. Everybody I know seems to be down there.'

Helen leaned over my shoulder and gazed at the long lines of boy scouts, girl guides, ex-servicemen, with half the population of the town packed on the pavements, watching. 'Yes, it's quite a sight, isn't it? Let's go down and see them move off.'

We trotted down the long flights of stairs and I followed her out through the front door. And as I appeared in the entrance I was suddenly conscious that I was the centre of attention. The citizens on the pavements, waiting patiently for the parade to start, had something else to look at now. The little brownies and wolf cubs waved at me from their ranks and there were nods and smiles from the people across the road and on all sides.

I could divine their thoughts. 'There's t'young vitnery coming out of his house. Not long married, too. That's his missus next to him.'

A feeling of wellbeing rose in me. I don't know whether other newly married men feel the same, but in those early days I was aware of a calm satisfaction and fulfilment. And I was proud to be the 'vitnery' and part of the life of the town. There was my plate on the wall beside me, a symbol of my solid importance. I was a man of substance now, I had arrived.

Looking around me, I acknowledged the greeting with a few dignified little smiles, raising a gracious hand now and then rather like a royal personage on view. Then I noticed that Helen hadn't much room by my side, so I stepped to the left to where the grating should have been and slid gracefully down into the cellar.

It would be a dramatic touch to say I disappeared from view; in fact I wish I had, because I would have stayed down there and avoided further embarrassment. But as it was I travelled only so far down the ramp and stuck there with my head and shoulders protruding into the street.

My little exhibition caused a sensation among the spectators. Nothing in the Gala parade could compete with this. One or two of the surrounding faces expressed alarm but loud laughter was the general response. The adults were almost holding each other up but the little brownies and wolf cubs made my most appreciative audience, breaking their ranks and staggering about helplessly in the roadway while their leaders tried to restore order.

I caused chaos, too, in the Houlton Silver Band, who were hoisting their instruments prior to marching off. If they had any ideas about bursting into tune they had to abandon them temporarily because I don't think any of them had breath to blow.

It was, in fact, two of the bandsmen who extricated me by linking their hands under my armpits. My wife was of no service at all in the crisis and I could only look up at her reproachfully as she leaned against the doorpost dabbing at her eyes.

It all became clear to me when I reached street level. I was flicking the coal dust from my trousers and trying to look unconcerned when I saw Wesley Binks doubled up with mirth, pointing triumphantly at me and at the hole over the cellar. He was quite near, jostling among the spectators, and I had my first close look at the wild-eyed little goblin who had plagued me. I may have made an unconscious movement towards him because he gave me a last malevolent grin and disappeared into the crowd.

Later I asked Helen about him. She could only tell me that Wesley's father had left home when he was about six years old, that his mother had remarried and the boy now lived with her and his stepfather.

Strangely, I had another opportunity to study him quite soon afterwards. It was about a week later and my feathers were still a little ruffled after the grating incident when I saw him sitting all alone in the waiting room. Alone, that is, except for a skinny black dog in his lap.

I could hardly believe it. I had often rehearsed the choice phrases which I would use on this very occasion but the sight of the animal restrained me; if he had come to consult me professionally I could hardly start pitching into him right away. Maybe later.

I pulled on a white coat and went in.

'Well, what can I do for you?' I asked coldly.

The boy stood up and his expression of mixed defiance and desperation showed that it had cost him something to enter this house.

'Summat matter wi' me dog,' he muttered.

'Right, bring him through.' I led the way along the passage to the consulting room.

'Put him on the table please,' I said, and as he lifted the little animal I decided that I couldn't let this opportunity pass. While I was carrying out my examination I would quite casually discuss recent events. Nothing nasty, no clever phrases, just a quiet probe into the situation. I was just about to say something like 'What's the idea of all those tricks you play on me?' when I took my first look at the dog and everything else fled from my mind.

He wasn't much more than a big puppy and an out-and-out mongrel. His shiny black coat could have come from a labrador and there was a suggestion of terrier in the pointed nose and pricked ears, but the long string-like tail and the knock-kneed fore limbs baffled me. For all that he was an attractive little creature with a sweetly expressive face.

But the things that seized my whole attention were the yellow blobs of pus in the corners of the eyes, the muco-purulent discharge from the nostrils and the photophobia which made the dog blink painfully at the light from the surgery window.

Classical canine distemper is so easy to diagnose but there is never any satisfaction in doing so.

'I didn't know you had a dog,' I said. 'How long have you had him?'

'A month. Feller got 'im from t'dog and cat home at Hartington and sold 'im to me.'

'I see.' I took the temperature and was not surprised to find it was 104°F.

'How old is he?'

'Nine months.'

I nodded. Just about the worst age.

I went ahead and asked all the usual questions but I knew the answers already.

Yes, the dog had been slightly off colour for a week or two. No, he wasn't really ill, but listless and coughing occasionally. And of course it was not until the eyes and nose began to discharge that the boy became worried and brought him to see me. That was when we usually saw these cases – when it was too late.

Wesley imparted the information defensively, looking at me under lowered brows as though he expected me to clip his ear at any moment. But as I studied him any aggressive feelings I may have harboured evaporated quickly. The imp of hell appeared on closer examination to be a neglected child. His elbows stuck out through holes in a filthy jersey, his shorts were similarly ragged, but what appalled me most was the sour smell of his unwashed little body. I hadn't thought there were children like this in Darrowby.

When he had answered my questions he made an effort and blurted out one of his own.

'What's matter with 'im?'

I hesitated a moment. 'He's got distemper, Wes.'

'What's that?'

'Well, it's a nasty infectious disease. He must have got it from another sick dog.'

'Will 'e get better?'

'I hope so. I'll do the best I can for him.' I couldn't bring myself to tell a small boy of his age that his pet was probably going to die.

I filled a syringe with a 'mixed macterin' which we used at that time against the secondary invaders of distemper. It never did much good and even now with all our antibiotics we cannot greatly influence the final outcome. If you can catch a case in the early viral phase then a shot of hyperimmune serum is curative, but people rarely bring their dogs in until that phase is over.

As I gave the injection the dog whimpered a little and the boy stretched out a hand and patted him.

'It's awright, Duke,' he said.

'That's what you call him, is it – Duke?'

'Aye.' He fondled the ears and the dog turned, whipped his strange long tail about and licked the hand quickly. Wes smiled and looked up at me and for a moment the tough mask dropped from the grubby features and in the dark wild eyes I read sheer delight. I swore under my breath. This made it worse.

I tipped some boracic crystals into a box and handed it over. 'Use this dissolved in water to keep his eyes and nose clean. See how his nostrils are all caked and blocked up – you can make him a lot more comfortable.'

He took the box without speaking and almost with the same movement dropped three and sixpence on the table. It was about our average charge and resolved my doubts on that score.

'When'll ah bring 'im back?' he asked.

I looked at him doubtfully for a moment. All I could do was repeat the injections, but was it going to make the slightest difference?

The boy misread my hesitation.

'Ah can pay!' he burst out. 'Ah can get t'money!'

'Oh I didn't mean that, Wes. I was just wondering when it would be suitable. How about bringing him in on Thursday?'

He nodded eagerly and left with his dog.

As I swabbed the table with disinfectant I had the old feeling of helplessness. The modern veterinary surgeon does not see nearly as many cases of distemper as we used to, simply because most people immunise their puppies at the earliest possible moment. But back in the thirties it was only the few fortunate dogs who were inoculated. The disease is so easy to prevent but almost impossible to cure.

The next three weeks saw an incredible change in Wesley Binks's character. He had built up a reputation as an idle scamp but now he was transformed into a model of industry, delivering papers in the mornings, digging people's gardens, helping to drive the beasts at the auction mart. I was perhaps the only one who knew he was doing it for Duke.

He brought the dog in every two or three days and paid on the nail. I naturally charged him as little as possible but the money he earned went on other things – fresh meat from the butcher, extra milk and biscuits.

'Duke's looking very smart today,' I said on one of the visits. 'I see you've been getting him a new collar and lead.'

The boy nodded shyly then looked up at me, dark eyes intent. 'Is 'e any better?'

'Well, he's about the same, Wes. That's how it goes – dragging on without much change.'

'When . . . when will ye know?'

I thought for a moment. Maybe he would worry less if he understood the situation. 'The thing is this. Duke will get better if he can avoid the nervous complications of distemper.'

'Wot's them?'

'Fits, paralysis and a thing called chorea which makes the muscles twitch.'

'Wot if he gets them?'

'It's a bad lookout in that case. But not all dogs develop them.' I tried to smile reassuringly. 'And there's one thing in Duke's favour – he's not a pure bred. Cross bred dogs have a thing called hybrid vigour which helps them to fight disease. After all, he's eating fairly well and he's quite lively, isn't he?'

'Aye, not bad.'

'Well then, we'll carry on. I'll give him another shot now.'

The boy was back in three days and I knew by his face he had momentous news.

'Duke's a lot better – 'is eyes and nose 'ave dried up and he's eatin' like a 'oss!' He was panting with excitement.

I lifted the dog on to the table. There was no doubt he was enormously improved and I did my best to join in the rejoicing.

'That's great, Wes,' I said, but a warning bell was tinkling in my mind. If nervous symptoms were going to supervene, this was the time – just when the dog was apparently recovering.

I forced myself to be optimistic. 'Well now, there's no need to come back any more but watch him carefully and if you see anything unusual bring him in.'

The ragged little figure was overjoyed. He almost pranced along the passage with his pet and I hoped fervently that I would not see them in there again.

That was on the Friday evening and by Monday I had put the whole thing out of my head and into the category of satisfying memories when the boy came in with Duke on the lead.

I looked up from the desk where I was writing in the day book. 'What is it, Wes?'

'He's dotherin'.'

I didn't bother going through to the consulting room but hastened from behind the desk and crouched on the floor, studying the dog intently. At first I saw nothing, then as I watched I could just discern a faint nodding of the head. I placed my hand on the top of the skull and waited. And it was there; the slight but regular twitching of the temporal muscles which I had dreaded.

'I'm afraid he's got chorea, Wes.' I said.

'What's that?'

'It's one of the things I was telling you about. Sometimes they call it St Vitus' Dance. I was hoping it wouldn't happen.'

The boy looked suddenly small and forlorn and he stood there silent, twisting the new leather lead between his fingers. It was such an effort for him to speak that he almost closed his eyes.

'Will 'e die?'

'Some dogs do get over it, Wes.' I didn't tell him that I had seen it happen only once. 'I've got some tablets which might help him. I'll get you some.'

I gave him a few of the arsenical tablets I had used in my only cure. I didn't even know if they had been responsible but I had nothing more to offer.

Duke's chorea pursued a text book course over the next two weeks. All the things which I had feared turned up in a relentless progression. The twitching spread from his head to his limbs, then his hindquarters began to sway as he walked.

His young master brought him in repeatedly and I went through the motions, trying at the same time to make it clear that it was all hopeless. The boy persisted doggedly, rushing about meanwhile with his paper deliveries and other jobs, insisting on paying though I didn't want his money. Then one afternoon he called in.

'Ah couldn't bring Duke,' he muttered. 'Can't walk now. Will you come and see 'im?'

We got into my car. It was a Sunday, about three o'clock and the streets were quiet. He led me up the cobbled yard and opened the door of one of the houses.

The stink of the place hit me as I went in. Country vets aren't easily sickened but I felt my stomach turning. Mrs Binks was very fat and a filthy dress hung shapelessly on her as she slumped, cigarette in mouth, over the kitchen table.

She was absorbed in a magazine which lay in a clearing among mounds of dirty dishes and her curlers nodded as she looked up briefly at us.

On a couch under the window her husband sprawled asleep, open-mouthed, snoring out the reek of beer. The sink, which held a further supply of greasy dishes, was covered in a revolting green scum. Clothes, newspapers and nameless rubbish littered the floor and over everything a radio blasted away at full strength.

The only clean new thing was the dog basket in the corner. I went across and bent over the little animal. Duke was now prostrate and helpless, his body emaciated and jerking uncontrollably. The sunken eyes had filled up again with pus and gazed apathetically ahead.

'Wes,' I said. 'You've got to let me put him to sleep.'

He didn't answer, and as I tried to explain, the blaring radio drowned my words. I looked over at his mother.

'Do you mind turning the radio down?' I asked.

She jerked her head at the boy and he went over and turned the knob. In the ensuing silence I spoke to him again.

'It's the only thing, believe me. You can't let him die by inches like this.'

He didn't look at me. All his attention was fixed desperately on his dog. Then he raised a hand and I heard his whisper.

'Awright.'

I hurried out to the car for the Nembutal.

'I promise you he'll feel no pain,' I said as I filled the syringe. And indeed the little creature merely sighed before lying motionless, the fateful twitching stilled at last.

I put the syringe in my pocket. 'Do you want me to take him away, Wes?'

He looked at me bewilderedly and his mother broke in.

'Aye, get 'im out. Ah never wanted t'bloody thing 'ere in t'first place.' She resumed her reading.

I quickly lifted the little body and went out. Wes followed me and watched as I opened the boot and laid Duke gently on top of my black working coat.

As I closed the lid he screwed his knuckles into his eyes and his body shook. I put my arm across his shoulder, and as he leaned against me for a moment and sobbed I wondered if he had ever been able to cry like this – like a little boy with somebody to comfort him.

But soon he stood back and smeared the tears across the dirt on his cheeks.

'Are you going back into the house, Wes?' I asked.

He blinked and looked at me with a return of his tough expression.

'Naw!' he said and turned and walked away. He didn't look back and I watched him cross the road, climb a wall and trail away across the fields towards the river.

And it has always seemed to me that at that moment Wes walked back into his old life. From then on there were no more odd jobs or useful activities. He never played any more tricks on me but in other ways he progressed into more serious misdemeanours. He set barns on fire, was up before the magistrates for theft and by the time he was thirteen he was stealing cars.

Finally he was sent to an approved school and then he disappeared from the district. Nobody knew where he went and most people forgot him. One person who didn't was the police sergeant.

'That young Wesley Binks,' he said to me ruminatively. 'He was a wrong 'un if ever I saw one. You know, I don't think he ever cared a damn for anybody or any living thing in his life.'

'I know how you feel sergeant,' I replied, 'But you're not entirely right. There was one living thing. .'.

Chapter Six

Tristan would never have won any prizes as an exponent of the haute cuisine.

We got better food in the RAF than most people in wartime Britain but it didn't compare with the Darrowby fare. I suppose I had been spoiled; first by Mrs Hall, then by Helen. There were only brief occasions at Skeldale House when we did not eat like kings and one of those was when Tristan was installed as temporary cook.

It began one morning at breakfast in the days when I was still a bachelor and Tristan and I were taking our places at the mahogany dining table. Siegfried bustled in, muttered a greeting and began to pour his coffee. He was unusually distrait as he buttered a slice of toast and cut into one of the rashers on his plate, then after a minute's thoughtful chewing he brought down his hand on the table with a suddenness that made me jump.

'I've got it!' he exclaimed.

'Got what?' I enquired.

Siegfried put down his knife and fork and wagged a finger at me. 'Silly, really, I've been sitting here puzzling about what to do and it's suddenly clear.'

'Why, what's the trouble?'

'It's Mrs Hall,' he said. 'She's just told me her sister has been taken ill and she has to go and look after her. She thinks she'll be away for a week and I've been wondering who I could get to look after the house.'

'I see.'

'Then it struck me.' He sliced a corner from a fried egg. 'Tristan can do it.'

'Eh?' His brother looked up, startled, from his *Daily Mirror*. 'Me?'

'Yes, you! You spend a lot of time on your arse. A bit of useful activity would be good for you.'

Tristan looked at him warily. 'What do you mean – useful activity?'

'Well, keeping the place straight,' Siegfried said. 'I wouldn't expect perfection but you could tidy up each day, and of course prepare the meals.'

'Meals?'

'That's right.' Siegfried gave him a level stare. 'You can cook, can't you?'

'Well, er, yes . . . I can cook sausage and mash.'

Siegfried waved an expansive hand. 'There you are, you see, no problem. Push over those fried tomatoes, will you, James?'

I passed the dish silently. I had only half heard the conversation because part of my mind was far away. Just before breakfast I had had a phone call from Ken Billings, one of our best farmers, and his words were still echoing in my head.

'Mr Herriot, that calf you saw yesterday is dead. That's the third 'un I've lost in a week and I'm flummoxed. I want ye out here this mornin' to have another look round.'

I sipped my coffee absently. He wasn't the only one who was flummoxed. Three fine calves had shown symptoms of acute gastric pain, I had treated them and they had died. That was bad enough but what made it worse was that I hadn't the faintest idea what was wrong with them.

I wiped my lips and got up quickly. 'Siegfried, I'd like to go to Billings' first. Then I've got the rest of the round you gave me.'

'Fine, James, by all means.' My boss gave me a sweet and encouraging smile, balanced a mushroom on a piece of fried bread and conveyed it to his mouth. He wasn't a big eater but he did love his breakfast.

On the way to the farm my mind beat about helplessly. What more could I do than I had already done? In these obscure cases one was driven to the conclusion that the animal had eaten something harmful. At times I had spent hours roaming around pastures looking for poisonous plants but that was pointless with Billings's calves because they had never been out; they were mere babies of a month old.

I had carried out post mortem examinations of the dead animals but had found only a non-specific gastro-enteritis. I had sent kidneys to the laboratory for lead estimation with negative result; like their owner, I was flummoxed.

Mr Billings was waiting for me in his yard.

'Good job I rang you!' he said breathlessly. 'There's another 'un startin'.'

I rushed with him into the buildings and found what I expected and dreaded; a small calf kicking at its stomach, getting up and down, occasionally rolling on its straw bed. Typical abdominal pain. But why?

I went over it as with the others. Temperature normal, lungs clear, only rumenal atony and extreme tenderness as I palpated the abdomen.

As I was putting the thermometer back in its case the calf suddenly toppled over and went into a frothing convulsion. Hastily I injected sedatives, calcium, magnesium, but with a feeling of doom. I had done it all before.

'What the hell is it?' the farmer asked, voicing my thoughts.

I shrugged. 'It's acute gastritis, Mr Billings, but I wish I knew the cause. I could swear this calf has eaten some irritant or corrosive poison.'

'Well, dang it, they've nobbut had milk and a few nuts.' The farmer spread his hands. 'There's nothing they can get to hurt them.'

Again, wearily, I went through the old routine; ferreting around in the calf pen, trying to find some clue. An old paint tin, a burst packet of sheep dip. It was amazing, the things you came across in the clutter of a farm building.

But not at Mr Billings's place. He was meticulously tidy, particularly with his calves, and the window sills and shelves were free from rubbish. It was the same with the milk buckets, scoured to spotless cleanliness after every feed.

Mr Billings had a thing about his calves. His two teenage sons were fanatically keen on farming and he encouraged them in all the agricultural skills; but he fed the calves himself.

'Feeding them calves is t'most important job in stock rearing,' he used to say. 'Get 'em over that first month and you're half-way there.'

And he knew what he was talking about. His charges never suffered from the normal ailments of the young; no scour, no joint ill, no pneumonia. I had often marvelled at it, but it made the present disaster all the more unbearable.

'All right,' I said with false breeziness as I left. 'Maybe this one won't be so bad. Give me a ring in the morning.'

I did the rest of my round in a state of gloom and at lunch I was still so preoccupied that I wondered what had happened when Tristan served the meal. I had entirely forgotten about Mrs Hall's absence.

However, the sausage and mash wasn't at all bad and Tristan was lavish with his helpings. The three of us cleaned our plates pretty thoroughly, because morning is the busiest working time in practice and I was always famished by midday.

My mind was still on Mr Billings's problem during the afternoon calls and when we sat down to supper I was only mildly surprised to find another offering of sausage and mash.

'Same again, eh?' Siegfried grunted, but he got through his plateful and left without further comment.

The next day started badly. I came into the dining room to find the table bare and Siegfried stamping around.

'Where the hell is our breakfast?' he burst out. 'And where the hell is Tristan?'

He pounded along the passage and I heard his shouts in the kitchen 'Tristan! Tristan!'

I knew he was wasting his time. His brother often slept in and it was just a bit more noticeable this morning.

My boss returned along the passage at a furious gallop and I steeled myself for some unpleasantness as the young man was rousted from his bed. But Tristan, as usual, was master of the situation. Siegfried had just begun to take the stairs three at a time when his brother descended from the landing, knotting his tie with perfect composure. It was uncanny. He always got more than his share of sleeping time but was rarely caught between the sheets.

'Sorry, chaps,' he murmured. 'Afraid I overslept.'

'Yes, that's all right!' shouted Siegfried. 'But how about our bloody breakfast? I gave you a job to do!'

Tristan was contrite. 'I really do apologise, but I was up late last night, peeling potatoes.'

His brother's face flushed. 'I know all about that!' he barked. 'You didn't start till after closing time at the Drovers!'

'Well, that's right.' Tristan swallowed and his face assumed the familiar expression of pained dignity. 'I did feel a bit dry last night. Think it must have been all the cleaning and dusting I did.'

Siegfried did not reply. He shot a single exasperated look at the young man then turned to me. 'We'll have to make do with bread and marmalade this morning, James. Come through to the kitchen and we'll . . .'

The jangling of the telephone cut off his words. I lifted the receiver and listened and it must have been the expression on my face which stopped him in the doorway.

'What's the matter, James?' he asked as I came away from the 'phone. 'You look as though you've had a kick in the belly.'

I nodded. 'That's how I feel. That calf is nearly dead at Billings's and there's another one ill. I wish you'd come out there with me, Siegfried.'

My boss stood very still as he looked over the side of the pen at the little animal. It didn't seem to know where to put itself, rising and lying down, kicking at some inward pain, writhing its hindquarters from side to side. As he watched it fell on its side and began to thrash around with all four limbs.

'James,' he said quietly. 'That calf has been poisoned.'

'That's what I thought, but how?'

Mr Billings broke in. 'It's no good talkin' like that, Mr Farnon. We've been over this place time and time again and there's nowt for them to get.'

'Well, we'll go over it again.' Siegfried stalked around the calf house as I had done and when he returned his face was expressionless.

'Where do you get the nuts from?' he grunted, crumbling one of the cubes between his fingers.

Mr Billings threw his arms wide. 'From t'local mill. Ryders' best. You can't fault them, surely.'

Siegfried said nothing. Ryders were noted for their meticulous preparation of cattle food. He went over the sick calf with stethoscope and thermometer, digging his fingers into the hairy abdominal wall, staring impassively at the calf's face to note its reaction. He did the same with my patient of yesterday whose glazing eyes and cold extremities told their grim tale. Then he gave the calves almost the same treatment as I had and we left.

He was silent for the first half mile, then he beat the wheel suddenly with one hand. 'There's an irritant poison there, James! As sure as God made little apples there is. But I'm damned if I know where it's coming from.'

Our visit had taken a long time and we returned to Skeldale House for lunch. Like myself, his mind was still wrestling with Mr Billings's problem and he hardly winced as Tristan placed a steaming plateful of sausage and mash before him. Then, as he prodded the mash with a fork, he appeared to come to the surface.

'God almighty!' he exclaimed. 'Have we got this again?'

Tristan smiled ingratiatingly. 'Yes, indeed. Mr Johnson told me they were a particularly fine batch of sausages today. Definitely superior, he said.'

'Is that so?' His brother gave him a sour glance. 'Well, they look the bloody same to me. Like supper yesterday – and like lunch.' His voice began to rise then he subsided.

'Oh, what the hell,' he muttered, and began to toy listlessly with the food. Clearly those calves had drained him and I knew how he felt.

I got through my share without much difficulty – I've always liked sausage and mash.

But my boss is a resilient character and when we met in the late afternoon he was bursting with his old spirit.

'That call to Billings's shook me, James, I can tell you.' he said. 'But I've revisited a few of my other cases since then and they're all improving nicely. Raises the morale tremendously. Here, let me get you a drink.'

He reached into the cupboard above the mantelpiece for the gin bottle and after pouring a couple of measures he looked benignly at his brother who was tidying the sitting room.

Tristan was making a big show, running a carpet-sweeper up and down, straightening cushions, flicking a duster at everything in sight. He sighed and panted with effort as he bustled around, the very picture of a harassed domestic. He needed only a mob cap and frilly apron to complete the image.

We finished our drinks and Siegfried immersed himself in the *Veterinary Record* as savoury smells began to issue from the kitchen. It was about seven o'clock when Tristan put his head round the door.

'Supper is on the table,' he said.

My boss put down the *Record*, rose and stretched expansively. 'Good, I'm ready for it, too.'

I followed him into the dining room and almost cannoned into his back as he halted abruptly. He was staring in disbelief at the tureen in the middle of the table.

'Not bloody sausage and mash again!' he bellowed.

Tristan shuffled his feet. 'Well, er, yes – it's very nice really.'

'Very nice! I'm beginning to dream about the blasted stuff. Can't you cook anything else?'

'Well, I told you.' Tristan looked wounded. 'I told you I could cook sausage and mash.'

'Yes, you did!' shouted his brother. 'But you didn't say you couldn't cook anything else BUT sausage and bloody mash!'

Tristan made a non-committal gesture and his brother sank wearily down at the table.

'Go on, then,' he sighed. 'Dish it out and heaven help us.'

He took a small mouthful from his plate then gripped at his stomach and emitted a low moan. 'This stuff is killing me. I don't think I'll ever be the same after this week.'

The following day opened in dramatic fashion. I had just got out of bed and was reaching for my dressing gown when an explosion shook the house. It was a great 'WHUFF' which rushed like a mighty wind through passages and rooms, rattling the windows and leaving an ominous silence in its wake.

I dashed out to the landing and ran into Siegfried, who stared wide-eyed at me for a moment before galloping downstairs.

In the kitchen Tristan was lying on his back amid a litter of pans and dishes. Several rashers of bacon and a few smashed eggs nestled on the flags.

'What the hell's going on?' Siegfried shouted.

His brother looked up at him with mild interest. 'I really don't know. I was lighting the fire and there was a bang.'

'Lighting the fire . . .?'

'Yes, I've had a little difficulty these last two mornings. The thing wouldn't go. I think the chimney needs sweeping. These old houses . . .'

'Yes, yes!' Siegfried burst out. 'We know, but what the hell happened?'

Tristan sat up. Even then, among the debris with smuts all over his face, he still retained his poise. 'Well, I thought I'd hurry things along a bit,' (His agile mind was forever seeking new methods of conserving energy.) 'I soaked a piece of cotton wool in ether and chucked that in.'

'Ether?'

'Well yes, it's inflammable, isn't it?'

'Inflammable!' His brother was pop-eyed. 'It's bloody well explosive! It's a wonder you didn't blow the whole place up.'

Tristan rose and dusted himself off. 'Ah well, never mind. I'll soon have breakfast ready.'

'You can forget that.' Siegfried took a long shuddering breath then went over to the bread tin, extracted a loaf and began to saw at it. 'The breakfast's on the floor, and anyway, by the time you've cleared up this mess we'll be gone. Bread and marmalade all right for you, James?'

We went out together again. My boss had arranged that Ken Billings should postpone his calf feeding till we got there so that we could witness the process.

It wasn't a happy arrival. Both the calves had died and the farmer's eyes held a look of desperation.

Siegfried's jaw clenched tight for a moment then he motioned with his hand. 'Please carry on, Mr Billings. I want to see you feed them.'

The nuts were always available for the little animals but we watched intently as the farmer poured the milk into the buckets and the calves started to drink. The poor man had obviously given up hope and I could tell by his apathetic manner that he hadn't much faith in this latest ploy.

Neither had I, but Siegfried prowled up and down like a caged panther as though willing something to happen. The calves raised white-slobbered muzzles enquiringly as he hung over them but they could offer no more explanation of the mystery than I could myself.

I looked across the long row of pens. There were still more than thirty calves left in the building and the terrible thought arose that the disease might spread through all of them. My mind was recoiling when Siegfried stabbed a finger at one of the buckets.

'What's that?' he snapped.

The farmer and I went over and gazed down at a circular black object about half an inch across floating on the surface of the milk.

592 *Vets Might Fly*

'Bit o' muck got in somehow,' Mr Billings mumbled. 'I'll 'ave it out.' He put his hand into the bucket.

'No, let me!' Siegfried carefully lifted the thing, shook the milk from his fingers and studied it with interest.

'This isn't muck,' he murmured. 'Look, it's concave – like a little cup.' He rubbed a corner between thumb and forefinger. 'I'll tell you what it is, it's a scab. Where the heck has it come from?'

He began to examine the neck and head of the calf, then became very still as he handled one of the little horn buds. 'There's a raw surface here. You can see where the scab belongs.' He placed the dark cup over the bud and it fitted perfectly.

The farmer shrugged. 'Aye, well, I can understand that. I disbudded all the calves about a fortnight sin'.'

'What did you use, Mr Billings?' My colleague's voice was soft.

'Oh, some new stuff. Feller came round sellin' it. You just paint it on – it's a lot easier than t'awd caustic stick.'

'Have you got the bottle?'

'Aye, it's in t'house. I'll get it.'

When the farmer returned Siegfried read the label and handed the bottle to me.

'Butter of Antimony, Jim. Now we know.'

'But . . . what are you on about?' asked the farmer bewilderedly.

Siegfried looked at him sympathetically. 'Antimony is a deadly poison, Mr Billings. Oh, it'll burn your horn buds off, all right, but if it gets in among the food, that's it.'

The farmer's eyes widened. 'Yes, dang it, and when they put their heads down to drink that's just when the scabs would fall off!'

'Exactly,' Siegfried said. 'Or they maybe knocked the horn buds on the sides of the bucket. Anyway, let's make sure the others are safe.'

We went round all the calves, removing the lethal crusts and scrubbing the buds clean, and when we finally drove away we knew that the brief but painful episode of the Billings calves was over.

In the car, my colleague put his elbows on the wheel and drove with his chin cupped in his hands. He often did this when in contemplative mood and it never failed to unnerve me.

'James,' he said, 'I've never seen anything like that before. It really is one for the book.'

His words were prophetic, for as I write about it now I realise that it has never been repeated in the thirty-five years that have passed since then.

At Skeldale House we parted to go our different ways. Tristan, no doubt anxious to redeem himself after the morning's explosive beginning, was plying mop and bucket and swabbing the passage with the zeal of one of Nelson's sailors.

But when Siegfried drove away, the activity stopped abruptly and as I was leaving with my pockets stuffed with the equipment for my round I glanced into the sitting room and saw the young man stretched in his favourite chair.

I went in and looked with some surprise at a pan of sausages balanced on the coals.

'What's this?' I asked.

Tristan lit a Woodbine, shook out his *Daily Mirror* and put his feet up. 'Just prepared lunch, old lad.'

'In here?'

'Yes, Jim, I've had enough of that hot stove – there's no comfort through there. And anyway, the kitchen's such a bloody long way away.'

I gazed down at the reclining form. 'No need to ask what's on the menu?'

'None at all, old son.' Tristan looked up from his paper with a seraphic smile. I was about to leave when a thought struck me. 'Where are the potatoes?'

'In the fire.'

'In the fire!'

'Yes, I just popped them in there to roast for a while. They're delicious that way.'

'Are you sure?'

'Absolutely, Jim. I'll tell you – you'll fall in love with my cooking all over again.'

I didn't get back till nearly one o'clock. Tristan was not in the sitting room but a haze of smoke hung on the air and a reek like a garden bonfire prickled in my nostrils.

I found the young man in the kitchen. His *savoir faire* had vanished and he was prodding desperately at a pile of coal black spheres.

I stared at him. 'What are those?'

'The bloody potatoes, Jim! I fell asleep for a bit and this happened!'

He gingerly sawed through one of the objects. In the centre of the carbonaceous ball I could discern a small whitish marble which seemed to be all that remained of the original vegetable.

'Hell's bells, Triss! What are you going to do?'

He gave me a stricken glance. 'Hack out the centres and mash 'em up together. It's all I CAN do.'

This was something I couldn't bear to watch. I went upstairs, had a wash then took my place at the dining table. Siegfried was already seated and I could see that the little triumph of the morning had cheered him. He greeted me jovially.

'James, wasn't that the damndest thing at Ken Billings'? It's so satisfying to get it cleared up.'

But his smile froze as Tristan appeared and set down the tureens before him. From one peeped the inevitable sausages and the other contained an amorphous dark grey mass liberally speckled with black foreign bodies of varying size.

'What in the name of God,' he enquired with ominous quiet, 'is this?'

His brother swallowed. 'Sausage and mash,' he said lightly.

Siegfried gave him a cold look. 'I am referring to this.' He poked warily at the dark mound.

'Well, er, it's the potatoes.' Tristan cleared his throat. 'Got a little burnt, I'm afraid.'

My boss made no comment. With dangerous calm he spooned some of the material on to his plate, raised a forkful and began to chew slowly. Once or twice he winced as a particularly tough fragment of carbon cracked between his molars, then he closed his eyes and swallowed.

For a moment he was still, then he grasped his midriff with both hands, groaned and jumped to his feet.

'No, that's enough!' he cried. 'I don't mind investigating poisonings on the farms but I object to being poisoned myself in my own home!' He strode away from the table and paused at the door. 'I'm going over to the Drovers for lunch.'

As he left another spasm seized him. He clutched his stomach again and looked back.

'Now I know just how those poor bloody calves felt!'

Chapter Seven

I suppose it was a little thoughtless of me to allow my scalpel to flash and flicker quite so close to Rory O'Hagan's fly buttons.

The incident came back to me as I sat in my room in St John's Wood reading Black's *Veterinary Dictionary*. It was a bulky volume to carry around and my RAF friends used to rib me about my 'vest pocket edition', but I had resolved to keep reading it in spare moments to remind me of my real life.

I had reached the letter 'C' and as the word 'Castration' looked up at me from the page I was jerked back to Rory.

I was castrating pigs. There were several litters to do and I was in a hurry and failed to notice the Irish farm worker's mounting apprehension. His young boss was catching the little animals and handing them to Rory who held them upside down, gripped between his thighs with their legs apart, and as I quickly incised the scrotums and drew out the testicles my blade almost touched the rough material of his trouser crutch.

'For God's sake, have a care, Mr Herriot!' he gasped at last.

I looked up from my work. 'What's wrong, Rory?'

'Watch what you're doin' with that bloody knife! You're whippin' it round between me legs like a bloody Red Indian. You'll do me a mischief afore you've finished!'

'Aye, be careful, Mr Herriot,' the young farmer cried. 'Don't geld Rory instead of the pig. His missus ud never forgive ye.' He burst into a loud peal of laughter, the Irishman grinned sheepishly and I giggled.

That was my undoing because the momentary inattention sent the blade slicing across my left forefinger. The razor-sharp edge went deep and in an instant the entire neighbourhood seemed flooded with my blood. I thought I would never staunch the flow. The red ooze continued, despite a long session of self-doctoring from the car boot, and when I finally drove away my finger was swathed in the biggest, clumsiest dressing I have ever seen. I had finally been forced to apply a large pad of cotton wool held in place with an enormous length of three-inch bandage.

It was dark when I left the farm. About five o'clock on a late December day, the light gone early and the stars beginning to show in a frosty sky. I drove slowly, the enormous finger jutting upwards from the wheel, pointing the way between the headlights like a guiding beacon. I was within half a mile of Darrowby with the lights of the little town beginning to wink between the bare roadside branches when a car approached, went past, then I heard a squeal of brakes as it stopped and began to double back.

It passed me again, drew into the side and I saw a frantically waving arm. I pulled up and a young man jumped from the driving seat and ran towards me.

He pushed his head in at the window. 'Are you the vet?' His voice was breathless, panic-stricken.

'Yes, I am.'

'Oh thank God! We're passing through on the way to Manchester and we've been to your surgery . . . they said you were out this way . . . described your car. Please help us!'

'What's the trouble?'

'It's our dog . . . in the back of the car. He's got a ball stuck in his throat. I . . . I think he might be dead.'

I was out of my seat and running along the road before he had finished. It was a big white saloon and in the darkness of the back seat a wailing chorus issued from several little heads silhouetted against the glass.

I tore open the door and the wailing took on words.

'Oh Benny, Benny, Benny . . .!'

I dimly discerned a large dog spread over the knees of four small children. 'Oh Daddy, he's dead, he's dead!'

'Let's have him out,' I gasped, and as the young man pulled on the forelegs I supported the body, which slid and toppled on to the tarmac with a horrible limpness.

I pawed at the hairy form. 'I can't see a bloody thing! Help me pull him round.'

We dragged the unresisting bulk into the headlights' glare and I could see it all. A huge, beautiful collie in his luxuriant prime, mouth gaping, tongue lolling, eyes staring lifelessly at nothing. He wasn't breathing.

The young father took one look then gripped his head with both hands. 'Oh God, oh God. . . .' From within the car I heard the quiet sobbing of his wife and the piercing cries from the back. 'Benny . . . Benny. . . .'

I grabbed the man's shoulder and shouted at him. 'What did you say about a ball?'

'It's in his throat . . . I've had my fingers in his mouth for ages but I couldn't move it.' The words came mumbling up from beneath the bent head.

I pushed my hand into the mouth and I could feel it all right. A sphere of hard solid rubber not much bigger than a golf ball and jammed like a cork in the pharynx, effectively blocking the trachea. I scrabbled feverishly at the wet smoothness but there was nothing to get hold of. It took me about three seconds to realise that no human agency would ever get the ball out that way and without thinking I withdrew my hands, braced both thumbs behind the angle of the lower jaw and pushed.

The ball shot forth, bounced on the frosty road and rolled sadly on to the grass verge. I touched the corneal surface of the eye. No reflex. I slumped to my knees, burdened by the hopeless regret that I hadn't had the chance to do this just a bit sooner. The only function I could perform now was to take the body back to Skeldale House for disposal. I couldn't allow the family to drive to Manchester with a dead dog. But I wished fervently that I had been able to do more, and as I passed my hand along the richly coloured coat over the ribs the vast bandaged finger stood out like a symbol of my helplessness.

It was when I was gazing dully at the finger, the heel of my hand resting in an intercostal space, that I felt the faintest flutter from below.

I jerked upright with a hoarse cry. 'His heart's still beating! He's not gone yet!' I began to work on the dog with all I had. And out there in the darkness of that lonely country road it wasn't much. No stimulant injections, no oxygen cylinders or intratracheal tubes. But I depressed his chest with my palms every three seconds in the old-fashioned way, willing the dog to breathe as the eyes still stared at nothing. Every now and then I blew desperately down the throat or probed between the ribs for that almost imperceptible beat.

I don't know which I noticed first, the slight twitch of an eyelid or the small lift of the ribs which pulled the icy Yorkshire air into his lungs. Maybe they both happened at once but from that moment everything was dreamlike and wonderful. I lost count of time as I sat there while the breathing became deep and regular and the animal began to be aware of his surroundings; and by the time he started to look around him and twitch his tail tentatively I realised suddenly that I was stiff-jointed and almost frozen to the spot.

With some difficulty I got up and watched in disbelief as the collie staggered to his feet. The young father ushered him round to the back where he was received with screams of delight.

The man seemed stunned. Throughout the recovery he had kept muttering, 'You just flicked that ball out . . . just flicked it out. Why didn't I think of that . . .?' And when he turned to me before leaving he appeared to be still in a state of shock.

'I don't . . . I don't know how to thank you,' he said huskily. 'It's a miracle.' He leaned against the car for a second. 'And now what is your fee? How much do I owe you?'

I rubbed my chin. I had used no drugs. The only expenditure had been time. 'Five bob,' I said. 'And never let him play with such a little ball again.'

He handed the money over, shook my hand and drove away. His wife, who had never left her place, waved as she left, but my greatest reward was in the last shadowy glimpse of the back seat where little arms twined around the dog, hugging him ecstatically, and in the cries, thankful and joyous, fading into the night.

'Benny . . . Benny . . . Benny. . . .'

Vets often wonder after a patient's recovery just how much credit they might take. Maybe it would have got better without treatment – it happened sometimes; it was difficult to be sure.

But when you know without a shadow of a doubt that, even without doing anything clever, you have pulled an animal back from the brink of death into the living, breathing world, it is a satisfaction which lingers, flowing like balm over the discomforts and frustrations of veterinary practice, making everything right.

Yet, in the case of Benny the whole thing had an unreal quality. I never even glimpsed the faces of those happy children nor that of their mother huddled in the front seat. I had a vague impression of their father but he had spent most of the time with his head in his hands. I wouldn't have known him if I met him in the street. Even the dog, in the unnatural glare of the headlights, was a blurred memory.

It seemed the family had the same feeling because a week later I had a pleasant letter from the mother. She apologised for skulking out of the way so shamelessly, she thanked me for saving the life of their beloved dog who was now prancing around with the children as though nothing had happened, and she finished with the regret that she hadn't even asked me my name.

Yes, it had been a strange episode, and not only were those people unaware of my name but I'd like to bet they would fail to recognise me if they saw me again.

In fact, looking back at the affair, the only thing which stood out unequivocal and substantial was my great white-bound digit which had hovered constantly over the scene, almost taking on a personality and significance of its own. I am sure that is what the family remembered best about me because of the way the mother's letter began.

'Dear Vet with the bandaged finger . . .'

Chapter Eight

My stint in London was nearing its end. Our breaking-in weeks were nearly over and we waited for news of posting to Initial Training Wing.

The air was thick with rumours. We were going to Aberystwyth in Wales; too far away for me, I wanted the north. Then we were going to Newquay in Cornwall; worse still. I was aware that the impending birth of AC2 Herriot's child did not influence the general war strategy but I still wanted to be as near to Helen as possible at the time.

The whole London phase is blurred in my memory. Possibly because everything was so new and different that the impressions could not be fully absorbed, and also perhaps because I was tired most of the time. I think we were all tired. Few of us were used to being jerked from slumber at 6 a.m. every morning and spending the day in continual physical activity. If we weren't being drilled we were being marched to meals, to classes, to talks. I had lived in a motor car for a few years and the rediscovery of my legs was painful.

There were times, too, when I wondered what it was all about. Like all the other young men I had imagined that after a few brisk preliminaries I would be sitting in an aeroplane, learning to fly, but it turned out that this was so far in the future that it was hardly mentioned. At the ITW we would spend months learning navigation, principles of flight, morse and many other things.

I was thankful for one blessing. I had passed the mathematics exam. I have always counted on my fingers and still do and I had been so nervous about this that I went to classes with the ATC in Darrowby before my call-up, dredging from my schooldays horrific calculations about trains passing each other at different speeds and water running in and out of bath tubs. But I had managed to scrape through and felt ready to face anything.

There were some unexpected shocks in London. I didn't anticipate spending days mucking out some of the dirtiest piggeries I had ever seen. Somebody must have had the idea of converting all the RAF waste food into pork and bacon and of course there was plenty of labour at hand. I had a strong feeling of unreality as, with other aspiring pilots, I threw muck and swill around hour after hour.

There was another time I had the same feeling. One night three of us decided to go to the cinema. We took pains to get to the front of the queue for the evening meal so that we would be in time for the start of the picture. When the doors of the huge dining room at the zoo were thrown open we were first in, but a sergeant cook met us in the entrance with: 'I want three volunteers for dishwashing – you, you and you,' and marched us away.

He probably had a kind heart because he patted our shoulders as we climbed miserably into greasy dungarees.

'Never mind, lads,' he said. 'I'll see you get a real good meal afterwards.'

My friends were taken somewhere else and I found myself alone in a kind of dungeon at the end of a metal chute. Very soon dirty plates began to cascade down the chute and my job was to knock the food remains off them and transfer them to a mechanical washer.

The menu that night was cottage pie and chips, a combination which has remained engraved on my memory. For more than two hours I stood at bay while a nonstop torrent of crockery poured down on me; thousands and thousands of plates, every one bearing a smear of cottage pie, a blob of cold gravy, a few adhering chips.

As I reeled around in the meaty steam a little tune tinkled repetitively in my mind; it was the song Siegfried and I were forever singing as we waited to enter the RAF, the popular jingle which in our innocence we thought typified the new life ahead.

> 'If I only had wings,
> Oh what a difference it would make to things,
> All day long I'd be in the sky, up on high,
> Talking to the birdies that pass me by.'

But in this reeking cavern with my hands, face, hair and every pore of my skin impregnated with cottage pie and chips, those birdies seemed far away.

At last, however, the plates began to slow down and finally stopped coming. The sergeant came in beaming and congratulated me on doing a fine job. He led me back to the dining hall, vast and empty save for my two friends. They both wore bemused, slightly stunned expressions and I am pretty sure I looked the same.

'Sit down here, lads,' the sergeant said. We took our places side by side in a corner with the bare boards of the table stretching away into the distance. 'I told you you'd get a real good meal, didn't I? Well, here it is.' He slid three heaped platefuls in front of us.

'There y'are,' he said. 'Cottage pie and chips, double helpin's!'

The following day I might have felt more disenchanted than ever, but news of the posting blotted out all other feelings. It seemed too good to be true – I was going to Scarborough. I had been there and I knew it as a beautiful seaside resort, but that wasn't why I was so delighted. It was because it was in Yorkshire.

Chapter Nine

As we marched out of the station into the streets of Scarborough I could hardly believe I was back in Yorkshire. But if there had been any doubt in my mind it would have been immediately resolved by my first breath of the crisp, tangy air. Even in winter there had been no 'feel' to the soft London air and I half closed my eyes as I followed the tingle all the way down to my lungs.

Mind you, it was cold. Yorkshire is a cold place and I could remember the sensation almost of shock at the start of my first winter in Darrowby.

It was after the first snow and I followed the clanging ploughs up the Dale, bumping along between high white mounds till I reached old Mr Stokill's gate. With my fingers on the handle I looked through the glass at the new world beneath me. The white blanket rolled down the hillside and lapped over the roofs of the dwelling and outbuildings of the little farm. Beyond, it smoothed out and concealed the familiar features, the stone walls bordering the fields, the stream on the valley floor, turning the whole scene into something unknown and exciting.

But the thrill I felt at the strange beauty was swept away as I got out and the wind struck me. It was an Arctic blast screaming from the east, picking up extra degrees of cold as it drove over the frozen white surface. I was wearing a heavy overcoat and woollen gloves but the gust whipped its way right into my bones. I gasped and leaned my back against the car while I buttoned the coat up under my chin, then I struggled forward to where the gate shook and rattled. I fought it open and my feet crunched as I went through.

Coming round the corner of the byre I found Mr Stokill forking muck on to a heap, making a churned brown trail across the whiteness.

'Now then,' he muttered along the side of a half-smoked cigarette. He was over seventy but still ran the smallholding single-handed. He told me once that he had worked as a farm hand for six shillings a day for thirty years, yet still managed to save enough to buy his own little place. Maybe that was why he didn't want to share it.

'How are you, Mr Stokill?' I said, but just then the wind tore through the yard, clutching icily at my face, snatching my breath away so that I turned involuntarily to one side with an explosive 'Aaahh!'

The old farmer looked at me in surprise, then glanced around as though he had just noticed the weather.

'Aye, blows a bit thin this mornin', lad.' Sparks flew from the end of his cigarette as he leaned for a moment on the fork.

He didn't seem to have much protection against the cold. A light khaki smock fluttered over a ragged navy waistcoat, clearly once part of his best suit, and his shirt bore neither collar nor stud. The white stubble on his fleshless jaw was a reproach to my twenty-four years and suddenly I felt an inadequate city-bred softie.

The old man dug his fork into the manure pile and turned towards the buildings. 'Ah've got a nice few cases for ye to see today. Fust 'un's in 'ere.' He opened a door and I staggered gratefully into a sweet bovine warmth where a few shaggy little bullocks stood hock deep in straw.

'That's the youth we want.' He pointed to a dark roan standing with one hind foot knuckled over. 'He's been on three legs for a couple o' days. Ah reckon he's got foul.'

I walked up to the little animal but he took off at a speed which made light of his infirmity.

'We'll have to run him into the passage. Mr Stokill,' I said. 'Just open the gate, will you?'

With the rough timbers pushed wide I got behind the bullock and sent him on to the opening. It seemed as though he was going straight through but at the entrance he stopped, peeped into the passage and broke away. I galloped a few times round the yard after him, then had another go. The result was the same. After half a dozen tries I wasn't cold any more. I'll back chasing young cattle against anything else for working up a sweat, and I had already forgotten the uncharitable world outside. And I could see I was going to get warmer still because the bullock was beginning to enjoy the game, kicking up his heels and frisking around after each attempt.

I put my hands on my hips, waited till I got my breath back then turned to the farmer.

'This is hopeless. He'll never go in there,' I said. 'We'd maybe better try to get a rope on him.'

'Nay, lad, there's no need for that. We'll get him through t'gate right enough.' The old man ambled to one end of the yard and returned with an armful of clean straw. He sprinkled it freely in the gate opening and beyond in the passage, then turned to me. 'Now send 'im on.'

I poked a finger into the animal's rump and he trotted forward, proceeded unhesitatingly between the posts and into the passage.

Mr Stokill must have noticed my look of bewilderment.

'Aye, 'e just didn't like t'look of them cobbles. Once they was covered over he was awright.'

'Yes . . . yes . . . I see.' I followed the bullock slowly through.

He was indeed suffering from foul of the foot, the mediaeval term given because of the stink of the necrotic tissue between the cleats, and I didn't have any antibiotics or sulphonamides to treat it. It is so nice and easy these days to give an injection, knowing that the beast will be sound in a day or two. But all I could do was wrestle with the lunging hind foot, dressing the infected cleft with a crude mixture of copper sulphate and Stockholm tar and finishing with a pad of cotton wool held by a tight bandage. When I had finished I took off my coat and hung it on a nail. I didn't need it any more.

Mr Stokill looked approvingly at the finished job. 'Capital, capital,' he murmured. 'Now there's some little pigs in this pen got a bit o' scour. I want you give 'em a jab wi' your needle.'

We had various *E coli* vaccines which sometimes did a bit of good in these cases and I entered the pen hopefully. But I left in a hurry because the piglets' mother didn't approve of a stranger wandering among her brood and she came at me open-mouthed, barking explosively. She looked as big as a donkey and when the cavernous jaws with the great yellowed teeth brushed my thigh I knew it was time to go. I hopped rapidly into the yard and crashed the door behind me.

I peered back ruminatively into the pen. 'We'll have to get her out of there before I can do anything, Mr Stokill.'

'Aye, you're right, young man, ah'll shift 'er.' He began to shuffle away.

I held up a hand. 'No, it's all right, I'll do it.' I couldn't let this frail old man go in there and maybe get knocked down and savaged, and I looked around for a means of protection. There was a battered shovel standing against a wall and I seized it.

'Open the door, please,' I said. 'I'll soon have her out.'

Once more inside the pen I held the shovel in front of me and tried to usher the huge sow towards the door. But my efforts at poking her rear end were fruitless; she faced me all the time, wide-mouthed and growling as I circled. When she got the blade of the shovel between her teeth and began to worry it I called a halt.

As I left the pen I saw Mr Stokill dragging a large object over the cobbles. 'What's that?' I asked.

'Dustbin,' the old man grunted in reply.

'Dustbin! What on earth . . .?'

He gave no further explanation but entered the pen. As the sow came at him he allowed her to run her head into the bin then, bent double, he began to back her towards the open door. The animal was clearly baffled. Suddenly finding herself in this strange dark place she naturally tried to retreat from it and all the farmer did was guide her.

Before she knew what was happening she was out in the yard. The old man calmly removed the bin and beckoned to me. 'Right you are, Mr Herriot, you can get on now.'

It had taken about twenty seconds.

Well, that was a relief, and anyway I knew what to do next. Lifting a sheet of corrugated iron which the farmer had ready I rushed in among the little pigs. I would pen them in a corner and the job would be over in no time.

But their mother's irritation had been communicated to the family. It was a big litter and there were sixteen of them hurtling around like little pink racehorses. I spent a long time diving frantically after them, jamming the sheet at a bunch only to see half of them streaking out the other end, and I might have gone on indefinitely had I not felt a gentle touch on my arm.

'Haud on, young man, haud on.' The old farmer looked at me kindly. 'If you'll nobbut stop runnin' after 'em they'll settle down. Just bide a minute.'

Slightly breathless, I stood by his side and listened as he addressed the little creatures.

'Giss-giss, giss-giss,' murmured Mr Stokill without moving. 'Giss-giss, giss-giss.'

The piglets slowed their headlong gallop to a trot, then, as though controlled by telepathy, they all stopped at once and stood in a pink group in one corner.

'Giss-giss,' said Mr Stokill approvingly, advancing almost imperceptibly with the sheet. 'Giss-giss.'

He unhurriedly placed the length of metal across the corner and jammed his foot against the bottom.

'Now then, put the toe of your wellington against t'other end and we 'ave 'em,' he said quietly.

After that the injection of the litter was a matter of a few minutes. Mr Stokill didn't say, 'Well, I'm teaching you a thing or two today, am I not?' There was no hint of triumph or self-congratulation in the calm old eyes. All he said was, 'I'm keepin' you busy this mornin', young man. I want you to look at a cow now. She's got a pea in her tit.'

'Peas' and other obstructions in the teats were very common in the days of hand milking. Some of them were floating milk calculi, others tiny pedunculated tumours, injuries to the teat lining, all sorts of things. It was a whole diverting little field in itself and I approached the cow with interest.

But I didn't get very near before Mr Stokill put his hand on my shoulder.

'Just a minute, Mr Herriot, don't touch 'er tit yet or she'll clout ye. She's an awd bitch. Wait a minute till ah rope 'er.'

'Oh right,' I said. 'But I'll do it.'

He hesitated. 'Ah reckon I ought to . . .'

'No, no, Mr Stokill that's quite unnecessary, I know how to stop a cow kicking.' I said primly. 'Kindly hand me that rope.'

'But . . . she's a bugger . . . kicks like a 'oss. She's a right good milker but . . .'

'Don't worry,' I said, smiling. 'I'll stop her little games.'

I began to unwind the rope. It was good to be able to demonstrate that I did know something about handling animals even though I had been qualified for only a few months. And it made a change to be told before and not after the job that a cow was a kicker. A cow once kicked me nearly to the other end of the byre and as I picked myself up the farmer said unemotionally, 'Aye, she's allus had a habit o' that.'

Yes, it was nice to be warned, and I passed the rope round the animal's body in front of the udder and pulled it tight in a slip knot. Just like they taught us at college. She was a scrawny red shorthorn with a woolly poll and she regarded me with a contemplative eye as I bent down.

'All right, lass,' I said soothingly, reaching under her and gently grasping the teat. I squirted a few jets of milk then something blocked the end. Ah yes, there it was, quite large and unattached. I felt sure I could work it through the orifice without cutting the sphincter.

I took a firmer grip, squeezed tightly and immediately a cloven foot shot out like a whip lash and smacked me solidly on the knee. It is a particularly painful spot to be kicked and I spent some time hopping round the byre and cursing in a fervent whisper.

The farmer followed me anxiously. 'Ee, ah'm sorry, Mr Herriot, she's a right awd bugger. Better let me . . .'

I held up a hand. 'No, Mr Stokill. I already have her roped. I just didn't tie it tight enough, that's all.' I hobbled back to the animal, loosened the knot then retied it, pulling till my eyes popped. When I had finished, her abdomen was lifted high and nipped in like a wasp-waisted Victorian lady of fashion.

'That'll fix you,' I grunted, and bent to my work again. A few spurts of milk then the thing was at the teat end again, a pinkish-white object peeping through the orifice. A little extra pressure and I would be able to fish it out with the hypodermic needle I had poised ready. I took a breath and gripped hard.

This time the hoof caught me half way up the shin bone. She hadn't been able to get so much height into it but it was just as painful. I sat down on a milking stool, rolled up my trouser leg and examined the roll of skin which hung like a diploma at the end of a long graze where the sharp hoof had dragged along.

'Now then, you've 'ad enough, young man.' Mr Stokill removed my rope and gazed at me with commiseration. 'Ordinary methods don't work with this 'un. I 'ave to milk her twice a day and ah knaw.'

He fetched a soiled length of plough cord which had obviously seen much service and fastened it round the cow's hock. The other end had a hook which he fitted into a ring on the byre wall. It was just the right length to stretch taut, pulling the leg slightly back.

The old man nodded. 'Now try.'

With a feeling of fatalism I grasped the teat again. And it was if the cow knew she was beaten. She never moved as I nipped hard and winkled out the offending obstruction. She couldn't do a thing about it.

'Ah, thank ye, lad,' the farmer said. 'That's champion. Been bothering me a bit has that. Didn't know what it was.' He held up a finger. 'One last job for ye. A young heifer with a bit o' stomach trouble, ah think. Saw her last night and she was a bit blown. She's in an outside buildin'.'

I put on my coat and we went out to where the wind welcomed us with savage glee. As the knife-like blast hit me, whistling up my nose and making my eyes water, I cowered in the lee of the stable.

'Where is this heifer?' I gasped.

Mr Stokill did not reply immediately. He was lighting another cigarette, apparently oblivious of the elements. He clamped the lid on an ancient brass lighter and jerked his thumb.

'Across the road. Up there.'

I followed his gesture over the buried walls, across the narrow roadway between the ploughed-out snow dunes to where the fell rose steeply in a sweep of unbroken white to join the leaden sky. Unbroken, that is, except for a tiny barn, a grey stone speck just visible on the last airy swell hundreds of feet up where the hillside joined the moorland above.

'Sorry,' I said, still crouching against the wall. 'I can't see anything.'

The old man, lounging in the teeth of the wind, looked at me in surprise. 'You can't? Why, t'barn's good enough to see, isn't it?'

'The barn?' I pointed a shaking finger at the heights. 'You mean that building? The heifer's surely not in there!'

'Aye, she is. Ah keep a lot o' me young beasts in them spots.'

'But . . . but . . .' I was gabbling now. 'We'll never get up there! That snow's three feet deep!'

He blew smoke pleasurably from his nostrils. 'We will, don't tha worry. Just hang on a second.'

He disappeared into the stable and after a few moments I peeped inside. He was saddling a fat brown cob and I stared as he led the little animal out, climbed stiffly on to a box and mounted.

Looking down at me he waved cheerfully. 'Well, let's be goin'. Have you got your stuff?'

Bewilderedly I filled my pockets. A bottle of bloat mixture, a trochar and cannula, a packet of gentian and nux vomica. I did it in the dull knowledge that there was no way I could get up that hill.

On the other side of the road an opening had been dug and Mr Stokill rode through. I slithered in his wake, looking up hopelessly at the great smooth wilderness rearing above us.

Mr Stokill turned in the saddle. 'Get haud on t'tail,' he said.

'I beg your pardon?'

'Get a haud of 'is tail.'

As in a dream I seized the bristly hairs.

'No, both 'ands,' the farmer said patiently.

'Like this?'

'That's grand, lad. Now 'ang on.'

He clicked his tongue, the cob plodded resolutely forward and so did I.

And it was easy! The whole world fell away beneath us as we soared upwards, and leaning back and enjoying it I watched the little valley unfold along its twisting length until I could see away into the main Dale with the great hills billowing round and white into the dark clouds.

At the barn the farmer dismounted. 'All right, young man?'

'All right, Mr Stokill.' As I followed him into the little building I smiled to myself. This old man had once told me that he left school when he was twelve, whereas I had spent most of the twenty-four years of my life in study. Yet when I looked back on the last hour or so I could come to only one conclusion.

He knew a lot more than I did.

Chapter Ten

I had plenty of company for Christmas that year. We were billeted in the Grand Hotel, the massive Victorian pile which dominated Scarborough in turreted splendour from its eminence above the sea, and the big dining room was packed with several hundred shouting airmen. The iron discipline was relaxed for a few hours to let the Yuletide spirit run free.

It was so different from other Christmases I had known that it ought to have remained like a beacon in my mind, but I know that my strongest memory of Christmas will always be bound up with a certain little cat.

I first saw her when I was called to see one of Mrs Ainsworth's dogs, and I looked in some surprise at the furry black creature sitting before the fire.

'I didn't know you had a cat,' I said.

The lady smiled. 'We haven't, this is Debbie.'

'Debbie?'

'Yes, at least that's what we call her. She's a stray. Comes here two or three times a week and we give her some food. I don't know where she lives but I believe she spends a lot of her time around one of the farms along the road.'

'Do you ever get the feeling that she wants to stay with you?'

'No.' Mrs Ainsworth shook her head. 'She's a timid little thing. Just creeps in, has some food then flits away. There's something so appealing about her but she doesn't seem to want to let me or anybody into her life.'

I looked again at the little cat. 'But she isn't just having food today.'

'That's right. It's a funny thing but every now and again she slips through here into the lounge and sits by the fire for a few minutes. It's as though she was giving herself a treat.'

'Yes ... I see what you mean.' There was no doubt there was something unusual in the attitude of the little animal. She was sitting bolt upright on the thick rug which lay before the fireplace in which the coals glowed and flamed. She made no effort to curl up or wash herself or do anything other than gaze quietly ahead. And there was something in the dusty black of her coat, the half-wild scrawny look of her, that gave me a clue. This was a special event in her life, a rare and wonderful thing; she was lapping up a comfort undreamed of in her daily existence.

As I watched she turned, crept soundlessly from the room and was gone.

'That's always the way with Debbie,' Mrs Ainsworth laughed. 'She never stays more than ten minutes or so, then she's off.'

She was a plumpish, pleasant-faced woman in her forties and the kind of client veterinary surgeons dream of; well off, generous, and the owner of three cosseted Basset hounds. And it only needed the habitually mournful expressions of one of the dogs to deepen a little and I was round there post haste. Today one of the Bassets had raised its paw and scratched its ear a couple of times and that was enough to send its mistress scurrying to the 'phone in great alarm.

So my visits to the Ainsworth home were frequent but undemanding, and I had ample opportunity to look out for the little cat which had intrigued me. On one occasion I spotted her nibbling daintily from a saucer at the kitchen door. As I watched she turned and almost floated on light footsteps into the hall then through the lounge door.

The three Bassets were already in residence, draped snoring on the fireside rug, but they seemed to be used to Debbie because two of them sniffed her in a bored manner and the third merely cocked a sleepy eye at her before flopping back on the rich pile.

Debbie sat among them in her usual posture; upright, intent, gazing absorbedly into the glowing coals. This time I tried to make friends with her. I approached her carefully but she leaned away as I stretched out my hand. However, by patient wheedling and soft talk I managed to touch her and gently stroked her cheek with one finger. There was a moment when she responded by putting her head on one side and rubbing back against my hand but soon she was ready to leave. Once outside the house she darted quickly along the road then through a gap in a hedge and the last I saw was the little black figure flitting over the rain-swept grass of a field.

'I wonder where she goes,' I murmured half to myself.

Mrs Ainsworth appeared at my elbow. 'That's something we've never been able to find out.'

It must have been nearly three months before I heard from Mrs Ainsworth, and in fact I had begun to wonder at the Bassets' long symptomless run when she came on the 'phone.

It was Christmas morning and she was apologetic. 'Mr Herriot, I'm so sorry to bother you today of all days. I should think you want a rest at Christmas like anybody else.' But her natural politeness could not hide the distress in her voice.

'Please don't worry about that,' I said. 'Which one is it this time?'

'It's not one of the dogs. It's . . . Debbie.'

'Debbie? She's at your house now?'

'Yes . . . but there's something wrong. Please come quickly.'

Driving through the market place I thought again that Darrowby on Christmas Day was like Dickens come to life; the empty square with the snow thick on the cobbles and hanging from the eaves of the fretted lines of roofs; the shops closed and the coloured lights of the Christmas trees winking at the windows of the clustering houses, warmly inviting against the cold white bulk of the fells behind.

Mrs Ainsworth's home was lavishly decorated with tinsel and holly, rows of drinks stood on the sideboard and the rich aroma of turkey and sage and onion stuffing wafted from the kitchen. But her eyes were full of pain as she led me through to the lounge.

Debbie was there all right, but this time everything was different. She wasn't sitting upright in her usual position; she was stretched quite motionless on her side, and huddled close to her lay a tiny black kitten.

I looked down in bewilderment. 'What's happened here?'

'It's the strangest thing,' Mrs Ainsworth replied. 'I haven't seen her for several weeks then she came in about two hours ago – sort of staggered into the kitchen, and she was carrying the kitten in her mouth. She took it through to the lounge and laid it on the rug and at first I was amused. But I could see all was not well because she sat as she usually does, but for a long time – over an hour – then she lay down like this and she hasn't moved.'

I knelt on the rug and passed my hand over Debbie's neck and ribs. She was thinner than ever, her fur dirty and mud-caked. She did not resist as I gently opened her mouth. The tongue and mucous membranes were abnormally pale and the lips ice-cold against my fingers. When I pulled down her eyelid and saw the dead white conjunctiva a knell sounded in my mind.

I palpated the abdomen with a grim certainty as to what I would find and there was no surprise, only a dull sadness as my fingers closed around a hard lobulated mass deep among the viscera. Massive lymphosarcoma. Terminal and hopeless. I put my stethoscope on her heart and listened to the increasingly faint, rapid beat then I straightened up and sat on the rug looking sightlessly into the fireplace, feeling the warmth of the flames on my face.

Mrs Ainsworth's voice seemed to come from afar. 'Is she ill, Mr Herriot?'

I hesitated. 'Yes . . . yes, I'm afraid so. She has a malignant growth.' I stood up. 'There's absolutely nothing I can do. I'm sorry.'

'Oh!' Her hand went to her mouth and she looked at me wide-eyed. When at last she spoke her voice trembled. 'Well, you must put her to sleep immediately. It's the only thing to do. We can't let her suffer.'

'Mrs Ainsworth,' I said. 'There's no need. She's dying now – in a coma – far beyond suffering.'

She turned quickly away from me and was very still as she fought with her emotions. Then she gave up the struggle and dropped on her knees beside Debbie.

'Oh, poor little thing!' she sobbed and stroked the cat's head again and again as the tears fell unchecked on the matted fur. 'What she must have come through. I feel I ought to have done more for her.'

For a few moments I was silent, feeling her sorrow, so discordant among the bright seasonal colours of this festive room. Then I spoke gently.

'Nobody could have done more than you,' I said. 'Nobody could have been kinder.'

'But I'd have kept her here – in comfort. It must have been terrible out there in the cold when she was so desperately ill – I daren't think about it. And having kittens, too – I . . . I wonder how many she did have?'

I shrugged. 'I don't suppose we'll ever know. Maybe just this one. It happens sometimes. And she brought it to you, didn't she?'

'Yes . . . that's right . . . she did . . . she did.' Mrs Ainsworth reached out and lifted the bedraggled black morsel. She smoothed her finger along the muddy fur and the tiny mouth opened in a soundless miaow. 'Isn't it strange? She was dying and she brought her kitten here. And on Christmas Day.'

I bent and put my hand on Debbie's heart. There was no beat.

I looked up. 'I'm afraid she's gone.' I lifted the small body, almost feather light, wrapped it in the sheet which had been spread on the rug and took it out to the car.

When I came back Mrs Ainsworth was still stroking the kitten. The tears had dried on her cheeks and she was bright-eyed as she looked at me.

'I've never had a cat before,' she said.

I smiled. 'Well it looks as though you've got one now.'

And she certainly had. That kitten grew rapidly into a sleek handsome cat with a boisterous nature which earned him the name of Buster. In every way he was the opposite to his timid little mother. Not for him the privations of the secret outdoor life; he stalked the rich carpets of the Ainsworth home like a king and the ornate collar he always wore added something more to his presence.

On my visits I watched his development with delight but the occasion which stays in my mind was the following Christmas Day, a year from his arrival.

I was out on my rounds as usual. I can't remember when I haven't had to work on Christmas Day because the animals have never got round to recognising it as a holiday; but with the passage of the years the vague resentment I used to feel has been replaced by philosophical acceptance. After all, as I tramped around the hillside barns in the frosty air I was working up a better appetite for my turkey than all the millions lying in bed or slumped by the fire; and this was aided by the innumerable aperitifs I received from the hospitable farmers.

I was on my way home, bathed in a rosy glow. I had consumed several whiskies – the kind the inexpert Yorkshiremen pour as though it was ginger ale – and I had finished with a glass of old Mrs Earnshaw's rhubarb wine which had seared its way straight to my toenails. I heard the cry as I was passing Mrs Ainsworth's house.

'Merry Christmas, Mr Herriot!' She was letting a visitor out of the front door and she waved at me gaily. 'Come in and have a drink to warm you up.'

I didn't need warming up but I pulled in to the kerb without hesitation. In the house there was all the festive cheer of last year and the same glorious whiff of sage and onion which set my gastric juices surging. But there was not the sorrow; there was Buster.

He was darting up to each of the dogs in turn, ears pricked, eyes blazing with devilment, dabbing a paw at them then streaking away.

Mrs Ainsworth laughed. 'You know, he plagues the life out of them. Gives them no peace.'

She was right. To the Bassets, Buster's arrival was rather like the intrusion of an irreverent outsider into an exclusive London club. For a long time they had led a life of measured grace; regular sedate walks with their mistress, superb food in ample quantities and long snoring sessions on the rugs and armchairs. Their days followed one upon another in unruffled calm. And then came Buster.

He was dancing up to the youngest dog again, sideways this time, head on one side, goading him. When he started boxing with both paws it was too much even for the Basset. He dropped his dignity and rolled over with the cat in a brief wrestling match.

'I want to show you something.' Mrs Ainsworth lifted a hard rubber ball from the sideboard and went out to the garden, followed by Buster. She threw the ball across the lawn and the cat bounded after it over the frosted grass, the muscles rippling under the black sheen of his coat. He seized the ball in his teeth, brought it back to his mistress, dropped it at her feet and waited expectantly. She threw it and he brought it back again.

I gasped incredulously. A feline retriever!

The Bassets looked on disdainfully. Nothing would ever have induced them to chase a ball, but Buster did it again and again as though he would never tire of it.

Mrs Ainsworth turned to me. 'Have you ever seen anything like that?'

'No,' I replied. 'I never have. He is a most remarkable cat.'

She snatched Buster from his play and we went back into the house where she held him close to her face, laughing as the big cat purred and arched himself ecstatically against her cheek.

Looking at him, a picture of health and contentment, my mind went back to his mother. Was it too much to think that that dying little creature with the last of her strength had carried her kitten to the only haven of comfort and warmth she had ever known in the hope that it would be cared for there? Maybe it was.

But it seemed I wasn't the only one with such fancies. Mrs Ainsworth turned to me and though she was smiling her eyes were wistful.

'Debbie would be pleased,' she said.

I nodded. 'Yes, she would. . . . It was just a year ago today she brought him, wasn't it?'

'That's right.' She hugged Buster to her again. 'The best Christmas present I ever had.'

Chapter Eleven

I stared in disbelief at the dial of the weighing machine. Nine stone seven pounds! I had lost two stones since joining the RAF. I was cowering in my usual corner in Boots' Chemist's shop in Scarborough, where I had developed the habit of a weekly weigh-in to keep a morbid eye on my progressive emaciation. It was incredible and it wasn't all due to the tough training.

On our arrival in Scarborough we had a talk from our Flight Commander, Flt Lieut Barnes. He looked us over with a contemplative eye and said, 'You won't know yourselves when you leave here.' That man wasn't kidding.

We were never at rest. It was PT and Drill, PT and Drill, over and over. Hours of bending and stretching and twisting down on the prom in singlets and shorts while the wind whipped over us from the wintry sea. Hours of marching under the bellowings of our sergeant; quick march, slow march, about turn. We even marched to our navigation classes, bustling along at the RAF quick time, arms swinging shoulder high.

They marched us regularly to the top of Castle Hill where we fired off every conceivable type of weapon; twelve bores, .22 rifles, revolvers, Browning machine guns. We even stabbed at dummies with bayonets. In between they had us swimming, playing football or rugby or running for miles along the beach and on the cliff tops towards Filey.

At first I was too busy to see any change in myself, but one morning after a few weeks our flight was coming to the end of a five-mile run. We dropped down from the Spa to a long stretch of empty beach and the sergeant shouted, 'Right, sprint to those rocks! Let's see who gets there first!'

We all took off on the last hundred yards' dash and I was mildly surprised to find that the first man past the post was myself – and I wasn't really out of breath. That was when the realisation hit me. Mr Barnes had been right. I didn't know myself.

When I left Helen I was a cosseted young husband with a little double chin and the beginnings of a spare tyre, and now I was a lithe, tireless greyhound. I was certainly fit, but there was something wrong. I shouldn't have been as thin as this. Another factor was at work.

In Yorkshire when a man goes into a decline during his wife's pregnancy they giggle behind their hands and say he is 'carrying' the baby. I never laugh at these remarks because I am convinced I 'carried' my son.

I base this conclusion on a variety of symptoms. It would be an exaggeration to say I suffered from morning sickness, but my suspicions were certainly aroused when I began to feel a little queasy in the early part of the day. This was followed by a growing uneasiness as Helen's time drew near and a sensation, despite my physical condition, of being drained and miserable. With the onset in the later stages of unmistakable labour pains in my lower abdomen all doubts were resolved and I knew I had to do something about it.

I had to see Helen. After all, she was just over that hill which I could see from the top windows of the Grand. Maybe that wasn't strictly true, but at least I was in Yorkshire and a bus would take me to her in three hours. The snag was that there was no leave from ITW. They left us in no doubt about that. They said the discipline was as tough as a Guards regiment and the restrictions just as rigid. I would get compassionate leave when the baby was born, but I couldn't wait till then. The grim knowledge that any attempt to dodge off unofficially would be like a minor desertion and would be followed by serious consequences, even prison, didn't weigh with me.

As one of my comrades put it: 'One bloke tried it and finished up in the Glasshouse. It isn't worth it, mate.'

But it was no good. I am normally a law-abiding citizen but I had not a single scruple. I had to see Helen. A surreptitious study of the timetables revealed that there was a bus at 2 p.m. which got to Darrowby at five o'clock, and another leaving Darrowby at six which arrived in Scarborough at nine. Six hours travelling to have one hour with Helen. It was worth it.

At first I couldn't see a way of getting to the bus station at two o'clock in the afternoon because we were never free at that time, but my chance came quite unexpectedly. One Friday lunchtime we learned that there were no more classes that day but we were confined to the Grand till evening. Most of my friends collapsed thankfully on to their beds, but I slunk down the long flights of stone stairs and took up a position in the foyer where I could watch the front door.

There was a glass-fronted office on one side of the entrance where the SPs sat and kept an eye on all departures. There was only one on duty today and I waited till he turned and moved to the back of the room then I walked quietly past him and out into the square.

That part had been almost too easy, but I felt naked and exposed as I crossed the deserted space between the Grand and the hotels on the opposite side. It was better once I had rounded the corner and I set off at a brisk pace for the west.

All I needed was a little bit of luck and as I pressed, dry-mouthed, along the empty street it seemed I had found it. The shock when I saw the two burly SPs strolling towards me was like a blow but was immediately followed by a strange calm.

They would ask me for the pass I didn't have, then they would want to know what I was doing there. It wouldn't be much good telling them I had just popped out for a breath of air – this street led to both the bus and railway stations and it wouldn't need a genius to rumble my little game. Anyway, there was no cover here, no escape, and I wondered idly if there had ever been a veterinary surgeon in the Glasshouse. Maybe I was about to set up some kind of a record.

Then behind me I heard the rhythmic tramp of marching feet and the shrill "eft 'ight, 'eft, 'ight,' that usually went with it. I turned and saw a long blue column approaching with a corporal in charge. As they swung past me I looked again at the SPs and my heart gave a thud. They were laughing into each other's faces at some private joke; they hadn't seen me. Without thinking I tagged on to the end of the marching men and within a few seconds was past the SPs unnoticed.

With my mind working with the speed of desperation, it seemed I would be safest where I was till I could break away in the direction of the bus station. For a while I had a glorious feeling of anonymity then the corporal, still shouting, glanced back. He faced to the front again then turned back more slowly for another look. He appeared to find something interesting because he shortened his stride till he was marching opposite me.

As he looked me up and down I examined him in turn from the corner of my eye. He was a shrivelled, runtish creature with fierce little eyes glinting from a pallid, skull-like face. It was some time before he spoke.

'Who the — hell are you?' he enquired conversationally. It was the number one awkward question but I discerned the faintest gleam of hope; he had spoken in the unmistakable harsh, glottal accent of my home town.

'Herriot, corporal. Two flight, four squadron,' I replied in my broadest Glasgow.

'Two flight, four . . .! This is one flight, three squadron. What the — hell are ye daein' here?'

Arms swinging high, staring rigidly ahead, I took a deep breath. Concealment was futile now.

'Tryin' to get tae see ma wife, corp. She's havin' a baby soon.'

I glanced quickly at him. His was not the kind of face to reveal weakness by showing surprise but his eyes widened fractionally. 'Get tae see yer wife? Are ye — daft or whit?'

'It's no' far, corp. She lives in Darrowby. Three hours in the bus. Ah wid be back tonight.'

'Back tonight! Ye want yer — heid examinin'!'

'I've got tae go!'

'Eyes front!' he screamed suddenly at the men before us. "eft 'ight, 'eft 'ight!' Then he turned and studied me as though I were an unbelievable phenomenon. He was interesting to me, too, as a typical product of the bad times in Glasgow between the wars. Stunted, undernourished, but as tough and belligerent as a ferret.

'D'ye no' ken,' he said at length, 'that ye get — leave when yer wife has the wean?'

'Aye, but a canna' wait that long. Gimme a break, corp.'

'Give ye a — break! D'ye want tae get me — shot?'

'No, corp, just want tae get to the bus station.'

'Jesus! Is that a'?' He gave me a final incredulous look before quickening his steps to the head of the column. When he returned he surveyed me again.

'Whit part o' Glesca are ye frae?'

'Scotstounhill,' I replied. 'How about you?'

'Govan.'

I turned my head slightly towards him. 'Ranger supporter, eh?'

He did not change expression, but an eyebrow flickered and I knew I had him.

'Whit a team!' I murmured reverently. 'Many's the time I've stood on the terraces at Ibrox.'

He said nothing and I began to recite the names of the great Rangers team of the thirties. 'Dawson, Gray, McDonald, Meiklejohn, Simpson, Brown.' His eyes took on a dreamy expression and by the time I had intoned 'Archibald, Marshall, English, McPhail and Morton,' there was something near to a wistful smile on his lips.

Then he appeared to shake himself back to normality.

"Eft 'ight, 'eft 'ight!' he bawled. 'C'mon, c'mon, pick it up!' Then he muttered to me from the corner of his mouth. 'There's the — bus station. When we march past it run like —!'

He took off again, shouting to the head of the flight, I saw the buses and the windows of the waiting room on my left and dived across the road and through the door. I snatched off my cap and sat trembling among a group of elderly farmers and their wives. Through the glass I could see the long lines of blue moving away down the street and I could still hear the shouts of the corporal.

But he didn't turn round and I saw only his receding back, the narrow shoulders squared, the bent legs stepping it out in time with his men. I never saw him again but to this day I wish I could take him to Ibrox and watch the Rangers with him and maybe buy him a half and half pint at one of the Govan pubs. It wouldn't have mattered if he had turned out to be a Celtic supporter at that decisive moment because I had the Celtic team on my tongue all ready to trot out, starting with Kennaway, Cook, McGonigle. It is not the only time my profound knowledge of football has stood me in good stead.

Sitting on the bus, still with my cap on my lap to avoid attracting attention, it struck me that the whole world changed within a mile or two as we left the town. Back there the war was everywhere, filling people's minds and eyes and thoughts; the teeming thousands of uniformed men, the RAF and army vehicles, the almost palpable atmosphere of anticipation and suspense. And suddenly it all just stopped.

It vanished as the wide sweep of grey-blue sea fell beneath the rising ground behind the town, and as the bus trundled westward I looked out on a landscape of untroubled peace. The long moist furrows of the new-turned soil glittered under the pale February sun, contrasting with the gold stubble fields and the grassy pastures where sheep clustered around their feeding troughs. There was no wind and the smoke rose straight from the farm chimneys and the bare branches of the roadside trees were still as they stretched across the cold sky.

There were many things that pulled at me. A man in breeches and leggings carrying on his shoulder a bale of hay to some outlying cattle; a group of farm men burning hedge clippings and the fragrance of the wood smoke finding its way into the bus. The pull was stronger as the hours passed and the beginnings of my own familiar countryside began to appear beyond the windows. Maybe it was a good thing I didn't see Darrowby; Helen's home was near the bus route and I dropped off well short of the town.

She was alone in the house and she turned her head as I walked into the kitchen. The delight on her face was mixed with astonishment; in fact I know we were both astonished, she because I was so skinny and I because she was so fat. Helen, with the baby only two weeks away, was very large indeed, but not too large for me to get my arms around her, and we stood there in the middle of the flagged floor clasped together for a long time with neither of us saying much.

She cooked me egg and chips and sat by me while I ate. We carried on a rather halting conversation and it came to me with a bump that my mind had been forced on to different tracks since I had left her. In those few months my brain had become saturated with the things of my new life – even my mouth was full of RAF slang and jargon. In our bed-sitter we used to talk about my cases, the funny things that happened on my rounds, but now, I thought helplessly, there wasn't much point in telling her that AC2 Phillips was on jankers again, that vector triangles were the very devil, that Don McGregor thought he had discovered the secret of Sergeant Hynd's phenomenally shiny boots.

But it really didn't matter. My worries melted as I looked at her. I had been wondering if she was well and there she was, bouncing with energy, shining-eyed, rosy-cheeked and beautiful. There was only one jarring note and it was a strange one. Helen was wearing a 'maternity dress' which expanded with the passage of time by means of an opening down one side. Anyway, I hated it. It was blue with a high red collar and I thought it cheap-looking and ugly. I was aware that austerity had taken over in England and that a lot of things were shoddy, but I desperately wished my wife had something better to wear. In all my life there have been very few occasions when I badly wanted more money and that was one of them, because on my wage of three shillings a day as an AC2 I was unable to drape her with expensive clothes.

The hour winged past and it seemed no time at all before I was back on the top road waiting in the gathering darkness for the Scarborough bus. The journey back was a bit dreary as the black-out vehicle bumped and rattled its way through the darkened villages and over the long stretches of anonymous country-side. It was cold, too, but I sat there happily with the memory of Helen wrapped around me like a warm quilt.

The whole day had been a triumph. I had got away by a lucky stroke and there would be no problem getting back into the Grand because one of my pals would be on sentry duty and it would be a case of 'pass friend'. Closing my eyes in the gloom I could still feel Helen in my arms and I smiled to myself at the memory of her bounding healthiness. She looked marvellous, the egg and chips tasted wonderful, everything was great.

Except that one discord which jangled still. Oh, how I hated that dress!

Chapter Twelve

'Hey you! Where the 'ell d'you think you're goin'?'

Coming from the RAF Special Police it was a typical mode of address and the man who barked it out wore the usual truculent expression.

'Extra navigation class, corporal,' I replied.

'Lemme see your pass!'

He snatched it from my hand, read it and returned it without looking at me. I slunk out into the street feeling like a prisoner on parole.

Not all the SPs were like that but I found most of them lacking in charm. And it brought home to me with a rush something which had been slowly dawning on me ever since I joined the Air Force; that I had been spoiled for quite a long time now. Spoiled by the fact that I had always been treated with respect because I was a veterinary surgeon, a member of an honourable profession. And I had taken it entirely for granted.

Now I was an AC2, the lowest form of life in the RAF, and the 'Hey you!' was a reflection of my status. The Yorkshire farmers don't rush out and kiss you, but their careful friendliness and politeness is something which I have valued even more since my service days. Because that was when I stopped taking it for granted.

Mind you, you have to put up with a certain amount of cheek in most jobs, and veterinary practice is no exception. Even now I can recall the glowering face of Ralph Beamish the racehorse trainer, as he watched me getting out of my car.

'Where's Mr Farnon?' he grunted.

My toes curled. I had heard that often enough, especially among the horse fraternity around Darrowby.

'I'm sorry, Mr Beamish, but he'll be away all day and I thought I'd better come along rather than leave it till tomorrow.'

He made no attempt to hide his disgust. He blew out his fat, purpled cheeks, dug his hands deep in his breeches pockets and looked at the sky with a martyred air.

'Well come on, then.' He turned and stumped away on his short, thick legs towards one of the boxes which bordered the yard. I sighed inwardly as I followed him. Being an unhorsey vet in Yorkshire was a penance at times, especially in a racing stable like this which was an equine shrine. Siegfried, apart altogether from his intuitive skill, was able to talk the horse language. He could discuss effortlessly and at length the breeding and points of his patients; he rode, he hunted, he even looked the part with his long aristocratic face, clipped moustache and lean frame.

The trainers loved him and some, like Beamish, took it as a mortal insult when he failed to come in person to minister to their valuable charges.

He called to one of the lads who opened a box door.

'He's in there,' he muttered. 'Came in lame from exercise this morning.'

The lad led out a bay gelding and there was no need to trot the animal to diagnose the affected leg; he nodded down on his near fore in an unmistakable way.

'I think he's lame in the shoulder,' Beamish said.

I went round the other side of the horse and picked up the off fore. I cleaned out the frog and sole with a hoof knife; there was no sign of bruising and no sensitivity when I tapped the handle of the knife against the horn.

I felt my way up over the coronet to the fetlock and after some palpation I located a spot near the distal end of the metacarpus which was painful on pressure.

I looked up from my crouching position. 'This seems to be the trouble, Mr Beamish. I think he must have struck into himself with his hind foot just there.'

'Where?' The trainer leaned over me and peered down at the leg. 'I can't see anything.'

'No, the skin isn't broken, but he flinches if you press here.'

Beamish prodded the place with a stubby forefinger.

'Well, he does,' he grunted. 'But he'd flinch anywhere if you squeeze him like you're doing.'

My hackles began to rise at his tone but I kept my voice calm. 'I'm sure that's what it is. I should apply a hot antiphlogistine poultice just above the fetlock and alternate with a cold hose on it twice a day.'

'Well, I'm just as sure you're wrong. It's not down there at all. The way that horse carries his leg he's hurt his shoulder.' He gestured to the lad. 'Harry, see that he gets some heat on that shoulder right away.'

If the man had struck me I couldn't have felt worse. I opened my mouth to argue but he was walking away.

'There's another horse I want you to look at,' he said. He led the way into a nearby box and pointed to a big brown animal with obvious signs of blistering on the tendons of a fore limb.

'Mr Farnon put a red blister on that leg six months ago. He's been resting in here ever since. He's going sound now – d'you think he's ready to go out?'

I went over and ran my fingers over the length of the flexor tendons, feeling for signs of thickening. There was none. Then I lifted the foot and as I explored further I found a tender area in the superficial flexor.

I straightened up. 'He's still a bit sore,' I said. 'I think it would be safer to keep him in for a bit longer.'

'Can't agree with you,' Beamish snapped. He turned to the lad. 'Turn him out, Harry.'

I stared at him. Was this a deliberate campaign to make me feel small? Was he trying to rub in the fact that he didn't think much of me? Anyway, he was beginning to get under my skin and I hoped my burning face wasn't too obvious.

'One thing more,' Beamish said. 'There's a horse through here been coughing. Have a look at him before you go.'

We went through a narrow passage into a smaller yard and Harry entered a box and got hold of a horse's head collar. I followed him, fishing out my thermometer.

As I approached the animal's rear end he laid back his ears, whickered and began to caper around. I hesitated, then nodded to the lad.

'Lift his fore leg while I take his temperature, will you?' I said.

The lad bent down and seized the foot but Beamish broke in. 'Don't bother, Harry, there's no need for that. He's quiet as a sheep.'

I paused for a moment. I felt I was right but my stock was low on this establishment. I shrugged, lifted the tail and pushed the thermometer into the rectum.

The two hind feet hit me almost simultaneously but as I sailed backwards through the door I remember thinking quite clearly that the one on the chest had made contact fractionally before the one on the abdomen. But my thoughts were rapidly clouded by the fact that the lower hoof had landed full on my solar plexus.

Stretched on the concrete of the yard I gasped and groaned in a frantic search for breath. There was a moment when I was convinced I was going to die but at last a long wailing respiration came to my aid and I struggled painfully into a sitting position. Through the open door I could see Harry hanging on to the horse's head and staring at me with frightened eyes. Mr Beamish, on the other hand, showed no interest in my plight; he was anxiously examining the horse's hind feet one after the other. Obviously he was worried lest they may have sustained some damage by coming into contact with my nasty hard ribs.

Slowly I got up and drew some long breaths. I was shaken but not really hurt. And I suppose it was instinct that had made me hang on to my thermometer; the delicate tube was still in my hand.

My only emotion as I went back into the box was cold rage.

'Lift that bloody foot like I told you!' I shouted at the unfortunate Harry.

'Right, sir! Sorry, sir!' He bent, lifted the foot and held it cupped firmly in his hands.

I turned to Beamish to see if he had any observation to make, but the trainer was silent, gazing at the big animal expressionlessly.

This time I took the temperature without incident. It was 101°F. I moved to the head and opened the nostril with finger and thumb, revealing a slight muco-purulent discharge. Submaxillary and post-pharyngeal glands were normal.

'He's got a bit of cold,' I said. 'I'll give him an injection and leave you some sulphonamide – that's what Mr Farnon uses in these cases' If my final sentence reassured him in any way he gave no sign, watching dead-faced as I injected 10 cc of Prontosil.

Before I left I took a half-pound packet of sulphonamide from the car boot. 'Give him three ounces of this immediately in a pint of water, then follow it with one and a half ounces night and morning and let us know if he isn't a lot better in two days.'

Mr Beamish received the medicine unsmilingly and as I opened the car door I felt a gush of relief that the uncomfortable visit was at an end. It seemed to have lasted a long time and there had been no glory for me in it. I was starting the engine when one of the little apprentices panted up to the trainer.

'It's Almira, sir. I think she's chokin'!'

'Choking!' Beamish stared at the boy then whipped round to me. 'Almira's the best filly I have. You'd better come!'

It wasn't over yet, then. With a feeling of doom I hurried after the squat figure back into the yard where another lad stood by the side of a beautiful chestnut filly. And as I saw her a cold hand closed around my heart. I had been dealing with trivia but this was different.

She stood immobile, staring ahead with a peculiar intensity. The rise and fall of her ribs was accompanied by a rasping, bubbling wheeze and at each intake her nostrils flared wildly. I had never seen a horse breathe like this. And there were other things; saliva drooled from her lips and every few seconds she gave a retching cough.

I turned to the apprentice. 'When did this start?'

'Not long ago, sir. I saw her an hour since and she were as right as a bobbin.'

'Are you sure?'

'Aye, I was givin' 'er some hay. There was nowt ailin' her then.'

'What the devil's wrong with her?' Beamish exclaimed.

Well, it was a good question and I didn't have a clue to the answer. As I walked bemusedly round the animal, taking in the trembling limbs and terrified eyes, a jumble of thoughts crowded my brain. I had seen 'choking' horses – the dry choke when the gullet becomes impacted with food – but they didn't look like this. I felt my way along the course of the oesophagus and it was perfectly clear. And anyway the respiration was quite different. This filly looked as though she had some obstruction in her airflow. But what . . .? And how . . .? Could there be a foreign body in there? Just possible, but that was something else I had never seen.

'Well, damn it, I'm asking you! What is it? What d'you make of her?' Mr Beamish was becoming impatient and I couldn't blame him.

I was aware that I was slightly breathless. 'Just a moment while I listen to her lungs.'

'Just a moment!' the trainer burst out. 'Good God, man, we haven't got many moments! This horse could die!'

He didn't have to tell me. I had seen that ominous trembling of the limbs before and now the filly was beginning to sway a little. Time was running out.

Dry mouthed, I auscultated the chest. I knew there was nothing wrong with her lungs – the trouble seemed to be in the throat area – but it gave me a little more time to think. Even with the stethoscope in my ears I could still hear Beamish's voice.

'It would have to be this one! Sir Eric Horrocks gave five thousand pounds for her last year. She's the most valuable animal in my stables. Why did this have to happen?'

Groping my way over the ribs, my heart thudding, I heartily agreed with him. Why in heaven's name did I have to walk into this nightmare? And with a man like Beamish who had no faith in me.

He stepped forward and clutched my arm. 'Are you sure Mr Farnon isn't available?'

'I'm sorry,' I replied huskily. 'He's over thirty miles away.'

The trainer seemed to shrivel within himself. 'That's it then. We're finished. She's dying.'

And he was right. The filly had begun to reel about, the breathing louder and more stertorous than ever, and I had difficulty in keeping the stethoscope on her chest wall. It was when I was resting my hand on her flank to steady her that I noticed the little swelling under the skin. It was a circular plaque, like a penny pushed under the tissue. I glanced sharply at it. Yes, it was clearly visible. And there was another one higher up on the back . . . and another and another. My heart gave a quick double thump . . . so that was it.

'What am I going to tell Sir Eric?' the trainer groaned. 'That his filly is dead and the vet didn't know what was wrong with her?' He glared desperately around him as though in the faint hope that Siegfried might magically appear from nowhere.

I called over my shoulder as I trotted towards the car. 'I never said I didn't know. I do know. She's got urticaria.'

He came shambling after me 'Urti . . . what the blazes is that?'

'Nettlerash,' I replied, fumbling among my bottles for the adrenalin.

'Nettlerash!' His eyes widened. 'But that couldn't cause all this!'

I drew 5 cc of the adrenalin into the syringe and started back. 'It's nothing to do with nettles. It's an allergic condition, usually pretty harmless, but in a very few cases it causes oedema of the larynx – that's what we've got here.'

It was difficult to raise the vein as the filly staggered around, but she came to rest for a few seconds and I dug my thumb into the jugular furrow. As the big vessel came up tense and turgid I thrust in the needle and injected the adrenalin. Then I stepped back and stood by the trainer's side.

Neither of us said anything. The spectacle of the toiling animal and the harrowing sound of the breathing absorbed us utterly.

The grim knowledge that she was on the verge of suffocation appalled me and when she stumbled and almost fell the hand in my pocket gripped more tightly on the scalpel which I had taken from my car along with the adrenalin. I knew only too well that tracheotomy was indicated here but I didn't have a tube with me. If the filly did go off her legs I should have to start cutting into her windpipe, but I put the thought away from me. For the moment I had to depend on the adrenalin.

Beamish stretched out a hand in a helpless gesture. 'It's hopeless, isn't it?' he whispered.

I shrugged. 'There's a small chance. If the injection can reduce the fluid in the larynx in time . . . we'll just have to wait.'

He nodded and I could read more than one emotion in his face; not just the dread of breaking the news to the famous owner but the distress of a horse-lover as he witnessed the plight of the beautiful animal.

At first I thought it was imagination, but it seemed that the breathing was becoming less stertorous. Then as I hovered in an agony of uncertainty I noticed that the salivation was diminishing; she was able to swallow.

From that moment events moved with unbelievable rapidity. The symptoms of allergies appear with dramatic suddenness but mercifully they often disappear as quickly following treatment. Within fifteen minutes the filly looked almost normal. There was still a slight wheeze in her respirations but she was looking around her, quite free from distress.

Beamish, who had been watching like a man in a daze, pulled a handful of hay from a bale and held it out to her. She snatched it eagerly from his hand and began to eat with great relish.

'I can't believe it,' the trainer muttered almost to himself. 'I've never seen anything work as fast as that injection.'

I felt as though I was riding on a pink cloud with all the tension and misery flowing from me in a joyful torrent. Thank God there were moments like this among the traumas of veterinary work; the sudden transition from despair to triumph, from shame to pride.

I almost floated to the car and as I settled in my seat Beamish put his face to the open window.

'Mr Herriot . . .' He was not a man to whom gracious speech came easily and his cheeks, roughened and weathered by years of riding on the open moor, twitched as he sought for words. 'Mr Herriot, I've been thinking . . . you don't have to be a horsey man to cure horses, do you?'

There was something like an appeal in his eyes as we gazed at each other. I laughed suddenly and his expression relaxed.

'That's right,' I said, and drove away.

Chapter Thirteen

Do dogs have a sense of humour?

I felt I needed all mine as I stood on guard outside the Grand. It was after midnight, with a biting wind swirling across the empty square, and I was so cold and bored that it was a relief even to slap the butt of my rifle in salute as a solitary officer went by.

Wryly I wondered how, after my romantic ideas of training to be a pilot, I came to be defending the Grand Hotel at Scarborough against all comers. No doubt there was something comic in the situation and I suppose that was what set my mind wandering in the direction of Farmer Bailes' dog, Shep.

Mr Bailes' little place was situated about half way along Highburn Village and to get into the farmyard you had to walk twenty yards or so between five-foot walls. On the left was the neighbouring house, on the right the front garden of the farm. In this garden Shep lurked for most of the day.

He was a huge dog, much larger than the average collie. In fact I am convinced he was part Alsatian because though he had a luxuriant black and white coat there was something significant in the massive limbs and in the noble brown-shaded head with its upstanding ears. He was quite different from the stringy little animals I saw on my daily round.

As I walked between the walls my mind was already in the byre, just visible at the far end of the yard. Because one of the Bailes cows, Rose by name, had the kind of obscure digestive ailment which interferes with veterinary surgeons' sleep. They are so difficult to diagnose. This animal had begun to grunt and go off her milk two days ago and when I had seen her yesterday I had flitted from one possibility to the other. Could be a wire. But the fourth stomach was contracting well and there were plenty of rumenal sounds. Also she was eating a little hay in a half-hearted way.

Could it be impaction . . .? Or a partial torsion of the gut . . .? There was abdominal pain without a doubt and that nagging temperature of 102.5° – that was damn like a wire. Of course I could settle the whole thing by opening the cow up, but Mr Bailes was an old-fashioned type and didn't like the idea of my diving into his animal unless I was certain of my diagnosis. And I wasn't – there was no getting away from that.

Anyway, I had built her up at the front end so that she was standing with her fore feet on a half door and had given her a strong oily purgative. 'Keep the bowels open and trust in God,' an elderly colleague had once told me. There was a lot in that.

I was half way down the alley between the walls with the hope bright before me that my patient would be improved when from nowhere an appalling explosion of sound blasted into my right ear. It was Shep again.

The wall was just the right height for the dog to make a leap and bark into the ear of the passers by. It was a favourite gambit of his and I had been caught before; but never so successfully as now. My attention had been so far away and the dog had timed his jump to a split second so that his bark came at the highest point, his teeth only inches from my face. And his voice befitted his size, a great bull bellow surging from the depths of his powerful chest and booming from his gaping jaws.

I rose several inches into the air and when I descended, heart thumping, head singing, I glared over the wall. But as usual all I saw was the hairy form bounding away out of sight round the corner of the house.

That was what puzzled me. Why did he do it? Was he a savage creature with evil designs on me or was it his idea of a joke? I never got near enough to him to find out.

I wasn't in the best of shape to receive bad news and that was what awaited me in the byre. I had only to look at the farmer's face to know that the cow was worse.

'Ah reckon she's got a stoppage,' Mr Bailes muttered gloomily.

I gritted my teeth. The entire spectrum of abdominal disorders were lumped as 'stoppages' by the older race of farmers. 'The oil hasn't worked, then?'

'Nay, she's nobbut passin' little hard bits. It's a proper stoppage, ah tell you.'

'Right, Mr Bailes,' I said with a twisted smile. 'We'll have to try something stronger.' I brought in from my car the gastric lavage outfit I loved so well and which has so sadly disappeared from my life. The long rubber stomach tube, the wooden gag with its leather straps to buckle behind the horns. As I pumped in the two gallons of warm water rich in formalin and sodium chloride I felt like Napoleon sending in the Old Guard at Waterloo. If this didn't work nothing would.

And yet I didn't feel my usual confidence. There was something different here. But I had to try. I had to do something to start this cow's insides functioning because I did not like the look of her today. The soft grunt was still there and her eyes had begun to retreat into her head – the worst sign of all in bovines. And she had stopped eating altogether.

Next morning I was driving down the single village street when I saw Mrs Bailes coming out of the shop. I drew up and pushed my head out of the window.

'How's Rose this morning, Mrs Bailes?'

She rested her basket on the ground and looked down at me gravely. 'Oh, she's bad, Mr Herriot. Me husband thinks she's goin' down fast. If you want to find him you'll have to go across the field there. He's mendin' the door in that little barn.'

A sudden misery enveloped me as I drove over to the gate leading into the field. I left the car in the road and lifted the latch.

'Damn! Damn! Damn!' I muttered as I trailed across the green. I had a nasty feeling that a little tragedy was building up here. If this animal died it would be a sickening blow to a small farmer with ten cows and a few pigs. I should be able to do something about it and it was a depressing thought that I was getting nowhere.

And yet, despite it all, I felt peace stealing into my soul. It was a large field and I could see the barn at the far end as I walked with the tall grass brushing my knees. It was a meadow ready for cutting and suddenly I realised that it was high summer, the sun was hot and that every step brought the fragrance of clover and warm grass rising about me into the crystal freshness of the air. Somewhere nearby a field of broad beans was in full flower and as the exotic scent drifted across I found myself inhaling with half-closed eyes as though straining to discern the ingredients of the glorious melange.

And then there was the silence; it was the most soothing thing of all. That and the feeling of being alone. I looked drowsily around at the empty green miles sleeping under the sunshine. Nothing stirred, there was no sound.

Then without warning the ground at my feet erupted in an incredible blast of noise. For a dreadful moment the blue sky was obscured by an enormous hairy form and a red mouth went 'WAAAHH!' in my face. Almost screaming, I staggered back and as I glared wildly I saw Shep disappearing at top speed towards the gate. Concealed in the deep herbage right in the middle of the field he had waited till he saw the whites of my eyes before making his assault.

Whether he had been there by accident or whether he had spotted me arriving and slunk into position I shall never know, but from his point of view the result must have been eminently satisfactory because it was certainly the worst fright I have ever had. I live a life which is well larded with scares and alarms, but this great dog rising bellowing from that empty landscape was something on its own. I have heard of cases where sudden terror and stress has caused involuntary evacuation of the bowels and I know without question that this was the occasion when I came nearest to suffering that unhappy fate.

I was still trembling when I reached the barn and hardly said a word as Mr Bailes led me back across the road to the farm.

And it was like rubbing it in when I saw my patient. The flesh had melted from her and she stared at the wall apathetically from sunken eyes. The doom-laden grunt was louder.

'She must have a wire!' I muttered. 'Let her loose for a minute, will you?'

Mr Bailes undid the chain and Rose walked along the byre. At the end she turned and almost trotted back to her stall, jumping quite freely over the gutter. My Bible in those days was Udall's *Practice of Veterinary Medicine* and the great man stated therein that if a cow moved freely she was unlikely to have a foreign body in her reticulum. I pinched her withers and she didn't complain . . . it had to be something else.

'It's worst stoppage ah've seen for a bit,' said Mr Bailes. 'Ah gave her a dose of some right powerful stuff this mornin' but it's done no good.'

I passed a weary hand over my brow. 'What was that, Mr Bailes?' It was always a bad sign when the client started using his own medicine.

The farmer reached to the cluttered windowsill and handed me a bottle. 'Doctor Hornibrook's Stomach Elixir. A sovereign remedy for all diseases of cattle.' The Doctor, in top hat and frock coat, looked confidently out at me from the label as I pulled out the cork and took a sniff. I blinked and staggered back with watering eyes. It smelt like pure ammonia but I was in no position to be superior about it.

'That dang grunt!' The farmer hunched his shoulders. 'What's cause of it?'

It was no good my saying it sounded like a circumscribed area of peritonitis because I didn't know what was behind it.

I decided to have one last go with the lavage. It was still the strongest weapon in my armoury but this time I added two pounds of black treacle to the mixture. Nearly every farmer had a barrel of the stuff in his cow house in those days and I had only to go into the corner and turn the tap.

I often mourn the passing of the treacle barrel because molasses was a good medicine for cattle, but I had no great hopes this time. The clinical instinct I was beginning to develop told me that something inside this animal was fundamentally awry.

It was not till the following afternoon that I drove into Highburn. I left the car outside the farm and was about to walk between the walls when I paused and stared at a cow in the field on the other side of the road. It was a pasture next to the hayfield of yesterday and that cow was Rose. There could be no mistake – she was a fine deep red with a distinctive white mark like a football on her left flank.

I opened the gate and within seconds my cares dropped from me. She was wonderfully, miraculously improved, in fact she looked like a normal animal. I walked up to her and scratched the root of her tail. She was a docile creature and merely looked round at me as she cropped the grass; and her eyes were no longer sunken but bright and full.

She seemed to take a fancy to a green patch further into the field and began to amble slowly towards it. I followed, entranced, as she moved along, shaking her head impatiently against the flies, eager for more of the delicious herbage. The grunt had disappeared and her udder hung heavy and turgid between her legs. The difference since yesterday was incredible.

As the wave of relief flooded through me I saw Mr Bailes climbing over the wall from the next field. He would still be mending that barn door.

As he approached I felt a pang of commiseration. I had to guard against any display of triumph. He must be feeling just a bit silly at the moment after showing his lack of faith in me yesterday with his home remedies and his general attitude. But after all the poor chap had been worried – I couldn't blame him. No, it wouldn't do to preen myself unduly.

'Ah, good morning to you, Mr Bailes,' I said expansively. 'Rose looks fine today, doesn't she?'

The farmer took off his cap and wiped his brow. 'Aye, she's a different cow, all right.'

'I don't think she needs any more treatment,' I said. I hesitated. Perhaps one little dig would do no harm. 'But it's a good thing I gave her that extra lavage yesterday.'

'Yon pumpin' job?' Mr Bailes raised his eyebrows. 'Oh that had nowt to do with it.'

'What . . . what do you mean? It cured her, surely.'

'Nay, lad, nay, Jim Oakley cured her.'

'Jim . . . what on earth . . .?'

'Aye, Jim was round 'ere last night. He often comes in of an evenin' and he took one look at the cow and told me what to do. Ah'll tell you she was like dyin' – that pumpin' job hadn't done no good at all. He told me to give her a bloody good gallop round t'field.'

'What!'

'Aye, that's what he said. He'd seen 'em like that afore and a good gallop put 'em right. So we got Rose out here and did as he said and by gaw it did the trick. She looked better right away.'

I drew myself up. 'And who,' I asked frigidly, 'is Jim Oakley?'

'He's t'postman, of course.'

'The postman!'

'Aye, but he used to keep a few beasts years ago. He's a very clever man wi' stock, is Jim.'

'No doubt, but I assure you, Mr Bailes . . .'

The farmer raised a hand. 'Say no more, lad. Jim put 'er right and there's no denyin' it. I wish you'd seen 'im chasin' 'er round. He's as awd as me, but by gaw 'e did go. He can run like 'ell, can Jim.' He chuckled reminiscently.

I had had about enough. During the farmer's eulogy I had been distractedly scratching the cow's tail and had soiled my hand in the process. Mustering the remains of my dignity I nodded to Mr Bailes.

'Well, I must be on my way. Do you mind if I go into the house to wash my hands?'

'You go right in,' he replied. 'T'missus will get you some hot water.'

Walking back down the field the cruel injustice of the thing bore down on me increasingly. I wandered as in a dream through the gate and across the road. Before entering the alley between the walls I glanced into the garden. It was empty. Shuffling beside the rough stones I sank deeper into my misery. There was no doubt I had emerged from that episode as a complete Charlie. No matter where I looked I couldn't see a gleam of light.

It seemed to take a long time to reach the end of the wall and I was about to turn right towards the door of the farm kitchen when from my left I heard the sudden rattle of a chain then a roaring creature launched itself at me, bayed once, mightily, into my face and was gone.

This time I thought my heart would stop. With my defences at their lowest I was in no state to withstand Shep. I had quite forgotten that Mrs Bailes occasionally tethered him in the kennel at the entrance to discourage unwelcome visitors, and as I half lay against the wall, the blood thundering in my ears, I looked dully at the long coil of chain on the cobbles.

I have no time for people who lose their temper with animals but something snapped in my mind then. All my frustration burst from me in a torrent of incoherent shouts and I grabbed the chain and began to pull on it frenziedly. That dog which had tortured me was there in that kennel. For once I knew where to get at him and this time I was going to have the matter out with him. The kennel would be about ten feet away and at first I saw nothing. There was only the dead weight on the end of the chain. Then as I hauled inexorably a nose appeared, then a head, then all of the big animal hanging limply by his collar. He showed no desire to get up and greet me but I was merciless and dragged him inch by inch over the cobbles till he was lying at my feet.

Beside myself with rage, I crouched, shook my fist under his nose and yelled at him from a few inches' range.

'You big bugger! If you do that to me again I'll knock your bloody head off! Do you hear me, I'll knock your bloody head clean off!'

Shep rolled frightened eyes at me and his tail flickered apologetically between his legs. When I continued to scream at him he bared his upper teeth in an ingratiating grin and finally rolled on his back where he lay inert with half-closed eyes.

So now I knew. He was a softie. All his ferocious attacks were just a game. I began to calm down but for all that I wanted him to get the message.

'Right, mate,' I said in a menacing whisper. 'Remember what I've said!' I let go the chain and gave a final shout. 'Now get back in there!'

Shep, almost on his knees, tail tucked well in, shot back into his kennel and I turned toward the farmhouse to wash my hands.

The memory of my discomfiture fermented in the back of my mind for some time. I had no doubt then that I had been unfairly judged, but I am older and wiser now and in retrospect I think I was wrong.

The symptoms displayed by Mr Bailes' cow were typical of displacement of the abomasum (when the fourth stomach slips round from the right to the left side) and it was a condition that was just not recognised in those early days.

At the present time we correct the condition by surgery – pushing the displaced organ back to the right side and tacking it there with sutures. But sometimes a similar result can be obtained by casting the cow and rolling her over, so why not by making her run . . .? I freely admit that I have many times adopted Jim Oakley's precept of a 'bloody good gallop,' often with spectacular results. To this day I frequently learn things from farmers, but that was one time when I learned from a postman.

I was surprised when, about a month later, I received another call to one of Mr Bailes' cows. I felt that after my performance with Rose he would have called on the services of Jim Oakley for any further trouble. But no, his voice on the 'phone was as polite and friendly as ever, with not a hint that he had lost faith. It was strange. . . .

Leaving my car outside the farm I looked warily into the front garden before venturing between the walls. A faint tinkle of metal told me that Shep was lurking there in his kennel and I slowed my steps; I wasn't going to be caught again. At the end of the alley I paused, waiting, but all I saw was the end of a nose which quietly withdrew as I stood there. So my outburst had got through to the big dog – he knew I wasn't going to stand any more nonsense from him.

And yet, as I drove away after the visit I didn't feel good about it. A victory over an animal is a hollow one and I had the uncomfortable feeling that I had deprived him of his chief pleasure. After all, every creature is entitled to some form of recreation and though Shep's hobby could result in the occasional heart failure it was, after all, his thing and part of him. The thought that I had crushed something out of his life was a disquieting one. I wasn't proud.

So that when, later that summer, I was driving through Highburn I paused in anticipation outside the Bailes farm. The village street, white and dusty, slumbered under the afternoon sun. In the blanketing silence nothing moved – except for one small man strolling towards the opening between the walls. He was fat and very dark – one of the tinkers from a camp outside the village – and he carried an armful of pots and pans.

From my vantage point I could see through the railings into the front garden where Shep was slinking noiselessly into position beneath the stones. Fascinated, I watched as the man turned unhurriedly into the opening and the dog followed the course of the disembodied head along the top of the wall.

As I expected it all happened half way along. The perfectly timed leap, the momentary pause at the summit then the tremendous 'WOOF!' into the unsuspecting ear.

It had its usual effect. I had a brief view of flailing arms and flying pans followed by a prolonged metallic clatter, then the little man reappeared like a projectile, turned right and sped away from me up the street. Considering his almost round physique he showed an astonishing turn of speed, his little legs pistoning, and he did not pause till he disappeared into the shop at the far end of the village.

I don't know why he went in there because he wouldn't find any stronger restorative than ginger pop.

Shep, apparently well satisfied, wandered back over the grass and collapsed in a cool patch where an apple tree threw its shade over the grass; head on paws he waited in comfort for his next victim.

I smiled to myself as I let in the clutch and moved off. I would stop at the shop and tell the little man that he could collect his pans without the slightest fear of being torn limb from limb, but my overriding emotion was one of relief that I had not cut the sparkle out of the big dog's life.

Shep was still having his fun.

Chapter Fourteen

I suppose once you embark on a life of crime it gets easier all the time. Making a start is the only hard bit.

At any rate that is how it seemed to me as I sat in the bus, playing hookey again. There had been absolutely no trouble about dodging out of the Grand, the streets of Scarborough had been empty of SPs and nobody had given me a second look as I strolled casually into the bus station.

It was Saturday, 13 February. Helen was expecting our baby this week-end. It could happen any time and I just didn't see how I could sit here these few miles away and do nothing. I had no classes today or tomorrow so I would miss nothing and nobody would miss me. It was, I told myself, a mere technical offence, and anyway I had no option. Like the first time, I just had to see Helen.

And it wouldn't be long now, I thought, as I hurried up to the familiar doorway of her home. I went inside and gazed disappointedly at the empty kitchen – somehow I had been sure she would be standing there waiting for me with her arms wide. I shouted her name but nothing stirred in the house. I was still there, listening, when her father came through from an inner room.

'You've got a son,' he said.

I put my hand on the back of a chair. 'What . . .?'

'You've got a son.' He was so calm.

'When . . .?'

'Few minutes ago. Nurse Brown's just been on the 'phone. Funny you should walk in.'

As I leaned on the chair he gave me a keen look. 'Would you like a drop of whisky?'

'Whisky? No – why?'

'Well you've gone a bit white, lad, that's all. Anyway, you'd better have something to eat.'

'No, no, no thanks, I've got to get out there.'

He smiled. 'There's no hurry, lad. Anyway, they won't want anybody there too soon. Better eat something.'

'Sorry, I couldn't. Would you – would you mind if I borrowed your car?'

I was still trembling a little as I drove away. If only Mr Alderson had led up to it gradually – he might have said, 'I've got some news for you,' or something like that, but his direct approach had shattered me. When I pulled up outside Nurse Brown's it still hadn't got through to me that I was a father.

Greenside Nursing Home sounded impressive, but it was in fact Nurse Brown's dwelling house. She was State Registered and usually had two or three of the local women in at a time to have their babies.

She opened the door herself and threw up her hands. 'Mr Herriot! It hasn't taken you long! Where did you spring from?' She was a cheerfully dynamic little woman with mischievous eyes.

I smiled sheepishly. 'Well, I just happened to drop in on Mr Alderson and got the news.'

'You might have given us time to get the little fellow properly washed,' she said. 'But never mind, come up and see him. He's a fine baby – nine pounds.'

Still in a dreamlike state I followed her up the stairs of the little house into a small bedroom. Helen was there, in the bed, looking flushed.

'Hello,' she said.

I went over and kissed her.

'What was it like?' I enquired nervously.

'Awful' Helen replied without enthusiasm. Then she nodded towards the cot beside her.

I took my first look at my son. Little Jimmy was brick red in colour and his face had a bloated, dissipated look. As I hung over him he twisted his tiny fists under his chin and appeared to be undergoing some mighty internal struggle. His face swelled and darkened as he contorted his features then from deep among the puffy flesh his eyes fixed me with a baleful glare and he stuck his tongue out of the corner of his mouth.

'My God!' I exclaimed.

The nurse looked at me, startled. 'What's the matter?'

'Well, he's a funny-looking little thing isn't he?'

'What!' She stared at me furiously. 'Mr Herriot, how can you say such a thing? He's a beautiful baby!'

I peered into the cot again. Jimmy greeted me with a lopsided leer, turned purple and blew a few bubbles.

'Are you sure he's all right?' I said.

There was a tired giggle from the bed but Nurse Brown was not amused.

'All right! What exactly do you mean?' She drew herself up stiffly.

I shuffled my feet. 'Well, er – is there anything wrong with him?'

I thought she was going to strike me 'Anything . . . how dare you! Whatever are you talking about? I've never heard such nonsense!' She turned appealingly towards the bed, but Helen, a weary smile on her face, had closed her eyes.

I drew the enraged little woman to one side. 'Look, Nurse, have you by chance got any others on the premises?'

'Any other what?' she asked icily.

'Babies – new babies. I want to compare Jimmy with another one.'

Her eyes widened. 'Compare him! Mr Herriot, I'm not going to listen to you any longer – I've lost patience with you!'

'I'm asking you, Nurse,' I repeated. 'Have you any more around?'

There was a long pause as she looked at me as though I was something new and incredible. 'Well – there's Mrs Dewburn in the next room. Little Sidney was born about the same time as Jimmy.'

'Can I have a look at him?' I gazed at her appealingly.

She hesitated then a pitying smile crept over her face. 'Oh you . . . you . . . just a minute, then.'

She went into the other room and I heard a mumble of voices. She reappeared and beckoned to me.

Mrs Dewburn was the butcher's wife and I knew her well. The face on the pillow was hot and tired like Helen's.

'Eee, Mr Herriot, I didn't expect to see you. I thought you were in the army.'

'RAF, actually, Mrs Dewburn. I'm on – er – leave at the moment.'

I looked in the cot. Sidney was dark red and bloated, too, and he, also, seemed to be wrestling with himself. The inner battle showed in a series of grotesque facial contortions culminating in a toothless snarl.

I stepped back involuntarily. 'What a beautiful child,' I said.

'Yes, isn't he lovely,' said his mother fondly.

'He is indeed, gorgeous.' I took another disbelieving glance into the cot. 'Well, thank you very much, Mrs Dewburn. It was kind of you to let me see him.'

'Not at all, Mr Herriot, it's nice of you to take an interest.'

Outside the door I took a long breath and wiped my brow. The relief was tremendous. Sidney was even funnier than Jimmy.

When I returned to Helen's room Nurse Brown was sitting on the bed and the two women were clearly laughing at me. And of course, looking back, I must have appeared silly. Sidney Dewburn and my son are now two big, strong, remarkably good-looking young men, so my fears were groundless.

The little nurse looked at me quizzically. I think she had forgiven me.

'I suppose you think all your calves and foals are beautiful right from the moment they are born?'

'Well yes,' I replied. 'I have to admit it – I think they are.'

As I have said before, ideas do not come readily to me, but on the bus journey back to Scarborough a devilish scheme began to hatch in my brain.

I was due for compassionate leave, but why should I take it now? Helen would be in the Nursing Home for a fortnight and there didn't seem any sense in my mooning round Darrowby on my own. The thing to do would be to send myself a telegram a fortnight from now announcing the birth, and we would be able to spend my leave together.

It was interesting how my moral scruples dissolved in the face of this attraction, but anyway, I told myself, where was the harm? I wasn't scrounging anything extra, I was just altering the time. The RAF or the war effort in general would suffer no mortal blow. Long before the darkened vehicle had rolled into the town I had made up my mind and on the following day I wrote to a friend in Darrowby and arranged about the telegram.

But I wasn't such a hardened criminal as I thought, because as the days passed doubts began to creep in. The rules at ITW were rigidly strict. I would be in trouble if I was found out. But the prospect of a holiday with Helen blotted out all other considerations.

When the fateful day arrived my room mates and I were stretched on our beds after lunch when a great voice boomed along the corridor.

'AC2 Herriot! Come on, let's have you, Herriot!'

My stomach lurched. Somehow I hadn't reckoned on Flight Sergeant Blackett coming into this. I had thought maybe an LAC or a corporal, even one of the sergeants might have handled it, not the great man himself.

Flight Sergeant Blackett was an unsmiling martinet of immense natural presence which a gaunt six feet two inch frame, wide bony shoulders and a craggy countenance did nothing to diminish. It was usually the junior NCOs who dealt with our misdemeanours, but if Flight Sergeant Blackett ever took a hand it was a withering experience.

I heard it again. The same bull bellow which echoed over our heads on the square every morning.

'Herriot! Let's be having you, Herriot!'

I was on my way at a brisk trot out of the room and along the polished surface of the corridor. I came to a halt stiffly in front of the tall figure.

'Yes, Flight Sergeant.'

'You Herriot?'

'Yes, Flight Sergeant.'

The telegram between his fingers scuffed softly against the blue serge of his trousers as he swung his hand to and fro. My pulse rate accelerated painfully as I waited.

'Well now, lad, I'm pleased to tell you that your wife has had her baby safely.' He raised the telegram to his eyes. 'It says 'ere, "A boy, both well. Nurse Brown." Let me be the first to congratulate you.' He held out his hand and as I took it he smiled. Suddenly he looked very like Gary Cooper.

'Now you'll want to get off right away and see them both, eh?'

I nodded dumbly. He must have thought I was an unemotional character.

He put a hand on my shoulder and guided me into the orderly room.

'Come on, you lot, get movin'!' The organ tones rolled over the heads of the airmen seated at the tables. 'This is important. Got a brand new father 'ere. Leave pass, railway warrant, pay, double quick!'

'Right, Flight. Very good, Flight.' The typewriters began to tap.

The big man went over to a railway timetable on the wall. 'You haven't far to go, anyway. Let's see – Darrowby, Darrowby . . . yes, there's a train out of here for York at three twenty.' He looked at his watch. 'You ought to make that if you get your skates on.'

A deepening sense of shame threatened to engulf me when he spoke again.

'Double back to your room and get packed. We'll have your documents ready.'

I changed into my best blue, filled my kit bag and threw it over my shoulder, then hurried back to the orderly room.

The Flight Sergeant was waiting. He handed me a long envelope. 'It's all there, son, and you've got plenty of time.' He looked me up and down, walked round me and straightened the white flash in my cap. 'Yes, very smart. We've got to have you lookin' right for your missus, haven't we?' He gave me the Gary Cooper smile again. He was a handsome, kind-eyed man and I'd never noticed it.

He strolled with me along the corridor. 'This'll be your first 'un, of course?'

'Yes, Flight.'

He nodded. 'Well, it's a great day for you. I've got three of 'em, meself. Getting big now but I miss 'em like hell with this ruddy war. I really envy you, walking in that door tonight and seeing your son for the very first time.'

Guilt drove through me in a searing flood and as we halted at the top of the stairs I was convinced my shifty eyes and furtive glances would betray me. But he wasn't really looking at me.

'You know, lad,' he said softly, gazing somewhere over my head. 'This is the best time of your life coming up.'

We weren't allowed to use the main stairways and as I clattered down the narrow stone service stairs I heard the big voice again.

'Give my regards to them both.'

I had a wonderful time with Helen, walking for miles, discovering the delights of pram pushing, with little Jimmy miraculously improved in appearance.

Everything was so much better than if I had taken my leave at the official time and there is no doubt my plan was a success.

But I was unable to gloat about it. The triumph was dimmed and to this day I have reservations about the whole thing.

Flight Sergeant Blackett spoiled it for me.

Chapter Fifteen

'You must have to be a bit of an idiot to be a country vet.' The young airman was laughing as he said it, but I felt there was some truth in his words. He had been telling me about his job in civil life and when I described my own working hours and conditions he had been incredulous.

There was one time I would have agreed with him wholeheartedly. It was nine o'clock on a filthy wet night and I was still at work. I gripped the steering wheel more tightly and shifted in my seat, groaning softly as my tired muscles complained.

Why had I entered this profession? I could have gone in for something easier and gentler – like coalmining or lumberjacking. I had started feeling sorry for myself three hours ago, driving across Darrowby market place on the way to a calving. The shops were shut and even through the wintry drizzle there was a suggestion of repose, of work done, of firesides and books and drifting tobacco smoke. I had all those things, plus Helen, back there in our bed-sitter.

I think the iron really entered when I saw the carload of young people setting off from the front of the Drovers; three girls and three young fellows, all dressed up and laughing and obviously on their way to a dance or party. Everybody was set for comfort and a good time; everybody except Herriot, rattling towards the cold wet hills and the certain prospect of toil.

And the case did nothing to raise my spirits. A skinny little heifer stretched on her side in a ramshackle open-fronted shed littered with old tin cans, half bricks and other junk; it was difficult to see what I was stumbling over since the only light came from a rusty oil lamp whose flame flickered and dipped in the wind.

I was two hours in that shed, easing out the calf inch by inch. It wasn't a malpresentation, just a tight fit, but the heifer never rose to her feet and I spent the whole time on the floor, rolling among the bricks and tins, getting up only to shiver my way to the water bucket while the rain hurled itself icily against the shrinking flesh of my chest and back.

And now here I was, driving home frozen-faced with my skin chafing under my clothes and feeling as though a group of strong men had been kicking me enthusiastically from head to foot for most of the evening. I was almost drowning in self-pity when I turned into the tiny village of Copton. In the warm days of summer it was idyllic, reminding me always of a corner of Perthshire, with its single street hugging the lower slopes of a green hillside and a dark drift of trees spreading to the heathery uplands high above.

But tonight it was a dead black place with the rain sweeping across the headlights against the tight-shut houses; except for a faint glow right in the middle where the light from the village pub fell softly on the streaming roadway.

I stopped the car under the swinging sign of the Fox and Hounds and on an impulse opened the door. A beer would do me good.

A pleasant warmth met me as I went into the pub. There was no bar counter, only high-backed settles and oak tables arranged under the whitewashed walls of what was simply a converted farm kitchen. At one end a wood fire crackled in an old black cooking range and above it the tick of a wall clock sounded above the murmur of voices. It wasn't as lively as the modern places but it was peaceful.

'Now then, Mr Herriot, you've been workin',' my neighbour said as I sank into the settle.

'Yes, Ted, how did you know?'

The man glanced over my soiled mackintosh and the wellingtons which I hadn't bothered to change on the farm. 'Well, that's not your Sunday suit, there's blood on your nose end and cow shit on your ear.' Ted Dobson was a burly cowman in his thirties and his white teeth showed suddenly in a wide grin.

I smiled too and plied my handkerchief. 'It's funny how you always want to scratch your nose at times like that.'

I looked around the room. There were about a dozen men drinking from pint glasses, some of them playing dominoes. They were all farm workers, the people I saw when I was called from my bed in the darkness before dawn; hunched figures they were then, shapeless in old greatcoats, cycling out to the farms, heads down against the wind and rain, accepting the facts of their hard existence. I often thought at those times that this happened to me only occasionally, but they did it every morning.

And they did it for thirty shillings a week; just seeing them here made me feel a little ashamed.

Mr Waters, the landlord, whose name let him in for a certain amount of ribbing, filled my glass, holding his tall jug high to produce the professional froth.

'There y'are, Mr Herriot, that'll be sixpence. Cheap at 'alf the price.'

Every drop of beer was brought up in that jug from the wooden barrels in the cellar. It would have been totally impracticable in a busy establishment, but the Fox and Hounds was seldom bustling and Mr Waters would never get rich as a publican. But he had four cows in the little byre adjoining this room, fifty hens pecked around in his long back garden and he reared a few litters of pigs every year from his two sows.

'Thank you, Mr Waters.' I took a deep pull at the glass. I had lost some sweat despite the cold and my thirst welcomed the flow of rich nutty ale. I had been in here a few times before and the faces were all familiar. Especially old Albert Close, a retired shepherd who sat in the same place every night at the end of the settle hard against the fire.

He sat as always, his hands and chin resting on the tall crook which he had carried through his working days, his eyes blank. Stretched half under the seat, half under the table lay his dog, Mick, old and retired like his master. The animal was clearly in the middle of a vivid dream; his paws pedalled the air spasmodically, his lips and ears twitched and now and then he emitted a stifled bark.

Ted Dobson nudged me and laughed. 'Ah reckon awd Mick's still rounding up them sheep.'

I nodded. There was little doubt the dog was reliving the great days, crouching and darting, speeding in a wide arc round the perimeter of the field at his master's whistle. And Albert himself. What lay behind those empty eyes? I could imagine him in his youth, striding the windy uplands, covering endless miles over the moor and rock and beck, digging that same crook into the turf at every step. There were no fitter men than the Dales shepherds, living in the open in all weathers, throwing a sack over their shoulders in snow and rain.

And there was Albert now, a broken, arthritic old man gazing apathetically from beneath the ragged peak of an ancient tweed cap. I noticed he had just drained his glass and I walked across the room.

'Good evening, Mr Close,' I said.

He cupped an ear with his hand and blinked up at me. 'Eh?'

I raised my voice to a shout. 'How are you, Mr Close?'

'Can't complain, young man,' he murmured. 'Can't complain.'

'Will you have a drink?'

'Aye, thank ye.' He directed a trembling finger at his glass. 'You can put a drop i' there, young man.'

I knew a drop meant a pint and beckoned to the landlord who plied his jug expertly. The old shepherd lifted the re-charged glass and looked up at me.

'Good 'ealth,' he grunted.

'All the best,' I said and was about to return to my seat when the old dog sat up. My shouts at his master must have wakened him from his dream because he stretched sleepily, shook his head a couple of times and looked around him. And as he turned and faced me I felt a sudden sense of shock.

His eyes were terrible. In fact I could hardly see them as they winked painfully at me through a sodden fringe of pus-caked lashes. Rivulets of discharge showed dark and ugly against the white hair on either side of the nose.

I stretched my hand out to him and the dog wagged his tail briefly before closing his eyes and keeping them closed. It seemed he felt better that way.

I put my hand on Albert's shoulder. 'Mr Close, how long has he been like this?'

'Eh?'

I increased my volume. 'Mick's eyes. They're in a bad state.'

'Oh aye.' The old man nodded in comprehension. 'He's got a bit o' caud in 'em. He's allus been subjeck to it ever since 'e were a pup.'

'No, it's more than cold, it's his eyelids'.

'Eh?'

I took a deep breath and let go at the top of my voice.

'He's got turned-in eyelids. It's rather a serious thing.'

The old man nodded again. 'Aye, 'e lies a lot wi' his head at foot of t'door. It's draughty there.'

'No, Mr Close!' I bawled. 'It's got nothing to do with that. It's a thing called entropion and it needs an operation to put it right.'

'That's right, young man.' He took a sip at his beer. 'Just a bit o' caud. Ever since he were a pup he's been subjeck . . .'

I turned away wearily and returned to my seat. Ted Dobson looked at me enquiringly.

'What was that about?'

'Well, it's a nasty thing, Ted. Entropion is when the eyelids are turned in and the lashes rub against the eyeball. Causes a lot of pain, sometimes ulceration or even blindness. Even a mild case is damned uncomfortable for a dog.'

'I see,' Ted said ruminatively. 'Ah've noticed awd Mick's had mucky eyes for a long time but they've got worse lately.'

'Yes, sometimes it happens like that, but often it's congenital. I should think Mick has had a touch of it all his life but for some reason it's suddenly developed to this horrible state.' I turned again towards the old dog, sitting patiently under the table, eyes still tight shut.

'He's sufferin' then?'

I shrugged my shoulders. 'Well, you know what it's like if you have a speck of dust in your eyes or even one lash turned in. I should say he feels pretty miserable.'

'Poor awd beggar. Ah never knew it was owt like that.' He drew on his cigarette. 'And could an operation cure it?'

'Yes, Ted, it's one of the most satisfying jobs a vet can do. I always feel I've done a dog a good turn when I've finished.'

'Aye, ah bet you do. It must be a nice feelin'. But it'll be a costly job, ah reckon?'

I smiled wryly. 'It depends how you look at it. It's a fiddly business and takes time. We usually charge about a pound for it.' A human surgeon would laugh at a sum like that, but it would still be too much for old Albert.

For a few moments we were both silent, looking across the room at the old man, at the threadbare coat, the long tatter of trouser bottoms falling over the broken boots. A pound was two weeks of the old age pension. It was a fortune.

Ted got up suddenly. 'Any road, somebody ought to tell 'im. Ah'll explain it to 'im.'

He crossed the room. 'Are ye ready for another, Albert?'

The old shepherd glanced at him absently then indicated his glass, empty again. 'Aye, ye can put a drop i' there, Ted.'

The cowman waved to Mr Waters then bent down. 'Did ye understand what Mr Herriot was tellin' ye, Albert?' he shouted.

'Aye .. aye ... Mick's got a bit o' caud in 'is eyes.'

'Nay, 'e hasn't! it's nowt of t'soart! It's a en ... a en ... summat different.'

'Keeps gettin' caud in 'em.' Albert mumbled, nose in glass.

Ted yelled in exasperation. 'Ye daft awd divil! Listen to what ah'm sayin' – ye've got to take care of 'im and ...'

But the old man was far away. 'Ever sin 'e were a pup ... allus been subjeck to it. ...'

Though Mick took my mind off my own troubles at the time, the memory of those eyes haunted me for days. I yearned to get my hands on them. I knew an hour's work would transport the old dog into a world he perhaps had not known for years, and every instinct told me to rush back to Copton, throw him in the car and bear him back to Darrowby for surgery. I wasn't worried about the money but you just can't run a practice that way.

I regularly saw lame dogs on farms, skinny cats on the streets and it would have been lovely to descend on each and every one and minister to them out of my knowledge. In fact I had tried a bit of it and it didn't work.

It was Ted Dobson who put me out of my pain. He had come in to the town to see his sister for the evening and he stood leaning on his bicycle in the surgery doorway, his cheerful, scrubbed face gleaming as if it would light up the street.

He came straight to the point. 'Will ye do that operation on awd Mick, Mr Herriot?'

'Yes, of course, but ... how about ... ?'

'Oh that'll be right. T'lads at Fox and Hounds are seein' to it. We're takin' it out of the club money.'

'Club money?'

'Aye, we put in a bit every week for an outin' in t'summer. Trip to t'seaside or summat like.'

'Well it's extremely kind of you, Ted, but are you quite sure? Won't any of them mind?'

Ted laughed. 'Nay, it's nowt, we won't miss a quid. We drink ower much on them do's anyway.' He paused. 'All t'lads want this job done – it's been gettin' on our bloody nerves watchin' t'awd dog ever since you told us about 'im.'

'Well, that's great,' I said. 'How will you get him down?'

'Me boss is lendin' me 'is van. Wednesday night be all right?'

'Fine.' I watched him ride away then turned back along the passage. It may seem to modern eyes that a lot of fuss had been made over a pound but in those days it was a very substantial sum, and some idea may be gained from the fact that four pounds a week was my commencing salary as a veterinary surgeon.

When Wednesday night arrived it was clear that Mick's operation had become something of a gala occasion. The little van was crammed with regulars from the Fox and Hounds and others rolled up on their bicycles.

The old dog slunk fearfully down the passage to the operating room, nostrils twitching at the unfamiliar odours of ether and antiseptic. Behind him trooped the noisy throng of farm men, their heavy boots clattering on the tiles.

Tristan, who was doing the anaesthesia, hoisted the dog on the table and I looked around at the unusual spectacle of rows of faces regarding me with keen anticipation. Normally I am not in favour of lay people witnessing operations but since these men were sponsoring the whole thing they would have to stay.

Under the lamp I got my first good look at Mick. He was a handsome, well-marked animal except for those dreadful eyes. As he sat there he opened them a fraction and peered at me for a painful moment before closing them against the bright light; that, I felt, was how he spent his life, squinting carefully and briefly at his surroundings. Giving him the intravenous barbiturate was like doing him a favour, ridding him of his torment for a while.

And when he was stretched unconscious on his side I was able to carry out my first examination. I parted the lids, wincing at the matted lashes, awash with tears and discharge; there was a long standing keratitis and conjunctivitis but with a gush of relief I found that the cornea was not ulcerated.

'You know,' I said. 'This is a mess, but I don't think there's any permanent damage.'

The farm men didn't exactly break into a cheer but they were enormously pleased. The carnival air was heightened as they chattered and laughed and when I poised my scalpel it struck me that I had never operated in such a noisy environment.

But I felt almost gleeful as I made the first incision; I had been looking forward so much to this moment. Starting with the left eye I cut along the full length parallel to the margin of the lid then made a semicircular sweep of the knife to include half an inch of the tissue above the eye. Seizing the skin with forceps I stripped it away, and as I drew the lips of the bleeding wound together with stitches I noticed with intense gratification how the lashes were pulled high and away from the corneal surface they had irritated, perhaps for years.

I cut away less skin from the lower lid – you never need to take so much there – then started on the right eye. I was slicing away happily when I realised that the noise had subsided; there were a few mutterings, but the chaff and laughter had died. I glanced up and saw big Ken Appleton, the horseman from Laurel Grove; it was natural that he should catch my eye, because he was six feet four and built like the Shires he cared for.

'By gaw, it's 'ot in 'ere,' he whispered, and I could see he meant it because sweat was streaming down his face.

I was engrossed in my work or I would have noticed that he wasn't only sweating but deadly pale. I was stripping the skin from the eyelid when I heard Tristan's yell.

'Catch him!'

The big man's surrounding friends supported him as he slid gently to the floor and he stayed there, sleeping peacefully, till I had inserted the last stitch. Then as Tristan and I cleaned up and put the instruments away he began to look around him and his companions helped him to his feet. Now that the cutting was over the life had returned to the party and Ken came in for some leg-pulling; but his was not the only white face.

'I think you could do with a drop of whisky, Ken,' Tristan said. He left the room and returned with a bottle which, with typical hospitality, he dispensed to all. Beakers, measuring glasses and test tubes were pressed into service and soon there was a boisterous throng around the sleeping dog. When the van finally roared off into the night the last thing I heard was the sound of singing from the packed interior.

They brought Mick back in ten days for removal of the stitches. The wounds had healed well but the keratitis had still not cleared and the old dog was still blinking painfully. I didn't see the final result of my work for another month.

It was when I was again driving home through Copton from an evening call that the lighted doorway of the Fox and Hounds recalled me to the little operation which had been almost forgotten in the rush of new work. I went in and sat down among the familiar faces.

Things were uncannily like before. Old Albert Close in his usual place, Mick stretched under the table, his twitching feet testifying to another vivid dream. I watched him closely until I could stand it no longer. As if drawn by a magnet I crossed the room and crouched by him.

'Mick!' I said. 'Hey, wake up, boy!'

The quivering limbs stilled and there was a long moment when I held my breath as the shaggy head turned towards me. Then with a kind of blissful disbelief I found myself gazing into the wide, clear, bright eyes of a young dog.

Warm wine flowed richly through my veins as he faced me, mouth open in a panting grin, tail swishing along the stone flags. There was no inflammation, no discharge, and the lashes, clean and dry, grew in a soft arc well clear of the corneal surface which they had chafed and rasped for so long. I stroked his head and as he began to look around him eagerly I felt a thrill of utter delight at the sight of the old animal exulting in his freedom, savouring the new world which had opened to him. I could see Ted Dobson and the other men smiling conspiratorially as I stood up.

'Mr Close,' I shouted. 'Will you have a drink?'

'Aye, you can put a drop i' there, young man.'

'Mick's eyes are a lot better.'

The old man raised his glass. 'Good 'ealth. Aye, it were nobbut a bit o' caud.'

'But Mr Close . . .!'

'Nasty thing, is caud in t'eyes. T'awd feller keeps lyin' in that door'ole and ah reckon he'll get it again. Ever since 'e were a pup 'e's been subjeck . . .'

Chapter Sixteen

As I bent over the wash basin in the 'ablutions' and went into another violent paroxysm of coughing I had a growing and uncomfortable conviction that I was a mere pawn.

The big difference between my present existence and my old life as a vet was that I used to make up my own mind as to how I would do things, whereas in the RAF all the decisions which affected me were made by other people. I didn't much like being a pawn because the lives of us lowly airmen were ruled by a lot of notions and ideas dreamed up by individuals so exalted that we never knew them.

And so many of these ideas seemed crazy to me.

For instance, who decided that all our bedroom windows should be nailed open throughout a Yorkshire winter so that the healthy mist could swirl straight from the black ocean and settle icily on our beds as we slept? The result was an almost one hundred per cent incidence of bronchitis in our flight, and in the mornings the Grand Hotel sounded like a chest sanatorium with a harrowing chorus of barks and wheezes.

The cough seized me again, racking my body, threatening to dislodge my eyeballs. It was a temptation to report sick but I hadn't done it yet. Most of the lads stuck it out till they had roaring fevers before going sick and by now, at the end of February, nearly all of them had spent a few days in hospital. I was one of the few who hadn't. Maybe there was a bit of bravado in my stand – because most of them were eighteen- or nineteen-year-olds and I was a comparatively old man in my twenties – but there were two other reasons. Firstly, it was very often after I had got dressed and been unable to eat breakfast that I felt really ill. But by then it was too late. You had to report sick before seven o'clock or suffer till next day.

Another reason was that I didn't like the look of the sick parade. As I went out to the corridor with my towel round my shoulders a sergeant was reading a list and inflating his lungs at the same time.

'Get on parade, the sick!' he shouted. 'C'mon, c'mon, let's be 'avin' you!'

From various doors an unhappy group of invalids began to appear, shuffling over the linoleum, each draped with his 'small kit', haversack containing pyjamas, canvas shoes, knife, fork, spoon, etc.

The sergeant unleashed another bellow. 'Get into line, there! Come on, you lot, hurry it up, look lively!'

I looked at the young men huddled there, white-faced and trembling. Most of them were coughing and spluttering and one of them clutched his abdomen as though he had a ruptured appendix.

'Parade!' bawled the sergeant. 'Parade, atten-shun! Parade stan'-at ease! Atten-shun! Le-eft turn! Qui-ick march! 'Eft-'ight, 'eft-'ight, 'eft-'ight, 'eft-'ight!'

The hapless band trailed wearily off. They had a march of nearly a mile through the rain to the sick quarters in another hotel above the Spa, and as I turned into my room it was with a renewed resolve to hang on as long as possible.

Another thing that frightened us all for a spell was the suggestion, drifting down from somewhere on high, that it wasn't enough to go jogging around Scarborough on our training runs; we ought to stop every now and then and do a bit of shadow boxing like fighters. This idea seemed too outrageous to be true but we had it from the sergeant himself, who came with us on our runs. Some VIP had passed it down, claiming that it would instil belligerence in us. We were thoroughly alarmed for a while, including the sergeant, who had no desire to be seen in charge of a bunch of apparent lunatics dancing around punching at the air. Mercifully, somebody had the strength to resist this one and the whole thing fell through.

But of all these brilliant schemes the one I remember best was the one that decided we had to scream at the end of our physical training session. Apart from running miles all over the place, we had long periods of PT down on the rain-swept prom with the wind cutting in from the sea on our goose-pimpled limbs. We became so good at these exercises that it was decided to put on a show for a visiting air marshal. Not only our flight but several squadrons all performing in unison in front of the Grand.

We trained for months for the big day, doing the same movements over and over again till we were perfect. At first the barrel-chested PT sergeant shouted instructions at us all the time, then as we got better all he did was call out 'Exercise three, commence'. And finally it all became so much a part of our being that he merely sounded a tiny peep on his whistle at the beginning of each exercise.

By spring we were really impressive. Hundreds of men in shorts and singlets swinging away as one out there on the square, with the PT sergeant up on the balcony above the doorway where he would stand with the air marshal on the day. The thing that made it so dramatic was the utter silence; the forest of waving limbs and swaying bodies with not a sound but the peep of the whistle.

Everything was lovely till somebody had the idea of the screaming. Up till then we had marched silently from the square at the end of the session, but that was apparently not good enough. What we had to do now was count up to five at the end of the last exercise, then leap into the air, scream at the top of our voices and run off the square at top speed.

And I had to admit that it seemed quite a brainwave. We tried it a few times, then we began to put our hearts into it, jumping high, yelling like dervishes then scuttling away into the various openings among the hotels around the square.

It must have looked marvellous from the balcony. The great mass of white-clad men going through the long routine in a cathedral hush, a few seconds of complete immobility at the end then the whole concourse erupting with a wild yell and disappearing, leaving the empty square echoing. And this last touch had another desirable aspect; it was further proof of our latent savagery. The enemy would have quaked at that chilling sound.

The sergeant had a little trouble with a lad in my flight, a tall gangling red-haired youth called Cromarty who stood in the line in front of me a few feet to my right. Cromarty seemed unable to enter into the spirit of the thing.

'Come on, lad,' the sergeant said one day. 'Put a bit of devil into it! You got to sound like a killer. You're floating up and down there like a ruddy fairy godmother.'

Cromarty did try, but the thing seemed to embarrass him. He gave a little hop, an apologetic jerk of his arms and a feeble cry.

The sergeant ran his hand through his hair. 'No, no, lad! You've got to let yourself go!' He looked around him. 'Here, Devlin, come out and show 'im how it's done.'

Devlin, a grinning Irishman, stepped forward. The scream was the high point of his day. He stood relaxed for a moment then without warning catapulted himself high in the air, legs and arms splayed, head back, while a dreadful animal cry burst from his gaping mouth.

The sergeant took an involuntary step backwards. 'Thanks, Devlin, that's fine,' he said a little shakily, then he turned to Cromarty. 'Now you see how I want it, boy, just like that. So work at it.'

Cromarty nodded. He had a long, serious face and you could see he wanted to oblige. After that I watched him each day and there was no doubt he was improving. His inhibitions were gradually being worn down.

It seemed that nature was smiling on our efforts because the great day dawned with blue skies and warm sunshine. Every man among the hundreds who marched out into the square had been individually prepared. Newly bathed, fresh haircut, spotless white shorts and singlet. We waited in our motionless lines before the newly painted door of the Grand while, on the balcony above, gold braid glinted on the air marshal's cap.

He stood among a knot of the top RAF brass of Scarborough, while in one corner I could see our sergeant, erect in long white flannels, his great chest sticking out further than ever. Beneath us the sea shimmered and the golden bay curved away to the Filey cliffs.

The sergeant raised his hand. 'Peep' went the whistle and we were off.

There was something exhilarating about being part of this smooth machine. I had a wonderful sense of oneness with the arms and legs which moved with mine all around. It was effortless. We had ten exercises to do and at the end of the first we stood rigid for ten seconds, then the whistle piped and we started again.

The time passed too quickly as I revelled in our perfection. At the end of exercise nine I came to attention, waiting for the whistle, counting under my breath. Nothing stirred, the silence was profound. Then, from the motionless ranks, as unexpected as an exploding bomb, Cromarty in front of me launched himself upwards in a tangle of flailing limbs and red hair and unleashed a long bubbling howl. He had put so much into his leap that he seemed to take a long time to come down and even after his descent the shattering sound echoed on.

Cromarty had made it at last. As fierce and warlike a scream, as high a jump as ever the sergeant could desire. The only snag was that he was too soon.

When the whistle went for the last exercise a lot of people didn't hear it because of the noise and many others were in a state of shock and came in late. Anyway, it was a shambles and the final yell and scuttle a sad anticlimax. I myself, though managing to get a few inches off the ground, was unable to make any sound at all.

Had Cromarty not been serving in the armed forces of a benign democracy he would probably have been taken quietly away and shot. As it was, there was really nothing anybody could do to him. NCOs weren't even allowed to swear at the men.

I felt for the PT sergeant. There must have been a lot he wanted to say but he was grievously restricted. I saw him with Cromarty later. He put his face close to the young man's.

'You . . . you . . .' His features worked as he fought for words 'You THING you!'

He turned and walked away with bowed shoulders. At that moment I'm sure he felt like a pawn too.

Chapter Seventeen

There is no doubt that when I looked back at my life in Darrowby I was inclined to bathe the whole thing in a rosy glow, but occasionally the unhappy things came to mind.

That man, distraught and gasping on the surgery steps. 'I's no good, I can't bring him in. He's as stiff as a board!'

My stomach lurched. It was another one. 'Jasper, you mean?'

'Yes, he's in the back of my car, right here.'

I ran across the pavement and opened the car door. It was as I feared; a handsome Dalmatian stretched in a dreadful tetanic spasm, spine arched, head craning deperately backward, legs like four wooden rods groping at nothing.

I didn't wait to talk but dashed back into the house for syringe and drugs.

I leaned into the car, tucked some papers under the dog's head, injected the apomorphine and waited.

The man looked at me with anxious eyes. 'What is it?'

'Strychnine poisoning, Mr Bartle. I've just given an emetic to make him vomit.' As I spoke the animal brought up the contents of his stomach on to the paper.

'Will that put him right?'

'It depends on how much of the poison has been absorbed.' I didn't feel like telling him that it was almost invariably fatal, that in fact I had treated six dogs in the last week with the same condition and they had all died. 'We'll just have to hope.'

He watched me as I filled another syringe with barbiturate. 'What are you doing now?'

'Anaesthetising him.' I slipped the needle into the radial vein and as I slowly trickled the fluid into the dog's bloodstream the taut muscles relaxed and he sank into a deep slumber.

'He looks better already,' Mr Bartle said.

'Yes, but the trouble is when the injection wears off he may go back into a spasm. As I say, it all depends on how much of the strychnine has got into his system. Keep him in a quiet place with as little noise as possible. Any sound can bring on a spasm. When he shows signs of coming out of it give me a ring.'

I went back into the house. Seven cases in a week! It was tragic and scarcely believable, but there was no doubt left in my mind now. This was malicious. Some psychopath in our little town was deliberately putting down poison to kill dogs. Strychnine poisoning was something that cropped up occasionally. Gamekeepers and other people used the deadly drug to kill vermin, but usually it was handled with great care and placed out of reach of domestic pets. Trouble started when a burrowing dog came across the poison by accident. But this was different.

I had to warn pet owners somehow. I lifted the 'phone and spoke to one of the reporters on the *Darrowby and Houlton Times*. He promised to put the story in the next edition, along with advice to keep dogs on their leads and otherwise supervise pets more carefully.

Then I rang the police. The sergeant listened to my account. 'Right, Mr

Herriot, I agree with you that there's some crackpot going around and we'll certainly investigate this matter. If you'll just give me the names of the dog owners involved ... thank you ... thank you. We'll see these people and check round the local chemists to see if anybody has been buying strychnine lately. And of course we'll keep our eyes open for anybody acting suspiciously.'

I came away from the 'phone feeling that I might have done something to halt the depressing series of events, but I couldn't rid myself of a gloomy apprehension that more trouble was round the corner. But my mood lightened when I saw Johnny Clifford in the waiting room.

Johnny always made me feel better because he was invariably optimistic and wore a cheerful grin which never altered, even though he was blind. He was about my own age and he sat there in his habitual pose, one hand on the head of his guide dog, Fergus.

'Is it inspection time again already, Johnny?' I asked.

'Aye, it is that, Mr Herriot, it's come round again. It's been a quick six months.' He laughed and held out his card.

I squatted and looked into the face of the big Alsatian sitting motionless and dignified by his master's side. 'Well, and how's Fergus these days?'

'Oh he's in grand fettle. Eatin' well and full of life.' The hand on the head moved round to the ears and at the other end the tail did a bit of sweeping along the waiting-room floor.

As I looked at the young man, his face alight with pride and affection, I realised afresh what this dog meant to him. He had told me that when his failing sight progressed to total blindness in his early twenties he was filled with a despair which did not lessen until he was sent to train with a guide dog and met Fergus; because he found something more than another living creature to act as his eyes, he found a friend and companion to share every moment of his days.

'Well, we'd better get started,' I said. 'Stand up a minute, old lad, while I take your temperature.' That was normal and I went over the big animal's chest with a stethoscope, listening to the reassuringly steady thud of the heart. As I parted the hair along the neck and back to examine the skin I laughed.

'I'm wasting my time here, Johnny. You've got his coat in perfect condition.'

'Aye, never a day goes by but he gets a good groomin'.'

I had seen him at it, brushing and combing tirelessly to bring extra lustre to the sleek swathes of hair. The nicest thing anybody could say to Johnny was, 'That's a beautiful dog you've got.' His pride in that beauty was boundless even though he had never seen it himself.

Treating guide dogs for the blind has always seemed to me to be one of a veterinary surgeon's most rewarding tasks. To be in a position to help and care for these magnificent animals is a privilege, not just because they are highly trained and valuable but because they represent in the ultimate way something which has always lain near the core and centre of my life: the mutually depending, trusting and loving association between man and animal.

Meeting these blind people was a humbling experience which sent me about my work with a new appreciation of my blessings.

I opened the dog's mouth and peered at the huge gleaming teeth. It was dicing with danger to do this with some Alsatians, but with Fergus you could haul the great jaws apart and nearly put your head in and he would only lick your ear. In fact he was at it now. My cheek was nicely within range and he gave it a quick wipe with his large wet tongue.

'Hey, just a minute, Fergus!' I withdrew and plied my handkerchief. 'I've had a wash this morning. And anyway, only little dogs lick – not big tough Alsatians.'

Johnny threw back his head and gave a great peal of laughter. 'There's nowt tough about him, he's the softest dog you could ever meet.'

'Well, that's the way I like them.' I said. I reached for a tooth scaler. 'There's just a bit of tartar on one of his back teeth. I'll scrape it off right now.'

When I had finished I looked in the ears with an auroscope. There was no canker but I cleaned out a little wax.

Then I went round the feet, examining paws and claws. They always fascinated me, these feet; wide, enormous, with great spreading toes. They had to be that size to support the big body and the massive bones of the limbs.

'All correct except that one funny claw, Johnny.'

'Aye, you allus have to trim that 'un don't you? I could feel it was growin' long again.'

'Yes, that toe seems to be slightly crooked or it would wear down like the others with all the walking he does. You have a great time going walks all day, don't you, Fergus?'

I dodged another attemped lick and closed my clippers around the claw. I had to squeeze till my eyes popped before the overgrown piece shot away with a loud crack.

'By gosh, we'd go through some clippers if all dogs had claws like that,' I gasped. 'It just about does them in every time he calls.'

Johnny laughed again and dropped his hand on the great head with a gesture which said so much.

I took the card entered my report on the dog's health along with the things I had done. Then I dated it and handed it back. 'That's it for this time, Johnny. He's in excellent order and there's nothing more I need do to him.'

'Thank you, Mr Herriot. See you next time round, then.' The young man took hold of the harness and I followed the two of them along the passage and out of the front door. I watched as Fergus halted by the kerb and waited till a car had passed before crossing the road.

They hadn't gone very far along the road when a woman with a shopping bag stopped them. She began to chatter animatedly, looking down repeatedly at the big dog. She was talking about Fergus and Johnny rested his hand on the noble head and nodded and smiled. Fergus was his favourite topic.

Shortly after midday Mr Bartle rang to say Jasper showed signs of returning spasms and before sitting down to lunch I rushed round to his house and repeated the barbiturate injection. Mr Bartle owned one of the local mills, producing cattle food for the district. He was a very bright man indeed.

'Mr Herriot,' he said. 'Please don't misunderstand me. I have every faith in you, but isn't there anything else you can do? I am so very fond of this dog.'

I shrugged helplessly 'I'm sorry, but I can't do any more.'

'But is there no antidote to this poison?'

'No, I'm afraid there isn't.'

'Well. . . .' He looked down with drawn face at the unconscious animal. 'What's going on? What's happening to Jasper when he goes stiff like he did? I'm only a layman but I like to understand things.'

'I'll try to explain it,' I said. 'Strychnine is absorbed into the nervous system and it increases the conductivity of the spinal cord.'

'What does that mean?'

'It means that the muscles become more sensitive to outside stimuli so that the slightest touch or sound throws them into violent contractions.'

'But why does a dog stretch out like that?'

'Because the extensor muscles are stronger than the flexors, causing the back to be arched and the legs extended.'

He nodded. 'I see, but . . . I believe it is usually fatal. What is it that . . . that kills them?'

'They die of asphyxia due to paralysis of the respiratory centre or contraction of the diaphragm.'

Maybe he wanted to ask more, but it was painful for him and he stayed silent.

'There's one thing I'd like you to know, Mr Bartle,' I said. 'It is almost certainly not a painful condition.'

'Thank you.' He bent and briefly stroked the sleeping dog. 'So nothing more can be done?'

I shook my head. 'The barbiturate keeps the spasms in abeyance and we'll go on hoping he hasn't absorbed too much strychnine. I'll call back later, or you can ring me if he gets worse. I can be here in a few minutes.'

Driving away, I pondered on the irony that made Darrowby a paradise for dog killers as well as dog lovers. There were grassy tracks everywhere; wandering by the river's edge, climbing the fell-sides and coiling green and tempting among the heather on the high tops. I often felt sympathy for pet owners in the big cities, trying to find places to walk their dogs. Here in Darrowby we could take our pick. But so could the poisoner. He could drop his deadly bait unobserved in a hundred different places.

I was finishing the afternoon surgery when the 'phone rang. It was Mr Bartle.

'Has he started the spasms again?' I asked.

There was a pause. 'No, I'm afraid Jasper is dead. He never regained consciousness.'

'Oh . . . I'm very sorry.' I felt a dull despair. That was the seventh death in a week.

'Well, thank you for your treatment, Mr Herriot. I'm sure nothing could have saved him.'

I hung up the 'phone wearily. He was right. Nothing or nobody could have done any good in this case, but it didn't help. If you finish up with a dead animal there is always the feeling of defeat.

Next day I was walking on to a farm when the farmer's wife called to me. 'I have a message for you to ring back to the surgery.'

I heard Helen's voice at the other end. 'Jack Brimham has just come in with his dog. I think it's another strychnine case.'

I excused myself and drove back to Darrowby at top speed. Jack Brimham was a builder. He ran a one-man business and whatever job he was on – repairing roofs or walls or chimneys – his little white rough-haired terrier went with him, and you could usually see the little animal nosing among the piles of bricks, exploring in the surrounding fields.

Jack was a friend, too. I often had a beer with him at the Drovers' Arms and I recognised his van outside the surgery. I trotted along the passage and found him leaning over the table in the consulting room. His dog was stretched there in that attitude which I dreaded.

'He's gone, Jim,' he muttered.

I looked at the shaggy little body. There was no movement, the eyes stared silently. The legs, even in death, strained across the smooth surface of the table. It was pointless, but I slipped my hand inside the thigh and felt for the femoral artery. There was no pulse.

'I'm sorry, Jack,' I said.

He didn't answer for a moment. 'I've been readin' about this in the paper, Jim, but I never thought it would happen to me. It's a bugger, isn't it?'

I nodded. He was a craggy-faced man, a tough Yorkshireman with a humour and integrity which I liked and a soft place inside which his dog had occupied. I did not know what to say to him.

'Who's doin' this?' he said, half to himself.

'I don't know, Jack. Nobody knows.'

'Well I wish I could have five minutes with him,' that's all.' He gathered the rigid little form into his arms and went out.

My troubles were not over for that day. It was about 11 p.m. and I had just got into bed when Helen nudged me.

'I think there's somebody knocking at the front door, Jim.'

I opened the window and looked out. Old Boardman, the lame veteran of the first war who did odd jobs for us, was standing on the steps.

'Mr Herriot,' he called up to me. 'I'm sorry to bother you at this hour, but Patch is ill.'

I leaned further out. 'What's he doing?'

'He's like a bit o' wood – stiff like, and laid on 'is side.'

I didn't bother to dress, just pulled my working corduroys over my pyjamas and went down the stairs two at a time. I grabbed what I needed from the dispensary and opened the front door. The old man, in shirt sleeves, caught at my arm.

'Come quickly, Mr Herriot!' He limped ahead of me to his little house about twenty yards away in the lane round the corner.

Patch was like all the others. The fat spaniel I had seen so often waddling round the top yard with his master was in that nightmare position on the kitchen floor, but he had vomited, which gave me hope. I administered the intravenous injection but as I withdrew the needle the breathing stopped.

Mrs Boardman, in nightgown and slippers, dropped on her knees and stretched a trembling hand towards the motionless animal.

'Patch. . . .' She turned and stared at me, wide-eyed. 'He's dead!'

I put my hand on the old woman's shoulder and said some sympathetic words. I thought grimly that I was getting good at it. As I left I looked back at the two old people. Boardman was kneeling now by his wife and even after I had closed the door I could hear their voices: 'Patch . . . oh Patch.'

I almost reeled over the few steps to Skeldale House and before going in I stood in the empty street breathing the cool air and trying to calm my racing thoughts. With Patch gone, this thing was getting very near home. I saw that dog every day. In fact all the dogs that had died were old friends – in a little town like Darrowby you came to know your patients personally. Where was it going to end?

I didn't sleep much that night and over the next few days I was obsessed with apprehension. I expected another poisoning with every 'phone call and took care never to let my own dog, Sam, out of the car in the region of the town. Thanks to my job I was able to exercise him miles away on the summits of the fells, but even there I kept him close to me.

By the fourth day I was beginning to feel more relaxed. Maybe the nightmare was over. I was driving home in the late afternoon past the row of grey cottages at the end of the Houlton Road when a woman ran waving into the road.

'Oh, Mr Herriot,' she cried when I stopped. 'I was just goin' to t'phone box when I saw you.'

I pulled up by the kerb. 'It's Mrs Clifford, isn't it?'

'Yes, Johnny's just come in and Fergus 'as gone queer. Collapsed and laid on t'floor.'

'Oh no!' An icy chill drove through me and for a moment I stared at her, unable to move. Then I threw open the car door and hurried after Johnny's mother into the end cottage. I halted abruptly in the little room and stared down in horror. The very sight of the splendid dignified animal scrabbling helplessly on the linoleum was a desecration, but strychnine is no respecter of such things.

'Oh God!' I breathed. 'Has he vomited, Johnny?'

'Aye, me mum said he was sick in t'back garden when we came in.' The young man was sitting very upright in a chair by the side of his dog. Even now there was a half smile on his face, but he looked strained as he put out his hand in the old gesture and failed to find the head that should have been there.

The bottle of barbiturate wobbled in my shaking hand as I filled the syringe. I tried to put away the thought that I was doing what I had done to all the others – all the dead ones. At my feet Fergus panted desperately, then as I bent over him he suddenly became still and went into the horrible distinctive spasm, the great limbs I knew so well straining frantically into space, the head pulled back grotesquely over the spine.

This was when they died, when the muscles were at full contraction. As the barbiturate flowed into the vein I waited for signs of relaxation but saw none. Fergus was about twice as heavy as any of the other victims I had treated and the plunger went to the end of the syringe without result.

Quickly I drew in another dose and began to inject it, my tension building as I saw how much I was administering. The recommended dose was 1 cc per 5 lb body weight and beyond that you could kill the animal. I watched the gradations on the glass barrel of the syringe and my mouth went dry when the dose crept far beyond the safety limit. But I knew I had to relieve this spasm and continued to depress the plunger relentlessly.

I did it in the grim knowledge that if he died now I would never know whether to blame the strychnine or myself for his death.

The big dog had received more than a lethal amount before peace began to return to the taut body and even then I sat back on my heels, almost afraid to look in case I had brought about his end. There was a long agonising moment when he lay still and apparently lifeless then the rib cage began to move almost imperceptibly as the breathing recommenced.

Even then I was in suspense. The anaesthesia was so deep that he was only just alive, yet I knew that the only hope was to keep him that way. I sent Mrs Clifford out to phone Siegfried that I would be tied up here for a while, then I pulled up a chair and settled down to wait.

The hours passed as Johnny and I sat there, the dog stretched between us. The young man discussed the case calmly and without self-pity. There was no suggestion that this was anything more than a pet animal lying at his feet – except for the tell-tale reaching for the head that was no longer there.

Several times Fergus showed signs of going into another spasm and each time I sent him back into his deep, deep insensibility, pushing him repeatedly to the brink with a fateful certainty that it was the only way.

It was well after midnight when I came sleepily out into the darkness. I felt drained. Watching the life of the friendly, clever, face-licking animal flicker as he lay inert and unheeding had been a tremendous strain, but I had left him sleeping – still anaesthetised but breathing deeply and regularly. Would he wake up and start the dread sequence again? I didn't know and I couldn't stay any longer. There was a practice with other animals to attend to.

But my anxiety jerked me into early wakefulness next morning. I tossed around till seven thirty telling myself this wasn't the way to be a veterinary surgeon, that you couldn't live like this. But my worry was stronger than the voice of reason and I slipped out before breakfast to the roadside cottage.

My nerves were like a bowstring as I knocked on the door. Mrs Clifford answered and I was about to blurt out my enquiries when Fergus trotted from the inner room.

He was still a little groggy from the vast dosage of barbiturate but he was relaxed and happy, the symptoms had gone, he was himself again. With a gush of pure joy I knelt and took the great head between my hands. He slobbered at me playfully with his wet tongue and I had to fight him off.

He followed me into the living room where Johnny was seated at the table, drinking tea. He took up his usual position, sitting upright and proud by his master's side.

'You'll have a cup, Mr Herriot?' Mrs Clifford asked, poising the teapot.

'Thanks, I'd love one, Mrs Clifford,' I replied.

No tea ever tasted better and as I sipped I watched the young man's smiling face.

'What a relief, Mr Herriot! I sat up with him all night, listenin' to the chimes of the church clock. It was just after four when I knew we'd won because I heard 'im get to his feet and sort o' stagger about. I stopped worryin' then, just listened to 'is feet patterin' on the linoleum. It was lovely!'

He turned his head to me and I looked at the slightly upturned eyes in the cheerful face.

'I'd have been lost without Fergus,' he said softly. 'I don't know how to thank you.'

But as he unthinkingly rested his hand on the head of the big dog who was his pride and delight I felt that the gesture alone was all the thanks I wanted.

That was the end of the strychnine poisoning outbreak in Darrowby. The older people still talk about it, but nobody ever had the slightest clue to the identity of the killer and it is a mystery to this day.

I feel that the vigilance of the police and the publicity in the press frightened this twisted person off, but anyway it just stopped and the only cases since then have been accidental ones.

To me it is a sad memory of failure and frustration. Fergus was my only cure and I'm not sure why he recovered. Maybe the fact that I pushed the injection to dangerous levels because I was desperate had something to do with it, or maybe he just didn't pick up as much poison as the others. I'll never know.

But over the years when I saw the big dog striding majestically in his harness, leading his master unerringly around the streets of Darrowby, I always had the same feeling.

If there had to be just one saved, I'm glad it was him.

Chapter Eighteen

A tender nerve twinged as the old lady passed me the cup of tea. She looked just like Mrs Beck.

One of the local churches was having a social evening to entertain us lonely airmen and as I accepted the cup and sat down I could hardly withdraw my eyes from the lady's face.

Mrs Beck! I could see her now standing by the surgery window.

'Oooh, I never thought you were such a 'eartless man, Mr Herriot.' Her chin trembled and she looked up at me reproachfully.

'But Mrs Beck,' I said. 'I assure you I am not being in the least heartless. I just cannot carry out a major operation on your cat for ten shillings.'

'Well, I thought you would've done it for a poor widder woman like me.'

I regarded her thoughtfully, taking in the small compact figure, the healthy cheeks, the neat helmet of grey hair pulled tightly into a bun. Was she really a poor widow? There was cause for doubt. Her next-door neighbour in Rayton village was a confirmed sceptic.

'It's all a tale, Mr Herriot,' he had said. 'She tries it on wi' everybody, but I'll tell you this – she's got a long stockin'. Owns property all over t'place.'

I took a deep breath. 'Mrs Beck. We often do work at reduced rates for people who can't afford to pay, but this is what we call a luxury operation.'

'Luxury!' The lady was aghast. 'Eee, ah've been tellin' you how Georgina keeps havin' them kittens. She's at it all the time and it's gettin' me down. Ah can't sleep for worryin' when t'next lot's comin'.' She dabbed her eyes.

'I understand and I'm sorry. I can only tell you again that the only way to prevent this trouble is to spay your cat and the charge is one pound.'

'Nay, I can't afford that much!'

I spread my hands. 'But you are asking me to do it for half the price. That's ridiculous. This operation involves the removal of the uterus and ovaries under a general anaesthetic. You just can't do a job like that for ten shillings.'

'Oh, you are cruel!' She turned and looked out of the window and her shoulders began to shake. 'You won't even take pity on a poor widder.'

This had been going on for ten minutes and it began to dawn on me that I was in the presence of a stronger character than myself. I glanced at my watch – I should have been on my round by now and it was becoming increasingly obvious that I wasn't going to win this argument.

I sighed. Maybe she really was a poor widow. 'All right, Mrs Beck, I'll do it for ten shillings, just this once. Will Tuesday afternoon be all right for you.'

She swung round from the window, her face crinkling magically into a smile. 'That'll suit me grand! Eee, that's right kind of you.' She tripped past me and I followed her along the passage.

'Just one thing,' I said as I held the front door open for her. 'Don't give Georgina any food from midday on Monday. She must have an empty stomach when you bring her in.'

'Bring 'er in?' She was a picture of bewilderment. 'But I 'aven't got no car. I thought you'd be collectin' her.'

'Collecting! But Rayton's five miles away!'

'Yes, and bring 'er back afterwards, too. I 'ave no transport.'

'Collect . . . operate on her . . . take her back! All for ten shillings!'

She was still smiling but a touch of steel glinted in her eyes. 'Well, that's what you agreed to charge – ten shillings.'

'But . . . but . . .'

'Oh now you're startin' again.' The smile faded and she put her head on one side. 'And I'm only a poor . . .'

'Okay, okay,' I said hastily. 'I'll call on Tuesday.'

And when Tuesday afternoon came round I cursed my softness. If that cat had been brought in I could have operated on her at two o'clock and been out on the road doing my farm calls by two thirty. I didn't mind working at a loss for half an hour, but how long was this business going to take?

On my way out I glanced through the open door of the sitting room. Tristan was supposed to be studying but was sleeping soundly in his favourite chair. I went in and looked down at him, marvelling at the utter relaxation, seen only in a dedicated sleeper. His face was as smooth and untroubled as a baby's, the *Daily Mirror*, open at the comic strips, had fallen across his chest and a burnt-out Woodbine hung from one dangling hand.

I shook him gently. 'Like to come with me, Triss? I've got to pick up a cat.'

He came round slowly, stretching and grimacing, but his fundamental good nature soon reasserted itself.

'Certainly, Jim,' he said with a final yawn. 'It will be a pleasure.'

Mrs Beck lived half way down the left side of Rayton village. I read 'Jasmine Cottage' on the brightly painted gate, and as we went up the garden path the door opened and the little woman waved gaily.

'Good afternoon, gentlemen, I'm right glad to see you both.' She ushered us into the living-room among good, solid-looking furniture which showed no sign of poverty. The open cupboard of a mahogany sideboard gave me a glimpse of glasses and bottles. I managed to identify Scotch, cherry brandy and sherry before she nudged the door shut with her knee.

I pointed to a cardboard box loosely tied with string. 'Ah, good, you've got her in there, have you?'

'Nay, bless you, she's in t'garden. She allus has a bit of play out there of an afternoon.'

'In the garden, eh?' I said nervously. 'Well, please get her in, we're in rather a hurry.'

We went through a tiled kitchen to the back door. Most of these cottages had a surprising amount of land behind them and Mrs Beck's patch was in very nice order. Flower beds bordered a smooth stretch of lawn and the sunshine drew glittering colours from the apples and pears among the branches of the trees.

'Georgina,' carolled Mrs Beck. 'Where are you, my pet?'

No cat appeared and she turned to me with a roguish smile. 'I think the little imp's playin' a game with us. She does that, you know.'

'Really?' I said without enthusiasm. 'Well, I wish she'd show herself. I really don't have much . . .'

At that moment a very fat tabby darted from a patch of chrysanthemums and flitted across the grass into a clump of rhododendrons with Tristan in close pursuit. The young man dived among the greenery and the cat emerged from the other end at top speed, did a couple of laps of the lawn then shot up a gnarled tree.

Tristan, eyes gleaming in anticipation, lifted a couple of windfall apples from the turf. 'I'll soon shift the bugger from there, Jim,' he whispered and took aim.

I grabbed his arm. 'For heaven's sake, Triss!' I hissed. 'You can't do that. Put those things down.'

'Oh . . . all right.' He dropped the apples and made for the tree. 'I'll get hold of her for you, anyway.'

'Wait a minute.' I seized his coat as he passed. 'I'll do it. You stay down here and try to catch her if she jumps.'

Tristan looked disappointed but I gave him a warning look. The way the cat had moved, it struck me that it only needed a bit of my colleague's ebullience to send the animal winging into the next county. I began to climb the tree.

I like cats, I've always liked them, and since I feel that animals recognise this in a person I have usually been able to approach and handle the most difficult types. It is not too much to say that I prided myself on my cat technique; I didn't foresee any trouble here.

Puffing slightly, I reached the top branch and extended a hand to the crouching animal.

'Pooss-pooss,' I cooed, using my irresistible cat tone.

Georgina eyed me coldly and gave no answering sign other than a higher arching of the back.

I leaned further along the branch. 'Pooss-pooss, pooss-pooss.' My voice was like molten honey, my finger near her face. I would rub her cheek ever so gently and she would be mine. It never failed.

'Pah!' replied Georgina warningly but I took no heed and touched the fur under her chin.

'Pah-pah!' Georgina spat and followed with a lightning left hook which opened a bloody track across the back of my hand.

Muttering fervently, I retreated and nursed my wounds. From below Mrs Beck gave a tinkling laugh.

'Oh, isn't she a little monkey! She's that playful, bless her.'

I snorted and began to ease my way along the branch again. This time, I thought grimly, I would dispense with finesse. The quick grab was indicated here.

As though reading my thoughts the little creature tripped to the end of the branch and as it bent low under her weight she dropped lightly to the grass.

Tristan was on her in a flash, throwing himself full length and seizing her by the hind leg. Georgina whipped round and unhesitatingly sank her teeth into his thumb but Tristan's core of resilience showed. After a single howl of agony he changed his grip at lightning speed to the scruff of the neck.

A moment later he was standing upright holding a dangling fighting fury high in the air.

'Right, Jim,' he called happily. 'I have her.'

'Good lad! Hang on!' I said breathlessly and slithered down the tree as quickly as I could. Too quickly, in fact, as an ominous ripping sound announced the removal of a triangular piece of my jacket elbow.

But I couldn't bother with trifles. Ushering Tristan at a gallop into the house I opened the cardboard box. There were no sophisticated cat containers in those days and it was a tricky job to enclose Georgina, who was lashing out in all directions and complaining bitterly in a bad-tempered wail.

It took a panting ten minutes to imprison the cat but even with several yards of rough twine round the floppy cardboard I still didn't feel very secure as I bore it to the car.

Mrs Beck raised a finger as we were about to drive away. I carefully explored my lacerated hand and Tristan sucked his thumb as we waited for her to speak.

'Mr Herriot, I 'ope you'll be gentle with 'er,' she said anxiously. 'She's very timid, you know.'

We had covered barely half a mile before sounds of strife arose from the back.

'Get back! Get in there. Get back, you bugger!'

I glanced behind me. Tristan was having trouble. Georgina clearly didn't care for the motion of the car and from the slits in the box clawed feet issued repeatedly; on one occasion an enraged spitting face got free as far as the neck. Tristan kept pushing everything back with great resolution but I could tell from the rising desperation of his cries that he was fighting a losing battle.

I heard the final shout with a feeling of inevitability.

'She's out, Jim! The bugger's out!'

Well this was great. Anybody who has driven a car with a hysterical cat hurtling around the interior will appreciate my situation. I crouched low over the wheel as the furry creature streaked round the sides or leaped clawing at the roof or windscreen with Tristan lunging vainly after her.

But cruel fate had not finished with us yet. My colleague's gasps and grunts from the rear ceased for a moment to be replaced by a horrified shriek.

'The bloody thing's shitting, Jim! She's shitting everywhere!'

The cat was obviously using every weapon at her disposal and he didn't have to tell me. My nose was away ahead of him, and I frantically wound down the window. But I closed it just as quickly at the rising image of Georgina escaping and disappearing into the unknown.

I don't like to think of the rest of that journey. I tried to breathe through my mouth and Tristan puffed out dense clouds of Woodbine smoke but it was still pretty terrible. Just outside Darrowby I stopped the car and we made a concerted onslaught of the animal; at the cost of a few more wounds, including a particularly painful scratch on my nose, we cornered her and fastened her once more in the box.

Even on the operating table Georgina had a few tricks left. We were using ether and oxygen as anaesthetic and she was particularly adept at holding her breath while the mask was on her face then returning suddenly to violent life when we thought she was asleep. We were both sweating when she finally went under.

I suppose it was inevitable, too, that she should be a difficult case. Ovarohysterectomy in the cat is a fairly straightforward procedure and nowadays we do innumerable cases uneventfully, but in the thirties, particularly in country practice, it was infrequently done and consequently a much larger undertaking.

I personally had my own preferences and aversions in this field. For instance, I found thin cats easy to do and fat cats difficult. Georgina was extremely fat.

When I opened her abdomen an ocean of fat welled up at me, obscuring everything, and I spent a long nerve-racking period lifting out portions of bowel or omentum with my forceps, surveying them gloomily and stuffing them back in again. A great weariness had began to creep over me by the time I at last managed to grip the pink ovary between the metallic jaws and drew forth the slender string of uterus. After that it was routine, but I still felt a strange sense of exhaustion as I inserted the last stitch.

I put the sleeping cat into the box and beckoned to Tristan. 'Come on, let's get her home before she comes round.' I was starting along the passage when he put his hand on my arm.

'Jim,' he said gravely. 'You know I'm your friend.'

'Yes, Triss, of course.'

'I'd do anything for you, Jim.'

'I'm sure you would.'

He took a deep breath. 'Except one thing. I'm not going back in that bloody car.'

I nodded dully. I really couldn't blame him.

'That's all right,' I said. 'I'll be off, then.'

Before leaving I sprinkled the interior with pine-smelling disinfectant but it didn't make much difference. In any case my main emotion was the hope that Georgina wouldn't wake up before I got to Rayton, and that was shattered before I had crossed Darrowby market place. The hair prickled on the back of my neck as an ominous droning issued from the box on the rear seat. It was like the sound of a distant swarm of bees but I knew what it meant; the anaesthetic was wearing off.

Once clear of the town I put my foot on the boards. This was something I rarely did because whenever I pushed my vehicle above forty miles an hour there was such a clamour of protest from engine and body that I always feared the thing would disintegrate around me. But at this moment I didn't care. Teeth clenched, eyes staring, I hurtled forward, but I didn't see the lonely strip of tarmac or the stone walls flitting past; all my attention was focused behind me, where the swarm of bees was getting nearer and the tone angrier.

When it developed into a bad-tempered yowling and was accompanied by the sound of strong claws tearing at cardboard I began to tremble. As I thundered into Rayton village I glanced behind me. Georgina was half out of the box. I reached back and grasped her scruff and when I stopped at the gate of Jasmine Cottage I pulled on the brake with one hand and lifted her on to my lap with the other.

I sagged in the seat, my breath escaping in a great explosion of relief; and my stiff features almost bent into a smile as I saw Mrs Beck pottering in her garden.

She took Georgina from me with a cry of joy but gasped in horror when she saw the shaven area and the two stitches on the cat's flank.

'Oooh, my darlin'! What 'ave those nasty men been doin' to you?' She hugged the animal to her and glared at me.

'She's all right, Mrs Beck, she's fine,' I said. 'You can give her a little milk tonight and some solid food tomorrow. There's nothing to worry about.'

She pouted. 'Oh, very well. And now . . .' She gave me a sidelong glance. 'I suppose you'll want your money?'

'Well, er . . .'

'Wait there, then. I'll get it.' She turned and went into the house.

Standing there, leaning against the reeking car, feeling the sting of the scratches on my hands and nose and examining the long tear on my jacket elbow I felt physically and emotionally spent. All I had done this afternoon was spay a cat but I had nothing more to offer.

Apathetically I watched the lady coming down the path. She was carrying a purse. At the gate she stopped and faced me.

'Ten shillin's, wasn't it?'

'That's right.'

She rummaged in the purse for some time before pulling out a ten-shilling note which was regarded sadly.

'Oh Georgina, Georgina, you *are* an expensive pussy,' she soliloquised.

Tentatively I began to extend my hand but she pulled the note away. 'Just a minute, I'm forgettin'. You 'ave to take the stitches out, don't you?'

'Yes, in ten days.'

She set her lips firmly. 'Well there's plenty of time to pay ye then – ye'll be here again.'

'Here again . . .? But you can't expect . . .'

'I allus think it's unlucky to pay afore a job's finished,' she said. 'Summat terrible might happen to Georgina.'

'But . . . but . . .'

'Nay, ah've made up me mind,' she said. She replaced the money and snapped her purse shut with an air of finality before turning towards the house. Halfway up the path she looked over her shoulder and smiled.

'Aye, that's what I'll do. I'll pay ye when ye come back.'

Chapter Nineteen

We were ready to march away from Scarborough. And it was ironical that we were leaving just when the place was beginning to smile on us.

In the May sunshine we stood on parade outside the Grand at 7 a.m. as we had done throughout the Yorkshire winter, mostly in darkness, often with the

icy rain blowing in our faces. But now I felt a pang of regret as I looked over
the heads at the wide beautiful bay stretching beneath its cliffs to the far
headland, the sand clean-washed and inviting, the great blue expanse of sea
shimmering and glittering and over everything the delicious sea-smell of salt
and seaweed, raising memories of holidays and happy things lost in the war.

'Atten-shun!' Flight Sergeant Blackett's bellow rolled over us as we stiffened
in our ranks, every man carrying full kit, our packs braced with sheets of
cardboard to give the sharp, rectangular look, hair cut short, boots gleaming,
buttons shining like gold. Without our knowing, No. ten ITW had moulded us
into a smart, disciplined unit, very different from the shambling, half-baked
crew of six months ago. We had all passed our exams and were no longer AC2s
but Leading Aircraftmen, and as LAC Herriot my wage had rocketed from
three shillings to a dizzying seven and threepence a day.

'Right turn!' Again the roar. 'By the left qui-ick march!'

Arms high, moving as one, we swung past the front of the Grand for the last
time. I shot a parting glance at the great building – like a dignified Victorian
lady stripped of her finery – and I made a resolve. I would come back some day,
when the war was over, and see the Grand Hotel as it should be.

And I did, too. Years later, Helen and I sat in deep armchairs in the lounge
where the SPs had barked. Waiters padded over the thick carpets with tea and
muffins while a string orchestra played selections from *Rose Marie*.

And in the evening we dined in the elegant room with its long unbroken line
of window looking down on the sea. This room had been the cold open terrace
where I learned to read the Aldis lamp flickering from the lighthouse, but now
we sat in luxurious warmth eating grilled sole and watching the lights of the
harbour and town beginning to wink in the gathering dusk.

But that was very much in the future as the tramping feet echoed along
Huntriss Row on the way to the station and the long lines of blue left the
emptying square. We didn't know where we were going, everything was
uncertain.

Black's *Veterinary Dictionary* dug into my back through the layer of cardboard.
It was an unwieldy article but it reminded me of good days and gave me hope
of more to come.

Chapter Twenty

'It's the same the whole world over, it's the poor wot gets the blame. It's the rich
wot gets the pleasure . . .'

We were on a 'toughening course', living under canvas in the depths of
Shropshire, and this was one of the occasions when we were all gathered together
– hundreds of sunburned men – in a huge marquee waiting to be addressed by
a visiting air commodore.

Before the great man arrived the platform was occupied by a lascivious
sergeant who was whittling away the time by leading us in a succession of bawdy
ditties accompanied by gestures. 'It's the rich wot gets the . . .', but instead of
'pleasure' he made a series of violent pumping movements with his forearm.

I was intrigued by the reaction of the airman on my right. He was a slim, pink-faced lad of about nineteen and his lank fair hair fell over his face as he jumped up and down. He was really throwing himself into it, bawling out the indelicate words, duplicating the sergeant's gesticulations with maniacal glee. He was, I had recently learned, the son of a bishop.

We had been joined on this course by the Oxford University Air Squadron. They were a group of superior and delicately nurtured young men and since I had spent three full days peeling potatoes with them I had come to know most of them very well. 'Spud bashing' is an unequalled method of becoming familiar with one's fellow men and as, hour after hour, we filled countless bins with our produce, the barriers crumbled steadily until at the end of three days we didn't have many secrets from each other.

The bishop's son had found something hilarious in the idea of a qualified veterinary surgeon leaving his practice to succour his country by removing the skins from thousands of tubers. And I, on the other hand, derived some reward from watching his antics. He was a charming and likeable lad but he seized avidly on anything with the faintest salacious slant. They say parsons' sons are a bit wild when let off the leash, and I suppose an escapee from a bishop's palace is even more susceptible to the blandishments of the big world.

I looked at him again. All round him men were yelling their heads off, but his voice, mouthing the four-letter words with relish, rang above the rest and he followed the actions of the conducting sergeant like a devoted acolyte.

It was all so different from Darrowby. My early days in the RAF with all the swearing and uninhibited conversation made me realise, perhaps for the first time, what kind of a community I had left behind me. Because I often think that one of the least permissive societies in the history of mankind was the agricultural community of rural Yorkshire in the thirties. Among the farmers anything to do with sex or the natural functions was unmentionable.

It made my work more difficult because if the animal's ailment had the slightest sexual connotation its owner would refuse to go into details if Helen or our secretary Miss Harbottle answered the 'phone. 'I want the vet to come and see a cow,' was as far as they would go.

Today's case was typical and I looked at Mr Hopps with some irritation.

'Why didn't you say your cow wasn't coming into season? There's a new injection for that now but I haven't got it with me. I can't carry everything in my car, you know.'

The farmer studied his feet. 'Well, it was a lady on t'phone and I didn't like to tell 'er that Snowdrop wasn't bullin'.' He looked up at me sheepishly. 'Can't you do owt about it, then?'

I sighed. 'Maybe I can. Bring me a bucket of hot water and some soap.'

As I lathered my arm I felt a twinge of disappointment. I'd have liked to try that new Prolan injection. But on the other hand there was a certain interest in these rectal examinations.

'Hold her tail, please,' I said, and began to work my hand carefully past the anal ring.

We were doing a lot of this lately. The profession had awakened quite suddenly to the fact that bovine infertility was no longer an impenetrable mystery. We were carrying out more and more of these examinations, and as I say, they had a strange fascination.

Siegfried put it with his usual succinctness one morning.

'James,' he said. 'There is more to be learned up a cow's arse than in many an encyclopaedia.'

And, groping my way into this animal, I could see what he meant. Through the rectal wall I gripped the uterine cervix, then I worked along the right horn. It felt perfectly normal, as did the fallopian tube when I reached it. In another moment the ovary rested between my fingers like a walnut; but it was a walnut with a significant bulge and I smiled to myself. That swelling was the corpus luteum, the 'yellow body' which was exerting its influence on the ovary and preventing the initiation of the normal oestral cycle.

I squeezed gently on the base of the bulge and felt it part from the ovary and swim off into space. That was lovely – just what was required – and I looked happily along the cow's back at the farmer.

'I think I've put things right, Mr Hopps. She should come on within the next day or two and you can get her served right away.'

I withdrew my arm, smeared with filth almost to the shoulder, and began to swill it with the warm water. This was the moment when young people with dewy-eyed ambitions to be veterinary surgeons usually decided to be lawyers or nurses instead. A lot of teenagers came round with me to see practice and it seemed to me that the sooner they witnessed the realities of the job the better it would be for them. A morning's pregnancy diagnoses or something similar had a salutary effect in sorting out the sheep from the goats.

As I left the farm I had the satisfied feeling that I had really done something, and a sensation of relief that Mr Hopps' delicacy hadn't resulted in an abortive visit.

It was strange, but when I returned to the surgery I immediately encountered another example of the same thing.

Mr Pinkerton, a smallholder, was sitting in the office next to Miss Harbottle's desk. By his side sat his farm collie.

'Well, what can I do for you, Mr Pinkerton?' I asked as I closed the door behind me.

The farmer hesitated. 'It's my dog – 'e isn't right.'

'What do you mean? Is he ill?' I bent down and stroked the shaggy head and as the dog leaped up in delight his tail began to beat a booming tom-tom rhythm against the side of the desk.

'Nay, nay, he's right enough in 'imself.' The man was clearly ill as ease.

'Well, what's the trouble? He looks the picture of health to me.'

'Aye, but ah'm a bit worried. Ye see it's 'is . . .' He glanced furtively towards Miss Harbottle. 'It's 'is pencil.'

'What d'you say?'

A faint flush mounted in Mr Pinkerton's thin cheeks. Again he shot a terrified glance at Miss Harbottle. 'It's 'is . . . pencil. There's summat matter with 'is pencil.' He indicated by the merest twitch of his forefinger somewhere in the direction of the animal's belly.

I looked. 'I'm sorry, but I can't see anything unusual.'

'Ah, but there is.' The farmer's face twisted in an agony of embarrassment and he pushed his face close to mine. 'There's summat there,' he said in a hoarse whisper. 'Summat comin' from 'is . . . 'is pencil.'

I got down on my knees and had a closer look, and suddenly all became clear.

'Is that what you mean?' I pointed to a tiny blob of semen on the end of the prepuce.

He nodded dumbly, his face a study in woe.

I laughed. 'Well you can stop worrying. That's nothing abnormal. You might call it an overflow. He's just a young dog, isn't he?'

'Aye, nobbut eighteen months.'

'Well, that's it. He's just too full of the joys. Plenty of good food and maybe not a lot of work to do, eh?'

'Aye, he gets good grub. Nowt but the best. And you're right – I 'aven't much work for him.'

'Well, there you are.' I held out a hand. 'Just cut down his diet and see he gets more exercise and this thing will sort itself out.'

Mr Pinkerton stared at me. 'But aren't you goin' to do anything to 'is . . . 'is . . .' Again he cast an anguished glance at our secretary.

'No, no,' I said. 'I assure you there's nothing wrong with his . . . er . . . pencil. No local trouble at all.'

I could see he was totally unconvinced so I threw in another ploy. 'I tell you what. I'll give you some mild sedative tablets for him. They'll help a bit.'

I went through to the dispensary and counted the tablets into a box. Back in the office I handed them to the farmer with a confident smile, but his face registered only a deepening misery. Obviously I hadn't explained the thing clearly enough and as I led him along the passage to the front door I talked incessantly, putting the whole business into simple words which I was sure he would understand.

As he stood on the doorstep I gave him a final comforting pat on the shoulder and though I was almost breathless with my own babbling I thought it best to sum up the entire oration before he left.

'So there you are,' I said with a light laugh. 'Reduce his food, see that he gets plenty of work and exercise and give him one of the tablets night and morning.'

The farmer's mouth dropped until I thought he would burst into tears then he turned and trailed down the steps into the street. He took a couple of indeterminate strides then swung round and his voice rose in a plaintive wail.

'But Mr Herriot . . . 'ow about 'is pencil?'

And when little Mr Gilby crashed moaning on the cobbles of his byre floor, my first thought was that it was unfair that it should happen to him of all people.

Because the natural delicacy and reticence of the times were embodied in him to an extreme degree. Even his physical makeup had something ethereal about it; nine stones of tiny bones, taut skin with no fat and a gentle, innocent face, almost child-like despite his fifty years. Nobody had ever heard Mr Gilby swear or use a vulgar expression; in fact he was the only farmer I have ever known who talked about cow's 'manure'.

Besides, as a strict methodist he didn't drink or indulge in worldly pleasures and had never been known to tell a lie. Altogether he was so good that I would have regarded him with deep suspicion if he had been anybody else. But I had come to know Mr Gilby. He was a nice little man, he was as honest as the day. I would have trusted him with my life.

That was why I was so sad to see him lying there. It had happened so quickly. We had only just come into the byre and he pointed to a black Angus Cross cow almost opposite the door.

'That's 'er. Got a touch o'cold, I think.' He knew I would want to take the temperature and grasped the tail before putting one foot across the channel so that he could slide between the cow and her neighbour. That was when it happened; when his legs were wide apart in the worst possible position.

In a way I wasn't surprised because that tail had been swishing bad-temperedly as we came in, and I am always a bit wary of black cows anyway. She didn't seem to like our sudden entry and lashed out with her right hind foot with the speed of light, catching him with her flinty hoof full in the crutch as his legs were splayed. He was wearing only frayed, much-washed overall trousers and the protection was nil.

I winced as the foot went home with an appalling thud, but Mr Gilby showed no emotion at all. He dropped as though on the receiving end of a firing squad and lay motionless on the hard stones, his hands clutched between his legs. It was only after several seconds that he began to moan softly.

As I hurried to his aid I felt it was wrong that I should be witnessing this disintegration of his modest façade. The little farmer, I was sure, would rather have died than be caught in this inelegant position, grovelling on the floor gripping frantically at an unmentionable area. I kneeled on the cobbles and patted his shoulder while he fought his inner battle with his agony.

After a while he felt well enough to sit up and I put my arm around him and supported him while perspiration bedewed the greenish pallor of his face. That was when the embarrassment began to creep in, because though he had removed his hands from their compromising position he was clearly deeply ashamed at being caught in a coarse attitude.

I felt strangely helpless. The little man couldn't relieve his feelings in the usual way by cursing the animal and fate in general, nor could I help him to laugh the thing off with a few earthly remarks. This sort of thing happens now and then in the present day and usually gives rise to a certain amount of ripe comment, often embracing the possible effect on the victim's future sex life. It all helps.

But here in Mr Gilby's byre there was only an uncomfortable silence. After a time the colour began to return to his cheeks and the little man struggled slowly to his feet. He took a couple of deep breaths then looked at me unhappily. Obviously he thought he owed me some explanation, even apology, for his tasteless behaviour.

As the minutes passed the tension rose. Mr Gilby's mouth twitched once or twice as though he were about to speak but he seemed unable to find the words. At length he appeared to come to a decision. He cleared his throat, looked around him carefully then put his lips close to my ear. He clarified the whole situation by one hoarsely whispered, deeply confidential sentence.

'Right in the privates, Mr Herriot.'

I referred earlier to the prevailing shyness about the natural functions and this did indeed give rise to problems.

One slight difficulty which all country vets encounter is that there comes a time on a long round when they have to urinate. When I first came to Yorkshire it seemed the most natural thing in the world for me to retire to a corner of a cow byre to relieve myself and it was utterly incomprehensible that anybody of my own sex should find this embarrassing. But it soon became obvious that the farmers were shuffling their feet, looking pointedly in the opposite direction or showing other signs of unease.

My attempts to laugh the incident off met with no success. Jocular remarks thrown over my shoulder like 'Just wringing out a kidney' or 'This method gives instant relief', were greeted with serious nods and mutterings of 'Aye . . . aye . . . aye . . . that's right.' I often had to resort to sneaking into some deserted outhouse as soon as I arrived, but very often the farmer would burst in and catch me in the act and retreat bashfully.

The farmers themselves added to my difficulties by their hospitable custom of pushing large mugs of tea into my hand at every opportunity. At times I shrank from causing offence in the buildings and when under stress took refuge in the open countryside. But even this was fraught with peril, because though I always selected a deserted road with the moors stretching empty to the far horizon the landscape within seconds invariably became black with cars, all driven by women and all bearing down on me at high speed.

I recall with quaking shame one occasion when a carload of middle-aged spinsters stopped and questioned me at length about the quickest way to Darrowby while a dark pool spread accusingly around my feet.

But I suppose there are exceptions to every rule, and there was one time when the reaction to my predicament was different. I had consumed my usual quota of tea and on top of this one kind chap had opened a couple of pint bottles of brown ale after a sweating session castrating calves in a tin-roofed shed. By the time I arrived at old Mr Ainsley's I was in dire straits.

But there was nobody around. I tiptoed into the byre, slunk into a corner and blessedly opened the flood gates. I was in mid flow when I heard the clatter of heavy boots on the cobbles behind me. The old man, shoulders hunched, hands in pockets, was standing there watching me.

Oh dear, it had happened again, but I wasn't going to stop now. With a sickly smile I looked over my shoulder at him.

'Sorry to make free with your cow house like this, Mr Ainsley,' I said in what I hoped was a light, bantering tone. 'But I had no option. When I have to go I just have to go. Maybe I have a weak bladder or something.'

The old man regarded me impassively for a few moments then he nodded his head several times.

'Aye, ah knaw, ah knaw,' he said gloomily. 'You're like me, Mr Herriot. Ah's allus pissin'.'

Chapter Twenty-one

Little pictures kept floating up into my mind. Memories from the very early days at Skeldale House. Before the RAF, before Helen. . . .

Siegfried and I were at breakfast in the big dining-room. My colleague looked up from a letter he was reading.

'James, do you remember Stewie Brannan?'

I smiled. 'I could hardly forget. That was quite a day at Brawton races.' I would always carry a vivid recollection of Siegfried's amiable college chum with me.

'Yes . . . yes, it was.' Siegfried nodded briefly. 'Well I've got a letter from him here. He's got six kids now, and though he doesn't complain, I don't think life is exactly a picnic working in a dump like Hensfield. Especially when he knocks a bare living out of it.' He pulled thoughtfully at the lobe of his ear. 'You know, James, it would be rather nice if he could have a break. Would you be willing to go through there and run his practice for a couple of weeks so that he could take his family on holiday?'

'Certainly. Glad to. But you'll be a bit pushed here on your own, won't you?'

Siegfried waved a hand. 'It'll do me good. Anyway it's the quiet time for us. I'll write back today.'

Stewie grasped the opportunity eagerly and within a few days I was on the road to Hensfield. Yorkshire is the biggest county in England and it must be the most varied. I could hardly believe it when, less than two hours after leaving the clean grassy fells and crystal air of Darrowby, I saw the forest of factory chimneys sprouting from the brown pall of grime.

This was the industrial West Riding and I drove past mills as dark and satanic as any I had dreamed of, past long rows of dreary featureless houses where the workers lived. Everything was black; houses, mills, walls, trees, even the surrounding hillsides, smeared and soiled from the smoke which drifted across the town from a hundred belching stacks.

Stewie's surgery was right in the heart of it, a gloomy edifice in a terrace of sooty stone. As I rang the bell I read the painted board: 'Stewart Brannan MRCVS, Veterinary Surgeon and Canine Specialist.' I was wondering what the Royal College would think about the last part when the door opened and my colleague stood before me.

He seemed to fill the entrance. If anything he was fatter than before, but that was the only difference. Since it was August I couldn't expect him to be wearing his navy nap overcoat, but otherwise he was as I remembered him in Darrowby; the big, meaty, good-natured face, the greasy black hair slicked across the brow which always seemed to carry a gentle dew of perspiration.

He reached out, grabbed my hand and pulled me delightedly through the doorway.

'Jim! Great to see you!' He put an arm round my shoulders as we crossed a dark hallway. 'It's good of you to help me out like this. The family are thrilled – they're all in the town shopping for the holiday. We've got fixed up in a flat at Blackpool.' His permanent smile widened.

We went into a room at the back where a rickety kitchen-type table stood on brown linoleum. I saw a sink in one corner, a few shelves with bottles and a white-painted cupboard. The atmosphere held a faint redolence of carbolic and cat's urine.

'This is where I see the animals,' Stewie said contentedly. He looked at his watch. 'Twenty past five – I have a surgery at five thirty. I'll show you round till then.'

It didn't take long because there wasn't much to see. I knew there was a more fashionable veterinary firm in Hensfield and that Stewie made his living from the poor people of the town; the whole set-up was an illustration of practice on a shoestring. There didn't seem to be more than one of anything – one straight suture needle, one curved needle, one pair of scissors, one syringe. There was a sparse selection of drugs and an extraordinary array of dispensing bottles and jars. These bottles were of many strange shapes – weird things which I had never seen in a dispensary before.

Stewie seemed to read my thoughts. 'It's nothing great, Jim. I haven't a smart practice and I don't make a lot, but we manage to clear the housekeeping and that's the main thing.'

The phrase was familiar. 'Clear the housekeeping' – that was how he had put it when I first met him at Brawton races. It seemed to be the lodestar of his life.

The end of the room was cut off by a curtain which my colleague drew to one side.

'This is what you might call the waiting room.' He smiled as I looked in some surprise at half a dozen wooden chairs arranged round the three walls. 'No high-powered stuff, Jim, no queues into the streets, but we get by.'

Some of Stewie's clients were already filing in; two little girls with a black dog, a cloth-capped old man with a terrier on a string, a teenage boy carrying a rabbit in a basket.

'Right,' the big man said. 'We'll get started.' He pulled on a white coat, opened the curtain and said, 'First, please.'

The little girls put their dog on the table. He was a long-tailed mixture of breeds and he stood trembling with fear, rolling his eyes apprehensively at the white coat.

'All right, lad,' Stewie murmured. 'I'm not going to hurt you.' He stroked and patted the quivering head before turning to the girls. 'What's the trouble, then?'

'It's 'is leg, 'e's lame,' one of them replied.

As if in confirmation the little dog raised a fore leg and held it up with a pitiful expression. Stewie engulfed the limb with his great hand and palpated it with the utmost care. And it struck me immediately – the gentleness of this shambling bear of a man.

'There's nothing broken,' he said. 'He's just sprained his shoulder. Try to rest it for a few days and rub this in night and morning.'

He poured some whitish liniment from a winchester bottle into one of the odd-shaped bottles and handed it over.

One of the little girls held out her hand and unclasped her fingers to reveal a shilling in her palm.

'Thanks,' said Stewie without surprise. 'Goodbye.'

He saw several other cases, then as he was on his way to the curtain two grubby urchins appeared through the door at the other end of the room. They carried a clothes basket containing a widely varied assortment of glassware.

Stewie bent over the basket, lifting out HP sauce bottles, pickle jars, ketchup containers and examining them with the air of a connoisseur. At length he appeared to come to a decision.

'Threepence,' he said.

'Sixpence,' said the urchins in unison.

'Fourpence,' grunted Stewie.

'Sixpence,' chorused the urchins.

'Fivepence,' my colleague muttered doggedly.

'Sixpence!' There was a hint of triumph in the cry.

Stewie sighed. 'Go on then.' He passed over the coin and began to stack the bottles under the sink.

'I just scrape off the labels and give them a good boil up, Jim.'

'I see.'

'It's a big saving.'

'Yes, of course.' The mystery of the strangely shaped dispensing bottles was suddenly resolved.

It was six thirty when the last client came through the curtain. I had watched Stewie examining each animal carefully, taking his time and treating their conditions ably within the confines of his limited resources. His charges were all around a shilling to two shillings and it was easy to see why he only just cleared the housekeeping.

One other thing I noticed; the people all seemed to like him. He had no 'front' but he was kind and concerned. I felt there was a lesson there.

The last arrival was a stout lady with a prim manner and a very correct manner of speech.

'My dog was bit last week,' she announced, 'and I'm afraid the wound is goin' antiseptic.'

'Ah yes.' Stewie nodded gravely. The banana fingers explored the tumefied area on the animal's neck with a gossamer touch. 'It's quite nasty, really. He could have an abscess there if we're not careful.'

He took a long time over clipping the hair away, swabbing out the deep puncture with peroxide of hydrogen. Then he puffed in some dusting powder, applied a pad of cotton wool and secured it with a bandage. He followed with an antistaphylococcal injection and finally handed over a sauce bottle filled to the rim with acriflavine solution.

'Use as directed on the label,' he said, then stood back as the lady opened her purse expectantly.

A long inward struggle showed in the occasional twitches of his cheeks and flickerings of his eyelids but finally he squared his shoulders.

'That,' he said resolutely, 'will be three and sixpence.'

It was a vast fee by Stewie's standards, but probably the minimum in other veterinary establishments, and I couldn't see how he could make any profit from the transaction.

As the lady left, a sudden uproar broke out within the house. Stewie gave me a seraphic smile.

'That'll be Meg and the kids. Come and meet them.'

We went out to the hall and into an incredible hubbub. Children shouted, screamed and laughed, spades and pails clattered, a large ball thumped from wall to wall and above it all a baby bawled relentlessly.

Stewie moved into the mob and extracted a small woman.

'This,' he murmured with quiet pride, 'is my wife.' He gazed at her like a small boy admiring a film star.

'How do you do,' I said.

Meg Brannan took my hand and smiled. Any glamour about her existed only in her husband's eyes. A ravaged prettiness still remained but her face bore the traces of some tough years. I could imagine her life of mother, housewife, cook, secretary, receptionist and animal nurse.

'Oh, Mr Herriot, it is good of you and Mr Farnon to help us out like this. We're so looking forward to going away.' Her eyes held a faintly desperate gleam but they were kind.

I shrugged. 'Oh it's a pleasure, Mrs Brannan. I'm sure I'll enjoy it and I hope you all have a marvellous holiday.' I really meant it – she looked as though she needed one.

I was introduced to the children but I never really got them sorted out. Apart from the baby, who yelled indefatigably from leather lungs, I think there were three little boys and two little girls, but I couldn't be sure – they moved around too quickly.

The only time they were silent was for a brief period at supper when Meg fed them and us from a kind of cauldron in which floated chunks of mutton, potatoes and carrots. It was very good, too, and was followed by a vast blancmange with jam on top.

The tumult broke out again very soon as the youngsters raced through their meal and began to play in the room. One thing I found disconcerting was that the two biggest boys kept throwing a large, new, painted ball from one to the other across the table as we ate. The parents said nothing about it – Meg, I felt, because she had stopped caring, and Stewie because he never had cared.

Only once when the ball whizzed past my nose and almost carried away a poised spoonful of blancmange did their father remonstrate.

'Now then, now then,' he murmured absently, and the throwing was re-sited more towards the middle of the table.

Next morning I saw the family off. Stewie had changed his dilapidated Austin Seven for a large rust-encrusted Ford V Eight. Seated at the wheel he waved and beamed through the cracked side windows with serene contentment. Meg, by his side, managed a harassed smile and at the other windows an assortment of dogs and children fought for a vantage point. As the car moved away a pram, several suitcases and a cot swayed perilously on the roof, the children yelled, the dogs barked, the baby bawled, then they were gone.

As I re-entered the house the unaccustomed silence settled around me, and with the silence came a faint unease. I had to look after this practice for two weeks and the memory of the thinly furnished surgery was not reassuring. I just didn't have the tools to tackle any major problem.

But it was easy to comfort myself. From what I had seen this wasn't the sort of place where dramatic things happened. Stewie had once said he made most of his living by castrating tom cats and I supposed if you threw in a few ear cankers and minor ailments that would be about it.

The morning surgery seemed to confirm this impression; a few humble folk led in nondescript pets with mild conditions and I happily dispensed a series of Bovril bottles and meat paste jars containing Stewie's limited drug store.

I had only one difficulty and that was with the table, which kept collapsing when I lifted the animals on to it. For some obscure reason it had folding legs held by metal struts underneath and these were apt to disengage at crucial moments, causing the patient to slide abruptly to the floor. After a while I got the hang of the thing and kept one leg jammed against the struts throughout the examination.

It was about 10.30 a.m. when I finally parted the curtains and found the waiting room empty and only the distinctive cat-dog smell lingering on the air. As I locked the door it struck me that I had very little to do till the afternoon surgery. At Darrowby I would have been dashing out to start the long day's driving round the countryside, but here almost all the work was done at the practice house.

I was wondering how I would put the time in after the single outside visit on the book when the door bell rang. Then it rang again followed by a frantic pounding on the wood. I hurried through the curtain and turned the handle. A well dressed young couple stood on the step. The man held a Golden Labrador in his arms and behind them a caravan drawn by a large gleaming car stood by the kerb.

'Are you the vet?' the girl gasped. She was in her twenties, auburn haired, extremely attractive, but her eyes were terrified.

I nodded. 'Yes – yes, I am. What's the trouble?'

'It's our dog.' The young man's voice was hoarse, his face deathly pale. 'A car hit him.'

I glanced over the motionless yellow form. 'Is he badly hurt?'

There were a few moments of silence then the girl spoke almost in a whisper. 'Look at his hind leg.'

I stepped forward and as I peered into the crook of the man's arm a freezing wave drove through me. The limb was hanging off at the hock. Not fractured but snapped through the joint and dangling from what looked like a mere shred of skin. In the bright morning sunshine the white ends of naked bones glittered with a sickening lustre.

It seemed a long time before I came out of my first shock and found myself staring stupidly at the animal. And when I spoke the voice didn't sound like my own.

'Bring him in,' I muttered, and as I led the way back through the odorous waiting room the realisation burst on me that I had been wrong when I thought that nothing ever happened here.

Chapter Twenty-two

I held the curtains apart as the young man staggered in and placed his burden on the table.

Now I could see the whole thing; the typical signs of a road accident; the dirt driven savagely into the glossy gold of the coat, the multiple abrasions. But that mangled leg wasn't typical. I had never seen anything like it before.

I dragged my eyes round to the girl. 'How did it happen?'

'Oh, just in a flash.' The tears welled in her eyes. 'We are on a caravanning holiday. We had no intention of staying in Hensfield' – (I could understand that) – 'but we stopped for a newspaper, Kim jumped out of the car and that was it.'

I looked at the big dog stretched motionless on the table. I reached out a hand and gently ran my fingers over the noble outlines of the head.

'Poor old lad,' I murmured and for an instant the beautiful hazel eyes turned to me and the tail thumped briefly against the wood.

'Where have you come from?' I asked.

'Surrey,' the young man replied. He looked rather like the prosperous young stockbroker that the name conjured up.

I rubbed my chin. 'I see. . . .' A way of escape shone for a moment in the tunnel. 'Perhaps if I patch him up you could get him back to your own vet there.'

He looked at his wife for a moment then back at me. 'And what would they do there? Amputate his leg?'

I was silent. If an animal in this condition arrived in one of those high-powered southern practices with plenty of skilled assistance and full surgical equipment that's what they probably would do. It would be the only sensible thing.

The girl broke in on my thoughts. 'Anyway, if it's at all possible to save his leg something has to be done right now. Isn't that so?' She gazed at me appealingly.

'Yes,' I said huskily. 'That's right.' I began to examine the dog. The abrasions on the skin were trivial. He was shocked but his mucous membranes were pink enough to suggest that there was no internal haemorrhage. He had escaped serious injury except for that terrible leg.

I stared at it intently, appalled by the smooth glistening articular surfaces of the tibio-tarsal joint. There was something obscene in its exposure in a living animal. It was as though the hock has been broken open by brutal inquisitive hands.

I began a feverish search of the premises, pulling open drawers, cupboards, opening tins and boxes. My heart leaped at each little find; a jar of catgut in spirit, a packet of lint, a sprinkler tin of iodoform, and – treasure trove indeed – a bottle of barbiturate anaesthetic.

Most of all I needed antibiotics, but it was pointless looking for those because they hadn't been discovered yet. But I did hope fervently for just an ounce or two of sulphanilamide, and there I was disappointed, because Stewie's menage didn't stretch to that. It was when I came upon the box of plaster of paris bandages that something seemed to click.

At that time in the late thirties the Spanish civil war was vivid in people's minds. In the chaos of the later stages there had been no proper medicaments to treat the terrible wounds. They had often been encased in plaster and left, in the grim phrase, to 'stew in their own juice'. Sometimes the results were surprisingly good.

I grabbed the bandages. I knew what I was going to do. Gripped by a fierce determination I inserted the needle into the radial vein and slowly injected the anaesthetic. Kim blinked, yawned lazily and went to sleep. I quickly laid out my meagre armoury then began to shift the dog into a better position. But I had forgotten about the table and as I lifted the hind quarters the whole thing gave way and the dog slithered helplessly towards the floor.

'Catch him!' At my frantic shout the man grabbed the inert form, then I reinserted the slots in their holes and got the wooden surface back on the level.

'Put your leg under there,' I gasped, then turned to the girl. 'And would you please do the same at the other end. This table mustn't fall over once I get started.'

Silently they complied and as I looked at them, each with a leg jammed against the underside, I felt a deep sense of shame. What sort of place did they think this was?

But for a long time after I forgot everything. First I put the joint back in place, slipping the ridges of the tibial-tarsal trochlea into the grooves at the distal end of the tibia as I had done so often in the anatomy lab at college. And I noticed with a flicker of hope that some of the ligaments were still intact and, most important, that a few good blood vessels still ran down to the lower part of the limb.

I never said a word as I cleaned and disinfected the area, puffed iodoform into every crevice and began to stitch. I stitched interminably, pulling together shattered tendons, torn joint capsule and fascia. It was a warm morning and as the sun beat on the surgery window the sweat broke out on my forehead. By the time I had sutured the skin a little river was flowing down my nose and dripping from the tip. Next, more iodoform, then the lint and finally two of the plaster bandages, making a firm cast above the hock down over the foot.

I straightened up and faced the young couple. They had never moved from their uncomfortable postures as they held the table upright but I gazed at them as though seeing them for the first time.

I mopped my brow and drew a long breath. 'Well, that's it. I'd be inclined to leave it as it is for a week, then wherever you are let a vet have a look at it.'

They were silent for a moment then the girl spoke. 'I would rather you saw it yourself.' Her husband nodded agreement.

'Really?' I was amazed. I had thought they would never want to see me, my smelly waiting room or my collapsible table again.

'Yes, of course we would,' the man said. 'You have taken such pains over him. Whatever happens we are deeply grateful to you, Mr Brannan.'

'Oh, I'm not Mr Brannan, he's on holiday. I'm his locum, my name is Herriot.'

He held out his hand. 'Well thank you again, Mr Herriot. I am Peter Gillard and this is my wife. Marjorie.'

We shook hands and he took the dog in his arms and went out to the car.

For the next few days I couldn't keep Kim's leg out of my mind. At times I felt I was crazy trying to salvage a limb that was joined to the dog only by a strip of skin. I had never met anything remotely like it before and in unoccupied moments that hock joint with all its imponderables would float across my vision.

There were plenty of these moments because Stewie's was a restful practice. Apart from the three daily surgeries there was little activity, and in particular the uncomfortable pre-breakfast call so common in Darrowby was unknown here.

The Brannans had left the house and me in the care of Mrs Holroyd, an elderly widow of raddled appearance who slouched around in a flowered overall down which ash cascaded from a permanently dangling cigarette. She wasn't a good riser but she soon had me trained, because after a few mornings when I couldn't find her I began to prepare my own breakfast and that was how it stayed.

However, at other times she looked after me very well. She was what you might call a good rough cook and pushed large tasty meals at me regularly with a 'There y'are, luv,' watching me impassively till I started to eat. The only thing that disturbed me was the long trembling finger of ash which always hung over my food from the cigarette that was part of her.

Mrs Holroyd also took telephone messages when I wasn't around. There weren't many outside visits but two have stuck in my memory.

The first was when I looked on the pad and read, 'Go to Mr Pimmarov to see bulldog,' in Mrs Holroyd's careful backsloped script.

'Pimmarov?' I asked her. 'Was he a Russian gentleman?'

'Dunno, luv, never asked 'im.'

'Well – did he sound foreign? I mean did he speak broken English?'

'Nay, luv, Yorkshire as me, 'e were.'

'Ah well, never mind, Mrs Holroyd. What's his address?'

She gave me a surprised look. 'How should ah know? He never said.'

'But . . . but Mrs Holroyd. How can I visit him when I don't know where he lives?'

'Well you'll know best about that, luv.'

I was baffled. 'But he must have told you.'

'Now then, young man, Pimmarov was all 'e told me. Said you would know.' She stuck out her chin, her cigarette quivered and she regarded me stonily. Maybe she had had similar sessions with Stewie, but she left me in no doubt that the interview was over.

During the day I tried to think about it but the knowledge that somewhere in the nighbourhood there was an ailing bulldog that I could not succour was worrying. I just hoped it was nothing fatal.

A phone call at 7 p.m. resolved my fears.

'Is that t'vet?' The voice was gruff and grumpy.

'Yes . . . speaking.'

'Well, ah've been waitin' all day for tha. When are you comin' to see ma flippin' bulldog?'

A light glimmered. But still . . . that accent . . . no suggestion of the Kremlin . . . not a hint of the Steppes.

'Oh, I'm terribly sorry,' I gabbled. 'I'm afraid there's been a little misunderstanding. I'm doing Mr Brannan's work and I don't know the district. I do hope your dog isn't seriously ill.'

'Nay, nay, nobbut a bit o' cough, but ah want 'im seein' to.'

'Certainly, certainly, I'll be right out, Mr . . . er . . .'

'Pym's ma name and ah live next to t'post office in Roff village.'

'Roff?'

'Aye, two miles outside Hensfield.'

I sighed with relief. 'Very good, Mr Pym, I'm on my way.'

'Thank ye.' The voice sounded mollified. 'Well, tha knows me now, don't tha – Pym o' Roff.'

The light was blinding. 'Pym o' Roff!' Such a simple explanation.

A lot of Mrs Holroyd's messages were eccentric but I could usually interpret them after some thought. However one bizarre entry jolted me later in the week. It read simply: 'Johnson, 12, Back Lane, Smiling Harry Syphilis.'

I wrestled with this for a long time before making a diffident approach to Mrs Holroyd.

She was kneading dough for scones and didn't look up as I entered the kitchen.

'Ah, Mrs Holroyd.' I rubbed my hands nervously. 'I see you have written down that I have to go to Mr Johnson's.'

'That's right, luv.'

'Well, er . . . fine, but I don't quite understand the other part – the Smiling Harry Syphilis.'

She shot a sidelong glance at me. 'Well that's 'ow you spell that word, isn't it? Ah looked it up once in a doctor's book in our 'ouse,' she said defensively.

'Oh yes, of course, yes, you've spelled it correctly. It's just the Smiling . . . and the Harry.'

Her eyes glinted dangerously and she blew a puff of smoke at me. 'Well, that's what t'feller said. Repeated it three times. Couldn't make no mistake.'

'I see. But did he mention any particular animal?'

'Naw, 'e didn't. That was what 'e said. That and no more.' A grey spicule of ash toppled into the basin and was immediately incorporated in the scones. 'Ah do ma best, tha knows!'

'Of course you do, Mrs Holroyd,' I said hastily. 'I'll just pop round to Back Lane now.'

And Mr Johnson put everything right within seconds as he led me to a shed on his allotment.

'It's me pig, guvnor. Covered wi' big red spots. Reckon it's Swine Erysipelas.'

Only he pronounced it arrysipelas and he did have a slurring mode of speech. I really couldn't blame Mrs Holroyd.

Little things like that enlivened the week but the tension still mounted as I awaited the return of Kim. And even when the seventh day came round I was still in suspense because the Gillards did not appear at the morning surgery. When they failed to show up at the afternoon session I began to conclude that they had had the good sense to return south to a more sophisticated establishment. But at five thirty they were there.

I knew it even before I pulled the curtains apart. The smell of doom was everywhere, filling the premises, and when I went through the curtains it hit me; the sickening stink of putrefaction.

Gangrene. It was the fear which had haunted me all week and now it was realised.

There were about half a dozen other people in the waiting room, all keeping as far away as possible from the young couple who looked up at me with strained smiles. Kim tried to rise when he saw me but I had eyes only for the dangling useless hind limb where my once stone-hard plaster hung in sodden folds.

Of course it had to happen that the Gillards were last in and I was forced to see all the other animals first. I examined them and prescribed treatment in a stupor of misery and shame. What had I done to that beautiful dog out there? I had been crazy to try that experiment. A gangrenous leg meant that even amputation might be too late to save his life. Death from septicaemia was likely now and what the hell could I do for him in this ramshackle surgery?

When at last it was their turn the Gillards came in with Kim limping between them, and it was an extra stab to realise afresh what a handsome animal he was. I bent over the great golden head and for a moment the friendly eyes looked into mine and the tail waved.

'Right,' I said to Peter Gillard, putting my arms under the chest. 'You take the back end and we'll lift him up.'

As we hoisted the heavy dog on to the table the flimsy structure disintegrated immediately, but this time the young people were ready for it and thrust their legs under the struts like a well-trained team till the surface was level again.

With Kim stretched on his side I fingered the bandage. It usually took time and patience with a special saw to remove a plaster but this was just a stinking pulp. My hand shook as I cut the bandage lengthways with scissors and removed it.

I had steeled myself against the sight of the cold dead limb with its green flesh but though there was pus and serous fluid everywhere the exposed flesh was a surprising, healthy pink. I took the foot in my hand and my heart gave a great bound. It was warm and so was the leg, right up to the hock. There was no gangrene.

Feeling suddenly weak I leaned against the table. 'I'm sorry about the terrible smell. All the pus and discharge have been decomposing under the bandage for a week but despite the mess it's not as bad as I feared.'

'Do you ... do you think you can save his leg?' Marjorie Gillard's voice trembled.

'I don't know. I honestly don't know. So much has to happen. But I'd say it was a case of so far so good.'

I cleaned the area thoroughly with spirit, gave a dusting of iodoform and applied fresh lint and two more plaster bandages.

'You'll feel a lot more comfortable now, Kim,' I said, and the big dog flapped his tail against the wood at the sound of his name.

I turned to his owners. 'I want him to have another week in plaster, so what would you like to do?'

'Oh, we'll stay around Hensfield,' Peter Gillard replied. 'We've found a place for our caravan by the river – it's not too bad.'

'Very well, till next Saturday, then.' I watched Kim hobble out, holding his new white cast high, and as I went back into the house relief flowed over me in a warm wave.

But at the back of my mind the voice of caution sounded. There was still a long way to go ...

Chapter Twenty-three

The second week went by without incident. I had a mildly indecent postcard from Stewie and a view of Blackpool Tower from his wife. The weather was scorching and they were having the best holiday of their lives. I tried to picture them enjoying themselves but I had to wait a few weeks for the evidence – a snap taken by a beach photographer. The whole family were standing in the sea, grinning delightedly into the camera as the wavelets lapped round their ankles. The children brandished buckets and spades, the baby dangled bandy legs towards the water, but it was Stewie who fascinated me. A smile of blissful contentment beamed from beneath a knotted handkerchief, sturdy braces supported baggy flannel trousers rolled decorously calf high. He was the archetype of the British father on holiday.

The last event of my stay in Hensfield was a visit to the local greyhound track. Stewie had an appointment there every other Friday to inspect the dogs.

The Hensfield stadium was not prepossessing from the outside. It had been built in a natural hollow in the sooty hills and was surrounded by ramshackle hoardings.

It was a cool night and as I drove down to the entrance I could hear the tinny blaring from the loudspeakers. It was George Formby singing 'When I'm Cleaning Windows' and strumming on his famous ukelele.

There are all kinds of greyhound tracks. My own experience had been as a student, accompanying vets who officiated under the auspices of the National Greyhound Racing Club, but this was an unlicensed or 'flapping' track, and vastly different. I know there are many highly reputable flapping tracks but this one had a seedy air. It was, I thought wryly, just the sort of place that would be under the care of Stewie.

First I had to go to the manager's office. Mr Coker was a hard-eyed man in a shiny pin-striped suit and he nodded briefly before giving me a calculating stare.

'Your duties here are just a formality,' he said, twisting his features into a smile. 'There'll be nothing to trouble you.'

I had the impression that he was assessing me with quiet satisfaction, looking me up and down, taking in my rumpled jacket and slacks, savouring my obvious youth and inexperience. He kept the smile going as he stubbed out his cigar. 'Well, I hope you'll have a pleasant evening.'

'Thank you,' I replied, and left.

I met the judge, timekeeper and other officials then went down to a long glass-fronted bar overlooking the track. Quite suddenly I felt I was in an alien environment. The place was rapidly filling up and the faces around me were out of a different mould from the wholesome rural countenances of Darrowby. There seemed to be a large proportion of fat men in camel coats with brassy blondes in tow. Shifty-looking characters studied race cards and glared intently at the flickering numbers on the tote board.

I looked at my watch. It was time to inspect the dogs for the first race. 'When I'm cleanin' winders!' bawled George Formby as I made my way round the edge of the track to the paddock, a paved enclosure with a wire-netting surround. Five dogs were being led round the perimeter and I stood in the centre and watched them for a minute or two. Then I halted them and went from one to the other, looking at their eyes, examining their mouths for salivation and finally palpating their abdomens.

They all appeared bright and normal except number four which seemed rather full in the stomach region. A greyhound should only have a light meal on the morning of a race and nothing thereafter and I turned to the man who was holding the animal.

'Has this dog been fed within the last hour or two?' I asked.

'No,' he replied. 'He's had nothing since breakfast.'

As I passed my fingers over the abdomen again I had the feeling that several of the onlookers were watching me with unusual intentness. But I dismissed it as imagination and passed on to the next animal.

Number four was second favourite but from the moment it left its trap it was flagging. It finished last and from the darkness on the far side of the track a storm of booing broke out. I was able to make out some of the remarks which came across on the night air. 'Open your bloody eyes, vet!' was one of them. And here, in the long, brightly lit bar I could see people nudging each other and looking at me.

I felt a thrill of anger. Maybe some of those gentlemen down there thought they could cash in on Stewie's absence. I probably looked a soft touch to them.

My next visit to the paddock was greeted with friendly nods and grins from all sides. In fact there was a strong atmosphere of joviality. When I went round the dogs all was well until I came to number five and this time I couldn't be mistaken. Under my probing fingers the stomach bulged tensely and the animal gave a soft grunt as I squeezed.

'You'll have to take this dog out of the race,' I said. 'He's got a full stomach.'

The owner was standing by the kennel lad.

'Can't 'ave?' he burst out. 'He's had nowt?'

I straightened up and looked him full in the face but his eyes were reluctant to meet mine. I knew some of the tricks; a couple of pounds of steak before the race; a bowlful of bread crumbs and two pints of milk – the crumbs swelled beautifully within a short time.

'Would you like me to vomit him?' I began to move away. 'I've got some washing soda in my car – we'll soon find out.'

The man held up a hand. 'Naw, naw, I don't want you messin' about with me dog.' He gave me a malevolent glare and trailed sulkily away.

I had only just got back to the bar when I heard the announcement over the loudspeakers. 'Will the vet please report to the manager's office.'

Mr Coker looked up from his desk and glared at me through a haze of cigar smoke. 'You've taken a dog out of the race!'

'That's right. I'm sorry, but his stomach was full.'

'But damn it . . . !' He stabbed a finger at me then subsided and forced a tortured smile across his face. 'Now, Mr Herriot, we have to be reasonable in these matters. I've no doubt you know your job, but don't you think there's just a chance you could be wrong?' He waved his cigar expansively. 'After all, anybody can make a mistake, so perhaps you would be kind enough to reconsider.' He stretched his smile wider.

'No, I'm sorry, Mr Coker, but that would be impossible.'

There was a long pause. 'That's your last word, then?'

'It is.'

The smile vanished and he gave me a threatening stare.

'Now look,' he said. 'You've mucked up that race and it's a serious matter. I don't want any repetition, do you understand?' He ground his cigar out savagely and his jaw jutted. 'So I hope we won't have any more trouble like this.'

'I hope so, too, Mr Coker,' I said as I went out.

It seemed a long way down to the paddock on my next visit. It was very dark now and I was conscious of the hum of the crowd, the shouts of the bookies and George and his ukelele still going full blast. 'Oh, don't the wind blow cold!' he roared.

This time it was dog number two. I could feel the tension as I examined him and found the same turgid belly.

'This one's out,' I said, and apart from a few black looks there was no argument.

They say bad news travels fast and I had hardly started my return journey when George was switched off and the loud-speaker asked me to report to the manager's office.

Mr Coker was no longer at his desk. He was pacing up and down agitatedly and when he saw me he did another length of the room before coming to a halt.

His expression was venomous and it was clear he had decided that the tough approach was best.

'What the bloody hell do you think you're playing at?' he barked. 'Are you trying to ruin this meeting?'

'No,' I replied. 'I've just taken out another dog which was unfit to run. That's my job. That's what I'm here for.'

His face flushed deep red. 'I don't think you know what you're here for. Mr Brannan goes off on holiday and leaves us at the mercy of a young clever clogs like you, throwing your weight about and spoiling people's pleasure. Wait till I see him!'

'Mr Brannan would have done just the same as I have. Any veterinary surgeon would.'

'Rubbish! Don't tell me what it's all about – you're still wet behind the ears.' He advanced slowly towards me. 'But I'll tell you this, I've had enough! So get it straight, once and for all – no more of this nonsense. Cut it out!'

I felt my heart thudding as I went down to see the dogs for the next race. As I examined the five animals the owners and kennel lads fixed me with a hypnotic stare as though I were some strange freak. My pulse began to slow down when I found there were no full stomachs this time and I glanced back in relief along the line. I was about to walk away when I noticed that number one looked a little unusual. I went back and bent over him, trying to decide what it was about him that had caught my attention. Then I realised what it was – he looked sleepy. The head was hanging slightly and he had an air of apathy.

I lifted his chin and looked into his eyes. The pupils were dilated and every now and then there was a faint twitch of nystagmus. There was absolutely no doubt about it – he had received some kind of sedative. He had been doped.

The men in the paddock was very still as I stood upright. For a few moments I gazed through the wire netting at the brightly lit green oval, feeling the night air cold on my cheeks. George was still at it on the loudspeakers.

'Oh Mr Wu,' he trilled. 'What can I do?'

Well I knew what I had to do, anyway. I tapped the dog on the back.

'This one's out,' I said.

I didn't wait for the announcement and was half way up the steps to the manager's office before I heard the request for my presence blared across the stadium.

When I opened the door I half expected Mr Coker to rush at me and attack me and I was surprised when I found him sitting at his desk, his head buried in his hands. I stood there on the carpet for some time before he raised a ghastly countenance to me.

'It it true?' he whispered despairingly. 'Have you done it again?'

I nodded. 'Afraid so.'

His lips trembled but he didn't say anything, and after a brief, disbelieving scrutiny he sank his head in his hands again.

I waited for a minute or two but when he stayed like that, quite motionless, I realised that the audience was at an end and took my leave.

I found no fault with the dogs for the next race and as I left the paddock an unaccustomed peace settled around me. I couldn't understand it when I heard the loudspeaker again – 'Will the vet please report . . .' But this time it was to the paddock and I wondered if a dog had been injured. Anyway, it would be a relief to do a bit of real vetting for a change.

But when I arrived there were no animals to be seen; only two men cradling a fat companion in their arms.

'What's this?' I asked one of them.

'Ambrose 'ere fell down the steps in the stand and skinned 'is knee.'

I stared at him. 'But I'm a vet, not a doctor.'

'Ain't no doctor on the track,' the man mumbled. 'We reckoned you could patch 'im up.'

Ah well, it was a funny night. 'Put him over on that bench,' I said.

I rolled up the trouser to reveal a rather revolting fat dimpled knee. Ambrose emitted a hollow groan as I touched a very minor abrasion on the patella.

'It's nothing much,' I said. 'You've just knocked a bit of skin off.'

Ambrose looked at me tremblingly. 'Aye, but it could go t'wrong way, couldn't it? I don't want no blood poisonin'.'

'All right, I'll put something on it.' I looked inside Stewie's medical bag. The selection was limited but I found some tincture of iodine and I poured a little on a pad of cotton wool and dabbed the wound.

Ambrose gave a shrill yelp. 'Bloody 'ell, that 'urts! What are you doin' to me?' His foot jerked up and rapped me sharply on the elbow.

Even my human patients kicked me, it seemed. I smiled reassuringly. 'Don't worry, it won't sting for long. I'll put a bandage on now.'

I bound up the knee, rolled down the trouser and patted the fat man's shoulder. 'There you are – good as new.'

He got off the bench, nodded, then grimacing painfully, prepared to leave. But an afterthought appeared to strike him and he pulled a handful of change from his pocket. He rummaged among it with a forefinger before selecting a coin which he pressed into my palm.

'There y'are,' he said.

I looked at the coin. It was a sixpence, the fee for my only piece of doctoring of my own species. I stared stupidly at it for a long time and when I finally looked up with the half-formed idea of throwing Ambrose's honorarium back at his head the man was limping into the crowd and was soon lost to sight.

Back in the bar I was gazing apathetically through the glass at the dogs parading round the track when I felt a hand on my arm. I turned and recognised a man I had spotted earlier in the evening. He was one of a group of three men and three women, the men dark, tight-suited, foreign-looking, the women loud and over-dressed. There was something sinister about them and I remembered thinking they could have passed without question as members of the Mafia.

The man put his face close to mine and I had a brief impression of black, darting eyes and a predatory smile.

'Is number three fit?' he whispered.

I couldn't understand the question. He seemed to know I was the vet and surely it was obvious that if I had passed the dog I considered him fit.

'Yes,' I replied. 'Yes, he is.'

The man nodded vigorously and gave me a knowing glance from hooded eyes. He returned and held a short, intimate conversation with his friends, then they all turned and looked over at me approvingly.

I was bewildered, then it struck me that they may have thought I was giving them an inside tip. To this day I am not really sure but I think that was it because when number three finished nowhere in the race their attitude changed dramatically and they flashed me some black glares which made them look more like the Mafia than ever.

Anyway I had no more trouble down at the paddock for the rest of the evening. No more dogs to take out, which was just as well, because I had made enough enemies for one night.

After the last race I looked around the long bar. Most of the tables were occupied by people having a final drink, but I noticed an empty one and sank wearily into a chair. Stewie had asked me to stay for half an hour after the finish to make sure all the dogs got away safely and I would stick to my bargain even though what I wanted most in the world was to get away from here and never come back.

George was still in splendid voice on the loudspeakers, 'I always get to bed by half past nine,' he warbled, and I felt strongly that he had a point there.

Along the bar counter were assembled most of the people with whom I had clashed; Mr Coker and other officials and dog owners. There was a lot of nudging and whispering and I didn't have to be told the subject of their discussion. The Mafia, too, were doing their bit with fierce side glances and I could almost feel the waves of antagonism beating against me.

My gloomy thoughts were interrupted by the arrival of a bookie and his clerk. The bookie dropped into a chair opposite me and tipped out a huge leather bag on to the table. I had never seen so much money in my life. I peered at the man over a mountain of fivers and pounds and ten-shilling notes while little streams and tributaries of coins ran down its flanks.

The two of them began a methodical stacking and counting of the loot while I watched hypnotically. They had eroded the mountain to about half its height when the bookie caught my eye. Maybe he thought I looked envious or poverty-stricken or just miserable because he put his finger behind a stray half crown and flicked it expertly across the smooth surface in my direction.

'Get yourself a drink, son,' he said.

It was the second time I had been offered money during the last hour and I was almost as much taken aback as the first time. The bookie looked at me expressionlessly for a moment then he grinned. He had an attractively ugly, good-natured face that I liked instinctively and suddenly I felt grateful to him, not for the money but for the sight of a friendly face. It was the only one I had seen all evening.

I smiled back. 'Thanks,' I said. I lifted the half crown and went over to the bar.

I awoke next morning with the knowledge that it was my last day at Hensfield. Stewie was due back at lunch time.

When I parted the now familiar curtains at the morning surgery I still felt a vague depression, a hangover from my unhappy night at the dog track.

But when I looked into the waiting room my mood lightened immediately. There was only one animal among the odd assortment of chairs but that animal was Kim, massive, golden and beautiful, sitting between his owners, and when he saw me he sprang up with swishing tail and laughing mouth.

There was none of the smell which had horrified me before but as I looked at the dog I could sniff something else – the sweet, sweet scent of success. Because he was touching the ground with that leg; not putting any weight on it but definitely dotting it down as he capered around me.

In an instant I was back in my world again and Mr Coker and the events of last night were but the dissolving mists of a bad dream.

I could hardly wait to get started.

'Get him on the table,' I cried, then began to laugh as the Gillards automatically pushed their legs against the collapsible struts. They knew the drill now.

I had to restrain myself from doing a dance of joy when I got the plaster off. There was a bit of discharge but when I cleaned it away I found healthy granulation tissue everywhere. Pink new flesh binding the shattered joint together, smoothing over and hiding the original mutilation.

'Is his leg safe now?' Marjorie Gillard asked softly.

I looked at her and smiled. 'Yes, it is. There's no doubt about it now.' I rubbed my hand under the big dog's chin and the tail beat ecstatically on the wood. 'He'll probably have a stiff joint but that won't matter, will it?'

I applied the last of Stewie's bandages then we hoisted Kim off the table.

'Well, that's it,' I said. 'Take him to your own vet in another fortnight. After that I don't think he'll need a bandage at all.'

The Gillards left on their journey back to the south and a couple of hours later Stewie and his family returned. The children were very brown; even the baby, still bawling resolutely, had a fine tan. The skin had peeled off Meg's nose but she looked wonderfully relaxed. Stewie, in open necked shirt and with a face like a boiled lobster, seemed to have put on weight.

'That holiday saved our lives, Jim,' he said. 'I can't thank you enough, and please tell Siegfried how grateful we are.' He looked fondly at his turbulent brood flooding through the house, then as an afterthought he turned to me.

'Is everything all right in the practice?'

'Yes, Stewie, it is. I had my ups and downs of course.'

He laughed. 'Don't we all.'

'We certainly do, but everything's fine now.'

And everything did seem fine as I drove away from the smoke. I watched the houses thin and fall away behind me till the whole world opened out clean and free and I saw the green line of the fells rising over Darrowby.

I suppose we all tend to remember the good things but as it turned out I had no option. The following Christmas I had a letter from the Gillards with a packet of snapshots showing a big golden dog clearing a gate, leaping high for a ball, strutting proudly with a stick in his mouth. There was hardly any stiffness in the leg, they said; he was perfectly sound.

So even now when I think of Hensfield the thing I remember best is Kim.

Chapter Twenty-four

There was a lot of shouting in the RAF. The NCOs always seemed to be shouting at me or at somebody else and a lot of them had impressively powerful voices. But for sheer volume I don't think any of them could beat Len Hampson.

I was on the way to Len's farm and on an impulse I pulled up the car and leaned for a moment on the wheel. It was a hot still day in late summer and this was one of the softer corners of the Dales, sheltered by the enclosing fells from the harsh winds which shrivelled all but the heather and the tough moorland grass.

Here, great trees, oak, elm and sycamore in full rich leaf, stood in gentle majesty in the green dips and hollows, their branches quite still in the windless air.

In all the grassy miles around me I could see no movement, nor could I hear anything except the fleeting hum of a bee and the distant bleating of a sheep.

Through the open window drifted the scents of summer; warm grass, clover and the sweetness of hidden flowers. But in the car they had to compete with the all-pervading smell of cow. I had spent the last hour injecting fifty wild cattle and I sat there in soiled breeches and sweat-soaked shirt looking out sleepily at the tranquil landscape.

I opened the door and Sam jumped out and trotted into a nearby wood. I followed him into the cool shade, into the damp secret fragrance of pine needles and fallen leaves which came from the dark heart of the crowding boles. From somewhere in the branches high above I could hear that most soothing of sounds, the cooing of a woodpigeon.

Then, although the farm was two fields away, I heard Len Hampson's voice. He wasn't calling the cattle home or anything like that. He was just conversing with his family as he always did in a long tireless shout.

I drove on to the farm and he opened the gate to let me into the yard.

'Good morning, Mr Hampson,' I said.

'NOW THEN, MR HERRIOT,' he bawled. 'IT'S A GRAND MORNIN'.'

The blast of sound drove me back a step but his three sons smiled contentedly. No doubt they were used to it.

I stayed at a safe distance. 'You want me to see a pig,'

'AYE, A GOOD BACON PIG. GONE RIGHT OFF. IT HASN'T ATE NOWT FOR TWO DAYS.'

We went into the pig pen and it was easy to pick out my patient. Most of the big white occupants careered around at the sight of a stranger, but one of them stood quietly in a corner.

It isn't often a pig will stand unresisting as you take its temperature but this one never stirred as I slipped the thermometer into its rectum. There was only a slight fever but the animal had the look of doom about it; back slightly arched, unwilling to move, eyes withdrawn and anxious.

I looked up at Len Hampson's red-faced bulk leaning over the wall of the pen.

'Did this start suddenly or gradually?' I asked.

'RIGHT SUDDEN!' In the confined space the full throated yell was deafening. 'HE WERE AS RIGHT AS NINEPENCE ON MONDAY NIGHT AND LIKE THIS ON TUESDAY MORNIN'.'

I felt my way over the pig's abdomen. The musculature was tense and boardlike and the abdominal contents were difficult to palpate because of this, but the whole area was tender to the touch.

'I've seen them like this before,' I said. 'This pig has a ruptured bowel. They do it when they are fighting or jostling each other, especially when they are full after a meal.'

'WHAT'S GOIN' TO 'APPEN THEN?'

'Well, the food material has leaked into the abdomen, causing peritonitis. I've opened up pigs like this and they are a mass of adhesions – the abdominal organs all growing together. I'm afraid the chances of recovery are very small.'

He took off his cap, scratched his bald head and replaced the tattered headgear. 'THAT'S A BUGGER. GOOD PIG AN' ALL. IS IT 'OPELESS?' He still gave tongue at the top of his voice despite his disappointment.

'Yes, I'm afraid it's pretty hopeless. They usually eat very little and just waste away. It would really be best to slaughter him.'

'NAY, AH DON'T LIKE THAT MUCH! AH ALLUS LIKE TO 'AVE A GO. ISN'T THERE SUMMAT WE CAN DO? WHERE THERE'S LIFE THERE'S 'OPE, THA KNAWS.'

I smiled. 'I suppose there's always some hope, Mr Hampson.'

'WELL THEN, LET'S GET ON. LET'S TRY!'

'All right.' I shrugged. 'He's not really in acute pain – more discomfort – so I suppose there's no harm in treating him. I'll leave you a course of powders.'

As I pushed my way from the pen I couldn't help noticing the superb sleek condition of the other pigs.

'My word,' I said. 'These pigs are in grand fettle. I've never seen a better lot. You must feed them well.'

It was a mistake. Enthusiasm added many decibels to his volume.

'*Aye!*' he bellowed. 'YOU'VE GOT TO GIVE STOCK A BIT O' GOOD STUFF TO MEK' EM DO RIGHT!'

My head was still ringing when I reached the car and opened the boot. I handed over a packet of my faithful sulphonamide powders. They had done great things for me but I didn't expect much here.

It was strange that I should go straight from the chief shouter of the practice to the chief whisperer. Elijah Wentworth made all his communications *sotto voce*.

I found Mr Wentworth hosing down his cow byre and he turned and looked at me with his habitual serious expression. He was a tall thin man, very precise in his speech and ways, and though he was a hard-working farmer he didn't look like one. This impression was heightened by his clothes which were more suited to office work than his rough trade.

A fairly new trilby hat sat straight on his head as he came over to me. I was able to examine it thoroughly because he came so close that we were almost touching noses.

He took a quick look around him. 'Mr Herriot,' he whispered, 'I've got a real bad case.' He spoke always as though every pronouncement was of the utmost gravity and secrecy.

'Oh I'm sorry to hear that. What's the trouble?'

'Fine big bullock, Mr Herriot. Goin' down fast.' He moved in closer till he could murmur directly into my ear. 'I suspect TB.' He backed away, face drawn.

'That doesn't sound so good,' I said. 'Where is he?'

The farmer crooked a finger and I followed him into a loose box. The bullock was a Hereford Cross and should have weighed about ten hundredweight, but was gaunt and emaciated. I could understand Mr Wentworth's fears, but I was beginning to develop a clinical sense and it didn't look like TB to me.

'Is he coughing?' I asked.

'No, never coughs, but he's a bit skittered.'

I went over the animal carefully and there were a few things – the submaxillary oedema, the pot-bellied appearance, the pallor of the mucous membranes – which made diagnosis straightforward.

'I think he's got liver fluke, Mr Wentworth. I'll take a dung sample and have it examined for fluke eggs but I want to treat him right away.'

'Liver fluke? Where would he pick that up?'

'Usually from a wet pasture. Where has be been running lately?'

The farmer pointed through the door. 'Over yonder. I'll show you.'

I walked with him a few hundred yards and through a couple of gates into a wide flat field lying at the base of the fell. The squelchy feel of the turf and the scattered tufts of bog grass told the whole story.

'This is just the place for it,' I said. 'As you know, it's a parasite which infests the liver, but during its life cycle it has to pass through a snail and that snail can only live where there is water.'

He nodded slowly and solemnly several times then began to look around him and I knew he was going to say something. Again he came very close then scanned the horizon anxiously. In all directions the grassland stretched empty and bare for miles but he still seemed worried he might be overheard.

We were almost cheek to cheek as he breathed the words into my ear. 'Ah know who's to blame for this.'

'Really? Who is that?'

He made another swift check to ensure that nobody had sprung up through the ground then I felt his hot breath again. 'It's me landlord.'

'How do you mean?'

'Won't do anything for me.' He brought his face round and looked at me wide-eyed before taking up his old position by my ear. 'Been goin' to drain this field for years but done nowt.'

I moved back. 'Ah well, I can't help that, Mr Wentworth. In any case there's other things you can do. You can kill the snails with copper sulphate – I'll tell you about that later – but in the meantime I want to dose your bullock.'

I had some hexachlorethane with me in the car and I mixed it in a bottle of water and administered it to the animal. Despite his bulk he offered no resistance as I held his lower jaw and poured the medicine down his throat.

'He's very weak, isn't he?' I said.

The farmer gave me a haggard look. 'He is that. I doubt he's a goner.'

'Oh don't give up hope, Mr Wentworth. I know he looks terrible but if it is fluke then the treatment will do a lot for him. Let me know how he goes on.'

It was about a month later, on a market day, and I was strolling among the stalls which packed the cobbles. In front of the entrance to the Drovers' Arms the usual press of farmers stood chatting among themselves, talking business with cattle dealers and corn merchants, while the shouts of the stallholders sounded over everything.

I was particularly fascinated by the man in charge of the sweet stall. He held up a paper bag and stuffed into it handfuls of assorted sweetmeats while he kept up a nonstop brazen-voiced commentary.

'Lovely peppermint drops! Delicious liquorice allsorts! How about some sugar candies! A couple o' bars o' chocolate! Let's 'ave some butterscotch an' all! Chuck in a beautiful slab o' Turkish Delight!' Then holding the bulging bag aloft in triumph "ere! 'ere! Who'll give me a tanner for the lot?'

Amazing, I thought as I moved on. How did he do it? I was passing the door of the Drovers when a familiar voice hailed me.

'HEY! MR HERRIOT!' There was no mistaking Len Hampson. He hove in front of me, red-faced and cheerful. 'REMEMBER THAT PIG YE DOCTORED FOR ME?' He had clearly consumed a few market-day beers and his voice was louder than ever.

The packed mass of farmers pricked up their ears. There is nothing so intriguing as the ailments of another farmer's livestock.

'Yes, of course, Mr Hampson,' I replied.

'WELL 'E NEVER DID NO GOOD!' bawled Len.

I could see the farmers' faces lighting up. It is more interesting still when things go wrong.

'Really? Well I'm sorry.'

'NAW 'E DIDN'T. AH'VE NEVER SEEN A PIG GO DOWN AS FAST!'

'Is that so?'

'AYE, FLESH JUST MELTED OFF 'IM!'

'Oh, what a pity. But if you recall I rather expected . . .'

'WENT DOWN TO SKIN AND BONE 'E DID!' The great bellow rolled over the market place, drowning the puny cries of the stallholders. In fact the man with the sweets had suspended operations and was listening with as much interest as the others.

I looked around me uneasily. 'Well, Mr Hampson, I did warn you at the time . . .'

'LIKE A WALKIN' SKELETON 'E WERE! NEVER SEEN SUCH A OBJECK!'

I realised Len wasn't in the least complaining. He was just telling me, but for all that I wished he would stop.

'Well, thank you for letting me know,' I said. 'Now I really must be off . . .'

'AH DON'T KNOW WHAT THEM POWDERS WERE YOU GAVE 'IM.'

I cleared my throat. 'Actually they were . . .'

'THEY DID 'IM NO BLOODY GOOD ANY ROAD!'

'I see. Well as I say, I have to run . . .'

'AH GOT MALLOCK TO KNOCK 'IM ON T'HEAD LAST WEEK.'

'Oh dear . . .'

'FINISHED UP AS DOG MEAT, POOR BUGGER!'

'Quite . . . quite . . .'

'WELL, GOOD DAY TO YE, MR HERRIOT.' He turned and walked away, leaving a quivering silence behind him.

With an uncomfortable feeling that I was the centre of attention I was about to retreat hastily when I felt a gentle hand on my arm. I turned and saw Elijah Wentworth.

'Mr Herriot,' he whispered. 'About that bullock.'

I stared at him, struck by the coincidence. The farmers stared, too, but expectantly.

'Yes, Mr Wentworth?'

'Well now, I'll tell you.' He came very near and breathed into my ear. 'It was like a miracle. He began to pick up straight away after you treated him.'

I stepped back. 'Oh marvellous! But speak up, will you, I can't quite hear you.' I looked around hopefully.

He came after me again and put his chin on my shoulder. 'Yes, I don't know what you gave 'im but it was wonderful stuff. I could hardly believe it. Every day I looked at 'im he had put on a bit more.'

'Great! But do speak a little louder,' I said eagerly.

'He's as fat as butter now.' The almost inaudible murmur wafted on my cheek. 'Ah'm sure he'll get top grade at the auction mart.'

I backed away again. 'Yes . . . yes . . . what was that you said?'

'I was sure he was dyin', Mr Herriot, but you saved him by your skill,' he said, but every word was pianissimo, sighed against my face.

The farmers had heard nothing and, their interest evaporating, they began to talk among themselves. Then as the man with the sweets started to fill his bags and shout again Mr Wentworth moved in and confided softly and secretly into my private ear.

'That was the most brilliant and marvellous cure I 'ave ever seen.'

Chapter Twenty-five

It must be unusual to feel senile in one's twenties, but it was happening to me. There were a few men of my own age among my RAF friends but for the most part I was surrounded by eighteen- and nineteen-year-olds.

It seemed that the selection boards thought this the optimum age for training pilots, navigators and air gunners and I often wondered how we elderly gentlemen had managed to creep in.

These boys used to pull my leg. The fact that I was not merely married but a father put me in the dotage class, and the saddest part was that I really did feel old in their company. They were all having the most marvellous time; chasing the local girls, drinking, going to dances and parties, carried along on the frothy insouciance which a war engenders. And I often thought that if it had all happened a few years ealier I would have been doing the same.

But it was no good now. Most of me was still back in Darrowby. During the day there was enough pressure to keep my mind occupied but in the evenings when I was off the leash all I wanted to do were the simple things I had done with Helen; the long games of bezique by the fireside in our bedsitter, tense battles on the push-ha'penny board; we even used to throw rings at hooks on a board on the wall. Kids' games after a hard slog round the practice, but even now as I look down the years I know I have never found a better way of living.

It was when we were lying in bed one night that Helen brought up the subject of Granville Bennett.

'Jim,' she murmured sleepily. 'Mr Bennett 'phoned again today. And his wife rang last week. They keep asking us to have a meal with them.'

'Yes . . . yes . . .' I didn't want to talk about anything at that moment. This was always a good time. The dying flames sent lights and shadows dancing across the ceiling, Oscar Rabin's band was playing *Deep Purple* on the bedside radio Ewan Ross gave us for a wedding present and I had just pulled off an unexpected victory at push-ha'penny. Helen was a dab hand at that game, urging the coins expertly up the board with the ball of her thumb, her lips pushed forward in a pout of concentration. Of course she had a lifetime of experience behind her while I was just learning, and it was inevitable that I seldom won. But I had done it tonight and I felt good.

My wife nudged me with her knee. 'Jim, I can't understand you. You never seem to do anything about it. And yet you say you like him.'

'Oh, I do, he's a grand chap, one of the best.' Everybody liked Granville, but at the same time there were many strong men who dived down alleys at the sight of him. I didn't like to tell Helen that every time I came into contact with him I got my wings singed. I fully realised that he meant well, that the whole thing was a natural extension of his extreme generosity. But it didn't help.

'And you said his wife was very nice, too.'

Zoe? Oh yes, she's lovely.' And she was, too, but thanks to her husband she had never seen me in any other role than a drunken hulk. My toes curled under the blankets. Zoe was beautiful, kind and intelligent – just the kind of woman you wanted to observe you staggering and hiccuping all over the place. In the darkness I could feel the hot blush of shame on my cheeks.

'Well then,' Helen continued, with the persistence that is part of even the sweetest women. 'Why don't we accept their invitation? I'd rather like to meet them – and it's a bit embarrassing when they keep 'phoning.'

I turned on my side. 'Okay, we'll go one of these days, I promise.'

But if it hadn't been for the little papilloma on Sam's lip I don't think we would ever have got there. I noticed the thing – a growth smaller than a pea – near the left commissure when I was giving our beagle an illicit chocolate biscuit. It was a typical benign tumour and on anybody else's dog I should have administered a quick local and whipped it off in a minute. But since it was Sam I turned pale and phoned Granville.

I have always been as soppy as any old lady over my pets and I suspect many of my colleagues are the same. I listened apprehensively to the buzz-buzz at the far end, then the big voice came on the line.

'Bennett here.'

'Hello, Granville, it's . . .'

'Jim!' The boom of delight was flattering. 'Where have you been hiding yourself, laddie?'

He didn't know how near he was to the truth. I told him about Sam.

'Doesn't sound much, old son, but I'll have a look at him with pleasure. Tell you what. We've been trying to get you over here for a meal – why not bring the little chap with you?'

'Well . . .' A whole evening in Granville's hands – it was a daunting prospect.

'Now don't mess about, Jim. You know, there's a wonderful Indian restaurant in Newcastle. Zoe and I would love to take you both out there. It's about time we met your wife, isn't it?'

'Yes . . . of course it is . . . Indian restaurant, eh?'

'Yes, laddie. Superb curries – mild, medium or blast your bloody head off. Onion bhajis, bhuna lamb, gorgeous nan bread.'

My mind was working fast. 'Sounds marvellous, Granville.' It did seem fairly secure. He was most dangerous on his own territory and it would take forty-five minutes' driving each way to Newcastle. Then maybe an hour and a half in the restaurant. I should be reasonably safe for most of the evening. There was just the bit at his house before we left – that was the only worry.

It was uncanny how he seemed to read my thoughts. 'Before we leave, Jim, we'll have a little session in my garden.'

'Your garden?' It sounded strange in November.

'That's right, old lad.'

Ah well, maybe he was proud of his late chrysanthemums, and I couldn't see myself coming to much harm there. 'Well, fine, Granville. Maybe Wednesday night?'

'Lovely, lovely, lovely – can't wait to meet Helen.'

Wednesday was one of those bright frosty late autumn days which turn misty in the afternoon and by six o'clock the countryside was blanketed by one of the thickest fogs I had ever seen in Yorkshire.

Creeping along in our little car, my nose almost on the windscreen, I muttered against the glass.

'God's truth, Helen, we'll never get to Newcastle tonight! I know Granville's some driver but you can't see ten yards out there.'

Almost at walking pace we covered the twenty miles to the Bennett residence and it was with a feeling of relief that I saw the brightly lit doorway rising out of the mirk.

Granville, as vast and impressive as ever, was there in the hall with arms outspread. Bashfulness had never been one of his problems and he folded my wife in a bear-like embrace.

'Helen, my pet,' he said and kissed her fondly and lingeringly. He stopped to take a breath, regarded her for a moment with deep appreciation then kissed her again.

I shook hands decorously with Zoe and the two girls were introduced. They made quite a picture standing there. An attractive woman is a gift from heaven and it was a rare bonus to see two of them in close proximity. Helen very dark and blue-eyed, Zoe brown-haired with eyes of greyish-green, but both of them warm and smiling.

Zoe had her usual effect on me. That old feeling was welling up; the desire to look my best, in fact better than my best. I cast a furtive glance at the hall mirror. Immaculately suited, clean shirted, freshly shaven, I was sure I projected the desired image of the clean-limbed young veterinary surgeon, the newly married man of high principles and impeccable behaviour.

I breathed a silent prayer of thanks that at last she was seeing me stone cold sober and normal. Tonight I would expunge all her squalid memories of me from her mind.

'Zoe, my sweet,' carolled Granville. 'Take Helen into the garden while I see Jim's dog.'

I blinked. The garden in this fog. I just didn't get it, but I was anxious about

Sam to give the thing much thought. I opened the car door and the beagle trotted into the house.

My colleague greeted him with delight. 'Come inside, my little man.' Then he hollered at the top of his voice. 'Phoebles! Victoria! Yoo-hoo! Come and meet cousin Sam!'

The obese Staffordshire bull terrier waddled in, closely followed by the Yorkie, who bared her teeth in an ingratiating smile at all present.

After the dogs had met and exchanged pleasantries Granville lifted Sam into his arms.

'Is that what you mean, Jim? Is that what you're worried about?'

I nodded dumbly.

'Good God, I could take a deep breath and blow the damn thing off!' He looked at me incredulously and smiled. 'Jim, old lad, why are you so daft about your dog?'

'Why do you call Phoebe Phoebles?' I countered swiftly.

'Oh well . . .' He cleared his throat. 'I'll get my equipment. Hang on a minute.'

He disappeared and came back with a syringe and scissors. About half a cc was enough to numb the part, then he snipped off the papilloma, applied some styptic and put the beagle on the floor. The operation took about two minutes but even in that brief spell his unique dexterity was manifest.

'That'll be ten guineas, Mr Herriot,' he murmured, then gave a shout of laughter. 'Come on, let's get into the garden. Sam will be quite happy with my dogs.'

He led me out of the back door and we stumbled through the fog by a rockery and rose bushes. I was just wondering how on earth he expected to show me anything in this weather when we came up against a stone outhouse. He threw open the door and I stepped into a brightly lit, sparkling Aladdin's cave.

It was quite simply a fully fitted bar. At the far end a polished counter with beer handles and, behind, a long row of bottles of every imaginable liquor. A fire crackled in the hearth and hunting prints, cartoons and bright posters looked down from the walls. It was completely authentic.

Granville saw my astonished face and laughed. 'All right, eh, Jim? I thought it would be a nice idea to have my own little pub in the garden. Rather cosy, isn't it?'

'Yes . . . yes indeed . . . charming.'

'Good, good.' My colleague slipped behind the counter. 'Now what are you going to have?'

Helen and Zoe took sherry and I made a quick decision to stick to one fairly harmless drink.

'Gin and tonic, please, Granville.'

The girls received a normal measure of sherry but when the big man took my glass over to the gin bottle hanging on the wall his hand seemed to be overcome by an uncontrollable trembling. The bottle was upended with one of those little optic attachments you push up with the rim of the glass to give a single measure.

But as I say, as Granville inserted the neck of the bottle into the glass his whole arm jerked repeatedly as though he were going into a convulsion. It was obvious that the result would be about six gins instead of one and I was about to remonstrate when he took the glass away and topped it up quickly with tonic, ice and sliced lemon.

I looked at it apprehensively. 'Rather a big one, isn't it?'

'Not at all, laddie, nearly all tonic. Well, cheers, so nice to see you both.'

And it certainly was. They were generous, warm people and veterinary folk like ourselves. I felt a gush of gratitude for the friendliness they had always shown me and as I sipped my drink, which was chokingly strong, I felt as I had often done that these contacts were one of the brightest rewards of my job.

Granville held out his hand. 'Have another, laddie.'

'Well, hadn't we better be getting on our way? It's a terrible night – in fact I don't see us ever getting to Newcastle in this fog.'

'Nonsense, old son.' He took my glass, reached up to the gin bottle and again was seized with a series of violent tremors of the forearm. 'No problem, Jim. Straight along the north road – half an hour or so – know it like the back of my hand.'

The four of us stood around the fire. The girls clearly had a lot to say to each other and Granville and I, like all vets, talked shop. It is wonderful how easy veterinary practice is in a warm room with good company and a dollop of alcohol in the stomach.

'One for the road, Jim,' my colleague said.

'No really, Granville, I've had enough,' I replied firmly. 'Let's be off.'

'Jim, Jim.' The familiar hurt look was creeping over his face. 'There's no rush. Look, we'll just have this last one while I tell you about this gorgeous restaurant.'

Once more he approached the gin bottle and this time the rigor lasted so long I wondered if he had some history of malaria.

Glass in hand he expounded. 'It's not just the curry, the cooking in general is exquisite.' He put his fingers to his lips and blew a reverent kiss into space. 'The flavours are unbelievable. All the spices of the orient, Jim.'

He went on at length and I wished he would stop because he was making me hungry. I had had a hard day round the farms and had eaten very little with the evening's feast in view, and as my colleague waved his hand around and drew word pictures of how they blended the rare herbs with the meat and fish, then served it on a bed of saffron rice, I was almost drooling.

I was relieved when I got through the third massive drink and Granville squeezed round to the front of the bar as if ready to go. We were on our way out when a man's bulk loomed in the doorway.

'Raymond!' cried Granville in delight. 'Come in, I've been wanting you to meet Jim Herriot. Jim, this is one of my neighbours – likes a bit of gardening, don't you Raymond?'

The man replied with a fat chuckle. 'Right, old boy! Splendid garden, this!' Granville seemed to know a lot of large, red-faced hearty men and this was one more.

My friend was behind the counter again. 'We must just have one with Raymond.'

I felt trapped as he again pressed my glass against the bottle and went into another paroxysm, but the girls didn't seem to mind. They were still deep in conversation and seemed unaware of the passage of time or the ravages of hunger.

Raymond was just leaving when Tubby Pinder dropped in. He was another enthusiastic horticulturist and I wasn't surprised to see that he was large, red-faced and hearty.

We had to have one with Tubby and I noticed with some alarm that after another palsied replenishment of my glass he had to replace the empty gin bottle with a fresh one. If the first one had been full then I had consumed nearly all of it.

I could hardly believe it when at last we were in the hall putting on our coats. Granville was almost purring with contentment.

'You two are going to love this place. It will be a joy to lead you through the menu.'

Outside the fog was thicker than ever. My colleague backed his enormous Bentley from the garage and began to usher us inside with great ceremony. He installed Helen and Zoe in the back, clucking solicitously over them, then he helped me into the passenger seat in front as though I were a disabled old man, tucking my coat in, adjusting the angle of the seat for maximum comfort, showing me how the cigar lighter worked, lighting up the glove compartment, enquiring which radio programme I desired.

At last he himself was in residence behind the wheel, massive and composed. Beyond the windscreen the fog parted for a second to show a steep, almost vertical grassy bank opposite the house, then it closed down like a dirty yellow curtain cutting off everything.

'Granville,' I said. 'We'll never get to Newcastle in this. It's over thirty miles.'

He turned and gave me a gentle smile. 'Absolutely no problem, laddie. We'll be there in half an hour, sampling that wonderful food. Tandoori chicken, all the spices of the orient, old son. Don't worry about a thing – I really know these roads. No chance of losing my way.'

He started the engine and drove confidently off, but unfortunately instead of taking the orthodox route along the road he proceeded straight up the grassy bank. He didn't seem to notice as the nose of the great car rose steadily higher, but when we had achieved an angle of forty-five degrees Zoe broke in gently from the back.

'Granville, dear, you're on the grass.'

My colleague looked round in some surprise. 'Not at all, my love. The road slopes a little here if you remember.' He kept his foot on the throttle.

I said nothing as my feet rose and my head went back. There was a point when the Bentley was almost perpendicular and I thought we were going over backwards, then I heard Zoe again.

'Granville, darling.' There was a hint of urgency in her tone. 'You're going up the bank.'

This time it seemed her husband was prepared to concede a little.

'Yes . . . yes, my pet,' he murmured as we hung there, all four of us gazing up at the fog-shrouded sky. 'Possibly I have strayed a little on to the verge.'

He took his foot off the brake and the car shot backwards at frightening speed into the darkness. We were brought up by a grinding crunch from the rear.

Zoe again: 'You've hit Mrs Thompson's wall, dear.'

'Have I, sweetheart? Ah, one moment. We'll soon be on our way.'

With undiminished aplomb he let in his clutch and we surged forward powerfully. But only for two seconds. From the gloom ahead there sounded a dull crash followed by a tinkling of glass and metal.

'Darling,' Zoe piped. 'That was the thirty miles an hour sign.

'Was it really, my angel?' Granville rubbed his hand on the window. 'You know, Jim, the visibility isn't too good.' He paused for a moment. 'Perhaps it would be a good idea if we postponed our visit till another time.'

He manoeuvred the big car back into the garage and we got out. We had covered, I should think, about five yards on our journey to Newcastle.

Back in the garden bar, Granville was soon in full cry again. And I was all for it because my earlier trepidation had vanished entirely. I was floating in a happy haze and I offered no resistance as my colleague jerked and twitched more samples from the gin bottle.

Suddenly he held up a hand. 'I'm sure we're all starving. Let's have some hot dogs!'

'Hot dogs?' I cried. 'Splendid idea!' It was a long call from all the spices of the orient but I was ready for anything.

'Zoe, sweet,' he said. 'We can use the big can of saveloy sausages if you would just heat it up.'

His wife left for the kitchen and Helen touched my arm.

'Jim,' she said. 'Saveloys . . . ?'

I knew what she meant. I have a pretty good digestion but there are certain things I can't eat. A single saveloy was enough to bring my entire metabolism to a halt, but at that moment it seemed a pettifogging detail.

'Oh don't worry, Helen,' I whispered, putting my arm round her. 'They won't hurt me.'

When Zoe came back with the food Granville was in his element, slicing the juicy smoked sausages lengthways, slapping mustard on them and enclosing them in rolls.

As I bit into the first one I thought I had never tasted anything so delicious. Chewing happily I found it difficult to comprehend my previous ridiculous prejudice.

'Ready for another, old son?' Granville held up a loaded roll.

'Sure! These are absolutely marvellous. Best hot dogs I've ever tasted!' I munched it down quickly and reached for a third.

I think it was when I had downed five of them that my friend prodded me in the ribs.

'Jim, lad,' he said between chews. 'We want a drop of beer to wash these down, don't you agree?'

I waved an arm extravagantly. 'Of course we do! Bloody gin's no good for this job!'

Granville pulled two pints of draught. Powerful delicious ale which flowed in a cooling wave over my inflamed mucous membranes, making me feel I had been waiting for it all my life. We each had three pints and another hot dog or two while waves of euphoria billowed around me.

The occasional anxious glance from Helen didn't worry me in the least. She was making signs that it was time to go home, but the very idea was unthinkable. I was having the time of my life, the world was a wonderful place and this little private pub was the finest corner of it.

Granville put down a half-eaten roll. 'Zoe, my precious, it would be nice to have something sweet to top this off. Why don't you bring out some of those little gooey things you made yesterday?'

She produced a plateful of very rich-looking cakelets. I do not have a sweet tooth and normally skip this part of the meal but I bit into one of Zoe's creations with relish. It was beautifully made and I could detect chocolate, marzipan, caramel and other things.

It was when I was eating the third that matters began to deteriorate. I found that my merry chatter had died and it was Granville doing all the talking, and as I listened to him owlishly I was surprised to see his face becoming two faces which floated apart and came together repeatedly. It was an astonishing phenomenon and it was happening with everything else in the room.

And I wasn't feeling so healthy now. That boundless vigour was no longer surging through my veins and I felt only a great weariness and a rising nausea.

I lost count of time around then. No doubt the conversation went on among the four of us but I can't remember any of it and my next recollection was of the party breaking up. Granville was helping Helen on with her coat and there was a general air of cheerful departure.

'Ready, Jim?' my friend said briskly.

I nodded and got slowly to my feet and as I swayed he put his arm round me and assisted me to the door. Outside, the fog had cleared and a bright pattern of stars overhung the village, but the clean cold air only made me feel worse and

I stumbled through the darkness like a sleepwalker. When I reached the car a long griping spasm drove through me, reminding me horribly of the sausages, the gin and the rest. I groaned and leaned on the roof.

'Maybe you'd better drive, Helen,' my colleague said. He was about to open the door when, with a dreadful feeling of helplessness, I began to slide along the metal.

Granville caught my shoulders. 'He'd be better in the back,' he gasped and began to lug me on to the seat. 'Zoe, sweetheart, Helen, love, grab a leg each, will you? Fine, now I'll get round the other side and pull him in.'

He trotted round to the far side, opened the door and hauled at my shoulders.

'Down a bit your side, Helen, dear. Now to me a little. Up a trifle your side, Zoe, pet. Now back to you a bit. Lovely, lovely.'

Clearly he was happy at his work. He sounded like an expert furniture remover and through the mists I wondered bitterly how many inert forms he had stuffed into their cars after an evening with him.

Finally they got me in, half lying across the back seat. My face was pressed against the side window and from the outside it must have been a grotesque sight with the nose squashed sideways and a solitary dead-mackerel eye staring sightlessly into the night.

With an effort I managed to focus and saw Zoe looking down at me anxiously. She gave a tentative wave of goodbye but I could produce only a slight twitch of the cheek in reply.

Granville kissed Helen fondly then slammed the car door. Moving back, he peered in at me and brandished his arms.

'See you soon, I hope, Jim. It's been a lovely evening!' His big face was wreathed in a happy smile and as I drove away my final impression was that he was thoroughly satisfied.

Chapter Twenty-six

Being away from Darrowby and living a different life I was able to stand back and assess certain things objectively. I asked myself many questions. Why, for instance, was my partnership with Siegfried so successful?

Even now, as we still jog along happily after thirty-five years, I wonder about it. I know I liked him instinctively when I first saw him in the garden at Skeldale House on that very first afternoon, but I feel there is another reason why we get on together.

Maybe it is because we are opposites. Siegfried's restless energy impels him constantly to try to alter things while I abhor change of any kind. A lot of people would call him brilliant, while not even my best friends would apply that description to me. His mind relentlessly churns out ideas of all grades – excellent, doubtful and very strange indeed. I, on the other hand, rarely have an idea of any sort. He likes hunting, shooting and fishing; I prefer football, cricket and tennis. I could go on and on – we are even opposite physical types – and yet, as I say, we get along.

This of course doesn't mean that we have never had our differences. Over the years there have been minor clashes on various points.

One, I recall, was over the plastic calcium injectors. They were something new so Siegfried liked them, and by the same token I regarded them with deep suspicion.

My doubts were nourished by my difficulties with them. Their early troubles have now been ironed out but at the beginning I found the things so temperamental that I abandoned them.

My colleague pulled me up about it when he saw me washing out my flutter valve by running the surgery tap through it.

'For God's sake, James, you're not still using that old thing, are you?'

'Yes, I'm afraid I am.'

'But haven't you tried the new plastics?'

'I have.'

'Well . . .?'

'Can't get away with them, Siegfried.'

'Can't . . . what on earth do you mean?'

I trickled the last drop of water through the tube, rolled it small and slipped it into its case. 'Well, the last time I used one the calcium squirted all over the place. And it's messy, sticky stuff. I had great white streaks down my coat.'

'But James!' He laughed incredulously. 'That's crazy! They're childishly simple to use. I haven't had the slightest trouble.'

'I believe you,' I said. 'But you know me. I haven't got a mechanical mind.'

'For heaven's sake, you don't need a mechanical mind. They're foolproof.'

'Not to me, they aren't. I've had enough of them.'

My colleague put his hand on my shoulder and his patient look began to creep across his face. 'James, James, you must persevere.' He raised a finger. 'There is another point at issue here, you know.

'What's that?'

'The matter of asepsis. How do you know that length of rubber you have there is clean?'

'Well, I wash it through after use, I use a boiled needle, and . . .'

'But don't you see, my boy, you're only trying to achieve what already exists in the plastic pack. Each one is self-contained and sterilised.'

'Oh I know all about that, but what's the good of it if I can't get the stuff into the cow?' I said querulously.

'Oh piffle, James!' Siegfried assumed a grave expression. 'It only needs a little application on your part, and I must stress that you are behaving in a reactionary manner by being stubborn. I put it to you seriously that we have to move with the times and every time you use that antiquated outfit of yours it is a retrograde step.'

We stood, as we often did, eyeball to eyeball, in mutual disagreement till he smiled suddenly. 'Look, you're going out now, aren't you, to see that milk-fever cow I treated at John Tillot's. I understand it's not up yet.'

'That's right.'

'Well, as a favour to me, will you give one of the new packs a try?'

I thought for a moment. 'All right, Siegfried, I'll have one more go.'

When I reached the farm I found the cow comfortably ensconced in a field, in the middle of a rolling yellow ocean of buttercups.

'She's had a few tries to get on 'er feet,' the farmer said. 'But she can't quite make it.'

'Probably just wants another shot.' I went to my car which I had driven, rocking and bumping, over the rig and furrow of the field, and took one of the plastic packs from the boot.

Mr Tillot raised his eyebrows when he saw me coming back. 'Is that one o' them new things?'

'Yes, it is, Mr Tillot, the very latest invention. All completely sterilised.'

'Ah don't care what it is, ah don't like it!'

'You don't?'

'Naw!'

'Well . . . why not?'

'Ah'll tell ye. Mr Farnon used one this mornin'. Some of the stuff went in me eye, some went in 'is ear 'ole and the rest went down 'is trousers. Ah don't think t'bloody cow got any!'

There was another time Siegfried had to take me to task. An old-age pensioner was leading a small mongrel dog along the passage on the end of a piece of string. I patted the consulting room table.

'Put him up here, will you?' I said.

The old man bent over slowly, groaning and puffing.

'Wait a minute.' I tapped his shoulder. 'Let me do it.' I hoisted the little animal on to the smooth surface.

'Thank ye, sir.' The man straightened up and rubbed his back and leg. 'I 'ave arthritis bad and I'm not much good at liftin'. My name's Bailey and I live at t'council houses.'

'Right, Mr Bailey, what's the trouble?'

'It's this cough He's allus at it. And 'e kind of retches at t'end of it.'

'I see. How old is he?'

'He were ten last month.'

'Yes . . ' I took the temperature and carefully auscultated the chest. As I moved the stethoscope over the ribs Siegfried came in and began to rummage in the cupboard.

'It's a chronic bronchitis, Mr Bailey,' I said. 'Many older dogs suffer from it just like old folks.'

He laughed. 'Aye, ah'm a bit wheezy meself sometimes.'

'That's right, but you're not so bad, really, are you?'

'Naw, naw.'

'Well neither is you little dog. I'm going to give him an injection and a course of tablets and it will help him quite a bit. I'm afraid he'll never quite get rid of this cough, but bring him in again if it gets very bad.'

He nodded vigorously. 'Very good, sir. Thank ye kindly, sir.'

As Siegfried banged about in the cupboard I gave the injection and counted out twenty of the new M&B 693 tablets.

The old man gazed at them with interest then put them in his pocket. 'Now what do ah owe ye, Mr Herriot?'

I looked at the ragged tie knotted carefully over the frayed shirt collar, at the threadbare antiquity of the jacket. His trouser knees had been darned but on one side I caught a pink glimpse of the flesh through the material.

'No, that's all right, Mr Bailey. Just see how he goes on.'

'Eh?'

'There's no charge.'

'But . . .'

'Now don't worry about it – it's nothing, really. Just see he gets his tablets regularly.'

'I will, sir, and it's very kind of you. I never expected . . .'

'I know you didn't, Mr Bailey. Goodbye for now and bring him back if he's not a lot better in a few days.'

The sound of the old man's footsteps had hardly died away when Siegfried emerged from the cupboard. He brandished a pair of horse tooth forceps in my face. 'God, I've been ages hunting these down. I'm sure you deliberately hide things from me, James.'

I smiled but made no reply and as I was replacing my syringe on the trolley my colleague spoke again.

'James, I don't like to mention this, but aren't you rather rash, doing work for nothing?'

I looked at him in surprise. 'He was an old-age pensioner. Pretty hard up I should think.'

'Maybe so, but really, you know, you just cannot give your services free.'

'Oh but surely occasionally, Siegfried – in a case like this . . .'

'No, James, not even occasionally. It's just not practical.'

'But I've seen you do it – time and time again!'

'Me?' His eyes widened in astonishment. 'Never! I'm too aware of the harsh realities of life for that. Everything has become so frightfully expensive. For instance, weren't those M&B 693 tablets you were dishing out? Heaven help us, do you know those things are threepence each? It's no good – you must never work without charging.'

'But dammit, you're always doing it!' I burst out. 'Only last week there was that . . .'

Siegfried held up a restraining hand. 'Please, James, please. You imagine things, that's your trouble.'

I must have given him one of my most exasperated stares because he reached out and patted my shoulder.

'Believe me, my boy, I do understand. You acted from the highest possible motives and I have often been tempted to do the same. But you must be firm. These are hard times and one must be hard to survive. So remember in future – no more Robin Hood stuff, we can't afford it.'

I nodded and went on my way somewhat bemusedly, but I soon forgot the incident and would have thought no more about it had I not seen Mr Bailey about a week later.

His dog was once more on the consulting room table and Siegfried was giving it an injection. I didn't want to interfere so I went back along the passage to the front office and sat down to write in the day book. It was a summer afternoon, the window was open and through a parting in the curtain I could see the front steps.

As I wrote I heard Siegfried and the old man passing on their way to the front door. They stopped on the steps. The little dog, still on the end of its string, looked much as it did before.

'All right, Mr Bailey,' my colleague said. 'I can only tell you the same as Mr Herriot. I'm afraid he's got that cough for life, but when it gets bad you must come and see us.'

'Very good, sir,' the old man put his hand in his pocket. 'And what is the charge, please?'

'The charge, oh yes . . . the charge . . .' Siegfried cleared his throat a few times but seemed unable to articulate. He kept looking from the mongrel dog to the old man's tattered clothing and back again. Then he glanced furtively into the house and spoke in a hoarse whisper.

'It's nothing, Mr Bailey.'

'But Mr Farnon, I can't let ye . . .'

'Shh! Shh!' Siegfried waved a hand agitatedly in the old man's face. 'Not a word now! I don't want to hear any more about it.'

Having silenced Mr Bailey he produced a large bag.

'There's about a hundred M&B tablets in here,' he said, throwing an anxious glance over his shoulder. 'He's going to keep needing them, so I've given you a good supply.'

I could see my colleague had spotted the hole in the trouser knee because he gazed down at it for a long time before putting his hand in his jacket pocket.

'Hang on a minute.' He extracted a handful of assorted chattels. A few coins fell and rolled down the steps as he prodded in his palm among scissors, thermometers, pieces of string, bottle openers. Finally his search was rewarded and he pulled out a bank note.

'Here's a quid,' he whispered and again nervously shushed the man's attempts to speak.

Mr Bailey, realising the futility of argument, pocketed the money.

'Well, thank ye, Mr Farnon. Ah'll take t'missus to Scarborough wi' that.'

'Good lad, good lad,' muttered Siegfried, still looking around him guiltily. 'Now off you go.'

The old man solemnly raised his cap and began to shuffle painfully down the street.

'Hey, hold on, there,' my colleague called after him. 'What's the matter? You're not going very well.'

'It's this dang arthritis. Ah go a long way in a long time.'

'And you've got to walk all the way to the council houses?' Siegfried rubbed his chin irresolutely. 'It's a fair step.' He took a last wary peep down the passage then beckoned with his hand.

'Look, my car's right here,' he whispered. 'Nip in and I'll run you home.'

Some of our disagreements were sharp and short.

I was sitting at the lunch table, rubbing and flexing my elbow. Siegfried, carving enthusiastically at a joint of roast mutton, looked up from his work.

'What's the trouble, James – rheumatism?'

'No, a cow belted me with her horn this morning. Right on the funny bone.'

'Oh, bad luck. Were you trying to get hold of her nose?'

'No, giving her an injection.'

My colleague, transporting a slice of mutton to my plate, paused in mid-air, 'Injecting her? Up there?'

'Yes, in the neck.'

'Is that where you do it?'

'Yes, always have done. Why?'

'Because if I may say so, it's rather a daft place. I always use the rump.'

'Is that so?' I helped myself to mashed potatoes. 'And what's wrong with the neck?'

'Well, you've illustrated it yourself, haven't you? It's too damn near the horns for a start.'

'Okay, well the rump is too damn near the hind feet.'

'Oh, come now, James, you know very well a cow very seldom kicks after a rump injection.'

'Maybe so, but once is enough.'

'And once is enough with a bloody horn, isn't it?'

I made no reply, Siegfried plied the gravy boat over both our plates and we started to eat. But he had hardly swallowed the first mouthful when he returned to the attack.

'Another thing, the rump is so handy. Your way you have to squeeze up between the cows.'

'Well, so what?'

'Simply that you get your ribs squashed and your toes stood on, that's all.'

'All right.' I spooned some green beans from the tureen. 'But your way you stand an excellent chance of receiving a faceful of cow shit.'

'Oh rubbish, James, you're just making excuses!' He hacked violently at his mutton.

'Not at all,' I said. 'It's what I believe. And anyway, you haven't made out a case against the neck.'

'Made out a case? I haven't started yet. I could go on indefinitely. For instance, the neck is more painful.'

'The rump is more subject to contamination,' I countered.

'The neck is often thinly muscled,' snapped Siegfried. 'You haven't got a nice pad to stick your needle into.'

'No, and you haven't got a tail either,' I growled.

'Tail? What the hell are you talking about?'

'I'm talking about the bloody tail! It's all right if you have somebody holding it but otherwise it's a menace, lashing about.'

Siegfried gave a few rapid chews and swallowed quickly. 'Lashing about? What in God's name has that got to do with it?'

'Quite a lot,' I replied. 'I don't like a whack across the face from a shitty tail, even if you do.'

There was a heavy-breathing lull then my colleague spoke in an ominously quiet voice. 'Anything else about the tail?'

'Yes, there is. Some cows can whip a syringe out of your hand with their tail. The other day one caught my big fifty cc and smashed it against a wall. Broken glass everywhere.'

Siegfried flushed slightly and put down his knife and fork. 'James, I don't like to speak to you in these terms, but I am bound to tell you that you are talking the most unmitigated balls, bullshit and poppycock.'

I gave him a sullen glare. 'That's your opinion, is it?'

'It is indeed, James.'

'Right.'

'Right.'

'Okay.'

'Very well.'

We continued our meal in silence.

But over the next few days my mind kept returning to the conversation. Siegfried has always had a persuasive way with him and the thought kept recurring that there might be a lot in what he said.

It was a week later that I paused, syringe in hand, before pushing between two cows. The animals, divining my intent as they usually did, swung their craggy hind ends together and blocked my way. Yes, by God, Siegfried had a point. Why should I fight my way in there when the other end was ready and waiting?

I came to a decision. 'Hold the tail, please,' I said to the farmer and pushed my needle into the rump.

The cow never moved and as I completed the injection and pulled the needle out I was conscious of a faint sense of shame. That lovely pad of gluteal muscle, the easy availability of the site – my colleague had been dead right and I had been a pig-headed fool. I knew what to do in future.

The farmer laughed as he stepped back across the dung channel. 'It's a funny thing how you fellers all have your different ways.'

'What do you mean?'

'Well, Mr Farnon was 'ere yesterday, injecting that cow over there.'

'He was?' A sudden light flashed in my mind. Could it be that Siegfried was not the only convincing talker in our practice . . ? 'What about it?'

'Just the 'e had a different system from you. He injected into the neck.'

Chapter Twenty-seven

I leaned on the handle of my spade, wiped away the sweat which had begun to run into my eyes and gazed around me at the hundreds of men scattered over the dusty green.

We were still on our toughening course. At least that's what they told us it was. I had a private suspicion that they just didn't know what to do with all the aircrews under training and that somebody had devised this method of getting us out of the way.

Anyway, we were building a reservoir near a charming little Shropshire town and a whole village of tents had sprung up to house us. Nobody was quite sure about the reservoir but we were supposed to be building something. They issued us with denim suits and pick-axes and spades and for hour after hour we pecked desultorily at a rocky hillside.

But, hot as I was, I couldn't help thinking that things could be a lot worse. The weather was wonderful and it was a treat to be in the open all day. I looked down the slope and away across the sweetly rolling countryside to where low hills rose in the blue distance; it was a gentler landscape than the stark fells and moors I had left behind in Yorkshire, but infinitely soothing.

And the roofs of the town showing above the trees held a rich promise. During the hours under the fierce sun, with the rock dust caking round our lips, we built up a gargantuan thirst which we nurtured carefully till the evening when we were allowed out of camp.

There, in cool taverns in the company of country folk, we slaked it with pints of glorious rough cider. I don't suppose you would find any there now. It is mostly factory-made cider which is drunk in the South of England these days, but many of the pubs used to have their own presses where they squeezed the juice from the local apples.

To me, there was something disturbing about sleeping in a tent. Each morning when I awoke with the early sun beating on the thin walls it was as if I were back in the hills above the Firth of Clyde long before the war was dreamed of. There was something very evocative about the tent smell of hot canvas and rubber groundsheet and crushed grass and the flies buzzing in a little cloud at the top of the pole. I was jerked back in an instant to Rosneath and when I opened my eyes I half expected to find Alex Taylor and Eddie Hutchison, the friends of my boyhood, lying there in their sleeping bags.

The three of us went camping at Rosneath every week-end from Easter to October, leaving the smoke and dirt of Glasgow behind us; and here in Shropshire, in the uncanny tent smell, when I closed my eyes I could see the little pine-wood behind the tent and the green hillside running down to the burn and, far below, the long blue mirror of the Gareloch glinting under the great mountains of Argyll. They have desecrated Rosneath and the Gareloch now, but to me, as a boy, it was a fairyland which led me into the full wonder and beauty of the world.

It was strange that I should dwell on that period when I was in my teens because Alex was in the Middle East, Eddie was in Burma and I was in another tent with a lot of different young men. And it was as though the time between had been rubbed away and Darrowby and Helen and all my struggles in veterinary practice had never happened. Yet those years in Darrowby had been the most important of my life. I used to sit up and shake myself, wondering at how my thoughts had been mixed up by the war.

But as I say, I quite enjoyed Shropshire. The only snag was that reservoir, or whatever it was that we were hacking out of the face of the hill. I could never get really involved with it. So that I pricked up my ears when our Flight Sergeant made an announcement one morning.

'Some of the local farmers want help with their harvest,' he called out at the early parade. 'Are there any volunteers?'

My hand was the first up and after a few moments' hesitation others followed, but none of my particular friends volunteered for the job. When everything had been sorted out I found I had been allotted to a farmer Edwards with three other airmen who were from a different flight and strangers to me.

Mr Edwards arrived the following day and packed the four of us into a typical big old-fashioned farmer's car. I sat in the front with him while the three others filled the back. He asked our names but nothing else, as though he felt that our station in civil life was none of his concern. He was about thirty-five with jet black hair above a sunburnt face in which his white teeth and clear blue eyes shone startlingly.

He looked us over with a good-humoured grin as we rolled into his farmyard.

'Well, here we are, lads,' he said. 'This is where we're going to put you through it.'

But I hardly heard him. I was looking around me at the scene which had been part of my life a few months ago. The cobbled yard, the rows of doors leading to cow byre, barn, pigsties and loose boxes. An old man was mucking out the byre and as the rich bovine smell drifted across, one of my companions wrinkled his nose. But I inhaled it like perfume.

The farmer led us all into the fields where a reaper and binder was at work, leaving the sheaves of corn lying in long golden swathes.

'Any of you ever done any stooking?' he asked.

We shook our heads dumbly.

'Never mind, you'll soon learn. You come with me, Jim.'

We spaced ourselves out in the big field, each of my colleagues with an old man while Mr Edwards took charge of me. It didn't take me long to realise that I had got the tough section.

The farmer grabbed a sheaf in each hand, tucked them under his arms, walked a few steps and planted them on end, resting against each other. I did the same till there were eight sheaves making up a stook. He showed me how to dig the stalks into the ground so that they stood upright and sometimes he gave a nudge with his knee to keep them in the right alignment.

I did my best but often my sheaves would fall over and I had to dart back and replace them. And I noticed with some alarm that Mr Edwards was going about twice as fast as the three old men. We had nearly finished the row while they were barely half way along, and my aching arms and back told me I was in for a testing time.

We went on like that for about two hours; bending, lifting, bending, lifting and shuffling forward without an instant's respite. One of the strongest impressions I had gained when I first came into country practice was that farming was the hardest way of all of making a living, and now I was finding out for myself. I was about ready to throw myself down on the stubble when Mrs Edwards came over the field with her young son and daughter. They carried baskets with the ingredients for our ten o'clock break; crusty apple tart and jugs of cider.

The farmer watched me quizzically as I sank gratefully down and began to drink like a parched traveller in the desert. The cider, from his own press, was superb, and I closed my eyes as I swallowed. The right thing, it seemed to me, would be to lie here in the sunshine for the rest of the day with about a gallon of this exquisite brew by my side, but Mr Edwards had other ideas. I was still chewing at the solid crust when he grasped a fresh pair of sheaves.

'Right, lad, must get on,' he grunted, and I was back on the treadmill.

With a pause at lunchtime for bread, cheese and more cider we went on at breakneck speed all day. I have always been grateful to the RAF for what they did for my physical well-being. When I was called up there was no doubt I was going slightly to seed under Helen's beneficent regime. Too much good cooking and the discovery of the charms of an armchair; I was getting fat. But the RAF changed all that and I don't think I have ever slipped back.

After the six months at Scarborough I am certain I didn't carry a surplus pound. Marching, drilling, PT, running – I could trot five miles along the beach and cliffs without trouble. When I arrived in Shropshire I was really fit. But I wasn't as fit as Mr Edwards.

He was a compact bundle of power. Not very big but with the wiry durability I remembered in the Yorkshire farmers. He seemed tireless, hardly breaking sweat as he moved along the rows, corded brown arms bulging from the sleeves of a faded collarless shirt, slightly bowed legs stumping effortlessly.

The sensible thing would have been to tell him straight that I couldn't go at his pace, but some demon of pride impelled me to keep up with him. I am quite sure he didn't mean to rub it in. Like any other farmer he had a job to do and was anxious to get on with it. At the lunch break he looked at me with some commiseration as I stood there, shirt sticking to my back, mouth hanging open, ribs heaving.

'You're doin' fine, Jim,' he said, then, as if noticing my distress for the first time, he shifted his feet awkwardly. 'I know you city lads ain't used to this kind of work and ... well ... it's not a question of strength, it's just knowin' how to do it.'

When we drove back to camp that night I could hear my companions groaning in the back of the car. They, too, had suffered, but not as badly as me.

After a few days I did begin to get the knack of the thing and though it still tested me to the utmost I was never on the border of collapse again.

Mr Edwards noticed the improvement and slapped me playfully on the shoulder. 'What did I tell you? It's just knowin' how to do it!'

But a new purgatory awaited me when we started to load the corn on to the stack. Forking the sheaves up on to the cart, roping them there then throwing them again, higher and higher as the stack grew in size. I realised with a jolt that stooking had been easy.

Mrs Edwards joined in this part. She stood on the top of the stack with her husband, expertly turning the sheaves towards him while he arranged them as they should be. I had the unskilled job way below, toiling as never before, back breaking, the handle of the fork blistering my palms.

I just couldn't go fast enough and Mr Edwards had to hop down to help me, grasping a fork and hurling the sheaves up with easy flicks of the wrist.

He looked at me as before and spoke the encouraging words. 'You're comin' along grand, Jim. It's just knowin' how to do it.'

But there were many compensations. The biggest was being among farming folk again. Mrs Edwards in her undemonstrative way was obviously anxious to show hospitality to these four rather bewildered city boys far from home, and set us down to a splendid meal every evening. She was dark like her husband, with large eyes which joined in her quick smile and a figure which managed to be thin and shapely at the same time. She hadn't much chance to get fat because she never stopped working. When she wasn't outside throwing the corn around like any man she was cooking and baking, looking after her children and scouring her great barn of a farmhouse.

Those evening meals were something to look forward to and remember. Steaming rabbit pies with fresh green beans and potatoes from the garden. Bilberry tarts and apple crumble and a massive jug of thick cream to pour ad lib. Home-baked bread and farm cheese.

The four of us revelled in the change from the RAF fare. It was said the aircrews got the best food in the services and I believed it, but after a while it all began to taste the same. Maybe it was the bulk cooking but it palled in time.

Sitting at the farm table, looking at Mrs Edwards serving us, at her husband eating stolidly and at the two children, a girl of ten whose dark eyes showed promise of her mother's attractiveness and a sturdy, brown-limbed boy of eight, the thought recurred; they were good stock.

The clever economists who tell us that we don't need British agriculture and that our farms should be turned into national parks seem to ignore the rather obvious snag that an unfriendly country could starve us into submission in a week. But to me a greater tragedy still would be the loss of a whole community of people like the Edwards.

It was late one afternoon and I was feeling more of a weakling than ever, with Mr Edwards throwing the sheaves around as though they were weightless while I groaned and strained. The farmer was called away to attend to a calving cow and as he hopped blithely from the stack he patted my shoulder as I leaned on my fork.

'Never mind, Jim,' he laughed. 'It's just knowin' how to do it.'

An hour later we were going into the kitchen for our meal when Mrs Edwards said 'My husband's still on with that cow. He must be having difficulty with her.'

I hesitated in the doorway. 'Do you mind if I go and see how he's getting on?'

She smiled. 'All right, if you like. I'll keep your food warm for you.'

I crossed the yard and went into the byre. One of the old men was holding the tail of a big Red Poll and puffing his pipe placidly. Mr Edwards, stripped to the waist, had his arm in the cow up to the shoulder. But it was a different Mr Edwards. His back and chest glistened and droplets of sweat ran down his nose and dripped steadily from the end. His mouth gaped and he panted as he fought his private battle somewhere inside.

He turned glazed eyes in my direction. At first he didn't appear to see me in his absorption, then recognition dawned.

''Ullo, Jim,' he muttered breathlessly. 'I've got a right job on 'ere.'

'Sorry to hear that. What's the trouble?'

He began to reply then screwed up his face. 'Aaah! The old bitch! She's squeezin' the life out of me arm again! She'll break it afore she's finished!' He paused, head hanging down, to recover, then he looked up at me. 'The calf's laid wrong, Jim. There's just a tail comin' into the passage and I can't get the hind legs round.'

A breech. My favourite presentation but one which always defeated farmers. I couldn't blame them really because they had never had the opportunity to read Franz Benesch's classical work on *Veterinary Obstetrics* which explains the

mechanics of parturition so lucidly. One phrase has always stuck in my mind:
'The necessity for simultaneous application of antagonistic forces'.

Benesch points out that in order to correct many mal-presentations it is
necessary to apply traction and repulsion at the same time, and to do that with
one hand in a straining cow is impossible.

As though to endorse my thoughts Mr Edwards burst out once more. 'Dang
it, I've missed it again! I keep pushin' the hock away then grabbin' for the foot
but the old bitch just shoves it all back at me. I've been doin' this for an hour
now and I'm about knackered.'

I never thought I would hear such words from this tough little man, but there
was no doubt he had suffered. The cow was a massive animal with a back like
a dining table and she was heaving the farmer back effortlessly every time she
strained. We didn't see many Red Polls in Yorkshire but the ones I had met
were self-willed and strong as elephants; the idea of pushing against one for an
hour made me quail.

Mr Edwards pulled his arm out and stood for a moment leaning against the
hairy rump. The animal was quite unperturbed by the interference of this puny
human but the farmer was a picture of exhaustion. He worked his dangling
fingers gingerly then looked up at me.

'By God!' he grunted. 'She's given me some stick. I've got hardly any feelin'
left in this arm.'

He didn't have to tell me. I had known that sensation many a time. Even
Benesch in the midst of his coldly scientific 'repositions', 'retropulsions', 'mal-
positions' and 'counteracting pressures' so far unbends as to state that 'Great
demands are made upon the strength of the operator'. Mr Edwards would agree
with him.

The farmer took a long shuddering breath and moved over to the bucket of
hot water on the floor. He washed his arms then turned back to the cow with
something like dread on his face.

'Look,' I said. 'Please let me help you.'

He gave me a pallid smile. 'Thanks, Jim, but there's nuthin' you can do.
Those legs have got to come round.'

'That's what I mean. I can do it.'

'What . . .?'

'With a bit of help from you. Have you got a piece of binder twine handy?'

'Aye, we've got yards of it, lad, but I'm tellin' you you need experience for
this job. You know nuthin' about . . .'

He stopped because I was already pulling my shirt over my head. He was too
tired to argue in any case.

Hanging the shirt on a nail on the wall, bending over the bucket and soaping
my arms with the scent of the antiseptic coming up to me brought a rush of
memories which was almost overwhelming. I held out my hand and Mr Edwards
wordlessly passed me a length of twine.

I soaked it in the water, then quickly tied a slip knot at one end and inserted
my hand into the cow. Ah yes, there was the tail, so familiar, hanging between
the calf's pelvic bones. Oh, I did love a breech, and I ran my hand with almost
voluptuous satisfaction along the hair of the limb till I reached the tiny foot. It
was a moment's work to push the loop over the fetlock and tighten it while I
passed the free end between the digits of the cloven foot.

'Hold that,' I said to the farmer, 'and pull it steadily when I tell you.'

I put my hand on the hock and began to push it away from me into the
uterus.

'Now pull,' I said. 'But carefully. Don't jerk.'

Like a man in a dream he did as I said and within seconds the foot popped out of the vulva.

'Hell!' said Mr Edwards.

'Now for the other one,' I murmured as I removed the loop.

I repeated the procedure, the farmer, slightly pop-eyed, pulling on the twine. The second little hoof, yellow and moist, joined its fellow on the outside almost immediately.

'Bloody hell!' said Mr Edwards.

'Right,' I said. 'Grab a leg and we'll have him out in a couple of ticks.'

We each took a hold and leaned back, but the big cow did the job for us, giving a great heave which deposited the calf wet and wriggling into my arms. I staggered back and dropped with it on to the straw.

'Grand bull calf, Mr Edwards,' I said. 'Better give him a rub down.'

The farmer shot me a disbelieving glance then twisted some hay into a wisp and began to dry off the little creature.

'If you ever get stuck with a breech presentation again,' I said, 'I'll show you what you ought to do. You have to push and pull at the same time and that's where the twine comes in. As you repel the hock with your hand somebody else pulls the foot round, but you'll notice I have the twine between the calf's cleats and that's important. That way it lifts the sharp little foot up and prevents injury to the vaginal wall.'

The farmer nodded dumbly and went on with his rubbing. When he had finished he looked up at me in bewilderment and his lips moved soundlessly a few times before he spoke.

'What the . . . how . . . how the heck do you know all that?'

I told him.

There was a long pause then he exploded.

'You young bugger! You kept that dark, didn't you?'

'Well . . . you never asked me.'

He scratched his head. 'Well, I don't want to be nosey with you lads that helps me. Some folks don't like it. . . .' His voice trailed away.

We dried our arms and donned our shirts in silence. Before leaving he looked over at the calf, already making strenuous efforts to rise as its mother licked it.

'He's a lively little beggar,' he said. 'And we might have lost 'im. I'm right grateful to you.' He put an arm round my shoulders. 'Anyway, come on, Mister Veterinary Surgeon, and we'll 'ave some supper.'

Half way across the yard he stopped and regarded me ruefully. 'You know, I must have looked proper daft to you, fumblin' away inside there for an hour and damn near killin' myself, then you step up and do it in a couple of minutes. I feel as weak as a girl.'

'Not in the least, Mr Edwards,' I replied. 'It's . . .' I hesitated a moment. 'It's not a question of strength, it's just knowing how to do it.'

He nodded, then became very still and the seconds stretched out as he stared at me. Suddenly his teeth shone as the brown face broke into an ever-widening grin which developed into a great shout of laughter.

He was still laughing helplessly when we reached the house and as I opened the kitchen door he leaned against the wall and wiped his eyes.

'You young divil!' he said. 'You really got a bit o' your own back there, didn't you?'

Chapter Twenty-eight

At last we were on our way to Flying School. It was at Windsor and that didn't seem far on the map, but it was a typical war-time journey of endless stops and changes and interminable waits. It went on all through the night and we took our sleep in snatches. I stole an hour's fitful slumber on the waiting-room table at a tiny nameless station and despite my hard pillowless bed I drifted deliciously back to Darrowby.

I was bumping along the rutted track to Nether Lees Farm, hanging on to the jerking wheel. I could see the house below me, its faded red tiles showing above the sheltering trees, and behind the buildings the scrubby hillside rose to the moor.

Up there the trees were stunted and sparse and dotted widely over the steep flanks. Higher still there was only scree and cliff and right at the top, beckoning in the sunshine, I saw the beginning of the moor – smooth, unbroken and bare.

A scar on the broad sweep of green showed where long ago they quarried the stones to build the massive farmhouses and the enduring walls which have stood against the unrelenting climate for hundreds of years. Those houses and those endlessly marching walls would still be there when I was gone and forgotten.

Helen was with me in the car. I loved it when she came with me on my rounds, and after the visit to the farm we climbed up the fell-side, panting through the scent of the warm bracken, feeling the old excitement as we neared the summit.

Then we were on the top, facing into the wide free moorland and the clean Yorkshire wind and the cloud shadows racing over the greens and browns. Helen's hand was warm in mine as we wandered among the heather through green islets nibbled to a velvet sward by the sheep. She raised a finger as a curlew's lonely cry sounded across the wild tapestry and the wonder in her eyes shone through the dark flurry of hair blowing across her face.

The gentle shaking at my shoulder pulled me back to wakefulness, to the hiss of steam and the clatter of boots. The table top was hard against my hip and my neck was stiff where it had rested on my pack.

'Train's in, Jim.' An airman was looking down at me. 'I hated to wake you – you were smiling.'

Two hours later, sweaty, unshaven, half asleep, laden with kit, we shuffled into the airfield at Windsor. Sitting in the wooden building we only half listened to the corporal giving us our introductory address. Then suddenly his words struck home.

There's one other thing,' he said. 'Remember to wear your identity discs at all times. We had two prangs last week – couple of fellers burned beyond recognition and neither of 'em was wearing his discs. We didn't know who they were.' He spread his hands appealingly. 'This sort of thing makes a lot of work for us, so remember what I've told you.'

In a moment we were all wide awake and listening intently. Probably thinking as I was – that we had only been playing at being airmen up till now.

I looked through the window at the wind sock blowing over the long flat stretch of green, at the scattered aircraft, the fire tender, the huddle of low wooden huts. The playing was over now. This was where everything started.

Vet in
a Spin

Vet in a Spin

With love to
ROSIE, JIM and GILL

Chapter One

This was a very different uniform. The wellingtons and breeches of my country vet days seemed far away as I climbed into the baggy flying suit and pulled on the sheepskin boots and the gloves – the silk ones first then the big clumsy pair on top. It was all new but I had a feeling of pride.

Leather helmet and goggles next, then I fastened on my parachute, passing the straps over my shoulders and between my legs and buckling them against my chest before shuffling out of the flight hut on to the long stretch of sunlit grass.

Flying Officer Woodham was waiting for me there. He was to be my instructor and he glanced at me apprehensively as though he didn't relish the prospect. With his dark boyish good looks he resembled all the pictures I had seen of Battle of Britain pilots and in fact, like all our instructors, he had been through this crisis in our history. They had been sent here as a kind of holiday after their tremendous experience but it was said that they regarded their operations against the enemy as a picnic compared with this. They had faced the might of the Luftwaffe without flinching but we terrified them.

As we walked over the grass I could see one of my friends coming in to land. The little biplane slewed and weaved crazily in the sky. It just missed a clump of trees, then about fifty feet from the ground it dropped like a stone, bounced high on its wheels, bounced twice again then zig-zagged to a halt. The helmeted head in the rear cockpit jerked and nodded as though it were making some pointed remarks to the head in front. Flying Officer Woodham's face was expressionless but I knew what he was thinking. It was his turn next.

The Tiger Moth looked very small and alone on the wide stretch of green. I climbed up and strapped myself into the cockpit while my instructor got in behind me. He went through the drill which I would soon know by heart like a piece of poetry. A fitter gave the propeller a few turns for priming. Then 'Contact!', the fitter swung the prop, the engine roared, the chocks were pulled away from the wheels and we were away, bumping over the grass, then suddenly and miraculously lifting and soaring high over the straggle of huts into the summer sky with the patchwork of the soft countryside of southern England unfolding beneath us.

I felt a sudden elation, not just because I liked the sensation but because I had waited so long for this moment. The months of drilling and marching and studying navigation had been leading up to the time when I would take to the air and now it had arrived.

FO Woodham's voice came over the intercom. 'Now you've got her. Take the stick and hold her steady. Watch the artificial horizon and keep it level. See that cloud ahead? Line yourself up with it and keep your nose on it.'

I gripped the joystick in my gauntleted hand. This was lovely. And easy, too. They had told me flying would be a simple matter and they had been right. It was child's play. Cruising along I glanced down at the grandstand of Ascot racecourse far below.

I was just beginning to smile happily when a voice crashed in my ear. 'Relax, for God's sake! What the hell are you playing at?'

I couldn't understand him. I felt perfectly relaxed and I thought I was doing fine, but in the mirror I could see my instructor's eyes glaring through his goggles.

'No, no, no! That's no bloody good! Relax, can't you hear me, relax!'

'Yes, sir,' I quavered and immediately began to stiffen up. I couldn't imagine what was troubling the man but as I began to stare with increasing desperation, now at the artificial horizon then at the nose of the aircraft against the cloud ahead, the noises over the intercom became increasingly apoplectic.

I didn't seem to have a single problem, yet all I could hear were curses and groans and on one occasion the voice rose to a scream. 'Get your bloody finger out, will you!'

I stopped enjoying myself and a faint misery welled in me. And as always when that happened I began to think of Helen and the happier life I had left behind. In the open cockpit the wind thundered in my ears, lending vivid life to the picture forming in my mind.

The wind was thundering here, too, but it was against the window of our bed-sitter. It was early November and a golden autumn had changed with brutal suddenness to arctic cold. For two weeks an icy rain had swept the grey towns and villages which huddled in the folds of the Yorkshire Dales, turning the fields into shallow lakes and the farmyards into squelching mud-holes.

Everybody had colds. Some said it was flu, but whatever it was it decimated the population. Half of Darrowby seemed to be in bed and the other half sneezing at each other.

I myself was on a knife edge, crouching over the fire, sucking an antiseptic lozenge and wincing every time I had to swallow. My throat felt raw and there was an ominous tickling at the back of my nose. I shivered as the rain hurled a drumming cascade of water against the glass. I was all alone in the practice. Siegfried had gone away for a few days and I just daren't catch cold.

It all depended on tonight. If only I could stay indoors and then have a good sleep I could throw this off, but as I glanced over at the phone on the bedside table it looked like a crouching beast ready to spring.

Helen was sitting on the other side of the fire, knitting. She didn't have a cold – she never did. And even in those early days of our marriage I couldn't help feeling it was a little unfair. Even now, thirty-five years later, things are just the same and, as I go around sniffling, I still feel tight-lipped at her obstinate refusal to join me.

I pulled my chair closer to the blaze. There was always a lot of night work in our kind of practice but maybe I would be lucky. It was eight o'clock with never a cheep and perhaps fate had decreed that I would not be hauled out into that sodden darkness in my weakened state.

Helen came to the end of a row and held up her knitting. It was a sweater for me, about half done.

'How does it look, Jim?' she asked.

I smiled. There was something in her gesture that seemed to epitomise our life together. I opened my mouth to tell her it was simply smashing when the phone pealed with a suddenness which made me bite my tongue.

Tremblingly I lifted the receiver while horrid visions of calving heifers floated before me. An hour with my shirt off would just tip me nicely over the brink.

'This is Sowden of Long Pasture,' a voice croaked.

'Yes, Mr Sowden?' I gripped the phone tightly. I would know my fate in a moment.

'I 'ave a big calf 'ere. Looks very dowly and gruntin' bad. Will ye come?'

A long breath of relief escaped me. A calf with probable stomach trouble. It could have been a lot worse.

'Right, I'll see you in twenty minutes,' I said.

As I turned back to the cosy warmth of the little room the injustice of life smote me.

'I've got to go out, Helen.'

'Oh, no.'

'Yes, and I have this cold coming on,' I whimpered. 'And just listen to that rain!'

'Yes, you must wrap up well, Jim.'

I scowled at her. 'That place is ten miles away, and a cheerless dump if ever there was one. There's not a warm corner anywhere.' I fingered my aching throat. 'A trip out there's just what I need – I'm sure I've got a temperature.' I don't know if all veterinary surgeons blame their wives when they get an unwanted call, but heaven help me, I've done it all my life.

Instead of giving me a swift kick in the pants Helen smiled up at me. 'I'm really sorry, Jim, but maybe it won't take you long. And you can have a bowl of hot soup when you get back.'

I nodded sulkily. Yes, that was something to look forward to. Helen had made some brisket broth that day, rich and meaty, crowded with celery, leeks and carrots and with a flavour to bring a man back from the dead. I kissed her and trailed off into the night.

Long Pasture Farm was in the little hamlet of Dowsett and I had travelled this narrow road many times. It snaked its way high into the wild country and on summer days the bare lonely hills had a serene beauty; treeless and austere, but with a clean wind sweeping over the grassy miles.

But tonight as I peered unhappily through the streaming windscreen the unseen surrounding black bulk pressed close and I could imagine the dripping stone walls climbing high to the summits where the rain drove across the moorland, drenching the heather and bracken, churning the dark mirrors of the bog water into liquid mud.

When I saw Mr Sowden I realised that I was really quite fit. He had obviously been suffering from the prevalent malady for some time, but like most farmers he just had to keep going at his hard ceaseless work. He looked at me from swimming eyes, gave a couple of racking coughs that almost tore him apart and led me into the buildings. He held an oil lamp high as we entered a lofty barn and in the feeble light I discerned various rusting farm implements, a heap of potatoes and another of turnips and in a corner a makeshift pen where my patient stood.

It wasn't the two week old baby calf I had half expected, but a little animal of six months, almost stirk age, but not well-grown. It had all the signs of a 'bad doer' – thin and pot-bellied with its light roan coat hanging in a thick overgrown fringe below its abdomen.

'Allus been a poor calf,' Mr Sowden wheezed between coughs. 'Never seemed to put on flesh. Rain stopped for a bit this afternoon, so ah let 'im out for a bit of fresh air and now look at 'im.'

I climbed into the pen and as I slipped the thermometer into the rectum I studied the little creature. He offered no resistance as I gently pushed him to one side, his head hung down and he gazed apathetically at the floor from deep sunk eyes. Worst of all was the noise he was making. It was more than a grunt – rather a long, painful groan repeated every few seconds.

'It certainly looks like his stomach,' I said. 'Which field was he in this afternoon?'

'I nobbut let 'im have a walk round t'orchard for a couple of hours.'

'I see.' I looked at the thermometer. The temperature was subnormal. 'I suppose there's a bit of fruit lying around there.'

Mr Sowden went into another paroxysm, then leaned on the boards of the pen to recover his breath. 'Aye, there's apples and pears all over t'grass. Had a helluva crop this year.'

I put the stethoscope over the rumen and instead of the normal surge and bubble of the healthy stomach I heard only a deathly silence. I palpated the flank and felt the typical doughy fullness of impaction.

'Well, Mr Sowden, I think he's got a bellyful of fruit and it's brought his digestion to a complete halt. He's in a bad way.'

The farmer shrugged. 'Well, if 'e's just a bit bunged up a good dose of linseed oil 'ud shift 'im.'

'I'm afraid it's not as simple as that,' I said. 'This is a serious condition.'

'Well what are we goin' to do about it then?' He wiped his nose and looked at me morosely.

I hesitated. It was bitterly cold in the old building and already I was feeling shivery and my throat ached. The thought of Helen and the bed-sitter and the warm fire was unbearably attractive. But I had seen impactions like this before and tried treating them with purgatives and it didn't work. This animal's temperature was falling to the moribund level and he had a sunken eye – if I didn't do something drastic he would be dead by morning.

'There's only one thing will save him,' I said. 'And that's a rumenotomy.'

'A what?'

'An operation. Open up his first stomach and clear out all the stuff that shouldn't be there.'

'Are you sure? D'ye not think a good pint of oil would put 'im right. It 'ud be a lot easier.'

It would indeed. For a moment the fireside and Helen glowed like a jewel in a cave, then I glanced at the calf. Scraggy and long-haired, he looked utterly unimportant, infinitely vulnerable and dependent. It would be the easiest thing in the world to leave him groaning in the dark till morning.

'I'm quite sure, Mr Sowden. He's so weak that I think I'll do it under a local anaesthetic, so we'll need some help.'

The farmer nodded slowly. 'Awright, ah'll go down t'village and get George Hindley.' He coughed again, painfully. 'But by gaw, ah could do without this tonight. Ah'm sure I've got brown chitis.'

Brown chitis was a common malady among the farmers of those days and there was no doubt this poor man was suffering from it but my pang of sympathy faded as he left because he took the lamp with him and the darkness closed tightly on me.

There are all kinds of barns. Some of them are small, cosy and fragrant with hay, but this was a terrible place. I had been in here on sunny afternoons and even then the dank gloom of crumbling walls and rotting beams was like a clammy blanket and all warmth and softness seemed to disappear among the cobwebbed rafters high above. I used to feel that people with starry eyed notions of farming ought to take a look inside that barn. It was evocative of the grim comfortless other side of the agricultural life.

I had it to myself now, and as I stood there listening to the wind rattling the door on its latch a variety of draughts whistled round me and a remorseless drip-drip from the broken pantiles on the roof sent icy droplets trickling over my head and neck. And as the minutes ticked away I began to hop from foot to foot in a vain effort to keep warm.

Dales farmers are never in a hurry and I hadn't expected a quick return, but after fifteen minutes in the impenetrable blackness bitter thoughts began to assail me. Where the hell was the man? Maybe he and George Hindley were brewing a pot of tea for themselves or perhaps settling down to a quick game of dominoes. My legs were trembling by the time the oil lamp reappeared in the entrance and Mr Sowden ushered his neighbour inside.

'Good evening, George,' I said. 'How are you?'

'Only moderate, Mr Herriot,' the newcomer sniffled. 'This bloody caud's just – ah – ah – whooosh – just gettin' a haud o' me.' He blew lustily into a red handkerchief and gazed at me blearily.

I looked around me. 'Well let's get started. We'll need an operating table. Perhaps you could stack up a few straw bales?'

The two men trailed out and returned, carrying a couple of bales apiece. When they were built up they were about the right height but rather wobbly.

'We could do with a board on top.' I blew on my freezing fingers and stamped my feet. 'Any ideas?'

Mr Sowden rubbed his chin. 'Aye, we'll get a door.' He shuffled out into the yard with his lamp and I watched him struggling to lift one of the cow byre doors from its hinges. George went to give him a hand and as the two of them pulled and heaved I thought wearily that veterinary operations didn't trouble me all that much but getting ready for them was a killer.

Finally the men staggered back into the barn, laid the door on top of the bales and the theatre was ready.

'Let's get him up,' I gasped.

We lifted the unresisting little creature on to the improvised table and stretched him on his right side. Mr Sowden held his head while George took charge of the tail and the rear end.

Quickly I laid out my instruments, removed coat and jacket and rolled up my shirt sleeves. 'Damn! We've no hot water. Will you bring some, Mr Sowden?'

I held the head and again waited interminably while the farmer went to the house. This time it was worse without my warm clothing and the cold ate into me as I pictured the farm kitchen and the slow scooping of the water from the side boiler into a bucket, then the unhurried journey back to the buildings.

When Mr Sowden finally reappeared I added antiseptic to the bucket and scrubbed my arms feverishly. Then I clipped the hair on the left side and filled the syringe with local anaesthetic. But as I infiltrated the area I felt my hopes sinking.

'I can hardly see a damn thing.' I looked helplessly at the oil lamp balanced on a nearby turnip chopper. 'That light's in the wrong place.'

Wordlessly Mr Sowden left his place and began to tie a length of plough cord to a beam. He threw it over another beam and made it fast before suspending the lamp above the calf. It was a big improvement but it took a long time and by the time he had finished I had abandoned all hope of ever throwing off my cold. I was frozen right through and a burning sensation had started in my chest. I would soon be in the same state as my helpers. Brown chitis was just round the corner.

Anyway, at least I could start now, and I incised skin, muscles, peritoneum and rumenal wall at record speed. I plunged an arm deep into the opened organ, through the fermenting mass of stomach contents, and in a flash all my troubles dissolved. Along the floor of the rumen apples and pears were spread in layers, some of them bitten but most of them whole and intact. Bovines take most of their food in big swallows and chew it over later at their leisure, but no animal could make cud out of this lot.

I looked up happily. 'It's just as I thought. He's full of fruit.'

'Hhrraaagh!' replied Mr Sowden. Coughs come in various forms but this one was tremendous and fundamental, starting at the soles of his hob-nailed boots and exploding right in my face. I hadn't realised how vulnerable I was with the farmer leaning over the calf's neck, his head a few inches from mine. 'Hhrraaagh!' he repeated, and a second shower of virus laden moisture struck me. Apparently Mr Sowden either didn't know or didn't care about droplet infection, but with my hands inside my patient there was nothing I could do about it.

Instinctively I turned my face a little in the other direction.

'Whoosh!' went George. It was a sneeze rather than a cough, but it sent a similar deadly spray against my other cheek. I realised there was no escape. I was hopelessly trapped between the two of them.

But as I say, my morale had received a boost. Eagerly I scooped out great handfuls of the offending fruit and within minutes the floor of the barn was littered with Bramley's seedlings and Conference pears.

'Enough here to start a shop,' I laughed.

'Hhrraaagh!' responded Mr Sowden.

'Whooosh!' added George, not to be outdone.

When I had sent the last apple and pear rolling into the darkness I scrubbed up again and started to stitch. This is the longest and most wearisome part of a rumenotomy. The excitement of diagnosis and discovery is over and it is a good time for idle chat, funny stories, anything to pass the time.

But there in the circle of yellow light with the wind whirling round my feet from the surrounding gloom and occasional icy trickles of rain running down my back I was singularly short of gossip, and my companions, sunk in their respective miseries, were in no mood for badinage.

I was half way down the skin sutures when a tickle mounted at the back of my nose and I had to stop and stand upright.

'Ah – ah – ashooo!' I rubbed my forearm along my nose.

'He's startin',' murmured George with mournful satisfaction.

'Aye, 'e's off,' agreed Mr Sowden, brightening visibly.

I was not greatly worried. I had long since come to the conclusion that my cause was lost. The long session of freezing in my shirt sleeves would have done it without the incessant germ bombardment from either side. I was resigned to my fate and besides, when I inserted the last stitch and helped the calf down from the table I felt a deep thrill of satisfaction. That horrible groan had vanished and the little animal was looking around him as though he had been away for a while. He wasn't cheerful yet, but I knew his pain had gone and that he would live.

'Bed him up well, Mr Sowden.' I started to wash my instruments in the bucket. 'And put a couple of sacks round him to keep him warm. I'll call in a fortnight to take out the stitches.'

That fortnight seemed to last a long time. My cold, as I had confidently expected, developed into a raging holocaust which settled down into the inevitable brown chitis with an accompanying cough which rivalled Mr Sowden's.

Mr Sowden was never an ebullient man but I expected him to look a little happier when I removed the stitches. Because the calf was bright and lively and I had to chase him round his pen to catch him.

Despite the fire in my chest I had that airy feeling of success.

'Well,' I said expansively. 'He's done very well. He'll make a good bullock some day.'

The farmer shrugged gloomily. 'Aye, reckon 'e will. But there was no need for all that carry on.'

'No need . . .?'

'Naw. Ah've been talkin' to one or two folk about t'job and they all said it was daft to open 'im up like that. Ah should just 'ave given 'im a pint of oil like I said.'

'Mr Sowden, I assure you . . .'

'And now ah'll have a big bill to pay.' He dug his hands deep into his pockets.

'Believe me, it was worth it.'

'Nay, nay, never.' He started to walk away, then looked over his shoulder. 'It would've been better if you 'adn't come.'

I had done three circuits with FO Woodham and on this third one he had kept fairly quiet. Obviously I was doing all right now and I could start enjoying myself again. Flying was lovely.

The voice came over the intercom again. 'I'm going to let you land her yourself this time. I've told you how to do it. Right, you've got her.'

'I've got her,' I replied. He had indeed told me how to do it – again and again – and I was sure I would have no trouble.

As we lost height the tops of the trees appeared, then the grass of the airfield came up to meet us. It was the moment of truth. Carefully I eased the stick back, then at what I thought was the right moment I slammed it back against my stomach. Maybe a bit soon because we bounced a couple of times and that made me forget to seesaw the rudder bar so that we careered from side to side over the turf before coming to a halt.

With the engine stilled I took a deep breath. That was my first landing and it hadn't been bad. In fact I had got better and better all the time and the conviction was growing in me that my instructor must have been impressed with my initial showing. We climbed out and after walking a few steps in silence FO Woodham halted and turned to me.

'What's your name?' he asked.

Ah yes, here was the proof. He knew I had done well. He was interested in me.

'Herriot, sir,' I replied smartly.

For a few moments he gave me a level stare. 'Well, Herriot,' he murmured, 'that was bloody awful.'

He turned and left me. I gazed down at my feet in their big sheepskin boots. Yes, the uniform was different, but things hadn't changed all that much.

Chapter Two

'Takes all kinds, doesn't it, chum?'

The airman grinned at me across the flight hut table. We had been listening to a monologue from a third man who had just left us after telling us what he intended to do after gaining his wings. The impression he left was that he was almost going to win the war on his own.

There were certainly all kinds in the RAF and this 'line shooting' was a common phenomenon when different types were thrown together.

There are all kinds of animals, too. Many people think my farm patients are all the same, but cows, pigs, sheep and horses can be moody, placid, vicious, docile, spiteful, loving.

There was one particular pig called Gertrude, but before I come to her I must start with Mr Barge.

Nowadays the young men from the pharmaceutical companies who call on veterinary surgeons are referred to as 'reps', but nobody would have dreamed of applying such a term to Mr Barge. He was definitely a 'representative' of Cargill and Sons, Manufacturers of Fine Chemicals since 1850, and he was so old that he might have been in on the beginning.

It was a frosty morning in late winter when I opened the front door at Skeldale House and saw Mr Barge standing on the front step. He raised his black homburg a few inches above the sparse strands of silver hair and his pink features relaxed into a smile of gentle benevolence. He had always treated me as a favourite son and I took it as a compliment because he was a man of immense prestige.

'Mr Herriot,' he murmured, and bowed slightly. The bow was rich in dignity and matched the dark morning coat, striped trousers and shiny leather brief case.

'Please come in, Mr Barge,' I said, and ushered him into the house.

He always called at midday and stayed for lunch. My young boss, Siegfried Farnon, a man not easily overawed, invariably treated him with deference and in fact the visit was something of a state occasion.

The modern rep breezes in, chats briefly about blood levels of antibiotics and steroids, says a word or two about bulk discounts, drops a few data sheets on the desk and hurries away. In a way I feel rather sorry for these young men because, with a few exceptions, they are all selling the same things.

Mr Barge, on the other hand, like all his contemporaries, carried a thick catalogue of exotic remedies, each one peculiar to its own firm.

Siegfried pulled out the chair at the head of the dining table. 'Come and sit here, Mr Barge.'

'You are very kind.' The old gentleman inclined his head slightly and took his place.

As usual there was no reference to business during the meal and it wasn't until the coffee appeared that Mr Barge dropped his brochure carelessly on the table as though this part of the visit was an unimportant afterthought.

Siegfried and I browsed through the pages, savouring the exciting whiff of witchcraft which has been blown from our profession by the wind of science. At intervals my boss placed an order.

'I think we'd better have a couple of dozen electuaries,' Mr Barge.

'Thank you so much.' The old gentleman flipped open a leather-bound notebook and made an entry with a silver pencil.

'And we're getting a bit low on fever drinks, aren't we, James?' Siegfried glanced round at me. 'Yes, we'll need a gross of them if you please.'

'I am most grateful,' Mr Barge breathed, noting that down, too.

My employer murmured his requests as he riffled through the catalogue. A Winchester of spirits of nitre and another of formalin, castration clams, triple bromide, Stockholm tar – all the things we never use now – and Mr Barge responded gravely to each with 'I do thank you' or 'Thank you indeed,' and a flourish of his silver pencil.

Finally Siegfried lay back in his chair. 'Well now, Mr Barge, I think that's it – unless you have anything new.'

'As it happens, my dear Mr Farnon, we have.' The eyes in the pink face twinkled. 'I can offer you our latest product, "Soothitt", an admirable sedative.'

In an instant Siegfried and I were all attention. Every animal doctor is keenly interested in sedatives. Anything which makes our patients more amenable is a blessing. Mr Barge extolled the unique properties of Soothitt and we probed for further information.

'How about unmaternal sows?' I asked. 'You know – the kind which savage their young. I don't suppose it's any good for that?'

'My dear young sir,' Mr Barge gave me the kind of sorrowing smile a bishop might bestow on an erring curate, 'Soothitt is a specific for this condition. A single injection to a farrowing sow and you will have no problems.'

'That's great,' I said. 'And does it have any effect on car sickness in dogs?'

The noble old features lit up with quiet triumph. 'Another classical indication, Mr Herriot. Soothitt comes in tablet form for that very purpose.'

'Splendid.' Siegfried drained his cup and stood up. 'Better send us a good supply then. And if you will excuse us, we must start the afternoon round, Mr Barge. Thank you so much for calling.'

We all shook hands, Mr Barge raised his homburg again on the front step and another gracious occasion was over.

Within a week the new supplies from Cargill and Sons arrived. Medicines were always sent in tea chests in those days and as I prised open the wooden lid I looked with interest at the beautifully packed phials and tablets of Soothitt. And it seemed uncanny that I had a call for the new product immediately.

That same day one of the town's bank managers, Mr Ronald Beresford, called to see me.

'Mr Herriot,' he said. 'As you know I have worked here for several years but I have been offered the managership of a bigger branch down south and I leave tomorrow for Portsmouth.' From his gaunt height he looked down at me with the unsmiling gaze which was characteristic of him.

'Portsmouth! Gosh, that's a long way.'

'Yes, it is – about three hundred miles. And I have a problem.'

'Really?'

'I have, I fear. I recently purchased a six-month-old cocker spaniel and he is an excellent little animal but for the fact that he behaves peculiarly in the car.'

'In what way?'

He hesitated. 'Well, he's outside now. If you've got a minute to spare I could demonstrate.'

'Of course,' I said. 'I'll come with you now.'

We went out to the car. His wife was in the passenger seat, as fat as her husband was thin, but with the same severe unbending manner. She nodded at me coldly but the attractive little animal on her lap gave me an enthusiastic welcome.

I stroked the long silky ears. 'He's a nice little fellow.'

Mr Beresford gave me a sidelong glance. 'Yes, his name is Coco and he really is quite charming. It's only when the engine is running that the trouble begins.'

I got in the back, he pressed the starter and we set off. And I saw immediately what he meant. The spaniel stiffened and raised his head till his nose pointed at the roof. He formed his lips into a cone and emitted a series of high-pitched howls.

'Hooo, hooo, hooo, hooo,' wailed Coco.

It really startled me because I had never heard anything quite like it. I don't know whether it was the perfectly even spacing of the hoots, their piercing, jarring quality, or the fact that they never stopped which drove the sound deep into my brain, but my head was singing after a two minute circuit of the town. I was vastly relieved when we drew up again outside the surgery.

Mr Beresford switched off the engine and it was as though he had switched off the noise, too, because the little animal relaxed instantly and began to lick my hand.

'Yes,' I said. 'You have a problem without a doubt.'

He pulled nervously at his tie. 'And it gets louder the longer you drive. Let me take you a bit further round and . . .'

'No-no, no-no,' I put in hastily. 'That won't be necessary. I can see exactly how you are placed. But you say you haven't had Coco for long. He isn't much more than a pup. I'm sure he'll get used to the car in time.'

'Very possibly he will.' Mr Beresford's voice was taut with apprehension. 'But I'm thinking of tomorrow. I've got to drive all the way to Portsmouth with my wife and this dog and I've tried car sickness tablets without result.'

A full day with that appalling din was unthinkable but at that moment the image of Mr Barge rose before me. He had sprouted wings and floated in front of my eyes like an elderly guardian angel. What an incredible piece of luck!

'As it happens,' I said with a reassuring smile, 'there is something new for this sort of thing, and by a coincidence we have just received a batch of it today. Come in and I'll fix you up.'

'Well, thank heavens for that.' Mr Beresford examined the box of tablets, 'I just give one half an hour before the journey and all will be well?'

'That's the idea,' I replied cheerfully. 'I've given you a few extra for future journeys.'

'I am most grateful, you've taken a great load off my mind.' He went out to the car and I watched as he started the engine. As if in response to a signal the little brown head on the back seat went up and the lips pursed.

'Hooo, hooo, hooo, hooo,' Coco yowled, and his master shot me a despairing look as he drove away.

I stood on the steps for some time, listening incredulously. Many people in Darrowby didn't like Mr Beresford very much, probably because of his cold manner, but I felt he wasn't a bad chap and he certainly had my sympathy. Long after the car had disappeared round the corner of Trengate I could still hear Coco.

'Hooo, hooo, hooo, hooo.'

About seven o'clock that evening I had a phone call from Will Hollin.

'Gertrude's started farrowin'!' he said urgently. 'And she's tryin' to worry her pigs!'

It was bad news. Sows occasionally attacked their piglets after birth and in fact would kill them if they were not removed from their reach. And of course it meant that suckling was impossible.

It was a tricky problem at any time but particularly so in this case because Gertrude was a pedigree sow – an expensive animal Will Hollin had bought to improve his strain of pigs.

'How many has she had?' I asked.

'Four – and she's gone for every one.' His voice was tense.

It was then I remembered Soothitt and again I blessed the coming of Mr Barge.

I smiled into the receiver. 'There's a new product I can use, Mr Hollin. Just arrived today. I'll be right out.'

I trotted through to the dispensary, opened the box of phials and had a quick read at the enclosed pamphlet. Ah yes, there it was. 'Ten cc intramuscularly and the sow will accept the piglets within twenty minutes.'

It wasn't a long drive to the Hollin farm but as I sped through the darkness I could discern the workings of fate in the day's events. The Soothitt had arrived this morning and right away I had two urgent calls for it. There was no doubt Mr Barge had been sent for a purpose – living proof, perhaps, that everything in our lives is preordained. It gave me a prickling at the back of my neck to think about it.

I could hardly wait to get the injection into the sow and climbed eagerly into the pen. Gertrude didn't appreciate having a needle rammed into her thigh and she swung round on me with an explosive bark. But I got the ten cc in before making my escape.

'We just wait twenty minutes, then?' Will Hollin leaned on the rail and looked down anxiously at his pig. He was a hard-working smallholder in his fifties and I knew this meant a lot to him.

I was about to make a comforting reply when Gertrude popped out another pink, squirming piglet. The farmer leaned over and gently nudged the little creature towards the udder as the sow lay on her side, but as soon as the nose made contact with the teat the big pig was up in a flash, all growls and yellow teeth.

He snatched the piglet away quickly and deposited it with the others in a tall cardboard box. 'Well, you see how it is, Mr Herriot.'

'I certainly do. How many have you got in there now?'

'There's six. And they're grand pigs, too.'

I peered into the box at the little animals. They all had the classical long-bodied shape. 'Yes, they are. And she looks as though she has a lot more in her yet.'

The farmer nodded and we waited.

It seemed to take a long time for the twenty minutes to pass but finally I lifted a couple of piglets and clambered into the pen. I was about to put them to the sow when one of them squealed. Gertrude rushed across with a ferocious roar, mouth gaping, and I leaped to safety with an agility which surprised me.

'She don't look very sleepy,' Mr Hollin said.

'No ... no ... she doesn't, does she? Maybe we'd better wait a bit longer.'

We gave her another ten minutes and tried again with the same result. I injected a further ten cc of the Soothitt, then about an hour later a third one. By nine o'clock Gertrude had produced fifteen beautiful young pigs and had chased me and her family from the pen six times. She was, if anything, livelier and fiercer than when I started.

'Well, she's cleansed,' Mr Hollin said gloomily. 'So it looks like she's finished.' He gazed, sad-faced, into the box. 'And now I've got fifteen pigs to rear without their mother's milk. I could lose all this lot.'

'Nay, nay.' The voice came from the open doorway. 'You won't lose 'em.'

I looked round. It was Grandad Hollin, his puckish features set in their customary smile. He marched to the pen and poked Gertrude's ribs with his stick.

She responded with a snarl and a malignant glare and the old man's smile grew broader.

'Ah'll soon fettle the awd beggar,' he said.

'Fettle her?' I shifted my feet uncomfortably. 'What do you mean?'

'Why, she just wants quietin', tha knaws.'

I took a long breath. 'Yes, Mr Hollin, that's exactly what I've been trying to do.'

'Aye, but you're not doin' it the right way, young man.'

I looked at him narrowly. The know-all with his liberal advice in a difficult situation is a familiar figure most veterinary surgeons have to tolerate, but in Grandad Hollin's case I didn't feel the usual irritation. I liked him. He was a nice man, the head of a fine family. Will was the eldest of his four sons and he had several farmer grandsons in the district.

Anyway, I had failed miserably. I was in no position to be uppity.

'Well, I've given her the latest injection,' I mumbled.

He shook his head. 'She don't want injections, she wants beer.'

'Eh?'

'Beer, young man. A drop o' good ale.' He turned to his son. 'Hasta got a clean bucket, Will, lad?'

'Aye, there's a new-scalded one in t'milk house.'

'Right, ah'll slip down to the pub. Won't be long.' Grandad swung on his heel and strode briskly into the night. He must have been around eighty but from the back he looked like a twenty-five-year-old – upright, square-shouldered, jaunty.

Will Hollin and I didn't have much to say to each other. He was sunk in disappointment and I was awash with shame. It was a relief when Grandad returned bearing an enamel bucket brimming with brown liquid.

'By gaw,' he chuckled. 'You should've seen their faces down at t'Wagon and Horses. Reckon they've never heard of a two gallon order afore.'

I gaped at him. 'You've got two gallons of beer?'

'That's right, young man, and she'll need it all.' He turned again to his son. 'She hasn't had a drink for a bit, has she, Will?'

'Naw I was goin' to give her some water when she'd finished piggin', but I haven't done it yet.'

Grandad poised his bucket. 'She'll be nice and thirsty, then.' He leaned over the rail and sent a dark cascade frothing into the empty trough.

Gertrude ambled moodily across and sniffed at the strange fluid. After some hesitation she dipped her snout and tried a tentative swallow, and within seconds the building echoed with a busy slobbering.

'By heck, she likes it!' Will exclaimed.

'She should,' Grandad murmured wistfully. 'It's John Smith's best bitter.'

It took a big sow a surprisingly short time to consume the two gallons and when she had finished she licked out every corner of the trough before turning away. She showed no inclination to return to her straw bed but began to saunter round the pen. Now and then she stopped at the trough to check that there was no more beer in it and from time to time she looked up at the three faces overhanging the timber walls.

On one of these occasions I cuaght her eye and saw with a sense of disbelief that the previously baleful little orb now registered only a gentle benevolence. In fact with a little effort I could have imagined she was smiling.

As the minutes passed her perambulations became increasingly erratic. There were times when she stumbled and almost fell and finally with an unmistakable hiccup she flopped on the straw and rolled on to her side.

Grandad regarded her expressionlessly for a few moments, whistling tunelessly, then he reached out again and pushed his stick against the fleshy thigh, but the only response he received from the motionless animal was a soft grunt of pleasure.

Gertrude was stoned to the wide.

The old man gestured towards the cardboard box. 'Put the little 'uns in now.'

Will went into the pen with a wriggling armful, then another, and like all new born creatures they didn't have to be told what to do. Fifteen ravenous little mouths fastened on to the teats and with mixed feelings I gazed at the sight which I had hoped to bring about with my modern veterinary skill, the long pink row filling their tiny stomachs with the life-giving fluid.

Well, I had fallen down on the job and an octogenarian farmer had wiped my eye with two gallons of strong ale. I didn't feel great.

Sheepishly I closed the box of Soothitt phials and was beating an unobtrusive retreat to my car when Will Hollin called after me.

'Come in and have a cup o' coffee afore you go, Mr Herriot.' His voice was friendly, with nothing to suggest that I had made no useful contribution all evening.

I made my way into the kitchen and as I went over to the table Will dug me in the ribs.

'Hey, look at this.' He held out the bucket in which a quantity of the good beer still sloshed around the bottom. 'There's summat better than coffee 'ere – enough for a couple of good drinks. I'll get two glasses.'

He was fumbling in the dresser when Grandad walked in. The old man hung his hat and stick on a hook on the wall and rubbed his hands.

'Tha can get another glass out, Will,' he said. 'Remember ah did the pourin' and ah left enough for three.'

Next morning I might have been inclined to dwell despondently on my chastening experience but I had a pre-breakfast call to a cow with a prolapsed uterus and there is nothing like an hour of feverish activity to rid the mind of brooding.

It was 8 a.m. when I drove back into Darrowby and I pulled in to the market place petrol station which was just opening. With a pleasantly blank mind I was watching Bob Cooper running the petrol into my tank when I heard the sound in the distance.

'Hooo, hooo, hooo, hooo.'

Tremblingly I scanned the square. There was no other vehicle in sight but the dread ululation approached inexorably until Mr Beresford's car rounded the far corner, heading my way.

I shrank behind a petrol pump but it was of no avail. I had been spotted and the car bumped over the strip of cobbles before screeching to a halt beside me.

'Hooo, hooo, hooo, hooo.' At close quarters the noise was insupportable.

I peeped round the pump and into the bulging eyes of the bank manager as he lowered his window. He switched off the engine and Coco stopped his howling and gave me a friendly wag through the glass.

His master, however, did not look at all friendly.

'Good morning, Mr Herriot,' he said, grim-faced.

'Good morning,' I replied hoarsely, then working up a smile I bent at the window. 'And good morning to you, Mrs Beresford.'

The lady withered me with a look and was about to speak when her husband went on.

'I administered one of the wonderful new tablets early this morning on your advice.' His chin quivered slightly.

'Oh, yes . . .?'

'Yes, I did, and it had no effect, so I gave him another.' He paused. 'Since this produced a similar result I tried a third and a fourth.'

I swallowed. 'Really . . .?'

'Indeed.' He gave me a cold stare. 'So I am driven to the conclusion that the tablets are useless.'

'Well . . . er . . . it certainly does look . . .'

He held up a hand. 'I cannot listen to explanations. I have already wasted enough time and there are three hundred miles' driving in front of me.'

'I'm truly sorry . . .' I began, but he was already closing the window. He started the engine and Coco froze immediately into his miniature wolf position, nose high, lips puckered into a small circle. I watched the car roll across the square and turn out of sight on the road to the south. For quite a while after it had gone I could still hear Coco.

'Hooo, hooo, hooo, hooo.'

Feeling suddenly weak, I leaned against the pump. My heart went out to Mr Beresford. As I have said, I felt sure he was a decent man.

In fact I quite liked him, but for all that I was profoundly grateful that I would probably never see him again.

Our audiences with Mr Barge usually took place every three months and it was mid June before I saw him again at the head of our luncheon table. The silvery head gleamed under the summer sunshine as he sipped his coffee and murmured politenesses. At the end of the meal he dabbed his lips with a napkin and slid his brochure unhurriedly along the table cloth.

Siegfried reached for it and asked the inevitable question. 'Anything new, Mr Barge?'

'My dear sir.' The old gentleman's smile seemed to convey that the follies of the young, though incomprehensible to him, were still delightful. 'Cargill and Sons never send me to you without a host of new products, many of them specific, all of them efficient. I have many sovereign remedies to offer you.'

I must have uttered some sort of strangled sound because he turned and regarded me quizzically. 'Ah, Mr Herriot, did you say something, young sir?'

I swallowed a couple of times and opened my mouth as the waves of benevolence flowed over me, but against that dignity and presence I was helpless.

'No . . . no, not really, Mr Barge,' I replied. I knew I would never be able to tell him about the Soothitt.

Chapter Three

Now that we were faced with the reality of life at flying school, the ties which bound me to my fellow airmen were strengthened. We had a common aim, a common worry.

The feeling of comradeship was very like my relationship with Siegfried, and his student brother, Tristan, back in Darrowby. But there, the pressures came not from learning to fly but from the daily challenge of veterinary practice. Our existence was ruled by sudden and unexpected alarms.

Tristan, however, didn't let it get him down. He and I were sitting in the big room at Skeldale House one night when the telephone burst into strident voice.

He reached from his chair and lifted the receiver.

'Allo, plis, oo is dis?' he enquired.

He listened attentively for a few moments then shook his head.

'Naw, naw, verree sorry, but Meester Farnon no at home. Yis, yis, I tell heem when he come. Hokey dokey, bye bye.'

I looked across at him wonderingly from the other side of the fireplace as he replaced the instrument. These strange accents were only one facet of his constant determination to extract amusement from every situation. He didn't do it all the time, only when the mood was on him, but it was not unusual for farmers to say that 'some foreign feller' had answered the phone.

Tristan settled comfortably behind his *Daily Mirror* and was fumbling for a Woodbine when the ringing started again. He stretched out once more.

'Yaas, yaas, goot efening, howdy do. Vat you vant, huh?'

I could just hear a deep rumble from the other end of the line and Tristan suddenly snapped upright in his chair. His *Daily Mirror* and cigarettes slithered to the floor.

'Yes, Mr Mount,' he said smartly. 'No, Mr Mount. Yes indeed, Mr Mount, I shall pass on your message immediately. Thank you very much, goodbye.'

He fell back in the chair and blew out his cheeks. 'That was Mr Mount.'

'So I gathered. And he certainly wiped the smile off your face, Triss.'

'Yes . . . yes . . . just a little unexpected.' He recovered his Woodbines and lit one thoughtfully.

'Quite,' I said. 'What did he ring for, anyway?'

'Oh, he has a cart horse to see tomorrow morning. Something wrong with its hind feet.'

I made a note on the pad and turned back to the young man. 'I don't know how you find the time in your hectic love life, but you're running around with that chap's daughter, aren't you?'

Tristan took the cigarette from his mouth and studied the glowing end. 'Yes, as a matter of fact I have taken Deborah Mount out a few times. Why do you ask?'

'Oh, no particular reason. Her old man seems a bit formidable, that's all.'

I could picture Mr Mount the last time I saw him. He was well named; a veritable massif of a man towering several inches over six feet. From shoulders like the great buttresses of the fell which overhung his farm rose a beetling cliff of head with craggy outcrops of jaw and cheek and brow. He had the biggest hands I have ever seen – approximately three times the size of my own.

'Oh, I don't know,' Tristan said. 'He's not a bad sort.'

'I agree, I've nothing against him.' Mr Mount was deeply religious and had the reputation of being hard but fair. 'It's just that I wouldn't like him to come up to me and ask if I was trifling with his daughter's affections.'

Tristan swallowed, and anxiety flitted briefly in his eyes. 'Oh, that's ridiculous. Deborah and I have a friendly relationship, that's all.'

'Well I'm glad to hear it,' I said. 'I've been told her father is very protective about her and I'd hate to feel those big hands round my throat.'

Tristan gave me a cold stare. 'You're a sadistic bugger at times, Jim. Just because I occasionally enjoy a little female company . . .'

'Oh, forget it, Triss, I'm only kidding. You've nothing to worry about. When I see old Mount tomorrow I promise I won't mention that Deborah is one of your harem.' I dodged a flying cushion and went through to the dispensary to stock up for the next day's round.

But I realised next morning that my joke was barbed when I saw Mr Mount coming out of the farm house. For a moment his bulk filled the doorway, then he advanced with measured tread over the cobbles till he loomed over me, blocking out the sunshine, throwing a large area around me into shade.

'That young man, Tristan,' he said without preamble. 'He was speakin' a bit funny like on the phone last night. What sort of a feller is he?'

I looked up at the great head poised above me, at the unwavering grey eyes probing into mine from beneath a bristling overhang of brow. 'Tristan?' I answered shakily. 'Oh, he's a splendid chap. A really fine type.'

'Mmm.' The huge man continued to look at me and one banana-like finger rubbed doubtfully along his chin. 'Does he drink?'

Mr Mount was renowned for his rigid antagonism to alcohol and I thought it unwise to reply that Tristan was a popular and esteemed figure at most of the local hostelries.

'Oh, er – ' I said. 'Hardly at all . . . in the strictest moderation . . .'

At that moment Deborah came out of the house and began to walk across the yard.

She was wearing a flowered cotton dress. About nineteen, shining golden hair falling below her shoulders, she radiated the healthy buxom beauty of the country girl. As she went by she flashed a smile at me and I had a heart-lifting glimpse of white teeth and warm brown eyes. It was in the early days before I had met Helen and I had as sharp an interest in a pretty lass as anybody. I found myself studying her legs appreciatively after she had passed.

It was then that I had an almost palpable awareness of her father's gaze upon me. I turned and saw a new expression there – a harsh disapproval which chilled me and left a deep conviction in my mind. Deborah was a little smasher all right, and she looked nice, but no . . . no . . . never. Tristan had more courage than I had.

Mr Mount turned away abruptly. 'This 'oss is in the stable,' he grunted.

In those late thirties the tractor had driven a lot of the draught horses from the land but most of the farmers kept a few around, perhaps because they had always worked horses and it was part of their way of life and maybe because of the sheer proud beauty of animals like the one which stood before me now.

It was a magnificent Shire gelding, standing all of eighteen hands. He was a picture of massively muscled power but when his master spoke, the great white-blazed face which turned to us was utterly docile.

The farmer slapped him on the rump. 'He's a good sort is Bobby and I think a bit about 'im. What ah noticed first was a strange smell about his hind feet and then ah had a look for meself. I've never seen owt like it.'

I bent and seized a handful of the long feathered hair behind the horse's pastern. Bobby did not resist as I lifted the huge spatulate foot and rested it on my knee. It seemed to occupy most of my lap but it was not the size which astonished me. Mr Mount had never seen owt like it and neither had I. The sole was a ragged, sodden mass with a stinking exudation oozing from the underrun horn, but what really bewildered me was the series of growths sprouting from every crevice.

They were like nightmare toadstools – long papillae with horny caps growing from the diseased surface. I had read about them in the books; they were called ergots, but I had never imagined them in such profusion. My thoughts raced as I moved behind the horse and lifted the other foot. It was just the same. Just as bad.

I had been qualified only a few months and was still trying to gain the confidence of the Darrowby farmers. This was just the sort of thing I didn't want.

'What is it?' Mr Mount asked, and again I felt that unwinking gaze piercing me.

I straightened up and rubbed my hands. 'It's canker, but a very bad case.' I knew all about the theory of the thing, in fact I was bursting with theory, but putting it into practice with this animal was a bit different.

'How are you going to cure it?' Mr Mount had an uncomfortable habit of going straight to the heart of things.

'Well, you see, all that loose horn and those growths will have to be cut away and then the surface dressed with caustic,' I replied, and it sounded easy when I said it.

'It won't get better on its own, then?'

'No, if you leave it the sole will disintegrate and the pedal bone will come through. Also the discharge will work up under the wall of the hoof and cause separation.'

The farmer nodded. 'So he'd never walk again, and that would be the end of Bobby.'

'I'm afraid so.'

'Right, then.' Mr Mount threw up his head with a decisive gesture. 'When are you going to do it?'

It was a nasty question, because I was preoccupied at that moment not so much with when I would do it but how I would do it.

'Well now, let's see,' I said huskily. 'Would it be . . .' The farmer broke in. 'We're busy hay-makin' all this week, and you'll be wantin' some men to help you. How about Monday next week?'

A wave of relief surged through me. Thank heavens he hadn't said tomorrow. I had a bit of time to think now.

'Very well, Mr Mount. That suits me fine. Don't feed him on the Sunday because he'll have to have an anaesthetic.'

Driving from the farm, a sense of doom oppressed me. Was I going to ruin that beautiful animal in my ignorance? Canker of the foot was unpleasant at any time and was not uncommon in the days of the draught horse, but this was something away out of the ordinary. No doubt many of my contemporaries have seen feet like Bobby's, but to the modern young veterinary surgeon it must be like a page from an ancient manual of farriery.

As is my wont when I have a worrying case I started mulling it over right away. As I drove, I rehearsed various procedures. Would that enormous horse go down with a chloroform muzzle? Or would I have to collect all Mr Mount's men and rope him and pull him down? But it would be like trying to pull down St Paul's Cathedral. And then how long would it take me to hack away all that horn – all those dreadful vegetations?

Within ten minutes my palms were sweating and I was tempted to throw the whole lot over to Siegfried. But I was restrained by the knowledge that I had to establish myself not only with the farmers but with my new boss. He wasn't going to think much of an assistant who couldn't handle a thing on his own.

I did what I usually did when I was worried; drove off the unfenced road, got out of the car and followed a track across the moor. The track wound beneath the brow of the fell which overlooked the Mount farm and when I had left the road far behind I flopped on the grass and looked down on the sunlit valley floor a thousand feet below.

In most places you could hear something – the call of a bird, a car in the distance – but here there was a silence which was absolute, except when the wind sighed over the hill top, rustling the bracken around me.

The farm lay in one of the soft places in a harsh countryside; lush flat fields where cattle grazed in comfort and the cut hay lay in long even swathes.

It was a placid scene, but it was up here in the airy heights that you found true serenity. Peace dwelt here in the high moorland, stealing across the empty miles, breathing from the silence and the tufted grass and the black, peaty earth.

The heady fragrance of the hay rose in the warm summer air and as always I felt my troubles dissolving. Even now, after all the years, I still count myself lucky that I can so often find tranquillity of mind in the high places.

As I rose to go I was filled with a calm resolve. I would do the job somehow. Surely I could manage the thing without troubling Siegfried.

In any case Siegfried had other things on his mind when I met him over the lunch table.

'I looked in at Granville Bennett's surgery at Hartington this morning,' he said, helping himself to some new potatoes which had been picked that morning from the garden. 'And I must say I was very impressed with his waiting room. All those magazines. I know we don't have the numbers to cater for, but there's often a lot of farmers in there.' He poured gravy on to a corner of his plate. 'Tristan, I'll give you the job. Slip round to Garlow's and order a few suitable things to be delivered every week, will you?'

'Okay,' his student brother replied. 'I'll do it this afternoon.'

'Splendid.' Siegfried chewed happily. 'We must keep progressing in every way. Do have some more of these potatoes, James, they really are very good.'

Tristan went into action right away and within two days the table and shelves in our waiting room carried a tasteful selection of periodicals. The *Illustrated London News*, *Farmer's Weekly*, *The Farmer and Stockbreeder*, *Punch*. But as usual he had to embroider the situation.

'Look at this, Jim,' he whispered one afternoon, guiding me through the door. 'I've been having a little harmless sport.'

'What do you mean?' I looked around me uncomprehendingly.

Tristan said nothing, but pointed to one of the shelves. There, among the innocent journals was a German naturist magazine displaying a startling frontispiece of full frontal nudity. Even in these permissive days it would have caused a raised eyebrow but in rural Yorkshire in the thirties it was cataclysmic.

'Where the devil did you get this?' I gasped, leafing through it hurriedly. It was just the same inside. 'And what's the idea, anyway?'

Tristan repressed a giggle. 'A fellow at college gave it to me. And it's rather a lark to sneak in quietly and find some solid citizen having a peek when he thinks nobody's looking. I've had some very successful incursions. My best bags so far have been a town councillor, a Justice of the Peace and a lay preacher.'

I shook my head. 'I think you're sticking you neck out. What if Siegfried comes across it?'

'No fear of that,' he said. 'He rarely comes in here and he's always in too much of a hurry. Anyway, it's well out of the way.'

I shrugged. Tristan had been blessed with an agile intelligence which I envied, but so much of it was misapplied. However, at the moment I hadn't time for his tricks. My mind was feverishly preoccupied.

Mentally I had cast that horse by innumerable methods and operated on his feet a thousand times by night and day. In daylight, riding round in the car, it wasn't so bad, but the operations I carried out in bed were truly bizarre. All the time I had the feeling that something was wrong, that there was some fatal flaw in the picture of myself carving away those hideous growths in one session. Finally I buried my pride.

'Siegfried,' I said, one afternoon when the practice was slack. 'I have rather a weird horse case.'

My boss's eyes glinted and the mouth beneath the small sandy moustache crooked into a smile. The word 'horse' usually had this effect.

'Really, James? Tell me.'

I told him.

'Yes ... yes ...' he murmured. 'Maybe we'd better have a look together.'

The Mount Farm was deserted when we arrived. Everybody was in the hayfields working frantically while the sunshine lasted.

'Where is he?' Siegfried asked.

'In here.' I led the way to the stable.

My boss lifted a hind foot and whistled softly. Then he moved round and examined the other one. For a full minute he gazed down at the obscene fungi thrusting from the tattered stinking horn. When he stood up he looked at me expressionlessly.

It was a few seconds before he spoke. 'And you were just going to pop round here on Monday, tip this big fellow on to the grass and do the job?'

'Yes,' I replied. 'That was the idea.'

A strange smile spread over my employer's face. It held something of wonder, sympathy, amusement and a tinge of admiration. Finally he laughed and shook his head.

'Ah, the innocence of youth,' he murmured.

'What do you mean?' After all, I was only six years younger than Siegfried.

He came over and patted my shoulder. 'I'm not mocking you, James. This is the worst case of canker I've ever seen and I've seen a few.'

'You mean I couldn't do it at one go?'

'That's exactly what I mean. There's six weeks' work here, James.'

'Six weeks . . .?'

'Yes, and there'll be three men involved. We'll have to get this horse into one of the loose boxes at Skeldale House and then the two of us plus a blacksmith will have a go at him. After that his feet will have to be dressed every day in the stocks.'

'I see.'

'Yes, yes.' Siegfried was warming to his subject. 'We'll use the strongest caustic – nitric acid – and he'll be shod with special shoes with a metal plate to exert pressure on the sole.' He stopped, probably because I was beginning to look bewildered, then he continued in a gentler tone. 'Believe me, James, all this is necessary. The alternative is to shoot a fine horse, because he can't go on much longer than this.'

I looked at Bobby, at the white face again turned towards us. The thought of a bullet entering that noble head was unbearable.

'All right, whatever you say, Siegfried,' I mumbled, and just then Mr Mount's vast bulk darkened the entrance to the stable.

'Ah, good afternoon to you, Mr Mount,' my boss said. 'I hope you're getting a good crop of hay.'

'Aye, thank ye, Mr Farnon. We're doing very nicely. We've been lucky with the weather.' The big man looked curiously from one of us to the other, and Siegfried went on quickly.

'Mr Herriot asked me to come and look at your horse. He's been thinking the matter over and has decided that it would be better to hospitalise him at our place for a few weeks. I must say I agree with him. It's a very bad case and the chances of a permanent cure would be increased.'

Bless you, Siegfried, I thought. I had expected to emerge from this meeting as the number one chump, but all was suddenly well. I congratulated myself, not for the first time, on having an employer who never let me down.

Mr Mount took off his hat and drew a forearm across his sweating brow. 'Aye well, if that's what you think, both of ye, we'd better do it. Ah want the best for Bobby. He's a favourite o' mine.'

'Yes, he's a grand sort, Mr Mount.' Siegfried went round the big animal, patting and stroking him, then as we walked back to the car he kept up an effortless conversation with the farmer. I had always found it difficult to speak to this formidable man, but in my colleague's presence he became quite chatty. In fact there were one or two occasions when he almost smiled.

Bobby came into the yard at Skeldale House the following day and when I saw the amount of sheer hard labour which the operation entailed I realised the utter impossibility of a single man doing it at one go.

Pat Jenner the blacksmith with his full tool kit was pressed into service and between us, taking it in turns, we removed all the vegetations and diseased tissue, leaving only healthy horn. Siegfried applied the acid to cauterise the area, then packed the sole with twists of tow which were held in place by the metal plate Pat had made to fit under the shoe. This pressure from the tow was essential to effect a cure.

After a week I was doing the daily dressings myself. This was when I began to appreciate the value of the stocks with their massive timbers sunk deep into the cobbles of the yard. It made everything so much easier when I was able to lead Bobby into the stocks, pull up a foot and make it fast in any position I wished.

Some days Pat Jenner came in to check on the shoes and he and I were busy in the yard when I heard the familiar rattle of my little Austin in the back lane. The big double doors were open and I looked up as the car turned in and drew alongside us. Pat looked too, and his eyes popped.

'Bloody 'ell!' he exclaimed, and I couldn't blame him, because the car had no driver. At least it looked that way since there was nobody in the seat as it swung in from the lane.

A driverless car in motion is quite a sight, and Pat gaped openmouthed for a few seconds. Then just as I was about to explain, Tristan shot up from the floor with a piercing cry.

'Hi there!' he shrieked.

Pat dropped his hammer and backed away. 'God 'elp us!' he breathed.

I was unaffected by the performance because it was old stuff to me. Whenever I was in the yard and a call came in, Tristan would drive my car round from the front street and this happened so many times that inevitably he grew bored and tried to find a less orthodox method.

After a bit of practice he mastered the driverless technique. He crouched on the floor with a foot on the accelerator and one hand on the wheel and nearly frightened the life out of me the first time he did it. But I was used to it now, and blasé.

Within a few days I was able to observe another of Tristan's little jokes. As I turned the corner of the passage at Skeldale House I found him lurking by the waiting room door which was slightly ajar.

'I think I've got a victim in there,' he whispered. 'Let's see what happens.' He gently pushed the door and tiptoed inside.

As I peeped through the crack I could see that he had indeed scored a success. A man was standing there with his back to him and he was poring over the nudist magazine with the greatest absorption. As he slowly turned the pages his enthralment showed in the way he frequently moved the pictures towards the light from the french window, inclining his head this way and that to take in all the angles. He looked as though he would have been happy to spend all day there but when he heard Tristan's exquisitely timed cough he dropped the magazine as though it was white hot, snatched hurriedly at the *Farmer's Weekly* and swung round.

That was when Tristan's victory went flat. It was Mr Mount.

The huge farmer loomed over him for a few seconds and the deep bass rumble came from between clenched teeth.

'It's you, is it?' He glanced quickly from the young man to the embarrassing magazine and back again and the eyes in the craggy face narrowed dangerously.

'Yes . . . yes . . . yes, Mr Mount,' Tristan replied unsteadily. 'And how are you, Mr Mount?'

'Ah'm awright?'

'Good . . . good . . . splendid.' Tristan backed away a few steps. 'And how is Deborah?'

The eyes beneath the sprouting bristles drew in further. 'She's awright.'

There was a silence which lingered interminably and I felt for my young friend. It was not a merry meeting.

At last he managed to work up a sickly smile. 'Ah well, yes, er . . . and what can we do for you, Mr Mount?'

'Ah've come to see me 'oss.'

'Yes, indeed, of course, certainly. I believe Mr Herriot is just outside the room.'

I led the big man down the long garden into the yard. His encounter with Tristan had clearly failed to improve his opinion of the young man and he glowered as I opened the loose box.

But his expression softened when he saw Bobby eating hay contentedly. He went in and patted the arching neck. 'How's he goin' on, then?'

'Oh, very well.' I lifted a hind foot and showed him the metal plate. 'I can take this off for you if you like.'

'Nay, nay ah don't want to disturb the job. As long as all's well, that's all ah want to know.'

The dressings went on for a few more weeks till finally Siegfried was satisfied that the last remnants of the diesease had been extirpated. Then he telephoned for Mr Mount to collect his horse the following morning.

It is always nice to be in on a little triumph, and I looked over my boss's shoulder as he lifted Bobby's feet and displayed the finished job to the owner. The necrotic jumble on the soles had been replaced by a clean, smooth surface with no sign of moisture anywhere.

Mr Mount was not enthusiastic by nature but he was obviously impressed. He nodded his head rapidly several times. 'Well now, that's champion. I'm right capped wi' that.'

Siegfried lowered the foot to the ground and straightened with a pleased smile. There was a general air of bonhomie in the yard, and then I heard my car in the back lane.

I felt a sudden tingle of apprehension. Oh no, Tristan, not this time, please. You don't know . . . My toes curled as I waited but I realised all was lost when the car turned in through the double doors. It had no driver.

With a dreadful feeling of imminent catastrophe I watched as it stopped within a few feet of Siegfried and Mr Mount who were staring at it in disbelief.

Nothing happened for a few seconds, then without warning Tristan catapulted like a jack-in-the-box into the open window.

'Yippeeee!' he screeched, but his happy grin froze as he found himself gazing into the faces of his brother and Mr Mount. Siegfried's expression of exasperation was familiar to me, but the farmer's was infinitely more menacing. The eyes in the stony visage were mere slits, the jaw jutted, the great tangle of eyebrows bristled fiercely. There was no doubt he had finally made up his mind about Tristan.

I felt the young man had suffered enough, and I kept off the subject for a week or two afterwards, but we were sitting in the big room at Skeldale House when he mentioned casually that he wouldn't be taking Deborah out any more.

'Seems her father has forbidden it,' he said.

I shrugged in sympathy, but said nothing. After all, it had been an ill-starred romance from the beginning.

Chapter Four

'Circuits and bumps' they called it. Taking off, circling the field and landing, over and over and over. After an hour of it with FO Woodham in full voice I had had enough and it was a blessed relief when we climbed out at the end.

As my instructor walked away, one of his fellow officers strolled by his side. 'How are you getting on with that chap, Woody?' he asked, smiling.

FO Woodham did not pause in his stride or turn his head. 'Oh God!' he said with a hollow groan, and that was all.

I knew I wasn't meant to hear the words but they bit deep. My spirits did not rise till I entered the barrack hut and was greeted by the cheerful voices of my fellow airmen.

'Hello, Jim!' 'How's it going, Jim?' The words were like balm.

I looked around at the young men sprawled on their beds, reading or smoking and I realised that I needed them and their friendship.

Animals are the same. They need friends. Have you ever watched two animals in a field? They may be of different species – a pony and a sheep – but they hang together. This comradeship between animals had always fascinated me, and I often think of Jack Sanders's two dogs as a perfect example of mutual devotion.

One of them was called Jingo and as I injected the local anaesthetic alongside the barbed wire tear in his skin the powerful white bull terrier whimpered just once. Then he decided to resign himself to his fate and looked stolidly to the front as I depressed the plunger.

Meanwhile his inseparable friend, Skipper the corgi, gnawed gently at Jingo's hind leg. It was odd to see two dogs on the table at once, but I knew the relationship between them and made no comment as their master hoisted them both up.

After I had infiltrated the area around the wound I began to stitch and Jingo relaxed noticeably when he found that he could feel nothing.

'Maybe this'll teach you to avoid barbed wire fences in future, Jing,' I said.

Jack Sanders laughed. 'I doubt if it will, Mr Herriot. I thought the coast was clear when I took him down the lane this morning, but he spotted a dog on the other side of the fence and he was through like a bullet. Fortunately it was a greyhound and he couldn't catch it.'

'You're a regular terror, Jing.' I patted my patient, and the big Roman-nosed face turned to me with an ear-to-ear grin and at the other end the tail whipped delightedly.

'Yes, it's amazing, isn't it?' his master said. 'He's always looking for a fight, yet people and children can do anything with him. He's the best natured dog in the world.'

I finished stitching and dropped the suture needle into a kidney dish on the trolley. 'Well, you've got to remember that the bull terrier is the original English fighting dog and Jing is only obeying an age-old instinct.'

'Oh I realise that. I'll just have to go on scanning the horizon every time I let him off the lead. No dog is safe from him.'

'Except this one, Jack.' I laughed and pointed to the little corgi who had tired of his companion's leg and was now chewing his ear.

'Yes, isn't it marvellous. I think he could bite Jing's ear off without reprisal.'

It was indeed rather wonderful. The corgi was eleven years old and beginning to show his age in stiffness of movement and impairment of sight while the bull terrier was only three, at the height of his strength and power. A squat, barrel-chested bundle of bone and muscle, he was a formidable animal. But when the ear-chewing became too violent, all he did was turn and gently engulf Skipper's head in his huge jaws till the little animal desisted. Those jaws could be as merciless as a steel trap but they held the tiny head in a loving embrace.

Ten days later their master brought both dogs back to the surgery for the removal of the stitches. He looked worried as he lifted the animals on to the table.

'Jingo isn't at all well, Mr Herriot,' he said. 'He's been off his food for a couple of days and he looks miserable. Could that wound make him ill if it turned septic?'

'Yes it could, of course.' I looked down anxiously at the area of the flank where I had stitched, and my fingers explored the long scar. 'But there's not the slightest sign of infection here. No swelling, no pain. He's healed beautifully.'

I stepped back and looked at the bull terrier. He was strangely disconsolate, tail tucked down, eyes gazing ahead with total lack of interest. Not even the busy nibbling of his friend at one of his paws relieved his apathy.

Clearly Skipper didn't like being ignored in this fashion. He transferred his operations to the front end and started on the big dog's ear. As his efforts still went unnoticed he began to chew and tug harder, dragging the massive head down to one side, but as far as Jingo was concerned he might as well not have been there.

'Hey, that's enough, Skipper,' I said. 'Jing isn't in the mood for rough stuff to-day.' I lifted him gently to the floor where he paced indignantly around the table legs.

I examined the bull terrier thoroughly and the only significant finding was an elevated temperature.

'It's a hundred and five, Jack. He's very ill, there's no doubt about that.'

'But what's the matter with him?'

'With a high fever like that he must have some acute infection. But at the moment it's difficult to pinpoint.' I reached out and stroked the broad skull, running my fingers over the curving white face as my thoughts raced.

For an instant the tail twitched between his hocks and the friendly eyes rolled round to me and then to his master. It was that movement of the eyes which seized my whole attention. I quickly raised the upper lid. The conjunctiva appeared to be a normal pink, but in the smooth white sclera I could discern the faintest tinge of yellow.

'He's got jaundice,' I said. 'Have you noticed anything peculiar about his urine?'

Jack Sanders nodded. 'Yes, now you mention it. I saw him cock his leg in the garden and his water looked a bit dark.'

'Those are bile pigments.' I gently squeezed the abdomen and the dog winced slightly. 'Yes, he's definitely tender in there.'

'Jaundice?' His master stared at me across the table. 'Where would he get that?'

I rubbed my chin. 'Well, when I see a dog like this I think firstly of two things – phosphorus poisoning and leptospirosis. In view of the high temperature I go for the leptospirosis.'

'Would he catch it from another dog?'

'Possibly, but more likely from rats. Does he come into contact with any rats?'

'Yes, now and then. There's a lot of them in an old hen house at the foot of the lane and Jing sometimes gets in there after them.'

'Well that's it.' I shrugged. 'I don't think we need to look any further for the cause.'

He nodded slowly. 'Anyway, it's something to know what's wrong with him. Now you can set about putting him right.'

I looked at him for a moment in silence. It wasn't like that at all. I didn't want to upset him, but on the other hand he was a highly intelligent and sensible man in his forties, a teacher at the local school. I felt I had to tell him the whole truth.

'Jack,' I said. 'This is a terrible condition to treat. If there's one thing I hate to see it's a jaundiced dog.'

'You mean it's serious?'

'I'm afraid so. In fact the mortality rate is very high.'

I felt for him when I saw the sudden pain and concern in his face, but a warning now was better than a shock later, because I knew that Jingo could be dead within a few days. Even now, thirty years later, I quail when I see that yellowish discoloration in a dog's eyes. Penicillin and other antibiotics have some effect against the causal organism of leptospirosis but the disease is still very often fatal.

'I see ... I see ...' He was collecting his thoughts. 'But surely you can do something?'

'Yes, yes, of course,' I said briskly. 'I'm going to give him a big shot of antileptospiral serum and some medicine to administer by the mouth. It isn't completely hopeless.'

I injected the serum in the knowledge that it didn't have much effect at this stage, but I had nothing else to offer. I gave Skipper a shot, too, with the happier feeling that it would protect him against the infection.

'One thing, more, Jack,' I added. 'This disease also affects humans, so please take all hygienic precautions when handling Jingo. All right?'

He nodded and lifted the bull terrier from the table. The big dog, as most of my patients do, tried to hurry away from the disturbing white-coat-and-antiseptic atmosphere of the surgery. As he trotted along the passage his master turned to me eagerly.

'Look at that! He doesn't seem too bad, does he?'

I didn't say anything. I hoped with all my heart that he was right, but I was fighting off the conviction that this nice animal was doomed. At any rate I would soon know.

I knew, in fact, next day. Jack Sanders was on the phone before nine o'clock in the morning.

'Jing's not so good,' he said, but the tremor in his voice belied the lightness of his words.

'Oh.' I experienced the familiar drooping of the spirits. 'What is he doing?'

'Nothing, I'm afraid. Won't eat a thing ... lying around ... just lifeless. And every now and then he vomits.'

It was what I expected, but I still felt like kicking the desk by my side. 'Very well, I'll be right round.'

There was no tail wags from Jing to-day. He was crouched before the fire, gazing listlessly into the coals. The yellow in his eyes had deepened to a rich orange and his temperature still soared. I repeated the serum injection, but the big dog did not heed the entry of the needle. Before I left I ran my hand over the smooth white body and Skipper as ever kept burrowing in on his friend, but Jingo's thoughts were elsewhere, sunk in his inner misery.

I visited him daily and on the fourth day I found him stretched almost comatose on his side. The conjunctiva, sclera, and the mucous membranes of the mouth were a dirty chocolate colour.

'Is he suffering?' Jack Sanders asked.

I hesitated for a moment. 'I honestly don't think he's in pain. Sickness, nausea, yes, but I'd say that's all.'

'Well I'd like to keep on trying,' he said. 'I don't want to put him down even though you think it's hopeless. You do . . . don't you?'

I made a non-committal gesture. I was watching Skipper who seemed bewildered. He had given up his worrying tactics and was sniffing round his friend in a puzzled manner. Only once did he pull very gently at the unresponsive ear.

I went through the motions with a feeling of helplessness and left with the unpleasant intuition that I would never see Jingo alive again.

And even though I was waiting for it, Jack Sanders' phone call next morning was a bad start to the day.

'Jing died during the night, Mr Herriot. I thought I'd better let you know. You said you were coming back this morning.' He was trying to be matter-of-fact.

'I'm sorry, Jack,' I said. 'I did rather expect . . .'

'Yes, I know. And thank you for what you did.'

It made it worse when people were nice at these times. The Sanders were a childless couple and devoted to their animals. I knew how he was feeling.

I stood there with the receiver in my hand. 'Anyway, Jack, you've still got Skipper.' It sounded a bit lame, but it did help to have the comfort of one remaining dog, even though he was old.

'That's right,' he replied. 'We're very thankful for Skipper.'

I went on with my work. Patients died sometimes and once it was over it was almost a relief, especially when I knew in Jingo's case that the end was inevitable.

But this thing wasn't over. Less than a week later Jack Sanders was on the phone again.

'It's Skipper,' he said. 'He seems to be going the same way as Jing.'

A cold hand took hold of my stomach and twisted it.

'But . . . but . . . he can't be! I gave him the protective injection!'

'Well, I don't know, but he's hanging around miserably and hardly eats a thing. He seems to be going down fast.'

I ran out and jumped into my car. And as I drove to the edge of the town where the Sanders lived my heart thudded and panicky thoughts jostled around in my mind. How could he have got the infection? I had little faith in the serum as a cure but as a prevention I felt it was safe. I had even given him a second shot to make sure. The idea of these people losing both their dogs was bad enough but I couldn't bear the thought the second one might be my fault.

The little corgi trailed unhappily across the carpet when he saw me and I lifted him quickly on to the kitchen table. I almost snatched at his eyelids in my anxiety but there was no sign of jaundice in the sclera nor in the mucous membranes of the mouth. The temperature was dead normal and I felt a wave of relief.

'He hasn't got leptospirosis, anyway,' I said.

Mrs Sanders clasped her hands. 'Oh thank God for that. We were sure it was the same thing. He looks so awful.'

I examined the little animal meticulously and when I finished I put my stethoscope in my pocket. 'Well, I can't find much wrong here. He's got a bit of a heart murmur but you've known about that for some time. He's old, after all.'

'Do you think he could be fretting for Jing?' Jack Sanders asked.

'Yes, I do. They were such friends. He must feel lost.'

'But he'll get over that, won't he?'

'Oh of course he will. I'll leave some mild sedative tablets for him and I'm sure they'll help.'

I met Jack a few days later in the market place.

'How is Skipper?' I asked.

He blew out his cheeks. 'About the same. Maybe a bit worse. The trouble is he eats practically nothing – he's getting very thin.'

I didn't see what else I could do but on the following day I looked in at the Sanders' as I was passing.

I was shocked at the little corgi's appearance, Despite his age he had been so cocky and full of bounce, and when Jing was alive he had been indisputably the boss dog. But now he was utterly deflated. He looked at me with lack-lustre eyes as I came in, then crept stiffly to his basket where he curled himself as though wishing to shut out the world.

I examined him again. The heart murmur seemed a little more pronounced but there was nothing else except that he looked old and decrepit and done.

'You know, I'm beginning to wonder if he really is fretting,' I said. 'It could be just his age catching up on him. After all, he'll be twelve in the spring, won't he?'

Mrs Sanders nodded. 'That's right. Then you think ... this could be the end?'

'It's possible.' I knew what she was thinking. A couple of weeks ago two healthy dogs rolling around and playing in this house and now there could soon be none.

'But isn't there anything else you can do?'

'Well I can give him a course of digitalis for his heart. And perhaps you would bring in a sample of his urine. I want to see how his kidneys are functioning.'

I tested the urine. There was a little albumen, but no more than you would expect in a dog of his age. I ruled out nephritis as a cause.

As the days passed I tried other things; vitamins, iron tonics, organo-phosphates, but the little animal declined steadily. It was about a month after Jing's death that I was called to the house again.

Skipper was in his basket and when I called to him he slowly raised his head. His face was pinched and fleshless and the filmed eyes regarded me without recognition.

'Come on, lad,' I said encouragingly. 'Let's see you get out of there.'

Jack Sanders shook his head. 'It's no good, Mr Herriot. He never leaves his basket now and when we lift him out he's almost too weak to walk. Another thing ... he makes a mess down here in the kitchen during the night. That's something he's never done.'

It was like the tolling of a sad bell. Everything he said pointed to a dog in the last stages of senility. I tried to pick my words.

'I'm sorry, Jack, but it all sounds as if the old chap has come to the end of the road. I don't think fretting could possibly cause all this.'

He didn't speak for a moment. He looked at his wife then down at the forlorn little creature. 'Well of course this has been in the back of our minds. But we've kept hoping he would start to eat. What ... what do you suggest?'

I could not bring myself to say the fateful words. 'It seems to me that we can't stand by and let him suffer. He's just a little skeleton and I can't think he's getting any pleasure out of his life now.'

'I see,' he said. 'And I agree. He lies there all day – he has no interest in anything.' He paused and looked at his wife again. 'I tell you what, Mr Herriot. Let us think it over till tomorrow. But you do think there's no hope?'

'Yes, Jack, I do. Old dogs often go this way at the end. Skipper has just cracked up . . . he's finished, I'm afraid.'

He drew a long breath. 'Right, if you don't hear from me by eight o'clock tomorrow morning, please come and put him to sleep.'

I had small hope of the call coming and it didn't. In those early days of our marriage Helen worked as a secretary for one of the local millers. We often started our day together by descending the long flights of stairs from our bed-sitter and I would see her out of the front door before getting ready for my round.

This morning she gave me her usual kiss before going out into the street but then she looked at me searchingly. 'You've been quiet all through breakfast, Jim. What's the matter?'

'It's nothing, really. Just part of the job,' I said. But when she kept her steady gaze on me I told her quickly about the Sanders.

She touched my arm. 'It's such a shame, Jim, but you can't let your sad cases depress you. You'd never survive.'

'Aagh, I know that. But I'm a softy, that's my trouble. Sometimes I think I should never have been a vet.'

'You're wrong there,' she said. 'I couldn't imagine you as anything else. You'll do what you have to do, and you'll do it the right way.' She kissed me again, turned and ran down the steps.

It was mid morning before I drew up outside the Sanders' home. I opened the car boot and took out the syringe and the bottle of concentrated anaesthetic which would give the old dog a peaceful and painless end.

The first thing I saw when I went into the kitchen was a fat little white puppy waddling across the floor.

I looked down in astonishment. 'What's this . . .?

Mrs Sanders gave me a strained smile, 'Jack and I had a talk yesterday. We couldn't bear the idea of not having a dog at all, so we went round to Mrs Palmer who bred Jing and found she had a litter for sale. It seemed like fate. We've called him Jingo, too.'

'What a splendid idea!' I lifted the pup which squirmed in my hand, grunted in an obese manner and tried to lick my face. This, I felt, would make my unpleasant task easier. 'I think you've been very sensible.'

I lifted the bottle of anaesthetic unobtrusively from my pocket and went over to the basket in the corner. Skipper was still curled in the unheeding ball of yesterday and the comforting thought came to me that all I was going to do was push him a little further along the journey he had already begun.

I pierced the rubber diaphragm on the bottle with my needle and was about to withdraw the barbiturate when I saw that Skipper had raised his head. Chin resting on the edge of the basket, he seemed to be watching the pup. Wearily his eyes followed the tiny creature as it made its way to a dish of milk and began to lap busily. And there was something in his intent expression which had not been there for a long time.

I stood very still as the corgi made a couple of attempts then heaved himself to a standing position. He almost fell out of the basket and staggered on shaking legs across the floor. When he came alongside the pup he remained there, swaying, for some time, a gaunt caricature of his former self, but as I watched in disbelief, he reached forward and seized the little white ear in his mouth.

Stoicism is not a characteristic of pups and Jingo the Second yelped shrilly as the teeth squeezed. Skipper, undeterred, continued to gnaw with rapt concentration.

I dropped bottle and syringe back in my pocket. 'Bring him some food,' I said quietly.

Mrs Sanders hurried to the pantry and came back with a few pieces of meat on a saucer. Skipper continued his ear-nibbling for a few moments then sniffed the pup unhurriedly from end to end before turning to the saucer. He hardly had the strength to chew but he lifted a portion of meat and his jaws moved slowly.

'Good heavens!' Jack Sanders burst out. 'That's the first thing he's eaten for days!'

His wife seized my arm. 'What's happened, Mr Herriot? We only got the puppy because we couldn't have a house without a dog.'

'Well, it looks to me as though you've got two again.' I went over to the door and smiled back at the two people watching fascinated as the corgi swallowed then started determinedly on another piece of meat. 'Good morning, I'm going now.'

About eight months later, Jack Sanders came into the surgery and put Jingo Two on the table. He was growing into a fine animal with the wide chest and powerful legs of the breed. His good-natured face and whipping tail reminded me strongly of his predecessor.

'He's got a bit of eczema between his pads,' Jack said, then he bent and lifted Skipper up.

At that moment I had no eyes for my patient. All my attention was on the corgi, plump and bright-eyed, nibbling at the big white dog's hind limbs with all his old bounce and vigour.

'Just look at that!' I murmured. 'It's like turning the clock back.'

Jack Sanders laughed. 'Yes, isn't it. They're tremendous friends – just like before.'

'Come here, Skipper.' I grabbed the little corgi and looked him over. When I had finished I held him for a moment as he tried to wriggle his way back to his friend. 'Do you know, I honestly think he'll go on for years yet.'

'Really?' Jack Sanders looked at me with a mischievous light in his eyes. 'But I seem to remember you saying quite a long time ago that his days were over – he was finished.'

I held up a hand. 'I know, I know. But sometimes it's lovely to be wrong.'

Chapter Five

'That young Herriot's a bloody thick-'ead.'

It wasn't the sort of statement to raise one's morale and for a moment the good ale turned to vinegar in my mouth. I was having a quiet pint all alone in the 'snug' of the Crown and Anchor on my way home from an evening colic case, and the words came clearly through the hatch from the public bar.

I suppose it was the fact that I had come to the conclusion that my flying instructor, FO Woodham, considered me to be a person of low intelligence that brought the incident back to my mind.

I shifted my position slightly so that I could see into the brightly lit room. The speaker was Seth Pilling, a casual labourer and a well known character in Darrowby. He was designated a labourer, but in truth he didn't labour unduly and his burly frame and red meaty face was a common sight around the Labour Exchange where he signed for his unemployment pay.

'Aye, 'e's got no idea. Knaws nowt about dogs.' The big man tipped about half a pint over his throat in one swallow.

'He's not a bad hand wi' cows,' another voice broke in.

'Aye, maybe, but I'm not talkin' about bloody awd cows,' Seth retorted witheringly. 'I'm talkin' about dogs. Ye need skill to doctor dogs.'

A third man spoke up. 'Well, 'e's a vitnery, isn't he?'

'Aye, a knaw he is, but there's all kind o' vitneries and this 'un's a dead loss. Ah could tell ye some tales about this feller.'

They say an eavesdropper never hears anything good about himself, and I knew the sensible thing would be to get out of there immediately rather than hear this man vilifying me in a crowded bar. But of course I didn't get out. I stayed, morbidly fascinated, listening with every nerve and fibre.

'What sort o' tales, Seth?' The company was as interested as I was.

'Well,' he replied. 'There's many a time folks 'ave brought dogs to me that he's made a mess of.'

'Tha knaws all about dogs, doesn't tha, Seth?'

It was perhaps wishful thinking that made me imagine a touch of sarcasm in the last remark, but if it were so it was lost on Mr Pilling. His big, stupid face creased into a self-satisfied smirk.

'Ah'll tell ye there's not a lot ah don't know about 'em. I've been among 'em all me life and I've studied t'job, too.' He slurped down more beer. 'I've got a houseful o' books and read 'em all. Ah ken everythin' about them diseases and the remedies.'

Another of the men in the bar spoke. 'Have ye never been beat wi' a dog job, Seth?'

There was a pause. 'Well ah'm not goin' to say I never 'ave,' he said judicially. 'It's very rare I'm beat, but if I am I don't go to Herriot.' He shook his head. 'Nay, nay, ah slip through to Brawton and consult wi' Dennaby Broome. He's a big friend o' mine.'

In the quiet of the snug I sipped at my glass. Dennaby Broome was one of the many 'quacks' who flourished in those days. He had started in the building trade – as a plasterer to be exact – and had gravitated mysteriously and without formal training into the field of veterinary science where he now made a comfortable living.

I had nothing against him for that – we all have to live. In any case he rarely bothered me because Brawton was mainly outside our practice orbit, but my colleagues around there used some unkind words about him. I had a private conviction that a lot of his success was due to his resounding name. To me, the very words 'Dennaby Broome' were profoundly imposing.

'Aye, that's what ah do,' Seth continued. 'Dennaby and me's big friends and we oft consult about dogs. Matter of fact ah took me own dog to 'im once – he looks well, eh?'

I stood on tiptoe and peered into the bar. I could just see Seth's keeshound sitting at his feet. A handsome creature with a luxuriant glossy coat. The big man leaned over and patted the fox-like head. 'He's a vallible animal is that. Ah couldn't trust 'im to a feller like Herriot.'

'What's the matter wi' Herriot, any road?' somebody asked.

'Well, ah'll tell tha.' Seth tapped his head. 'He hasn't got ower much up 'ere.'

I didn't want to hear any more. I put down my glass and stole out into the night.

After that experience I took more notice of Seth Pilling. He was often to be seen strolling round the town because, despite his vast store of knowledge on many subjects, he was frequently out of work. He wasn't an expert only on dogs – he pontificated in the Crown and Anchor on politics, gardening, cage birds, agriculture, the state of the economy, cricket, fishing and many other matters. There were few topics which his wide intellect did not effortlessly embrace, so that it was surprising that employers seemed to dispense with his services after a very brief period.

He usually took his dog with him on his strolls, and the attractive animal began to appear to me as a symbol of my shortcomings. Instinctively I kept out of his way but one morning I came right up against him.

It was at the little shelter in the market place and a group of people were waiting for the Brawton bus. Among them was Seth Pilling and the keeshound, and as I passed within a few feet of them on my way to the post office I stopped involuntarily and stared. The dog was almost unrecognisable.

The dense, off-standing ash-grey coat I knew so well had become sparse and lustreless. The thick ruff, so characteristic of the breed, had shrunk to nothing.

'You're lookin' at me dog?' Mr Pilling tightened the lead and pulled the little animal towards him protectively as though he feared I might put my contaminating hand on him.

'Yes . . . I'm sorry, but I couldn't help noticing. He has a skin condition . . .?'

The big man looked down his nose at me. 'Aye, 'e has, a bit. I'm just takin' him through to Brawton to see Dennaby Broome.'

'I see.'

'Yes, ah thought ah'd better take 'im to somebody as knows summat about dogs.' He smirked as he looked around at the people in the shelter who were listening with interest. 'He's a vallible dog is that.'

'I'm sure he is,' I said.

He raised his voice further. 'Mind you, ah've been givin' him some of me own treatment.' He didn't have to tell me. There was a strong smell of tar, and the dog's hair was streaked with some oily substance. 'But it's maybe better to make sure. We're lucky to 'ave a man like Dennaby Broome to turn to.'

'Quite.'

He looked around his audience appreciatively. 'Especially with a vallible dog like this. You can't 'ave any Tom Dick or Harry muckin' around with 'im.'

'Well,' I said. 'I hope you get him put right.'

'Oh, ah will.' The big man was enjoying the interlude, and he laughed. 'Don't *you* worry about *that*.'

This little session did not enliven my day, but it gave me more reason to watch out for Mr Pilling. For the next two weeks I observed his movements with the deepest interest because his dog was losing its hair at an alarming rate. Not only that, but the animal's whole demeanour had changed and instead of tripping along in his old sprightly way he dragged one foot after another as though he were on the point of death.

Towards the end of the period I was horrified to see the big man with something like a shorn ewe on the end of the lead. It was all that was left of the beautiful keeshound, but as I started to walk towards him his master spotted me and hurried off in the opposite direction, dragging the unfortunate animal behind him.

I did, however, succeed in having a look at the dog a few days afterwards. He was in the waiting room at Skeldale House, and this time he was accompanied by his mistress instead of his master.

Mrs Pilling was sitting very upright, and when I asked her to come through to the consulting room she jumped to her feet, marched past me and stumped quickly along the passage in front of me.

She was quite small, but broad hipped and stocky, and she always walked rapidly, her head nodding forward aggressively at each step, her jaw thrust out. She never smiled.

I had heard it said that Seth Pilling was a big talker outside, but under his own roof he was scared to death of his little wife. And as the tight-mouthed fiery-eyed face turned to me I could believe it.

She bent, pushed powerful arms under the keeshound and hoisted him on to the table.

'Just look at me good dog, Mr Herriot!' she rapped out.

I looked. 'Good heavens!' I gasped.

The little animal was almost completely bald. His skin was dry, scaly and wrinkled, and his head hung down as though he were under sedation.

'Aye, you're surprised, aren't you?' she barked. 'And no wonder. He's in a terrible state, isn't he?'

'I'm afraid so. I wouldn't have known him.'

'No, nobody would. Ah think the world 'o this dog and just look at 'im!' She paused and snorted a few times. 'And I know who's responsible, don't you?'

'Well . . .'

'Oh, you do. It's that husband o' mine.' She paused and glared at me, breathing rapidly. 'What d'you think of my husband, Mr Herriot?'

'I really don't know him very well. I . . .'

'Well ah know 'im and he's a gawp. He's a great gawp. Knows everything and knows nowt. He's played around wi' me good dog till he's ruined 'im.'

I didn't say anything. I was studying the keeshound. It was the first time I had been able to observe him closely and I was certain I knew the cause of his trouble.

Mrs Pilling stuck her jaw out further and continued.

'First me husband said it was eczema. Is it?'

'No.'

'Then 'e said it was mange. Is it?'

'No.'

'D'you know what it is?'

'Yes.'

'Well, will you tell me please?'

'It's myxoedema.'

'Myx . . .?'

'Wait a minute,' I said. 'I'll just make absolutely sure.' I reached for my stethoscope and put it on the dog's chest. And the bradycardia was there as I expected, the slow, slow heartbeat of hypothyriodism. 'Yes, that's it. Not a shadow of a doubt about it.'

'What did you call it?'

'Myxoedema. It's a thyroid deficiency – there's a gland in his neck which isn't doing its job properly.'

'And that makes 'is hair fall out?'

'Oh yes. And it also cuases this typical scaliness and wrinkling of the skin.'

'Aye, but he's half asleep all t'time. How about that?'

'Another classical symptom. Dogs with this condition become very lethargic – lose all their energy.'

She reached out and touched the dog's skin, bare and leathery where once the coat had grown in bushy glory. 'And can you cure it?'

'Yes.'

'Now Mr Herriot, don't take this the wrong way, but could you be mistaken? Are ye positive it's this myxi-whatever-it-is?'

'Of course I am. It's a straightforward case.'

'Straightforward to you, maybe.' She flushed and appeared to be grinding her teeth. 'But not straightforward to that clever husband o' mine. The great lubbert! When ah think what he's put me good dog through – ah could kill 'im.'

'Well, I suppose he thought he was acting for the best, Mrs Pilling.'

'Ah don't care what he thought, he's made this poor dog suffer, the big fool. Wait till ah get hold of 'im.'

I gave her a supply of tablets. 'These are thyroid extract, and I want you to give him one night and morning.' I also handed her a bottle of potassium iodide which I had found helpful in these cases.

She looked at me doubtfully. 'But surely he'll want summat rubbed on 'is skin.'

'No,' I replied. 'Applications to the skin do no good at all.'

'Then you mean.' She turned a dark purple colour and began snorting again. 'You mean all them bottles o' filthy stuff me husband put on 'im were a waste o' time?'

'Afraid so.'

'Oh ah'll murder 'im!' she burst out. 'Mucky, oily rubbish, it was. And that fancy feller in Brawton sent some 'orrible lotion – yeller it was, and stank the place out. Ruined me carpets and good chair covers an' all!'

Sulphur, whale oil and creosote, I thought. Splendid old fashioned ingredients, but quite useless in this case and definitely antisocial.

Mrs Pilling heaved the keeshound to the floor and strode along the passage, head down, powerful shoulders hunched. I could hear her muttering to herself as she went.

'By gaw, just wait till ah get home. Ah'll sort 'im, by gaw ah will!'

I was naturally interested in the progress of my patient, and when I failed to see him around for the next fortnight I could only conclude that Seth Pilling was keeping out of my way. Indeed there was one occasion when I thought I saw him and the dog disappearing down an alley, but I couldn't be sure.

When I did see them both it was by accident. I was driving round the corner into the market place and I came upon a man and dog coming away from one of the stalls on the cobbles.

And as I peered through the window I caught my breath. Even in that short space of time the animal's skin was covered with a healthy down of new hair, and he was stepping out with something very like his old vitality.

His master swung round as I slowed down. He gave me a single hunted look then tugged on the lead and scuttled away.

I could only imagine the turmoil in his mind, the conflict of emotions. No doubt he wanted to see his dog recover, but not this way. And as it turned out, the dice were loaded against the poor man because this was an unbelievably rapid recovery. I have seen some spectacular cures in myxoedema, but none so dramatic as that keeshound.

Mr Pilling's sufferings were communicated to me in various ways. For instance I heard he had changed his pub and now went to the Red Bear of an evening. In a little place like Darrowby, news fairly crackles around and I had a good idea that the farm men in the Crown and Anchor would have had a bit of quiet Yorkshire sport with the expert.

But his main martyrdom was at home. It was about six weeks after I had finished treating the dog that Mrs Pilling brought him to the surgery.

As before, she lifted him easily on to the table and looked at me, her face as always grim and unsmiling.

'Mr Herriot,' she said. 'Ah've just come to say thank ye, and ah thought you'd be interested to see me dog now.'

'I am indeed, Mrs Pilling. It's nice of you to come.' I gazed wonderingly at the thick coat, bushy, shining and new, and at the sparkling eyes and alert expression. 'I think you can say he's about back to normal.'

She nodded. 'That's what I thought and ah'm grateful to ye for what you've done.'

I walked with her to the front door and as she led her dog onto the street she turned her tough little face to me again. As the stern eyes met mine she looked very menacing.

'There's one thing,' she said. 'Ah'll never forgive that man o' mine for what he did to me dog. By gum, I've given 'im some stick, the great goof! He'll never hear the last of it from me.'

As she made off down the street, the little animal trotting briskly by her side, I brimmed with pleasant emotions. It is always warming to see a case recover so well, but in this instance there was an additional bonus.

For a long time little Mrs Pilling was going to give her husband pure hell.

Chapter Six

'Today,' said FO Woodham, 'We're going to try a few new things. Spinning, side-slipping and how to come out of a stall.' His voice was gentle, and before he pulled on his helmet he turned his dark, fine-featured face towards me and smiled. Walking over the grass I thought what a likeable chap he was. I could have made a friend of him.

But he was always like that on the ground. He was altogether different in the air.

Yet I could never understand it. Flying was no trouble at all, and as we spun and dropped and soared about the summer sky his instructions appeared simple and easy to carry out. But the rot, as always, began to set in very soon.

'Didn't I tell you opposite rudder and stick to sideslip?' he bawled over the intercom.

'Yes, sir,' was all I replied, instead of the more appropriate, 'That's just what I'm doing, you stupid bugger!' which I might have used in civil life.

The goggled eyes bulged in the mirror. 'Well why the bloody hell aren't you doing it?' His voice rose to a wild shriek.

'Sorry, sir.'

'Well take her up. We'll try again. And for God's sake keep your wits about you!'

It was the same with the spins and stalls. I hadn't the slightest difficulty in pulling out of them but at times I thought my instructor was going out of his mind.

Berserk cries rang in my ears. 'Full opposite rudder and centralise the stick! Centralise it! Can't you hear me? Oh God, God!'

And of course the panic gradually crept in and I began to crack. One moment

I could see a railway station in front of me whirling around in crazy circles, then there was nothing but the empty heavens and within seconds fields and trees would start to rush at me. Everything kept changing bewilderingly except the enraged eyes in the mirror and the exasperated yells.

'Centralise it, you bloody fool! Keep your eye on that cloud! Watch your artificial horizon! Don't you know what the altimeter's for? I told you to keep at 1,000 feet but it's like talking to a bloody wall!'

After a while a kind of numbness took over and the words rang meaninglessly in my head, one sentence seeming to contradict another. Desperately I tried to sort out the volleys of advice, but the whole thing began to slip from my grasp.

I had felt like this somewhere before. There was a familiar ring about this jumble in my brain. Then it came back to me. It was like being back at the Birtwhistles.

The trouble with the Birtwhistles was that they all spoke at once. Mr Birtwhistle invariably discussed his livestock, his wife concentrated on family matters and Len, their massive eighteen-year-old son, talked of nothing but football.

I was examining Nellie, the big white cow that always stood opposite the doorway in the grey stone byre. She had been lame for over a week and I didn't like the look of her.

'Lift her foot, will you, Len,' I said. It was wonderful to have a muscular giant to hoist the hind limb instead of going through the tedious business of hauling it up with a rope over a beam.

With the cloven hoof cradled in the great hands I could see that my fears were realised. The space between the cleats was clear but there was a significant swelling around the interphalangeal joint.

I looked up from my stooping position. 'Can you see that, Mr Birtwhistle? The infection is spreading upwards.'

'Aye . . . aye . . .' The farmer thrust a finger against the tumefied area and Nellie flinched. 'It's goin' up her leg on that side right enough. Ah thought it was nowt but a bit o' foul and I've been puttin' . . .'

'By gaw,' Len interjected. 'The lads 'ad a good win against Hellerby on Saturday. Johnnie Nudd got another couple o' goals and . . .'

'. . . puttin' that caustic lotion between 'er cleats.' Mr Birtwhistle didn't appear to have heard his son, but it was always like that. 'Done it regular night and morning'. And ah'll tell ye the best way to do it. Get a hen feather an' . . .'

'. . . ah wouldn't be surprised if 'e scores a few more this Saturday,' continued Len unheedingly. 'He's a right bobby dazzler when 'e . . .'

'. . . ye just dip it in t'lotion and push the feather in between t'cleats. It works like a . . .'

'. . . gets that ball on 'is right foot. He just whacks 'em in . . .'

I raised a hand. 'Wait a minute. You must realise this cow hasn't got foul. She has suppurative arthritis in this little joint just at the coronet here. I don't want to use a lot of big words but she has pus – matter – right inside the joint cavity, and it's a very nasty thing.'

Mr Birtwhistle nodded slowly. 'Sort of a abscess, you mean? Well, maybe it ud be best to lance it. Once you let t'matter out it would . . .'

'. . . just like a rocket,' went on Len. 'Ah'll tell ye, Johnnie could get a trial for Darlington one o' these days and then . . .'

I always think it is polite to look at a person when they are talking to you, but it is difficult when they are both talking at once, especially when one of them is bent double and the other standing behind you.

'Thank you, Len,' I said. 'You can put her foot down now.' I straightened up and directed my gaze somewhere between them. 'The trouble with this condition is that you can't just stick a knife into it and relieve it. Very often the smooth surfaces of the joint are eaten away and it's terribly painful.'

Nellie would agree with me. It was the outside cleat which was affected and she was standing with her leg splayed sideways in an attempt to take the weight on the healthy inner digit.

The farmer asked the inevitable question. 'Well, what are we goin' to do?'

I had an uncomfortable conviction that it wasn't going to make much difference what we did, but I had to make an effort.

'We'll give her a course of sulphanilamide powders and I also want you to put a poultice on that foot three times daily.'

'Poultice?' The farmer brightened. 'Ah've been doin' that. Ah've been . . .'

'If Darlington signed Johnnie Nudd I reckon . . .'

'Hold on, Len,' I said. 'What poultice have you been using, Mr Birtwhistle?'

'Cow shit,' the farmer replied confidently. 'Ye can't beat a good cow shit poultice to bring t'bad out. Ah've used it for them bad cases o' . . .'

'. . . ah'd have to go through to Darlington now and then instead of watchin' the Kestrels,' Len broke in. 'Ah'd have to see how Johnnie was gettin' on wi' them professionals because . . .'

I managed a twisted smile. I like football myself and I found it touching that Len ignored the great panorama of league football to concentrate on a village team who played in front of about twenty spectators. 'Yes, yes, Len, I quite understand how you feel.' Then I turned to his father. 'I was thinking of a rather different type of poultice, Mr Birtwhistle.'

The farmer's face lengthened and the corners of his mouth drooped. 'Well, ah've never found owt better than cow shit and ah've been among stock all my life.'

I clenched my teeth. This earthy medicament was highly regarded among the Dales farmers of the thirties and the damnable thing was that it often achieved its objective. There was no doubt that a sackful of bovine faeces applied to an inflamed area set up a tremendous heat and counter-irritation. In those days I had to go along with many of the ancient cures and keep my tongue between my teeth but I had never prescribed cow shit and I wasn't going to start now.

'Maybe so,' I said firmly, 'But what I was thinking of was kaolin. You could call down at the surgery for some. You just heat the tin in a pan of hot water and apply the poultice to the foot. It keeps its heat for several hours.'

Mr Birtwhistle showed no great enthusiasm so I tried again.

'Or you could use bran. I see you've got a sack over there.'

He cheered up a little. 'Aye . . . that's right.'

'Okay, put on some hot bran three times a day and give her the powders and I'll see her again in a few days.' I knew the farmer would do as I said, because he was a conscientious stockman, but I had seen cases like this before and I wasn't happy. Nothing seems to pull a good cow down quicker than a painful foot. Big fat animals could be reduced to skeletons within weeks because of the agony of septic arthritis. I could only hope.

'Very good, Mr Herriot,' Mr Birtwhistle said. 'And now come into the house. T'missus has a cup o' tea ready for you.'

I seldom refuse such an invitation but as I entered the kitchen I knew this was where the going got really tough.

'Now then, Mr Herriot,' the farmer's wife said, beaming as she handed me a steaming mug. 'I was talkin' to your good lady in the market place yesterday, and she said . . .'

'And ye think them powders o' yours might do the trick?' Her husband looked at me seriously. 'I 'ope so, because Nellie's a right good milker. Ah reckon last lactation she gave . . .'

'Kestrels is drawn agin Dibham in t'Hulton cup.' Len chimed in. 'It'll be some game. Last time . . .'

Mrs Birtwhistle continued without drawing breath. '. . . you were nicely settled in at top of Skeldale House. It must be right pleasant up there with the lovely view and . . .'

'. . . five gallons when she fust calved and she kept it up for . . .'

'. . . they nearly kicked us off t'pitch, but by gaw ah'll tell ye, we'll . . .'

'. . . you can see right over Darrowby. But it wouldn't do for a fat body like me. I was sayin' to your missus that you 'ave to be young and slim to live up there. All them stairs and . . .'

I took a long draught from my cup. It gave me a chance to focus my eyes and attention on just one thing as the conversation crackled unceasingly around me. I invariably found it wearing trying to listen to all three Birtwhistles in full cry and of course it was impossible to look at them all simultaneously and adjust my expression to their different remarks.

The thing that amazed me was that none of them ever became angry at the others butting in. Nobody ever said, 'I'm speaking, do you mind?' or 'Don't interrupt!' or 'For Pete's sake, shut up!' They lived together in perfect harmony with all of them talking at once and none paying the slightest heed to what the other was saying.

When I saw the cow during the following week she was worse. Mr Birtwhistle had followed my instructions faithfully but Nellie could scarcely hobble as he brought her in from the field.

Len was there to lift the foot and I gloomily surveyed the increased swelling. It ran right round the coronet from the heel to the interdigital cleft in front, and the slightest touch from my finger caused the big cow to jerk her leg in pain.

I didn't say much, because I knew what was in store for Nellie and I knew too, that Mr Birtwhistle wasn't going to like it when I told him.

When I visited again at the end of the week I had only to look at the farmer's face to realise that everything had turned out as I feared. For once he was on his own and he led me silently into the byre.

Nellie was on three legs now, not daring even to bring the infected foot into momentary contact with the cobbled flooring. And worse, she was in an advanced state of emaciation, the sleek healthy animal of two weeks ago reduced to little more than bone and hide.

'I doubt she's 'ad it,' Mr Birtwhistle muttered.

Cow's hind feet are difficult to lift, but today I didn't need any help because Nellie had stopped caring. I examined the swollen digit. It was now vast – a great ugly club of tissue with a trickle of pus discharging down the wall.

'I see it's bust there.' The farmer poked a finger at the ragged opening. 'But it hasn't given 'er no relief.'

'Well, I wouldn't expect it to,' I said. 'Remember I told you the trouble is all inside the joint.'

'Well, these things 'appen,' he replied. 'Ah might as well telephone for Mallock. She's hardly givin' a drop o' milk, poor awd lass, she's nowt but a screw now.'

I always had to wait for the threat of the knacker man's humane killer before I said what I had to say now. Right from the start this had been a case for surgery, but it would have been a waste of time to suggest it at the beginning. Amputation of the bovine digit has always filled farmers with horror and even now I knew I would have trouble convincing Mr Birtwhistle.

'There's no need to slaughter her,' I said. 'There's another way of curing this.'

'Another way? We've tried 'ard enough, surely.'

I bent and lifted the foot again. 'Look at this.' I seized the inner cleat and moved it freely around. 'This side is perfectly healthy. There's nothing wrong with it. It would bear Nellie's full weight.'

'Aye, but . . . how about t'other 'orrible thing?'

'I could remove it.'

'You mean . . . cut it off?'

'Yes.'

He shook his head vigorously 'Nay, nay, I'm not havin' that. She's suffered enough. Far better send for Jeff Mallock and get the job over.'

Here it was again. Farmers are anything but shrinking violets, but there was something about this business which appalled them.

'But Mr Birtwhistle,' I said. 'Don't you see – the pain is immediately relieved. The pressure is off and all the weight rests on the good side.'

'Ah said no, Mr Herriot, and ah mean no. You've done your best and I thank ye, but I'm not havin' her foot cut off and that's all about it.' He turned and began to walk away.

I looked after him helplessly. One thing I hate to do is talk a man into an operation on one of his beasts for the simple reason that if anything goes wrong I get the blame. But I was just about certain that an hour's work could restore this good cow to her former state, I couldn't let it go at this.

I trotted from the byre. The farmer was already half way across the yard on his way to the phone.

I panted up to him as he reached the farmhouse door. 'Mr Birtwhistle, listen to me for a minute. I never said anything about cutting off her foot. Just one cleat.'

'Well that's half a foot, isn't it?' he looked down at his boots. 'And it's ower much for me.'

'But she wouldn't know a thing,' I pleaded. 'She'd be under a general anaesthetic. And I'm nearly sure it would be a success.'

'Mr Herriot, I just don't fancy it. I don't like t'idea. And even if it did work it would be like havin' a crippled cow walkin' about.'

'Not at all. She would grow a little stump of horn there and I'd like to bet you'd never notice a thing.'

He gave me a long sideways look and I could see he was weakening.

'Mr Birtwhistle,' I said, pressing home the attack. 'Within a month Nellie could be a fat cow again, giving five gallons of milk a day.'

This was silly talk, not to be recommended to any veterinary surgeon, but I was seized by a kind of madness. I couldn't bear the thought of that cow being cut up for dog food when I was convinced I could put her right. And there was another thing; I was already savouring the pleasure, childish perhaps, of instantly relieving an animal's pain, of bringing off a spectacular cure. There aren't many operations in the field of bovine surgery where you can do this but digit amputation is one of them.

Something of my fervour must have been communicated to the farmer because he looked at me steadily for a few moments then shrugged.

'When do you want to do it?' he asked.

'Tomorrow.'

'Right. Will you need a lot o' fellers to help?'

'No, just you and Len. I'll see you at ten o'clock.'

Next day the sun was warm on my back as I laid out my equipment on a small field near the house. It was a typical setting for many large animal operations I have carried out over the years; the sweet stretch of green, the grey stone buildings and the peaceful bulk of the fells rising calm and unheeding into the white scattering of clouds.

It took a long time for them to lead Nellie out, though she didn't have far to go, and as the bony scarecrow hopped painfully towards me, dangling her useless limb, the brave words of yesterday seemed foolhardy.

'All right,' I said. 'Stop there. That's a good spot.' On the grass, nearby, lay my tray with the saw, chloroform, bandages, cotton wool and iodoform. I had my long casting rope too, which we used to pull cattle down, but I had a feeling Nellie wouldn't need it.

I was right. I buckled on the muzzle, poured some chloroform on to the sponge and the big white cow sank almost thankfully on to the cool green herbage.

'Kestrels had a smashin' match on Wednesday night,' Len chuckled happily. 'Johnnie Nudd didn't score but Len Bottomley . . .'

'I 'ope we're doin' t'right thing,' muttered Mr Birtwhistle. 'The way she staggered out 'ere I'd say it was a waste of time to . . .'

'. . . cracked in a couple o' beauties.' Len's face lit up at the memory. 'Kestrels is lucky to 'ave two fellers like . . .'

'Get hold of that bad foot, Len!' I barked, playing them at their own game. 'And keep it steady on that block of wood. And you, Mr Birtwhistle, hold her head down. I don't suppose she'll move, but if she does we'll have to give her more chloroform.'

Cows are good subjects for chloroform anaesthesia but I don't like to keep them laid out too long in case of regurgitation of food. I was in a hurry.

I quickly tied a bandage above the hoof, pulling it tight to serve as a tourniquet, then I reached back to the tray for the saw. The books are full of sophisticated methods of digit amputation with much talk of curved incisions, reflections of skin to expose the region of the articulations, and the like. But I have whipped off hundreds of cleats with a few brisk strokes of the saw below the coronary band with complete success.

I took a long breath. 'Hold tight, Len.' And set to work.

For a few moments there was silence except for the rhythmic grating of metal on bone, then the offending digit was lying on the grass, leaving a flat stump from which a few capillary vessels spurted. Using curved scissors I speedily disarticulated the remains of the pedal bone from the second phalanx and held it up.

'Look at that!' I cried. 'Almost eaten away.' I pointed to the necrotic tissue in and around the joint. 'And d'you see all that rubbish? No wonder she was in pain.' I did a bit of quick curetting, dusted the surface with iodoform, applied a thick pad of cotton wool and prepared to bandage.

And as I tore the paper from the white rolls I felt a stab of remorse. In my absorption I had been rather rude. I had never replied to Len's remark about his beloved team. Maybe I could pass the next few minutes with a little gentle banter.

'Hey Len,' I said. 'When you're talking about the Kestrels you never mentioned the time Willerton beat them five nil. How is that?'

In reply the young man hurled himself unhesitatingly at me, butting me savagely on the forehead. The assault of the great coarse-haired head against my skin was like being attacked by a curly-polled bull, and the impact sent me flying backwards on to the grass. At first the inside of my cranium was illuminated by a firework display but as consciousness slipped away my last sensation was of astonishment and disbelief.

I loved football myself but never had I thought that Len's devotion to the

Kestrels would lead him to physical violence. He had always seemed a most gentle and harmless boy.

I suppose I was out for only a few seconds but I fancy I might have spent a good deal longer lying on the cool turf but for the fact that something kept hammering out the message that I was in the middle of a surgical procedure. I blinked and sat up.

Nellie was still sleeping peacefully against the green background of hills. Mr Birtwhistle, hands on her neck, was regarding me anxiously, and Len was lying unconscious face down across the cow's body.

'Has he hurt tha, Mr Herriot?'

'No ... no ... not really. What happened?'

'I owt to have told ye. He can't stand the sight o' blood. Great daft beggar.' The farmer directed an exasperated glare at his slumbering son. 'But ah've never seen 'im go down as fast as that. Pitched right into you, 'e did!'

I rolled the young man's inert form to one side and began again. I bandaged slowly and carefully because of the danger of post operative haemorrhage. I finished with several layers of zinc oxide plaster then turned to the farmer.

'You can take her muzzle off now, Mr Birtwhistle. The job's done.'

I was starting to wash my instruments in the bucket when Len sat up almost as suddenly as he had slumped down. He was deathly pale but he looked at me with his usual friendly smile.

'What was that ye were sayin' about t'Kestrels, Mr Herriot?'

'Nothing, Len,' I replied hastily. 'Nothing át all.'

After three days I returned and removed the original dressing which was caked hard with blood and pus. I dusted the stump with powder again and bandaged on a clean soft pad of cotton wool.

'She'll feel a lot more comfortable now,' I said, and indeed Nellie was already looking vastly happier. She was taking some weight on the affected foot – rather gingerly, as though she couldn't believe that terrible thing had gone from her life.

As she walked away I crossed my fingers. The only thing that can ruin these operations is if the infection spreads to the other side. The inevitable result then is immediate slaughter and terrible disappointment.

But it never happened to Nellie. When I took off the second dressing she was almost sound and I didn't see her again until about five weeks after the operation.

I had finished injecting one of Mr Birtwhistle's pigs when I asked casually, 'And how's Nellie?'

'Come and 'ave a look at her,' the farmer replied. 'She's just in that field at side of t'road.'

We walked together over the grass to where the white cow was standing among her companions, head down, munching busily. And she must have done a lot of that since I saw her because she was fat again.

'Get on, lass.' The farmer gently nudged her rump with his thumb and she ambled forward a few places before setting to work on another patch of grass. There wasn't the slightest trace of lameness.

'Well, that's grand,' I said. 'And is she milking well, too?'

'Aye, back to five gallons.' He pulled a much dented tobacco tin from his pocket, unscrewed the lid and produced an ancient watch. 'It's ten o'clock, young man. Len'll have gone into t'house for his tea, and 'lowance. Will ye come in and have a cup?'

I squared my shoulders and followed him inside, and the barrage began immediately.

'Summat right funny happened on Saturday,' Len said with a roar of laughter.

'Walter Gimmett was refereein' and 'e gave two penalties agin t'Kestrels. So what did the lads do, they . . .'

'Eee, wasn't it sad about old Mr Brent?' Mrs Birtwhistle put her head on one side and looked at me piteously. 'We buried 'im on Saturday and . . .'

'You know, Mr Herriot,' her husband put in. 'Ah thought you were pullin' ma leg when you said Nellie would be givin' five gallons again. I never . . .'

'. . . dumped the beggar in a 'oss trough. He won't give no more penalties agin t'Kestrels. You should 'ave seen . . .'

'. . . it would 'ave been his ninetieth birthday today, poor old man. He was well liked in t'village and there was a big congregation. Parson said . . .'

'. . . expected owt like that. Ah thought she might maybe put on a bit of flesh so we could get 'er off for beef. Ah'm right grateful to . . .'

At that moment, fingers clenched tensely around my cup, I happened to catch sight of my reflection in a cracked mirror above the kitchen sink. It was a frightening experience because I was staring glassily into space with my features contorted almost out of recognition. There was something of an idiot smile as I acknowledged the humour of Walter in the horse trough, a touch of sorrow at Mr Brent's demise, and, I swear, a suggestion of gratification at the successful outcome of Nellie's operation. And since I was also trying to look in three directions at once, I had to give myself full marks for effort.

But as I say, I found it a little unnerving and excused myself soon afterwards. The men were still busy with Mrs Birtwhistle's apple pie and scones and the conversation was raging unabated when I left. The closure of the door behind me brought a sudden peace. The feeling of tranquillity stayed with me as I got into my car and drove out of the yard and onto the narrow country road. It persisted as I stopped the car after less than a hundred yards and wound down the window to have a look at my patient.

Nellie was lying down now. She had eaten her fill and was resting comfortably on her chest as she chewed her cud. To a doctor of farm animals there is nothing more reassuring than that slow lateral grinding. It means contentment and health. She gazed at me across the stone wall and the placid eyes in the white face added to the restfulness of the scene, accentuating the silence after the babel of voices in the farmhouse.

Nellie couldn't talk, but those calmly moving jaws told me all I wanted to know.

Chapter Seven

To me there are few things more appealing than a dog begging. This one was tied to a lamp post outside a shop in Windsor. Its eyes were fixed steadfastly on the shop doorway, willing its owner to come out, and every now and then it sat up in mute entreaty.

Flying had been suspended for an afternoon. It gave us all a chance to relax and no doubt it eased the frayed nerves of our instructors, but as I looked at that dog all the pressures of the RAF fell away and I was back in Darrowby.

It was when Siegfried and I were making one of our market day sorties that we noticed the little dog among the stalls.

When things were quiet in the surgery we often used to walk together across the cobbles and have a word with the farmers gathered round the doorway of the Drovers' Arms. Sometimes we collected a few outstanding bills or drummed up a bit of work for the forthcoming week – and if nothing like that happened we still enjoyed the fresh air.

The thing that made us notice the dog was that he was sitting up begging in front of the biscuit stall.

'Look at that little chap,' Siegfried said. 'I wonder where he's sprung from.'

As he spoke, the stallholder threw a biscuit which the dog devoured eagerly but when the man came round and stretched out a hand the little animal trotted away.

He stopped, however, at another stall which sold produce; eggs, cheese, butter, cakes and scones. Without hesitation he sat up again in the begging position, rock steady, paws dangling, head pointing expectantly.

I nudged Siegfried. 'There he goes again.'

My colleague nodded. 'Yes, he's an engaging little thing, isn't he? What breed would you call him?'

'A cross, I'd say. He's like a little brown sheepdog, but there's a touch of something else – maybe terrier.'

It wasn't long before he was munching a bun, and this time we walked over to him. And as we drew near I spoke gently.

'Here, boy,' I said, squatting down a yard away. 'Come on, let's have a look at you.'

He faced me and for a moment two friendly brown eyes gazed at me from a singularly attractive little face. The fringed tail waved in response to my words but as I inched nearer he turned and ambled unhurriedly among the market day crowd till he was lost to sight. I didn't want to make a thing out of the encounter because I could never quite divine Siegfried's attitude to the small animals. He was eminently wrapped up in his horse work and often seemed amused at the way I rushed around after dogs and cats.

At that time, in fact, Siegfried was strongly opposed to the whole idea of keeping animals as pets. He was quite vociferous on the subject – said it was utterly foolish – despite the fact that five assorted dogs travelled everywhere with him in his car. Now, thirty-five years later, he is just as strongly in favour of keeping pets, though he now carries only one dog in his car. So, as I say, it was difficult to assess his reactions in this field and I refrained from following the little animal.

I was standing there when a young policeman came up to me.

'I've been watching that little dog begging among the stalls all morning,' he said. 'But like you, I haven't been able to get near him.'

'Yes, it's strange. He's obviously friendly, yet he's afraid. I wonder who owns him.'

'I reckon he's a stray, Mr Herriot. I'm interested in dogs myself and I fancy I know just about all of them around here. But this 'un's a stranger to me.'

I nodded. 'I bet you're right. So anything could have happened to him. He could have been ill-treated by somebody and run away, or he could have been dumped from a car.'

'Yes,' he replied 'There's some lovely people around. It beats me how anybody can leave a helpless animal to fend for itself like that. I've had a few goes at catching him myself but it's no good.'

The memory stayed with me for the rest of the day and even when I lay in bed that night I was unable to dispel the disturbing image of the little brown creature wandering in a strange world, sitting up asking for help in the only way he knew.

I was still a bachelor at that time and on the Friday night of the same week Siegfried and I were arraying outselves in evening dress in preparation for the Hunt Ball at East Hirdsley, about ten miles away.

It was a tortuous business because those were the days of starched shirt fronts and stiff high collars and I kept hearing explosions of colourful language from Siegfried's room as he wrestled with his studs.

I was in an even worse plight because I had outgrown my suit and even when I had managed to secure the strangling collar I had to fight my way into the dinner jacket which nipped me cruelly under the arms. I had just managed to don the complete outfit and was trying out a few careful breaths when the phone rang.

It was the same young policeman I had been speaking to earlier in the week. 'We've got that dog round here, Mr Herriot. You know – the one that was begging in the market place.'

'Oh yes? Somebody's managed to catch him, then?'

There was a pause. 'No, not really. One of our men found him lying by the roadside about a mile out of town and brought him in. He's been in an accident.'

I told Siegfried. He looked at his watch. 'Always happens, doesn't it, James. Just when we're ready to go out. It's nine o'clock now and we should be on our way.' He thought for a moment. 'Anyway, slip round there and have a look and I'll wait for you. It would be better if we could go to this affair together.'

As I drove round to the Police Station I hoped fervently that there wouldn't be much to do. This Hunt Ball meant a lot to my boss because it would be a gathering of the horse-loving fraternity of the district and he would have a wonderful time just chatting and drinking with so many kindred spirits even though he hardly danced at all. Also, he maintained, it was good for business to meet the clients socially.

The kennels were at the bottom of a yard behind the Station and the policeman led me down and opened one of the doors. The little dog was lying very still under the single electric bulb and when I bent and stroked the brown coat his tail stirred briefly among the straw of his bed.

'He can still manage a way, anyway,' I said.

The policeman nodded. 'Aye, there's no doubt he's a good-natured little thing.'

I tried to examine him as much as possible without touching. I didn't want to hurt him and there was no saying what the extent of his injuries might be. But even at a glance certain things were obvious; he had multiple lacerations, one hind leg was crooked in the unmistakable posture of a fracture and there was blood on his lips.

This could be from damaged teeth and I gently raised the head with a view to looking into his mouth. He was lying on his right side and as the head came round it was as though somebody had struck me in the face.

The right eye had been violently dislodged from its socket and it spouted like some hideous growth from above the cheek bone, a great glistening orb with the eyelids tucked behind the white expanse of sclera.

I seemed to squat there for a long time, stunned by the obscenity, and as the seconds dragged by I looked into the little dog's face and he looked back at me – trustingly from one soft brown eye, glaring meaninglessly from the grotesque ball on the other side.

The policeman's voice broke my thoughts. 'He's a mess, isn't he?'

'Yes . . . yes . . . must have been struck by some vehicle – maybe dragged along by the look of all those wounds.'

'What d'you think, Mr Herriot?'

I knew what he meant. It was the sensible thing to ease this lost unwanted creature from the world. He was grievously hurt and he didn't seem to belong to anybody. A quick overdose of anaesthetic – his troubles would be over and I'd be on my way to the dance.

But the policemean didn't say anything of the sort. Maybe, like me, he was looking into the soft depths of that one trusting eye.

I stood up quickly. 'Can I use your phone?'

At the other end of the line Siegfried's voice crackled with impatience. 'Hell, James, it's half-past nine! If we're going to this thing we've got to go now or we might as well not bother. A stray dog, badly injured. It doesn't sound such a great problem.'

'I know, Siegfried. I'm sorry to hold you up but I can't make up my mind. I wish you'd come round and tell me what you think.'

There was a silence then a long sigh. 'All right, James. See you in five minutes.'

He created a slight stir as he entered the Station. Even in his casual working clothes Siegfied always managed to look distinguished, but as he swept into the station newly bathed and shaved, a camel coat thrown over the sparkling white shirt and black tie there was something ducal about him.

He drew respectful glances from the men sitting around, then my young policeman stepped forward.

'This way, sir' he said, and we went back to the kennels.

Siegfried was silent as he crouched over the dog, looking him over as I had done without touching him. Then he carefully raised the head and the monstrous eye glared.

'My God!' he said softly, and at the sound of his voice the long fringed tail moved along the ground.

For a few seconds he stayed very still looking fixedly at the dog's face while in the silence, the whisking tail rustled the straw.

Then he straightened up. 'Let's get him round there,' he murmured.

In the surgery we anaesthetised the little animal and as he lay unconscious on the table we were able to examine him thoroughly. After a few minutes Siegfried stuffed his stethoscope into the pocket of his white coat and leaned both hands on the table.

'Luxated eyeball, fractured femur, umpteen deep lacerations, broken claws. There's enough here to keep us going till midnight, James.'

I didn't say anything.

My boss pulled the knot from his black tie and undid the front stud. He peeled off the stiff collar and hung it on the cross bar of the surgery lamp.

'By God, that's better,' he muttered, and began to lay out suture materials.

I looked at him across the table. 'How about the Hunt Ball?'

'Oh bugger the Hunt Ball,' Siegfried said. 'Let's get busy.'

We were busy, too, for a long time. I hung up my collar next to my colleague's and we began on the eye. I know we both felt the same – we wanted to get rid of that horror before we did anything else.

I lubricated the great ball and pulled the eyelids apart while Siegfried gently manoeuvred it back into the orbital cavity. I sighed as everything slid out of sight, leaving only the cornea visible.

Siegfried chuckled with satisfaction. 'Looks like an eye again, doesn't it.' He seized an ophthalmoscope and peered into the depths.

'And there's no major damage – could be as good as new again. But we'll just stitch the lids together to protect it for a few days.'

The broken ends of the fractured tibia were badly displaced and we had a struggle to bring them into apposition before applying the plaster of paris. But at last we finished and started on the long job of stitching the many cuts and lacerations.

We worked separately for this, and for a long time it was quiet in the operating room except for the snip of scissors as we clipped the brown hair away from the wounds. I knew and Siegfried knew that we were almost certainly working without payment, but the most disturbing thought was that after all our efforts we might still have to put him down. He was still in the care of the police and if nobody claimed him within ten days it meant euthanasia. And if his late owners were really interested in his fate, why hadn't they tried to contact the police before now ...

By the time we had completed our work and washed the instruments it was after midnight. Siegfried dropped the last suture needle into its tray and looked at the sleeping animal.

'I think he's beginning to come round,' he said. 'Let's take him through to the fire and we can have a drink while he recovers.'

We stretchered the dog through to the sitting-room on a blanket and laid him on the rug before the brightly burning coals. My colleague reached a long arm up to the glass-fronted cabinet above the mantelpiece and pulled down the whisky bottle and two glasses. Drinks in hand, collarless, still in shirt sleeves, with our starched white fronts and braided evening trousers to remind us of the lost dance we lay back in our chairs on either side of the fireplace and between us our patient stretched peacefully.

He was a happier sight now. One eye was closed by the protecting stitches and his hind leg projected stiffly in its white cast, but he was tidy, cleaned up, cared for. He look as though he belonged to somebody – but then there was a great big doubt about that.

It was nearly one o'clock in the morning and we were getting well down the bottle when the shaggy brown head began to move.

Siegfried leaned forward and touched one of the ears and immediately the tail flapped against the rug and a pink tongue lazily licked his fingers.

'What an absolutely grand little dog,' he murmured, but his voice had a distant quality. I knew he was worried too.

I took the stiches out of the eyelids in two days and was delighted to find a normal eye underneath.

The young policeman was as pleased as I was. 'Look at that!' he exclaimed. 'You'd never know anything had happened there.'

'Yes, it's done wonderfully well. All the swelling and inflammation has gone.' I hesitated for a moment. 'Has anybody enquired about him?'

He shook his head. 'Nothing yet. But there's anothing eight days to go and we're taking good care of him here.'

I visited the Police Station several times and the little animal greeted me with undisguised joy, all his fear gone, standing upright against my legs on his plastered limb, his tail swishing.

But all the time my sense of foreboding increased, and on the tenth day I made my way almost with dread to the police kennels. I had heard nothing. My course of action seemed inevitable. Putting down old or hopelessly ill dogs was often an act of mercy but when it was a young healthy dog it was terrible. I hated it, but it was one of the things veterinary surgeons had to do.

The young policeman was standing in the doorway.

'Still no news?' I asked, and he shook his head.

I went past him into the kennel and the shaggy little creature stood up against my legs as before, laughing into my face, mouth open, eyes shining.

I turned away quickly. I'd have to do this right now or I'd never do it.

'Mr Herriot.' The policeman put his hand on my arm. 'I think I'll take him.'

'You?' I stared at him.

'Aye, that's right. We get a lot o' stray dogs in here and though I feel sorry for them you can't give them all a home, can you?'

'No, you can't,' I said. 'I have the same problem.'

He nodded slowly. 'But somehow this 'un's different, and it seems to me he's just come at the right time. I have two little girls and they've been at me for a bit to get 'em a dog. This little bloke looks just right for the job.'

Warm relief began to ebb through me. 'I couldn't agree more. He's the soul of good nature. I bet he'll be wonderful with children.'

'Good. That's settled then. I thought I'd ask your advice first.' He smiled happily.

I looked at him as though I had never seen him before, 'What's your name?'

'Phelps,' he replied. 'PC Phelps.'

He was a good-looking young fellow, clear-skinned, with cheerful blue eyes and a solid dependable look about him. I had to fight against an impulse to wring his hand and thump him on the back. But I managed to preserve the professional exterior.

'Well, that's fine.' I bent and stroked the little dog. 'Don't forget to bring him along to the surgery in ten days for removal of the stitches, and we'll have to get that plaster off in about a month.'

It was Siegfried who took out the stitches, and I didn't see our patient again until four weeks later.

PC Phelps had his little girls, aged four and six, with him as well as the dog.

'You said the plaster ought to come off about now,' he said, and I nodded.

He looked down at the children. 'Well, come on, you two, lift him on the table.'

Eagerly the little girls put their arms around their new pet and as they hoisted him the tail wagged furiously and the wide mouth panted in delight.

'Looks as though he's been a success,' I said.

He smiled. 'That's an understatement. He's perfect with these two. I can't tell you what pleasure he's given us. He's one of the family.'

I got out my little saw and began to hack at the plaster.

'It's worked both ways, I should say. A dog loves a secure home.'

'Well, he couldn't be more secure.' He ran his hand along the brown coat and laughed as he addressed the little dog. 'That's what you get for begging among the stalls on market day, my lad. You're in the hands of the law now.'

Chapter Eight

When I entered the RAF I had a secret fear. All my life I have suffered from vertigo and even now I have only to look down from the smallest height to be engulfed by that dreadful dizziness and panic. What would I feel, then, when I started to fly?

As it turned out, I felt nothing. I could gaze downwards from the open cockpit through thousands of feet of space without a qualm, so my fear was groundless.

I had my fears in veterinary practice, too, and in the early days the thing which raised the greatest terror in my breast was the Ministry of Agriculture.

An extraordinary statement, perhaps, but true. It was the clerical side that scared me – all those forms. As to the practical Ministry work itself, I felt in all modesty that I was quite good at it. My thoughts often turned back to all the tuberculin testing I used to do – clipping a clean little area from just the right place in the cow's neck, inserting the needle into the thickness of the skin and injecting one tenth of a c.c. of tuberculin.

It was on Mr Hill's farm, and I watched the satisfactory intradermal 'pea' rise up under my needle. That was the way it should be, and when it came up like that you knew you were really doing your job and testing the animal for tuberculosis.

'That 'un's number 65,' the farmer said, then a slightly injured look spread over his face as I checked the number in the ear.

'You're wastin' your time, Mr Herriot. I 'ave the whole list, all in t'correct order. Wrote it out special for you so you could take it away with you.'

I had my doubts. All farmers were convinced that their herd records were flawless but I had been caught out before. I seemed to have the gift of making every possible clerical mistake and I didn't need any help from the farmers.

But still . . . it was tempting. I looked at the long list of figures dangling from the horny fingers. If I accepted it I would save a lot of time. There were still more than fifty animals to test here and I had to get through two more herds before lunch time.

I looked at my watch. Damn! I was well behind my programme and I felt the old stab of frustration.

'Right, Mr Hill, I'll take it and thank you very much.' I stuffed the sheet of paper into my pocket and began to move along the byre, clipping and injecting at top speed.

A week later the dread words leaped out at me from the open day book. 'Ring Min.' The cryptic phrase in Miss Harbottle's writing had the power to freeze my blood quicker than anything else. It meant simply that I had to telephone the Ministry of Agriculture office, and whenever our secretary wrote those words in the book it meant that I was in trouble again. I extended a trembling hand towards the receiver.

As always, Kitty Pattison answered my call and I could detect the note of pity in her voice. She was the attractive girl in charge of the office staff and she knew all about my misdemeanours. In fact when it was something very trivial she sometimes brought it to my attention herself, but when I had really dropped a large brick I was dealt with by the boss, Charles Harcourt the Divisional Inspector.

'Ah, Mr Herriot,' Kitty said lightly. I knew she sympathised with me but she couldn't do a thing about it. 'Mr Harcourt wants a word with you.'

There it was. The terrible sentence that always set my heart thumping.

'Thank you,' I said huskily, and waited an eternity as the phone was switched through.

'Herriot!' The booming voice made me jump.

I swallowed. 'Good morning, Mr Harcourt. How are you?'

'I'll tell you how I am, I'm bloody annoyed!' I could imagine vividly the handsome, high-coloured, choleric face flushing deeper, the greenish eyes glaring. 'In fact I'm hopping bloody mad!'

'Oh.'

'It's no use saying "oh". That's what you said the last time when you tested that cow of Frankland's that had been dead for two years! That was very clever – I don't know how you managed it. Now I've been going over your test at Hill's of High View and there are two cows here that you've tested – numbers

74 and 103. Now our records show that he sold both of them at Brawton Auction Mart six months ago, so you've performed another miracle.'

'I'm sorry . . .'

'Please don't be sorry, it's bloody marvellous how you do it. I have all the figures here – skin measurements, the lot. I see you found they were both thin-skinned animals even though they were about fifteen miles away at the time. Clever stuff!'

'Well I . . .'

'All right, Herriot, I'll dispense with the comedy. I'm going to tell you once more, for the last time, and I hope you're listening.' He paused and I could almost see the big shoulders hunching as he barked into the phone. '*Look in the bloody ears in future!*'

I broke into a rapid gabble. 'I will indeed, Mr Harcourt, I assure you from now on . . .'

'All right, all right, but there's something else.'

'Something else?'

'Yes, I'm not finished yet.' The voice took on a great weariness. 'Can I ask you to cast your mind back to that cow you took under the TB order from Wilson of Low Parks?'

I dug my nails into my palm. We were heading for deep water. 'Yes – I remember it.'

'Well now, Herriot, lad, do you remember a little chat we had about the forms?' Charles was trying to be patient, because he was a decent man, but it was costing him dearly. 'Didn't anything I told you sink in?'

'Well, yes, of course.'

'Then why, why didn't you sent me a receipt for slaughter?'

'Receipt for . . . didn't I . . .?'

'No, you didn't,' he said. 'And honestly I can't understand it. I went over it with you step by step last time when you forgot to forward a copy of the valuation agreement.'

'Oh dear, I really am sorry.'

A deep sigh came from the other end. 'And there's nothing to it.' He paused. 'Tell you what we'll do. Let's go over the procedure once more, shall we?'

'Yes, by all means.'

'Very well,' he said. 'First of all, when you find an infected animal you serve B. 205 DT Form A, which is the notice requiring detention and isolation of the animal. Next,' and I could hear the slap of finger on palm as he enumerated his points, 'next, there is B. 207 DT, Form C, Notice of intended slaughter. Then B. 208 DT, Form D, Post Mortem Certificate. Then B. 196 DT, Veterinary Inspector's report. Then B. 209 DT, Valuation agreement, and in cases where the owner objects, there is B. 213 DT, Appointment of valuer. Then we have B. 212 DT, Notice to owner of time and place of slaughter, followed by B. 227 DT, Receipt for animal for slaughter, and finally B. 230 DT, Notice requiring cleansing and disinfection. Dammit, a child could understand that. It's perfectly simple, isn't it?'

'Yes, yes, certainly, absolutely.' It wasn't simple to me, but I didn't mention the fact. He had calmed down nicely and I didn't want to inflame him again.

'Well thank you, Mr Harcourt,' I said. 'I'll see it doesn't happen again.' I put down the receiver with the feeling that things could have turned out a lot worse, but for all that my nerves didn't stop jangling for some time. The trouble was that the Ministry work was desperately important to general practitioners. In fact, in those precarious days it was the main rent payer.

This business of the Tuberculosis Order. When a veterinary surgeon came upon a cow with open TB it was his duty to see that the animal was slaughtered immediately because its milk could be a danger to the public. That sounds easy, but unfortunately the law insisted that the demise of each unhappy creature be commemorated by a confetti-like shower of the doom-laden forms.

It wasn't just that there were so many of these forms, but they had to be sent to an amazing variety of people. Sometimes I used to think that there were very few people in England who didn't get one. Apart from Charles Harcourt, other recipients included the farmer concerned, the police, the Head Office of the Ministry, the knacker man, the local authority. I nearly always managed to forget one of them. I used to have nightmares about standing in the middle of the market place, throwing the forms around me at the passers-by and laughing hysterically.

Looking back, I can hardly believe that for all this wear and tear on the nervous system the payment was one guinea plus ten and sixpence for the post mortem.

It was a mere two days after my interview with the Divisional Inspector that I had to take another cow under the TB Order. When I came to fill in the forms I sat at the surgery desk in a dither of apprehension, going over them again and again, laying them out side by side and enclosing them one by one in their various envelopes. This time there must be no mistake.

I took them over to the post myself and uttered a silent prayer as I dropped them into the box. Charles would have them the following morning, and I would soon know if I had done it again. When two days passed without incident I felt I was safe, but midway through the third morning I dropped in at the surgery and read the message in letters of fire. 'RING MIN!'

Kitty Pattison sounded strained. She didn't even try to appear casual. 'Oh yes, Mr Herriot,' she said hurriedly. 'Mr Harcourt asked me to call you. I'm putting you through now.'

My heart almost stopped as I waited for the familiar bellow, but when the quiet voice came on the line it frightened me even more.

'Good morning, Herriot.' Charles was curt and impersonal. 'I'd like to discuss that last cow you took under the Order.'

'Oh yes?' I croaked.

'But not over the telephone. I want to see you here in the office.'

'In the . . . the office?'

'Yes, right away if you can.'

I put down the phone and went out to the car with my knees knocking. Charles Harcourt was really upset this time. There was a kind of restrained fury in his words, and this business of going to the office – that was reserved for serious transgressions.

Twenty minutes later my footsteps echoed in the corridor of the Ministry building. Marching stiffly like a condemned man I passed the windows where I could see the typists at work, then I read 'Divisional Inspector' on the door at the end.

I took one long shuddering breath, then knocked.

'Come in.' The voice was still quiet and controlled.

Charles looked up unsmilingly from his desk as I entered. He motioned me to a chair and directed a cold stare at me.

'Herriot,' he said unemotionally. 'You're really on the carpet this time.'

Charles had been a major in the Punjabi Rifles and he was very much the Indian Army officer at this moment. A fine looking man, clear-skinned and ruddy, with massive cheek bones above a powerful jaw. Looking at the danger-ously glinting eyes it struck me that only a fool would trifle with somebody like him – and I had a nasty feeling that I had been trifling.

Dry-mouthed, I waited.

'You know, Herriot,' he went on. 'After our last telephone conversation about TB forms I thought you might give me a little peace.'

'Peace . . .?'

'Yes, yes, it was silly of me, I know, but when I took all that time to go over the procedure with you I actually thought you were listening.'

'Oh I was, I was!'

'You were? Oh good.' He gave me a mirthless smile. 'Then I suppose it was even more foolish of me to expect you to act upon my instructions. In my innocence I thought you cared about what I was telling you.'

'Mr Harcourt, believe me, I do care, I . . .'

'*Then why*,' he bawled without warning, bringing his great hand flailing down on the desk with a crash that made pens and inkwells dance. '*Why the bloody hell do you keep making a balls of it?*'

I resisted a strong impulse to run away. 'Making a . . . I don't quite understand.'

'You don't?' He kept up his pounding on the desk. 'Well I'll tell you. One of my veterinary officers was on that farm, and he found that you hadn't served a Notice of Cleansing and Disinfection!'

'Is that so?'

'Yes, it bloody well is so! You didn't give one to the farmer but you sent one to me. Maybe you want me to go and disinfect the place, is that it? Would you like me to slip along there and get busy with a hosepipe – I'll go now if it'll make you feel any happier!'

'Oh no, no, no . . . no.'

He was apparently not satisfied with the thunderous noise he was making because he began to use both hands, bringing them down simultaneously with sickening force on the wood while he glared wildly.

'Herriot!' he shouted. 'There's just one thing I want to know from you – do you want this bloody work or don't you? Just say the word and I'll give it to another practice and then maybe we'd both be able to live a quiet life!'

'Please, Mr Harcourt, I give you my word, I . . . we . . . we do want the work very much.' And I meant it with all my heart.

The big man slumped back in his chair and regarded me for a few moments in silence. Then he glanced at his wrist watch.

'Ten past twelve,' he murmured. 'Just time to have a beer at the Red Lion before lunch.'

In the pub lounge he took a long pull at his glass, placed it carefully on the table in front of him, then turned to me with a touch of weariness.

'You know, Herriot, I do wish you'd stop doing this sort of thing. It takes it out of me.'

I believed him. His face had lost a little of its colour and his hand trembled slightly as he raised his glass again.

'I'm truly sorry, Mr Harcourt, I don't know how it happened. I did try to get it right this time and I'll do my best to avoid troubling you in future.'

He nodded a few times then clapped me on the shoulder. 'Good, good – let's just have one more.'

He moved over to the bar, brought back the drinks then fished out a brown paper parcel from his pocket.

'Little wedding present, Herriot. Understand you're getting married soon – this is from my missus and me with our best wishes.'

I didn't know what to say. I fumbled the wrapping away and uncovered a small square barometer.

Shame engulfed me as I muttered a few words of thanks. This man was the head of the Ministry in the area while I was the newest and lowest of his minions. Not only that, but I was pretty sure I caused him more trouble than all the others put together – I was like a hair shirt to him. There was no earthly reason why he should give me a barometer.

This last experience deepened my dread of form filling to the extent that I hoped it would be a long time before I encountered another tuberculous animal, but fate decreed that I had some concentrated days of clinical inspections and it was with a feeling of inevitability that I surveyed Mr Moverley's Ayrshire cow.

It was the soft cough which made me stop and look at her more closely, and as I studied her my spirits sank. This was another one. The skin stretched tightly over the bony frame, the slightly accelerated respirations and that deep careful cough. Mercifully you don't see cows like that now, but in those days they were all too common.

I moved along her side and examined the wall in front of her. The-tell-tale blobs of sputum were clearly visible on the rough stones and I quickly lifted a sample and smeared it on a glass slide.

Back at the surgery I stained the smear by Ziehl-Nielson's method and pushed the slide under the microscope. The red clumps of tubercle bacilli lay among the scattered cells, tiny, iridescent and deadly. I hadn't really needed the grim proof but it was there.

Mr Moverley was not amused when I told him next morning that the animal would have to be slaughtered.

'It's nobbut got a bit of a chill,' he grunted. The farmers were never pleased when one of their milk producers was removed by a petty bureaucrat like me. 'But ah suppose it's no use arguin'.'

'I assure you, Mr Moverley, there's no doubt about it. I examined that sample last night and . . .'

'Oh never mind about that.' The farmer waved an impatient hand. 'If t'bloody government says me cow's got to go she's got to go. But ah get compensation, don't I?'

'Yes, you do.'

'How much?'

I thought rapidly. The rules stated that the animal be valued as if it were up for sale in the open market in its present condition. The minimum was five pounds and there was no doubt that this emaciated cow came into that category.

'The statutory value is five pounds,' I said.

'Shit!' replied Mr Moverley.

'We can appoint a valuer if you don't agree.'

'Oh 'ell, let's get t'job over with.' He was clearly disgusted and I thought it imprudent to tell him that he would only get a proportion of the five pounds, depending on the post mortem.

'Very well,' I said. 'I'll tell Jeff Mallock to collect her as soon as possible.'

The fact that I was unpopular with Mr Moverley didn't worry me as much as the prospect of dealing with the dreaded forms. The very thought of sending another batch winging hopefully on its way to Charles Harcourt brought me out in a sweat.

Then I had a flash of inspiration. Such things don't often happen to me, but this struck me as brilliant. I wouldn't send off the forms till I'd had them vetted by Kitty Pattison.

I couldn't wait to get the plan under way. Almost gleefully I laid the papers out in a long row, signed them and laid them by their envelopes, ready for their varied journeys. Then I phoned the Ministry office.

Kitty was patient and kind. I am sure she realised that I did my work conscientiously but that I was a clerical numbskull and she sympathised.

When I had finished going through the list she congratulated me. 'Well done, Mr Herriot, you've got them right this time! All you need now is the knacker man's signature and your post mortem report and you're home and dry.'

'Bless you, Kitty,' I said. 'You've made my day.'

And she had. The airy sensation of relief was tremendous. The knowledge that there would be no come-back from Charles this time was like the sun bursting through dark clouds. I felt like singing as I went round to Mallock's yard and arranged with him to pick up the cow.

'Have her ready for me to inspect tomorrow, Jeff,' I said, and went on my way with a light heart.

I couldn't understand it when Mr Moverley waved me down from his farm gate next day. As I drew up I could see he was extremely agitated.

'Hey!' he cried. 'Ah've just got back from the market and my missus tells me Mallock's been!'

I smiled. 'That's right, Mr Moverley. Remember I told you I was going to send him round for your cow.'

'Aye, ah know all about that!' He paused and glared at me. 'But he's took the wrong one!'

'Wrong . . . wrong what?'

'Wrong cow, that's what! He's off wi' the best cow in me herd. Pedigree Ayrshire – ah bought 'er in Dumfries last week and they only delivered 'er this mornin'.'

Horror drove through me in a freezing wave. I had told the knacker man to collect the Ayrshire which would be isolated in the loose box in the yard. The new animal would be in a box, too, after her arrival. I could see Jeff and his man leading her up the ramp into his wagon with a dreadful clarity.

'This is your responsibility, tha knaws!' The farmer waved a threatening finger. 'If he kills me good cow you'll 'ave to answer for it!'

He didn't have to tell me. I'd have to answer for it to a lot of people, including Charles Harcourt.

'Get on the phone to the knacker yard right away!' I gasped.

The farmer waved his arms about 'Ah've tried that and there's no reply. Ah tell ye he'll shoot 'er afore we can stop 'im. Do you know how much ah paid for that cow?'

'Never mind about that! Which way did he go?'

'T'missus said he went towards Grampton – about ten minutes ago.'

I started my engine. 'He'll maybe be picking up other beasts – I'll go after him.'

Teeth clenched, eyes popping, I roared along the Grampton road. The enormity of this latest catastrophe was almost more than I could assimilate. The wrong form was bad enough, but the wrong cow was unthinkable. But it had happened. Charles would crucify me this time. He was a good bloke but he would have no option, because the higher-ups in the Ministry would get wind of an immortal boner like this and they would howl for blood.

Feverishly but vainly I scanned each farm entrance in Grampton village as I shot through, and when I saw the open countryside ahead of me again the tension was almost unbearable. I was telling myself that the whole thing was hopeless when in the far distance above a row of trees I spotted the familiar top of Mallock's wagon.

It was a high, wooden-sided vehicle and I couldn't mistake it. Repressing a shout of triumph I put my foot on the boards and set off in that direction with the fanatical zeal of the hunter. But it was a long way off and I hadn't travelled a mile before I realised I had lost it.

Over the years many things have stayed in my memory, but the Great Cow Chase is engraven deeper than most. The sheer terror I felt is vivid to this day. I kept sighting the wagon among the maze of lanes and side roads but by the time I had cut across country my quarry had disappeared behind a hillside or dipped into one of the many hollows in the wide vista. I was constantly deceived by the fact that I expected him to be turning towards Darrowby after passing through a village, but he never did. Clearly he had other business on the way.

The whole thing seemed to last a very long time and there was no fun in it for me. I was gripped throughout by a cold dread, and the violent swings – the alternating scents of hope and despair – were wearing to the point of exhaustion. I was utterly drained when at last I saw the tall lorry rocking along a straight road in front of me.

I had him now! Forcing my little car to the limit, I drew abreast of him, sounding my horn repeatedly till he stopped. Breathlessly I pulled up in front of him and ran round to offer my explanations. But as I looked up into the driver's cab my eager smile vanished. It wasn't Jeff Mallock at all. I had been following the wrong man.

It was the 'ket feller'. He had exactly the same type of wagon as Mallock and he went round a wide area of Yorkshire picking up the nameless odds and ends of the dead animals which even the knacker men didn't want. It was a strange job and he was a strange-looking man. The oddly piercing eyes glittered uncannily from under a tattered army peaked cap.

'Wot's up, guvnor?' He removed a cigarette from his mouth and spat companionably into the roadway.

My throat was tight. 'I – I'm sorry. I thought you were Jeff Mallock.'

The eyes did not change expression, but the corner of his mouth twitched briefly. 'If tha wants Jeff he'll be back at his yard now, ah reckon.' He spat again and replaced his cigarette.

I nodded dully. Jeff would be there now all right – long ago. I had been chasing the wrong wagon for about an hour and that cow would be dead and hanging up on hooks at this moment. The knacker man was a fast and skilful worker and wasted no time when he got back with his beasts.

'Well, ah'm off 'ome now,' the ket feller said. 'So long, boss.' He winked at me, started his engine and the big vehicle rumbled away.

I trailed back to my car. There was no hurry now. And strangely, now that all was lost my mood relaxed. In fact, as I drove away, a great calm settled on me and I began to assess my future with cool objectivity. I would be drummed out of the Ministry's service for sure, and idly I wondered if they had any special ceremony for the occasion – perhaps a ritual stripping of the Panel Certificates or something of the sort.

I tried to put away the thought that more than the Ministry would be interested in my latest exploit. How about the Royal College? Did they strike you off for something like this? Well, it was possible, and in my serene state of mind I toyed with the possibilities of alternative avenues of employment. I had often thought it must be fun to run a secondhand book shop and now that I began to consider it seriously I felt sure there was an opening for one in Darrowby. I experienced a comfortable glow at the vision of myself sitting under the rows of dusty volumes, pulling one down from the shelf when I felt like it or maybe just looking out into the street through the window from my safe little world where there were no forms or telephones or messages saying, 'Ring Min.'

In Darrowby I drove round without haste to the knacker yard. I left my car outside the grim little building with the black smoke drifting from its chimney.

I pulled back the sliding door and saw Jeff seated at his ease on a pile of cow hides, holding a slice of apple pie in blood-stained fingers. And, ah yes, there, just behind him hung the two great sides of beef and on the floor, the lungs, bowels and other viscera – the sad remnants of Mr Moverley's pedigree Ayrshire.

'Hello, Jeff,' I said.

'Now then, Mr Herriot.' He gave me the beatific smile which mirrored his personality so well. 'Ah'm just havin' a little snack. I allus like a bite about this time.' He sank his teeth into the pie and chewed appreciatively.

'So I see.' I sorrowfully scanned the hanging carcase. Just dog meat and not even much of that. Ayrshires were never very fat. I was wondering how to break the news to him when he spoke again.

'Ah'm sorry you've caught me out this time, Mr Herriot,' he said, reaching for a greasy mug of tea.

'What do you mean?'

'Well, I allus reckon to have t'beast dressed and ready for you but you've come a bit early.'

I stared at him. 'But . . . everything's here, surely.' I waved a hand around me.

'Nay, nay, that's not 'er.'

'You mean . . . that isn't the cow from Moverley's.'

'That's right.' He took a long draught from the mug and wiped his mouth with the back of his hand. 'I 'ad to do this 'un first. Moverley's cow's still in t'wagon out at the back.'

'Alive?'

He looked mildly surprised. 'Aye, of course. She's never had a finger on 'er. Nice cow for a screw, too.'

I could have fainted with relief. 'She's no screw, Jeff. That's the wrong cow you've got there?'

'Wrong cow?' Nothing ever startled him but he obviously desired more information. I told him the whole story.

When I had finished, his shoulders began to shake gently and the beautiful clear eyes twinkled in the pink face.

'Well, that's a licker,' he murmured, and continued to laugh gently. There was nothing immoderate in his mirth and indeed nothing I had said disturbed him in the least. The fact that he had wasted his journey or that the farmer might be annoyed was of no moment to him.

Again, looking at Jeff Mallock, it struck me, as many times before, that there was nothing like a lifetime of dabbling among diseased carcases and lethal bacteria for breeding tranquillity of mind.

'You'll slip back and change the cow?' I said.

'Aye, in a minute or two. There's nowt spoilin'. Ah never likes to hurry me grub.' He belched contentedly. 'And how about you, Mr Herriot? You could do with summat to keep your strength up.' He produced another mug and broke off a generous wedge of pie which he offered to me.

'No . . . no . . . er . . . no, thank you, Jeff. It's kind of you, but no . . . no . . . not just now.'

He shrugged his shoulders and smiled as he stretched an arm for his pipe which was balanced on a sheep's skull. Flicking away some shreds of stray tissue from the stem he applied a match and settled down blissfully on the hides.

'I'll see ye later, then,' he said. 'Come round tonight and everything'll be ready for you.' He closed his eyes and again his shoulders quivered. 'Ah'd better get the right 'un this time.'

It must be more than twenty years since I took a cow under the TB Order, because the clinical cases so rarely exist now. 'Ring Min' no longer has the power to chill my blood, and the dread forms which scarred my soul lie unused and yellowing in the bottom of a drawer.

All these things have gone from my life. Charles Harcourt has gone too, but I think of him every day when I look at the little barometer which still hangs on my wall.

Chapter Nine

'Oh Mr Herriot!' Mrs Ridge said delightedly. 'Somebody stole our car last night.' She looked at me with a radiant smile.

I was lying on my bed in the barrack hut at Winkfield listening to somebody on the radio adjuring people to immobilise their cars in wartime when this lady's strange remark bubbled back from my veterinary days.

I stopped in the doorway of her house. 'Mrs Ridge, I'm terribly sorry. How . . .?'

'Yes, yes, oh I can't wait to tell you!' Her voice trembled with excitement and joy. 'There must have been some prowlers around here last night, and I'm such a silly about leaving the car unlocked.'

'I see . . . how unfortunate.'

'But do come in,' she giggled. 'Forgive me for keeping you standing on the step, but I'm all of a dither!'

I went past her into the lounge. 'Well, it's very understandable. It must have been quite a shock.'

'Shock? Oh, but you don't see what I mean. It's wonderful!'

'Eh?'

'Yes, of course!' She clasped her hands and looked up at the ceiling. 'Do you know what happened?'

'Well yes,' I said. 'You've just told me.'

'No, I haven't told you half.'

'You haven't?'

'No, but do sit down. I know you'll want to hear all about it.'

To explain this I have to go back ten days to the afternoon when Mrs Ridge ran tearfully up the steps of Skeldale House.

'My little dog's had an accident,' she gasped.

I looked past her. 'Where is he?'

'In the car. I didn't know whether I should move him.'

I crossed the pavement and opened the door. Her Cairn terrier, Joshua, lay very still on a blanket on the back seat.

'What happened?' I asked.

She put a hand over her eyes. 'Oh it was terrible. You know he often plays in the farmer's field opposite our house – well about half an hour ago he started to chase a rabbit and ran under the wheels of a tractor.'

I looked from her face to the motionless animal and back again. 'Did the wheels go over him?'

She nodded as the tears streamed down her cheeks.

I took her by the arm. 'Mrs Ridge, this is important. Are you absolutely sure that wheel passed right over his body?'

'Yes, I am – quite certain. I saw it happen. I couldn't believe he'd be alive when I ran to pick him up.' She took a long breath. 'I don't suppose he can live after that, can he?'

I didn't want to depress her but it seemed impossible that a small dog like this could survive being crushed under that great weight. Massive internal damage would be inevitable apart altogether from broken bones. It was sad to see the little sandy form lying still and unheeding when I had watched him so often running and leaping in the fields.

'Let's have a look at him,' I said.

I climbed into the car and sat down on the seat beside him. With the utmost care I felt my way over the limbs, expecting every moment to feel the crepitus which would indicate a fracture. I put my hand underneath him very slowly, supporting his weight every inch of the way. The only time Joshua showed any reaction was when I moved the pelvic girdle.

The best sign of all was the pinkness of the mucous membranes of eye and mouth and I turned to Mrs Ridge rather more hopefully.

'Miraculously he doesn't seem to have any internal haemorrhage and there are no limb bones broken. I'm pretty sure he has a fractured pelvis, but that's not so bad.'

She drew her fingers over the smears on her cheeks and looked at me, wide-eyed. 'You really think he has a chance?'

'Well I don't want to raise your hopes unduly, but at this moment I can't find any sign of severe injury.'

'But it doesn't seem possible.'

I shrugged. 'I agree, it doesn't, but if he has got away with it I can only think it was because he was on soft ground which yielded as the wheel squeezed him down. Anyway, let's get him X-rayed to make sure.'

At that time, in common with most large animal practices, we didn't have an X-ray machine, but the local hospital helped us out in times of need. I took Joshua round there and the picture confirmed my diagnosis of pelvic fracture.

'There's not much I can do,' I said to his mistress. 'This type of injury usually heals itself. He'll probably have difficulty in standing on his hind legs for a while and for several weeks he'll be weak in the rear end, but with rest and time he ought to recover.'

'Oh marvellous!' She watched me place the little animal back on the car seat. 'I suppose it's just a matter of waiting, then?'

'That's what I hope.'

My fears that Joshua might have some internal damage were finally allayed when I saw him two days later. His membranes were a rich deep pink and all natural functions were operating.

Mrs Ridge, however, was still worried. 'He's such a sorrowful little thing,' she said. 'Just look at him he's lifeless.'

'Well you know he must be bruised and sore after that squashing he had. And he was very shocked, too. You must be patient.'

As I spoke, the little dog stood up, wobbled a few feet across the carpet and flopped down again. He showed no interest in me or his surroundings.

Before I left I gave his mistress some salicylate tablets to give him. 'These will ease his discomfort,' I said. 'Let me know if he doesn't improve.'

She did let me know – within forty-eight hours. 'I wish you'd come and see Joshua again,' she said on the phone. 'I'm not at all happy about him.'

The little animal was as before. I looked down at him as he lay dejectedly on the rug, head on his paws, looking into the fireplace.

'Come on, Joshua, old lad,' I said. 'You must be feeling better now.' I bent and rubbed my fingers along the wiry coat, but neither word or gesture made any impression. I might as well not have been there.

Mrs Ridge turned to me worriedly. 'That's what he's like all the time. And you know how he is normally.'

'Yes, he's always been a ball of fire.' Again I recalled him jumping round my legs, gazing up at me eagerly. 'It's very strange.'

'And another thing,' she went on. 'He never utters a sound. And you know, that worries me more than anything because he's always been such a good little watch dog. We used to hear him barking when the early post came, he barked at the milk boy, the dustman, everybody. He was never a yappy dog, but he let us know when anybody was around.'

'Yes . . .' That was another thing I remembered. The tumult of sound from within whenever I rang the door bell.

'And now there's just this dreadful silence. People come and go but he never even looks up.' She shook her head slowly. 'Oh, if only he'd bark! Just once! I think it would mean he was getting better.'

'It probably would,' I said.

'Is there something else wrong with him, do you think?' she asked.

I thought for a moment or two. 'No, I'm convinced there isn't. Not physically, anyway. He's had a tremendous fright and he has withdrawn within himself. He'll come out of it in time.'

As I left I had the feeling I was trying to convince myself as much as Mrs Ridge. And as, over the next few days she kept phoning me with bad reports about the little dog my confidence began to ebb.

It was a week after the accident that she begged me to come to the house again. Joshua was unchanged. Apathetic, tail tucked down, sad-eyed – and still soundless.

His mistress was obviously under strain.

'Mr Herriot,' she said. 'What are we going to do? I can't sleep for thinking about him.'

I produced stethoscope and thermometer and examined the little animal again. Then I palpated him thoroughly from head to tail. When I had finished I squatted on the rug and looked up at Mrs Ridge.

'I can't find anything new. You'll just have to be patient.'

'But that's what you said before, and I feel I can't go on much longer like this.'

'Still no barking?'

She shook her head. 'No, and that's what I'm waiting for. He eats a little, walks around a little, but we never hear a sound from him. I know I'd stop worrying if I heard him bark, just once, but otherwise I have a horrible feeling he's going to die . . .'

I had hoped that my next visit would be more cheerful but though I was greatly relieved at Mrs Ridge's high spirits I was surprised, too.

I sat down in one of the comfortable chairs in the lounge.

'Well I hope you'll soon recover your car,' I said.

She waved a hand negligently. 'Oh, it'll turn up somewhere, I'm sure.'

'But still – you must be very upset.'

'Upset? Not a bit! I'm so happy!

'Happy? About losing the car . . .?'

'No, not about that. About Joshua.'

'Joshua?'

'Yes.' She sat down in the chair opposite and leaned forward. 'Do you know what he did when those people were driving the car away?'

'No, tell me.'

'He *barked*, Mr Herriot! Joshua *barked*!'

Chapter Ten

The food was so good at the Winkfield flying school that it was said that those airmen whose homes were within visiting distance wouldn't take a day's leave because they might miss some culinary speciality. Difficult to believe, maybe, but I often think that few people in wartime Britain fared as well as the handful of young men in the scatter of wooden huts on that flat green stretch outside Windsor.

It wasn't as though we had a French chef, either. The cooking was done by two grizzled old men – civilians who wore cloth caps and smoked pipes and went about their business with unsmiling taciturnity.

It was rumoured that they were two ex-army cooks from the First World War, but whatever their origins they were artists. In their hands, simple stews and pies assumed a new significance and it was possible to rhapsodise even over the perfect flouriness of their potatoes.

So it was surprising when at lunch time my neighbour on the left drew down his spoon pushed away his plate and groaned. We ate on trestle tables, sitting in rows on long forms, and I was right up against the young man.

'What's wrong?' I asked. 'This apple dumpling is terrific.'

'Ah, it's not the grub.' He buried his face in his hands for a few seconds then looked at me with tortured eyes. 'I've been doing circuits and bumps this morning with Routledge and he's torn the knackers off me – all the time, it never stopped.'

Suddenly my own meal lost some of its flavour. I knew just what he meant. FO Woodham did the same to me.

He gave me another despairing glance then stared straight ahead.

'I know one thing, Jim. I'll never make a bloody pilot.'

His words sent a chill through me. He was voicing the conviction which had been gradually growing in me. I never seemed to make any progress – whatever I did was wrong, and I was losing heart. Like all the others I was hoping to be graded pilot, but after every session with FO Woodham the idea of ever flying an aeroplane all on my own seemed more and more ludicrous. And I had another date with him at 2 pm.

He was as quiet and charming as ever when I met him – till we got up into the sky and the shouting started again.

'Relax! For heavens sake, relax!' or 'Watch your height! Where the hell d'you think you're going?' or 'Didn't I tell you to centralise the stick? Are you bloody deaf or something?' And finally, after the first circuit when we juddered to a halt on the grass. 'That was an absolutely bloody ropy landing! Take off again!'

On the second circuit he fell strangely silent. And though I should have felt relieved I found something ominous in the unaccustomed peace. It could mean only one thing – he had finally given me up as a bad job. When we landed he told me to switch off the engine and climbed out of the rear cockpit. I was about to unbuckle my straps and follow him when he signalled me to remain in my seat.

'Stay where you are,' he said. 'You can take her up now.'

I stared down at him through my goggles. 'What . . .?'

'I said take her up.'

'You mean, on my own . . .? Go solo . . .?'

'Yes, of course. Come and see me in the flight hut after you've landed and taxied in.' He turned and walked away over the green. He didn't look back.

After a few minutes a fitter came over to where I sat trembling in my seat. He spat on the turf then looked at me with deep distaste.

'Look, mate,' he said. 'That's a — good aircraft you've got there.'

I nodded agreement.

'Well I don't want it — well smashed up, okay?'

'Okay.'

He gave me a final disgusted glance then went round to the propeller.

Panic-stricken though I was, I did not forget the cockpit drill which had been dinned in to me so often. I never thought I'd have to use it in earnest but now I automatically tested the controls – rudder, ailerons and elevator. Fuel on, switch off, throttle closed, then switch on, throttle slightly open.

'Contact!' I cried.

The fitter swung the propeller and the engine roared. I pushed the throttle full open and the Tiger Moth began to bump its way over the grass. As we gathered speed I eased the stick forward to lift the tail, then as I pulled it back again the bumping stopped and we climbed smoothly into the air with the long dining hut at the end of the airfield flashing away beneath.

I was gripped by exhilaration and triumph. The impossible had happened. I was up here on my own, flying, really flying at last. I had been so certain of failure that the feeling of relief was over-powering. In fact it intoxicated me, so that for a long time I just sailed along, grinning foolishly to myself.

When I finally came to my senses I looked down happily over the side. It must be time to turn now, but as I stared downwards cold reality began to roll over me in a gathering flood. I couldn't recognise a thing in the great hazy tapestry beneath me. And everything seemed smaller than usual. Dry-mouthed, I looked at the altimeter. I was well over 2,000 feet.

And suddenly it came to me that FO Woodham's shouts had not been meaningless; he had been talking sense, giving me good advice, and as soon as I got up in the air by myself I had ignored it all. I hadn't lined myself up on a cloud, I hadn't watched my artificial horizon, I hadn't kept an eye on the altimeter. And I was lost.

It was a terrible feeling, this sense of utter isolation as I desperately scanned the great chequered landscape for a familiar object. What did you do in a case like this? Soar around southern England till I found some farmer's field big enough to land in, then make my own abject way back to Winkfield? But that way I was going to look the complete fool, and also I'd stand an excellent chance of smashing up that fitter's beloved aeroplane and maybe myself.

It seemed to me that one way or another I was going to make a name for myself. Funny things had happened to some of the other lads – many had been air-sick and vomited in the cockpit, one had gone through a hedge, another on his first solo had circled the airfield again and again – seven times he had gone round – trying to find the courage to land while his instructor sweated blood and cursed on the ground. But nobody had really got lost like me. Nobody had flown off into the blue and returned on foot without his aeroplane.

My visions of my immediate fate were reaching horrific proportions and my heart was hammering uncontrollably when far away on my left I spotted the dear familiar bulk of the big stand on Ascot racecourse. Almost weeping with joy, I turned towards it and within minutes I was banking above its roof as I had done so often.

And there, far below and approaching with uncomfortable speed was the belt of trees which fringed the airfield and beyond, the windsock blowing over the wide green. But I was still far too high – I could never drop down there in time to hit that landing strip, I would have to go round again.

The ignominy of it went deep. They would all be watching on the ground and some would have a good laugh at the sight of Herriot over-shooting the field by several hundred feet and cruising off again into the clouds. But what was I thinking about? There was a way of losing height rapidly and, bless you FO Woodham, I knew how to do it.

Opposite rudder and stick. He had told me a hundred times how to side slip and I did it now as hard as I could, sending the little machine slewing like an airborne crab down, down towards those trees.

And by golly it worked! The green copse rushed up at me and before I knew I was almost skimming the branches. I straightened up and headed for the long stretch of grass. At fifty feet I rounded out then checked the stick gradually back till just above the ground when I slammed it into my abdomen. The undercarriage made contact with the earth with hardly a tremor and I worked the rudder bar to keep straight until I came to a halt. Then I taxied in, climbed from the cockpit and walked over to the flight hut.

FO Woodham was sitting at a table, cup in hand, and he looked up as I entered. He had got out of his flying suit and was wearing a battle dress jacket with the wings we all dreamed about and the ribbon of the DFC.

'Ah, Herriot, I'm just having some coffee. Will you join me?'

'Thank you, sir.'

I sat down and he pushed a cup towards me.

'I saw your landing,' he said. 'Delightful, quite delightful.'

'Thank you, sir.'

'And that side-slip.' One corner of his mouth twitched upwards. 'Very good indeed, really masterly.'

He reached for the coffee pot and went on. 'You've done awfully well, Herriot. Solo after nine hours' instruction, eh? Splendid. But then I never had the slightest doubt about you at any time.'

He poised the pot over my cup. 'How do you like your coffee – black or white?'

Chapter Eleven

I was only the third man in our Flight of fifty to go solo and it was a matter of particular pride to me because so many of my comrades were eighteen and nineteen year olds. They didn't say so but I often had the impression that they felt that an elderly gentleman like me in my twenties with a wife and baby had no right to be there, training for aircrew. In the nicest possible way they thought I was past it.

Of course, in many ways they had a point. The pull I had from home was probably stronger than theirs. When our sergeant handed out the letters on the daily parade I used to secrete mine away till I had a few minutes of solitude to read about how fast little Jimmy was growing, how much he weighed, the unmistakable signs of outstanding intelligence, even genius, which Helen could already discern in him.

I was missing his babyhood and it saddened me. It is still something I deeply regret because it comes only once and is gone so quickly. But I still have the bundles of letters which his proud mother wrote to keep me in touch with every fascinating stage, and when I read them now it is almost as though I had been there to see it all.

At the time, those letters pulled me back almost painfully to the comforts of home but on the other hand there were occasions when life in Darrowby hadn't been all that comfortable . . .

I think it was the early morning calls in the winter which were the worst. It was a fairly common experience to be walking sleepy-eyed into a cow byre at 6 am for a calving but at Mr Blackburn's farm there was a difference. In fact several differences.

Firstly, there was usually an anxious-faced farmer to greet me with the news of how the calf was coming, when labour had started, but today I was like an unwelcome stranger. Secondly, I had grown accustomed to the sight of a few cows tied up in a cobbled byre with wooden partitions and an oil lamp, and now I was gazing down a long avenue of concrete under blazing electric light with a seemingly endless succession of bovine backsides protruding from tubular metal standings. Thirdly, instead of the early morning peace there was a clattering of buckets, the rhythmic pulsing of a milking machine and the blaring of a radio loudspeaker. There was also a frantic scurrying of white-coated, white-capped men, but none of them paid the slightest attention to me.

This was one of the new big dairy farms. In place of a solitary figure on a milk stool, head buried in the cow's side, pulling forth the milk with a gentle 'hiss-hiss' there was this impersonal hustle and bustle.

I stood just inside the doorway while out in the yard a particularly cold snow drifted from the blackness above. I had left a comfortable bed and a warm wife to come here and it seemed somebody ought at least to say 'hello'. Then I noticed the owner hurrying past with a bucket. He was moving as fast as any of his men.

'Hey, Mr Blackburn!' I cried. 'You rang me – you've got a cow calving?'

He stopped and looked at me uncomprehendingly for a moment. 'Oh aye . . . aye . . . she's down there on t'right.' He pointed to a light roan animal half way along the byre. She was easy to pick out – the only one lying down.

'How long has she been on?' I asked, but when I turned round Mr Blackburn had gone. I trotted after him, cornered him in the milk house and repeated my question.

'Oh, she should've calved last night. Must be summat amiss.' He began to pour his bucket of milk over the cooler into the churn.

'Have you had a feel inside her?'

'Nay, haven't had time.' He turned harassed eyes towards me. 'We're a bit behind with milkin' this mornin'. We can't be late for t'milk man.'

I knew what he meant. The drivers who collected the churns for the big dairy companies were a fierce body of men. Probably kind husbands and fathers at normal times but subject to violent outbursts of rage if they were kept waiting even for an instant. I couldn't blame them, because they had a lot of territory to cover and many farms to visit, but I had seen them when provoked and their anger was frightening to behold.

'All right,' I said. 'Can I have some hot water, soap and a towel, please?'

Mr Blackburn jerked his head at the corner of the milk house. 'You'll 'ave to help yourself. There's everythin' there. Ah must get on.' He went off again at a brisk walk. Clearly he was more in fear of the milk man than he was of me.

I filled a bucket, found a piece of soap and threw a towel over my shoulder. When I reached my patient I looked in vain for some sign of a name. So many of the cows of those days had their names printed above their stalls but there were no Marigolds, Alices or Snowdrops here, just numbers.

Before taking off my jacket I looked casually in the ear where the tattoo marks stood out plainly against the creamy white surface. She was number eighty seven.

I was in more trouble when I stripped off my shirt. In a modern byre like this there were no nails jutting from the walls to serve as hangers. I had to roll my clothes into a ball and carry them through to the milk house. There I found a sack which I tied round my middle with a length of binder twine.

Still ignored by everybody, I returned, soaped my arm and inserted it into the cow. I had to go a long way in to reach the calf, which was strange considering the birth should have taken place last night. It was the top of the little creature's head I touched first; the nose was tucked downwards instead of thrusting its way along the vagina towards the outside world, and the legs were similarly coiled under the body.

And I noticed something else. The entry of my arm did not provoke any answering strain from the cow, nor did she try to rise to her feet. There was something else troubling Number Eighty Seven.

Lying flat on the concrete, still buried to the shoulder in the cow, I raised my head and looked along the shaggy back with its speckle of light red and white hairs, and when I reached the neck I knew I need seek no further. The lateral kink was very obvious. Number Eighty Seven, slumped on her chest, was gazing wearily and without interest at the wall in front of her but there was that funny little bend in her neck that told me everything.

I got up, washed and dried my arm and looked for Mr Blackburn. I found him bending by the side of a fat brown animal, pulling the cups from her teats. I tapped him on the shoulder.

'She's got milk fever.' I said.

'Oh aye,' he replied, then he hoisted the bucket, brushed past me and made off down the byre.

I kept pace with him. 'That's why she can't strain. Her uterus has lost its tone. She'll never calve till she gets some calcium.'

'Right.' He still didn't look at me. 'Ye'll give 'er some, then?'

'Yes,' I said to his retreating back.

The snow still swirled in the outer darkness and I toyed with the idea of getting dressed. But I'd only have to strip again so I decided to make a dash for it. With the car boot open it seemed to take a long time to fish out the bottles and flutter valve with the flakes settling thickly on my naked flesh.

Back in the byre I looked around for a spare man to help me but there was no lessening of the feverish activity. I would have to roll this cow onto her side and inject into her milk vein without assistance. It all depended on how comatose she was.

And she must have been pretty far gone because when I braced my feet against the tubular steel and pushed both hands against her shoulder she flopped over without resistance. To keep her there I lay on top of her as I pushed in the needle and ran the calcium into the vein.

One snag was that my sprawling position took me right underneath the neighbouring cow on the right, a skittish sort of animal who didn't welcome the rubber-booted legs tangling with her hind feet. She expressed her disapproval by treading painfully on my ankles and giving me a few smart kicks on the thigh, but I dared not move because the calcium was flowing in beautifully.

When the bottle was empty I kneed my patient back onto her chest and ran another bottle of calcium magnesium and phosphorus under her skin. By the time I had finished and rubbed away the subcutaneous fluid Number Eighty Seven was looking decidedly happier.

I didn't hurry over cleaning and putting away my injection outfit and re-soaping my arms because I knew that every minute would bring back strength to my patient.

The lightning response to intravenous calcium has always afforded me a simple pleasure and when I pushed my arm in again the difference was remarkable. The previously flaccid uterus gripped at my hand and as the cow went into a long expulsive effort she turned her head, looked back at me and opened her mouth in a muffled bellow. It was not a sound of pain but rather as though she was saying, 'I'm back in business now.'

'All right, my lass,' I replied. 'I'll stay with you till it's all over.'

At other times I might have been a little chary of being overheard conversing with a cow, but with the clamour of buckets and the nonstop blasting of the radio there was no chance of that happening.

I knew that I had to guide the calf back into the correct position and that it would take time, but I had a strange sense of one-ness with this animal because neither of us seemed to be of the slightest importance in the present setting. As I lay there face down on the concrete which grew harder all the time and with the milkers stumbling over my prostrate form I felt very much alone. There was just myself and Number Eighty Seven for it.

Another thing I missed was the sense of occasion. There was a compensation in many an arduous calving in the feeling of a little drama being enacted; the worried farmer, attentive stocksmen, the danger of losing the calf or even the mother – it was a gripping play and there was no doubt the vet was the leading man. He may even be the villain but he was number one. And here I was now, a scrabbling nonentity with hardly a mention in the cast. It was the shape of things to come.

And yet . . . and yet . . . the job was still there. I lifted the calf's lower jaw and as the cow gave a heave I eased it over the brim of the pelvis. Then I groped for the tiny legs and straightened them as another expulsive effort pushed the little creature towards me. He was definitely on his way now.

I didn't rush things – just lay there and let the cow get on with it. My worst moment was when one of the men came to put the milking machine on the temperamental animal on my right. As he tried to step up beside her she swung round, cocked her tail and sent a jet of faeces cascading across my back.

The man pushed her back into place, slipped on the teat cups then lifted the hose which was lying ready for swilling down the byre. A moment later I felt the icy flow of water playing from my shoulders to my hips then the application of a spare udder cloth as the helpful fellow cleaned me off.

'Thanks very much,' I gasped. And I was really grateful. It was the only attention I had received all morning.

Within half an hour the feet appeared at the vulva followed by a wet nose whose nostrils twitched reassuringly. But they were big feet – this would be a bull calf and his final entry into the world could be a tight squeeze.

I got into a sitting position and gripped a slippery cloven hoof in each hand. Leaning back, feet against the dung channel, I addressed Number Eighty Seven again.

'Come on, old lass. A couple of good shoves and we're there.'

She responded with a mighty inflation of the abdomen and the calf surged towards me as I pulled, giving me a glimpse of a broad forehead and a pair of slightly puzzled eyes. For a moment I thought the ears were going to slip through but then the cow relaxed and the head disappeared back inside.

'Once more, girl!' I pleaded, and this time it seemed that she had decided to stop playing around and get the job over with. She gave a prolonged strain which sent head and shoulders through, and as I hauled away I had only that momentary panic I always feel that the hips might jam in the pelvis. But this one didn't stick and came sliding beautifully on to my lap.

Puffing slightly, I got to my feet and parted the hind legs. Sure enough the little scrotum was there; he was a fine bull calf. I pulled some hay from the rack and dried him off and within minutes he was sitting up, sniffing and snorting, looking around him with interest.

He wasn't the only interested party. His mother, craning round in her neck chain, gazed fascinatedly at the new arrival before releasing a deafening bellow. I seized the front feet again and pulled the calf up to the front of the stall where the cow after a brief examination began to lick him from head to tail. Then as I watched, entranced, she suddenly rose to her feet so that she could reach some of the little creature's more inaccessible corners.

I smiled to myself. So that was that. She had got over the milk fever and had a nice live calf, too. All was well with Number Eighty Seven.

Mr Blackburn came up and stood by my side and I realised that the noise in the byre had subsided. The milking was finished.

The farmer took off his white hat and wiped away the sweat from his brow. 'By gaw, that was a rush. We were shorthanded this mornin' and I was sure we were goin' to miss that milk feller. He's a terror – won't wait a minute, and I've had to chase after 'im in a tractor with the churns afore now.'

As he finished speaking a hen leaped with a squawk from the rack, Mr Blackburn reached forward and lifted a warm new-laid egg out of the hay.

He inspected it for a moment then turned to me. 'Have you 'ad your breakfast?'

'No, of course not.'

'Well tell your missus to put this in the fryin' pan,' he said, handing me the egg.

'Oh, thank you very much, Mr Blackburn, I'll enjoy that.'

He nodded and continued to stand there, gazing at the cow and calf. Dairy farming is one of the hardest ways of making a living and this pre-dawn turmoil was an every day occurrence in his life. But I knew he was pleased with my efforts because he faced me suddenly and his weathered features broke into a delighted grin. Without warning he gave me a friendly thump on the chest.

'Good old Jim!' he said, and walked away.

I dressed, got into the car and placed my egg with the utmost care on the dash, then I eased myself gingerly on to the seat, because that hosing had sent a pint or two of dirty water down into my underpants and sitting down was intensely uncomfortable.

As I drove away the darkness was thinning into the grey beginning of a new day and around me the white bulk of the fells began to lift from the half light – massive, smooth and inexpressibly cold.

I looked at the egg rocking gently on the dash, and smiled to myself. I could still see Mr Blackburn's sudden grin, still feel his punch on the chest, and my main sensation was of reassurance.

Systems may be changing, but cows and calves and Yorkshire farmers were just the same.

Chapter Twelve

On my wage of seven and threepence a day, out of which was deducted maintenance for wife and child, I was unable to indulge in high living even if I had wanted to, but one evening in Windsor I decided to allow myself the luxury of one glass of beer, and as I pushed open the pub doorway the first thing I saw was a man sitting at the corner of the bar with a small dog under his chair.

Little things like that could lift me effortlessly back to my old life, and I could almost hear George Wilks, the auctioneer, in the Drovers' Arms at Darrowby.

'I reckon that's the best pub terrier I've ever seen.' He bent down from the bar counter and patted Theo's shaggy head as it protruded from beneath his master's stool.

It struck me that 'pub terrier' wasn't a bad description. Theo was small and mainly white, though there were odd streaks of black on his flanks, and his muzzle had a bushy outgrowth of hair which made him undeniably attractive but still more mysterious.

I warmed to a Scottish colleague recently who, when pressed by a lady client to diagnose her dog's breed and lineage replied finally, 'Madam, I think it would be best just to call him a wee broon dug.'

By the same token Theo could be safely be described as a wee white dug, but in Yorkshire the expression 'pub terrier' would be more easily understood.

His master, Paul Cotterell, looked down from his high perch.

'What's he saying about you, old chap?' he murmured languidly, and at the sound of his voice the little animal leaped, eager and wagging, from his retreat.

Theo spent a considerable part of his life between the four metal legs of that stool, as did his master on the seat. And it often seemed to me to be a waste of time for both of them. I often took my own dog, Sam, into pubs and he would squat beneath my seat, but whereas it was an occasional thing with me – maybe once or twice a week – with Paul Cotterell it was an unvarying ritual. Every night from eight o'clock onwards he could be found sitting there at the end of the bar of the Drovers' Arms, pint glass in front of him, little curly pipe drooping over his chin.

For a young man like him – he was a bachelor in his late thirties – and a person of education and intelligence, it seemed a sterile existence.

He turned to me as I approached the counter. 'Hello, Jim, let me get you a drink.'

'That's very kind of you, Paul,' I replied. 'I'll have a pint.'

'Splendid.' He turned to the barmaid with easy courtesy. 'Could I trouble you, Moyra?'

We sipped our beer and we chatted. This time it was about the music festival at Brawton and then we got on to music in general. As with any other topic I had discussed with him he seemed to know a lot about it.

'So you're not all that keen on Bach?' he enquired lazily.

'No, not really. Some of it, yes, but on the whole I like something a bit more emotional. Elgar, Beethoven, Mozart. Even Tchaikovsky – I suppose you highbrows look down your noses at him?'

He shrugged, puffed his little pipe and regarded me with a half smile, one eyebrow raised. He often looked like that and it made me feel he ought to wear a monocle. But he didn't enthuse about Bach, though it seemed he was his favourite composer. He never enthused about anything, and he listened with that funny look on his face while I rhapsodised about the Elgar violin concerto.

Paul Cotterell was from the south of England, but the locals had long since forgiven him for that because he was likeable, amusing, and always ready to buy anybody a drink from his corner in the Drovers'. To me, he had a charm which was very English; casual, effortless. He never got excited, he was always polite and utterly self-contained.

'While you're here, Jim,' he said. 'I wonder if you'd have a look at Theo's foot?'

'Of course.' It is one of a vet's occupational hazards that wherever he goes socially it is taken for granted that there is nothing he would rather do than dole out advice or listen to symptoms. 'Let's have him up.'

'Here, boy, come on.' Paul patted his knee and the little dog jumped up and sat there, eyes sparkling with pleasure. And I thought as I always did that Theo should be in pictures. He was the perfect film dog with that extraordinarily fuzzy laugh-face. People paid good money to see dogs just like him in cinemas all over the world.

'All right, Theo,' I said, scooping him from his master's knee. 'Where's the trouble?'

Paul indicated the right fore foot with the stem of his pipe. 'It's that one. He's been going a bit lame off and on for the last few days.'

'I see.' I rolled the little animal on his back and then laughed. 'Oh, he's only got a broken claw. There's a little big hanging off here. He must have caught it on a stone. Hang on a minute.' I delved in my pocket for the scissors which always dwelt there. A quick snip and the job was done.

'Is that all?' asked Paul.

'Yes, that's it.'

One eyebrow went up mockingly as he looked at Theo. 'So that's what you were making all the fuss about, eh? Silly old trout.' He snapped his fingers. 'Back you go.'

The little dog obediently leaped to the carpet and disappeared into his sanctuary beneath the stool. And at that moment I had a flash of intuition about Paul – about his charm which I had often admired and envied. He didn't really care. He was fond of his dog, of course. He took him everywhere with him, exercised him regularly by the river, but there was none of the anxiety, the almost desperate concern which I had so often seen in the eyes of my clients when I dealt with even the most trivial of their ailments. They cared too much – as I have always done with my own animals.

And of course he was right. It was an easier and more comfortable way to live. Caring made you vulnerable while Paul cruised along, impregnable. That attractive casualness, the nonchalant good manners, the imperturbability – they all had their roots in the fact that nothing touched him very deeply.

And despite my snap diagnosis of his character I still envied him. I have always been blown around too easily by my emotions; it must be lovely to be like Paul. And the more I thought about it the more I realised how everything fitted in. He had never cared enough to get married. Even Bach, with his mathematical music, was part of the pattern.

'I think that major operation deserves another pint, Jim.' He smiled his lop-sided smile. 'Unless you demand a higher fee?'

I laughed. I would always like him. We are all different and we have to act as we are made, but as I started my second glass I thought again of his carefree life. He had a good job in the government offices in Brawton, no domestic responsibilities, and every night he sat on that same stool drinking beer with his dog underneath. He hadn't a worry in the world.

Anyway, he was part of the Darrowby scene, part of something I liked, and since I have always hated change it was in a sense reassuring to know that no matter what night you went into the Drovers' you would find Paul Cotterell in the corner and Theo's shaggy muzzle peeping from below.

I felt like that one night when I dropped in near closing time.

'D'you think he's got worms?' The question was typically off-hand.

'I don't know, Paul. Why do you ask?'

He drew on his pipe. 'Oh I just thought he looked a bit thin lately. Come up, Theo!'

The little dog, perched on his master's knee, looked as chirpy as ever and when I reached over and lifted him he licked my hand. But his ribs did feel rather prominent.

'Mmm, yes,' I said. 'Maybe he has lost a bit of weight. Have you noticed him passing any worms?'

'I haven't, actually.'

'Not even little bits – whitish segments sticking round his rear?'

'No, Jim.' He shook his head and smiled. 'But I haven't looked all that closely, old boy.'

'Okay,' I said. 'Let's worm him, just in case. I'll bring in some tablets tomorrow night. You'll be here . . .?'

The eyebrow went up. 'I think that's highly probable.'

Theo duly got his worm tablets and after that there was a space of several weeks when I was too busy to visit the Drovers'. When I finally did get in it was a Saturday night and the Athletic Club dance was in full spate. A rhythmic beat drifted from the ballroom, the little bar was packed, and the domino players were under pressure, squashed into a corner by the crush of dinner jackets and backless dresses.

In the noise and heat I struggled towards the bar, thinking that the place was unrecognisable. But there was one feature unchanged – Paul Cotterell on his stool at the far end of the counter.

I squeezed in next to him and saw he was wearing his usual tweed jacket. 'Not dancing, Paul?'

He half closed his eyes, shook his head slowly and smiled at me over his bent little pipe. 'Not for me, old boy,' he murmured. 'Too much like work.'

I glanced down and saw that something else hadn't changed. Theo was there, too, keeping his nose well clear of the milling feet. I ordered two beers and we tried to converse, but it was difficult to shout above the babel. Arms kept poking between us towards the counter, red faces pushed into ours and shouted greetings. Most of the time we just looked around us.

Then Paul leaned close and spoke into my ear. 'I gave Theo those pills but he's still getting thinner.'

'Really?' I shouted back. 'That's unusual.'

'Yes . . . perhaps you'd have a look at him?'

I nodded, he snapped his fingers and the little dog was on his knee in an instant. I reached and lifted him onto mine and I noticed immediately that he was lighter in my hands.

'You're right,' I said. 'He's still losing weight.'

Balancing the dog in my lap, I pulled down an eyelid and saw that the conjunctiva was pale.

I shouted again. 'He's anaemic.' I felt my way back over his face and behind the angle of the jaw I found that the post pharyngeal lymph glands were greatly enlarged. This was strange. Could he have some form of mouth or throat infection? I looked helplessly around me, wishing fervently that Paul wouldn't invariably consult me about his dog in a pub. I wanted to examine the animal, but I couldn't very well deposit him among the glasses on the bar.

I was trying to get a better grip with a view to looking down his throat when my hand slipped behind his fore leg and my heart gave a sudden thump as I encountered the axillary gland. It, too, was grossly enlarged. I whipped my fingers back into his groin and there was the inguinal gland, prominent as an egg. The prescapular was the same, and as I groped feverishly I realised that every superficial lymph gland was several times its normal size.

Hodgkin's disease. For a few moments I was oblivious of the shouting and laughter, the muffled blare of music. Then I looked at Paul who was regarding me calmly as he puffed his pipe. How could I tell him in these surroundings? He would ask me what Hodgkin's disease was and I would have to explain that it was a cancer of the lymphatic system and that his dog was surely going to die.

As my thoughts raced I stroked the shaggy head and Theo's comic whiskered face turned towards me. People jostled past, hands reached out and bore gins and whiskies and beers past my face, a fat man threw his arm round my neck.

I leaned across. 'Paul,' I said.

'Yes, Jim?'

'Will you . . . will you bring Theo round to the surgery tomorrow morning. It's ten o'clock on a Sunday.'

Momentarily the eyebrow twitched upwards, then he nodded.

'Right, old boy.'

I didn't bother to finish my drink. I began to push my way towards the door and as the crush closed around me I glanced back. The little dog's tail was just disappearing under the stool.

Next day I had one of those early waking mornings when I started tossing around at six o'clock and finished by staring at the ceiling.

Even after I had got my feet on the ground and brought Helen a cup of tea the waiting was interminable until the moment arrived which I had been dreading – when I faced Paul across the surgery table with Theo standing between us.

I told him straight away. I couldn't think of any easy way to lead up to it.

His expression did not change, but he took his pipe out of his mouth and looked steadily at me, then at the dog and back again at me.

'Oh,' he said at last. 'I see.'

I didn't say anything and he slowly ran his hand along the little animal's back. 'Are you quite sure, Jim?'

'Absolutely. I'm terribly sorry.'

'Is there no treatment?'

'There are various palliatives, Paul, but I've never seen any of them do any good. The end result is always the same.'

'Yes . . .' He nodded slowly. 'But he doesn't look so bad. What will happen if we don't do anything?'

I paused. 'Well, as the internal glands enlarge, various things will happen. Ascites – dropsy – will develop in the abdomen. In fact you see he's a little bit pot-bellied now.'

'Yes . . . I do see, now you mention it. Anything else?'

'As the thoracic glands get bigger he'll begin to pant.'

'I've noticed that already. He's breathless after a short walk.'

'And all the time he'll get thinner and thinner and more debilitated.'

Paul looked down at his feet for a few moments then faced me. 'So what it amounts to is that he's going to be pretty miserable for the rest of his life.' He swallowed. 'And how long is that going to be?'

'A few weeks. It varies. Maybe up to three months.'

'Well, Jim.' He smoothed back his hair. 'I can't let that happen. It's my responsibility. You must put him to sleep now, before he really starts to suffer. Don't you agree?'

'Yes, Paul, it's the kindest thing to do.'

'Will you do it immediately – as soon as I am out of that door?'

'I will,' I replied. 'And I promise you he won't know a thing.'

His face held a curious fixity of expression. He put his pipe in his mouth, but it had gone out so he stuffed it into his pocket. Then he leaned forward and patted his dog once on the head. The bushy face with the funny shock of hair round the muzzle turned to him and for a few seconds they looked at each other.

Then, 'Goodbye, old chap,' he muttered and strode quickly from the room.

I kept my promise.

'Good lad, good old Theo,' I murmured, and stroked the face and ears again and again as the little creature slipped peacefully away. Like all vets I hated doing this, painless though it was, but to me there has always been a comfort in the knowledge that the last thing these helpless animals knew was the sound of a friendly voice and the touch of a gentle hand.

Sentimental, maybe. Not like Paul. He had been practical and utterly rational in the way he had acted. He had been able to do the right thing because he was not at the mercy of his emotions.

Later, over a Sunday lunch which I didn't enjoy as much as usual I told Helen about Theo.

I had to say something because she had produced a delicious pot roast on the gas ring which was our only means of cooking and I wasn't doing justice to her skill.

Sitting at our bench I looked down at her. It was my turn for the high stool.

'You know, Helen,' I said. 'That was an object lesson for me. The way Paul acted, I mean. If I'd been in his position I'd have shilly-shallied – tried to put off something which was inevitable.'

She thought for a moment. 'Well, a lot of people would.'

'Yes, but he didn't.' I put down my knife and fork and stared at the wall. 'He behaved in a mature way. I suppose Paul has one of those personalities you read about. Well-adjusted, completely adequate.'

'Come on, Jim, eat your lunch. I know it was a sad thing but it had to be done and you mustn't start criticising yourself. Paul is Paul and you are you.'

I started again on the meat but I couldn't repress the rising sense of my own inadequacy. Then as I glanced to one side I saw that my wife was smiling up at me.

I felt suddenly reassured. It seemed that she at least didn't seem to mind that I was me.

That was on the Sunday, and on Tuesday morning I was handing out some wart lotion to Mr Sangster who kept a few dairy cows down by the station.

'Dab that on the udder night and morning after milking,' I said. 'I think you'll find that the warts will start to drop off after a week or two.'

'Thank ye.' He handed over half a crown and I was dropping it into the desk drawer when he spoke again.

'Bad job about Paul Cotterell, wasn't it?'

'What do you mean?'

'Ah thought you'd have heard,' he said. 'He's dead.'

'Dead!' I stared at him stupidly. 'How . . . what . . .?'

'Found 'im this mornin'. He did away with 'isself.'

I leaned with both hands on the desk. 'Do you mean . . . suicide?'

'Aye, that's what they say. Took a lot o' pills. It's all ower t'town.'

I found myself hunching over the day book, sightlessly scanning the list of calls while the farmer's voice seemed to come from far away.

'It's a bad job, right enough. He were a nice feller. Reckon everybody liked 'im.'

Later that day I was passing Paul's lodgings when I saw his landlady, Mrs Clayton, in the doorway. I pulled up and got out of the car.

'Mrs Clayton,' I said. 'I still can't believe this.'

'Nor can I, Mr Herriot, it's terrible.' Her face was pale, her eyes red. 'He was with me six years, you know – he was like a son.'

'But why on earth . . .?'

'Oh, it was losin' his dog that did it. He just couldn't stand it.'

A great wave of misery rose and engulfed me and she put her hand on my arm.

'Don't look like that, Mr Herriot. It wasn't your fault. Paul told me all about it and nobody could have saved Theo. People die of that, never mind dogs.'

I nodded dumbly and she went on.

'But I'll tell you something in confidence, Mr Herriot. Paul wasn't able to stand things like you or me. It was the way he was made – you see he suffered from depression.'

'Depression! Paul . . .?'

'Oh yes, he's been under the doctor for a long time and takin' pills regular. He allus put a brave face on, but he's had nervous trouble off and on for years.'

'Nervous trouble . . . I'd never have dreamed . . .'

'No, nobody would, but that's how it was. He had an unhappy childhood from what I made out. Maybe that's why he was so fond of his dog. He got too attached to him, really.'

'Yes . . . yes . . .'

She took out a screwed up handkerchief and blew her nose. 'Well, as I said, the poor lad had a rough time most of his life, but he was brave.'

There didn't seem anything else to say. I drove away out of the town and the calm green hills offered a quiet contrast to the turmoil which can fill a man's mind. So much for Herriot as a judge of character. I couldn't have been more wrong, but Paul had fought his secret battle with a courage which had deceived everybody.

I reflected on the object lesson which I thought he had given me, but in fact it was a lesson of another kind and one which I have never forgotten; that there are countless people like Paul who are not what they seem.

Chapter Thirteen

The shock of Paul Cotterell's death stayed with me for a long time, and in fact I know I have never quite got over it because even now when the company in the bar of the Drovers' has changed and I am one of the few old faces left from thirty-five years ago I can still see the jaunty figure on the corner stool and the bushy face peeping from beneath.

It was the kind of experience I didn't want repeated in my lifetime yet, uncannily, I ran into the same sort of thing almost immediately afterwards.

It couldn't have been more than a week after Paul's funeral that Andrew Vine brought his fox terrier to the surgery.

I put the little dog on the table and examined each of his eyes carefully in turn.

'I'm afraid he's getting worse,' I said.

Without warning the man slumped across the table and buried his face in his hands.

I put my hand on his shoulder. 'What is it, Andrew? What on earth's the matter?'

At first he did not answer but stayed there, huddled grotesquely by the side of his dog as great sobs shook his body.

When he spoke at last it was into his hands and his voice was hoarse and desperate. 'I can't stand it! If Digger goes blind I'll kill myself!'

I looked down at the bowed head in horrified disbelief. It couldn't be happening again. Not so soon after Paul. And yet there were similarities. Andrew was another bachelor in his thirties and the terrier was his constant companion. He lived in lodgings and appeared to have no worries though he was a shy, diffident man with a fragile look about his tall stooping frame and pallid face.

He had first consulted me about Digger several months ago.

'I call him that because he's dug large holes in the garden ever since his puppy days,' he said with a half smile, looking at me almost apprehensively from large dark eyes.

I laughed. 'I hope you haven't brought him to me to cure that, because I've never read anything in the books about it.'

'No, no, it's about something else – his eyes. And he's had that trouble since he was a pup, too.'

'Really? Tell me.'

'Well, when I first got him he had sort of mattery eyes, but the breeder said he'd probably just got some irritant in them and it would soon clear up. And in fact it did. But he's never been quite right. He always seems to have a little discomfort in his eyes.'

'How do you mean?'

'He rubs the side of his face along the carpet and he blinks in bright light.'

'I see.' I pulled the little animal's face round towards me and looked intently at the eyelids. My mind had been busy as he spoke and I was fairly sure I should find either entropion (inversion of the eyelids) or distichiasis (an extra row of lashes rubbing against the eyeball) but there was no sign of either. The surface of the cornea, too, looked normal, except perhaps that the deeper structure of lens and iris were not as easy to define as usual.

I moved over to a cupboard for the ophthalmoscope. 'How old is he now?'

'About a year.'

'So he's had this for about ten months?'

'Yes, about that. But it varies a lot. Most of the time he seems normal then there are days when he goes and lies in his basket with his eyes half closed and you can tell there's something wrong. Not pain, really. More like discomfort, as I said.'

I nodded and hoped I was looking wise but none of this added up to anything familiar. I switched on the little light on the ophthalmoscope and peered into the depths of that most magical and delicate of all organs, down through the lens to the brilliant tapestry of the retina with its optic papilla and branching blood vessels. I couldn't find a thing wrong.

'Does he still dig holes?' I asked. When baffled I often snatch at straws and I wondered if the dog was suffering from a soil irritation.

Andrew shook his head. 'No, very seldom now, and anyway, his bad days are never associated with his digging.'

'Is that so?' I rubbed my chin. The man was obviously ahead of me with his thinking and I had an uncomfortable feeling of bewilderment. People were always bringing their dogs in with 'bad eyes' and there was invariably something to be seen, some cause to be found. 'And would you say that this was one of his bad days?'

'Well I thought so this morning, but he seems a bit better now. Still, he's a bit blinky, don't you think?'

'Yes . . . maybe so.' Digger did appear to be reluctant to open his eyes fully to the sunshine streaming through the surgery window. And occasionally he kept them closed for a second or two as though he wasn't very happy. But damn it, nothing gave me the slightest clue.

I didn't tell the owner that I hadn't the faintest idea what was wrong with his dog. Such remarks do not inspire confidence. Instead, I took refuge in businesslike activity.

'I'm going to give you some lotion,' I said briskly. 'Put a few drops into his eyes three times daily. And let me know how he goes on. It's possible he has some long-standing infection in there.'

I handed over a bottle of 2% boric acid solution and patted Digger's head. 'I hope that will clear things up for you, lad,' I said, and the stumpy tail wagged in reply. He was a sharp looking little animal, attractive and good-natured and a fine specimen of the smooth-haired breed with his long head and neck, pointed nose and beautifully straight limbs.

He jumped from the table and leaped excitedly around his master's legs.

I laughed. 'He's eager to go, like most of my patients.' I bent and slapped him playfully on the rump. 'My word, doesn't he look fit!'

'He is fit.' Andrew smiled proudly. 'In fact I often think that apart from those eyes he's a perfect little physical machine. You should see him out in the fields – he can run like a whippet.'

'I'll bet he can. Keep in touch, will you?' I waved them out of the door and turned to my other work, mercifully unaware that I had just embarked on one of the most frustrating and traumatic cases of my career.

After that first time I took special notice of Digger and his owner. Andrew, a sensitive likeable man, was a representative for a firm of agricultural chemists and, like myself, spent most of his time driving around the Darrowby district. His dog was always with him and I had been perfunctorily amused by the fact that the little animal was invariably peering intently through the windscreen, his paws either on the dash or balanced on his master's hand as he operated the gear lever.

But now that I was personally interested I could discern the obvious delight which the little animal derived from taking in every detail of his surroundings. He missed nothing in his daily journeys. The road ahead, the houses and people, trees and fields which flashed by the windows – these made up his world.

I met him one day when I was exercising Sam up on the high moors which crown the windy summits of the fells. But this was May, the air was soft and a week's hot sunshine had dried the green paths which wandered among the heather. I saw Digger flashing like a white streak over the velvet turf and when he spotted Sam he darted up to him, set himself teasingly for a moment then shot back to Andrew who was standing in a natural circular glade among the harsh brown growth.

Here gorse bushes blazed in full yellow glory and the little dog hurtled round and round the arena, exulting in his health and speed.

'That's what I'd call sheer joy of living,' I said.

Andrew smiled shyly. 'Yes, isn't he beautiful,' he murmured.

'How are the eyes?' I asked.

He shrugged. 'Sometimes good, sometimes not so good. Much the same as before. But I must say he seems easier whenever I put the drops in.'

'But he still has days when he looks unhappy?'

'Yes . . . I have to say yes. Some days they bother him a lot.'

Again the frustration welled in me. 'Let's walk back to the car,' I said. 'I might as well have a look at him.'

I lifted Digger on to the bonnet and examined him again. There wasn't a single abnormality in the eyelids – I had wondered if I had missed something last time – but as the bright sunshine slanted across the eyeballs I could just discern the faintest cloudiness in the cornea. There was a slight keratitis there which hadn't been visible before. But why . . . why?

'He'd better have some stronger lotion.' I rummaged in the car boot. 'I've got some here. We'll try silver nitrate this time.'

Andrew brought him in about a week later. The corneal discoloration had gone – probably the silver nitrate had moved it – but the underlying trouble was unchanged. There was still something sadly wrong. Something I couldn't diagnose.

That was when I started to get really worried. As the weeks passed I bombarded those eyes with everything in the book; oxide of mercury, chinosol, zinc sulphide, ichthyol and a host of other things which are now buried in history.

I had none of the modern sophisticated antibiotic and steroid applications but it would have made no difference if I had. I know that now.

The real nightmare started when I saw the first of the pigment cells beginning to invade the cornea. Sinister brown specks gathering at the limbus and pushing out dark tendrils into the smooth membrane which was Digger's window on the world. I had seen cells like them before. When they came they usually stayed. And they were opaque.

Over the next month I fought them with my pathetic remedies, but they crept inwards, slowly but inexorably, blurring and narrowing Digger's field of vision. Andrew noticed them too, and when he brought the little dog into the surgery he clasped and unclasped his hands anxiously.

'You know, he's seeing less all the time, Mr Herriot. I can tell. He still looks out of the car windows but he used to bark at all sorts of things he didn't like – other dogs for instance – and now he just doesn't spot them. He's – he's losing his sight.'

I felt like screaming or kicking the table, but since that wouldn't have helped I just looked at him.

'It's that brown stuff isn't it?' he said. 'What is it?'

'It's called pigmentary keratitis, Andrew. It sometimes happens when the cornea – the front of the eyeball – has been inflamed over a long period, and it is very difficult to treat. I'll do the best I can.'

My best wasn't enough. That slow, creeping tide was pitiless, and as the pigment cells were laid down thicker and thicker the resulting layer was almost black, lowering a dingy curtain between Digger and all the things he had gazed at so eagerly.

And all the time I suffered a long gnawing worry, a helpless wretchedness as I contemplated the inevitable.

It was when I examined the eyes five months after I had first seen them that Andrew broke down. There was hardly anything to be seen of the original corneal structure now; just a brown-black opacity which left only minute chinks for moments of sight. Blindness was not far away.

I patted the man's shoulder again. 'Come on, Andrew. Come over here and sit down.' I pulled over the single wooden chair in the consulting room.

He staggered across the floor and almost collapsed on the seat. He sat there, head in hands, for some time then raised a tearstained face to me. His expression was distraught.

'I can't bear the thought of it,' he gasped. 'A friendly little thing like Digger – he loves everybody. What has he ever done to deserve this?'

'Nothing, Andrew. It's just one of the sad things which happen. I'm terribly sorry.'

He rolled his head from side to side. 'Oh God, but it's worse for him. You've seen him in the car – he's so interested in everything. Life wouldn't be worth living for him if he lost his sight. And I don't want to live any more either!'

'You mustn't talk like that, Andrew,' I said. 'That's going too far.' I hesitated. 'Please don't be offended, but you ought to see your doctor.'

'Oh I'm always at the doctor,' he replied dully. 'I'm full of pills right now. He tells me I have a depression.'

The word was like a mournful knell. Coming so soon after Paul it sent a wave of panic through me.

'How long have you been like this?'

'Oh, weeks. I seem to be getting worse.'

'Have you ever had it before?'

'No, never.' He wrung his hands and looked at the floor. 'The doctor says that if I keep on taking the pills I'll get over it, but I'm reaching the end of my tether now.'

'But the doctor is right, Andrew. You've got to stick it and you'll be as good as new.'

'I don't believe it,' he muttered. 'Every day lasts a year. I never enjoy anything. And every morning when I wake up I dread having to face the world again.'

I didn't know what to say or how to help. 'Can I get you a glass of water?'

'No . . . no thanks.'

He turned his deathly pale face up to me again and the dark eyes held a terrible blankness. 'What's the use of going on? I know I'm going to be miserable for the rest of my life.'

I am no psychiatrist but I knew better than to tell somebody in Andrew's condition to snap out of it. And I had a flash of intuition.

'All right,' I said. 'Be miserable for the rest of your life, but while you're about it you've got to look after this dog.'

'Look after him? What can I do? He's going blind. There's nothing anybody can do for him now.'

'You're wrong, Andrew. This is where you start doing things for him. He's going to be lost without your help.'

'How do you mean?'

'Well, you know all those walks you take him – you've got to get him used to the same tracks and paths so that he can trot along on familiar ground without fear. Keep him clear of holes and ditches.'

He screwed up his face. 'Yes, but he won't enjoy the walks any more.'

'He will,' I said. 'You'll be surprised.'

'Oh, but . . .'

'And that nice big lawn at the back of your house where he runs. You'll have to be on the lookout all the time in case there are things left lying around on the grass that he might bump into. And the eye drops – you say they make him more comfortable. Who's going to put them in if you don't?'

'But Mr Herriot . . . you've seen how he always looks out of the car when he's with me . . .'

'He'll still look out.'

'Even if he can't see?'

'Yes.' I put my hand on his arm. 'You must understand, Andrew, when an animal loses his sight he doesn't realise what's happened to him. It's a terrible thing, I know, but he doesn't suffer the mental agony of a human being.'

He stood up and took a long shuddering breath. 'But I'm having the agony. I've been dreading this happening for so long. I haven't been able to sleep for thinking about it. It seems so cruel and unjust for this to strike a helpless animal – a little creature who's never done anybody any harm.' He began to wring his hands again and pace about the room.

'You're just torturing yourself!' I said sharply. 'That's part of your trouble. You're using Digger to punish yourself instead of doing something useful.'

'Oh but what can I do that will really help? All those things you talked about – they can't give him a happy life.'

'Oh but they can. Digger can be happy for years and years if you really work at it. It's up to you.'

Like a man in a dream he bent and gathered his dog into his arms and shuffled along the passage to the front door. As he went down the steps into the street I called out to him.

'Keep in touch with your doctor, Andrew. Take your pills regularly – and remember.' I raised my voice to a shout. 'Remember you've got a job to do with that dog!'

After Paul I was on a knife edge of apprehension but this time there was no tragic news to shatter me. Instead I saw Andrew Vine frequently, sometimes in the town with Digger on a lead, occasionally in his car with the little white head framed always in the windscreen, and most often in the fields by the river where he seemed to be carrying out my advice by following the good open tracks again and again.

It was by the river that I stopped him one day. 'How are things going, Andrew?'

He looked at me unsmilingly. 'Oh, he's finding his way around not too badly. I keep my eye on him. I always avoid that field over there – there's a lot of boggy places in it.'

'Good, that's the idea. And how are you yourself?'

'Do you really want to know?'

'Yes, of course.'

He tried to smile. 'Well this is one of my good days. I'm just tense and dreadfully unhappy. On my bad days I'm terror-stricken, despairing, utterly desolate.'

'I'm sorry, Andrew.'

He shrugged. 'Don't think I'm wallowing in self-pity. You asked me. Anyway, I have a system. Every morning I look at myself in the mirror and I say, "Okay, Vine, here's another bloody awful day coming up, but you're going to do your job and you're going to look after your dog." '

'That's good, Andrew. And it will all pass. The whole thing will go away and you'll be all right one day.'

'That's what the doctor says.' He gave me a sidelong glance. 'But in the meantime . . .' He looked down at his dog. 'Come on, Digger.'

He turned and strode away abruptly with the little dog trotting after him, and there was something in the set of the man's shoulders and the forward thrust of his head which gave me hope. He was a picture of fierce determination.

My hopes were fulfilled. Both Andrew and Digger won through. I knew that within months, but the final picture in my mind is of a meeting I had with the two of them about two years later. It was on the flat table-land above Darrowby where I had first seen Digger hurtling joyously among the gorse bushes.

He wasn't doing so badly now, running freely over the smooth green turf, sniffing among the herbage, cocking a leg now and then with deep contentment against the drystone wall which ran along the hillside.

Andrew laughed when he saw me. He had put on weight and looked a different person. 'Digger knows every inch of this walk,' he said. 'I think it's just about his favourite spot – you can see how he's enjoying himself.'

I nodded. 'He certainly looks a happy little dog.'

'Yes, he's happy all right. He has a good life and honestly I often forget that he can't see.' He paused. 'You were right, that day in your surgery. You said this would happen.'

'Well that's great, Andrew,' I said. 'And you're happy, too, aren't you?'

'I am, Mr Herriot. Thank God, I am.' A shadow crossed his face. 'When I think how it was then, I can't believe my luck. It was like being in a dark valley, and bit by bit I've climbed out into the sunshine.'

'I can see that. You're as good as new, now.'

He smiled. 'I'm better than that – better than I was before. That terrible experience did me good. Remember you said I was torturing myself? I realised I had spent all my days doing that. I used to take every little mishap of life and beat myself over the head with it.'

'You don't have to tell me, Andrew,' I said ruefully. 'I've always been pretty good at that myself.'

'Well yes, I suppose a lot of us are. But I became an expert and see where it got me. It helped so much to have Digger to look after.' His face lit up and he pointed over the grass. 'Just look at that!'

The little dog had been inspecting an ancient fence, a few rotting planks which were probably part of an old sheep fold, and as we watched he leaped effortlessly between the spars to the other side.

'Marvellous!' I said delightedly. 'You'd think there was nothing wrong with him.'

Andrew turned to me. 'Mr Herriot, when I see a thing like that it makes me wonder. Can a blind dog do such a thing. Do you think . . . do you think there's a chance he can see just a little?'

I hesitated. 'Maybe he can see a bit through that pigment, but it can't be much – a flicker of light and shade, perhaps. I really don't know. But in any case, he's become so clever in his familiar surroundings that it doesn't make much difference.'

'Yes . . . yes.' He smiled philosophically. 'Anyway, we must get on our way. Come on, Digger!'

He snapped his fingers and set off along a track which pushed a vivid green finger through the heather, pointing clean and unbroken to the sunny skyline. His dog bounded ahead of him, not just at a trot but at a gallop.

I have made no secret of the fact that I never really knew the cause of Digger's blindness, but in the light of modern developments in eye surgery I believe it was a condition called keratitis sicca. This was simply not recognised in those early days and anyway, if I had known I could have done little about it. The name means 'dryness of the cornea' and it occurs when the dog is not producing enough tears. At the present time it is treated by instilling artificial tears or by an intricate operation whereby the salivary ducts are transferred to the eyes. But even now, despite these things, I have seen that dread pigmentation taking over in the end.

When I look back on the whole episode my feeling is of thankfulness. All sorts of things help people to pull out of a depression. Mostly it is their family – the knowledge that wife and children are dependent on them – sometimes it is a cause to work for, but in Andrew Vine's case it was a dog.

I often think of the dark valley which closed around him at that time and I am convinced he came out of it on the end of Digger's lead.

Chapter Fourteen

Now that I had done my first solo I was beginning to appreciate the qualities of my instructor. There was no doubt FO Woodham was a very good teacher.

There was a war on and no time for niceties. He had to get green young men into the air on their own without delay and he had done it with me.

I used to fancy myself as a teacher, too, with the boys who came to see practice in Darrowby. I could see myself now, smiling indulgently at one of my pupils.

'You don't see this sort of thing in country practice, David,' I said. He was one of the young people who occasionally came with me on my rounds. Fifteen years old, and like all the others he thought he wanted to be a veterinary surgeon. But at the moment he looked a little bewildered.

I really couldn't blame him. It was his first visit and he had expected to spend a day with me in the rough and tumble of large animal practice in the Yorkshire Dales and now there was this lady with the poodle and Emmeline. The lady's progress along the passage to the consulting room had been punctuated by a series of squeaking noises produced by her squeezing a small rubber doll. At each squeak Lucy advanced a few reluctant steps until a final pressure lured her on to the table. There she stood trembling and looking soulfully around her.

'She won't go anywhere without Emmeline,' the lady explained.

'Emmeline?'

'The doll.' She held up the rubber toy. 'Since this trouble started Lucy has become devoted to her.'

'I see. And what trouble is that?'

'Well, it's been going on for about two weeks now. She's so listless and strange, and she hardly eats anything.'

I reached behind me to the trolley for the thermometer. 'Right, we'll have a look at her. There's something wrong when a dog won't eat.'

The temperature was normal. I went over her chest thoroughly with my stethoscope without finding any unusual sounds. The heart thudded steadily in my ears. Careful palpation of the abdomen revealed nothing out of the way.

The lady stroked Lucy's curly poll and the little animal looked up at her with sorrowful liquid eyes. 'I'm getting really worried about her. She doesn't want to go walks. In fact we can't even entice her from the house without Emmeline.'

'Eh?'

'I say she won't take a step outside unless we squeak Emmeline at her, and then they both go out together. Even then she just trails along like an old dog, and she's only three after all. You know how lively she is normally.'

I nodded. I did know. This little poodle was a bundle of energy. I had seen her racing around the fields down by the river, jumping to enormous heights as she chased a ball. She must be suffering from something pretty severe, but so far I was baffled.

And I wished the lady wouldn't keep on about Emmeline and the squeaking. I shot a side glance at David. I had been holding forth to him, telling him how ours was a scientific profession and that he would have to be really hot at physics, chemistry and biology to gain entrance to a veterinary school, and it didn't fit in with all this.

Maybe I could guide the conversation along more clinical lines.

'Any more symptoms?' I asked. 'Any cough, constipation, diarrhoea? Does she ever cry out in pain?'

The lady shook her head. 'No, nothing like that. She just moons around looking at us with such a pitiful expression and searching for Emmeline.'

Oh dear, there it was again. I cleared my throat. 'She never vomits at all? Especially after a meal?'

'Never. When she does eat a little she goes straight away to find Emmeline and takes her to her basket.'

'Really? Well I can't see that that has anything to do with it. Are you sure she isn't lame at times?'

The lady didn't seem to be listening. 'And when she gets Emmeline into her basket she sort of circles around, scratching the blanket as though she was making a bed for the little thing.'

I gritted my teeth. Would she never stop? Then a light flashed in the darkness. 'Wait a minute,' I said. 'Did you say making a bed?'

'Yes, she scratches around for ages then puts Emmeline down.'

'Ah yes.' The next question would settle it. 'When was she last in season?'

The lady tapped a finger against her cheek. 'Let me see. It was in the middle of May – that would be about nine weeks ago.'

There wasn't a mystery any more.

'Roll her over, please,' I said.

With Lucy stretched on her back, her eyes regarding the surgery ceiling with deep emotion, I ran my fingers over the mammary glands. They were turgid and swollen. I gently squeezed one of the teats and a bead of milk appeared.

'She's got false pregnancy,' I said.

'What on earth is that?' The lady looked at me, round-eyed.

'Oh, it's quite common in bitches. They get the idea they are going to have pups and around the end of the gestation period they start this business. Making a bed for the pups is typical, but some of them actually swell in the abdomen. They do all sorts of peculiar things.'

'My goodness, how extraordinary!' The lady began to laugh. 'Lucy, you silly little thing, worrying us over nothing.' She looked at me across the table. 'How long is she going to be like this?'

I turned on the hot tap and began to wash my hands. 'Not for long. I'll give you some tablets for her. If she's not much better in a week come back for more. But you needn't worry – even if it takes a little bit longer she'll be her old self in the end.'

I went through to the dispensary, put the tablets in a box and handed them over. The lady thanked me then turned to her pet who was sitting on the tiled floor looking dreamily into space.

'Come along, Lucy,' she said, but the poodle took no notice. 'Lucy! Do you hear me? We're going now!' She began to walk briskly along the passage but the little animal merely put her head on one side and appeared to be hearkening to inward music. After a minute her mistress reappeared and regarded her with some exasperation. 'Oh really, you are naughty. I suppose there's only one way.' She opened her handbag and produced the rubber toy.

'Squeak-squeak,' went Emmeline and the poodle raised her eyes with misty adoration. 'Squeak-squeak, squeak-squeak.' The sound retreated along the passage and Lucy followed entranced until she disappeared round the corner.

I turned to David with an apologetic grin. 'Right,' I said, 'we'll get out on the road. I know you want to see farm practice and I assure you it's vastly different from what you've seen here.'

Sitting in the car, I continued. 'Mind you, don't get me wrong. I'm not decrying small animal work. In fact I'd have to admit that it is the most highly skilled branch of the profession and I personally think that small animal surgery is tremendously demanding. Just don't judge it all by Emmeline. Anyway, we have one doggy visit before we go out into the country.'

'What's that?' the lad asked.

'Well, I've had a call from a Mr Rington to say that his dalmatian bitch has completely altered her behaviour. In fact she's acting so strangely that he doesn't want to bring her to the surgery.'

'What do you think that might be?'

I thought for a moment. 'It seems a bit silly, but the first thing that comes to my mind is rabies. This is the most dreadful dog disease of all, but thank heaven we've managed to keep it out of this country so far by strict quarantine regulations. But at college it was hammered into us so forcibly that it is always at the back of my mind even though I don't really expect to see it. But this case of the dalmatian could be anything. I only hope she hasn't turned savage because that's the sort of thing that leads to a dog being put down and I hate that.'

Mr Rington's opening remark didn't cheer me.

'Tessa's become really fierce lately, Mr Herriot. Started moping about and growling a few days ago and frankly I daren't trust her with strangers now. She nailed the postman by the ankle this morning. Most embarrassing.'

My spirits sank lower. 'Actually bit somebody! It's unbelievable – she's such a softie. I've always been able to do anything with her.'

'I know, I know,' he muttered. 'She's marvellous with children, too. I can't understand it. But come and have a look at her.'

The dalmatian was sitting in a corner of the lounge and she glanced up sulkily as we entered. She was a favourite patient and I approached her confidently.

'Hello, Tessa,' I said, and held out my hand. I usually had a tail-lashing, tongue-lolling welcome from this animal but today she froze into complete immobility and her lips withdrew silently from her teeth. It wasn't an ordinary snarl – it was as though the upper lip was operated by strings and there was something unnerving about it.

'What's the matter, old girl?' I enquired, and again the gleaming incisors were soundlessly exposed. And as I stared uncomprehendingly I could see that the eyes were glaring at me with blazing primitive hatred. Tessa was unrecognisable.

'Mr Herriot.' Her owner looked at me apprehensively. 'I don't think I'd go any nearer if I were you.'

I withdrew a pace. 'Yes, I'm inclined to agree with you. I don't think she'd cooperate if I tried to examine her. But never mind, tell me all about her.'

'Well, there's really nothing more to tell,' Mr Rington said helplessly. 'She's just different – like this.'

'Appetite good?'

'Yes, fine. Eats everything in front of her.'

'No unusual symptoms at all?'

'None, apart from the altered temperament. The family can handle her, but quite frankly I think she'd bite any stranger who came too near.'

I ran my fingers through my hair. 'Any change in family circumstances? New baby? Different domestic help? Unusual people coming to the house?'

'No, nothing like that. There's been no change.'

'I ask because animals sometimes act like this out of jealousy or disapproval.'

'Sorry.' Mr Rington shrugged his shoulders. 'Everything is just as it's always been. Only this morning my wife was wondering if Tessa was still cross with us because we kept her indoors for three weeks while she was in season. But that was a long time ago – about two months now.'

I whipped round and faced him. 'Two months?'

'Yes, about that.'

'Surely not again!' I gestured to the owner. 'Would you please lift her up so that she's standing on her hind legs?'

'Like this?' He put his arms round the dalmatian's chest and hoisted till she was in the upright position with her abdomen facing me.

And it was as if I knew beforehand. Because I felt not the slightest surprise when I saw the twin row of engorged teats. It was unnecessary, but I leaned forward, grasped a little nipple and sent a white jet spurting.

'She's bulging with milk,' I said.

'Milk?'

'Yes, she's got a false pregnancy. This is one of the more unusual side effects, but I'll give you some tablets and she'll soon be the docile Tessa again.'

As we got back into the car I had a good idea what the schoolboy was thinking. He would be wondering where the chemistry, physics and biology came in.

'Sorry about that, David,' I said. 'I've been telling you all about the constant variety of a vet's life and the first two cases you see are the same condition. But we are going out to the farms now and as I said, you'll find it very different. I mean, those two cases were really psychological things. You don't get that in country practice. It's a bit rough but it's real and down to earth.'

As we drove into the farmyard I saw the farmer carrying a bag of meal over the cobbles.

I got out of the car with David. 'You've got a pig ill, Mr Fisher?'

'Aye, a big sow. She's in 'ere.' He led the way into a pen and pointed to a huge white pig lying on her side.

'She's been off it for a few days,' he said. 'Hardly eats owt – just picks at her food. And she just lays there all t'time. Ah don't think she's got strength to get to her feet.'

My thermometer had been in the pig's rectum as he spoke and I fished it out and read the temperature. It was 102·2 – dead normal. I auscultated the chest and palpated the abdomen with growing puzzlement. Nothing wrong. I looked over at the trough nearby. It was filled to the brim with fresh meal and water – untouched. And pigs do love their food.

I nudged her thigh with my fist. 'Come on, lass, get up.' And I followed it with a brisk slap across the rump. A healthy pig would have leaped to her feet but the sow never moved.

I tried not to scratch my head. There was something very funny here. 'Has she ever been ill before, Mr Fisher?'

'Nay, never ailed a thing and she's allus been a real lively pig, too. Ah can't reckon it up.'

Nor could I. 'What beats me,' I said, 'is that she doesn't look like a sick animal. She's not trembling or anxious, she's lying there as if she hadn't a care in the world.'

'Aye, you're right, Mr Herriot. She's as 'appy as Larry, but she'll neither move nor eat. It's a rum 'un, isn't it?'

It was very rum indeed. I squatted on my heels, watching the big sow. She reached forward and pushed gently with her snout at the straw bedding round her head. Sick pigs never did that. It was a gesture of well-being. And those little grunts which issued from deep in her chest. They were grunts of deep contentment and there was something familiar about the sound of them ... something lurking at the back of my mind which wouldn't come forward. It was the same with the way the sow eased herself further on to her side, pushing the great stretch of abdomen outward as though in offering.

I had heard and seen it so many times before – the happy sounds, the careful movements. Then I remembered. Of course! She was like a sow with a litter, only there was no litter.

A wave of disbelief flowed over me. Oh no, no, please not a third time! It was dark in the pen and I couldn't get a clear view of the mammary glands.

I turned to the farmer. 'Open the door a little will you, please.'

As the sunshine flooded in everything was obvious. It was mere routine to reach out to the long tumefied udder and squirt the milk against the wall.

I straightened up wearily and was about to make my now commonplace announcement when David did it for me.

'False pregnancy?' he said.

I nodded dumbly.

'What was that?' enquired Mr Fisher.

'Well your sow has got it into her head that she is pregnant,' I said. 'Not only that, but she thinks she has given birth to a litter and she's suckling the imaginary piglets now. You can see it, can't you?'

The farmer gave a long soft whistle. 'Aye ... aye ... you're right. That's what she's doin' ... enjoyin' it, too.' He took off his cap, rubbed the top of his head and put the cap on again. 'Well, there's allus summat new, isn't there?'

It wasn't new to David, of course. Old stuff, in fact, and I didn't want to bore him further with a lengthy dissertation.

'Nothing to worry about, Mr Fisher,' I said hastily. 'Call down to the surgery and I'll give you something to put in her food. She'll soon be back to normal.'

As I left the pen the sow gave a deep sigh of utter fulfilment and moved her position with the utmost care to avoid crushing her phantom family. I looked back to her and I could almost see the long pink row of piglets sucking busily. I shook my head to dispel the vision and went out to the car.

I was opening the door when the farmer's wife trotted towards me. 'I've just had a phone call from your surgery, Mr Herriot. They want you to go to Mr Rogers of East Farm. There's a cow calving.'

An emergency like this in the middle of a round was usually an irritant, but today the news came as a relief. I had promised this schoolboy some genuine country practice and I was beginning to feel embarrassed.

'Well, David,' I said with a light laugh as we drove away. 'You must be thinking all my patients are neurotic. But you're going to see a bit of the real thing now – there's nothing airy-fairy about a calving cow. This is where the hard work of our job comes in. It's often pretty tough fighting against a big straining cow, because you must remember the vet only sees the difficult cases where the calf is laid wrong.'

The situation of East Farm seemed to add weight to my words. We were bumping up the fellside along a narrow track which was never meant for motor cars and I winced as the exhaust grated against the jutting rocks.

The farm was perched almost on the edge of the hilltop and behind it the sparse fields, stolen from the moorland, rolled away to the skyline. The crumbling stonework and broken roof tiles testified to the age of the squat grey house.

I pointed to some figures, faintly visible on the massive stone lintel above the front door. 'What does that date mean to you, David?'

'Sixteen sixty-six, the Great Fire of London,' he replied promptly.

'Well done. Strange to think they were building this place in the same year as old London burned down.'

Mr Rogers appeared, carrying a steaming bucket and a towel. 'She's out in t'field, Mr Herriot, but she's a quiet cow and easy to catch.'

'All right.' I followed him through the gate. It was another little annoyance when the farmer didn't have the cow inside for me but again I felt that if David wanted to be a vet he ought to know that a lot of our work was carried out in the open, often in the cold and rain.

Even now on this July morning a cool breeze whipped round my chest and back as I pulled off my shirt. It was never very warm in the high country of the Dales but I felt at home here. With the cow standing patiently as the farmer held her halter, the bucket perched among the tufts of wiry grass, and only a few stunted wind-bent trees breaking the harsh sweep of green, it seemed that at last this boy was seeing me in my proper place.

I soaped my arms to the shoulders. 'Hold the tail, will you, David. This is where I find out what kind of job it's going to be.'

As I slipped my hand into the cow it struck me that it would be no bad thing if it was a hard calving. If the lad saw me losing a bit of sweat it would give him a truer picture of the life in front of him.

'Sometimes these jobs take an hour or more,' I said. 'But you have the reward of delivering a new living creature. Seeing a calf wriggling on the ground at the end of it is the biggest thrill in practice.'

I reached forward, my mind alive with the possibilities. Posterior? Head back? Breech? But as I groped through the open cervix into the uterus I felt a growing astonishment. There was nothing there.

I withdrew my arm and leaned for a moment on the hairy rump. The day's events were taking on a dreamlike quality. Then I looked up at the farmer.

'There's no calf in this cow, Mr Rogers.'

'Eh?'

'She's empty. She's calved already.'

The farmer gazed around him, scanning the acres of bare grass. 'Well where the hangment is the thing? This cow was messin' about last night and I thought she'd calve, but there was nowt to find this mornin'.'

His attention was caught by a cry from the right.

'Hey, Willie! Just a minute, Willie!' It was Bob Sellars from the next farm. He was leaning over the drystone wall about twenty yards away.

'What's matter, Bob?'

'Ah thowt ah'd better tell ye. Ah saw that cow hidin' her calf this mornin'.'

'Hidin' . . .? What are ye on about?'

'Ah'm not jokin' nor jestin', Willie. She hid it on yon gutter ower there and every time t'calf tried to get out she pushed it back in again.'

'But . . . nay, nay, I can't 'ave that. I've never heard of such a thing. Have you, Mr Herriot?'

I shook my head, but the whole thing seemed to fit in with the air of fantasy which had begun to pervade the day's work.

Bob Sellars began to climb over the wall. 'Awright, if ye won't believe me I'll show ye.'

He led the way to the far end of the field where a dry ditch ran along the base of the wall. 'There 'e is!' he said triumphantly.

And there indeed he was. A tiny red and white calf half concealed by the long herbage. He was curled comfortably in his grassy bed, his nose resting on his fore legs.

When the little creature saw his mother he staggered to his feet and clambered shakily up the side of the ditch, but no sooner had he gained the level of the field than the big cow, released now from her halter, lowered her head and gently nudged him back in again.

Bob waved his arm. 'There y'are, she's hidin' it, isn't she?'

Mr Rogers said nothing and I merely shrugged my shoulders, but twice more the calf managed to scramble from the ditch and twice more his mother returned him firmly with her head.

'Well it teks a bit o' believin,' the farmer murmured, half to himself. 'She's had five calves afore this and we've taken 'em straight away from 'er as we allus do. Maybe she wants to keep this 'un for 'erself? I dunno . . . I dunno . . .' His voice trailed away.

Later, as we rattled down the stony track, David turned to me. 'Do you think that cow really hid her calf . . . so that she could keep it for herself?'

I stared helplessly through the glass of the windscreen. 'Well anybody would tell you it's impossible, but you saw what happened. I'm like Mr Rogers, I just don't know.' I paused as the car dipped into a deep rut and sent us bobbing about. 'But you see some funny things at our job.'

The schoolboy nodded thoughtfully. 'Yes, it seems to me that yours is a funny life altogether.'

Chapter Fifteen

'Would you care to come and dice with death?'

Flight Lieutenant Cramond looked down at me, his puckish features creased into a mischievous smile. I was sitting at a table in my flying suit waiting to be called for a grading test and I stood up hurriedly.

'You mean . . . go up with you, sir?'

'Yes, that's right.'

'Well, I'm just waiting for . . .'

'Oh I know all about that.' He waved a careless hand. 'But there's no hurry. You've time for a bit of fun first.'

'Just as you say, sir,' I said, and followed him out of the hut. Nobody was quite sure of Flt Lt Cramond's status at the flying school. He wasn't one of the regular instructors – he was a much older man – but he was obviously regarded with respect by his fellow officers and seemed to adopt a freelance role.

He occasionally descended on an unsuspecting trainee pilot with his familiar request, 'Would you care to dice with death?' and this was invariably followed by a joy ride round the sky, a dazzling display of aerobatics which looked wonderful from the ground but could be shattering in the air.

I had seen pupils tottering green-faced from the Tiger Moth after these sessions, and there seemed to be no particular reason why he did it at all. But there was no doubt he was a brilliant flyer. It was rumoured that he had been a stunt pilot with Alan Cobham's famous air circus, but there were so many rumours in the RAF – like the one about the bromide in the tea – that I never really knew if it was true.

However, I got into the aircraft with a feeling of pleasant anticipation. Whatever happened I wouldn't feel ill, being blessed with a stomach which never got queasy with motion. Over-indulgence can have disastrous effects on my digestive apparatus but otherwise I am immune. I have been on little cattle boats in force nine gales when even the crew were groaning in their bunks, but land-lubber Herriot was still enjoying his four meals a day. It was the same in the air.

I soon had reason to be grateful for this blessing because Flt Lt Cramond threw the little aircraft around the sky in an alarming manner, climbing high then fluttering earthwards like a falling autumn leaf, doing repeated loops and spins. Most of it I enjoyed because he was a likeable man and the eyes in the mirror were humorous and friendly.

He kept up a running commentary as he went through his repertoire.

'This is Cramond's famous hangover cure,' he announced before going into a violent manoeuvre which involved a lot of flying upside down. To a novice like myself it was a strange sensation to be hanging in my straps, looking up at farmhouses and down at the cloud-strewn sky.

That was the only time I didn't feel too happy, because those canvas straps were attached to the sides of the cockpit by frayed wires which twanged and groaned disturbingly as I hung there. It was a long way to the ground and I kept a hand on the parachute release just in case.

I was wondering how long we were going to stay in this position when he rolled over and went into a long dive. Down and down we roared, heading nose first for the peaceful farm land, and just as I had concluded that we must certainly plunge straight into the earth he levelled off and we skimmed through a long cornfield with the wheels of the undercarriage trailing among the golden ears.

'This is nice, isn't it?' Flt Lt Cramond murmured.

And it was nice, too. There was no crop spraying in those days and the scent of the wild flowers growing among the corn drifted into the open cockpit. The heady fragrance took me back in a moment to that picnic with Helen.

There were many things leading up to the picnic. It all started when I caught Helen in the pantry, stealing the porridge oats. She was standing with the packet in her hand, scooping the contents into her mouth with a spoon, and she started guiltily when she saw me.

'You're at it again!' I exclaimed. I snatched the packet from her fingers. 'It's nearly empty! How many do you go through a week?'

She looked at me with a stricken face and shook her head. 'I don't know.'

'But Helen – raw porridge oats! You're not supposed to eat them that way. Not a packet at a time, anyway. You'll give yourself indigestion.'

'I'm all right so far.' Her spoon twitched and I could see she wanted more.

'But why don't you cook them and eat ordinary porridge – do you good that way.'

She pouted. 'Don't want ordinary porridge.'

I gave her an exasperated stare and left her to it. I'd had no experience with pregnant women but I had heard of these cravings and no doubt they were to be respected. With Helen it had started with oranges – oranges morning noon and night – and I was rather pleased because I thought they would be good for her with all those vitamins. But it wasn't long before she went off the oranges and on to the porridge and I started to worry.

However it was needless. Within a week or two the porridge had lost all its attractions and Helen was on the custard. And it was cooked custard, good wholesome stuff made with plenty of milk, and though Helen drank it by the gallon instead of the pint I felt sure it must be beneficial.

The custard phase lasted for some time. Whatever I was doing around our bed-sitter Helen would be crouched over her bowl of custard, imbibing it effortlessly, spoonful by spoonful, watching me with inward-looking eyes. When I was working in the garden I had only to glance up to the little window under the tiles to see that rapt face looking out at me and the spoon rising and falling from the custard bowl.

Such nourishing material, I thought, could no nothing but good both for my wife and for our first born, but before I knew where I was the trouble with the smells began.

It was totally unexpected. We both accepted the fact that our dining arrangements were somewhat primitive. Bare boards, a wooden bench against the wall and a gas ring was all we had. But it was all we wanted, so that it was something of a shock to me when Helen complained.

It was one lunchtime and she looked around her, sniffing suspiciously. 'There's a funny smell in here,' she said.

'A funny smell? What do you mean?' I was utterly at a loss because just about the only thing that annoyed me about my new wife was that she spent far too much time scrubbing and cleaning our premises. There just couldn't be any smells.

But it began to happen every day. Each lunchtime when we climbed the long flights of stairs to our kitchen Helen's nose began to wrinkle almost as soon as the door closed behind her. Matters came to a head at the end of a week.

'Jim' she said mournfully. 'I can't eat here any more. Not with this smell about.'

It was a problem. Lunch was our main meal of the day and she had almost stopped eating breakfast. Also, the reassuring consumption of custard had dwindled. If this went on she would suffer from malnutrition. Then I had one of my infrequent ideas.

'Let's go out to lunch,' I said.

'Where?'

'The Lilac Cafe. They say it's very good.'

She nodded uncertainly. 'All right, we'll try it. I just can't eat up here, anyway.'

For a couple of weeks I was sure the problem was solved. The food at the Lilac was excellent and didn't put any strain on our limited financial resources. You could get soup, meat, potatoes and two veg., apple pie and cream, coffee and biscuits all for one and sixpence. Helen enjoyed it all and I was triumphant.

It was only on market days that the Lilac was full, with the farmers and their wives packing the place, and it was on a market day that the blow fell. I was sipping my coffee and making conversation with two stout ladies at the next table when my wife nudged me.

'Jim,' she whispered, and I felt a premonition as I saw the familiar hunted look on her face. 'There's a funny smell in here.'

I stared at her. 'What kind of smell – the same as the one at home?'

'No.' She shook her head miserably. 'But it's funny.'

'But Helen, this is pure imagination.' I raised my head and gave a few ostentatious sniffs. 'There's nothing here at all.'

But she was already on her way out and I realised with a sense of loss that that was the end of the Lilac.

For the next few days we tried the Dickon Street Cafe. It was much smaller and the food was definitely uninspiring but Helen seemed content, so I was thankful. After all, I told myself as I chewed at a toughish piece of rump steak, she was the one who was having the baby and it was only right that I should humour her. And I was just thinking that matters could be a lot worse when she leaned across the table.

'Can't you smell it?' she asked, wide-eyed.

I felt a surge of despair. 'Smell what?'

'That funny smell. Surely you must be able to . . .' She gazed at me appealingly.

'No, I can't,' I said. 'But never mind, we'll try somewhere else tomorrow.'

Darrowby didn't run to many cafes and there was only one left. It was known simply as Mrs Ackerley's and consisted of one tiny room in that lady's house down a side street. The cuisine there was frankly sub-standard and Mrs Ackerley herself didn't seem to have much faith in it because she invariably added 'Praps not' to every suggestion.

'Would you like some liver – or praps not? Or some toad in the hole – or praps not?' Then for dessert it would be the same. 'How about prunes and rice – or praps not?'

Everything was badly cooked and yet it fascinated me that she had her faithful clientele; an old man who worked at the shoe shop, a middle-aged spinster school teacher and a pale dyspeptic-looking young man whom I recognised as a clerk from the bank. They came every day and I realised I was exploring a hitherto unknown stratum of Darrowby society.

Helen seemed to find some humour in the situation. 'Let's get round to Praps Not's,' she would say each day and I hoped this was a good sign. But I could not stifle the lurking conviction within me that Mrs Ackerley wouldn't last.

I was pushing some particularly tired-looking cabbage round my plate when I heard a sharp intake of breath. My wife was sitting bolt upright, snuffing the air like a hound on the scent.

'Jim,' she muttered urgently, 'There's a . . .'

I held up a hand. 'Okay, okay, you don't have to tell me. Let's go.'

Our position was critical. We had run out of cafes and yet we couldn't live without eating. It was Helen who found the answer.

'It's lovely weather,' she said, slipping her arm through mine. 'Let's have a picnic tomorrow.'

One thing about living in Darrowby is that you don't have to drive very far to leave the town behind. Next day we sat down on a grassy bank and as we opened our packet of sandwiches the September sun flooded down, warming the grey stones of the wall behind us, slanting dazzlingly against the tumbling water of the river far below.

Beyond the wall lay the wide golden sweep of a corn field and a little breeze stirred the ripe ears into a long slow whisper, bringing with· it the sweet scent of a thousand growing things.

Helen sliced a tomato, shook some salt on to it and drew a long contented breath.

'Nice smell here,' she said.

Chapter Sixteen

The doctor put down the folder containing my case history and gave me a friendly smile across the desk.

'I'm sorry, Herriot, but you've got to have an operation.'

His words, though gentle, were like a slap in the face. After flying school we had been posted to Heaton Park, Manchester, and I heard within two days that I had been graded pilot. Everything seemed at last to be going smoothly.

'An operation . . . are you sure?'

'Absolutely, I'm afraid,' he said, and he looked like a man who knew his business. He was a Wing Commander, almost certainly a specialist in civil life, and I had been sent to him after a medical inspection by one of the regular doctors.

'This old surgical scar they mention in your documents,' he went on. 'You've already had surgery there, haven't you?'

'Yes, a few years ago.'

'Well, I'm afraid the thing is opening up again and needs attention.'

I seemed to have run out of words and could think of only one.

'When?'

'Immediately. Within a few days, anyway.'

I stared at him. 'But my flight's going overseas at the end of the week.'

'Ah well, that's a pity.' He spread his hands and smiled again. 'But they'll be going without you. You will be in hospital.'

I had a sudden feeling of loss, of something coming to an end, and it lingered after I had left the Wing Commander's office. I realised painfully that the fifty men with whom I had sweated my way through all those new experiences had become my friends. The first breaking-in at St John's Wood in London, the hard training at Scarborough ITW, the 'toughening course' in Shropshire and the final flying instruction at Winkfield; it had bound us together and I had come to think of myself not as an individual but as part of a group. My mind could hardly accept the fact that I was going to be on my own.

The others were sorry, too, my own particular chums looking almost bereaved, but they were all too busy to pay me much attention. They were being pushed around all over the place, getting briefed and kitted out for their posting, and it was a hectic time for the whole flight – except me. I sat on my bed in the Nissen hut while the excitement billowed around me.

I thought my departure would go unnoticed but when I got my summons and prepared to leave I found, tucked in the webbing of my pack, an envelope filled with the precious coupons with which we drew our ration of cigarettes in those days. It seemed that nearly everybody had chipped in and the final gesture squeezed at my throat as I made my lonely way from the camp.

The hospital was at Creden Hill, near Hereford, and I suppose it is one of the consolations of service life that you can't feel lonely for very long. The beds in the long ward were filled with people like myself who had been torn from their comrades and were eager to be friendly.

In the few days before my operation we came to know each other pretty well. The young man in the bed on my left spent his time writing excruciating poetry to his girl friend and insisted on reading it out to me, stanza by stanza. The lad on the right seemed a pensive type. Everybody addressed him as 'Sammy' but he replied only in grunts.

When he found out I was a vet he leaned from the sheets and beckoned to me.

'I got fed up wi' them blokes callin' me Sammy,' he muttered in a ripe Birmingham accent. 'Because me name's not Sammy, it's Desmond.'

'Really? Why do they do it, then?'

He leaned out further. 'That's what I want to talk to you about. You bein' a vet – you'll know about these things. It's because of what's wrong with me – why I'm in 'ere.'

'Well, why are you here? What's your trouble?'

He looked around him then spoke in a confidential whisper. 'I gotta big ball.'

'A what?'

'A big ball. One of me balls is a right whopper.'

'Ah, I see, but I still don't understand . . .'

'Well, it's like this,' he said. 'All the fellers in the ward keep sayin' the doctor's goin' to cut it off – then I'd be like Sammy Hall.'

I nodded in comprehension. Memories from my college days filtered back. It had been a popular ditty at the parties. 'My name is Sammy Hall and I've only got one ball . . .'

'Oh, nonsense, they're pulling your leg,' I said. 'An enlarged testicle can be all sorts of things. Can you remember what the doctor called it?'

He screwed up his face. 'It was a funny name. Like vorry or varry something.'

'Do you mean varicocele?'

'That's it!' He threw up an arm. 'That's the word!'

'Well, you can stop worrying,' I said. 'It's quite a simple little operation. Trifling, in fact.'

'You mean they won't cut me ball off?'

'Definitely not. Just remove a few surplus blood vessels, that's all. No trouble.'

He fell back on the pillow and gazed ecstatically at the ceiling. 'Thanks mate,' he breathed. 'You've done me a world o' good. I'm gettin' done tomorrow and I've been dreadin' it.'

He was like a different person all that day, laughing and joking with everybody, and next morning when the nurse came to give him his pre-med injection he turned to me with a last appeal in his eyes.

'You wouldn't kid me, mate, would you? They're not goin' to . . .?'

I held up a hand. 'I assure you, Sammy – er – Desmond, you've nothing to worry about. I give you my word.'

Again the beatific smile crept over his face and it stayed there until the 'blood wagon', the operating room trolley pushed by a male orderly, came to collect him.

The blood wagon was very busy each morning and it was customary to raise a cheer as each man was wheeled out. Most of the victims responded with a sleepy wave before the swing doors closed behind them, but when I saw Desmond grinning cheerfully and giving the thumbs-up sign I felt I had really done something.

Next morning it was my turn. I had my injection at around eight o'clock and by the time the trolley appeared I was pleasantly woozy. They removed my pyjamas and arrayed me in a sort of nightgown with laces at the neck and pulled thick woollen socks over my feet. As the orderly wheeled me away the inmates of the ward broke into a ragged chorus of encouragement and I managed the ritual flourish of an arm as I left.

It was a cheerless journey along white-tiled corridors until the trolley pushed its way into the anaesthetics room. As I entered, the doors at the far end parted as a doctor came towards me bearing a loaded syringe. I had a chilling slimpse of the operating theatre beyond, with the lights beating on the long table and the masked surgeons waiting.

The doctor pushed up my sleeve and swabbed my forearm with surgical spirit. I decided I had seen enough and closed my eyes, but an exclamation from above made me open them.

'Good God, it's Jim Herriot!'

I looked up at the man with the syringe. It was Teddy McQueen. He had been in my class at school and I hadn't seen him since the day I left.

My throat was dry after the injection but I felt I had to say something.

'Hello, Teddy,' I croaked.

His eyes were wide. 'What the hell are you doing here?'

'What the hell do you think?' I rasped crossly. 'I'm going in there for an operation.'

'Oh, I know that – I'm the anaesthetist here – but I remember you telling me at school that you were going to be a vet.'

'That's right. I am a vet.'

'You are?' His face was a picture of amazement. 'But what the devil is a vet doing in the RAF?'

It was a good question. 'Nothing very much, Teddy,' I replied.

He began to laugh. Obviously he found the whole situation intriguing.

'Well, Jim, I can't get over this!' He leaned over me and giggled uncontrollably. 'Imagine our meeting here after all these years. I think it's an absolute hoot!' His whole body began to shake and he had to dab away the tears from his eyes.

Lying there on the blood wagon in my nightie and woolly socks I didn't find it all that funny, and my numbed brain was searching for a withering riposte when a voice barked from the theatre.

'What's keeping you, McQueen? We can't wait all morning!'

Teddy stopped laughing. 'Sorry, Jim old chum,' he said. 'But your presence is requested within.' He pushed the needle into my vein and my last memory as I drifted away was of his lingering amused smile.

I spent three weeks at Creden Hill and towards the end of that time those of us who were almost fully recovered were allowed out to visit the nearby town of Hereford. This was embarrassing because we were all clad in the regulation suit of hospital blue with white shirt and red tie and it was obvious from the respectful glances we received that people thought we had been wounded in action.

When a veteran of the First World War came up to me and asked, 'Where did you get your packet, mate?' I stopped going altogether.

I left the RAF hospital with a feeling of gratitude – particularly towards the hard-working, cheerful nurses. They gave us many a tongue lashing for chattering after lights out, for smoking under the blankets, for messing up our beds, but all the time I marvelled at their dedication.

I used to lie there and wonder what it was in a girl's character that made her go in for the arduous life of nursing. A concern for people's welfare? A natural caring instinct? Whatever it was, I was sure a person was born with it.

This trait is part of the personalities of some animals and it was exemplified in Eric Abbot's sheepdog, Judy.

I first met Judy when I was treating Eric's bullock for wooden tongue. The bullock was only a young one and the farmer admitted ruefully that he had neglected it because it was almost a walking skeleton.

'Damn!' Eric grunted. 'He's been runnin' out with that bunch in the far fields and I must have missed 'im. I never knew he'd got to this state.'

When actinobacillosis affects the tongue it should be treated right at the start, when the first symptons of salivation and swelling beneath the jaw appear. Otherwise the tongue becomes harder and harder till finally it sticks out of the front of the mouth, as unyielding as the wood which gives the disease its ancient name.

This skinny little creature had reached that state, so that he not only looked pathetic but also slightly comic as though he were making a derisive gesture at me. But with a tongue like that he just couldn't eat and was literally starving to death. He lay quietly as though he didn't care.

'There's one thing, Eric,' I said. 'Giving him an intravenous injection won't be any problem. He hasn't the strength to resist.'

The great new treatment at that time was sodium iodide into the vein – modern and spectacular. Before that the farmers used to paint the tongue with tincture of iodine, a tedious procedure which sometimes worked and sometimes didn't. The sodium iodide was a magical improvement and showed results within a few days.

I inserted the needle into the jugular and tipped up the bottle of clear fluid. Two drachms of the iodide I used to use, in eight ounces of distilled water and it didn't take long to flow in. In fact the bottle was nearly empty before I noticed Judy.

I had been aware of a big dog sitting near me all the time, but as I neared the end of the injection a black nose moved ever closer till it was almost touching the needle. Then the nose moved along the rubber tube up to the bottle and back again, sniffing with the utmost concentration. When I removed the needle the nose began a careful inspection of the injection site. Then a tongue appeared and began to lick the bullock's neck methodically.

I squatted back on my heels and watched. This was something more than mere curiosity; everything in the dog's attitude suggested intense interest and concern.

'You know, Eric,' I said. 'I have the impression that this dog isn't just watching me. She's supervising the whole job.'

The farmer laughed. 'You're right there. She's a funny old bitch is Judy – sort of a nurse. If there's anything amiss she's on duty. You can't keep her away.'

Judy looked up quickly at the sound of her name. She was a handsome animal; not the usual colour, but a variegated brindle with waving lines of brown and grey mingling with the normal black and white of the farm collie. Maybe there was a cross somewhere but the result was very attractive and the effect was heightened by her bright-eyed, laughing-mouthed friendliness.

I reached out and tickled the backs of her ears and she wagged mightily – not just her tail but her entire rear end. 'I suppose she's just good-natured.'

'Oh aye, she is,' the farmer said. 'But it's not only that. It sounds daft but I think Judy feels a sense of responsibility to all the stock on t'farm.'

I nodded. 'I believe you. Anyway, let's get this beast on to his chest.'

We got down in the straw and with our hands under the back bone, rolled the bullock till he was resting on his sternum. We balanced him there with straw bales on either side then covered him with a horse rug.

In that position he didn't look as moribund as before, but the emaciated head with the useless jutting tongue lolled feebly on his shoulders and the saliva drooled uncontrolled on to the straw. I wondered if I'd ever see him alive again.

Judy however didn't appear to share my pessimism. After a thorough sniffing examination of rug and bales she moved to the front, applied an encouraging tongue to the shaggy forehead then stationed herself comfortably facing the bullock, very like a night nurse keeping an eye on her patient.

'Will she stay there?' I closed the half door and took a last look inside.

'Aye, nothing'll shift her till he's dead or better,' Eric replied. 'She's in her element now.'

'Well, you never know, she may give him an interest in life, just sitting there. He certainly needs some help. You must keep him alive with milk or gruel till the injection starts to work. If he'll drink it it'll do him most good but otherwise you'll have to bottle it into him. But be careful – you can choke a beast that way.'

A case like this had more than the usual share of the old fascination because I was using a therapeutic agent which really worked – something that didn't happen too often at that time. So I was eager to get back to see if I had been able to pull that bullock from the brink of death. But I knew I had to give the drug a chance and kept away for five days.

When I walked across the yard to the box I knew there would be no further doubts. He would either be dead or on the road to recovery.

The sound of my steps on the cobbles hadn't gone unnoticed. Judy's head, ears cocked, appeared above the half door. A little well of triumph brimmed in me. If the nurse was still on duty then the patient must be alive. And I felt even more certain when the big dog disappeared for a second then came soaring effortlessly over the door and capered up to me, working her hind end into convolutions of delight. She seemed to be doing her best to tell me all was well.

Inside the box the bullock was still lying down but he turned to look at me and I noticed a strand of hay hanging from his mouth. The tongue itself had disappeared behind the lips.

'Well, we're winnin', aren't we?' Eric Abbot came in from the yard.

'Without a doubt,' I said. 'The tongue's much softer and I see he's been trying to eat hay.'

'Aye, can't quite manage it yet, but he's suppin' the milk and gruel like a good 'un. He's been up a time or two but he's very wobbly on his pins.'

I produced another bottle of sodium iodide and repeated the injection with Judy's nose again almost touching the needle as she sniffed avidly. Her eyes were focused on the injection site with fierce concentration and so intent was she on extracting the full savour that she occasionally blew out her nostrils with a sharp blast before recommencing her inspection.

When I had finished she took up her position at the head and as I prepared to leave I noticed a voluptuous swaying of her hips which were embedded in the straw. I was a little puzzled until I realised she was wagging in the sitting position.

'Well, Judy's happy at the way things are going,' I said.

The farmer nodded. 'Yes, she is, She likes to be in charge. Do you know, she gives every new-born calf a good lick over as soon as it comes into t'world and it's the same whenever one of our cats 'as kittens.'

'Bit of a midwife, too, eh?'

'You could say that. And another funny thing about 'er – she lives with the livestock in the buildings. She's got a nice warm kennel but she never bothers with it – sleeps with the beasts in the straw every night.'

I revisited the bullock a week later and this time he galloped round the box like a racehorse when I approached him. When I finally trapped him in a corner and caught his nose I was breathless but happy. I slipped my fingers into his mouth; the tongue was pliable and almost normal.

'One more shot, Eric,' I said. 'Wooden tongue is the very devil for recurring if you don't get it cleared up thoroughly.' I began to unwind the rubber tube. 'By the way, I don't see Judy around.'

'Oh, I reckon she feels he's cured now, and anyway, she has summat else on her plate this mornin'. Can you see her over there?'

I looked through the doorway. Judy was stalking importantly across the yard. She had something in her mouth – a yellow, fluffy object.

I craned out further. 'What is she carrying?'

'It's a chicken.'

'A chicken?'

'Aye, there's a brood of them runnin' around just now. They're only a month old and t'awd bitch seems to think they'd be better off in the stable. She's made a bed for them in there and she keeps tryin' to curl herself around them. But the little things won't 'ave it.'

I watched Judy disappear into the stable. Very soon she came out, trotted after a group of tiny chicks which were pecking happily among the cobbles and gently scooped one up. Busily she made her way back to the stable but as she entered the previous chick reappeared in the doorway and pottered over to rejoin his friends.

She was having a frustrating time but I knew she would keep at it because that was the way she was.

Judy the nurse dog was still on duty.

Chapter Seventeen

My experience in the RAF hospital made me think. As a veterinary surgeon I had become used to being on the other end of the knife and I preferred it that way.

As I remembered, I was quite happy that morning a couple of years ago as I poised my knife over a swollen ear. Tristan, one elbow leaning wearily on the table, was holding an anaesthetic mask over the nose of the sleeping dog when Siegfried came into the room.

He glanced briefly at the patient. 'Ah yes, that haematoma you were telling me about, James.' Then he looked across the table at his brother. 'Good God, you're a lovely sight this morning! When did you get in last night?'

Tristan raised a pallid countenance. His eyes were bloodshot slits between puffy lids. 'Oh, I don't quite know. Fairly late, I should think.'

'Fairly late! I got back from a farrowing at four o'clock and you hadn't arrived then. Where the hell were you, anyway?'

'I was at the Licensed Victuallers' Ball. Very good do, actually.'

'I bet it was!' Siegfried snorted. 'You don't miss a thing, do you? Darts Team Dinner, Bellringers' Outing, Pigeon Club Dance and now it's the Licensed Victuallers' Ball. If there's a good booze-up going on anywhere you'll find it.'

When under fire Tristan always retained his dignity and he drew it around him now like a threadbare cloak.

'As a matter of fact,' he said, 'many of the Licensed Victuallers are my friends.'

His brother flushed. 'I believe you. I should think you're the best bloody customer they've ever had!'

Tristan made no reply but began to make a careful check of the flow of oxygen into the ether bottle.

'And another thing,' Siegfried continued. 'I keep seeing you slinking around with about a dozen different women. And you're supposed to be studying for an exam.'

'That's an exaggeration.' The young man gave him a pained look. 'I admit I enjoy a little female company now and then – just like yourself.'

Tristan believed in attack as the best form of defence, and it was a telling blow because there was a constant stream of attractive girls laying siege to Siegfried at Skeldale House.

But the elder brother was only temporarily halted. 'Never mind me!' he shouted. 'I've passed all my exams. I'm talking about you! Didn't I see you with that new barmaid from the Drovers' the other night? You dodged rapidly into a shop doorway but I'm bloody sure it was you.'

Tristan cleared his throat. 'It quite possibly was. I have recently become friendly with Lydia – she's a very nice girl.'

'I'm not saying she isn't. What I am saying is that I want to see you indoors at night with your books instead of boozing and chasing women. Is that clear?'

'Quite.' The young man inclined his head gracefully and turned down the knob on the anaesthetic machine.

His brother regarded him balefully for a few moments, breathing deeply. These remonstrations always took it out of him. Then he turned away quickly and left.

Tristan's façade crumbled as soon as the door closed.

'Watch the anaesthetic for a minute, Jim,' he croaked. He went over to the basin in the corner, filled a measuring jar with cold water and drank it at a long gulp. Then he soaked some cotton wool under the tap and applied it to his brow.

'I wish he hadn't come in just then. I'm in no mood for the raised voices and angry words.' He reached up to a large bottle of aspirins, swallowed a few and washed them down with another gargantuan draught. 'All right then, Jim,' he murmured as he returned to the table and took over the mask again. 'Let's go.'

I bent once more over the sleeping dog. He was a Scottie called Hamish and his mistress, Miss Westerman, had brought him in two days ago.

She was a retired school teacher and I always used to think she must have had little trouble in keeping her class in order. The chilly pale eyes looking straight into mine reminded me that she was as tall as I was and the square jaw between the muscular shoulders completed a redoubtable presence.

'Mr Herriot,' she barked. 'I want you to have a look at Hamish. I do hope it's nothing serious but his ear has become very swollen and painful. They don't get – er – cancer there, do they?' For a moment the steady gaze wavered.

'Oh that's most unlikely.' I lifted the little animal's chin and looked at the left ear which was drooping over the side of his face. His whole head, in fact, was askew as though dragged down by pain.

Carefully I lifted the ear and touched the tense swelling with a forefinger. Hamish looked around at me and whimpered.

'Yes, I know, old chap. It's tender, isn't it?' As I turned to Miss Westerman I almost bumped into the close-cropped iron-grey head which was hovering close over the little dog.

'He's got an aural haematoma,' I said.

'What on earth is that?'

'It's when the little blood vessels between the skin and cartilage of the ear rupture and the blood flows out and causes this acute distension.'

She patted the jet black shaggy coat. 'But what causes it?'

'Canker, usually. Has he been shaking his head lately?'

'Yes, now you mention it he has. Just as though he had got something in his ear and was trying to get rid of it.'

'Well that's what bursts the blood vessels. I can see he has a touch of canker though it isn't common in this breed.'

She nodded. 'I see. And how can you cure it?'

'Only by an operation, I'm afraid.'

'Oh dear!' She put her hand to her mouth. 'I'm not keen on that.'

'There's nothing to worry about,' I said. 'It's just a case of letting the blood out and stitching the layers of the ear together. If we don't do this soon he'll suffer a lot of pain and finish up with a cauliflower ear, and we don't want that because he's a bonny little chap.'

I meant it, too. Hamish was a proud-strutting, trim little dog. The Scottish terrier is an attractive creature and I often lament that there are so few around in these modern days.

After some hesitation Miss Westerman agreed and we fixed a date two days from then. When she brough him in for the operation she deposited Hamish in my arms, stroked his head again and again then looked from Tristan to me and back again.

'You'll take care of him, won't you,' she said, and the jaw jutted and the pale blue eyes stabbed. For a moment I felt like a little boy caught in mischief, and I think my colleague felt the same because he blew out his breath as the lady departed.

'By gum, Jim, that's a tough baby,' he muttered. 'I wouldn't like to get on the wrong side of her.'

I nodded. 'Yes, and she thinks all the world of this dog, so let's make a good job of him.

After Siegfried's departure I lifted the ear which was now a turgid cone and made an incision along the inner skin. As the pent up blood gushed forth I caught it in an enamel dish, then I squeezed several big clots through the wound.

'No wonder the poor little chap was in pain,' I said softly. 'He'll feel a lot better when he wakes up.'

I filled the cavity between skin and cartilage with sulphanilamide then began to stitch the layers together, using a row of buttons. You had to do something like this or the thing filled up again within a few days. When I first began to operate on aural haematomata I used to pack the interior with gauze then bandage the ear to the head. The owners often made little granny-hats to try to keep the bandage in place, but a frisky dog usually had it off very soon.

The buttons were a far better idea and kept the layers in close contact, lessening the chance of distortion.

By lunchtime Hamish had come round from the anaesthetic and though still slightly dopey he already seemed to be relieved that his bulging ear had been deflated. Miss Westerman had gone away for the day and was due to pick him up in the evening. The little dog, curled in his basket, waited philosophically.

At tea time, Siegfried glanced across the table at his brother. 'I'm going off to Brawton for a few hours, Tristan,' he said. 'I want you to stay in the house and give Miss Westerman her dog when she arrives. I don't know just when she'll come.' He scooped out a spoonful of jam. 'You can keep an eye on the patient and do a bit of studying, too. It's about time you had a night at home.'

Tristan nodded. 'Right, I'll do that.' But I could see he wasn't enthusiastic.

When Siegfried had driven away Tristan rubbed his chin and gazed reflectively through the french window into the darkening garden. 'This is distinctly awkward, Jim.'

'Why?'

'Well, Lydia has tonight off and I promised to see her.' He whistled a few bars under his breath. 'It seems a pity to waste the opportunity just when things are building up nicely. I've got a strong feeling that girl fancies me. In fact she's nearly eating out of my hand.'

I looked at him wonderingly. 'My God, I thought you'd want a bit of peace and quiet and an early bed after last night!'

'Not me,' he said. 'I'm raring to go again.'

And indeed he looked fresh and fit, eyes sparkling, roses back in his cheeks.

'Look, Jim,' he went on. 'I don't suppose you could stick around with this dog?'

I shrugged. 'Sorry, Triss. I'm going back to see that cow of Ted Binns' – right at the top of the Dale. I'll be away for nearly two hours.'

For a few moments he was silent, then he raised a finger. 'I think I have the solution. It's quite simple, in fact it's perfect. I'll bring Lydia in here.'

'What! Into the house?'

'Yes, into this very room. I can put Hamish in his basket by the fire and Lydia and I can occupy the sofa. Marvellous! What could be nicer on a cold winter's night. Cheap, too.'

'But Triss! How about Siegfried's lecture this morning? What if he comes home early and catches the two of you here?'

Tristan lit a Woodbine and blew out an expansive cloud. 'Not a chance. You worry about such tiny things, Jim. He's always late when he goes to Brawton. There's no problem at all.'

'Well, please yourself,' I said. 'But I think you're asking for trouble. Anyway, shouldn't you be doing a bit of bacteriology? The exams are getting close.'

He smiled seraphically through the smoke. 'Oh, I'll have a quick read through it all in good time.'

I couldn't argue with him there. I always had to go over a thing about six times before it finally sank in, but with his brain the quick read would no doubt suffice. I went out on my call.

I got back about eight o'clock and as I opened the front door my mind was far from Tristan. Ted Binns's cow wasn't responding to my treatment and I was beginning to wonder if I was on the right track. When in doubt I liked to look the subject up and the books were on the shelves in the sitting room. I hurried along the passage and threw open the door.

For a moment I stood there bewildered, trying to reorientate my thoughts. The sofa was drawn close to the bright fire, the atmosphere was heavy with cigarette smoke and the scent of perfume, but there was nobody to be seen.

The most striking feature was the long curtain over the french window. It was wafting slowly downwards as though some object had just hurtled through it at great speed. I trotted over the carpet and peered out into the dark garden. From somewhere in the gloom I heard a scuffling noise, a thud and a muffled cry, then there was a pitter-patter followed by a shrill yelping. I stood for some time listening, then as my eyes grew accustomed to the darkness I walked down the long path under the high brick wall to the yard at the foot. The yard door was open as were the big double doors into the back lane, but there was no sign of life.

Slowly I retraced my steps to the warm oblong of light at the foot of the tall old house. I was about to close the french window when I heard a stealthy movement and an urgent whisper.

'Is that you, Jim?'

'Triss! Where the hell have you sprung from?'

The young man tiptoed past me into the room and looked around him anxiously. 'It was you, then, not Siegfried?'

'Yes, I've just come in.'

He flopped on the sofa and sunk his head in his hands. 'Oh damn! I was just lying here a few minutes ago with Lydia in my arms. At peace with the world. Everything was wonderful. Then I heard the front door open.'

'But you knew I was coming back.'

'Yes, and I'd have given you a shout, but for some reason I thought, "God help us, it's Siegfried!" It sounded like his step in the passage.'

'Then what happened?'

He churned his hair around with his fingers. 'Oh, I panicked. I was whispering lovely things into Lydia's ear, then the next second I grabbed her, threw her off the couch and out of the french window.'

'I heard a thud . . .'

'Yes, that was Lydia falling into the rockery.'

'And then some sort of high-pitched cries . . .'

He sighed and closed his eyes. 'That was Lydia in the rose bushes. She doesn't know the geography of the place, poor lass.'

'Gosh, Triss,' I said. 'I'm really sorry. I shouldn't have burst in on you like that. I was thinking of something else.'

He rose wearily and put a hand on my shoulder. 'Not your fault, Jim, not your fault. You did warn me.' He reached for his cigarettes. 'I don't know how I'm going to face that girl again. I just chucked her out into the lane and told her to beat it home with all speed. She must think I'm stone balmy.' He gave a hollow groan.

I tried to be cheerful. 'Oh, you'll get round her again. You'll have a laugh about it later.'

But he wasn't listening. His eyes, wide with horror, were staring past me. Slowly he raised a trembling finger and pointed towards the fireplace. His mouth worked for a few seconds before he spoke.

'Christ, Jim, it's gone!' he gasped.

For a moment I thought the shock had deranged him. 'Gone . . .? What's gone?'

'The bloody dog! He was there when I dashed outside. Right there!'

I looked down at the empty basket and a cold hand clutched at me. 'Oh no! He must have got out through the open window. We're in trouble.'

We rushed into the garden and searched in vain. We came back for torches and searched once more, prowling around the yard and back lane, shouting the little dog's name with diminishing hope.

After ten minutes we trailed back to the brightly lit room and stared at each other.

Tristan was the first to voice our thoughts. 'What do we tell Miss Westerman when she calls?'

I shook my head. My mind fled from the thought of informing that lady that we had lost her dog.

Just at that moment the front door bell pealed in the passage and Tristan almost leaped in the air.

'Oh God!' he quavered. 'That'll be her now. Go and see her, Jim. Tell her it was my fault – anything you like – but I daren't face her.'

I squared my shoulders, marched over the long stretch of tiles and opened the door. It wasn't Miss Westerman, it was a well-built platinum blonde and she glared at me angrily.

'Where's Tristan?' she rasped in a voice which told me we had more than one tough female to deal with tonight.

'Well, he's – er –.'

'Oh, I know he's in there!' As she brushed past me I noticed she had a smear of soil on her cheek and her hair was sadly disarranged. I followed her into the room where she stalked up to my friend.

'Look at my bloody stockings!' she burst out. 'They're ruined!'

Tristan peered nervously at the shapely legs. 'I'm sorry, Lydia. I'll get you another pair. Honestly, love, I will.'

'You'd better, you bugger!' she replied. 'And don't "love" me – I've never been so insulted in my life. What did you think you were playing at?'

'It was all a misunderstanding. Let me explain . . .' Tristan advanced on her with a brave attempt at a winning smile, but she backed away.

'Keep your distance,' she said frigidly. 'I've had enough of you for one night.'

She swept out and Tristan leaned his head against the mantelpiece. 'The end of a lovely friendship, Jim.' Then he shook himself. 'But we've got to find that dog. Come on.'

I set off in one direction and he went in the other. It was a moonless night of impenetrable darkness and we were looking for a jet black dog. I think we both knew it was hopeless but we had to try.

In a little town like Darrowby you are soon out on the country roads where there are no lights and as I stumbled around peering vainly over invisible fields the utter pointlessness of the activity became more and more obvious.

Occasionally I came within Tristan's orbit and heard his despairing cries echoing over the empty landscape. 'Haamiish! Haamiish! Haamiish . . .!'

After half an hour we met at Skeldale House. Tristan faced me and as I shook my head he seemed to shrink within himself. His chest heaved as he fought for breath. Obviously he had been running while I had been walking and I suppose that was natural enough. We were both in an awkward situation but the final devastating blow would inevitably fall on him.

'Well, we'd better get out on the road again,' he gasped, and as he spoke the front door bell rang again.

The colour drained rapidly from his face and he clutched my arm. 'That must be Miss Westerman this time. God almighty, she's coming in!'

Rapid footsteps sounded in the passage and the sitting room door opened. But it wasn't Miss Westerman, it was Lydia again. She strode over to the sofa, reached underneath and extracted her handbag. She didn't say anything but merely shrivelled Tristan with a sidelong glance before leaving.

'What a night!' he moaned, putting a hand to his forehead. 'I can't stand much more of this.'

Over the next hour we made innumerable sorties but we couldn't find Hamish and nobody else seemed to have seen him. I came in to find Tristan collapsed in an armchair. His mouth hung open and he showed every sign of advanced exhaustion. I shook my head and he shook his then I heard the telephone.

I lifted the receiver, listened for a minute and turned to the young man. 'I've got to go out, Triss. Mr Drew's old pony has colic again.'

He reached out a hand from the depths of his chair. 'You're not going to leave me, Jim?'

'Sorry, I must. But I won't be long. It's only a mile away.'

'But what if Miss Westerman comes?'

I shrugged. 'You'll just have to apologise. Hamish is bound to turn up – maybe in the morning.'

'You make it sound easy . . .' He ran a hand inside his collar. 'And another thing – how about Siegfried? What if he arrives and asks about the dog? What do I tell him?'

'Oh, I shouldn't worry about that.' I replied airily. 'Just say you were too busy on the sofa with the Drovers' barmaid to bother about such things. He'll understand.'

But my attempt at jocularity fell flat. The young man fixed me with a cold eye and ignited a quivering Woodbine. 'I believe I've told you this before, Jim, but there's a nasty cruel streak in you.'

Mr Drew's pony had almost recovered when I got there but I gave it a mild sedative injection before turning for home. On the way back a thought struck me and I took a road round the edge of the town to the row of modern bungalows where Miss Westerman lived. I parked the car and walked up the path of number ten.

And there was Hamish in the porch, coiled up comfortably on the mat, looking up at me with mild surprise as I hovered over him.

'Come on, lad,' I said. 'You've got more sense than we had. Why didn't we think of this before?'

I deposited him on the passenger seat and as I drove away he hoisted his paws on to the dash and gazed out interestedly at the road unfolding in the headlights. Truly a phlegmatic little hound.

Outside Skeldale House I tucked him under my arm and was about to turn the handle of the front door when I paused. Tristan had notched up a long succession of successful pranks against me – fake telephone calls, the ghost in my bedroom and many others – and in fact, good friends as we were, he never neglected a chance to take the mickey out of me. In this situation, with the positions reversed, he would be merciless. I put my finger on the bell and leaned on it for several long seconds.

For some time there was neither sound nor movement from within and I pictured the cowering figure mustering his courage before marching to his doom. Then the light came on in the passage and as I peered expectantly through the glass a nose appeared round the far corner followed very gingerly by a wary eye. By degrees the full face inched into view and when Tristan recognised my grinning countenance he unleashed a cry of rage and bounded along the passage with upraised fist.

I really think that in his distraught state he would have attacked me, but the sight of Hamish banished all else. He grabbed the hairy creature and began to fondle him.

'Good little dog, nice little dog,' he crooned as he trotted through to the sitting room. 'What a beautiful thing you are.' He laid him lovingly in the basket, and Hamish, after a 'heigh-ho, here we are again' glance around him, put his head along his side and promptly went to sleep.

Tristan fell limply into the armchair and gazed at me with glazed eyes.

'Well, we're saved, Jim,' he whispered. 'But I'll never be the same after tonight. I've run bloody miles and I've nearly lost my voice with shouting. I tell you I'm about knackered.'

I too was vastly relieved, and the nearness of catastrophe was brought home to us when Miss Westerman arrived within ten minutes.

'Oh, my darling!' she cried as Hamish leaped at her, mouth open, short tail wagging furiously. 'I've been so worried about you all day.'

She looked tentatively at the ear with its rows of buttons. 'Oh, it does look a lot better without that horrid swelling – and what a nice neat job you have made. Thank you, Mr Herriot, and thank you, too, young man.'

Tristan, who had staggered to his feet, bowed slightly as I showed the lady out.

'Bring him back in six weeks to have the stitches out,' I called to her as she left, then I rushed back into the room.

'Siegfried's just pulled up outside! You'd better look as if you've been working.'

He rushed to the bookshelves, pulled down Gaiger and Davis's *Bacteriology* and a notebook and dived into a chair. When his brother came in he was utterly engrossed.

Siegfried moved over to the fire and warmed his hands. He looked pink and mellow.

'I've just been speaking to Miss Westerman,' he said. 'She's really pleased. Well done, both of you.'

'Thank you,' I said, but Tristan was too busy to reply, scanning the pages anxiously and scribbling repeatedly in the notebook.

Siegfried walked behind the young man's chair and looked down at the open volume.

'Ah yes, Clostridium septique,' he murmured, smiling indulgently. 'That's a good one to study. Keeps coming up in exams.' He rested a hand briefly on his brother's shoulder. 'I'm glad to see you at work. You've been raking about too much lately and it's getting you down. A night at your books will have been good for you.'

He yawned, stretched, and made for the door. 'I'm off to bed. I'm rather sleepy.' He paused with his hand on the door. 'You know, Tristan, I quite envy you – there's nothing like a nice restful evening at home.'

Chapter Eighteen

When I was discharged from hospital I expected to be posted straight overseas and I wondered if I would be able to catch up with my old flight and my friends.

However, I learned with surprise that I had to go to a convalescent home for a fortnight before any further action could be taken. This was in Puddlestone, near Leominster – a lovely mansion house in acres of beautiful gardens. It was presided over by a delightful old matron with whom we fortunate airmen played sedate games of croquet or walked in the cool woods; it was easy to imagine there was no such thing as a war. Two weeks of this treatment left me feeling revitalised. It wouldn't be long, I felt, before I was back on the job.

From Puddlestone it was back to Manchester and Heaton Park again and this time it was strange to think that in all the great sprawl of huts and the crowding thousands of men in blue there wasn't a soul who knew me.

Except, of course, the Wing Commander who had sent me to hospital in the first place. I had an interview with him on my arrival and he came straight to the point.

'Herriot,' he said. 'I'm afraid you can't fly any more.'

'But ... I've had the operation ... I'm a lot better.'

'I know that, but you can no longer be classed as 100% fit. You have been officially downgraded and I'm sure you realise that pilots have to be grade one.'

'Yes ... of course.'

He glanced at the file in his hand. 'I see you are a veterinary surgeon. Mmm – this poses a problem. Normally when an aircrew man is grounded he remusters on the ground staff, but yours is a reserved occupation. You really can't serve in any capacity but aircrew. Yes . . . yes . . . we'll have to see.'

It was all very impersonal and businesslike. Those few words coming from a man like him left no room for argument and they obliterated at a stroke every picture I had ever had of my future in the RAF.

I was fairly certain that if my flying days were over I would be discharged from the service and as I left the Wing Commander's office and walked slowly back to my hut at the other end of the park I pondered on my contribution to the war effort.

I hadn't fired a shot in anger. I had peeled mountains of potatoes, washed countless dishes, shovelled coke, mucked out pigs, marched for miles, drilled interminably, finally and magically learned to fly and now it was all for nothing. I passed the big dining hall and the RAF march blared out at me from the loudspeakers.

The familiar sound reminded me of so many experiences, so many friends, and suddenly I felt intensely lonely. I wanted somebody to talk to. It was a new sensation for me, and there, in those unlikely surroundings, I began to realise how much I used to enjoy chatting to the farmers during my veterinary calls.

It is one of the nicest things about country practice, but you have to keep your mind on the job at the same time or you could be in trouble. And at Mr Duggleby's I nearly landed in the biggest trouble of all. He was a smallholder who kept a few sows and reared the litters to pork weight in some ramshackle sheds behind the railway line outside Darrowby.

He was also a cricket fanatic, steeped in the lore and history of the game, and he would talk about it for hours on end. He never tired of it.

I was a willing listener because cricket has always fascinated me, even though I grew up in Scotland where it is little played. As I moved among the pigs only part of my attention was focused on the little animals – most of me was out on the great green oval at Headingley with the Yorkshire heroes.

'By gaw, you should've seen Len Hutton on Saturday,' he breathed reverently. 'A hundred and eighty and never gave a chance. It was lovely to watch 'im.' He gave a fair imitation of the great man's cover drive.

'Yes, I can imagine it.' I nodded and smiled. 'You said these pigs were lame, Mr Duggleby?'

'Aye, noticed a few of 'em hoppin' about with a leg up this mornin'. And you know, Maurice Leyland was nearly as good. Not as classy as Len, tha knows, but by heck 'e can clump 'em.'

'Yes, he's a lion-hearted little player is Maurice,' I said. I reached down, grabbed a pig by the tail and thrust my thermometer into its rectum. 'Remember him and Eddie Paynter in the test match against Australia?'

He gave a dreamy smile. 'Remember it? By gaw, that's summat I'll never forget. What a day that was.'

I withdrew the thermometer. 'This little chap's got a temperature of a hundred and five. Must be some infection somewhere – maybe a touch of joint ill.' I felt my way along the small pink limbs. 'And yet it's funny, the joints aren't swollen.'

'Ah reckon Bill Bowes'll skittle Somerset out when they start their innings today. This wicket's just to 'is liking.'

'Yes, he's a great bowler, isn't he?' I said. 'I love watching a good fast bowler. I suppose you'll have seen them all – Larwood, Voce, G.O. Allen and the rest?'

'Aye, that I have. I could go on all day about those men.'

I caught another of the lame pigs and examined it. 'This is rather strange, Mr Duggleby. About half the pigs in this pen seem to be lame but there's nothing to see.'

'Aye well, happen it's like you said – joint ill. You can give 'em a jab for that,

can't you? And while you're doin' it I'll tell you of the time I saw Wilfred
Rhodes take eight wickets in an afternoon.'

I filled a syringe. 'Right, we'd better give them all a shot. Have you got a
marking pencil there?'

The farmer nodded and lifted one of the little animals which promptly
unleashed a protesting scream. 'There was never anybody like awd Wilfred,' he
shouted above the noise. 'It was about half past two and the wicket had had a
shower of rain on it when t'skipper threw 'im the ball.'

I smiled and raised my syringe. It passed the time so pleasantly listening to
these reminiscences. Well content, I was about to plunge the needle into the
pink thigh when one of the pigs began to nibble at the heel of my wellington.
I looked down at a ring of the little creatures all looking up at me, alarmed by
the shrill screeches of their friend.

My mind was still with Wilfred Rhodes when I noticed what looked like a
small white knob on one of the uptilted snouts. And there was another on that
one – and that one . . . I had been unable to see their faces until now because
they had been trying to run away from me, but a warning bell clanged suddenly
in my head.

I reached down and seized a pig, and as I squeezed the swelling on the snout
a cold wind blew through me, scattering the gentle vision of cricket and sunshine
and green grass. It wasn't a knob, it was a vesicle, a delicate blister which
ruptured easily on pressure.

I could feel my arms shaking as I turned the piglet up and began to examine
the tiny cloven feet. There were more vesicles there, flatter and more diffuse, but
telling the same dread story.

Dry-mouthed, I lifted two other pigs. They were just the same. As I turned
to the farmer I felt bowed down by a crushing weight of pity, almost of guilt.
He was still smiling eagerly, anxious to get on with his tale, and I was about
to give him the worst news a veterinary surgeon can give a stocksman.

'Mr Duggleby,' I said. 'I'm afraid I'll have to telephone the Ministry of
Agriculture.'

'The Ministry . . .? What for?'

'To tell them I have a case of suspected Foot and Mouth Disease.'

'Foot and Mouth? Never!'

'Yes, I'm terribly sorry.'

'Are you sure?'

'It's not up to me to be definite about it, Mr Duggleby. One of the Ministry
officers will have to do that – I must phone them right away.'

It was an unlikely place to find a telephone but Mr Duggleby ran a little coal
delivery round on the side. I was quickly through to the Ministry and I spoke
to Neville Craggs, one of the full time officers.

He groaned. 'Sounds awful like it, Jim. Anyway, stay put till I see you.'

In the farm kitchen Mr Duggleby looked at me enquiringly. 'What now?'

'You'll just have to put up with me for a bit,' I said. 'I can't leave till I get
the verdict.'

He was silent for a moment. 'What happens if it's what you think?'

'I'm afraid your pigs will have to be slaughtered.'

'Every one of 'em?'

'That is the law – I'm sorry. But you'll get compensation.' He scratched his
head. 'But they can get better. Why do you have to kill 'em all?'

'You're quite right.' I shrugged. 'Many animals do recover, but Foot and
Mouth is fiercely infectious. While you were treating them it would have spread
to neighbouring farms, then all over the country.'

'Aye, but look at the expense. Slaughtering must cost thousands o' pounds.'

'I agree, but it would cost a lot more the other way. Apart from the animals that die, just think of the loss of milk, loss of flesh in cows, pigs and sheep. It would come to millions every year. It's lucky Britain is an island.'

'Reckon you'll be right.' He felt for his pipe. 'And you're pretty sure I've got it?'

'Yes.'

'Aye well,' he murmured. 'These things 'appen.'

The old Yorkshire words. I had heard them so often under circumstances which would make most city folk, including myself, beat their heads against a wall. Mr Duggleby's smallholding would soon be a silent place of death, but he just chewed his pipe and said, 'These things 'appen.'

It didn't take the Ministry long to make up their minds. The source of the infection was almost certainly some imported meat which Mr Duggleby hadn't boiled properly with his swill. The disease was confirmed and a fifteen mile radius standstill order was imposed. I disinfected myself and my car and went home. I undressed, my clothes were taken away for fumigation and I climbed into a hot antiseptic bath.

Lying there in the steam, I pondered on what might have been. If I had failed to spot the disease I would have gone merrily on my way, spreading destruction and havoc. I always washed my boots before leaving a farm, but how about those little pigs nibbling round the hem of my long coat, how about my syringe, even my thermometer? My next call was to have been to Terence Bailey's pedigree herd of dairy shorthorns – two hundred peerless cows, a strain built up over generations. Foreigners came from all over the world to buy them and I could have been the cause of their annihilation.

And then there was Mr Duggleby himself. I could picture him rattling around the farms in his coal wagon. He would have done his bit of spreading, too. And like as not he would have taken a few store pigs to the auction mart this week, sending the deadly contagion all over Yorkshire and beyond. It was easy to see how a major outbreak could have started – a disaster of national importance costing millions.

If I hadn't been sweating already I would have started now at the very thought of it. I would have joined the unhappy band of practitioners who had missed Foot and Mouth.

I knew of some of these people and my heart bled for them. It could happen so easily. Busy men trying to examine kicking, struggling animals in dark buildings with perhaps part of their mind on the list of calls ahead. And the other hazards – the total unexpectedness, the atypical case, various distractions. My distraction had been cricket and it had nearly caused my downfall. But I had escaped and, huddling lower in the hot water, I said a silent prayer of thanks.

Later, with a complete change of clothes and instruments, I continued on my rounds and as I stood in Terence Bailey's long byre I realised my luck again. The long rows of beautiful animals, meticulously groomed, firm high udders pushing between their hocks, delicate heads, fine legs deep in straw; they were a picture of bovine perfection and quite irreplaceable.

Once Foot and Mouth is confirmed in a district there is a tense period of waiting. Farmers, veterinary surgeons and most of all, Ministry officials are on the rack, wondering if there has been any dissemination before diagnosis, bracing themselves against the telephone message which could herald the raging spread which they dreaded and which would tear their lives apart.

To the city dwellers a big Foot and Mouth outbreak is something remote which they read about in the newspapers. To the country folk it means the transformation of the quiet farms and fields into charnel houses and funeral pyres. It means heartbreak and ruin.

We waited in Darrowby. And as the days passed and no frightening news of lame or salivating animals came over the wires it seemed that the Duggleby episode was what we hoped – an isolated case caused by a few shreds of imported meat.

I almost bathed in disinfectant on every farm, sloshing a strong solution of lysol over my boots and protective clothing so that my car reeked of the stuff and I caused wrinkled noses when I entered a shop, the post office, the bank.

After nearly two weeks I had begun to feel reasonably safe but when I had a call from the famous Bailey farm I felt a twinge of apprehension.

It was Terence Bailey himself. 'Will you come and see one of my cows, Mr Herriot. She's got blisters on one of her teats.'

'Blisters!' My heart went bump. 'Is she slavering, is she lame?'

'Nay, nay, she just has these nasty blisters. Seem to have fluid in them.'

I was breathless as I put down the receiver. One nasty blister would be enough. It sometimes started like that in cows. I almost ran out to my car and on the journey my mind beat about like a trapped bird.

Bailey's was the farm I had visited straight from Duggleby's. Could I possibly have carried it there? But the change of clothes, the bath, the fresh thermometer and instruments. What more could I do? How about my car wheels? Well, I had disinfected them, too – I couldn't possibly be blamed, but . . . but . . .

It was Mr Bailey's wife who met me.

'I noticed this cow when I was milking this morning, Mr Herriot.' The herd was still hand-milked and in the hard-working family tradition Mrs Bailey did her stint night and morning with her husband and the farm men.

'As soon as I got hold of the teats I could see the cow was uneasy,' she continued. 'Then I saw there was a lot of little blisters and one big one. I managed to milk her and most of the little blisters burst, but the big one's still there.'

I bent and peered anxiously at the udder. It was as she said – lots of small ruptured vesicles and one large one, intact and fluctuating. It was all horribly evocative and without speaking I moved along, grasped the cow's nose and pulled her head round. I prised the mouth open and stared desperately at lips, cheek and dental pad. I think I would have fainted if I had found anything in there but it was all clean and normal.

I lifted each forefoot in turn and scrubbed out the clefts with soap and water – nothing. I tied a rope round the hind leg, threw it over a beam and with the help of one of the men pulled the foot up. More scrubbing and searching without success then the same with the other hind foot. When I finished I was perspiring but no further forward.

I took the temperature and found it slightly elevated, then I walked up and down the byre.

'Is there any trouble among these other cows?' I asked.

Mrs Bailey shook her head. 'No, there's just this one.' She was a good-looking woman in her thirties with the red, roughened complexion of the outdoor worker. 'What do you think it is?'

I didn't dare tell her. I had a cow with vesicles on the teats right in the middle of a district under Foot and Mouth restrictions. I just couldn't take a chance. I had to bring the Ministry in.

Even then I was unable to speak the dread words. All I could say was, 'Can I use your phone, please?'

She looked surprised, but smiled quickly. 'Yes, of course. Come into the house.'

As I walked down the byre I looked again at the beautiful cows and then beyond, at the fold yard where I could see the young heifers and the tiny calves in their pens. All of them carrying the Bailey blood which had been produced and perfected by generations of careful breeding and selection. But a humane killer is no respecter of such things and if my fears were realised a quick series of bang-bangs would wipe out all this in an hour or two.

We went into the farm kitchen and Mrs Bailey pointed to the door at the far end.

'The phone's through there in the front room,' she said.

I kicked off my wellingtons and was padding across the floor in my stockinged feet when I almost fell over Giles, the lusty one-year-old baby of the family, as he waddled across my path. I bent to ease him out of the way and he looked up at me with an enormous cheesy grin.

His mother laughed. 'Just look at him. Full of the devil, and he's had such a painful arm since his smallpox vaccination.'

'Poor lad,' I said absently, patting his head as I opened the door, my mind already busy with the uncomfortable conversation ahead. I had taken a few strides over the carpet beyond, when I halted abruptly.

I turned and looked back into the kitchen. 'Did you say smallpox vaccination?'

'Yes, all our other children have been done when they were his age but they've never reacted like this. I've had to change his dressing every day.'

'You changed his dressing . . . and you milked that cow . . .?'

'Yes, that's right.'

A great light beamed suddenly, spilling sunshine into my dark troubled world. I returned to the kitchen and closed the door behind me.

Mrs Bailey looked at me for a moment in silence, then she spoke hesitantly. 'Aren't you going to use the phone?'

'No . . . no . . .' I replied. 'I've changed my mind.'

'I see.' She raised her eyebrows and seemed at a loss for words. Then she smiled and lifted the kettle. 'Well maybe you'll have a cup of tea, then?'

'Thank you, that would be lovely.' I sank happily on to one of the hard wooden chairs.

Mrs Bailey put the kettle on and turned to me. 'By the way, you've never told me what's wrong with that cow.'

'Oh yes, of course, I'm sorry,' I said airily as though I'd just forgotten to mention it. 'She's got cow pox. In fact you gave it to her.'

'I gave it . . .? What do you mean?'

'Well, the vaccine they use for babies is made from the cow pox virus. You carried it on your hands from the baby to the cow.' I smiled, enjoying my big moment.

Her mouth fell open slightly, then she began to giggle. 'Oh dear, I don't know what my husband's going to say. I've never heard of anything like that.' She wiggled her fingers in front of her eyes. 'And I'm always so careful, too. But I've been a bit harassed with the poor little chap's arm.'

'Oh well, it isn't serious,' I said. 'I've got some ointment in the car which will cure it quite quickly.'

I sipped my tea and watched Giles's activities. In a short time he had spread chaos throughout the kitchen and at the moment was busily engaged in removing all the contents of a cupboard in the corner. Bent double, small bottom out-thrust, he hurled pans, lids, brushes behind him with intense dedication till the cupboard was empty. Then, as he looked around for further employment, he spotted me and tacked towards me on straddled legs.

My stocking-clad toes seemed to fascinate him and as I wiggled them at him he grasped at them with fat little hands. When he had finally trapped my big toe he looked up at me with his huge grin in which four tiny teeth glittered.

I smiled back at him with sincere affection as the relief flowed through me. It wasn't just that I was grateful to him – I really liked him. I still like Giles today. He is one of my clients, a burly farmer with a family of his own, a deep love and knowledge of pedigree cows and the same big grin, except that there are a few more teeth in it.

But he'll never know how near his smallpox vaccination came to giving me heart failure.

Chapter Nineteen

I looked around me at the heap of boots, the piled mounds of shirts, the rows of empty shelves and pigeon holes. I was employed in the stores at Heaton Park, living proof that the RAF was finding me something of a problem.

The big war machine was rumbling along pretty smoothly by this time, turning out pilots, navigators, air-gunners in a steady stream and slotting them into different jobs if they failed to make the grade. It ticked over like a well-oiled engine as long as nothing disturbed the rhythm.

I was like a speck of sand in the works, and I could tell from various interviews that I had caused the administrators a certain amount of puzzlement. I don't suppose Mr Churchill was losing any sleep over me but since I wasn't allowed to fly and was ineligible for the ground staff I was obviously a bit of a nuisance. Nobody seemed to have come across a grounded vet before.

Of course it was inevitable that I would be sent back to my practice, but I could see that it was going to take some time for the RAF to regurgitate me into civil life. Apparently I had to go through the motions even though some of them were meaningless.

One of the interviews was with three officers. They were very nice and they sat behind a table, beaming, friendly, reassuring. Their task, apparently, was to find out what ground staff job might suit me. I think they were probably psychologists and they asked me all kinds of questions, nodding and smiling kindly all the time.

'Well now, Herriot,' the middle officer said. 'We are going to put you through a series of aptitude tests. It will last two days, starting tomorrow, and by the end of it I think we'll know all about you.' He laughed. 'It's nothing to worry about. You might rather enjoy it.'

I did enjoy it, in fact. I filled up great long sheets with my answers, I drew diagrams, fitted odd-shaped pieces of wood into holes. It was fun.

I had to wait another two days before I was called before the tribunal again. The three were if anything more charming than before and I seemed to sense an air of subdued excitement about them this time. They were all smiling broadly as the middle one spoke.

'Herriot, we have really found out something about you,' he said.

'You have?'

'Yes, indeed. We have found that you have an outstanding mechanical aptitude.'

I stared at him. This was a facer, because if ever there was a mechanical idiot that man is J. Herriot. I have a loathing for engines, wheels, pistons, cylinders, cogs. I can't mend anything and if a garage mechanic tries to explain something to me I just can't take it in.

I told the officers this and the three smiles became rather fixed.

'But surely,' said the one on the left. 'you drive a car in the course of your professional work?'

'Yes, sir, I do. I've driven one for years, but I still don't know how it works and if I break down I have to scream for help.'

'I see, I see.' The smiles were very thin now and the three heads came together for a whispered consultation.

Finally the middle one leaned across the table.

'Tell you what, Herriot. How would you like to be a meteorologist?'

'Fine,' I replied.

I sympathised with them, because they were obviously kind men, but I've never had any faith in aptitude tests since then.

Of course there was never the slightest chance of my becoming a meteorologist and I suppose that's how I landed in the stores. It was one of the bizarre periods of my life, mercifully brief but vivid. They had told me to report to Corporal Weekes at the stores hut and I made my way through the maze of roads of a Heaton Park populated by strangers.

Corporal Weekes was fat and he gave me a quick look over with crafty eyes.

'Herriot, eh? Well you can make yourself useful around 'ere. Not much to do, really. This ain't a main stores – we deal mainly wiv laundry and boot repairs.'

As he spoke a fair-haired young man came in.

'A.C.2 Morgan, Corporal,' he said. 'Come for my boots. They've been re-soled.'

Weekes jerked his head and I had my first sight of the boot mountain. 'They're in there. They'll be labelled.'

The young man looked surprised but he came round behind the counter and began to delve among the hundreds of identical black objects. It took him nearly an hour to find his own pair during which the corporal puffed at cigarettes with a total lack of interest. When the boots were finally unearthed he wordlessly ticked off the name on a long list.

'This is the sort of thing you'll be doin',' he said to me. 'Nothin' to it.'

He wasn't exaggerating. There was nothing to life in those stores. It took me only a day or two to realise the sweet existence Weekes had carved out for himself. Store-bashing is an honourable trade but not the way he did it. The innumerable compartments, niches and alcoves around the big hut were all marked with letters or numbers and there is no doubt the incoming boots and shirts should have been tucked away in order for easy recovery. But that would have involved work and the corporal was clearly averse to that.

When the boots came in they were tipped out in the middle of the floor and the string-tied packages of laundry were stacked, shirts-uppermost where they formed a blue tumulus reaching almost to the roof.

After three days I could stand it no longer.

'Look,' I said. 'It would pass the time if I had something to do. Do you mind if I start putting all this stuff on the shelves? It would be a lot easier to hand out.'

Weekes continued to study his magazine – he was a big reader – and at first I thought he hadn't heard me. Then he tongued his cigarette to the corner of his mouth and glanced at me through the smoke.

'Now just get this through your 'ead, mate,' he drawled. 'If I want any ——
thing doin' I'll —— well tell you. I'm the boss in 'ere and I give the —— orders,
awright?' He resumed his perusal of the magazine.

I subsided in my chair. Clearly I had offended my overseer and I would have
to leave things as they were.

But overseer is a misnomer for Weekes because on the following day, after
a final brain-washing that the procedure must remain unchanged he disappeared
and except for a few minutes each morning he left me on my own. I had nothing
to do but sit there behind the wooden counter, ticking off the comings and goings
of the boots and shirts and I had the feeling that I was only one of many
displaced persons who had fallen under his thrall.

I found it acutely embarrassing to watch the lads scrabbling for their belongings
and the strongest impression left with me was of the infinite tolerance of the
British race. Since I was in charge they thought I was responsible for the whole
system but despite the fact that I was of lowly rank nobody attacked me
physically. Most of them muttered and grumbled as they searched and one large
chap came over to the counter and said, 'You should be filing away these boots
in their proper order instead of sitting there on your arse, you lazy sod!' But he
didn't punch me on the nose and I marvelled at it.

But still, the knowledge that great numbers of decent young men shared his
opinion was uncomfortable and I found I was developing a permanently
ingratiating smile.

The only time I came very near to being lynched was when a mob suddenly
appeared one afternoon. An unexpected leave pass had been granted and there
were hundreds of men milling around on the tarmac and grass outside the stores.
They wanted their laundry – and quick, because they had trains to catch.

For a moment panic seized me. I couldn't let them all inside to fight for their
shirts. Then inspiration came. I grabbed an armful of the flat packets from the
table shouted the name on the label.

'Walters!' And from somewhere among the surging heads an eager voice
replied, 'Here!'

I located the source, held the packet between thumb and finger and with a
back-hand flick sent it skimming over the crowd.

'Reilly!'
'Here!'
'McDonald!'
'Here!'
'Gibson!'
'Here!'

I was getting quite skilful at it, propelling the blue oblongs unerringly towards
their owners, but it was a slow method of distribution. Also, there were occasional
disasters when the strings broke in mid-air, sending a shower of collars on the
upturned faces. Sometimes the shirts themselves burst free from their wrappings
and plunged to earth.

It wasn't long before the voices had turned from eager to angry. As my
projectiles planed and glided, volleys of abuse came back at me.

'You've made me miss my train, you useless bugger!'

'Bloody skiver, you want locking up!'

Much of it was in stronger language which I would rather not record here,
but I have a particularly vivid memory of one young man scraping up his
laundry from the dusty ground and approaching me with rapid strides. He
pushed his face to within inches of mine. Despite the rage which disfigured it
I could see it was a gentle, good-natured face. He looked a well-bred lad, the

type who didn't even swear, but as he stared into my eyes his lips trembled and his cheeks twitched.

'This is a . . .' he stammered. 'This is a . . . a *bastard* system!'

He spat the words out and strode away.

I agreed entirely with him, of course, but continued to hurl the packets doggedly while somewhere in the back of my mind a little voice kept enquiring how James Herriot, Member of the Royal College of Veterinary Surgeons and trainee pilot had ever got into this.

After half an hour there was no appreciable dimunution in the size of the multitude and I began to be aware of an increasing restlessness among the medley of waiting faces.

Suddenly there was a concerted movement and the packed mass of men surged at me in a great wave. I shrank back, clutching an armful of shirts, quite certain that this was when they rushed me and beat me up, but my fears were groundless. All they wanted was a speedier delivery and about a dozen of them swept past me behind the counter and began to follow my example.

Whereas there had been only a single missile winging over the heads the sky was now dark with the flying objects. Mid-air collisions were frequent. Collars sprayed, handkerchiefs fluttered, underpants parachuted gracefully, but after an unbearably long period of chaos the last airman had picked up his scattered laundry, given me a disgusted glance and departed.

I was left alone in the hut with the sad knowledge that my prestige was very low and the equally sad conviction that the RAF still did not know what to do with me.

Chapter Twenty

Occasionally my period in limbo was relieved when I was allowed out of camp into the city of Manchester. And I suppose it was the fact that I was a new-fangled parent that made me look at the various prams in the streets. Mostly the prams were pushed by women but now and then I saw a man doing the job.

I suppose it isn't unusual to see a man pushing a pram in a town, but on a lonely moorland road the sight merits a second glance. Especially when the pram contains a large dog.

That was what I saw in the hills above Darrowby one morning and I slowed down as I drove past. I had noticed the strange combination before – on several occasions over the last few weeks – and it was clear that man and dog had recently moved into the district.

As the car drew abreast of him the man turned, smiled and raised his hand. It was a smile of rare sweetness in a very brown face. A forty-year-old face, I thought, above a brown neck which bore neither collar nor tie, and a faded striped shirt lying open over a bare chest despite the coldness of the day.

I couldn't help wondering who or what he was. The outfit of scuffed suede golf jacket, corduroy trousers and sturdy boots didn't give much clue. Some people might have put him down as an ordinary tramp, but there was a businesslike energetic look about him which didn't fit the term.

I wound the window down and the thin wind of a Yorkshire March bit at my cheeks.

'Nippy this morning,' I said.

The man seemed surprised. 'Aye,' he replied after a moment. 'Aye, reckon it is.'

I looked at the pram, ancient and rusty, and at the big animal sitting upright inside it. He was a lurcher, a cross-bred greyhound, and he gazed back at me with unruffled dignity.

'Nice dog,' I said.

'Aye, that's Jake.' The man smiled again, showing good regular teeth. 'He's a grand 'un.'

I waved and drove on. In the mirror I could see the compact figure stepping out briskly, head up, shoulders squared, and, rising like a statue from the middle of the pram, the huge brindled form of Jake.

I didn't have to wait long to meet the unlikely pair again. I was examining a carthorse's teeth in a farmyard when on the hillside beyond the stable I saw a figure kneeling by a dry stone wall. And by his side, a pram and a big dog sitting patiently on the grass.

'Hey, just a minute.' I pointed at the hill. 'Who is that?'

The farmer laughed. 'That's Roddy Travers. D'you ken 'im?'

'No, no I don't. I had a word with him on the road the other day, that's all.'

'Aye, on the road.' He nodded knowingly. 'That's where you'd see Roddy, right enough.'

'But what is he? Where does he come from?'

'He comes from somewhere in Yorkshire, but ah don't rightly know where and ah don't think anybody else does. But I'll tell you this – he can turn 'is hand to anything.'

'Yes,' I said, watching the man expertly laying the flat slabs of stone as he repaired a gap in the wall. 'There's not many can do what he's doing now.'

'That's true. Wallin' is a skilled job and it's dying out, but Roddy's a dab hand at it. But he can do owt – hedgin', ditchin', lookin' after stock, it's all the same to him.'

I lifted the tooth rasp and began to rub a few sharp corners off the horse's molars. 'And how long will he stay here?'

'Oh, when he's finished that wall he'll be off. Ah could do with 'im stoppin' around for a bit but he never stays in one place for long.'

'But hasn't he got a home anywhere?'

'Nay, nay.' The farmer laughed again. 'Roddy's got nowt. All 'e has in the world is in that there pram.'

Over the next weeks as the harsh spring began to soften and the sunshine brought a bright speckle of primroses on to the grassy banks I saw Roddy quite often, sometimes on the road, occasionally wielding a spade busily on the ditches around the fields. Jake was always there, either loping by his side or watching him at work. But we didn't actually meet again till I was inoculating Mr Pawson's sheep for pulpy kidney.

There were three hundred to do and they drove them in batches into a small pen where Roddy caught and held them for me. And I could see he was an expert at this, too. The wild hill sheep whipped past him like bullets but he seized their fleece effortlessly, sometimes in mid-air, and held the fore leg up to expose that bare clean area of skin behind the elbow that nature seemed to provide for the veterinary surgeon's needle.

Outside, on the windy slopes the big lurcher sat upright in typical pose, looking with mild interest at the farm dogs prowling intently around the pens, but not interfering in any way.

'You've got him well trained,' I said.

Roddy smiled. 'Yes, ye'll never find Jake dashin' about annoyin' people. He knows 'e has to sit there till I'm finished and there he'll sit.'

'And quite happy to do so, by the look of him.' I glanced again at the dog, a picture of contentment. 'He must live a wonderful life, travelling everywhere with you.'

'You're right there,' Mr Pawson broke in as he ushered another bunch of sheep into the pen. 'He hasn't a care in t'world, just like his master.'

Roddy didn't say anything, but as the sheep ran in he straightened up and took a long steady breath. He had been working hard and a little trickle of sweat ran down the side of his forehead but as he gazed over the wide sweep of moor and fell I could read utter serenity in his face. After a few moments he spoke.

'I reckon that's true. We haven't much to worry us, Jake and me.'

Mr Pawson grinned mischievously. 'By gaw, Roddy, you never spoke a truer word. No wife, no kids, no life insurance, no overdraft at t'bank – you must have a right peaceful existence.'

'Ah suppose so,' Roddy said. 'But then ah've no money either.'

The farmer gave him a quizzical look. 'Aye, how about that, then? Wouldn't you feel a bit more secure, like, if you had a bit o' brass put by?'

'Nay, nay. Ye can't take it with you and any road, as long as a man can pay 'is way, he's got enough.'

There was nothing original about the words, but they have stayed with me all my life because they came from his lips and were spoken with such profound assurance.

When I finished the inoculations and the ewes were turned out to trot back happily over the open fields I turned to Roddy. 'Well, thanks very much. It makes my job a lot quicker when I have a good catcher like you.' I pulled out a packet of Gold Flake. 'Will you have a cigarette?'

'No, thank ye, Mr Herriot. I don't smoke.'

'You don't?'

'No – don't drink either.' He gave me his gentle smile and again I had the impression of physical and mental purity. No drinking, no smoking, a life of constant movement in the open air without material possessions or ambitions – it all showed in the unclouded eyes, the fresh skin and the hard muscular frame. He wasn't very big but he looked indestructible.

'C'mon, Jake, it's dinner time,' he said and the big lurcher bounded around him in delight. I went over and spoke to the dog and he responded with tremendous body-swaying wags, his handsome face looking up at me, full of friendliness.

I stroked the long pointed head and tickled the ears. 'He's a beauty, Roddy – a grand 'un, as you said.'

I walked to the house to wash my hands and before I went inside I glanced back at the two of them. They were sitting in the shelter of a wall and Roddy was laying out a thermos flask and a parcel of food while Jake watched eagerly. The hard bright sunshine beat on them as the wind whistled over the top of the wall. They looked supremely comfortable and at peace.

'He's independent, you see,' the farmer's wife said as I stood at the kitchen sink. 'He's welcome to come in for a bit o' dinner but he'd rather stay outside with his dog.'

I nodded. 'Where does he sleep when he's going round the farms like this?'

'Oh, anywhere,' she replied. 'In hay barns or granaries or sometimes out in the open, but when he's with us he sleeps upstairs in one of our rooms. Ah know for a fact any of the farmers would be willin' to have him in the house because he allus keeps himself spotless clean.'

'I see.' I pulled the towel from behind the door. 'He's quite a character, isn't he?'

She smiled ruminatively. 'Aye, he certainly is. Just him and his dog!' She lifted a fragrant dishful of hot roast ham from the oven and set it on the table. 'But I'll tell you this. The feller's all right. Everybody likes Roddy Travers – he's a very nice man.'

Roddy stayed around the Darrowby district throughout the summer and I grew used to the sight of him on the farms or pushing his pram along the roads. When it was raining he wore a tattered over-long gaberdine coat, but at other times it was always the golf jacket and corduroys. I don't know where he had accumulated his wardrobe. It was a safe bet he had never been on a golf course in his life and it was just another of the little mysteries about him.

I saw him early one morning on a hill path in early October. It had been a night of iron frost and the tussocky pastures beyond the walls were held in a pitiless white grip with every blade of grass stiffly ensheathed in rime.

I was muffled to the eyes and had been beating my gloved fingers against my knees to thaw them out, but when I pulled up and wound down the window the first thing I saw was the bare chest under the collarless unbuttoned shirt.

'Mornin', Mr Herriot,' he said. 'Ah'm glad I've seen ye.' He paused and gave me his tranquil smile. 'There's a job along t'road for a couple of weeks, then I'm movin' on.'

'I see.' I knew enough about him now not to ask where he was going. Instead I looked down at Jake who was sniffling the herbage. 'I see he's walking this morning.'

Roddy laughed. 'Yes, sometimes 'e likes to walk, sometimes 'e likes to ride. He pleases 'imself.'

'Right, Roddy,' I said. 'No doubt we'll meet again. All the best to you.'

He waved and set off jauntily over the icebound road and I felt that a little vein of richness had gone from my life.

But I was wrong. That same evening about eight o'clock the front door bell rang. I answered it and found Roddy on the front door steps. Behind him, just visible in the frosty darkness, stood the ubiquitous pram.

'I want you to look at me dog, Mr Herriot,' he said.

'Why, what's the trouble?'

'Ah don't rightly know. He's havin' sort of . . . faintin' fits.'

'Fainting fits? That doesn't sound like Jake. Where is he, anyway?'

He pointed behind him 'In t'pram, under t'cover.'

'All right.' I threw the door wide. 'Bring him in.'

Roddy adroitly manhandled the rusty old vehicle up the steps and pushed it, squeaking and rattling, along the passage to the consulting room. There, under the bright lights he snapped back the fasteners and threw off the cover to reveal Jake stretched beneath.

His head was pillowed on the familiar gaberdine coat and around him lay his master's worldly goods; a string-tied bundle of spare shirt and socks, a packet of tea, a thermos, knife and spoon and an ex-army haversack.

The big dog looked up at me with terrified eyes and as I patted him I could feel his whole frame quivering.

'Let him lie there a minute, Roddy,' I said. 'And tell me exactly what you've seen.'

He rubbed his palms together and his fingers trembled. 'Well it only started this afternoon. He was right as rain, larkin' about on the grass, then he went into a sort o'fit.'

'How do you mean?'

'Just kind of seized up and toppled over on 'is side. He lay there for a bit, gaspin' and slaverin'. Ah'll tell ye, I thought he was a goner.' His eyes widened and a corner of his mouth twitched at the memory.

'How long did that last?'

'Nobbut a few seconds. Then he got up and you'd say there was nowt wrong with 'im.'

'But he did it again?'

'Aye, time and time again. Drove me near daft. But in between 'e was normal. Normal, Mr Herriot!'

It sounded ominously like the onset of epilepsy. 'How old is he?' I asked.

'Five gone last February.'

Ah well, it was a bit old for that. I reached for a stethoscope and auscultated the heart. I listened intently but heard only the racing beat of a frightened animal. There was no abnormality. My thermometer showed no rise in temperature.

'Let's have him on the table, Roddy. You take the back end.'

The big animal was limp in our arms as we hoisted him on to the smooth surface, but after lying there for a moment he looked timidly around him then sat up with a slow and careful movement. As we watched he reached out and licked his master's face while his tail flickered between his legs.

'Look at that!' the man exclaimed. 'He's all right again. You'd think he didn't ail a thing.'

And indeed Jake was recovering his confidence rapidly. He peered tentatively at the floor a few times then suddenly jumped down, trotted to his master and put his paws against his chest.

I looked at the dog standing there, tail wagging furiously. 'Well, that's a relief, anyway. I didn't like the look of him just then, but whatever's been troubling him seems to have righted itself. I'll . . .'

My happy flow was cut off. I stared at the lurcher. His fore legs were on the floor again and his mouth was gaping as he fought for breath. Frantically he gasped and retched then he blundered across the floor, collided with the pram wheels and fell on his side.

'What the hell . . .! Quick, get him up again!' I grabbed the animal round the middle and we lifted him back on to the table.

I watched in disbelief as the huge form lay there. There was no fight for breath now – he wasn't breathing at all, he was unconscious. I pushed my fingers inside his thigh and felt the pulse. It was still going, rapid and feeble, but yet he didn't breathe.

He could die any moment and I stood there helpless, all my scientific training useless. Finally my frustration burst from me and I struck the dog on the ribs with the flat of my hand.

'Jake!' I yelled. 'Jake, what's the matter with you?'

As though in reply, the lurcher immediately started to take great wheezing breaths, his eyelids twitched back to consciousness and he began to look about him. But he was still mortally afraid and he lay prone as I gently stroked his head.

There was a long silence while the animal's terror slowly subsided, then he sat up on the table and regarded us placidly.

'There you are,' Roddy said softly. 'Same thing again. Ah can't reckon it up and ah thought ah knew summat about dogs.'

I didn't say anything. I couldn't reckon it up either, and I was supposed to be a veterinary surgeon.

I spoke at last. 'Roddy, that wasn't a fit. He was choking. Something was interfering with his air flow.' I took my hand torch from my breast pocket. 'I'm going to have a look at his throat.'

I pushed Jake's jaws apart, depressed his tongue with a forefinger and shone the light into the depths. He was the kind of good-natured dog who offered no resistance as I prodded around, but despite my floodlit view of the pharynx I could find nothing wrong. I had been hoping desperately to come across a bit of bone stuck there somewhere but I ranged feverishly over pink tongue, healthy tonsils and gleaming molars without success. Everything looked perfect.

I was tilting his head a little further when I felt him stiffen and heard Roddy's cry.

'He's goin' again!'

And he was, too. I stared in horror as the brindled body slid away from me and lay prostrate once more on the table. And again the mouth strained wide and froth bubbled round the lips. As before, the breathing had stopped and the rib cage was motionless. As the seconds ticked away I beat on the chest with my hand but it didn't work this time. I pulled the lower eyelid down from the staring orb – the conjunctiva was blue, Jake hadn't long to live. The tragedy of the thing bore down on me. This wasn't just a dog, he was this man's family and I was watching him die.

It was at that moment that I heard the faint sound. It was a strangled cough which barely stirred the dog's lips.

'Damn it!' I shouted. 'He *is* choking. There must be something down there.'

Again I seized the head and pushed my torch into the mouth and I shall always be thankful that at that very instant the dog coughed again, opening the cartilages of the larynx and giving me a glimpse of the cause of all the trouble. There, beyond the drooping epiglottis I saw for a fleeting moment a smooth round object no bigger than a pea.

'I think it's a pebble,' I gasped. 'Right inside his larynx.'

'You mean, in 'is Adam's apple?'

'That's right, and it's acting like a ball valve, blocking his windpipe every now and then.' I shook the dog's head. 'You see, look, I've dislodged it for the moment. He's coming round again.'

Once more Jake was reviving and breathing steadily.

Roddy ran his hand over the head, along the back and down the great muscles of the hind limbs. 'But . . . but . . . it'll happen again, won't it?'

I nodded. 'I'm afraid so.'

'And one of these times it isn't goin' to shift and that'll be the end of 'im?' He had gone very pale.

'That's about it, Roddy, I'll have to get that pebble out.'

'But how . . .?'

'Cut into the larynx. And right now – it's the only way.'

'All right.' He swallowed. 'Let's get on. I don't think ah could stand it if he went down again.'

I knew what he meant. My knees had begun to shake, and I had a strong conviction that if Jake collapsed once more then so would I.

I seized a pair of scissors and clipped away the hair from the ventral surface of the larynx. I dared not use a general anaesthetic and infiltrated the area with local before swabbing with antiseptic. Mercifully there was a freshly boiled set of instruments lying in the steriliser and I lifted out the tray and set it on the trolley by the side of the table.

'Hold his head steady,' I said hoarsely, and gripped a scalpel.

I cut down through skin, fascia and the thin layers of the sterno-hyoid and omo-hyoid muscles till the ventral surface of the larynx was revealed. This was something I had never done to a live dog before, but desperation abolished any hesitancy and it took me only another few seconds to incise the thin membrane and peer into the interior.

And there it was. A pebble right enough – grey and glistening and tiny, but big enough to kill.

I had to fish it out quickly and cleanly without pushing it into the trachea. I leaned back and rummaged in the tray till I found some broad-bladed forceps then I poised them over the wound. Great surgeons' hands, I felt sure, didn't shake like this, nor did such men pant as I was doing. But I clenched my teeth, introduced the forceps and my hand magically steadied as I clamped them over the pebble.

I stopped panting, too. In fact I didn't breathe at all as I bore the shining little object slowly and tenderly through the opening and dropped it with a gentle rat-tat on the table.

'Is that it?' asked Roddy, almost in a whisper.

'That's it.' I reached for needle and suture silk. 'All is well now.'

The stitching took only a few minutes and by the end of it Jake was bright-eyed and alert, paws shifting impatiently, ready for anything. He seemed to know his troubles were over.

Roddy brought him back in ten days to have the stitches removed. It was, in fact, the very morning he was leaving the Darrowby district, and after I had picked the few loops of silk from the nicely healed wound I walked with him to the front door while Jake capered round our feet.

On the pavement outside Skeldale House the ancient pram stood in all its high, rusted dignity. Roddy pulled back the cover.

'Up, boy,' he murmured, and the big dog leaped effortlessly into his accustomed place.

Roddy took hold of the handle with both hands and as the autumn sunshine broke suddenly through the clouds it lit up a picture which had grown familiar and part of the daily scene. The golf jacket, the open shirt and brown chest, the handsome animal sitting up, looking around him with natural grace.

'Well, so long, Roddy,' I said. 'I suppose you'll be round these parts again.'

He turned and I saw that smile again. 'Aye, reckon ah'll be back.'

He gave a push and they were off, the strange vehicle creaking, Jake swaying gently as they went down the street. The memory came back to me of what I had seen under the cover that night in the surgery. The haversack, which would contain his razor, towel, soap and a few other things. The packet of tea and the thermos. And something else – a tiny dog collar. Could it have belonged to Jake as a pup or to another loved animal? It added a little more mystery to the man . . . and explained other things, too. That farmer had been right – all Roddy possessed was in that pram.

And it seemed it was all he desired, too, because as he turned the corner and disappeared from my view I could hear him whistling.

Chapter Twenty-one

They had sent me to Eastchurch on the Isle of Sheppey and I knew it was the last stop.

As I looked along the disorderly line of men I realised I wouldn't be taking part in many more parades. And it came to me with a pang that at the Scarborough Initial Training Wing this would not have been classed as a parade at all. I could remember the ranks of blue outside the Grand Hotel, straight as the Grenadier Guards and every man standing stiffly, looking neither to left nor right. Our boots gleaming, buttons shining like gold and not a movement anywhere as the flight sergeant led the officer round on morning inspection.

I had moaned as loudly as anybody at the rigid discipline, the 'bull', the scrubbing and polishing, marching and drilling, but now that it had all gone it seemed good and meaningful and I missed it.

Here the files of airmen lounged, chatted among themselves and occasionally took a surreptitious drag at a cigarette as a sergeant out in front called the names from a list and gave us our leisurely instructions for the day.

This particular morning he was taking a long time over it, consulting sheaves of papers and making laboured notes with a pencil. A big Irishman on my right was becoming increasingly restive and finally he shouted testily:

'For —— sake, sergeant, get us off this —— square. Me —— feet's killin ' me!'

The sergeant didn't even look up. 'Shut your mouth, Brady,' he replied. 'You'll get off the square when I say so and not before.'

It was like that at Eastchurch, the great filter tank of the RAF, where what I had heard described as the 'odds and sods' were finally sorted out. It was a big sprawling camp filled with a widely varied mixture of airmen who had one thing in common; they were all waiting – some of them for remuster, but most for discharge from the service.

There was a resigned air about the whole place, an acceptance of the fact that we were all just putting in time. There was a token discipline but it was of the most benign kind. And as I said, every man there was just waiting . . . waiting . . .

Little Ned Finch in his remote corner of the high Yorkshire Dales always seemed to me to be waiting, too. I could remember his boss yelling at him.

'For God's sake, shape up to t'job! You're not farmin' at all!' Mr Daggett grabbed hold of a leaping calf and glared in exasperation.

Ned gazed back at him impassively. His face registered no particular emotion, but in the pale blue eyes I read the expression that was always there – as though he was waiting for something to happen, but without much hope. He made a tentative attempt to catch a calf but was brushed aside, then he put his arms round the neck of another one, a chunky little animal of three months, and was borne along a few yards before being deposited on his back in the straw.

'Oh, dang it, do this one, Mr Herriot!' Mr Daggett barked, turning the hairy neck towards me. 'It looks as though I'll have to catch 'em all myself.'

I injected the animal. I was inoculating a batch of twenty with preventive pneumonia vaccine and Ned was suffering. With his diminutive stature and skinny, small-boned limbs he had always seemed to me to be in the wrong job; but he had been a farm worker all his life and he was over sixty now, grizzled, balding and slightly bent, but still battling on.

Mr Daggett reached out and as one of the shaggy creatures sped past he scooped the head into one of his great hands and seized the ear with the other. The little animal seemed to realise it was useless to struggle and stood unresisting as I inserted the needle. At the other end Ned put his knee against the calf's rear and listlessly pushed it against the wall. He wasn't doing much good and his boss gave him a withering glance.

We finished the bunch with hardly any help from the little man, and as we left the pen and came out into the yard Mr Daggett wiped his brow. It was a raw November day but he was sweating profusely and for a moment he leaned his gaunt six foot frame against the wall as the wind from the bare moorland blew over him.

'By gaw, he's a useless little beggar is that,' he grunted. 'Ah don't know how ah put up with 'im.' He muttered to himself for a few moments then gave tongue again. 'Hey, Ned!'

The little man who had been trailing aimlessly over the cobbles turned his pinched face and looked at him with his submissive but strangely expectant eyes.

'Get them bags o' corn up into the granary!' his boss ordered.

Wordlessly Ned went over to the cart and with an effort shouldered a sack of corn. As he painfully mounted the stone steps to the granary his frail little legs trembled and bent under the weight.

Mr Daggett shook his head and turned to me. His long cadaverous face was set in its usual cast of melancholy.

'You know what's wrong wi' Ned?' he murmured confidentially.

'What do you mean?'

'Well, you know why 'e can't catch them calves?'

My own view was that Ned wasn't big enough or strong enough and anyway he was naturally ineffectual, but I shook my head.

'No,' I said. 'Why is it?'

'Well I'll tell ye.' Mr Daggett glanced furtively across the yard then spoke from behind his hand. 'He's ower fond of t'bright lights.'

'Eh?'

'Ah'm tellin' ye he's crazed over t'bright lights.'

'Bright . . . what . . . where . . .?'

Mr Daggett leaned closer. 'He gets over to Briston every night.'

'Briston . . .?' I looked across from the isolated farm to the village three miles away on the other side of the Dale. It was the only settlement in that bleak vista – a straggle of ancient houses dark and silent against the green fellside. I could recall that at night the oil lamps made yellow flickers of light in the windows but they weren't very bright. 'I don't understand.'

'Well . . . 'e gets into t'pub.'

'Ah, the pub.'

Mr Daggett nodded slowly and portentously but I was still puzzled. The Hulton Arms was a square kitchen where you could get a glass of beer and where a few old men played dominoes of an evening. It wasn't my idea of a den of vice.

'Does he get drunk there?' I asked.

'Nay, nay.' The farmer shook his head. 'It's not that. It's the hours 'e keeps.'

'Comes back late, eh?'

'Aye, that 'e does!' The eyes widened in their cavernous sockets. 'Sometimes 'e doesn't get back till 'alf past nine or ten o'clock!'

'Gosh, is that so?'

'Sure as ah'm standin' here. And there's another thing. He can't get out of 'is bed next day. Ah've done half a day's work before 'e starts.' He paused and glanced again across the yard. 'You can believe me or believe me not, but sometimes 'e isn't on the job till seven o'clock in t'morning!'

'Good heavens!'

He shrugged wearily. 'Aye well, you see how it is. Come into t'house, you'll want to wash your hands.'

In the huge flagged kitchen I bent low over the brown earthenware sink. Scar Farm was four hundred years old and the various tenants hadn't altered it much since the days of Henry the Eighth. Gnarled beams, rough whitewashed walls and hard wooden chairs. But comfort had never been important to Mr Daggett or his wife who was ladling hot water from the primitive boiler by the side of the fire and pouring it into her scrubbing bucket.

She clopped around over the flags in her clogs, hair pulled back tightly from her weathered face into a bun, a coarse sacking apron tied round her waist. She had no children but her life was one of constant activity; indoors or outside, she worked all the time.

At one end of the room wooden steps led up through a hole in the ceiling to a loft where Ned slept. That had been the little man's room for nearly fifty years ever since he had come to work for Mr Daggett's father as a boy from school. And in all that time he had never travelled further than Darrowby, never done anything outside his daily routine. Wifeless, friendless, he plodded through his life, endlessly milking, feeding and mucking out, and waiting, I suspected with diminishing hope, for something to happen.

With my hand on the car door I looked back at Scar Farm, at the sagging roof tiles, the great stone lintel over the door. It typified the harshness of the lives of the people within. Little Ned was no bargain as a stocksman, and his boss's exasperation was understandable. Mr Daggett was not a cruel or an unjust man. He and his wife had been hardened and squeezed dry by the pitiless austerity of their existence in this lonely corner of the high Pennines.

There was no softness up here, no frills. The stone walls, sparse grass and stunted trees; the narrow road with its smears of cow muck. Everything was down to fundamentals, and it was a miracle to me that most of the Dalesmen were not like the Daggetts but cheerful and humorous.

But as I drove away, the sombre beauty of the place overwhelmed me. The lowering hillsides burst magically into life as a shaft of sunshine stabbed through the clouds, flooding the bare flanks with warm gold. Suddenly I was aware of the delicate shadings of green, the rich glowing bronze of the dead bracken spilling from the high tops, the whole peaceful majesty of my work-a-day world.

I hadn't far to drive to my next call – just about a mile – and it was in a vastly different atmosphere. Miss Tremayne, a rich lady from the south, had bought a tumbledown manor house and spent many thousands of pounds in converting it into a luxury home. As my feet crunched on the gravel I looked up at the large windows with their leaded panes, at the smooth, freshly-pointed stones.

Elsie opened the door to me. She was Miss Tremayne's cook-housekeeper, and one of my favourite people. Aged about fifty, no more than five feet high and as round as a ball with short bandy legs sticking out from beneath a tight black dress.

'Good morning, Elsie,' I said, and she burst into a peal of laughter. This, more then her remarkable physical appearance, was what delighted me. She laughed uproariously at every statement and occurrence; in fact she laughed at the things she said herself.

'Come in, Mr Herriot, ha-ha-ha,' she said. 'It's been a bit nippy today, he-he, but I think it'll get out this afternoon, ho-ho-ho.'

All the mirth may have seemed somewhat unnecessary, and indeed, it made her rather difficult to understand, but the general effect was cheering. She led me into the drawing room and her mistress rose with some difficulty from her chair.

Miss Tremayne was elderly and half crippled with arthritis but bore her affliction without fuss.

'Ah, Mr Herriot,' she said. 'How good of you to come.' She put her head on one side and beamed at me as though I was the most delightful thing she had seen for a long time.

She, too, had a bubbling, happy personality, and since she owned three dogs, two cats and an elderly donkey I had come to know her very well in her six months' residence in the Dale.

My visit was to dress the donkey's overgrown hooves, and a pair of clippers and a blacksmith's knife dangled from my right hand.

'Oh, put those grisly instruments down over there,' she said. 'Elsie's bringing some tea – I'm sure you've time for a cup.'

I sank willingly into one of the brightly covered armchairs and was looking round the comfortable room when Elsie reappeared, gliding over the carpet as though on wheels. She put the tray on the table by my side.

'There's yer tea,' she said, and went into a paroxysm so hearty that she had to lean on the back of my chair. She had no visible neck and the laughter caused the fat little body to shake all over.

When she had recovered she rolled back into the kitchen and I heard her clattering about with pans. Despite her idiosyncrasies she was a wonderful cook and very efficient in all she did.

I spent a pleasant ten minutes with Miss Tremayne and the tea, then I went outside and attended to the donkey. When I had finished I made my way round the back of the house and as I was passing the kitchen I saw Elsie at the open window.

'Many thanks for the tea, Elsie,' I said.

The little woman gripped the sides of the sink to steady herself. 'Ha-ha-ha, that's all right. That's, he-he, quite all right, ha-ha-ho-ho-ho.'

Wonderingly I got into the car and as I drove away, the disturbing thought came to me that one day I might say something really witty to Elsie and cause her to do herself an injury.

I was called back to Mr Daggett's quite soon afterwards to see a cow which wouldn't get up. The farmer thought she was paralysed.

I drove there in a thin drizzle and the light was fading at about four o'clock in the afternoon when I arrived at Scar Farm.

When I examined the cow I was convinced she had just got herself into an awkward position in the stall with her legs jammed under the broken timbers of the partition.

'I think she's sulking, Mr Daggett,' I said. 'She's had a few goes at rising and now she's decided not to try any more. Some cows are like that.'

'Maybe you're right,' the farmer replied. 'She's allus been a stupid bitch.'

'And she's a big one, too. She'll take a bit of moving.' I lifted a rope from the byre wall and tied it round the hocks. 'I'll push the feet from the other side while you and Ned pull the legs round.'

'Pull?' Mr Daggett gave the little man a sour look. 'He couldn't pull the skin off a rice puddin'.'

Ned said nothing, just gazed dully to his front, arms hanging limp. He looked as though he didn't care, wasn't even there with us. His mind was certainly elsewhere if his thoughts were mirrored in his eyes – vacant, unheeding, but as always, expectant.

I went behind the partition and thrust steadily at the feet while the men pulled. At least Mr Daggett pulled, mouth open, gasping with effort, while Ned leaned languidly on the rope.

Inch by inch the big animal came round till she was lying almost in the middle of the stall, but as I was about to call a halt the rope broke and Mr Daggett flew backwards on to the hard cobbles. Ned of course did not fall down because he hand't been trying, and his employer, stretched flat, glared up at him with frustrated rage.

'Ye little bugger, ye let me do that all by myself! Ah don't know why ah bother with you, you're bloody useless.'

At that moment the cow, as I had expected, rose to her feet, and the farmer gesticulated at the little man. 'Well, go on, dang ye, get some straw and rub her legs! They'll be numb.'

Meekly Ned twisted some straw into a wisp and began to do a bit of massage. Mr Daggett got up stiffly, felt gingerly along his back then walked up beside the cow to make sure the chain hadn't tightened round her neck. He was on his way back when the big animal swung round suddenly and brought her cloven hoof down solidly on the farmer's toe.

If he had been wearing heavy boots it wouldn't have been so bad, but his feet were encased in ancient cracked wellingtons which offered no protection.

'Ow! Ow! Ow!' yelled Mr Daggett, beating on the hairy back with his fists. 'Gerroff, ye awd bitch!' He heaved, pushed and writhed but the ten hundred-weight of beef ground down inexorably.

The farmer was only released when the cow slid off his foot, and I know from experience that that sliding is the worst part.

Mr Daggett hopped around on one leg, nursing the bruised extremity in his hands. 'Bloody 'ell,' he moaned. 'Oh, bloody 'ell.'

Just then I happened to glance towards Ned and was amazed to see the apathetic little face crinkle suddenly into a wide grin of unholy glee. I couldn't recall him even smiling before, and my astonishment must have shown in my face because his boss whipped round suddenly and stared at him. As if by magic the sad mask slipped back into place and he went on with his rubbing.

Mr Daggett hobbled out to the car with me and as I was about to leave he nudged me.

'Look at 'im,' he whispered.

Ned, milk pail in hand, was bustling along the byre with unwonted energy.

His employer gave a bitter smile. 'It's t'only time 'e ever hurries. Can't wait to get out t'pub.'

'Oh well, you say he doesn't get drunk. There can't be any harm in it.'

The deep sunk eyes held me. 'Don't you believe it. He'll come to a bad end gaddin' about the way 'e does.'

'But surely the odd glass of beer . . .'

'Ah but there's more than that to it.' He glanced around him. 'There's women!'

I laughed incredulously. 'Oh come now, Mr Daggett, what women?'

'Over at t'pub,' he muttered. 'Them Bradley lasses.'

'The landlord's daughters? Oh really, I can't believe . . .'

'All right, ye can say what ye like. He's got 'is eye on 'em. Ah knaw – ah've only been in that pub once but ah've seen for meself.'

I didn't know what to say, but in any case I had no opportunity because he turned and strode into the house.

Alone in the cold darkness I looked at the gaunt silhouette of the old farmhouse above me. In the dying light of the November day the rain streamed down the rough stones and the wind caught at the thin tendril of smoke from the chimney, hurling it in ragged streamers across the slate blue pallor of the western sky. The fell hung over everything, a black featureless bulk, oppressive and menacing.

Through the kitchen window I could see the oil lamp casting its dim light over the bare table, the cheerless hearth with its tiny flicker of fire. In the shadows at the far end the steps rose into Ned's loft and I could imagine the little figure clambering up to get changed and escape to Briston.

Across the valley the single street of the village was a broken grey thread in the gloom but in the cottage windows the lamps winked faintly. These were Ned Finch's bright lights and I could understand how he felt. After Scar Farm, Briston would be like Monte Carlo.

The image stayed in my mind so vividly that after two more calls that evening I decided to go a few miles out of my way as I returned homeward. I cut across the Dale and it was about half past eight when I drove into Briston. It was difficult to find the Hulton Arms because there was no lighted entrance, no attempt to advertise its presence, but I persevered because I had to find out what was behind Mr Daggett's tale of debauchery.

I located it at last. Just like the door of an ordinary house with a faded wooden sign hanging above it. Inside, the usual domino game was in progress, a few farmers sat chatting quietly. The Misses Bradley, plain but pleasant-faced women in their forties, sat on either side of the fire, and sure enough there was Ned with a half pint glass in front of him.

I sat down by his side. 'Hello, Ned.'

'Now then, Mr Herriot,' he murmured absently, glancing at me with his strange expectant eyes.

One of the Bradley ladies put down her knitting and came over.

'Pint of bitter, please,' I said. 'What will you have, Ned?'

'Nay, thank ye, Mr Herriot. This'll do for me. It's me second and ah'm not a big drinker, tha knows.'

Miss Bradley laughed. 'Yes, he nobbut has 'is two glasses a night, but he enjoys them, don't you, Ned?'

'That's right, ah do.' He looked up at her and she smiled kindly down at him before going for my beer.

He took a sip at his glass. 'Ah really come for t'company, Mr Herriot.'

'Yes, of course,' I said. I knew what he meant. He probably sat on his own most of the time, but around him was warmth and comfort and friendliness. A great log sent flames crackling up to the wide chimney, there was electric light and shining mirrors with whisky slogans painted on their surface. It wasn't anything like Scar Farm.

The little man said very little. He spun out his drink for another hour, looking around him as the dominoes clicked and I lowered another contemplative pint. The Misses Bradley knitted and brewed tea in a big black kettle over the fire and when they had to get up to serve their customers they occasionally patted Ned playfully on the cheek as they passed.

By the time he tipped down the last drop and rose to go it was a quarter to ten and he still had to cycle across to the other side of the Dale. Another late night for Ned.

It was a Tuesday lunchtime in early spring. Helen always cooked steak and kidney pie on Tuesdays and I used to think about it all morning on my rounds. My thoughts that morning had been particularly evocative because lambing had started and I had spent most of the time in my shirt sleeves in the biting wind as my hunger grew and grew.

Helen cut into her blissful creation and began to scoop the fragrant contents on to my plate.

'I met Miss Tremayne in the market place this morning, Jim.'

'Oh yes?' I was almost drooling as my wife stopped shovelling out the pie, sliced open some jacket potatoes and dropped pats of farm butter on to the steaming surfaces.

'Yes, she wants you to go out there this afternoon and put some canker drops in Wilberforce's ears if you have time.'

'Oh I have time for that,' I said. Wilberforce was Miss Tremayne's ancient tabby cat and it was just the kind of job I wanted after my arm-aching morning.

I was raising a luscious forkful when Helen spoke again. 'Oh and she had an interesting item of news.'

'Really?' But I had begun to chew and my thoughts were distant.

'It's about the little woman who works for her – Elsie. You know her?'

I nodded and took another mouthful. 'Of course, of course.'

'Well it's quite unexpected, I suppose, but Elsie's getting married.'

I choked on my pie. 'What!'

'It's true. And maybe you know the bridegroom.'

'Tell me.'

'He works on one of the neighbouring farms. His name is Ned Finch.'

This time my breath was cut off completely and Helen had to beat me on the back as I spluttered and retched. It wasn't until an occluding morsel of potato skin had shot down my nose that I was able to utter a weak croak. 'Ned Finch?'

'That's what she said.'

I finished my lunch in a dream, but by the end of it I had accepted the extraordinary fact. Helen and Miss Tremayne were two sensible people – there couldn't be any mistake. And yet . . . even as I drew up outside the old Manor House a feeling of unreality persisted.

Elsie opened the door as usual. I looked at her for a moment.

'What's this I hear, Elsie?'

She started a giggle which rapidly spread over her spherical frame.

I put my hand on her shoulder. 'Is it true?'

The giggle developed into a mighty gale of laughter, and if she hadn't been holding the handle I am sure she would have fallen over.

'Aye, it's right enough,' she gasped. 'Ah've found a man at last and ah'm goin' to get wed!' She leaned helplessly on the door.

'Well, I'm pleased to hear it, Elsie. I hope you'll be very happy.'

She hadn't the strength to speak but merely nodded as she lay against the door. Then she led me to the drawing room.

'In ye go,' she chuckled. 'Ah'll bring ye some tea.'

Miss Tremayne rose to greet me with parted lips and shining eyes. 'Oh, Mr Herriot, have you heard?'

'Yes, but how . . .?'

'It all started when I asked Mr Daggett for some fresh eggs. He sent Ned on his bicycle with the eggs and it was like fate.'

'Well, how wonderful.'

'Yes, and I actually saw it happen. Ned walked in that door with his basket, Elsie was clearing the table here, and, Mr Herriot.' She clasped her hands under her chin, smiled ecstatically and her eyes rolled upwards. 'Oh, Mr Herriot, it was love at first sight!'

'Yes . . . yes, indeed. Marvellous!'

'And ever since that day Ned has been calling round and now he comes every evening and sits with Elsie in the kitchen. Isn't it romantic!'

'It certainly is. And when did they decide to get married?'

'Oh, he popped the question within a month, and I'm so happy for Elsie because Ned is such a dear little man, don't you think so?'

'Yes he is.' I said. 'He's a very nice chap.'

Elsie simpered and tittered her way in with the tea then put her hand over her face and fled in confusion, and as Miss Tremayne began to pour I sank into one of the armchairs and lifted Wilberforce on to my lap.

The big cat purred as I instilled a few drops of lotion into his ear. He had a chronic canker condition – not very bad but now and then it became painful and needed treatment. It was because Miss Tremayne didn't like putting the lotion in that I was pressed into service.

As I turned the ear over and genlty massaged the oily liquid into the depths. Wilberforce groaned softly with pleasure and rubbed his cheek against my hand. He loved this anointing of the tender area beyond his reach and when I had finished he curled up on my knee.

I leaned back and sipped my tea. At that moment, with my back and shoulders weary and my hands red and chapped with countless washings on the open hillsides this seemed to be veterinary practice at its best.

Miss Tremayne continued. 'We shall have a little reception after the wedding and then the happy couple will take up residence here.'

'You mean, in this house?'

'Yes, of course. There's heaps of room in this big old place, and I have furnished two rooms for them on the east side. I'm sure they'll be very comfortable. Oh, I'm so excited about it all!'

She refilled my cup. 'Before you go you must let Elsie show you where they are going to live.'

On my way out the little woman took me through to the far end of the house.

'This, hee-hee-hee,' she said, 'is where we'll sit of a night, and this, ha-ha-ho-ho, oh dear me, is our bedroom.' She staggered around for a bit, wiped her eyes and turned to me for my opinion.

'It's really lovely, Elsie,' I said.

There were bright carpets, chairs with flowered covers and a fine mahogany-ended bed. It was nothing like the loft.

And as I looked at Elsie I realised the things Ned would see in his bride. Laughter, warmth, vivacity, and – I had no doubt at all – beauty and glamour.

I seemed to get round to most farms that lambing time and in due course I landed at Mr Daggett's. I delivered a fine pair of twins for him but it didn't seem to cheer him at all. Lifting the towel from the grass he handed it to me.

'Well, what did ah tell ye about Ned, eh? Got mixed up wi' a woman just like ah said.' He sniffed disapprovingly. 'All that rakin' and chasin' about – ah knew he'd get into mischief at t'finish.'

I walked back over the sunlit fields to the farm and as I passed the byre door Ned came out pushing a wheelbarrow.

'Good morning, Ned,' I said.

He glanced up at me in his vague way. 'How do, Mr Herriot.'

There was something different about him and it took me a few moments to discern what it was; his eyes had lost the expectant look which had been there for so long, and, after all, that was perfectly natural.

Because it had happened at last for Ned.

Chapter Twenty-two

Despite the crowds of men milling around Eastchurch I felt cut off and apart. It made me think of old Mr Potts from my veterinary days. He must have felt like that.

'How are you, Mr Herriot?'

Ordinary words, but the eagerness, almost desperation in the old man's voice made them urgent and meaningful.

I saw him nearly every day. In my unpredictable life it was difficult to do anything regularly but I did like a stroll by the river before lunch and so did my beagle, Sam. That was when we met Mr Potts and Nip, his elderly sheepdog – they seemed to have the same habits as us. His house backed on to the riverside fields and he spent a lot of time just walking around with his dog.

Many retired farmers kept a bit of land and a few stock to occupy their minds and ease the transition from their arduous existence to day-long leisure, but Mr Potts had bought a little bungalow with a scrap of garden and it was obvious that time dragged.

Probably his health had dictated this. As he faced me he leaned on his stick and his bluish cheeks rose and fell with his breathing. He was a heart case if ever I saw one.

'I'm fine, Mr Potts,' I replied. 'And how are things with you?'

'Nobbut middlin', lad. Ah soon get short o' wind.' He coughed a couple of times then asked the inevitable question.

'And what have you been doin' this morning'?' That was when his eyes grew intent and wide. He really wanted to know.

I thought for a moment. 'Well now, let's see.' I always tried to give him a detailed answer because I knew it meant a lot to him and brought back the life he missed so much. 'I've done a couple of cleansings, seen a lame bullock, treated two cows with mastitis and another with milk fever.'

He nodded eagerly at every word.

'By gaw!' he exclaimed. 'It's a beggar, that milk fever. When I were a lad, good cows used to die like flies with it. Allus good milkers after their third or fourth calf. Couldn't get to their feet and we used to dose 'em with all sorts, but they died, every one of 'em.'

'Yes,' I said. 'It must have been heartbreaking in those days.'

'But then.' He smiled delightedly, digging a forefinger into my chest. 'Then we started blowin' up their udders wi' a bicycle pump, and d'you know – they jumped up and walked away. Like magic it were.' His eyes sparkled at the memory.

'I know, Mr Potts, I've blown up a few myself, only I didn't use a bicycle pump – I had a special little inflation apparatus.'

That black box with its shining cylinders and filter is now in my personal museum, and it is the best place for it. It had got me out of some difficult situations but in the background there had always been the gnawing dread of transmitting tuberculosis. I had heard of it happening and was glad that calcium borogluconate had arrived.

As we spoke, Sam and Nip played on the grass beside us, I watched as the beagle frisked round the old animal while Nip pawed at him stiff-jointedly, his tail waving with pleasure. You could see that he enjoyed these meetings as much as his master and for a brief time the years fell away from him as he rolled on his back with Sam astride him, nibbling gently at his chest.

I walked with the old farmer as far as the little wooden bridge, then I had to turn for home. I watched the two of them pottering slowly over the narrow strip of timber to the other side of the river. Sam and I had our work pressing, but they had nothing else to do.

I used to see Mr Potts at other times, too. Wandering aimlessly among the stalls on market days or standing on the fringe of the group of farmers who always gathered in front of the Drovers' Arms to meet cattle dealers, cow feed merchants, or just to talk business among themselves.

Or I saw him at the auction mart, leaning on his stick, listening to the rapid-fire chanting of the auctioneer, watching listlessly as the beasts were bought and sold. And all the time I knew there was an emptiness in him, because there were none of his cattle in the stalls, none of his sheep in the long rows of pens. He was out of it all, old and done.

I saw him the day before he died. It was in the usual place and I was standing at the river's edge watching a heron rising from a rush-lined island and flapping lazily away over the fields.

The old man stopped as he came abreast of me and the two dogs began their friendly wrestling.

'Well now, Mr Herriot.' He paused and bowed his head over the stick which he had dug into the grass of his farm for half a century. 'What have you been doin' today?'

Perhaps his cheeks were a deeper shade of blue and the breath whistled through his pursed lips as he exhaled, but I can't recall that he looked any worse than usual.

'I'll tell you, Mr Potts,' I said. 'I'm feeling a bit weary. I ran into a real snorter of a foaling this morning – took me over two hours and I ache all over.'

'Foaling, eh? Foal would be laid wrong, I reckon?'

'Yes, cross-ways on, and I had a struggle to turn it.'

'By gaw, yes, it's hard work is that.' He smiled reminiscently. 'Doesta remember that Clydesdale mare you foaled at ma place? Must 'ave been one of your first jobs when you came to Darrowby.'

'Of course I do,' I replied. And I remembered too, how kind the old man had been. Seeing I was young and green and unsure of myself he had taken pains, in his quiet way, to put me at my ease and give me confidence. 'Yes,' I went on, 'it was late on a Sunday night and we had a right tussle with it. There was just the two of us but we managed, didn't we?'

He squared his shoulders and for a moment his eyes looked past me at something I couldn't see. 'Aye, that's right. We made a job of 'er, you and me. Ah could push and pull a bit then.'

'You certainly could. There's no doubt about that.'

He sucked the air in with difficulty and blew it out again with that peculiar pursing of the lips. Then he turned to me with a strange dignity.

'They were good days, Mr Herriot, weren't they?'

'They were, Mr Potts, they were indeed.'

'Aye, aye.' He nodded slowly. 'Ah've had a lot o' them days. Hard but good.' He looked down at his dog. 'And awd Nip shared 'em with me, didn't ye, lad?'

His words took me back to the very first time I had seen Mr Potts. He was perched on a stool, milking one of his few cows, his cloth-capped head thrusting into the hairy flank, and as he pulled at the teats old Nip dropped a stone on the toe of his boot. The farmer reached down, lifted the stone between two fingers and flicked it out through the open door into the yard. Nip scurried delightedly after it and was back within seconds, dropping the stone on the boot and panting hopefully.

He wasn't disappointed. His master repeated the throw automatically as if it was something he did all the time, and as I watched it happening again and again I realised that this was a daily ritual between the two. I had a piercing impression of infinite patience and devotion.

'Right, then, Mr Herriot, we'll be off,' Mr Potts said, jerking me back to the present. 'Come on, Nip.' He waved his stick and I watched him till a low-hanging willow branch hid man and dog from my sight.

That was the last time I saw him. Next day the man at the petrol pumps mumbled casually. 'See old Mr Potts got his time in, eh?'

And that was it. There was no excitement, and only a handful of his old friends turned up at the funeral.

For me it was a stab of sorrow. Another familiar face gone, and I should miss him as my busy life went on. I knew our daily conversations had cheered him but I felt with a sad finality that there was nothing else I could do for Mr Potts.

It was about a fortnight later and as I opened the gate to let Sam into the riverside fields I glanced at my watch. Twelve thirty – plenty of time for our pre-lunch walk and the long stretch of green was empty. Then I noticed a single dog away on the left. It was Nip, and as I watched he got up, took a few indeterminate steps over the grass then turned and sat down again at the gate of his back garden.

Instead of taking my usual route I cut along behind the houses till I reached the old dog. He had been looking around him aimlessly but when we came up to him he seemed to come to life, sniffing Sam over and wagging his tail at me.

On the other side of the gate Mrs Potts was doing a bit of weeding, bending painfully as she plied her trowel.

'How are you, Mrs Potts?' I said.

With an effort she straightened up. 'Oh, not too bad, thank you, Mr Herriot.' She came over and leaned on the gate. 'I see you're lookin' at the awd dog. My word he's missin' his master.'

I didn't say anything and she went on. 'He's eating all right and I can give him plenty of good food, but what I can't do is take 'im for walks.' She rubbed her back. 'I'm plagued with rheumaticks, Mr Herriot, and it takes me all my time to get around the house and garden.'

'I can understand that,' I said. 'And I don't suppose he'll walk by himself.'

'Nay, he won't. There's the path he went along every day.' She pointed to the winding strip of beaten earth among the grass. 'But he won't go more'n a few yards.'

'Ah well, dogs like a bit of company just the same as we do.' I bent and ran my hand over the old animal's head and ears. 'How would you like to come with us, Nip?'

I set off along the path and he followed unhesitatingly, trotting alongside Sam with swinging tail.

'Eee, look!' the old lady cried. 'Isn't that grand to see!'

I followed his usual route down to the river where the water ran dark and silent under the branches of the gnarled willows. Then we went over the bridge and in front of us the river widened into pebbly shallows and murmured and chattered among the stones.

It was peaceful down there with only the endless water sound and the piping of birds in my ears and the long curtain of leaves parting here and there to give glimpses of the green flanks of the fells.

I watched the two dogs frisking ahead of me and the decision came to me quite naturally; I would do this regularly. From that day I altered my route and went along behind the houses first. Nip was happy again, Sam loved the whole idea, and for me there was a strange comfort in the knowledge that there was still something I could do for Mr Potts.

Chapter Twenty-three

I had plenty of time on my hands at Eastchurch, plenty of time to think, and like most servicemen I thought of home. Only my home wasn't there any more.

When I left Darrowby Helen had gone back to live with her father and the little rooms under the tiles of Skeldale House would be empty and dusty now. But they lived on in my mind, clear in every detail.

I could see the ivy-fringed window looking over the tumble of roofs to the green hills, our few pieces of furniture, the bed and side table and the old wardrobe which only stayed shut with the aid of one of my socks jammed in the door. Strangely, it was that dangling woollen toe which gave me the sharpest stab as I remembered.

And even though it was all gone I could hear the bedside radio playing, my wife's voice from the other side of the fire and on that winter evening Tristan shouting up the stairs from the passage far below.

'Jim! Jim!'

I went out and stuck my head over the bannisters. 'What is it, Triss?'

'Sorry to bother you, Jim, but could you come down for a minute?' The upturned face had an anxious look.

I went down the long flights of steps two at a time and when I arrived slightly breathless on the ground floor Tristan beckoned me through to the consulting room at the back of the house. A teenage girl was standing by the table, her hand resting on a stained roll of blanket.

'It's a cat,' Tristan said. He pulled back a fold of the blanket and I looked down at a large, deeply striped tabby. At least he would have been large if he had had any flesh on his bones, but ribs and pelvis stood out painfully through the fur and as I passed my hand over the motionless body I could feel only a thin covering of skin.

Tristan cleared his throat. 'There's something else, Jim.'

I looked at him curiously. For once he didn't seem to have a joke in him. I watched as he gently lifted one of the cat's hind legs and rolled the abdomen into view. There was a gash on the ventral surface through which a coiled cluster of intestines spilled grotesquely on to the cloth. I was still shocked and staring when the girl spoke.

'I saw this cat sittin' in the dark, down Brown's yard. I thought 'e looked skinny, like, and a bit quiet and I bent down to give 'im a pat. Then I saw 'e was badly hurt and I went home for a blanket and brought 'im round to you.'

'That was kind of you,' I said. 'Have you any idea who he belongs to?'

The girl shook her head. 'No, he looks like a stray to me.'

'He does indeed.' I dragged my eyes away from the terrible wound. 'You're Marjorie Simpson, aren't you?'

'Yes.'

'I know your Dad well. He's our postman.'

'That's right.' She gave a half smile then her lips trembled. 'Well, I reckon I'd better leave 'im with you. You'll be goin to put him out of his misery. There's nothing anybody can do about . . . about that?'

I shrugged and shook my head. The girl's eyes filled with tears, she stretched out a hand and touched the emaciated animal then turned and walked quickly to the door.

'Thanks again, Marjorie,' I called after the retreating back. 'And don't worry – we'll look after him.'

In the silence that followed, Tristan and I looked down at the shattered animal. Under the surgery lamp it was all too easy to see. He had almost been disembowelled and the pile of intestines was covered in dirt and mud.

'What d'you think did this?' Tristan said at length. 'Has he been run over?'

'Maybe,' I replied. 'Could be anything. An attack by a big dog or somebody could have kicked him or struck him.' All things were possible with cats because some people seemed to regard them as fair game for any cruelty.

Tristan nodded. 'Anyway, whatever happened, he must have been on the verge of starvation. He's a skeleton. I bet he's wandered miles from home.'

'Ah well,' I sighed. 'There's only one thing to do. Those guts are perforated in several places. It's hopeless.'

Tristan didn't say anything but he whistled under his breath and drew the tip of his forefinger again and again across the furry cheek. And, unbelievably, from somewhere in the scraggy chest a gentle purring arose.

The young man looked at me, round eyed. 'My God, do you hear that?'

'Yes . . . amazing in that condition. He's a good natured cat.'

Tristan, head bowed, continued his stroking. I knew how he felt because, although he preserved a cheerfully hard-boiled attitude to our patients he couldn't kid me about one thing; he had a soft spot for cats. Even now, when we are both around the sixty mark, he often talks to me over a beer about the cat he has had for many years. It is a typical relationship – they tease each other unmercifully – but it is based on real affection.

'It's no good, Triss,' I said gently. 'It's got to be done.' I reached for the syringe but something in me rebelled against plunging a needle into that mutilated body. Instead I pulled a fold of the blanket over the cat's head.

'Pour a little ether on to the cloth,' I said. 'He'll just sleep away.'

Wordlessly Tristan unscrewed the cap of the ether bottle and poised it above the head. Then from under the shapeless heap of blanket we heard it again; the deep purring which increased in volume till it boomed in our ears like a distant motor cycle.

Tristan was like a man turned to stone, hand gripping the bottle rigidly, eyes staring down at the mound of cloth from which the purring rose in waves of warm friendly sound.

At last he looked up at me and gulped. 'I don't fancy this much, Jim. Can't we do something?'

'You mean, put that lot back?'

'Yes.'

'But the bowels are damaged – they're like a sieve in parts.'

'We could stitch them, couldn't we?'

I lifted the blanket and looked again. 'Honestly, Triss, I wouldn't know where to start. And the whole thing is filthy.'

He didn't say anything, but continued to look at me steadily. And I didn't need much persuading. I had no more desire to pour ether on to that comradely purring than he had.

'Come on, then,' I said. 'We'll have a go.'

With the oxygen bubbling and the cat's head in the anaesthetic mask we washed the whole prolapse with warm saline. We did it again and again but it was impossible to remove every fragment of caked dirt. Then we started the painfully slow business of stitching the many holes in the tiny intestines, and here I was glad of Tristan's nimble fingers which seemed better able to manipulate the small round-bodied needles than mine.

Two hours and yards of catgut later, we dusted the patched up peritoneal surface with sulphonamide and pushed the entire mass back into the abdomen. When I had sutured muscle layers and skin everything looked tidy but I had a nasty feeling of sweeping undesirable things under the carpet. The extensive damage, all that contamination – peritonitis was inevitable.

'He's alive, anyway, Triss,' I said as we began to wash the instruments. 'We'll put him on to sulphapyridine and keep our fingers crossed.' There were still no antibiotics at that time but the new drug was a big advance.

The door opened and Helen came in. 'You've been a long time, Jim.' She walked over to the table and looked down at the sleeping cat. 'What a poor skinny little thing. He's all bones.'

'You should have seen him when he came in.' Tristan switched off the steriliser and screwed shut the valve on the anaesthetic machine. 'He looks a lot better now.'

She stroked the little animal for a moment. 'Is he badly injured?'

'I'm afraid so, Helen,' I said. 'We've done our best for him but I honestly don't think he has much chance.'

'What a shame. And he's pretty, too. Four white feet and all those unusual colours.' With her fingers she traced the faint bands of auburn and copper-gold among the grey and black.

Tristan laughed. 'Yes, I think that chap has a ginger Tom somewhere in his ancestry.'

Helen smiled, too, but absently, and I noticed a broody look about her. She hurried out to the stock room and returned with an empty box.

'Yes . . . yes . . .' she said thoughtfully. 'I can make a bed in this box for him and he'll sleep in our room, Jim.'

'He will?'

'Yes, he must be warm, mustn't he?'

'Of course.'

Later, in the darkness of our bed-sitter, I looked from my pillow at a cosy scene; Sam in his basket on one side of the flickering fire and the cat cushioned and blanketed in his box on the other.

As I floated off into sleep it was good to know that my patient was so comfortable, but I wondered if he would be alive in the morning . . .

I knew he was alive at 7.30 a.m. because my wife was already up and talking to him. I trailed across the room in my pyjamas and the cat and I looked at each other. I rubbed him under the chin and he opened his mouth in a rusty miaow. But he didn't try to move.

'Helen,' I said. 'This little thing is tied together inside with catgut. He'll have to live on fluids for a week and even then he probably won't make it. If he stays up here you'll be spooning milk into him umpteen times a day.'

'Okay, okay.' She had that broody look again.

It wasn't only milk she spooned into him over the next few days. Beef essence, strained broth and a succession of sophisticated baby foods found their way down his throat at regular intervals. One lunch time I found Helen kneeling by the box.

'We shall call him Oscar,' she said.

'You mean we're keeping him?'

'Yes.'

I am fond of cats but we already had a dog in our cramped quarters and I could see difficulties. Still I decided to let it go.

'Why Oscar?'

'I don't know.' Helen tipped a few drops of chop gravy onto the little red tongue and watched intently as he swallowed.

One of the things I like about women is their mystery, the unfathomable part of them, and I didn't press the matter further. But I was pleased at the way things were going. I had been giving the sulphapyridine every six hours and taking the temperature night and morning, expecting all the time to encounter the roaring fever, the vomiting and the tense abdomen of peritonitis. But it never happened.

It was as though Oscar's animal instinct told him he had to move as little as possible because he lay absolutely still day after day and looked up at us – and purred.

His purr became part of our lives and when he eventually left his bed, sauntered through to our kitchen and began to sample Sam's dinner of meat and biscuit it was a moment of triumph. And I didn't spoil it by wondering if he was ready for solid food; I felt he knew.

From then on it was sheer joy to watch the furry scarecrow fill out and grow strong, and as he ate and ate and the flesh spread over his bones the true beauty of his coat showed in the glossy medley of auburn, black and gold. We had a handsome cat on our hands.

Once Oscar had recovered, Tristan was a regular visitor.

He probably felt, and rightly, that he, more than I, had saved Oscar's life in the first place, and he used to play with him for long periods. His favourite ploy was to push his leg round the corner of the table and withdraw it repeatedly just as the cat pawed at it.

Oscar was justifiably irritated by this teasing but showed his character by lying in wait for Tristan one night and biting him smartly in the ankle before he could start his tricks.

From my own point of view Oscar added many things to our menage. Sam was delighted with him and the two soon became firm friends, Helen adored him and each evening I thought afresh that a nice cat washing his face by the hearth gave extra comfort to a room.

Oscar had been established as one of the family for several weeks when I came in from a late call to find Helen waiting for me with a stricken face.

What's happened?' I asked.

'It's Oscar – he's gone!'

'Gone? What do you mean?'

'Oh, Jim, I think he's run away.'

I stared at her. 'He wouldn't do that. He often goes down to the garden at night. Are you sure he isn't there?'

'Absolutely. I've searched right into the yard. I've even had a walk round the town. And remember.' Her chin quivered. 'He . . . he ran away from somewhere before.'

I looked at my watch. 'Ten o'clock. Yes, that is strange. He shouldn't be out at this time.'

As I spoke the front door bell jangled. I galloped down the stairs and as I rounded the corner in the passage I could see Mrs Heslington, the vicar's wife, through the glass. I threw open the door. She was holding Oscar in her arms.

'I believe this is your cat, Mr Herriot,' she said.

'It is indeed, Mrs Heslington. Where did you find him?'

She smiled. 'Well it was rather odd. We were having a meeting of the Mothers' Union at the church house and we noticed the cat sitting there in the room.'

'Just sitting . . .?'

'Yes, as though he were listening to what we were saying and enjoying it all. It was unusual. When the meeting ended I thought I'd better bring him along to you.'

'I'm most grateful, Mrs Heslington.' I snatched Oscar and tucked him under my arm. 'My wife is distraught – she thought he was lost.'

It was a little mystery. Why should he suddenly take off like that? But since he showed no change in his manner over the ensuing week we put it out of our minds.

Then one evening a man brought in a dog for a distemper inoculation and left the front door open. When I went up to our flat I found that Oscar had disappeared again. This time Helen and I scoured the market place and side alleys in vain and when we returned at half past nine we were both despondent. It was nearly eleven and we were thinking of bed when the door bell rang.

It was Oscar again, this time resting on the ample stomach of Jack Newbould. Jack was leaning against a doorpost and the fresh country air drifting in from the dark street was richly intermingled with beer fumes.

Jack was a gardener at one of the big houses. He hiccuped gently and gave me a huge benevolent smile. 'Brought your cat, Mr Herriot.'

'Gosh, thanks, Jack!' I said, scooping up Oscar gratefully. 'Where the devil did you find him?'

'Well, s'matter o' fact, 'e sort of found me.'

'What do you mean?'

Jack closed his eyes for a few moments before articulating carefully. 'Thish is a big night, tha knows, Mr Herriot. Darts championship. Lots of t'lads round at t'Dog and Gun – lotsh and lotsh of 'em. Big gatherin'.'

'And our cat was there?'

'Aye, he were there, all right. Sittin' among t'lads. Shpent t'whole evenin' with us.'

'Just sat there, eh?'

'That e' did.' Jack giggled reminiscently. 'By gaw 'e enjoyed isself. Ah gave 'im a drop o' best bitter out of me own glass and once or twice ah thought 'e was goin' to have a go at chuckin' a dart. He's some cat.' He laughed again.

As I bore Oscar upstairs I was deep in thought. What was going on here? These sudden desertions were upsetting Helen and I felt they could get on my nerves in time.

I didn't have long to wait till the next one. Three nights later he was missing again. This time Helen and I didn't bother to search – we just waited.

He was back earlier than usual. I heard the door bell at nine o'clock. It was the elderly Miss Simpson peering through the glass. And she wasn't holding Oscar – he was prowling on the mat waiting to come in.

Miss Simpson watched with interest as the cat stalked inside and made for the stairs. 'Ah, good, I'm so glad he's come home safely. I knew he was your cat and I've been intrigued by his behaviour all evening.'

'Where . . . may I ask?'

'Oh, at the Women's Institute. He came in shortly after we started and stayed till the end.'

'Really? What exactly was your programme, Miss Simpson?'

'Well, there was a bit of committee stuff, then a short talk with lantern slides by Mr Walters from the water company and we finished with a cake-making competition.'

'Yes . . . yes . . . and what did Oscar do?'

She laughed. 'Mixed with the company, apparently enjoyed the slides and showed great interest in the cakes.'

'I see. And you didn't bring him home?'

'No, he made his own way here. As you know, I have to pass your house and I merely rang your bell to make sure you knew he had arrived.'

'I'm obliged to you, Miss Simpson. We were a little worried.'

I mounted the stairs in record time. Helen was sitting with the cat on her knee and she looked up as I burst in.

'I know about Oscar now,' I said.

'Know what?'

'Why he goes on these nightly outings. He's not running away – he's visiting.'

'Visiting?'

'Yes,' I said. 'Don't you see? He likes getting around, he loves people, especially in groups, and he's interested in what they do. He's a natural mixer.'

Helen looked down at the attractive mound of fur curled on her lap. 'Of course . . . that's it . . . he's a socialite!'

'Exactly, a high stepper!'

'A cat-about-town!'

It all afforded us some innocent laughter and Oscar sat up and looked at us with evident pleasure, adding his own throbbing purr to the merriment. But for Helen and me there was a lot of relief behind it; ever since our cat had started his excursions there had been the gnawing fear that we would lose him, and now we felt secure.

From that night our delight in him increased. There was endless joy in watching this facet of his character unfolding. He did the social round meticulously, taking in most of the activities of the town. He became a familiar figure at whist drives, jumble sales, school concerts and scout bazaars. Most of the time he was made welcome, but was twice ejected from meetings of the Rural District Council who did not seem to relish the idea of a cat sitting in on their deliberations.

At first I was apprehensive about his making his way through the streets but I watched him once or twice and saw that he looked both ways before tripping daintily across. Clearly he had excellent traffic sense and this made me feel that his original injury had not been caused by a car.

Taking it all in all, Helen and I felt that it was a kind stroke of fortune which had brought Oscar to us. He was a warm and cherished part of our home life. He added to our happiness.

When the blow fell it was totally unexpected.

I was finishing the evening surgery. I looked round the door and saw only a man and two little boys.

'Next, please,' I said.

The man stood up. He had no animal with him. He was middle-aged, with the rough weathered face of a farm worker. He twirled a cloth cap nervously in his hands.

'Mr Herriot?' he said.

'Yes, what can I do for you?'

He swallowed and looked me straight in the eyes. 'Ah think you've got ma cat.'

'What?'

'Ah lost ma cat a bit since.' He cleared his throat. 'We used to live at Missdon but ah got a job as ploughman to Mr Horne of Wederly. It was after we moved to Wederly that t'cat went missin'. Ah reckon he was tryin' to find 'is way back to his old home.'

'Wederly? That's on the other side of Brawton – over thirty miles away.'

'Aye, ah knaw, but cats is funny things.'

'But what makes you think I've got him?'

He twisted the cap around a bit more. 'There's a cousin o' mine lives in Darrowby and ah heard tell from 'im about this cat that goes around to meetin's. I 'ad to come. We've been huntin' everywhere.'

'Tell me,' I said. 'This cat you lost. What did he look like?'

'Grey and black and sort o' gingery. Right bonny 'e was. And 'e was allus goin' out to gatherin's.'

A cold hand clutched at my heart. 'You'd better come upstairs. Bring the boys with you.'

Helen was putting some coal on the fire of the bed-sitter.

'Helen,' I said. 'This is Mr – er – I'm sorry, I don't know your name.'

'Gibbons, Sep Gibbons. They called me Septimus because ah was the seventh in family and it looks like ah'm goin' t'same way 'cause we've got six already. These are our two youngest.' The two boys, obvious twins of about eight, looked up at us solemnly.

I wished my heart would stop hammering. 'Mr Gibbons thinks Oscar is his. He lost his cat some time ago.'

My wife put down her little shovel. 'Oh . . . oh . . . I see.' She stood very still for a moment then smiled faintly. 'Do sit down. Oscar's in the kitchen, I'll bring him through.'

She went out and reappeared with the cat in her arms. She hadn't got through the door before the little boys gave tongue.

'Tiger!' they cried. 'Oh, Tiger, Tiger!'

The man's face seemed lit from within. He walked quickly across the floor and ran his big work-roughened hand along the fur.

'Hullo, awd lad,' he said, and turned to me with a radiant smile. 'It's 'im, Mr Herriot, It's 'im awright, and don't 'e look well!'

'You call him Tiger, eh?' I said.

'Aye,' he replied happily. 'It's them gingery stripes. The kids called 'im that. They were broken hearted when we lost 'im.'

As the two little boys rolled on the floor our Oscar rolled with them, pawing playfully, purring with delight.

Sep Gibbons sat down again. 'That's the way 'e allus went on wi' the family. They used to play with 'im for hours. By gaw we did miss 'im. He were a right favourite.'

I looked at the broken nails on the edge of the cap, at the decent, honest, uncomplicated Yorkshire face so like the many I had grown to like and respect. Farm men like him got thirty shillings a week in those days and it was reflected in the threadbare jacket, the cracked, shiny boots and the obvious hand-me-downs of the boys.

But all three were scrubbed and tidy, the man's face like a red beacon, the children's knees gleaming and their hair carefully slicked across their foreheads. They looked like nice people to me. I didn't know what to say.

Helen said it for me. 'Well, Mr Gibbons.' Her tone had an unnatural brightness. 'You'd better take him.'

The man hesitated. 'Now then, are ye sure, Missis Herriot?'

'Yes . . . yes, I'm sure. He was your cat first.'

'Aye, but some folks 'ud say finders keepers or summat like that. Ah didn't come 'ere to demand 'im back or owt of t'sort.'

'I know you didn't, Mr Gibbons, but you've had him all those years and you've searched for him so hard. We couldn't possibly keep him from you.'

He nodded quickly. 'Well, that's right good of ye.' He paused for a moment, his face serious, then he stooped and picked Oscar up. 'We'll have to be off if we're goin' to catch the eight o'clock bus.'

Helen reached forward, cupped the cat's head in her hands and looked at him steadily for a few seconds. Then she patted the boys' heads. 'You'll take good care of him, won't you?'

'Aye, missis, thank ye, we will that.' The two small faces looked up at her and smiled.

'I'll see you down the stairs, Mr Gibbons,' I said.

On the descent I tickled the furry cheek resting on the man's shoulder and heard for the last time the rich purring. On the front door step we shook hands and they set off down the street. As they rounded the corner of Trengate they stopped and waved, and I waved back at the man, the two children and the cat's head looking back at me over the shoulder.

It was my habit at that time in my life to mount the stairs two or three at a time but on this occasion I trailed upwards like an old man, slightly breathless, throat tight, eyes prickling.

I cursed myself for a sentimental fool but as I reached our door I found a flash of consolation. Helen had taken it remarkably well. She had nursed that cat and grown deeply attached to him, and I'd have thought an unforeseen calamity like this would have upset her terribly. But no, she had behaved calmly and rationally. You never knew with women, but I was thankful.

It was up to me to do as well. I adjusted my features into the semblance of a cheerful smile and marched into the room.

Helen had pulled a chair close to the table and was slumped face down against the wood. One arm cradled her head while the other was stretched in front of her as her body shook with an utterly abandoned weeping.

I had never seen her like this and I was appalled. I tried to say something comforting but nothing stemmed the flow of racking sobs.

Feeling helpless and inadequate I could only sit close to her and stroke the back of her head. Maybe I could have said something if I hadn't felt just about as bad myself.

You get over these things in time. After all, we told ourselves, it wasn't as though Oscar had died or got lost again – he had gone to a good family who would look after him. In fact he had really gone home.

And of course, we still had our much-loved Sam, although he didn't help in the early stages by sniffing disconsolately where Oscar's bed used to lie, then collapsing on the rug with a long lugubrious sigh.

There was one other thing, too. I had a little notion forming in my mind, an idea which I would spring on Helen when the time was right. It was about a month after that shattering night and we were coming out of the cinema at Brawton at the end of our half day. I looked at my watch.

'Only eight o'clock,' I said. 'How about going to see Oscar?'

Helen looked at me in surprise. 'You mean – drive on to Wederly?'

'Yes, it's only about five miles.'

A smile crept slowly across her face. 'That would be lovely. But do you think they would mind?'

'The Gibbons? No, I'm sure they wouldn't. Let's go.'

Wederly was a big village and the ploughman's cottage was at the far end a few yards beyond the Methodist chapel. I pushed open the garden gate and we walked down the path.

A busy-looking little woman answered my knock. She was drying her hands on a striped towel.

'Mrs Gibbons?' I said.

'Aye, that's me.'

'I'm James Herriot – and this is my wife.'

Her eyes widened uncomprehendingly. Clearly the name meant nothing to her.

'We had your cat for a while,' I added.

Suddenly she grinned and waved her towel at us. 'Oh aye, ah remember now. Sep told me about you. Come in, come in!'

The big kitchen-living room was a tableau of life with six children and thirty shillings a week. Battered furniture, rows of much-mended washing on a pulley, black cooking range and a general air of chaos.

Sep got up from his place by the fire, put down his newspaper, took off a pair of steel-rimmed spectacles and shook hands.

He waved Helen to a sagging armchair. 'Well, it's right nice to see you. Ah've often spoke of ye to t'missis.'

His wife hung up her towel. 'Yes, and I'm glad to meet ye both. I'll get some tea in a minnit.'

She laughed and dragged a bucket of muddy water into a corner. 'I've been washin' football jerseys. Them lads just handed them to me tonight – as if I haven't enough to do.'

As she ran the water into the kettle I peeped surreptitiously around me and I noticed Helen doing the same. But we searched in vain. There was no sign of a cat. Surely he couldn't have run away again? With a growing feeling of dismay I realised that my little scheme could backfire devastatingly.

It wasn't until the tea had been made and poured that I dared to raise the subject.

'How –' I asked diffidently. 'How is – er – Tiger?'

'Oh he's grand,' the little woman replied briskly. She glanced up at the clock on the mantelpiece. 'He should be back any time now, then you'll be able to see 'im.'

As she spoke, Sep raised a finger. 'Ah think ah can hear 'im now.'

He walked over and opened the door and our Oscar strode in with all his old grace and majesty. He took one look at Helen and leaped on to her lap. With a cry of delight she put down her cup and stroked the beautiful fur as the cat arched himself against her hand and the familiar purr echoed round the room.

'He knows me,' she murmured. 'He knows me.'

Sep nodded and smiled. 'He does that. You were good to 'im. He'll never forget ye, and we won't either, will we mother?'

'No, we won't, Mrs Herriot,' his wife said as she applied butter to a slice of gingerbread. 'That was a kind thing ye did for us and I 'ope you'll come and see us all whenever you're near.'

'Well, thank you,' I said. 'We'd love to – we're often in Brawton.'

I went over and tickled Oscar's chin, then I turned again to Mrs Gibbons. 'By the way, it's after nine o'clock. Where has he been till now?'

She poised her butter knife and looked into space.

'Let's see, now,' she said. 'It's Thursday, isn't it? Ah yes, it's 'is night for the Yoga class.'

Chapter Twenty-four

I knew it was the end of the chapter when I slammed the carriage door behind me and squeezed into a seat between a fat WAAF and a sleeping corporal.

I suppose I was an entirely typical discharged serviceman. They had taken away my blue uniform and fitted me with a 'demob suit', a ghastly garment of stiff brown serge with purple stripes which made me look like an old-time gangster, but they had allowed me to retain my RAF shirt and tie and the shiny boots which were like old friends.

My few belongings, including Black's *Veterinary Dictionary* lay in the rack above in a small cardboard suitcase of a type very popular among the lower ranks of the services. They were all I possessed and I could have done with a coat because it was cold in the train and a long journey stretched between Eastchurch and Darrowby.

It took an age to chug and jolt as far as London then there was a lengthy wait before I boarded the train for the north. It was about midnight when we set off, and for seven hours I sat there in the freezing darkness, feet numb, teeth chattering.

The last lap was by bus and it was the same rattling little vehicle which had carried me to my first job those years ago. The driver was the same too, and the time between seemed to melt away as the fells began to rise again from the blue distance in the early light and I saw the familiar farmhouses, the walls creeping up the grassy slopes, the fringe of trees by the river's edge.

It was mid morning when we rumbled into the market place and I read 'Darrowby Co-operative Society' above the shop on the far side. The sun was high, warming the tiles of the fretted line of roofs with their swelling green background of hills. I got out and the bus went on its way, leaving me standing by my case.

And it was just the same as before. The sweet air, the silence and the cobbled square deserted except for the old men sitting around the clock tower. One of them looked up at me.

'Now then, Mr Herriot,' he said quietly as though he had seen me only yesterday.

Before me Trengate curved away till it disappeared round the grocer's shop on the corner. Most of the quiet street with the church at its foot was beyond my view and it was a long time since I had been down there, but with my eyes closed I could see Skeldale House with the ivy climbing over the old brick walls to the little rooms under the eaves.

That was where I would have to make another start; where I would find out how much I had forgotten, whether I was fit to be an animal doctor again. But I wouldn't go along there yet, not just yet . . .

A lot had happened since that first day when I arrived in Darrowby in search of a job but it came to me suddenly that my circumstances hadn't changed much. All I had possessed then was an old case and the suit I stood in and it was about the same now. Except for one great and wonderful thing. I had Helen and Jimmy.

That made all the difference. I had no money, not even a house to call my own, but any roof which covered my wife and son was personal and special. Sam would be with them, too, waiting for me. They were outside the town and it was a fair walk from here, but I looked down at the blunt toes of my boots sticking from the purple striped trousers. The RAF hadn't only taught me to fly, they had taught me to march, and a few miles didn't bother me.

I took a fresh grip on my cardboard case, turned towards the exit from the square and set off, left-right, left-right, left-right on the road for home.